BASIC BOOKS FOR JUNIOR COLLEGE LIBRARIES:

20,000 VITAL TITLES.

VOLUME NUMBER ONE

BASIC BOOKS FOR JUNIOR COLLEGE LIBRARIES:

20,000 VITAL TITLES.

Edited by

CHARLES L. TRINKNER

Chairman, Library Service Division
Pensacola Junior College
Pensacola, Florida

Introduction by

DR. HENRY L. ASHMORE
President, Pensacola Junior College
Pensacola, Florida

COLONIAL   PRESS

Northport, Alabama

LIBRARY OF CONGRESS CATALOG CARD NUMBER:

63-14932

Dedicated to

MY WIFE, MARIAN THE LIBRARIAN.

ABOUT THE EDITOR

Charles L. Trinkner is Chairman, Library Services Division, Pensacola Junior College, Pensacola, Florida. He is author of <u>Better Libraries Make Better Schools</u> c1962 and <u>Library Services for Junior Colleges</u> c1963.

He has four earned degrees from the University of Florida and Louisiana State University and received an honorary doctorate in 1961. He has taught Library Science at North Texas State University, Arkansas State College, Texas Woman's University, Pensacola Junior College, and the University of Oregon. He has also worked with library evaluations at Appalachian State Teachers College, North Carolina; Arlington State College, Texas; and Florida Schools.

He served with the U. S. Marine Corps during World War II and participated in the Battle of Pearl Harbor, Battle of Coral Sea, Battle of Midway and others. He is listed in Who's Who in America-Supplement 1957; Who's Who in American Education 1955--; Who's Who in the South and Southwest 1959--; American Men of Science 1962; and the American Library Directory.

INTRODUCTION

By Dr. Henry L. Ashmore, President
Pensacola Junior College

There is no doubt that a vast majority of educators and leaders agree that the heart of any institution of learning is the instructional program. This is the purpose for being. All activities occurring on the campus of an institution of higher learning, important though they may be, exist, or should exist, in order to undergird the instructional program. The quality of the faculty, the status and quality of the physical facilities, the level of campus maintenance, existance of extra-curricular activities, should be such to enhance the primary purpose for which the institution was created.

There are many factors which determine the quality of an instructional program. The two most important are the faculty and the library. It is impossible to have a high level of instruction without having a high concomitant level of faculty. This statement would hold true for the library and library services. It would be impossible to have a high level instructional program without having a well developed library, both in terms of physical facilities and in terms of library holdings. In a very real sense, the entire instructional program of the institution of higher learning should be centered around the library. It should serve as a reference center, it should serve as a study center; it should serve to stimulate; it should serve in providing materials to increase the productivity of the mind.

Most knowledgeable educators would agree that the extent to which a library is used determines in a very real way the quality of an instructional program. It is for this reason that this publication is so important. It brings together the titles of those vital works which are essential to a well equipped and well functioning library. This is not to state that a library should have all 20,000 volumes included herein. It is to state that an institution should be growing toward this as a minimum standard. To achieve this many titles would depend on a great many factors. It would depend upon the size of the institution, the breadth and depth of the program offered and the finances available. However, each institution should reach out in providing the best possible library center, thereby enhancing its total instructional program.

It is significant that the development of junior colleges has been one of the fastest growing developments in the area of higher education in the United States. This came about because many of the junior colleges and community colleges are located in the population centers and attempt to serve in a real way the needs of the students' in these areas. This means there will be a diverse offering of curriculums, particularly in the larger junior colleges. The more curriculums offered, the greater is the responsibility which must be placed upon the libraries. The range of materials would necessarily have to be greater to provide for a wider range of offerings. It is significant that a group of librarians in the junior colleges in the United States, recognizing the problems created by the rapid growth of the junior colleges, should join together in an effort to present this basic book list. It comes directly from the institutions affected. Therefore, it has the strength which comes from being specifically germane to the needs of the institutions involved.

As the junior colleges develop with rapidity throughout the United States, it becomes necessary for these institutions to become quality institutions. To become quality institutions as it has already been pointed out, these institutions must have quality programs. To have quality programs, they must have quality library services. I am sure that judicial use of this volume will help in a very concrete way the development of quality holdings for these junior colleges.

Henry L. Ashmore

June 15, 1963

PREFACE

The purpose of this book list is to provide junior college librarians with a ready reference tool listing in-print books for their basic collections. There has been a very significant and pertinent need for an authoritative up-to-date core of books during this period of growth and expansion of the American junior college system. The project was prepared by 225 librarian-coordinators and 2600 subject specialists representing junior college institutions in the United States, including Hawaii and Alaska, Canada, Guam, Puerto Rico, and the Panama Canal Zone. A coordinator-contributor section lists the individual authorities responsible for coordinating and leading their institution's subject specialists in the task of selecting 20,000 vital entries.

The cooperative efforts of junior college subject specialists and librarians yielded nearly a half-million votes for first choice titles. The criteria for book selection was based on each coordinator's institutional curriculum, personal book knowledge, subject specialist recommendations, reviewing sources and book collection needs. The building of a comprehensive book list requires a proportional distribution of titles so as to have an overall balance of resources particularly in the broad areas of humanities, social sciences and sciences. Each coordinator determined final selections with the balance aspect in mind coupled with the unique aims and objectives of the junior college program.

The control figure of 20,000 volumes was determined through three related factors drawn from the general framework of the nation's junior college library program. These are: (1) the national standard of 20,000 volumes prescribed as a guide for junior college library evaluations; (2) preliminary research and pilot studies involving the range of basic book needs and breadth and depth of resource needs in specific subject areas and (3) national statistics report that six out of ten junior college libraries have less than 20,000 volumes.

The book is organized into four parts. Part I contains 20,000 basic nonfictional works arranged by subject. Part II lists 1200 recommended literary works for the junior college. Part III provides a basic reference collection of 500 in-print titles and Part IV has a list of 150 recommended periodicals. The appendix section includes a list of coordinating librarians, a Dewey Classification Index, and a Directory of Publishers.

Dewey Classification numbers have been assigned to subject headings mainly as an aid to relating the titles to particular areas of knowledge. Classification designations were drawn from the 16th Edition of the Dewey System and it should be kept in mind by the user that this classification scheme does not analyze and classify each individual entry but rather a broad classification assignment is made for the more practical purpose of grouping related materials.

The latest edition of in-print books was included whenever possible and paper back items were listed when hardbound copies were not available. Bibliographical information for each entry has been reduced to author, title, date, price, and publisher. Publishing firms are in brief one-word form; however, a Directory of Publishers provides full name and address of each publisher. An (R) appearing at the end of an entry denotes reference material.

Up-to-dateness and availability of titles is the key problem of a junior college book list. A follow-up plan has been designed to provide continuity and prevent the list from becoming inactive. Library teams will recommend replacements for out-dated items in assigned subject areas and supplements will be issued until a new revision is made available. This plan also provides for the reprinting of vital out-of-print titles.

It is not possible to list all the junior college l i b r a r i a n s, subject specialists, administrators, and consultants who have contributed ideas, content, and organization to this task of building better book collections for America's junior colleges. Special recognition is due the coordinating librarians for their cooperative spirit, knowledge of book resources, selection skills, and leadership of their individual institution's faculty resources. Without their cooperation this project would not have the authority, national scope, and quality that has been interwoven throughout the preparation of this project.

I particularly wish to extend my gratitude to Mrs. Gay Hildreth for proofreading, Mr. Charles J. Laubenthal, Mrs. Dorothy Ingram and Mrs. Ruth McCormick for their helpful suggestions, inspiration, and encouragement throughout the project. Finally, thanks are due my wife who has stimulated and comforted me from day to day from the creation to the finish-line.

CHARLES L. TRINKNER

Pensacola, Florida
May, 1963

The following junior college consultants, administrators, and national leaders in the American junior college movement have indicated their approval and support of this basic core of books designed to help build better libraries for the nation's junior colleges.

Dr. Henry L. Ashmore, President, Pensacola Junior College, Pensacola, Florida; President, Florida Association of Colleges and Universities, 1961-63; Secretary, Executive Council, Southern Association of Colleges and Schools 1962-63.

   (6 or 8 lines)

C. C. Bussey, President, Sinclair College, Dayton, Ohio and President, Ohio Association of Junior Colleges, 1961-62.

"We commend your committee for its diligent work in compiling this vital list. It should prove very useful to all junior colleges. I hope there will be a way found to keep this list up-to-date from year to year."

Dr. Bruce G. Carter, President, Northeastern Oklahoma A & M College, Miami, Oklahoma and President, Oklahoma Association of Junior Colleges, 1961-62.

"The junior college library or the college library plays such an important part in the life of any college and we certainly want to make available to our students the right books at the right time to provide for their needs."

Dr. G. A. Collyer, President, Shasta College, Redding, California and President, California Junior College Association, 1962-63.

"I heartily endorse your project, and I am sure other administrators in our junior college association will be very interested in its accomplishment and availability. I believe your project in developing a basic book list for junior college libraries is an excellent one."

Dr. C. C. Colvert, Professor and Consultant in Junior College Education, The University of Texas, Austin, Texas.

"This is very much needed for our junior colleges since there are so many new ones now being established and they need some authoritative source to use for building up the library in a hurry. I am sure your list of more than 20,000 titles will be of great value to these new libraries as well as to the older ones who wish to fill in the gap. I heartily endorse such a project and wish you every success in it."

Dr. W. L. Compare, President, Clark Memorial College, Newton, Mississippi and President, Southern Association of Junior Colleges, 1962.

"The compilation Basic Books for Junior College Libraries should meet a real need in this area. Every junior college librarian should find it most helpful in building and maintaining library holdings adequate for the needs of an advancing educational program."

Donald E. Deyo, President, American Association of Junior Colleges and Dean, Montgomery Junior College, Takoma Park 12, Maryland.

"In these days when we stand on the threshold of an immense growth in the number of new junior colleges, such a list for the guidance of new librarians who are probably themselves unfamiliar with the junior college concept would be of inestimable value. You are to be congratulated on the project you have undertaken."

Lee E. Dulgar, Dean, Thornton Junior College, Harvey, Illinois and President, Illinois Association of Junior Colleges, 1961-62.

"This list can contribute materially to improving junior college libraries."

Jack P. Hudnall, Dean, Hibbing Junior College, Hibbing, Minnesota and President, Minnesota Association of Junior Colleges, 1961-63.

"...result in a more dynamic library program for junior colleges..."

Dr. Lamar Johnson, University of California, Los Angeles, California and Consultant for Junior Colleges and Professor of Higher Education.

"Such a publication is greatly needed..."

Dr. Fred Koschmann, Dean, Sheldon Jackson Junior College, Sitka, Alaska and President, Northwest Association of Junior Colleges, 1962-63.

"I am interested in the Basic Books for Junior College Libraries: 20,000 Vital Titles, because we need help in this area. There is a shortage of competant librarians and most junior colleges, especially new ones, have the huge task of building an adequate library in a short time with inadequate funds. Those who have initiated and carried out this program are making a splendid contribution to the junior college movement."

Dr. Leland L. Medsker, Vice Chairman, University of California, Center of the Study of Higher Education, Berkeley, California.

Project Endorsement - 20,000 Vital Titles (Ed.)

Dr. Clyde E. Nail, Vice-President, San Antonio Jr. College, San Antonio,

Dr. Clyde E. Nail, Vice-President, San Antonio Jr. College, San Antonio, Texas.

"Your core list will be of interest for practical use, just as it is of interest to me as an administrator because it affords one method of evaluating our own collection."

Dr. Charles E. Rollins, President, Edison Junior College, Fort Myers, Florida and President, Pennsylvania Association of Junior Colleges, 1961-62.

"I certainly feel that (this) tool will aid the thinking and planning of our library committee and librarian in building our new library. Since the library is the heart of any institution, the need for careful planning is of the utmost importance. Assistance as can be obtained from your book will make available to us the best thinking in the field."

Elbridge M. Smith, Chairman, Division of General Education, New York State Agricultural and Technical Institute, Cobleskill, New York and Executive Secretary, New York State Junior College Association.

"This basic list should be extremely valuable to all of us in the rapidly changing and expanding junior college field. It would seem to me that librarians would welcome the considered judgement of their colleagues and certainly faculty members pressured by the multiplicity of their responsibilities will welcome up-to-date professional advice on books which they might have overlooked or to which they have seen only passing reference."

Dr. Thomas M. Spencer, President, San Jacinto College, Pasadena, Texas and President, Texas Public Junior College Association, 1961-62.

"Surely it will answer a vital and pressing need, a need felt by trained librarians as well as faculty members..."

Dr. Laurence E. Spring, President, Erie County Technical Institute, Buffalo, New York and President, New York State Association of Junior Colleges, 1962-63.

"... there is a definite need for the list which you propose."

Stanley E. Van Lare, Director, Alpena Community College, Alpena, Michigan.

"... I wish to commend the junior college librarians for their action in establishing this project. It is greatly needed. The '20,000 Vital Titles', will be a valuable assist to junior college librarians; and it shows promise of becoming the criterion of greatest use for the selection of books for junior college libraries."

Dr. Rolo E. Wicks, Chairman, Dept. of English and Social Studies. Agricultural and Technical Institute, Canton, New York and President, The Junior College Council of the Middle Atlantic States, 1962-63.

"... I am more than pleased to indicate my hearty approval of your proposed publication: Basic Book List for Junior College Libraries: 20,000 Vital Titles. This publication should meet a very real need which has been long felt by many teachers, as well as librarians, who are identified with the development of junior colleges. Those responsible for this publication are to be commended for their initiative in undertaking such an ambitious project and for bringing it to such admirable fruition."

Dr. Horace J. Wubbon, President, Mesa College, Grand Junction, Colorado and President, Council of North Central Junior Colleges, 1961-62.

"... your program is a very desirable one. It is my impression that junior colleges, the country over, would benefit greatly from the common knowledge of what consists of a good junior college library."

TABLE OF CONTENTS

CONTENTS

APPENDIX:

20,000 VITAL TITLES FOR JUNIOR COLLEGES
ARRANGED ALPHABETICALLY BY SUBJECT

A

ABACUS (511.2078)
Crook, Welton J. Abacus arithmetic. 3.50. Pacific Bks.
ABBEYS (726.7)
Pennington, John. English cathedrals and abbeys. il. 1959. 3.95. Norton
Smith, Edwin, and Olive Cook. English abbeys and priories. il. 1960. 12.00.
   Viking
ABBREVIATIONS (421.8)
Collins, F. H. Authors' and printers' dictionary. 1956. 1.70. Oxford U. P. (R)
De Sola, Ralph. Abbreviations dictionary. 1958. 4.00. Duell (R)
Mayberry, George. Concise dictionary of abbreviations. 1961. 3.75. Tudor
Schwartz, Robert J. Complete dictionary of abbreviations. 1959. 4.95. Crowell
   (R)
ABDOMEN (611.95)
Friedman, Sydney M. Visual anatomy: Thorax and abdomen. il. 1952. 10.50.
   Thomas, C. C.
Michels, Nicholas A. Blood supply and anatomy of the upper abdominal organs.
   il. 1955. 24.00. Lippincott
ABELARD, PETER, 1079-1142 (921.4)
Gilson, Etienne. Heloise and Abelard. 1960. 4.40. U. of Mich.
Waddell, Helen J. Peter Abelard. 1959. 3.25. Smith, Peter
Worthington, Marjorie. Immortal lovers: Heloise and Abelard. 1960. 3.95.
   Doubleday
ABILITY (151)
Bingham, Walter V. Aptitudes and aptitude testing. 1937. 6.00. Harper
Bond, Horace M. Search for talent. 1959. 1.50. Harvard
Brueckner, Leo J. Educational diagnosis. NSSE, 34th yrbk. 1935. 4.50. U. of
   Chicago
Driscoll, Justin A. Factors in intelligence and achievement. 1952. 1.50. Catholic
   U. of Am. Pr.
Lawshe, Charles H., Jr. Principles of personnel testing. il. 1948. 5.75. McGraw
McClelland, David C., and others. Talent and society. 1958. 3.75. Van Nostrand
Thorndike, R. L. Personnel selection. 1949. 5.95. Wiley
Vernon, P. E. Structure of human abilities. 1950. 3.50. Wiley
ACCIDENTS (614.8)
American Public Health Association. Accident prevention. by Maxwell N. Halsey.
   il. 1961. 12.00. McGraw
Schulzinger, Morris S. Accident syndrome: The genesis of accidental injury, a
   clinical approach. il. 1956. 6.50. Thomas, C. C.
ACCOUNTING (657)
Backer, M. Handbook of modern accounting theory. 1954. 10.60. Prentice-Hall
Bray, F. S. Interpretation of accounts. 1957. 4,80. Oxford U. P.
Carson, A. B., and others. College accounting. 1962. 5.40. Southwestern Pub.
Carson, A. B., and others. Secretarial accounting. 1962. 4.00. Southwestern Pub.
Childs, William H. Accounting for management control. 10.50. Simmons-Boardman
Edwards, James D. History of public accounting in the United States. 1960. 6.50.
   Bur. of Bus. & Econ. Res., Mich. State
Eiteman, Wilford J. Essentials of accounting theory. 3.00. Masterco
Finney, Harry A., and Herbert E. Miller. Principles of accounting, intermediate.
   1958. 11.95. 8.75. Prentice-Hall
Fischer, Harry C. Accounting and office manual for labor unions. il. 5.50. Bur.
   of Nat. Affairs

Goldberg, Louis., and Vivian R. Hill. Elements of accounting. 1958. 4.50. Cambridge U. P.

Haller, Frederick J. Suggestions for an accounting plan. 1936. 2.00. Whiteside

Isaacson, Bernard B. Guides to successful accounting practice. 1959. 3.50. Am. Inst. of C. P. A.

Jackson, Paul R. Elementary college accounting. 1949. 4.35. Prentice-Hall

Keller, I. Wayne. Management accounting for profit control. il. 1957. 7.75. McGraw

Kennedy, R. D., and F. C. Kurtz. Introductory accounting. 9.50. Int. Textbook

Kohler, Eric L. Dictionary for accountants. 1957. 11.35. Prentice-Hall

Lasser, Jacob K. Handbook of accounting methods. il. 1954. 15.00. Van Nostrand

Lasser, Jacob K. Standard handbook for accountants. 1956. 15.00. McGraw

Littleton, A. C., and B. S. Yamey. Studies in the history of accounting. 1956. 7.00. Irwin

Mackenzie, Donald H. Fundamentals of accounting. il. 1956. 7.25; workforms for chapter problems, rev. ed. 3.50; practice sets; rev. ed. pap. 1.75; Panton Door Manufacturing Co., 1.75; R. S. Stewart Co., 1.75; Suburban Style Shop, 1.75. Macmillan

Mason, Perry, and others. Fundamentals of accounting. 1959. 7.95. Holt, Rinehart & Winston

May George O. Financial accounting. 1943. 5.25. Macmillan

Midgett, E. W. Introduction to accounting. 1962. 5.00. Humphries

Minrath, William. Simplified accounting. 1959. pap. 1.00. Van Nostrand

Murphy, M. E. Accounting. 1957. 5.50. Cambridge U. P.

Paton, William A. Accounting. 1924. 7.50; problems and cases for advanced accounting, 4.75. Macmillan

Ray, Delmas D. Accounting and business fluctuations. 6.50. U. of Fla.

Shugerman, A. L. Accounting for lawyers. 1952. 15.00. problems manual for text ed. 1.00. Bobbs

Vatter, William J. Fund theory of accounting and its implications for financial reports. 1947. pap. 2.50. U. of Chicago

ACCULTURATION (301.23)

Foster, George M. Culture and conquest: America's Spanish heritage. il. 6.00. Quadrangle

Frazier, E. Franklin. Race and culture contacts in the modern world. 1957. 5.00. Knopf

Handlin, Oscar. Uprooted. 1951. 4.75. Little

Malinowski, Bronislaw. Dynamics of culture change. by Phyllis M. Kaberry. il. 1945. 4.00. Yale

Mead, Margaret. Cultural patterns and technical change. (UNESCO) 2.50. Int. Doc. Service-Columbia

Mead, Margaret. New lives for old: A cultural transformation--Manus, 1928-1953. il. 1956. 6.75. Morrow

Patai, Raphael. Cultures in conflict. 1961. pap. 0.65. Herzl

Warner, W. Lloyd, and Leo Srole. Social systems of American ethnic groups. 1945. 6.00. Yale

ACIDS (661.2)

Bell, Ronald P. Acids and bases. 1952. 2.25. Wiley

ACTING (792.028)

Baldwin, Thomas W. Organization and personnel of the Shakespearean company. 1960. 10.00. Russell

Chambers, E. K. Elizabethan stage. il. 4 vol. 1923. 26.90. Oxford U. P.

Cole, Toby. Acting: A handbook of the Stanislavski method. 1955. 3.50. Crown

Dean, Alexander. Fundamentals of play directing. 1941. 5.50. Rinehart

Dolman, John Jr. Art of acting. il. 1949. 6.00. Harper

Dolman, John, Jr. Art of play production. 1946. 5.00. Harper

Franklin, Miriam A. Rehearsal. Principles and practice of acting for the stage. 1950. 6.75. Prentice-Hall

Funke, Lewis, and John Booth. Actors talk about acting. 1961. 6.95. Random

Gaye, Freda. Who's who in the theatre. 1962. 20.00. Pitman
Herman, Lewis, and Marguerite. Foreign dialects. 8.50. Theatre Arts
Kahan, Stanley. Introduction to acting. il. 1962. 5.95. Harcourt
McGraw, Charles J. Acting is believing. 1955. 4.35. Holt, Rinehart & Winston
Ommanney, Katharine A., and P. C. Stage and the school. 1960. 5.00. McGraw
Selden, Samuel. First steps in acting. 3.00. Appleton
Selden, Samuel. Stage in action. il. 3.50. Appleton
Stanislavski, Constantin. Actor prepares. 3.50. Theatre Arts
Stanislavski, Constantin. Building a character. 3.50. Theatre Arts
Stanislavski, Constantin. Creating a role. by Hermine E. Popper. tr. by
    Elizabeth R. Hapgood. 1961. 4.00. Theatre Arts
Stanislavski, Constantin. On the art of the stage. by David Magarshack. il. 1961.
    4.50. Hill & Wang
Stanislavski, Constantin. Stanislavski's legacy. by Elizabeth R. Hapgood. 3.50.
    Theatre Arts
ADAMS, HENRY, 1838-1918 (923.7)
Adams, Henry. Eudcation of Henry Adams. 6.00. Houghton
Levenson, J. C. Mind and art of Henry Adams. 1957. 6.00. Houghton
Stevenson, Elizabeth. Henry Adams. il. 1955. 6.50. Macmillan
ADAMS, JOHN, PRES. U.S., 1735-1826 (923.173)
Bowen, Catherine Drinker. John Adams and the American Revolution. il. 1950.
    7.50. Little
Kurtz, Stephen G. Presidency of John Adams. 1957. 8.50. U. of Pa.
ADAMS, JOHN QUINCY, PRES. U. S., 1767-1848 (923.173)
Bemis, Samuel Flagg. John Quincy Adams and the foundations of American foreign
    policy. il. 1949. 8.75. Knopf
Bemis, Samuel Flagg. John Quincy Adams and the Union. 1956. 8.75. Knopf
ADAPTATION (BIOLOGY) (574.5)
Gale, E. F., and R. Davies. Adaptation in micro-organisma. 1953. 6.50.
    Cambridge U. P.
Huxley, Julian S. Wonderful world of life. il. 1958. 2.95. Doubleday
Srb, Adrian M., and Bruce Wallace. Adaptation. 1961. 3.75. Prentice-Hall
Welch, William H. Adaptation in pathological processes, 1897. 1937. 1.50. Johns
    Hopkins
ADDAMS, JANE, 1860-1935. (923)
Addams, Jane. Centennial reader. by Emily C. Johnson. 1960. 6.00. Macmillan
Tims, Margaret. Jane Addams of Hull House. 1961. 4.25. Macmillan
ADDISON, JOSEPH, 1672-1719 (928)
Smithers, Peter. Life of Joseph Addison. il. 1954. 7.20. Oxford U. P.
ADJUSTMENT (PSYCHOLOGY) (137)
Coleman, James C. Personality dynamics and effective behavior. 1960. 6.00.
    Scott
Heyns, Roger W. Psychology of personal adjustment. 1958. 5.50. Holt, Rinehart
    & Winston
Jouard, Sidney M. Personal adjustment. 5.95. Macmillan
Lazarus, Richard S. Adjustment and personality. il. 1961. 6.95. McGraw
Smith, Henry C. Personality adjustment. 1961. 7.50. McGraw
Young, Kimball. Personality and problems of adjustment. il. 6.50. Appleton
ADLER, ALFRED, 1870-1937 (131.3463)
Bottome, Phyllis. Alfred Adler. 5.00. Vanguard
Brachfeld, Oliver. Inferiority feelings. 1951. 4.50. Grune
Ganz, Madelaine. Psychology of Alfred Adler, and Development of the child. 1953.
    5.00. Humanities
Way, Lewis. Adler's place in psychology. 1950. 4.50. Macmillan
ADMINISTRATIVE LAW (350)
Auerbach, Carl A., and others. Legal process: An introduction to decision-making
    by judicial, legislative, executive, and administrative agencies. 1961. 10.00.
    Chandler-Pub.
Hart, James. Introduction to administrative law. 1950. 7.50. Appleton

Pfiffner, J. M., and R. V. Presthus. Public administration. 1960. 7.50. Ronald

ADOLESCENCE (136.7354)

Ausubel, D. P. Theory and problems of adolescent development. 1954. 8.50. Grune

Baruch, Dorothy W. How to live with your teen-ager. il. 1953. 4.95. McGraw

Blos, Peter. On adolescence. 1961. 5.00. Free Press

Cole, Luella. Psychology of adolescence. 1959. 7.00. Rinehart

Coleman, James S. Adolescent. 1961. 6.95. Free Press

Crow, Lester D., and Alice. Adolescent development and adjustment. 1956. 6.95. McGraw

Crow, Lester D., and Alice. Readings in child and adolescent psychology. 1961. pap. 3.95. McKay

Gallagher, James R., and Herbert I. Harris. Emotional problems of adolescents. 1958. 4.00. Oxford U. P.

Garrison, Karl C. Psychology of adolescence. 1951. 6.95. Prentice-Hall

Gesell, Arnold, and others. Infant and child in the culture of today and The child from five to ten, and Youth. 15.95. Harper

Gesell, Arnold, and others. Youth: The years from ten to sixteen. 1956. 5.95. Harper

Gordon, Ira J. Human development: From birth through adolescence. 1962. 5.75. Harper

Havighurst, Robert J. and H. Taba. Adolescent character and personality. 1949. 5.95. Wiley

Hurlock, Elizabeth B. Adolescent development. 1955. 7.25. McGraw

Jersild, Arthur T. Psychology of adolescence. il. 1957. 6.00. Macmillan

Jones, Harold E. Adolescence. NSSE, 43rd yrbk. pt. 1. 1944. 3.00. U. of Chicago

Josselyn, Irene M. Adolescent and his world. 1952. 1.75. Family Service Assn.

Kunkel, Fritz. What it means to grow up. 1955. 3.00. Scribner

Landis, Paul H. Adolescence and youth: The process of maturing. 1952. 6.95. McGraw

Mead, Margaret. Coming of age in Samoa. 3.75. Smith, Peter

Mead, Margaret. From the South Seas: Studies of adolescence and sex in Primitive societies. 1939. 5.00. Morrow

Menninger, William C. and others. How to understand the opposite sex. 1956. 2.95. Sterling

Merry, Frieda K., and Ralph V. First two decades of life. 1958. 6.75. Harper

Pearson, Gerald H. J. Adolescence and the conflict of generations. 1958. 4.50. Norton

Rogers, Dorothy. Psychology of adolescence. il. 1962. 6.00. Appleton

Schneiders, Alexander A. Personality development and adjustment in adolescence. 1960. 5.75. Bruce

Seidman, Jerome M. Adolescent: A book of readings. 1960. 6.50. Holt, Rinehart & Winston

Smith, Ernest A. American youth culture: Group life in teenage society. 1962. 6.00. Free Press

Stone, L. Joseph, and Joseph Church. Childhood and adolescence. il. 1957. 7.75. Random

Strain, Frances B. Teen days. il. 1946. 3.75. Meredith

Strang, Ruth. Adolescent views himself: A psychology of adolescence. 1957. 9.00. McGraw

Tanner, James M. Growth at adolescence. il. 1961. 9.00. Davis

Vattenberg, William W. Adolescent years. 9.25. Harcourt

Wilkes, E. T. Family guide to teenage health. 1958. 4.50. Ronald

Wittenberg, Rudolph M. Adolescence and discipline: A mental hygiene primer. 1959. 4.95. Assn. Pr.

ADOPTION (362.73)

Charnley, Jean. Art of child placement. 1961. 5.00. U. of Minn.

Glickman, E. Child placement through clinically oriented casework. 1957. 7.50. Columbia

Raymond, Louise. Adoption - and after. 1955. 3.50. Harper

Trasler, G. In place of parents: A study of foster care. 5.00. Humanities
ADRENAL GLANDS (612.45)
Gardner, L. I. Adrenal function in infants and children. 1956. 7.00. Grune
Soffer, Louis J., and others. Human adrenal gland. 8.50. Lea & F
ADVERTISING (659.1)
Baker, Samm S. Casebook of successful ideas for advertising and selling. 1959.
     3.95. Doubleday
Baker, Stephen. Visual persuasion. il. 1961. 13.50. McGraw
Committee on Advertising. Principles of advertising. 1962. 7.50. Pitman
Dunn, S. Watson. Advertising: Its role in modern marketing. 1961. 10.20. Holt,
     Rinehart & Winston
Fortune. Amazing advertising business. by the Editors of Fortune. 1957. 3.50.
     S. and S.
Frey, A. W. Advertising. 1961. 7.50. Ronald
Gaw, Walter A. Advertising: Methods and media. il. 1961. 7.95. Wadsworth
Graham, Irvin. Encyclopedia of advertising. 1952. 6.50. Fairchild
Kirkpatrick, C. A. Advertising: Mass communication in marketing. 1960. 11.00.
     Houghton
Mayer, Martin. Madison Avenue, U.S.A. 1958. 4.95. Harper
Packard, Vance O. Hidden persuaders. 1957. 5.75. McKay'
Rowse, Edward J., and Carroll A. Nolan. Fundamentals of advertising. 1957.
     3.72. South-Western Pub.
Sandage, Charles H., and Vernon Fryburger. Role of advertising. 1960. 8.00.
     Irwin
Tyler, Poyntz. Advertising in America. 1959. 2.50. Wilson
Zacher, Robert V. Advertising techniques and management. 1961. 10.00. Irwin
AERODYNAMICS (629.1323)
Etkin, Bernard. Dyanmics of flight. il. 1959. 13.50. Wiley
Kolk, W. Richard. Modern flight dynamics. 1960. 10.00. Prentice-Hall
Kuethe, Arnold M., and J. D. Schetzer. Foundations of aerodynamics. il. 1959.
     9.95. Wiley
Mises, Richard von. Theory of flight. 5.00. Smith, Peter
Perkins, C. D., and R. E. Hage. Airplane performance, stability and control.
     1949. 7.95. Wiley
AERONAUTICS (629.13)
Bernardo, James V. Aviation in the modern world. il. 1960. 5.95. Dutton
Bridgman, Leonard. Jane's all the world's aircraft. 1963. 35.00. McGraw
De la Croix, Robert. They flew the Atlantic. il. 1959. 3.95. Norton
Desoutter, Dennis M. Aircraft and missiles. 1959. 7.50. De Graff
Gentle, Ernest J., and Charles Edward Chapel. Aviation and space dictionary.
     il. 1961. 10.00.
Gunston, W. T. Flight handbook: Theory and practice of powered flight. il. 1962.
     7.50. Aero
Hoare, Robert. Wings over the Atlantic. 3.00. Branford
Lindbergh, Anne Morrow. Listen! The wind. il. 3.95. Harcourt
Lindbergh, Charles A. Spirit of St. Louis. il. 1957. 5.95. Scribner
Tower, Merrill E. Basic aeronautics. il. 1952. 4.00. Aero
Van Sickle, Neil D. Modern airmanship. il. 1961. 9.75. Van Nostrand
AFGHANISTAN (958.1)
Weston, Christine. Afghanistan. il. 1962. 3.95. Scribner
Wilber, Donald N. Afghanistan. 1962. 8.75. Taplinger
AFRICA (960)
Alimen, H. Prehistory of Africa. 12.50. Humanities
Boyd, Andrew, and Patrick Van Rensburg. Atlas of African affairs. 3.50. Praeger
Drachler, Jacob. African heritage. 1962. 3.95. Crowell-Collier
Italiaander, Rolf. New leaders of Africa. 1961. 5.00. Prentice-Hall
Legum, Colin. Africa: A handbook to the continent. il. 1962. 15.00. Praeger
Lewis, William H., and others. New forces in Africa. 1962. 3.50. Pub. Affairs

Panikkar, Kavalam M. Afro-Asian states and their problems. 1960. 3.00. Day

Williams, John A. Africa: Her history, lands and people. 4.50. Cooper

AFRICA--CIVILIZATION (960)

Davidson, Basil. Lost cities of Africa. il. 1959. 6.00. Little

Herskovits, Melville J. Human factor in changing Africa. 1962. 6.95. Knopf

Murdock, George P. Africa: Its people and their cultural history. 1959. 11.75. McGraw

AFRICA--DESCRIPTION AND TRAVEL (916)

Franck, Frederck. African sketchbook. 1961. 5.95. Holt, Rinehart & Winston

Gunther, John. Inside Africa. 1955. 7.95. Harper

Johnson, Osa. I married adventure. il. 1940. 5.00. Lippincott

Kane, Robert S. Africa A to Z: A guide for travelers. il. 1961. 4.95. Doubleday

AFRICA--POLITICS (960)

Elias, Taslim O. Government and politics in Africa. 1961. 6.50? Taplinger

Hatch, John. Africa today - and tomorrow. il. 1962. 5.00. Praeger

MacLure, Millar, and Douglas G. Anglin. Africa: Political pattern. 1961. 2.50. U. of Toronto

Phillips, John. Kwame Nkrumah and the future of Africa. 6.50. Praeger

AGASSIZ, LOUIS, 1807-1873) (925)

Forsee, Aylesa. Louis Agassiz: The pied piper of science. il. 1958. 4.00. Viking

Lurie, Edward. Louis Agassiz: A life in science. il. 1960. 7.50. U. of Chicago

AGED (301.435)

Barron, Milton L. Aging American. il. 1961. 7.50. Crowell

Burgess, Ernest W. Aging in Western societies. il. 1960. 7.50. U. of Chicago

Drake, J. T. Aged in American society. 1958. 6.00. Ronald

Hazell, Kenneth. Social and medical problems of the elderly. il. 1960. 6.75. Thomas, C. C.

Kaplan, J. and G. Aldridge. Social welfare of the aging. 1962. 9.00. Columbia

Maves, Paul B. Best is yet to be. 1951. 2..00. Westminster

AGGREGATES (512.817)

Berge, Claude. Theory of graphs and its applications. 1962. 6.50. Wiley

Hamilton, Norman T., and Joseph Landin. Set theory: The structure of arithmetic. il. 1961. 7.75. Allyn & Bacon

Keene, Geoffrey B. Abstract sets and finite ordinals. il. 1962. 3.50. Pergamon

Kuratowski, Casimir. Introduction to set theory and topology. il. 1962. 6.50. Addison-Wesley

Suppes, Patrick. Axiomatic set theory. 1960. 6.00. Van Nostrand

AGING (612.67)

Birren, James E. Handbook of aging and the individual. il. 1960. 12.50. U. of Chicago

Smith, Ethel Sabin. Dynamics of aging. 1956. 3.95. Norton

Tibbitts, Clark, and Wilma Donahue. Aging in today's society. 1960. 7.00. Prentice-Hall

Wolff, Kurt. Biological, sociological and psychological aspects of aging. 1959. 3.75. Thomas, C. C.

AGRICULTURE (630)

Black, John Donald. Introduction to economics for agriculture. il. 6.75. Macmillan

Blanck, F. C. Handbook of food and agriculture. 1955. 15.00. Reinhold (R)

Bromfield, Louis. Out of the earth. il. 1950. 5.00. Harper

Donahue, Roy L., and E. F. Evans. Exploring agriculture. 1957. 7.55. Prentice-Hall

Heady, Earl, and John Dillon. Agricultural production functions. 1961. 6.95. Iowa State

Hockensmith, Roy D. Water and agriculture. 1960. 5.00. A.A.A.S.

Kolb, John H., and Edmund de S. Brunner. Study of rural society. 7.50. Houghton

Land Economics Institute. Modern land policy. il. 1960. 8.50. U. of Ill.

Osborn, Fairfield. Our plundered planet. 1948. 3.75. Little

Pearson, Frank A., and Floyd A. Harper. World's hunger. 1945. 1.50. Cornell

Williams, W. R., and G. V. Jacks. Principles of agriculture. 1952. 3.75. Tudor

White, John M. Farmer's handbook. il. 1956. 4.95. U. of Okla.

Winburne, John N., and others. Dictionary of agricultural and allied terminology. 1962. 15.00. Mich. State (R)

AIR--POLLUTION (614.71)

Farber, Seymour M., and Roger H. L. Wilson. Air we breathe: A study of man and his environment. 1960. 14.00. Thomas, C. C.

Jacobs, Morris B. Chemical analysis of air pollutants. il. 1960. 14.00. Wiley

Leighton, P. A. Photochemical aspects of air pollution. il. 1961. 11.00. Academic Press

Mallette, F. S. Problems and control of air pollution. 1955. 7.50. Reinhold

Meetham, A. Roger. Atmospheric pollution: Its origins and prevention. 1956. 11.00. Pergamon

Mills, Clarence A. This air we breathe. 1962. 4.00. Christopher

AIR CONDITIONING (697)

Althouse, Andrew D., and C. H. Turnquist. Modern refrigeration and air conditioning. il. 1960. 7.45. Goodheart

Burkhardt, C. H. Residential and commercial air conditioning. 1959. 9.50. McGraw

Harris, Norman C. Modern air conditioning practice. 1959. 6.75. McGraw

Laub, J. Air conditioning and heating practice. 1962. 11.00. Holt, Rinehart & Winston

Strock, Clifford. Handbook of air conditioning, heating and ventilating. il. 1959. 15.00. Industrial Pr.

AIRPLANES, MILITARY (623.746)

Green, William. War planes of the Second World War: Fighters. 4 vols. il. 1961. 2.75 ea. 'Doubleday

Green, William, and Gerald Pollinger. World's fighting planes. il. 1959. 3.50. Doubleday

Swanborough, F. G. Combat aircraft of the world. 1962. 6.50. Taplinger

Wagner, Ray. American combat planes. il. 9.95. Doubleday

ALABAMA (976.1)

Carmer, Carl. Stars fell on Alabama. 1961. pap. 1.75. Hill & Wang

Writers' Project. Alabama. 6.50. Hastings

Summersell, Charles G. Alabama history for schools. il. 1957. 3.87. Colonial Pr.

ALASKA (979.8)

Adams, Ben. Last frontier: A short history of Alaska. il. 1961. 3.50. Hill & Wang

Alaska: story of our nothern treasureland. il. 1960. 9.95. Doubleday

Colby, Merle. Alaska: A guide to the last American frontier. il. 7.50. Macmillan

Emerson, William C. Land of the midnight sun. il. 1956. 3.00. Dorrance

Kursh, Harry. This is Alaska. 1961. 5.95. Prentice-Hall

Rogers, George W. Future of Alaska: Economic consequences of statehood. 1962. 6.50. Johns Hopkins

ALCHEMY (540.1)

Caron, M., and S. Hutin. Alchemists. il. 3.35. Smith, Peter

Jung, Carl G. Psychology and alchemy. by Herbert Read, and others. 1953. 5.00. Pantheon

ALCOHOLICS (616.861)

Alcoholics Anonymous. Twelve steps and twelve traditions. 1953. 2.75. Harper

Bier, W. C. Problems in addiction: Alcoholism and narcotics. 1962. 5.00. Fordham

Chafetz, Morris E., and Harold W. Demone, Jr. Alcoholism and society. 1962. 6.95. Oxford U. P.

Clinebell, Howard J., Jr. Understanding and counseling the alcoholic. 1956. 3.75. Abingdon

Courville, Cyril B. Effects of alcohol on the nervous system of man. il. 1955. 4.50. Univ. Pub.

Fox, Ruth, and Peter Lyon. Alcoholism: Its scope, causes and treatment. 1955. 3.00. Random

Jellinek, Elvin M. Disease concept of alcoholism. 1960. 6.00. Rutgers Center of Alcohol Studies

Kessel, Joseph. Road back: A report on Alcoholics Anonymous. tr. by Francis Partridge. 1962. 3.95. Knopf

Pfau, Father. Prodigal shepherd. 1958. 3.95. S. M. T.

Pittman, David J., and C. Wayne Gordon. Revolving door. 1958. 4.00. Free Press

Taylor, G. Aiken. Sober faith. Religion and Alcoholics Anonymous. 1953. 3.50. Macmillan

ALEXANDER THE GREAT, 356-323 B. C. (923.5)

Fuller, J. F. C. Generalship of Alexander the Great. il. 1959. 7.50. Rutgers

Quintus Curtius. History of Alexander. 2 vols. 3.50 ea. Harvard

Tarn, William W. Alexander the Great. 1948. 4.00. Cambridge U. P.

ALGAE (589.3)

Dawson, E. Yale. How to know the seaweeds. by H. E. Jaques. 1956. 2.75. Brown, W. C.

Prescott, Gerald W. How to know the freshwater algae. by Harry E. Jaques. 1954. 2.75. Brown, W. C.

Smith, Gilbert M. Freshwater algae of the United States. il. 1950. 14.00. McGraw

Tiffany, Lewis H. Algae. il. 1958. 6.50. Thomas, C. C

ALGEBRA (512)

Asimov, Isaac. Realm of algebra. 1961. 3.00. Houghton

Birkhoff, Garrett, and Saunders MacLane. Survey of modern algebra. 1953. 7.50. Macmillan

Brink, Raymond W. College algebra. 1951. 4.25. Appleton

Britton, Jack R., and L. Clifton Snively. Algebra for college students. 1954. 4.50. Rinehart

Crouch, R. B., and E. A. Walker. Introduction to modern algebra and analysis. 1962. 4.00. Holt, Rinehart & Winston

Fisher, Robert C., and Allen D. Zieber. Integrated algebra and trigonometry. 1958. 10.60. Prentice-Hall

Fuller, Gordon. College algebra. 1956. 4.75. Van Nostrand

Hafstrom, J. E. Basic concepts in modern mathematics. 1961. 5.75. Addison-Wesley

Hart, William L. Intermediate algebra for colleges. 1948. 4.75. Heath

Herrick, Marian, and others. Essential skills in algebra. 1962. 2.40. Harcourt

Lehmann, Charles H. College algebra. il. 1962. 5.95. Wiley

Leonhardy, A. College algebra. il. 1961. 5.95. Wiley

Mancill, Julian D., and Mario O. Gonzalez. Modern college algebra. il. 1960. 8.65. Allyn & Bacon

Mueller, Francis J. Essential mathematics for college students. 1958. 3.95. Prentice-Hall

Peters, Max. College algebra. il. 1961. 4.25. Barron's

Peterson, Thurman S. Intermediate algebra for college students. 1954. 4.50. Harper

Rider, Paul R. College algebra. 4.90. Macmillan

Toskey, B. R. College algebra: A modern approach. 1962. Addison-Wesley

ALGEBRA, ABSTRACT (512.8)

Andree, Richard V. Selections from modern abstract algebra. 1958. 6.50. Holt, Rinehart & Winston

Halmos, Paul R. Algebraic logic. 1962. 3.75. Chelsea

Moore, John T. Elements of abstract algebra. il. 1962. 6.50. Macmillan

ALGERIA (965)

Behr, Edward. Algerian problem. il. 1962. 4.50. Norton

Fisher, Godfrey. Barbary legend: War, trade and piracy in North Africa, 1415-1830. 1957. 8.80. Oxford U. P.

Gillespie, Joan. Algeria: rebellion and revolution. 1960. 6.50. Praeger

Tillion, Germaine. Algeria. 1958. 3.00. Knopf

ALLERGY (616.97)

Feinberg, Samuel M. Living with your allergy. 2.75. Lippincott

Jamar, J. M. International textbook of allergy. il. 1959. 17.50. Thomas, C. C

Prigal, Samuel J. Fundamentals of modern allergy. 1960. 18.50. McGraw

Sammis, Florence E. Allergic patient and his world: Including sources of allergens. il. 1953. 4.75. Thomas, C. C

Scott, Michael J. Hypnosis in skin and allergic diseases. 1961. 6.50. Thomas, C. C.

Swartz, Harry. How to master your allergy. 1961. 5.00. Nelson

ALLUSIONS (803)

Brewer's dictionary of phrase and fable. 1953. 5.95. Harper (R)

ALMANACS (317)

Franklin, Benjamin. Poor Richard's almanac. 1.50. McKay

Golenpaul, Dan. Information please almanac. 1959. 2.50. Macmillan (R)

ALPHABET (411)

Doblhofer, Ernst. Voices in stone: The decipherment of ancient scripts and writings. tr. by Mervyn Savill. il. 1961. 6.00. Viking

Driver, Godfrey R. Semitic writing: From pictograph to alphabet. 1954. 6.90. Oxford U. P.

Moorhouse, Alfred C. Triumph of the alphabet. il. 1953. 3.50. Abelard

Ogg, Oscar. 26 letters. il. 1961. 5.50. Crowell

Russell, J. Alphabets, ancient and modern. 2.00. Wehman

AMATEUR THEATRICALS (792.022)

Bailey, Howard. ABC's of play producing: A handbook for the non professional. 1955. 3.95. McKay

Cartmell, Van H. Amateur theater. 1961. 3.95. Van Nostrand

Corry, Percy. Amateur theatrecraft. 1962. 3.95. Pitman

Dolman, John, Jr. Art of play production. 1946. 5.00. Harper

Downs, Harold. Theatre and stage. 2 vols. 1951. 25.00. Pitman

Smith, Milton M. Play production. il. 1948. 5.50. Appleton

Young, John Wray. Directing the play: From selection to opening night. 1958. 3.50. Harper

AMERICA (973.1)

Hibben, Frank C. Lost Americans. il. 3.25. Smith, Peter

Pohl, Frederick J. Atlantic crossings before Columbus. il. 1961. 4.50. Norton

Larned, Josephus N. Literature of American history. 1953. 15.00. Long's College Bk.

AMERICA--DISCOVERY AND EXPLORATION (973.1)

Bakeless, John E. Eyes of discovery. il. 1962. 4.00. Smith, Peter

Channing, Edward. Planting of the nation in the new world, 1000-1660. 7.00. Macmillan

Cheyney, E. P. European background of American history, 1300-1600. 3.00. Smith, Peter

De Voto, Bernard. Course of empire. 1952. 6.50. Houghton

Lamb, Harold. New found world. 1955. 5.75. Doubleday

Lowery, Woodbury. Spanish settlements within the present limits of the United States. vol. 1, 1513-1561; vol. 2, Florida, 1562-1574. il. set, 15.00. Russell

Morse, Jarvis M. American beginnings. 1952. 3.75. Pub. Affairs

O'Gorman, Edmundo. Invention of America. il. 1961. 5.00. Indiana

AMERICAN BALLADS AND SONGS (784.4)

Greenway, John. American folksongs of protest. 4.00. Smith, Peter

Ives, Burl. Song in America. 1961. 10.00. Duell

Leach, MacEdward. Ballad book. 1955. 10.00. Harper

Sandburg, Carl. American songbag. il. 1927. 5.95. Harcourt

Wells, Evelyn K. Ballad tree. 1950. 6.00. Ronald

AMERICAN DRAMA (COLLECTIONS) (812.08)
Clark, Barrett H., and William H. Davenport. Nine modern American plays. 1951.
  2.90. Appleton
Cordell, Richard A. Twentieth century plays - American. 1947. 3.00. Ronald
Cordell, Richard A. Twentieth century plays - British, American, Continental.
  1947. 3.50. Ronald
Gassner, John. Best American plays, 1918-1958. suppl. vol. 5.95. Lothrop
Gassner, John. Best American plays: 1945-1951. 5.95. Crown
Gassner, John. Best plays of the modern American theatre. 1939-1946. 1952-1957.
  2 vols. 5.95 ea. Crown
Gassner, John. Library of best American plays. 5 vols. 5.95 ea. Crown
Gassner, John. Twenty best plays of the modern American theatre. 5.95. Crown
Gassner, John. Twenty five best plays of the modern American theatre: Early
  series. 5.95. Crown
Hatcher, Harlan. Modern American dramas. 1949. 3.00. Harcourt
Kozlenko, William. 100 non-royalty one-act plays. 4.95. Grosset
Miller, Jordan Y. American dramatic literature: Ten modern plays in historical
  perspective. 1961. 6.75. McGraw
Quinn, Arthur H. Representative American plays. 1953. 7.00. Appleton
Sixteen famous American plays. 2.95. Modern Lib.
Warnock, Robert. Representative modern plays, American. 1952. 2.95. Scott
AMERICAN DRAMA--HISTORY AND CRITICISM (812.09)
Krutch, Joseph Wood. American drama since 1918. 1957. 5.00. Braziller
Quinn, Arthur H. History of American drama: vol. 1, From the beginnings to
  the Civil War. 7.00. vol. 2, From the Civil War to the present day, 1943.
  7.00. Appleton
AMERICAN ESSAYS (814.08)
Beaver, Harold L. American critical essays. 1961. 2.25. Oxford U. P.
Jameson, Robert U. Essays old and new. 1955. 2.12. Harcourt
Leary, Lewis. American literary essays. 1960. 5.95. Crowell
Nye, Russel. Modern essays. 1957. 2.95. Scott
Smithberger, Andrew Thomas. Essays: British and American. 1953. 3.50.
  Houghton
Wann, Louis. Century readings in the English essay. il. 1931. 5.00. Appleton
AMERICAN FICTION (COLLECTIONS) (813.08)
Blackmur, Richard P. American short novels. 1960. 5.95. Crowell
Phillips, William. Great American short novels. 1947. 4.50. Holt, Rinehart &
  Winston
Solomon, Eric. Faded banners, a treasury of nineteenth-century Civil War fiction.
  1960. 10.00. Yoseloff
Thurston, Jarvis, and others. Short fiction criticism: A checklist of interpretation
  since 1925 of stories and novelettes (American, British, continental) 1800-1958.
  1959. 4.00. Swallow, A. (R)
AMERICAN FICTION--HISTORY AND CRITICISM (813.09)
Aldridge, John W. After the lost generation. 1958. pap. 1.45. Farrar, Straus
Aldridge, J. W. Critiques and essays on modern fiction, 1920-1951. 1952. 7.50.
  Ronald
Beach, Joseph W. American fiction 1920-1940. 1960. 6.00. Russell
Bewley, Marius. Eccentric design: Form in the classic American novel. 1959.
  4.00. Columbia
Brown, Herbert R. Sentimental novel in America, 1789-1860. 1959. 6.00. Cooper
Chase, Richard. American novel and its tradition. 3.00. Smith, Peter
Cowie, Alexander. Rise of the American novel. 7.00. Am. Bk. Co.
Cowley, Malcolm. After the genteel tradition, American writers since 1910. 1959.
  3.75. Smith, Peter
Fiedler, Leslie. Love and death in the American novel. il. 1959. 8.50. Criterion
Frohock, W. M. Novel of violence in America. 1957. 4.50. S. M. U.
Fuller, Edmund. Man in modern fiction. 1958. 3.50. Random

Geismar, Maxwell. American moderns: From rebellion to conformity. 1958. 3.95. Hill & Wang

Geismar, Maxwell. Last of the provincials. 5.00. Houghton

Geismar, Maxwell. Rebels and ancestors. 1953. 4.50. Houghton

Geismar, Maxwell. Writers in crisis. 1942. 5.00. Houghton

Hicks, Granville. Living novel. 4.50. Macmillan

Hoffman, Daniel G. Form and fable in American fiction. 1961. 7.00. Oxford U. P.

Leisy, Ernest E. American historical novel. 1952. 3.75. U. of Okla.

Quinn, Arthur H. American fiction: An historical and critical survey. 1936. 6.50. Appleton

Rubin, Louis D., and John R. Moore. Idea of an American novel. 1961. 7.50. Crowell

Snell, George. Shapers of American fiction. 4.95. Cooper

Van Doren, Carl. American novel. 1789-1939. 5.50. Macmillan

Wagenknecht, Edward. Cavalcade of the American novel. 1952. 9.45. Holt, Rinehart & Winston

Wright, Austin M. American short story in the twenties. 1961. 7.50. U. of Chicago

Zabel, Morton Dauwen. Craft and character in modern fiction. 1957. 4.75. Viking

AMERICAN LANGUAGE (427)

Horwill, H. W. Dictionary of modern American usage. 1944. 4.50. Oxford U. P. (R)

Krapp, George P. English language in America. 2 vols. 12.00. Ungar

Mencken, Henry L. American language. 3 vols. 1936-1948. 10.00 ea; set 25.00. Knopf

Morehead, Albert H., and others. New American Roget's college thesaurus in dictionary form. 1957. 2.75. Grosset

Evans, Bergen, and Cornelia. Dictionary of contemporary American usage. 1957. 5.95. Random (R)

Nicholson, Margaret. Dictionary of American-English usage. 1957. 5.00. Oxford U. P. (R)

Webster's new world dictionary of the American language. 29.50. World Pub.

AMERICAN LITERATURE (COLLECTIONS) (810.08)

Burnett, Whit. This is my best. 4.95. World Pub.

Grebanier, Bernard D. N., and Seymour Reiter. Introduction to imaginative literature. 1960. 7.50. Crowell

Hunt, Kellogg W., and Paul Stoakes. Our living language. 1961. 4.75. Houghton

Miller, Perry. American Putitans, their prose and poetry. 1959. 3.25. Smith, Peter

Miller, Perry. American transcendentalists: Their prose and poetry. 3.25. Smith, Peter

Saturday Review. Saturday Review treasury. by the Editors of Saturday Review. 1957. 6.00. S. and S.

Stewart, Randall, and Dorothy Bethurum. Living masterpieces of American literature. 1954. 8.75. Whitman

Stewart, Randall, and Dorothy Bethurum. Living masterpieces of English literature. 1954. 8.75. Whitman

Wann, Louis. Rise of realism. 1933. 5.75. Macmillan

AMERICAN LITERATURE (SELECTIONS: EXTRACTS, ETC.) (810)

Benet, William, and N. H. Pearson. Oxford anthology of American literature; 2 vols. 6.00 ea. Oxford U. P.

Bradley, Sculley, and others. American tradition in literature. 1957. complete 2 vol. ed. 6.50 ea; short ed. 1. vol. 7.25. Norton

Cady, Edwin Harrison, and others. Growth of American literature. 2 vols. vol. 1 7.00; vol. 2, 6.75. Am. Bk. Co.

Chase, Mary Ellen, and Henry W. Sams. Constructive theme writing. 1957. 5.25. Holt

Commager, Henry Steele, and Allan Nevins. Heritage of America. il. 1949. 8.00. Little

Fadiman, Clifton, and Charles Van Doren. American Treasury, 1455-1955. 8.95. 1955. Harper

Hart, James D., and Clarence Gohdes. America's literature. 1955. 9.75. Holt, Rinehart & Winston

Havighurst, Walter, and others. Selection: A reader for college writings. 1955. 6.75. Holt, Rinehart & Winston

McNamee, Maurice B. Reading for understanding. 1958. 5.25. Holt, Rinehart & Winston

McNamee, Maurice, and others. Literary types and themes. 1960. 6.95; manual 0.50; gratis to teachers. Holt, Rinehart & Winston

Miller, Perry. Major writers of America. 2 vols. 1962. 3.95 ea. Harcourt

Stallman, R. W., and Arthur Waldhorn. American literature: Readings and critiques. 1961. 8.50. Putnam

Thorp, Willard, and others. American literary record. 1961. 10.00. 7.50. Lippincott

AMERICAN LITERATURE--ADDRESSES, ESSAYS, LECTURES (810)

Davidson, Donald. Still Rebels, still Yankees and other essays. 1957. 4.50. La. State

Feidelson, Charles, and Paul Brodtkorb. Interpretations of American literature. 1959. 4.75. Smith, Peter

Wilson, Edmund. Literary chronicle, 1920-1950. 1956. pap. 1.45. Doubleday

Wilson, Edmund. Literary chronicle: 1920-1950. 3.50. Smith, Peter

Wilson, Edmund. Shores of light. 1952. 6.50. Farrar, Straus

AMERICAN LITERATURE--BIBLIOGRAPHY (016.81)

Altick, Richard D., and Andrew Wright. Selective bibliography for the study of English and American literature. pap. 2.50. Macmillan

Blanck, Jacob, comp. Bibliography of American literature. 3. vols. 17.50 ea. Yale

Jones, Howard Mumford. Guide to American literature and its backgrounds since 1890. 1959. pap. 2.50. Harvard

Richards, Robert L. Dictionary of American literature. 1956. pap. 1.50. Littlefield (R)

AMERICAN LITERATURE--DICTIONARIES, INDEXES, ETC. (810.03)

Hart, J. D. Oxford companion to American literature. 1956. 10.00. Oxford U.P. (R)

Herzberg, Max J. Reader's encyclopedia of American literature. il. 1962. 12.95. Crowell (R)

AMERICAN LITERATURE--HISTORY AND CRITICISM (810.09)

Blair, Walter, and others. Literature of the United States. 1957. 12.75. Whitman

Blankenship, Russell. American literature as an expression of the national mind. 1949. 7.50. Holt

Bradbury, John M. Fugitives: A critical account. 1958. 5.00. U. of N. C.

Brooks, Van Wyck. Makers and finders. 5 vols. 2.95 ea. Dutton

Brooks, Van Wyck, and Otto L. Bettmann. Our literary heritage: A pictorial history of the writer in America. il. 1956. 8.50. Dutton

Cowan, Louise S. Fugitive group: A literary history. 1959. 5.00. La. State

Foerster, Norman. American criticism: A study in literary theory from Poe to the present day. 1962. 7.50. Russell

Horton, Rod W., and Herbert W. Edwards. Backgrounds of American literary thought. 1952. 3.25. Appleton

Hubbell, Jay B. South in American literature, 1607-1900. 1954. 10.00. Duke

Lawrence, David H. Studies in classic American literature. 1953. pap. 0.95. Doubleday

Parrington, Vernon Louis. Main currents in American thought. 1 vol. 10.50. vol. 1, Colonial mind, 1620-1800; and vol. 2, Romantic revolution in America, 1800-1860. pap. 1.75 ea. Harcourt

Rourke, Constance. American humor: A study of national character. 1953. pap.
0.95. Doubleday
Spiller, Robert E. Cycle of American literature. 1955. 5.95. Macmillan
Wilson, Edmund. Shock of recognition. 2.95. Modern Lib.
Canby, Henry S. Classic Americans. 6.00. Russell
Miller, P. G. E. New England mind: The seventeenth century. 1954. 7.50.
Harvard
Morison, Samuel E. Intellectual life in colonial New England. 1956. 4.95. N. Y. U.
Beer, Thomas. Mauve decade. 1961. pap. 1.10. Vintage
Blair, Walter. Native American humor. 1960. pap. 2.75. Chandler Pub.
Brooks, Van Wyck. Confident years: 1885-1915. 2.95. Dutton
Brooks, Van Wyck. Flowering of New England. 2.95. Dutton
Brooks, Van Wyck. New England: Indian summer, 1865-1915. 2.95. Dutton
Brooks, Van. Wyck. Times of Melville and Whitman. 1953. 2.95. Dutton
Brooks, Van Wyck. World of Washington Irving. 2.95. Dutton
Fiedeison, Charles N., Jr. Symbolism and American literature. 1953. 6.50.
1959. U. of Chicago
Matthiesen, F. O. American renaisance: Art and expression in the age of
Emerson and Whitman. il. 1941. 10.00. Oxford U. P.
Mumford, Lewis. Golden day, a study in American literature and culture. 3.50.
Smith, Peter
Cowley, Malcolm. Exile's return. 1959. 3.25. Smith, Peter
Gardiner, Harold C. In all conscience. 1959. 3.95. Doubleday
Heiney, Donald W. Recent American literature. 4.95. Barron's
Kazin, Alfred. On native grounds. 6.75. Harcourt
Nyren, Dorothy. Library of literary criticism. 11.00. Ungar (R)
Spiller, Robert E. Time of harvest: American literature, 1910-1960. 1962. 3.50.
Hill & Wang
Thorp, Willard. American writing in the twentieth century. 1960. 5.00. Harvard
Thrall, William F., and others. Handbook to literature. 1960. 3.75. Odyssey (R)

AMERICAN ORATIONS (815)
Baird, A. Craig. American public addresses. 1956. 5.50. McGraw
Birley, Robert. Speeches and documents in American history. 4 vols. 2.25 ea.
Oxford U. P.
Brandt, Carl G., and Edward M. Shafter, Jr. Selected American speeches on
basic issues, 1850-1950. 1960. 5.00. Houghton
Hurd, Charles. Treasury of great American speeches. il. 1959. 5.95. Hawthorn
Sutton, Roberta B. Speech index, 1935-1955. 1956. 8.50. Scarecrow

AMERICAN PERIODICALS (805)
Mott, Frank Luther. History of American magazines. 4 vols. il. Harvard
Peterson, Theodore. Magazines in the twentieth century. 1956. 6.50. U. of Ill.

AMERICAN POETRY (COLLECTIONS) (811.08)
Aiken, Conrad. Comprehensive anthology of American poetry. 1.95. Modern Lib.
Aldington, Richard. Viking book of poetry of the English-speaking world. 2 vols.
1958. boxed. 12.50; 2 vols in 1. 7.95. Viking
Gillis, Adolph, and William R. Benet. Poems for modern youth. 3.28. Houghton
Gordon, Margery, and Marie B. King. Magic world: An anthology of poetry. il.
1930. 1.85. Appleton
Gwynn, Frederick L., and others. Case for poetry: A new anthology. 1954. 4.25.
Prentice-Hall
Lieberman, Elias, Poems for enjoyment. 1931. 4.40. McGraw
Main, Charles F., and Peter J. Seng. Poems: Wadsworth handbook and anthology.
1961. 2.95. Wadsworth
Matthiessen, F. O. Oxford book of American verse. 1950. 7.00. Oxford U. P.
Miles, Josephine. Poem, a critical anthology. 1959. 4.95. Prentice-Hall
Miles, Josephine. Ways of the poem. 1961. 3.25. Prentice-Hall
Miller, James E., Jr., and Bernice Slote. Dimension of poetry: A critical
anthology. 1962. 5.50. Dodd

Page, C. H. Chief American poets. 7.00. Houghton
Perrine, Laurence. Sound and sense: An introduction to poetry. 1956. pap. 2.50.
    Harcourt
Pratt, John C. Meaning of modern poetry. 5.95. Doubleday
Shapiro, Karl. American poetry. 1960. 5.95. Crowell
Smith, Arthur J. M. Seven centuries of verse. 1957. 4.25. Scribner
Smith, Paul J. Poetry from hidden springs. 1962. 3.95. Doubleday
Thomas, Charles Wright, and S. G. Brown. Reading poems: An introduction to
    critical study. 1941. 4.50. Oxford U. P.
Untermeyer, Louis. Anthology of the New England poets. 4.95. Random
Untermeyer, Louis, and others. Doorways to poetry. 1938. 3.16. Harcourt
Winters, Yvor. Poets of the Pacific. 3.00. Stanford
Woods, Ralph L. Famous poems and the little-known stories behind them. 1961.
    5.00. Hawthorn
AMERICAN POETRY (COLLECTIONS)--19TH CENTURY (811.08)
Steinmetz, Lee. Poetry of the American Civil War. 1960. 5.75. Mich, State
Untermeyer, Louis. Yesterday and today. 2.20. Harcourt
AMERICAN POETRY (COLLECTIONS)--20TH CENTURY (811.08)
Aiken, Conrad. Twentieth century American poetry. 1.95. Modern Lib.
Allen, Donald. New American poetry, 1945-1960. 5.00. Smith, Peter
Carrier, Warren, and Paul Engle. Reading modern poetry. 1955. 2.95. Scott
Ciardi, John. Mid-Century American poets. 5.00. Twayne
Clark, Thomas Curtis. One thousand quotable poems. 1937. 5.00. Harper
Derleth, August W. Fire and sleet and candlelight. 1961. 4.00. Arkham
Untermeyer, Louis. Modern American poetry. 1962. 8.25. Harcourt
Untermeyer, Louis. Yesterday and today. 2.20. Harcourt
AMERICAN POETRY--BIBLIOGRAPHY (811.016)
Kuntz, Joseph M., and George Arms. Poetry explication. 1962. 4.75. Swallow, A.
AMERICAN POETRY--HISTORY AND CRITICISM (811.9)
Cambon, Glauco. Recent American poetry. 1962. pap. 0.65. U. of Minn.
Coffman, Stanley K., Jr. Imagism: A chapter for the history of modern poetry.
Gregory, Horace and Marya A. Zaturenska. History of American poetry, 1900-
    1940. 5.00. Harcourt
Hughes, Glenn. Imagism and the imagists. 6.00. Humanities
Lutyens, David B. Creative encounter. 1960. 5.50. Humanities
Raiziss, Sona. Metaphysical passion: Seven modern American poets and the
    17th-century tradition. 1952. 5.00. U. of Pa.
Rosenthal, Macha L. Modern poets. 1960. 6.50. Oxford U. P.
AMERICAN PROSE LITERATURE (COLLECTIONS) (810.08)
Cerf, Bennett. Reading for pleasure. 1957. 6.50. Harper
Hohenberg, John. Pulitzer prize story. il. 1959. 6.50. Columbia
Prescott, F. C., and G. D. Sanders. Introduction to American prose. 1931. 4.75.
    Appleton
Schorer, Mark, and others. Harbrace college reader. 1959. 3.75. Harcourt
AMERICAN WIT AND HUMOR (817)
Becker, Stephen. Comic art in America. 1959. 7.50. S. and S.
Blair, Walter. Native American humor. 1960. pap. 2.75. Chandler Pub.
Braude, Jacob M. Speaker's encyclopedia of humor. 1961. 5.95. Prentice-Hall
Cerf, Bennett. Encyclopedia of modern humor. il. 1954. 3.95. Doubleday
Droke, Maxwell. Speaker's handbook of humor. 1956. 4.95. Harper
Edmund, Peggy, and Harold W. Williams. Toaster's handbook. 1916. 3.00. Wilson
Linscott, R. N. Best American humorous short stories. 1.95. Modern Lib.
Lynn, Kenneth S. Comic tradition in America: An anthology of American humor.
    1958. pap. 1.45. Doubleday
Phelan, P. J. Time to laugh. 1949. 4.50. McKay
Seldes, Gilbert. Seven lively arts. 1957. 4.95. Sagamore
Weber, Brom. Anthology of American humor. 1962. 8.75. Crowell
Wells, Carolyn. Nonsense anthology. pap. 1.25. Dover

White, E. B., and Katherine S. Subtreasury of American humor. 1962. pap. 1.85. Putnam

AMERICANISMS (427.97)

Fries, Charles C. American English grammar. 1940. 3.75. Appleton

Hogan, Homer. Dictionary of American synonyms. 1959. pap. 1.75. Littlefield (R)

Horwill, H. W. Dictionary of modern American usage. 1944. 4.50 Oxford U. P.

Mathews, Mitford McLeod. Dictionary of Americanisms on historical principles. 2 vols. il. 1956. 12.50. U. of Chicago (R)

Partridge, Eric. Dictionary of the underworld. 1961. 12.75. Macmillan

Wentworth, Harold, and Stuart B. Flexner. Dictionary of American slang. 1960. 7.50. Crowell (R)

AMINO ACIDS (547.637)

Albanese, Anthony A. Protein and amino acid nutrition. 1959. 16.00. Academic Press

Brady, Roscoe O., and Donald B. Tower. Neurochemistry of nucleotides and amino acids. il. 1960. 10.00. Wiley

Greenberg, David M. Amino acids and proteins: Theory, methods, application. il. 1950. 15.00. Thomas, C. C

Meister, A. Biochemistry of the amino acids. 1957. 10.00. Academic Press

AMMONIA (661.34)

Harding, A. J. Ammonia, manufacture and uses. 1959. 1.05. Oxford U. P.

ANARCHISM AND ANARCHISTS (321.9)

Adamic, Louis. Dynamite, the story of class violence in America. il. 1959. 6.00. Smith, Peter

David, Henry. History of the Haymarket affair. 6.75. Russell

Eltzbacher, Paul. Anarchism. 1960. 6.00. Chip's

ANATOMY (591.1)

Corner, George W. Anatomist at large. 4.00. Basic Books

Singer, Charles. Short history of anatomy and physiology. il. 1957. pap. 1.75. Dover

Smout, C. F. V. Baisc anatomy and physiology. 1962. 3.50. Williams & Wilkins

Smout, C. F. V., and R. J. S. McDowall. Anatomy and physiology for students of physiotherapy, occupational therapy and gymnastics. il. 1956. 10.00. Williams & Wilkins

Tompsett, D. H. Anatomical techniques. il. 1956. 7.50. Williams & Wilkins

Leonardo da Vinci. Leonardo da Vinci on the human body. by John B. de C. M. Saunders and Charles D. O'Malley. il. 1952. 25.00. Abelard

ANATOMY, ARTISTIC (743.4)

Barcsay, Jeno. Anatomy for the artist. il. 1958. 7.95. Tudor

Bridgman, George B. Complete guide to drawing from life. 12.00. Sterling

Bridgman, George B. Constructive anatomy. pap. 1.00. Sterling

Bridgman, George B. Heads, features and faces. 1962. pap. 1.00. Sterling

Clarke, Carl D. Molding and casting. il. 7.50. Standard Arts

Ellenberger, Wilhelm., and others. Atlas of animal anatomy for artists. il. tr. by Helene Weinbaum. 1957. 6.00. Dover

Peck, S. R. Atlas of human anatomy for the artist. il. 1951. 8.50. Oxford U. P.

ANATOMY, COMPARATIVE (591.4)

Breland, Osmond. Manual of comparative anatomy. il. 1953. 5.95. McGraw

Cole, Francis J. History of comparative anatomy. 1949. 6.00. St. Martins

Gans, C., and John F. Storr. Comparative anatomy atlas. 1962. 2.50? Academic Press

Hyman, Libbie H. Comparative vertebrate anatomy. il. 1942. 5.00. U. of Chicago

Kent, G. C. Comparative anatomy of the vertebrates. 1954. 7.95. McGraw

Leach, William J. Functional anatomy: Mammalian and comparative. 1961. 6.50. McGraw

Montagna, William. Comparative anatomy. 1959. 6.50. Wiley

ANATOMY, HUMAN (611)

Anthony, Catherine P. Structure and function of the body. il. 1960. 3.00. Mosby

Anthony, Catherine P. Textbook of anatomy and physiology. il. 1959. 6.00. Mosby
Bocock, E. J., and R. Wheeler Haines. Applied anatomy for nurses. il. 1959.
   4.25. Williams & Wilkins
Buchanan, A. M. Buchanan's manual of anatomy. il. by Frederick W. Jones.
   1950. 10.00. Williams & Wilkins
Cates, H. A. Cates' primary anatomy. by J. V. Basmajian. 1960. 6.50. Williams
   & Wilkins
Cunningham, D. J. Textbook of anatomy. il. 1951. by J. C. Brash. 17.50.

Flitter, Hessel H., and Harold R. Rowe. Teaching physiology and anatomy in
   nursing. 1955. 2.00. Lippincott
Gray, Henry. Anatomy of the human body. by Charles M. Goss. il. 1959. 17.50.
   Lea & F
Lockhart, R. D. Living anatomy. il. 1959. 4.00. Oxford U. P.
Romer, Alfred S. Vertebrate story. il. 1959. 7.00. U. of Chicago
Whillis, James. Whillis's elementary anatomy and physiology. 1961. 7.00.
   Little
Zuckerman, Solly. New system of anatomy. il. 1961. 17.25. Oxford U. P.
Frohse, Franz, and others. Atlas of human anatomy. 1961. 4.50. Barnes &
   Noble
Grant, John C. B. Atlas of anatomy. il. 1962. 19.95. Williams & Wilkins
ANDERSEN, HANS CHRISTIAN, 1805-1875 (928)
Godden, Rumer. Hans Christian Andersen. 1955. 3.00. Knopf
ANDERSON, MAXWELL, 1888- (928)
Bailey, Mabel Driscoll. Maxwell Anderson: The playwright as prophet. 1957. 3.50.
   Abelard
ANDERSON, SHERWOOD, 1876-1941 (928)
Anderson, David. Sherwood Anderson. 1962. 2.95. Barnes & Noble
ANECDOTES (808.87)
Braude, Jacob M. New treasury of stories for every speaking and writing occa-
   ssion. 1959. 5.95. Prentice-Hall
Braude, Jacob M. Speaker's encyclopedia of stories, quotations, and anecdotes.
   1955. 5.95. Prentice-Hall
Droke, Maxwell. Speaker's treasury of anecdotes. 1948. 1.95. Grosset
Friedman, Edward L. Toastmaster's treasury. 1960. 4.95. Harper
Hovey, E. Paul. Treasury of inspirational anecdotes, quotations and illustrations.
   1959. 3.95. Revell
Prochnow, Herbert V., comp. Complete toastmaster. 1960. bds. 4.95. Prentice-
   Hall
Prochnow, Herbert V. New guide for toastmasters and speakers. 1956. 5.95.
   Prentice-Hall
Prochnow, Herbert V. New speaker's treasury of wit and wisdom. 1958. 4.95?
   Harper
Prochnow, Herbert V. Public speaker's treasure chest. 1942. 5.50. Harper
Prochnow, H. V. Speaker's treasury of stories for all occasions. 1955. 4.95.
   Prentice-Hall
ANESTHESIA (617.96)
Adriani, John Appraisal of current concepts in anesthesiology. 1961. 7.75. Mosby
Adriani, John. Chemistry and physics of anesthesia. il. 1962. 28.50. Thomas,
   C. C.
Adriani, John. Techniques and procedures of anesthesia. 1960. 8.75. Thomas, C. C.
Artusio, Joseph F., Jr., and Valentine D. B. Mazzia. Practical anesthesiology.
   1962. 7.75. Mosby
Goldman, Victor. Aids to anesthesia. 1958. 3.50. Williams & Wilkins
Lee, John Alfred. Synopsis of anesthesia. il. 1960. 6.50. Williams & Wilkins
Pryor, William J. Manual of anesthetic techniques. il. 1958. 7.00. Williams &
   Wilkins
Woolmer, Ronald F. Conquest of pain. 1961. 4.50. Knopf

Wylie, W. D., and H. D. Churchill-Davidson. Practice of anesthesia. 1960.
20.00. Year Bk.

ANGER (179.8)

Petritz, M. M. Philosophy of anger and the virtues. 1953. 0.75. Catholic U. of
Am. Pr.

Saul, Leon J. Hostile mind: The sources and consequences of rage and hate. 1956.
3.50. Random House

ANGLO-SAXON LANGUAGE (429)

Alston, R. C. Introduction to Old English. 1961. 4.25. Harper

Clark, J. W. Early English: A study of Old and Middle English. 1957. 3.75.
Oxford U. P.

Anderson, Marjorie, and B. C. Williams. Old English handbook. 6.50.
Houghton

Wyatt, Alfred John. Anglo-Saxon reader. 1919. 4.75. Cambridge U. P.

Hall, J. R. Clark and Herbert D. Meritt. Concise Anglo-Saxon dictionary.
1961. 6.50. Cambridge U. P.

ANGLO-SAXON LITERATURE--HISTORY AND CRITICISM (829.08)

Anderson, George K. Literature of the Anglo-Saxons. il. 1962. 8.50. Russell

Ker, W. P. English literature: Medieval. 1.70. Oxford U. P.

Sisam, Kenneth. Studies in the history of Old English literature. 1953. 4.80.
Oxford U. P.

ANGLO-SAXON POETRY (829.1)

Anglo-Saxon poetry. 1.95. Dutton

Bone, Gavin. Anglo-Saxon poetry: An essay with specimen translations in verse.
1943. 2.40 Oxford U. P.

Kennedy, Charles W. Anthology of Old English poetry. 1960. 4.50. 1.50. Oxford
U. P.

ANIMAL INDUSTRY (636)

Acker, Duane C. Animal science and industry. il. 1962. 10.35. Prentice-Hall

Peters, Walter H., and R. H. Grummer. Livestock production. il. 1954. 7.50.
McGraw

ANIMAL INTELLIGENCE (591.5)

Adamson, Joy. Living free. il. 1961. 5.95. Harcourt

Bierens De Haan, Johan A. Animal psychology. 2.50. Hillary

Kohler, Wolfgang. Mentality of apes. 5.00. Humanities

Lilly, John C. Man and dolphin. il. 4.95. Doubleday

ANIMAL MIGRATION (591.52)

Blond, Georges. Great migrations. tr. by Frances Frenaye. 4.00. Macmillan

Milne, Lorus J., and Margery J. Paths across the earth. il. 1958. 3.95. Harper

ANIMALS (591)

Milne, Lorus J., and Margery. Balance of nature. 1960. 5.00. Knopf

Slobodkin, Lawrence B. Growth and regulation of animal populations. 1961. 5.00.
Holt, Rinehart & Winston

Krutch, Joseph Wood. World of animals. il. 1961. 10.00. S. and S.

Tomkins, T. L. C. Wild animals of the world. il. 1962. 3.95. Pitman

ANIMALS, HABITS AND BEHAVIOR OF (591.5)

Adamson, Joy. Born free: A lioness of two worlds. il. 1960. 4.95. Pantheon

Adamson, Joy. Elsa. il. 1961. 3.50. Pantheon

Allee, W. C. Social life of animals. pap. 1.45. Beacon

Cloudsley-Thompson, J. L. Animal behavior. il. 1961. 4.50. Macmillan

Ditmars, Raymond L. Strange animals I have known. il. 4.00. Harcourt

Ditmars, Raymond L. Thrills of a naturalist's quest. il. 1932. 5.95. Macmillan

Eibl-Eibesfeldt, Irenaus. Galapagos: The Noah's ark of the Pacific. tr. by Alan
H. Brodrick. il. 1960. 3.95. Doubleday

Farre, Rowena. Seal morning. il. by Raymond Sheppard. 1957. 3.50. Rinehart

Kellogg, Winthrop N. Porpoises and sonar. 1961. 4.50. U. of Chicago

Krutch, Joseph W. Great chain of life. 1956. 4.50. Houghton

Lorenz, Konrad Z. King Solomon's ring. il. 1952. 4.95. Crowell

Morgan, Ann. Field book of animals in winter. il. 1939. 5.00. Putnam
Murie, Olaus. Field guide to animal tracks. 1954. 4.50. Houghton
Schweitzer, Albert. Animal world of Albert Schweitzer. by Charles R. Joy.
  il. 1962. 3.75. Smith, Peter
Scientific American. Twentieth-Century Bestiary. 1956. 1.45. S. and S.
Scott, John Paul. Animal behavior. il. 1958. 5.00. U. of Chicago
Seton, Ernest Thompson. Ernest Thompson Seton's America. 5.00. Seton
Terres, John K. Discovery: Great moments in the lives of outstanding naturalists.
  il. 1961. 6.50. Lippincott
Weyer, Edward M. Strangest creatures on earth. il. 1953. 5.00. Sheridan
ANTARCTIC REGIONS (999)
Bixby, William. McMurdo Antartica. il. 1962. 3.50. McKay
Bowman, Gerald. Men of Antarctica. il. 1951. 3.95. Fleet
Kearns, William H. J., and Beverley Britton. Silent continent: Antarctica. il.
  1955. 3.95. Harper
Scott, Robert F. Scott's last expedition. il. 1951. 4.25. Transatlantic
Shackleton, Ernest H. South! il. 1962. 4.50. Macmillan
Sullivan, Walter. Quest for a continent. il. 1957. 5.95. McGraw
ANTHROPOLOGY (572)
Ashley, Montagu, M. F. Humanization of man. 1962. 6.00. World Pub.
Barnett, Anthony. Human species. 3.75. Smith, Peter
Benedict, Ruth. Patterns of culture. 4.00. Houghton
Benedict, Ruth F., and Margaret Mead. Anthropologist at work. il. 1959. 6.00.
  Houghton
Boas, Franz. Anthropology and modern life. 1962. 1.85. Norton
Boas, Franz. Race, language and culture. 7.25. Macmillan
Chase, Stuart. Proper study of mankind. 1956. 4.50. Harper
Coon, Carleton S. Origin of races. il. 1962. 10.00. Knopf
Coon, Carleton S. Story of man. il. 1962. 7.50. Knopf
Gillin, John. Ways of men. 1948. 5.50. Appleton
Goldschmidt, Walter. Man's way. 1959. 3.25. Holt, Rinehart & Winston
Hallowell, A. Irving. Culture and experience. 1957. 8.50. U. of Pa.
Hays, H. R. From ape to angel. il. 1958. 7.50. Knopf
Herskovits, Melville Jean. Cultural anthropology. il. 1955. 5.50. Knopf
Honigmann, John J. World of man. 1959. 8.00. Harper
Hooton, Earnest Albert. Up from the ape. il. 8.50. Macmillan
Kluckhohn, Clyde. Culture and behavior. 1961. 6.75. Free Press
Kluckhohn, Clyde. Mirror for man. 1949. 5.00. McGraw
Linton, Ralph. Study of man: An introduction. 1936. 5.50. Appleton
Linton, Ralph. Tree of culture. il. 1955. 9.75. Knopf
Lowie, R. H. Introduction to cultural anthropology. 1940. 6.50. Rinehart
Malinowski, Bronislaw. Scientific theory of culture. 1944. 3.00. U. of N. C.
Mead, Margaret. Cooperation and competition among primitive peoples. 1961.
  2.95. Beacon
Murdock, George Peter. Social structure. 1949. 5.00. Macmillan
Piddington, Ralph. Introduction to social anthropology. 2 vols. il. 4.75 ea.
  Macmillan
Shapiro, Harry L. Man, culture, and society. 1956. 7.75. 2.25. Oxford U. P.
Titiev, Mischa. Introduction to cultural anthropology. il. 1959. 9.45. Holt,
  Rinehart & Winston
Titiev, Mischa. Science of man: An intorduction to anthropology. il. 1954. 9.45.
  Holt, Rinehart & Winston
Ashley, Montagu, M. F. Anthropology and human nature. 1957. 6.00. Sargent
Kroeber, Alfred L. Nature of culture. il. 1952. 10.00. U. of Chicago
Mead, Margaret, and Ruth Bunzel. Golden age of American anthropology. 10.00.
  Braziller
White, Lynn, Jr. Frontiers of knowledge: In the study of man. 1956. 4.50. Harper

ANTIBIOTICS (615.329)
Gause, G. F. Search for new antibiotics. il. 1960. 4.75. Yale
Reinfeld, Fred. Miracle drugs and the new age of medicine. 1959. 3.95. Sterling
Welch, Henry. Guide to antibiotic therapy. 1959. 3.00. Medical Encyclopedia
ANTIGENS AND ANTIBODIES (612.1182)
Burnet, F. Macfarlane. Enzyme, antigen and virus. 1957. 3.75. Cambridge U. P.
Henry Ford Hospital Symposium. Mechanisms of hypersensitivity. 1959. 18.50.
    Little
Najjar, Victor A. Immunity and virus infection. il. 1959. 10.50. Wiley
Talmage, David W., and John R. Cann. Chemistry of immunity in health and
    disease. 1961. 5.75. Thomas, C. C.
ANTS (595.796)
Goetsch, Wilhelm. Ants. il. 1957. 4.50. U. of Mich.
Wheeler, William M. Ants. il. 1960. 17.50. Columbia
ANXIETY (157.1)
Bender, Lauretta. Aggression, hostility and anxiety in children. il. 1953. 5.50.
    Thomas, C. C
Hoffman, Richard H., and A. W. Pezet. Conquest of tension. 1961. 3.95. Holt,
    Rinehart & Winston
Janis, Irving. L. Psychological stress. il. 1958. 7.50. Wiley
Stein, Maurice R., and others. Identity and anxiety: Survival of the person in
    mass society. 7.50. Free Press
APOPLEXY (616.81)
D'Alonzo, Constance A. Heart disease, blood pressure and strokes. il. 1960.
    3.50. Gulf
Page, Irving H., and others. Strokes: How they occur and what can be done about
    them. il. 1961. 4.50. Dutton
Van Rosen, Robert E. Comeback: The story of my stroke. 1962. 3.95. Bobbs
APOSTLES (229.92)
Barker, William P. Twelve who were chosen: The disciples of Jesus. 2.50.
    Revell
Goodspeed, Edgar J. Twelve: The story of Christ's apostles. 0.95. Collier
Oursler, Fulton, and April O. Armstrong. Greatest faith ever known. il. 1953.
    3.95. Doubleday
Smith, Asbury. Twelve Christ chose. 1958. 3.00. Harper
AQUARIUMS (574.92074)
Axelrod, Herbert R., and William Vorderwinkler. Encyclopedia of tropical fishes.
    il. 1957. 8.95. Sterling
Barker, Philip. Life in the aquarium. il. 1960. 3.50. Branford
Boulenger, Edward G. Keep an aquarium. il. 1.50. Warne
Gray, William B. Creatures of the sea. 1960. il. 3.95. Funk
McInery, Derek, and Geoffrey Gerard. All about tropical fish. il. 1959. 15.00.
    Macmillan
Schneider, E., and L. Whitney. Complete guide to tropical fishes. 10.00. Nelson
AQUATIC SPORTS (797)
Gabrielsen, M. Alexander, and others. Aquatics handbook. il. 1960. 8.35 Pren-
    tice-Hall
Liebers, Arthur. Complete book of water sports. 1962. 4.50. Coward
Smith, Hope M. Water games. il. 1962. 3.50. Ronald
ARABIA (953)
Ingrams, H. Arabia and the Isles. il. 6.75. Transatlantic
Bisch, Jorgen. Behind Arabia's veil. il. 5.95. Dutton
Sanger, Richard H. Arabian Peninsula. il. 1954. 5.00. Cornell
Hitti, Philip Khuri, History of the Arabs. 9.00. St. Martins
Marston, Thomas E. Red Sea. 1961. 10.00. Shoe String
ARABS (953)
Ellis, Harry B. Arabs. 1958. 3.50. World Pub.
Gabrieli, Francesco. Arabs: A short history. 1962. 3.95. Hawthorn

Lawrence, T. E. Seven pillars of wisdom: A triumph. il. 1947. 6.00. Doubleday
Villiers, Alan. Sons of Sinbad. il. 1940. 6.00. Scribner
ARBITRATION (331.155)
Braun, Kurt. Labor disputes and their settlement. 1955. 6.00. Johns Hopkins
Elkouri, Frank, and Edna A. How arbitration works. 9.65. Bur. of Nat. Affairs
Jones, Dallas L. Arbitration and industrial discipline. 1961. 5.00. Bur. of Ind.
    Rel., U. of Mich.
Trotta, Maurice. Labor arbitration. 10.00. Simmons-Boardman
Horlacher, John Perry. Guides for labor arbitration. 1953. 1.00. U. of Pa.
Pierson, Frank. Collective bargaining systems. 1942. 3.00. Pub. Affairs
ARCHAEOLOGY (913)
Childe, V. Gordon. Dawn of European civilization. 1958. 7.50. Knopf
Childe, V. G. Short introduction to archaeology. il. 2.50. Macmillan
Churchward, James. Lost continent of Mu. il. 1931. 4.25. Washburn
Clark, Grahame. World prehistory: An outline. 1961. 6.00. Cambridge U. P.
Cottrell, Leonard. Concise encyclopedia of archaeology. il. 1960. 15.00. Hawthorn
    (R)
Kenyon, Kathleen M. Beginning in archaeology. il. 1953. 5.00. Praeger
Piggott, Stuart. Approach to archaeology. il. 1959. 3.00. Harvard
Ceram, C. W. Gods, graves and scholars. il. 1951. 5.75. Knopf
Ceram, C. W. March of archaeology. il. 1958. 15.00. Knopf
Daniel, Glyn E. Hundred years of archaeology. 1950. 3.50. Macmillan
Silverberg, Robert. Lost cities and vanished civilizations. il. 1962. 3.95. Chilton
Marriott, Alice L. First comers: Indians of America's dawn. il. 1960. 4.50.
    McKay
Wheeler, Mortimer. Archaeology. from the earth. 1954. 4.80. Oxford U. P.
ARCHERY (799.32)
Burke, Edmund H. Archery handbook. il. 1960. 2.50. Arco
Burke, Edmund H. History of archery. il. 1957. 4.50. Morrow
Forbes, Thomas A. New guide to better archery. il. 1960. 5.50. Stackpole
Hochman, Louis. Complete archery handbook. 1957. 2.50. Arco
Reichart, N., and G. Keasey. Archery. 1961. 3.50. Ronald
ARCHITECTURAL DRAWING (744.424)
Bellis, H. F., and W. A. Schmidt. Architectural drafting. 1961. 5.50. 2.95.
    McGraw
Hornung, William J. Architectural drafting. 1959. 8.75. Prentice-Hall
Morgan, Sherley W. Architectural drawing. 1950. 10.00. McGraw
Svensen, C. L., and Edgar Greer Shelton. Architectural drafting. il. 1929. 3.50.
    Van Nostrand
ARCHITECTURE (720)
Gropius, Walter. New architecture and Bauhaus. 3.50. Branford
Hamlin, T. F. Architecture - an art for all men. 1947. 4.50. Columbia
Hudnut, Joseph. Architecture and the spirit of man. 1949. 4.75. Harvard
LeCorbusier. Towards a new architecture. il. 1959. 4.95. Praeger
Michaels, L. Contemporary structure in architecture. 1950. 12.00. Reinhold
Ruskin, John. Seven lamps of architecture. il. 1.95. Dutton
Wright, Frank Lloyd. Frank Lloyd Wright on architecture. by Frederick Gutheim.
    1941. 7.00. Duell
Wright, Frank Lloyd. Living city. il. 1958. 7.50. Horizon
Wright, Frank Lloyd. Writings and buildings. by Edgar Kaufmann, and Ben Raeburn
    il. 3.95. Horizon
Zevi, Bruno. Architecture as space: How to look at architecture. il. 1957. 7.50.
    Horizon
ARCHITECTURE--DESIGNS AND PLANS (729)
Architectural Record. Buildings for industry. by the Editors of Architectural
    Record. 1957. 9.75. McGraw
Architectural Record. Buildings for research. by the Editors of Architectural
    Record. 1958. 9.50. McGraw

Dorgelo, A.   Modern European architecture. il. 1960. 27.50. Am. Elsevier

Joedicke, Jurgen.   New frontiers in architecture. 1961. 15.00. Universe

ARCHITECTURE--DICTIONARIES (720)

Briggs, Martin S.   Everyman's concise encyclopaedia of architecture. il. 1959.
   6.50. Dutton

Saylor, Henry.   Dictionary of architecture. 1952. 5.95. Wiley

ARCHITECTURE--HISTORY (720.9)

Fletcher, Banister.   History of architecture. 1961. 16.75. Scribner

Giedion, Siegfried.   Space, time and architecture: The growth of a new tradition.
   1962. 12.50. Harvard

Hamlin, A. D. F.   History of architecture. 1928. 4.00. McKay

Hamlin, Talbot.   Architecture through the ages. il. 1953. 8.50. Putnam

Smith, W. Stevenson.   Art and architecture of ancient Egypt. 12.50. Penguin

Jordan, Robert F., and Bodo Cichy.   World of great architecture, from the Greeks
   to the nineteenth century. il. 1961. 22.50. Viking

Whittick, Arnold.   European architecture in the 20th century. 2 vols. il. 12.00.
   ea. Transatlantic

ARCHITECTURE--U.S. (720.973)

Andrews, Wayne.   Architecture ambition and Americans: History of American
   architecture. il. 1955. 7.95. Harper

Connely, Willard.   Louis Sullivan as he lived.il. 1960. 6.50. Horizon

Gutheim, Frederick.   One hundred years of architecture in America. 1957. 1.95.
   Reinhold

Maass, John.   Gingerbread age: A view of Victorian America. il. 1957. 7.95.
   Rinehart

McCallum, I.   Architecture U. S. A. 1959. 7.95. Reinhold

Morrison, Hugh.   Early American architecture. 1952. 15.00. Oxford U. P.

Mumford, Lewis.   Brown decades: A study of the arts of America 1865-1895. il.
   1960. 3.50. Smith, Peter

Mumford, Lewis.   South in architecture. 2.00. Harcourt

Sloane, Eric.   American yesterday. il. 1956. 4.50. Funk

Wright, Frank Lloyd.   American architecture. by Edgar Kaufmann. il. 12.50.
   Horizon

ARCHITECTURE, GOTHIC (720)

Frankl, P.   Gothic: Literary sources and interpretation through eight centuries.
   1960. 17.50. Princeton

Worringer, Wilhelm.   Form in gothic. il. 6.75. Transatlantic

ARCHITECTURE, GREEK (722)

Fyfe, T.   Hellenistic architecture. 1936. 9.50. Cambridge U. P.

Lawrence, Arnold W.   Greek architecture. 1957. 16.50. Penguin

Robertson, D. S.   Greek and Roman architecture. 1943. 8.50. Cambridge U. P.

Scranton, Robert L.   Greek architecture. il. 1962. bds. 4.95. Braziller

ARCHITECTURE, MODERN (724)

Blake, Peter.   Master builders. il. 1960. 8.00. Knopf

Dorgelo, A.   Modern European architecture. il. 1960. 27.50. Am. Elsevier

Hoffman, H., and others.   New German architecture. il. 1956. 12.50. Praeger

Joedicke, Jurgen.   New frontiers in architecture. 1961. 15.00. Universe

Le Corbusier.   Complete works. by W. Boesiger and H. Girsberger. il. 1960.
   15.00. Wittenborn

Wright, Frank Lloyd.   Future of architecture. il. 7.50. Horizon

Wright, Frank Lloyd.   Natural house. il. 7.50. Horizon

ARCHIVES (025.171)

Hamer, Philip M.   Guide to archives and manuscripts in the United States. 1961.
   15.00. Yale

ARCTIC REGIONS (998)

Anderson, William R., and Clay Blair, Jr.   Nautilus 90 North. il. 1959. 3.95.
   World Pub.

Ellsberg, Edward.   Hell on ice, the saga of the "Jeannette". 1938. 5.00. Dodd

Freuchen, Peter. Peter Freuchen's men of the frozen north. il. 1962. 6.00.
World Pub.
Freuchen, Dagmar. Peter Freuchen's adventures in the arctic. 1960. 4.95.
Messner
Kimble, George H. G., and Dorothy Good. Geography of the Northlands. 1955.
9.25. Wiley
Lindbergh, Anne Morrow, North to the Orient. il. 2.50. Harcourt
Rodahl, Kaare. North: Nature and drama of the polar world. il. 1953. 5.00.
Harper
Scherman, Katherine. Spring on an Arctic island. 1956. 5.00. Little
Stefansson, Vilhjalmur. Arctic manual. il. 1944. 8.50. Macmillan
ARISTOTLE (185)
Allan, D. J. Philosophy of Aristotle. 1952. 1.70. Oxford U. P.
Anscombe, G. E. M., and Peter T. Geach. Three philosophers. 1961. 3.50.
Cornell
Barker, Ernest. Political thought of Plato and Aristotle. 1959. 7.50. Russell
Butcher, Samuel H. Aristotle's theory of poetry and fine art. 1955. pap. 2.00.
Dover
Cooper, Lane. Poetics of Aristotle: Its Meaning and influence. 1923. 1.75. Cornell
During, I. Aristotle in the ancient biographical tradition. 10.00. Humanities
Elders, L. Aristotle's theory of the one. 6.00. Humanities
Jaeger, Werner. Aristotle: Fundamentals of the history of his development. 1948.
5.60. Oxford U. P.
Joachim, H. H. Aristotle: The Nicomachean ethics. by D. A. Rees. 1951. 4.50.
Oxford U. P.
Lucas, F. L. Tragedy. 1953. 2.50. Macmillan
Lyons, Lawrence F. Material and formal causality in the philosophy of Aristotle
and St. Thomas. 1958. 1.50. Catholic U. of Am. Pr.
Randall, John H. Aristotle. 1960. 5.00. Columbia
Ross, William D. Aristotle. 5.00. Barnes & Noble
Steenberghen, Fernaud van. Aristotle in the west. 1958. 2.25. Duquesne
Thomson, James A. Ethics of Aristotle. 1962. 3.50. Barnes & Noble
ARITHMETIC (511)
Adams, Lovincy J. Arithmetic for college students. 1961. 3.75. Holt, Rinehart
& Winston
Asimov, Isaac. Realm of numbers. il. 1959. 2.75. Houghton
Bakst, Aaron, Arithmetic for the modern age. 1960. 4.95. Van Nostrand
Barden, Agnes, and John Carter. How to work with numbers. 1st no. bk. 0.80;
2nd no. bk. 0.95. Rand McNally
Brumfiel, Charles F., and others. Rundamental concepts of elementary mathema-
tics. il. 1962. 6.50. Addison-Wesley
Huffman, H., and others. Arithmetic for business and consumer use. 1962. 4.48.
McGraw
Larsen, Harold D. Arithmetic for colleges. 1950. il. 1958. 5.75. Macmillan
Reckless, M. W. Understanding arithmetic. 3.96. Prentice-Hall
Duncan, D. C. Arithmetic in general education. 1954. pap. 2.25. Brown, W. C.
National Council of Teachers of Mathematics. Instruction in arithmetic. 25th
yearbook. by Foster E. Grossnickle. 1960. 4.50. Nat. Council of Teachers
of Math.
National Education Association, National Council of Teachers of Mathematics.
Instruction in arithmetic, yearbook. 1960. 4.50. N. E. A.
ARIZONA (979.1)
Cross, Jack L., and others. Arizona: Its people and resources. il. 1961. 6.50.
U. of Ariz.
Miller, Joseph. Arizona story. 1952. 5.50. Hastings
Writers' Project. Arizona. 1955. 6.50. Hastings
ARKANSAS (976.7)
Wilson, Charles Morrow. Bodacious Ozarks: True tales of the backhills. 1959.
4.50. Hastings

Writers' Project. Arkansas. 1941. 6.50. Hastings
ARNOLD, MATTHEW, 1822-1888 (821.8)
Baum, Paull F. Ten studies in the poetry of Matthew Arnold. 1958. 4.00. Duke
Connell, W. F. Education thought and influence of Matthew Arnold. 1950. 4.50. Humanities
James, David G. Matthew Arnold and the decline of English romanticism. 2.90. Oxford U. P.
Johnson, Wendell S. Voices of Matthew Arnold. 1961. 5.75. Yale
Raleigh, John H. Matthew Arnold and the American culture. 1962. 4.00. Smith, Peter
Trilling, Lionel. Matthew Arnold. 1949. 5.50. Columbia
ART (700)
Baldinger, Wallace S., and Harry B. Green. Visual arts. il. 1960. 10.50. Holt, Rinehart & Winston
Beam, P. C. Language of art. 1958. 8.00. Ronald
Faulkner, Ray, and others. Art today: An introduction to the fine and functional arts. il. 1956. 10.10. Holt, Rinehart & Winston
Gardner, Helen. Understanding the arts. il. 1932. 5.00. Harcourt
Goldstein, Harriet, and Vetta. Art in everyday life. il. 1954. 7.50. Macmillan
Gombrich, Eric H. Art and illusion. il. 1961. 10.00. Pantheon
Lowry, Bates. Visual experience. il. 1961. 10.00. Abrams
Munro, Thomas. Art in American life and education. NSSE, 40th yearbook. 1941. 4.00. U. of Chicago
Read, H. Icon and idea: The function of art in the development of human consciousness. il. 1955. 7.50. Harvard
Read, Herbert E. Meaning of art. 1951. 5.50. Pitman
Ruskin, John. Lamp of beauty. by Joan Evans. il. 1959. 6.95. N. Y. Graphic
Fry, Roger. Vision and design. il. 3.50. Smith, Peter
Greenberg, Clement. Art and culture. 1961. 6.00. Beacon
Huxley, Aldous. On art and artists. 1960. 4.50. Harper
Mumford, Lewis. Art and technics. 1952. 2.50. Columbia
Panofsky, Erwin. Meaning in the visual arts. il. 3.50. Smith, Peter
Shahn, B. Shape of content. il. 1957. 4.00. Harvard
ART--DICTIONARIES, INDEXES, ETC. (700.03)
Clapp, Jane. Art in life. 1959. 12.50. Scarecrow.
Encyclopedia of world art. 5 vols. 39.80 ea. McGraw
Haggar, Reginald C. Dictionary of art terms. il. 1962. 5.95. Hawthorn
Larousse. Larousse encyclopedia of prehistoric and ancient art. 1962. 17.95. Putnam (R)
ART--HISTORY (709)
Bazin, Germain. History of art. 1959. 9.00. Houghton
Biederman, Charles. Art as the evolution of visual knowledge. il. 1948. 10.00. Art History
Canaday, John. Mainstreams of modern art. il. 1959. 9.75. Holt, Rinehart & Winston
Cheney, Sheldon. New world history of art. il. 1956. 8.50. Viking
Cheney, Sheldon. Story of modern art. 1958. 7.95. Viking
Fleming, William. Arts and ideas. il. 1955. 13.90. Holt, Rinehart & Winston
Gardner, Helen. Art through the ages. by Sumner McK. Crosby. il. 1959. 9.50. Harcourt
Gombrich, E. H. Story of art. il. 1958. 5.50. Oxford U. P.
Hauser, Arnold. Social history of art. 2 vols. il. 1951. 17.50. Knopf
Janson, H. W. History of art. il. 1962. 18.50. Abrams
Janson, H. W. Key monuments of the history of art. il. 1962. 12.50. Abrams
Myers, Bernard. Art and civilization. il. 1957. 10.95. McGraw
Orpen, William. Outline of art. il. 1955. 11.25. Transatlantic
ART--HISTORY (709)
Read, Herbert E. Meaning of art. 1951. 5.50. Pitman

ART--INDEXES(700)
Art index. 5 vols. 1947-1959. vol. 12. 1959-1961. Wilson
ART--PHILOSOPHY (701)
Cary, Joyce. Art and reality. 1958. 3.50. Harper
Collingwood, R. G. Principles of art. 1938. 4.50; Oxford U. P.
Guggenheimer, Richard. Creative vision. 1960. 3.50. Harper
Huyghe, Rene. Art and the spirit of man. il. 1962. 15.00. Abrams
Kepes, Gyorgy. Language of vision. il. 1945. 19.50. Theobald
Mumford, Lewis. Art and technics. 1952. 2.50· Columbia
Rothschild, Lincoln. Style in art. 3.95. Yoseloff
Weiss, Paul. World of art. 1961. 4.50. Southern Ill.
ART--PSYCHOLOGY (701.15)
Arnheim, Rudolf. Art and visual perception: A psychology of the creative eye.
   il. 1957. 12.50. U. of Calif.
Gombrich, Eric H. Art and illusion. il. 1961. 19.00. Pantheon
Hauser, Arnold. Philosophy of art history. 1959. 7.50. Knopf
Lowenfeld, Viktor. Creative and mental growth. il. 6.50. Macmillan
Lowenfeld, Viktor. Nature of creative activity. 6.50. Humanties
Read, Herbert E. Education through art. il. 1958. 7.50. Pantheon
ART--STUDY AND TEACHING (707)
Bethers, Ray. Composition in pictures. 1962. 6.75. Pitman
Conant, Howard, and Arne Randall. Art in education. 1959. 6.00. Bennett
D'Amico, Victor, and others. Art for the family. il. 1958. 2.95. Mus. of Mod.
   Art, or Doubleday
De Francesco, Italo. Art education: Its means and ends. 1958. 7.25. Harper
Erdt, Margaret H. Teaching art in the elementary school. 1962. 6.75. Holt,
   Rinehart & Winston
File, Mary Jeanne, Sister. Critical analysis of current concepts of art in American
   higher education. 1958. 1.75. Catholic U. of Am. Pr.
Gaitskell, Charles D. Children and their art. il. 1958. 8.75. Harcourt
Lee, Carval. Art guide. 1959. 4.95. Denison
Logan, Frederick M. Growth of art in American schools. 1955. 4.50. Harper
Lowenfeld, Viktor. Creative and mental growth. il. 6.50. Macmillan
Munro, Thomas. Art in American life and education. NSSE. 40th yearbook. 1941.
   4.00; pap. 3.00. U. of Chicago (R)
Munro, Thomas, and Herbert Read. Creative arts in American education. 1960.
   2.50. Harvard
National Education Association, National Art Education Association. Art and human
   values, yearbook. 1953. 3.00. N. E. A. (R)
National Education Association, National Art Education Association. Art in the
   secondary school. 1961. 2.50. N. E. A.
Ocvirk, O. G., and others. Art fundamentals, theory and practice. 1960. pap. 5.75.
   Brown, W. C.
Pearson, Ralph M. New art education. il. 1953. 7.50. Harper
Pepper, Stephen C. Principles of art appreciation. il. 1949. 9.00 Harcourt
Read, Herbert. Education through art. il. 1958. 7.50. Pantheon
Read, and Orze. Art from scrap. 1960. 3.95.
Riley, Olive L. Your art heritage. 1952. 5.36. McGraw
Taylor, J. F. A., and others. Introduction to literature and the fine arts. il.
   1950. pap. 6.00. Mich. State
Tolces, Toska. Creative disciplines: Explorations in awareness. 1956. 3.50.
   Wheelwright
ART--TECHNIQUE (701.8)
Herberts, Kurt. Complete book of artists' techniques. il. 1958. 15.00. Praeger (R)
Moholy-Nagy, Laszlo. Vision in motion. il. 1947. 13.75. Theobald
Vasari, Giorgio. Vasari on technique. ed. by G. Baldwin Brown. tr. by Louisa
   S. Maclehose. pap. 2.00. Dover
Zaidenberg, Arthur. Anyone can paint. il. 1942. 3.95. Crown

ART--YEARBOOKS (703)
Teachers College, Fine Arts Staff. Art education today. il. Annuals, 1935-1943.
    1948-1952. 1948. pap. 2.75; 1949-50: Teacher. pap. 2.75; 1951-52; Secondary
    school program. pap. 2.25. T. C.
Writers' and artists' yearbook. 4.50. Writer (R)
ART, ABSTRACT (709.04)
Alloway, L. Nine abstract artists. il. 1955. 2.75. Transatlantic
Henning, Edward B. Paths of abstract art. il. 1960. '5..00. Abrams
Kuhn, Charles L. German expressionism and abstract art: The Harvard
Laidman, Hugh. How to make abstract paintings. il. 1961. 6.50. Viking
Lynch, John. How to make mobiles. il. 1953.3.50. Viking
Rathbun, Mary C., and Bartlett H. Hayes, Jr. Layman's guide to modern art.
    1954. 2.75; Addison Gallery
Seuphor, Michel. Abstract painting: Fifty years of accomplishment, from
    Kandinsky to the present. il. 1962. 20.00. Abrams (R)
Seuphor, M., ed. Dictionary of abstract painting. il. 1957. 7.95. Tudor (R)
ART, AFRICAN (709.6)
Museum of Primitive Art. Traditional art of the African nations. il. 1961.
    6.00. Univ. Pub.
Schmalenbach, Werber. African art. 10.00. Boston Bk. (R)
ART--AMERICAN (709.73)
Antiques magazine and Alice Winchester. Antiques treasury of furniture and
    decorative arts. il. 13.50. Dutton (R)
Baur, John Ireland Howe. Revolution and tradition in modern American art.
    il. 1951. 6.50. Harvard
Dover, Cedric. American Negro art. il. 1962. 10.00. N. Y. Graphic
Goodrich, Lloyd, and John I. Baur. American art of our century. il. 15.00.
    Praeger
Larkin, Oliver W. Art and life in America. il. 1960; 14.55. Holt, Rinehart &
    Winston (R)
Lynes, Russell. Tastemakers. il. 1954. 6.00. Harper
McCausland, Elizabeth. Careers in the arts: Fine and applied. 1950. 4.Q0.
    Day
Miller, Dorothy C., ed. Sixteen Americans. il. 1959. pap. 1.95. Mus. of Mod.
    Art.
Mumford, Lewis. Brown decades, a study of the arts of America 1865-1895.
    il. 1960. 3.50. Smith, Peter
Pierson, William H., and Martha Davidson. Arts of the United States: A
    pictorial survey. 1960. 10.95 McGraw (R)
ART, AMERICAN--HISTORY (709)
Blesh, Rudi. Modern art USA. il. 1956. 5.00. Knopf
Dorra, Henri. American muse. il. 1961. 10.00. Viking
Kouwenhoven, John Atlee. Made in America. 5.00. Branford
Larkin, Oliver W. Samuel F. B. Morse and American democratic art. 1954.
    3.75. Little
Mendelowitz, Daniel. History of American art. il. 1960. 13.00 Holt, Rinehart &
    Winston
Torbert, Donald R. Century art and architecture in Minnesota. 1958. 1.00.
    U. Of Minn.
ART, ANCIENT (709.3)
Larousse. Larousse encyclopedia of prehistoric and ancient art. 1962. 17.95.
    Putnam (R)
Lloyd, Seton. Art of the ancient Near East. il. 8.95. Praeger (R)
Loud, Gordon. Khorsabad. vol. 1, Excavations in the palace and at a city gate.
    il. 1936. 10.00. U. of Chicago
Macht, Carol. Classical Wedgewood designs. 1957. 5.00. Barrows
Parrot, Andre. Arts of Assyria. 1961. 25.00. Golden Press (R)
Parrot, Andre. Sumer, the dawn of art. il. 1961. 25.00. Golden Press

Smith, Joseph L. Tombs, temples, and ancient art. ed. by Corinna L. Smith. il. 1956. 5.00. U. of Okla.

Woolley, C. Leonard. Art of the Middle East. il. 1961. 5.95. Crown

ART, ASIAN (709.5)

Japan Cultural Forum. Modern art of Asia: New movements and old traditions. il. 1961. 8.50. Tuttle

ART, AUSTRALIAN (709.9)

Read, Herbert and C. Mountford. Australia, aboriginal paintings: Arnhem land. il. 1954. 18.00. N. Y. Graphic

ART, BAROQUE (709.033)

Hauser, Arnold. Renaissance to Baroque (Social history of art. vol. 2) pap. 1.45. Vintage

Kelemen, Pal. Baroque and rococo in Latin America. il. 16.50. Macmillan

Lees-Milne, James. Baroque in Italy. il. 1959. 7.00. Macmillan

Lees-Milne, James. Baroque in Spain and Portugal. il. 1960. 7.00. Macmillan

Tapie, Victor L. Age of Grandeur: Baroque art and architecture. il. 1961. 12.50 Praeger (R)

ART, BRITISH (709.42)

Cranfill, Thomas M., ed. Image of Britain. 2 vols. il. 1961. 4.00 ea. U. of Tex.

Edwards, Ralph, and L. G. G. Ramsey, eds. Connoisseur period guides: vol. 1, Tudor period 1500-1603; vol. 2, Stuart period 1603- 1714; vol. 3, Early (R) Georgian period 1714-1760; vol. 4, Late Georgian period 1760-1810; vol. 5, Regency period 1810-1830; vol. 6, Early Victorian period, 1830-1860. 1958. 6.95 ea. Crown

Rothenstein, John. British art since 1900. il. 1962. 13.50. N. Y. Graphic

Toynbee, Jocelyn. Art in Roman Britain. il. 1962. 15.00. N. Y. Graphic (R)

ART, BRITISH--HISTORY (709.42)

Boase, Thomas S. R., ed. English art, 1100-1216. il. 1953. 7.20. Oxford U. P.

Brieger, Peter. English art, 1216-1307. 1957. 8.00. Oxford U. P.

Evans, Joan. English art, 1307-1461. il. 1949. 7.20. Oxford U. P.

Rice, David Talbot. English art, 871-1100. il. 1952. 7.20. Oxford U. P.

ART, BUDDHIST (709.52)

Ecke, G., and P. Demieville. Twin Pagodas of Zayton. il. 1935. 6.00. Harvard

Saunders, Ernest D. Mudra: A study of sumbolic gestures in Japanese Buddhist sculpture. il. 1960. 7.50. Pantheon

Warner, Langdon. Japanese sculpture of the Tempyo period: Masterpieces of the eighth century. ed. by James Marshall Plumer. il. 1959. 50.00. Harvard

ART, BYZANTINE (709.02)

Demus, Otto. Byzantine mosiac decoration. il. 1955. 8.50. Boston Bk.

Rice, David T., ed. Masterpieces of Byzantine art. il. 3.00. Aldine

Talbot-Rice, David. Byzantine art. (Pelican A287). il. 1961. Penguin

Weitzmann, K. Greek mythology in Byzantine art. 1951. 12.00. Princeton (R)

ART, CANADIAN (709.71)

Hubbard, Robert H., ed. Anthology of Canadian art. il. 1960. 7.50. Oxford U. P.

McInnes, Graham. Canadian art. 1950. 6.00. St. Martins

Ross, Malcolm, ed. Arts in Canada. 12.50. St. Martins

ART, CHINESE (709.51)

Arts of the Ming dynasty. il. 1958. 14.00. Int. Pub. Service

Carter, D. Four thousand years of China's art. 1951. 8.00. Ronald

Feddersen, Martin. Chinese decorative art. il. 1961. 6.95. Yoseloff

Fitzgerald, Charles P. China, a short cultural history. il. 1954. 12.50. Praeger

Grousset, Rene. Chinese art and culture. tr. by Haakon Chevalier. il. 1961. Grove

Lin, Yu-tang. Imperial Peking. il. 1961. 10.00. Crown

Sullivan, Michael. Chinese art in the twentieth century. il. 1959. 10.00. U. of Calif.

ART, DECORATIVE (700)
Moody, Ella. Decorative art. vol. 52. il. 1962. 10.95. Viking
Moody, Ella, ed. Decorative art in modern interiors. il. 1961. 9.50. Viking

ART, DUTCH (709.492)
Timmers, J. J. M. History of Dutch life and art. 1959. 15.00. Nelson
ART, EGYPTIAN (709.32)
Aldred, Cyril. Development of ancient Egyptian art. il. 7.75. Transatlantic
Aldred, Cyril. New kingdom art in ancient Egypt. il. 4.75. Transatlantic
Lange, Kurt, and Max Hirmer. Egypt, architecture, sculpture, painting in
     3000 years. il. 1956. 15.00. N. Y. Graphic
Rachewiltz, Boris de. Egyptian art. il. 1960. 6.95. Viking
Smith, Joseph L. Tombs, temples, and ancient art. ed. by Corinna L. Smith.
Smith, William S. Ancient Egypt. il. 1961. 7.50. Beacon
Smith, W. Stevenson. Art and architecture of ancient Egypt. (Z14) 12.50. Pen-
     guin
ART, ETRUSCAN (709)
Bloch, Raymond. Etruscan art. il. 1959. 25.00. N. Y. Graphic
ART, EUROPEAN (709.4)
Damaz, Paul. Art in European architecture. 1956. 3.95. Reinhold
Focillon, Henri. Art of the West. il. 1962. 2 vols. 7.95 ea. N. Y. Graphic
Matejcek, Antonin. Art and architecture in Europe. ed. by Jan Krofta. il.
     9.95. Crown
Stadler, Wolfgang. European art. 1960. 7.95. Herder & Herder, N. Y. C.
ART, FLEMISH(709.49)
Ninane, Lucie and others. Flanders in the fifteenth century: Art and civilization.
     il. 1960. 4.50. Detroit Inst. or Wayne
ART, FRENCH (709.44)
Blunt, Anthony. Art and architecture in France, 1500-1700. (Z4) 12.50. Penguin
Canaday, John. Mainstreams of modern art. il. 1959. 9.75. Holt, Rinehart &
     Winston
Canaday, John. Mainstreams of modern art: David to Picasso. il. 1959. 12.50.
     S. and S.
Evans, Joan. Art in Mediaeval France, 987-1498. 12.00. Oxford U. P.
Faniel, Stephane. French art of the 18th century. 20.00. Boston Bk.
George, Andre. Paris. ed. by J. H. and J. M. Denis. 1957. 10.00. Oxford U. P.
     (R)
Huyghe, Rene, and Francois Cali. Wonders of France. il. 1961. 25.00. Viking
     Viking
Male, Emile. Gothic image: Religious art in France in the thirteenth century.
     1958. 4.00. Smith, Peter
ART, GERMAN (709)
Bithell, J. Germany: Companion to German studies. 5th ed. 1955. 8.50. Pitman
Haftmann, Werner, and others. German art of the twentieth century. ed. by
     Andrew Carnduff Ritchie. il. 1958. 9.50. Mus. of Mod. Art
Kuhn, Charles L. German expressionism and abstract art: The Harvard
     collections. 1957. 8.75. Harvard
Muehsam, Alice, ed. German readings, vol. 2: A brief survey of art from the
     Middle Ages to the twentieth century. 1959. pap. 3.50. Wittenborn
Ritchie, Andrew Carduff. ed. German art of the twentieth century. il. 1958.
     9.50. Doubleday
Wolfflin, H. Sense of form in art. 6.50. Chelsea
ART, GREEK (709.38)
Bieber, Margarete. German readings. vol. 1. 1950. pap. 3.00. Wittenborn
Bothmer, Dietrich von. Amazons in Greek art. 1957. 26.90. Oxford U. P.
Carpenter, Rhys. Esthetic basis of Greek art. il. 1959. 3.50. Indiana
Carpenter, Rhys. Greek art: A study of the formal evolution of style. il. 1962.
     12.50. U. of Pa.

Matz, F. Art of Crete and early Greece. 5.95. Crown

Oakeshott, Walter. Classical inspiration in medieval art. il. 1960. 20.00. Praeger

Richter, Gisela M. A. Ancient Italy. 1955. 15.00. U. of Mich.

Richter, G. M. A. Archaic Greek art against its historical background. il. 1949. 25.00. Oxford U. P.

Richter, Gisela. Handibook of Greek art. il. 1960. 7.95. N. Y. Graphic (R) N. Y. Graphic (R)

Richter, Gisela M. A. Handbook of Greek art. 1960. 5.75. Oxford U. P. (W) U. P. (W)

Rodenwaldt, Gerhart. Acropolis. 1958. 8.75. U. of Okla.

Webster, T. B. L. Art and literature in fourth century Athens. 1956. 4.00. Oxford U. P.

Wegner, Max. Greek masterworks of art. tr. by Charlotte La Rue. il. 1961. 12.50. Braziller (R)

ART, HINDU (709)

Anand, Mulk Raj. Hindu view of art. il. 1960. 8.00. Taplinger

Zimmer, Heinrich. Myths and symbols in Indian art and civilization. il. ed. by Joseph Campbell. 1946. 4.50. Pantheon

ART, HITTITE (709)

Akurgal, Ekrem. Art of the Hittites. il. 1962. 25.00. Abrams (R)

ART, ITALIAN (709.45)

American Heritage. Horizon book of the Renaissance. by the Editors of American Heritage. il. 17.50. Doubleday (R)

Berenson, Bernard. Passionate sightseer. il. 1960. 10.00. S. and S.

Decker, Hans. Romanesque art in Italy. il. 1959. 15.00. Abrams (R)

Hutton, Edward. Florence. 1952. 5.00. McKay

McCarthy, Mary T. Stones of Florence. il. 1959. 15.00. Harcourt

Wall, Bernard. Italian art, life and landscape. 1957. 5.00. Sloane

Wolfflin, Heinrich. Classic art: An introduction to the Italian Renaissance. tr. by Peter and Linda Murray. 1953. 5.50. Oxford U. P.

ART, JAPANESE (709.52)

Munsterberg, Hugo. Folk arts of Japan. 6.75. Tuttle

Yashiro, Yukio. 2000 years of Japanese art. ed. by Peter C. Swann. il. 1958. 25.00. Abrams (R)

ART, JAPANESE--HISTORY (709.52)

Terry, Charles S. Masterworks of Japanese art. il. 1957. 17.50. Tuttle

Warner, Langdon. Enduring art of Japan. il. 1952. 6.50. Harvard

ART, JEWISH (709.33)

Roth, Cecil. Jewish art. 1961. 14.95. McGraw (R)

ART, LATIN-AMERICAN (709.8)

Cali, Francois. Spanish arts of Latin America. il. 1961. 12.50. Viking (R)

Groth-Kimball, I and F. Feuchtwanger. Art of ancient Mexico. il. 1954. 12.50. Vanguard. (R)

ART, MEDIEVAL (709.02)

Crump, C. G., and E. F. Jacob, ed. Legacy of the Middle Ages. il. 1926. 6.00. Oxford U. P.

Jackson, Esther. Early English church art, 597-1066. il. 1962. 5.00? Smith, Richard R.

Morey, Charles R. Medieval art. il. 1942. 10.00. Norton (R)

Oakeshott, Walter. Classical inspiration in medieval art. il. 1960. 20.00. Praeger

Syndicus, Edward. Early Christian art. tr. by J. R. Foster. il. 1962. 3.50. Hawthorn

Taylor, Henry Osborn. Classical heritage of the Middle Ages. 4.50. Ungar

ART, MODERN--20TH CENTURY (709.04)

Ashton, Dore. Unknown shore: A view of contemporary art. il. 1962. 6.00. (Atlantic Monthly Press) Little

Barr, Alfred H., Jr. Masters of modern art. il. 1959. 16.50. Mus. of Mod. Art, or Doubleday (R)

Baur, John Ireland Howe. Revolution and tradition in modern American art. il. 1951. 6.50. Harvard

Bernier, Georges, and Rosamond, eds. Aspects of modern art: Selective eye III. il. 9.75. Reynal

Biddle, George. Yes and no of contemporary art: An artist's evaluation. 1957. 5.00. Harvard

Blesh, Rudi. Modern art USA. il. 1956. 5.00. Knopf

Canaday, John. Mainstreams of modern art. il. 1959. 9.75. Holt, Rinehart & Winston

Cassou, J., and others. Gateway to the twentieth century: Art and culture in a changing world. 1962. 25.00. McGraw

Cheney, Sheldon. Primer of modern art. 1958. 5.95. Liveright

Damaz, Paul. Art in European architecture. 1956. 3.95. Reinhold

Getlein, Frank and Dorothy. Christianity in modern art. il. 1961. 5.00. Bruce

Goodrich, Lloyd, and John I. H. Baur. American art of our century. il. 1961. 15.00. Praeger (R)

Kepes, Gyorgy, ed. Visual arts today. il. 1960. 6.00. Wesleyan U. P.

Kuh, Katharine. Art has many faces. il. 1951. 7.95. Harper

Langui, Emile. Fifty years of modern art. il. 6.50. Boston Bk.

Motherwell, R., and others, eds. Modern artists in America. 1st ser. il. 1952. 6.50. Wittenborn

Raynal, Maurice. Modern painting. il. 1956. in English and French. 27.50. World Pub. (R)

Read, Herbert. Art now. il. 1960. 8.50. Pitman

Read, Herbert E. Concise history of modern painting. il. 1959. 7.50; pap. 3.95. Praeger

Rodman, Selden. Eye of man. 1955. 10.00. Devin

Rosenblum, Robert. Cubism and twentieth century art. il. 1960. 25.00. Abrams

Soby, James T. Modern art and the New past. 1957. 3.75. U. of Okla.

Wilenski, R. H. Modern movement in art. 1957. 8.50. Yoseloff

Wilson, Frank. Art into life: An interpretation of contemporary trends in painting. il. 1958. 6.95. Citadel

ART, ORIENTAL (709)

Lloyd, Seton. Art of the ancient Near East. il. 1961. 8.95. Praeger

ART, PACIFIC ISLAND (709.9)

Buehler, A., and others. Art of the South Sea Islands. 5.95. Crown

Linton, Ralph, and Paul Wingert. Arts of the south seas. il. 1958. 3.95. Mus. of Mod. Art.

ART, PERSIAN (709.55)

Pope, Arthur Upham. Masterpieces of Persian art. il. 6.00. Holt, Rinehart & Winston

ART, PRIMITIVE (709.011)

Bandi, Hans-Georg. Art of the Stone Age. il. 5.95. Crown

Boas, Franz. Primitive art. il. 1962. 4.00. Smith, Peter

Dark, Philip J. C. Bush Negro art. il. 1954. 2.50. Transatlantic

Forman, Werner and Bedrich. Art of far lands. 12.95. Tudor (R)

Hajek, L. Exotic art. 12.95. Tudor (R)

Museum of Primitive art. Traditional art of the African nations. il. 1961. 6.00. Univ. Pub.

ART, RENAISSANCE (709.4)

Clements, Robert J. Michelangelo's theory of art. il. 1961. 10.00. N. Y. U. (R)

Panofsky, E.. Renaissance and Renascences in Western art. 22.50. Humanities

Thompson, James Westfall, and others. Civilization of the Renaissance. 1959. 3.00. Ungar

Wolfflin, H. Classic art: An introduction to the Italian Renaissance. 2nd ed. il. 1953. 7.50. N. Y. Graphic

ART, ROCOCO (709.033)

Schonberger, Arno, and Halldor Soener. Rococo age. 1960. 23.50. McGraw (R)

ART, ROMAN (709.37)

Richter, Gisela M. A. Ancient Italy. 1955. 15.00. U. of Mich.

ART, RUSSIAN (709.47)

Gray, Camilla. Great experiment: Russian art, 1863-1922. il. 1962. 25.00.
   Abrams

Hamilton, G. H. Art and architecture of Russia. (Z6) 1955. 8.50. Penguin

ART, SPANISH (709.46)

Hagen, Oskar. Patterns and principles of Spanish art. il. 2nd ptg. 1948. 5.00.
   U. of Wis.

Peers, E. Allison. Spain: A companion to Spanish studies. 1957. 6.00. Pitman

ART, THAILAND (709)

Bowie, Theodore R., ed. Arts of Thailand. il. 1961. 8.95. Indiana

ART, VATICIAN CITY (709)

Calvesi, Maurizio. Treasures of the Vatican. il. 1962. 27.50. World Pub.

Matt, Leonard von. Art in the Vatican. 1962. 4.75. Universe

ART AND INDUSTRY (745.1)

Biegeleisen, J. I. Careers in commercial art. rev. ed. il. 1952. 4.00. Dutton

ART AND LITERATURE (709)

Hagstrum. Jean H. Sister arts. il. 1958. 7.50. U. of Chicago

Webster, T. B. L. Art and literature in fourth century Athens. 1956. 4.00.
   Oxford U. P.

Webster, T. B. L. Greek art and literature, 700-530 B. C. il. 1960. 5.95.
   Praeger

ART AND MORALS (701)

Maritain, Jacques. Responsibility of the artist. 1960. 2.95. Scribner

Taylor, Harold. Art and the intellect. 1960. pap. 0.75. Mus. of Mod. Art

Tolstoy, Leo N. What is art? tr. by A. Maude. 1960. pap. 1.00. Bobbs

Tolstoy, Leo. What is art? and Essays on art. (WC 331) tr. by Aylmer
   Msude. 2.75. Oxford U. P.

ART AND RELIGION (701)

Christie, M. J., Sister, ed. Art for Christian living. 1958. 3.50. Catholic U.
   of Am. Pr.

Eversole, Finley, ed. Christian faith and the contemporary arts. il. 1962. 5.00.
   Abingdon

Wilder, Amos N. Theology and modern literature. 1958. 3.50. Harvard

ART AND SCIENCE (709)

Cassidy, Harold G. Sciences and the arts. il. 1962. bds. 4.75. Harper

Kepes, Gyorgy. New landscape in art and science. 1956. 15.50. Theobald

Sypher, Wylie. Loss of the self in modern literature and art. 1962. 4.00.
   Random

ART AND SOCIETY (701)

Hauser, Arnold. Philosophy of art history. 1959. 7.50. Knopf

Hauser, Arnold. Social history of art. 2 vols. il. 1951. 17.50. Knopf

Moholy-Nagy, Laszlo. Vision in motion. il. 1947. 13.75. Theobald

Myers, Bernard. Art and civilization. il. 1957. 10.95; text ed. 7.95. McGraw
   (R)

Read, Herbert E. Grass roots of art. rev. ed. il. 1955. pap. 2.50. Wittenborn

ART AS A PROFESSION (700)

Harris, Kenneth. How to make a living as a painter. 1954. 2.95. Watson

ART CRITICISM (701.18)

Baudelaire, Charles. Mirror of art. (Anchor A84) ed. by Jonathan Mayne. 1956
   pap. 1.45. Doubleday

Beigel, Hugo G. Art appreciation. il. 6.50. Ungar

Beigel, Hugo G. Wake up to art. il. 5.50. (Daye, S.) Ungar

Biederman, Charles. Art as the evolution of visual knowledge. il. 1948. 10.00.
   Art History

Boas, George. Wingless Pegasus: A handbook of art criticism. 1950. 3.50. Johns Hopkins

Rosenthal, Erwin. Changing concept of reality in art. il. 1962. 6.50. Wittenborn

ART DEALERS (709)

Rheims, Maurice. Strange life of objects. il. 1961. 6.95. Atheneum

ART DEALERS--DIRECTORIES (708.1)

Spaeth, Eloise. American art museums and galleries. il. 1960. 5.95. Harper (R)

ART INDUSTRIES AND TRADE (709)

Boe, A. From Gothic revival to functional form. 3.50. Humanities

Cole, Ann Kilborn. Antiques: How to identify, buy, sell, refinish, and care for them. il. 1957. 4.95. McKay

Drexler, Arthur, and Greta Daniel. Introduction to twentieth century design. il. 1959. pap. 2.95. Mus. of Mod. Art

Faulkner, Ray, and others. Art today: An introduction to the fine and functional arts, il. 1956. 10.10. Holt, Rinehart & Winston

Robertson, S. Crafts and contemporary culture. (UNESCO) 3.50. Int. Doc. Service-Columbia

Willoughby, George A. General crafts. 1959. 4.00. Bennett

ART INDUSTRIES AND TRADE--DICTIONARIES (709)

Boger, Louise A., and H. Batterson. Dictionary of antiques and the decorative arts. il. 1957. 13.95. Scribner (R)

Connoisseur. Concise encyclopedia of antiques. 5 vols. by the Editors of Connoisseur. il. vols. 1-3, 1955; vol 4, 1959; vol. 5. 1961. 12.50 ea. Hawthorn

Hayward, Helena, ed. Connoisseur's handbook of antique collecting. il. 1960. 5.95. Hawthorn (R)

ART LIBRARIES (709)

Chamberlin, Mary W. Guide to art reference books. 1959. 10.00. A. L. A. (R)

ART METAL-WORK (709)

Aitchison, L. History of metals. 2 vols. il. 1960. 30.00. Wiley (R)

Baxter, William T. Jewelry, gem cutting and metalcraft. 1950. 7.50. McGraw (R)

Bick, Alexander F. Artistic metalwork. 1940. 4.50. Bruce

Kronquist, Emil. Art metal work. 1942. 5.95. McGraw

Miller, John G. Metal art crafts. 2nd ed. Van Nostrand

Untracht, Oppi. Enameling on metal. il. 1957. 7.50. Chilton

ART OBJECTS--COLLECTORS AND COLLECTING (709)

Lee, Ruth Webb. Antique fakes and reproductions. il. 7.50. Lee Pub.

ART OBJECTS--CONSERVATION AND RESTORATION (708)

Freeman, Larry. How to restore antiques. 6.00. Century House

ART THERAPY (709)

Dax, E. Cunningham. Experimental studies in psychiatric art. il. 1953. 5.00. Lippincott

Meares, Ainslie. Door of serenity: A study in the therapeutic use of symbolic painting. il. 1958. 4.50. Thomas, C. C

ART TREASURES IN WAR (709)

Flanner, Janet. Men and monuments. il. 1957. 5.00. Harper

ARTERIOSCLEROSIS (616.13)

Katz, Louis N., and others. Nutrition and atherosclerosis. il. 1958. 5.00. Lea & F.

ARTHRITIS (616.7)

Alexander, Dan Dale. Arthritis and common sense. 1953. 3.95. Witkower

Broadman, Joseph. Bee venom. 1962. 3.95. Putnam

Brugsch, Heinrich G. Rheumatic diseases, rheumatism and arthritis. il. 1957. 10.00. Lippincott

ARTHUR, KING (398.2)

Bruce, J. D. Evolution of the Arthurian romance. 2 vols. 13.00. Smith, Peter

Jones, W. Lewis. King Arthur in history and legend. 1914. 1.75. Cambridge U. P.

Loomis, Roger Sherman, ed. Arthurian literature in the Middle Ages. 1959.
10.10. Oxford U. P.

Malory, Thomas. King Arthur and his noble knights. 3.75. Dodd

ARTHUR, CHESTER ALAN, PRES. U. S., 1830-1886 (923.173)

Howe, George F. Chester A. Arthur: A quarter century of machine politics. il
5.00. Ungar

ARTICULATION (EDUCATION) (370)

Brown, Nicholas C., ed. Orientation to college learning, a reappraisal. il.
1961. pap. 2.00. A. C. E.

Diamond, Esther E. Preparing students for college. 1962. il. pap. 1.50. Sci. Res.
Assoc.

General education in school and college: A committee report by members of the
faculties of Andover, Exeter, Lawrenceville, Harvard, Princeton, and Yale.
1952. 2.50. Harvard

ARTIFICIAL INSEMINATION (636.082)

Herman, H. A., and F. W. Madden. Artificial insemination of dairy cattle. rev.
ed. 4.00. Lucas Bros.

Perry, Enos J. Artificial insemination of farm animals. 1960. 6.50. Rutgers

ARTIFICIAL INSEMINATION, HUMAN (636)

Williams, Glanville. Sancitity of life and the criminal law. 1957. 5.00. Knopf

ARTIFICIAL RESPIRATION (610.9)

Karpovich, Peter V. Adventures in artificial respiration. 1953. 7.50. Assn
Press

ARTISTS (709)

Gaunt, William, ed. Dictionary of pictorial art. 2 vols. il. set, 13.00. Dutton
(R)

Greenberg, Clement. Art and culture. 1961. 6.00. Beacon (R)

Mallett, D. T. Index of artists: International and biographical. 12.00. suppl.
8.50. Smith, Peter (R)

Read, Herbert. Philosophy of modern art. 1955. pap. 1.55. Meridian

Rosenberg, Jakob. Great draughtsmen from Pisanello to Picasso. il. 1959.
12.50. Harvard

Schneider, Daniel E. Psychoanalyst and the artist. 1954. 4.00. Int. Univs.

Strange, T. A. English furniture, decoration, woodwork and allied arts. il.
1950. 15.00. Museum Bks.

Vasari, Giorgio. Lives of the artists. ed. by Betty Burroughs. 1959. 5.00;
A. and S. (R)

Vasari, Giorgio. Lives of the painters, sculptors, and architects. 4 vols.
1.95 ea. Dutton (R)

ARTISTS--CORRESPONDENCE, REMINISCENCES, ETC. (927)

Chagall, Marc. My life. tr. by Elisabeth Abbott. il. 1960. 6.00. Orion Press
(R)

Courthion, Pierre, and P. Cailler, eds. Portrait of Manet. 6.50. Rou Pub.

Gauguin, Paul. Noa, Noa. 1957. pap. 1.45. Farrar, Straus

Leslie, C. R. Memoirs of the life of John Constable. ed. by Jonathon Mayne. il.
1952. 2.95. Doubleday

Moses, Anna Mary Robertson. Grandma Moses: My life's history. ed. by
Otto Kallir. il. 1952. 5.50. Harper

Rodman, Selden. Conversations with artists. 4.00. Devin

Van Gough, Vincent. Van Gogh: A self portrait. ed. by W. H. Auden. il. 1961.
10.00. N. Y. Graphic (R)

ARTISTS, AMERICAN (927)

American prints today. il. 1962. 1.50. Print Council of Am.

Brooks, Van Wyck. Dream of Arcadia: American writers and artists in
Italy, 1760-1915. 1958. 4.50. Dutton

Gilbert, Dorothy B., ed. Who's who in American art. 9th ed. 1962. 22.50.
Bowker (R)

Groce, G., and D. Wallace. Dictionary of artists in America, 1564-1860. 1957.
15.00. Yale (R)
ARTISTS' MARKS (709)
MacDonald-Taylor, Margaret. Dictionary of marks. il. 1962. 5.95. Hawthorn (R)
ARTISTS' MATERIALS (751)
Bazzi, Maria. Artist's methods and materials. il. 1960. 6.00. Pitman
Mayer, Ralph. Artist's handbook of materials and techniques. rev. ed. il. 1957.
6.75; text ed. 5.25. Viking (R)
Taubes, Frederic. Oil and tempera painting. 3.75. Watson
ARYAN LANGUAGES (491)
Scott, Harry F., and others. Language and its growth. 1957. 6.75. Scott
ASCETICISM (248)
Colliander, Tito. Way of the ascetics. ed. by R. M. French. tr. by Katharine
Ferre. 1960. 2.50. Harper
Goodier, Alban. Introduction to the study of ascetical and mystical theology.
1938. 3.50. Bruce
Guibert, Joseph de. Theology of the spiritual life. 1953. 4.50. Sheed
ASIA (950)
American Library Association. Richer by Asia: Bibliography of books and
other materials for promoting West-East understanding. 1959. pap. 1.25.
A. L. A. (R)
Cressey, George B. Asia's lands and peoples. il. 1951. 9.50. McGraw
Dhingra, Baldoon, ed. Asia through Asian eyes. 1959. 5.75. Tuttle
Gunther, John. Inside Asia. 1942. 6.95. Harper
ASIA--DESCRIPTION AND TRAVEL (915)
Dobby, E. H. G. Monsoon Asia. il. 1961. 5.95. Quadrangle
Hurlimann, Martin. Journey through the Orient. il. 1960. 15.00. Viking
Kennedy, Robert F. Just friends and brave enemies. 1962. 3.95? Harper
Pollock, John C. Earth's remotest end. 1961. 5.95. Macmillan
Polo, Marco. Travels. ed. by Manuel Kimroff. 1926. 3.95. Liveright
Roosevelt, Eleanor. India and the awakening East. il. 1953. 3.95. Harper
Waldron, D'Lynn. Further than at home. il. 1959. 3.50. Harper
ASIA, DESCRIPTION AND TRAVEL--VIEWS (915)
Hurlimann, Martin. Asia. il. 1957. 12.50. (Studio) Viking
ASIA--ECONOMIC CONDITIONS (950)
Bonne, Alfred. State and economics in the Middle East. il. 1948. 8.00.
Humanities
Economic survey of Asia and the Far East, 1960. 1961. 3.00. U. N.
ASIA--HISTORY (950)
Edwardes, Michael. Asia in the European age: 1498-1955. il. 1962. 8.50.
Praeger
Lensen, George A. World beyond Europe. il. 1960. pap. 1.95. Houghton
Panikkar, Kavalam M. Asia and Western dominance: A survey of the Vasco
Da Gama epoch of Asian history. 1498-1945. il. 1959. 5.00. Hillary
Vernadsky, G. Mongols and Russia. 1953. 7.50. Yale
ASIA--POLITICS (950)
Bonne, Alfred. State and economics in the Middle East. il. 1948. 8.00.
Humanities
Buss, Claude A. Arc of crisis. 1961. 5.95. Doubleday
Lattimore, Owen. Situation in Asia. 1949. 3.50. Little
Thomson, Ian. Rise of modern Asia. 1958. 4.95. Pitman
ASIA--RELIGION (181)
Fitch, Florence. Their search for God. 1944. 3.00. Lothrop
Kitagawa, Joseph M. Religions of the East. 1960. 4.50. Westminster
ASIA--RELISION--BIBLIOGRAPHY (181) G
James. E. O. Comparative study of religions of the eastern world. 1959.
DeVorss

ASIA--SOCIAL CONDITIONS (950)
Deverall, Richard L. G. Asia and the Democratic Revolution. il. 1952. pap.
   2.50. Tuttle
Rowan, Carl T. Pitiful and the proud. 1956. 5.00. Random House
ASIA--SOCIAL LIFE AND CUSTOMS (915)
Michener, James A. Voice of Asia. 1951. 3.50. Random
ASIA, CENTRAL--DESCRIPTION AND TRAVEL (915.8)
Rawicz, Slavomir. Long walk: A gamble for life. ed. by Ronald Downing. il.
   1956. 4.50. Harper
ASIA, SOUTHEASTERN (959)
Calder, Ritchie. Men against the jungle. il. 1954. 3.50. Macmillan
Hall, D. G. E. History of South-East Asia. 1955. 10.00. St. Martins
Harrison, Brian. Southeast Asia: A short history. 1954. 3.50. St. Martins
ASIA, SOUTHEASTERN--POLITICS (959)
Butwell, Richard. Southeast Asia today - and tomorrow. 4.25; pap. 1.75.
   Praeger
ASIA, WESTERN (956)
Hall, H. R. Ancient history of the Near East. 8.50. Macmillan
ASIA, WESTERN-.-DESCRIPTION AND TRAVEL (915.6)
Cressey, George B. Crossroads: Land and life in Southwest Asia. il. 1960.
   12.00 9.50. Lippincott
Douglas, William O. West of the Indus. 1958. 5.00. Doubleday
ASIA MINOR (939.2)
Muller, Herbert J. Loom of history. il. 1958. 7.50. Harper
Osward, Maxim. Asia Minor. il. 1958. 10.00. Morrow
ASSAM (954.16)
Bertrand, Gabrielle. Secret lands where women reign. il. 5.75. Transatlantic
ASSEMBLY, RIGHT OF (323.47)
Drinker, Henry S. Some observations on the Four Freedoms of the First
   Amendment. 1957. 3.00. Boston U.
ASSEMBLY-LINE METHODS (658.54)
Walker, Charles Rumford, and Robert H. Guest. Man on the assembly line.
   il. 1952. 3.25. Harvard
ASSIMILATION(SOCIOLOGY) (301.23)
Kaplan, Ben. Eternal stranger. 1957. 4.00. Twayne
Knapp, Robert B. Social integration in urban communities. 1960. 5.75. T. C.
ASSOCIATION OF IDEAS(153.2)
Bjorkman, Mats. Measurement of learning. 3.00. Humanities (R)
Freud, Sigmund. Psychopathology of everyday life. 3.75. Macmillan
ASSOCIATIONS, INSTITUTIONS, ETC. (301.158)
Barnard, Chester Irving. Functions of the executive. 1938. 5.50. Harvard
Buttress, F. A. World list of abbreviations of scientific, technological
   commercial organizations. 1960. 4.25. Hafner (R)
Dby, Kermit. Protests of an ex-organization man. 1961. 3.50. Beacon
Leiserson, Avery. Administrative regulation: A study in representation of
   interests. 1942. 5.50. U. of Chicago
ASSOCIATIONS, INSTITUTIONS, ETC.--DIRECTORIES (061)
Encyclopedia of Associations. vol. 1. National Organizations of the U. S. 25.00;
   vol. 2. Gale (R)
ASSYRIA (935)
Contenau, G. Everyday life in Babylon and Assyria. 1954. 6.00. St. Martins
Olmstead, A. T. History of Assyria. 1923. 12.50. U. of Chicago
ASSYRO-BABYLONIAN LITERATURE (892.19)
Lambert, W. G. Babylonian wisdom literature. il. 1960. 16.00. Oxford U. P.
ASTRODYNAMICS (523)
Baker, Robert M., and Maud W. Makemson. Introduction to astrodynamics.
   1960. 7.50. Academic Press
Kolk, W. Richard. Modern flight dynamics. 1960. 10.00 7.50. Prentice-Hall

Thomson, William T. Introduction to space dynamics. 1961. 10.50. Wiley

ASTROLOGY (133)
Righter, Carroll. Astrology and you. 4.65. Fleet

ASTROLOGY, EARLY (133)
Cumont, Franz. Astrology and religion among the Greeks and Romans. 3.35. Smith, Peter.

Moran, Hugh A. Alphabet and the ancient calendar signs. 1952. 3.50. Pacific Bks.

ASTRONAUTICS (629)
Bergaust, Erik. Reaching for the stars. il. 1960. 4.95. Doubleday

Berman, Arthur I. Physical principles of astronautics. il. 1961. 8.50. Wiley

Bucheim, Robert W., and Rand Corporation. Space handbook. 1959. 3.95. Random

Clarke, Arthur C. Exploration of space. 4.50. Harper

Clarke, Arthur C. Interplanetary flight. il. 1960. 3.50. Harper

Cleator, P. E. Introduction to space travel. 1961. 3.95. Pitman

De Leeuw, Hendrik. Conquest of the air. il. 1960. 4.95. Vantage

Haley, Andrew G. Rocketry and space exploration. il. 1958. 6.75. Van Nostrand

Holmes, Jay. America on the Moon. 1962. 4.50. Lippincott

Jones, Harold Spencer, and others. Space encyclopedia. il. 1959. 8.95. Dutton (R)

Kaiser, Hans K. Rockets and spaceflight. il. 1962. 4.75. Pitman

Koelle, Heinz H., ed. Handbook of astronautical engineering. 1961. 27.50. McGraw (R)

Lapp, Ralph E. Man and space: The next decade. il. 1961. 4.95. Harper

Ley, Willy. Rockets, missiles, and space travel. il. 1957. 6.75. Viking

Marcus, A., and R. Tomorrow the moon. 3.50. Prentice-Hall

Medaris, John B. Countdown for decision. il. 1960. 5.00. Putnam

Newlon, Clarke. 1001 questions answered about space. il. 1962. 6.00. Dodd (R)

Stokley, James. Atoms to galaxies. 1961. 6.00. Ronald

ASTRONAUTICS--DICTIONARIES (629)
Besserer, C., and H. Guide to the space age. 1959. 7.95. Prentice-Hall (R)

Van Nostrand. Van Nostrand's dictionary of guided missiles and space flight. il. 1959. 19.50. Van Nostrand (R)

ASTRONAUTICS AND CIVILIZATION (629)
American Assembly. Outer space prospects for man and society. ed. by Lincoln P. Bloomfield. 1962. 3.95 Prentice-Hall

Cox, Donald, and Michael Stoiko. Spacepower. il. 1958. 4.50. Winston

Ramo, Simon, ed. Peacetime uses of outer space. il. 1961. 6.95. McGraw

ASTRONAUTICS AS A PROFESSION (629)
Adams, C. C., and W. von Braun. Careers in astronautics and rocketry. in prep. McGraw

Ely, Lawrence D. Your future in aerospace technology. 2.95. 2.65. Richards Rosen

ASTRONAUTS (629)
Americans in space. 1962. 6.50? S. and S.

Bell, Joseph N. Seven into space. il. 1960. 3.95. Hawthorn

ASTRONOMICAL INSTRUMENTS (522)
Chauvenet, William. Manual of spherical and practical astronomy. 2 vols. 9.50. Smith, Peter (R)

ASTRONOMICAL PHOTOGRAPHY (522)
Fassero, James S. Photographic giants of Palomar. 1953. 1.50. Westernlore

Paul, Henry E. Outer space photography for amateurs. 1960. bds. 2.50. Hastings

Rackham, Thomas. Astronomical photography at the telescope. 2nd ed. il. 1961. 8.50. Macmillan

ASTRONOMY (520)
Baker, Robert H. Astronomy. il. 1959. 7.50. Van Nostrand

Baker, Robert H. Introduction to astronomy. il. 1960. 5.50. Van Nostrand

Beet, E. A. Guide to the sky. 1950. 3.00. Cambridge U. P.

Beet, Ernest A. Sky and its mysteries. il. 3.50. Dover

Bok, Bart J. Astronomer's universe. 1959. 3.75. Cambridge U. P.

Bova, Ben. Milky Way galaxy: Man's exploration of the stars. 5.00. Holt, Rinehart & Winston

Davidson, Martin, ed. Astronomy for everyman. il. 1953. 4.00. Dutton

Evans, David S. Teach yourself astronomy. 2.50. Roy Pub.

Hawkins, Gerald S. Splendor in the sky. il. 1961. 5.95. Harper

Hoyle, Fred. Frontiers of astronomy. 1955. 5.95. Harper

Hoyle, Fred. Nature of the universe. 1960. 3.00. Harper

Inglis, S. J. Planets, stars and galaxies. il. 1961. 6.95. Wiley

Jeans, James. Astronomy and cosmogony. pap. 2.45. Dover

Jeans, J. H. Universe around us. 1944. 5.00. 1960. Cambridge U. P.

Jones, H. Spencer. General astronomy. 1961. 12.00. St. Martins

Kahn, Fritz. Design of the universe: The heavens and the earth. il. 1954. 6.95. Crown

Larousse. Larousse encyclopedia of astronomy. il. 1959. 15.00. Putnam (R)

Lee, Oliver J. Measuring our universe. 1950. 4.50. Ronald

Lyttleton, Raymond A. Man's view of the universe. il. 1961. 4.50. Little

McLaughlin, Dean B. Introduction to astronomy. 7.50. Houghton

Marshall, Roy K. Sun, moon, and planets. il. 1952. 3.00. Holt

Moore, Patrick. Amateur astronomer. 1957. 5.95. Norton

Moore, Patrick. Guide to the stars. il. 1960. 4.95. Norton

Pickering, James S. 1001 questions answered about astronomy. 1958. 6.00. Dodd (R)

Richardson, R. S. Fascinating world of astronomy. 1960. 5.95. McGraw

Schneider, Leo. Space in your future. 1961. 3.75. Harcourt

Scientific American, ed. New astronomy. by the Editors of Scientific American. 1956. 1.45. S. and S.

Stokley, J. Atoms to galaxies. 1961. 6.00. Ronald

Van de Kamp, Peter. Basic astronomy. 1952. 4.95. Random

Whitrow, G. J. Structure and evolution of the universe. 4.50. Hillary

ASTRONOMY--EARLY WORKS TO 1800 (520.1)

Copernicus, Nicolaus. Three Copernicus treatises. rev. by Edward Rosen, with annotated bibliography, 1939-1958. 3.75. Smith, Peter

Galilei, Galileo. Dialogue concerning the two chief world systems, Ptolemaic and Copernican. tr. by Stillman Drake. il. 1953. 10.00. U. of Calif.

Galilei, Galileo. Dialogue on the great world systems, ed. by Giorgio de Santillana. il. 1953. 12.50. U. of Chicago

ASTRONOMY--HISTORY (520)

Abetti, Giorgio. History of astronomy. tr. by Betty Burr Abetti. il. 1952. 6.00. Abelard

Dreyer, John L. E. History of astronomy from Thales to Kepler. 3.75. Smith, Peter

King, Henry C. Background of astronomy. 1958. 5.00. Braziller

Lodge, Oliver J. Pioneers of science. il. 1960. pap. 1.50. Dover

Lodge, Oliver. Pioneers of science and the development of their scientific theories. 3.50. Smith, Peter

Pannekoek, Antonie. History of astronomy. il. 1961. 9.75. Wiley

Rousseau, Pierre. Man's conquest of the stars. il. 1961. 5.00. Norton

Thiel, Rudolf. And there was light. 1957. 6.95. Knopf

ASTRONOMY--OBSERVERS' MANUALS (522)

Bernhard, Hubert, and others. New handbook of the heavens. il. 1948. 5.50. McGraw (R)

Olcott, William, and others. Field book of the skies. 1954. 5.00. Putnam

Sidgwick, J. B. Observational astronomy for amateurs. il. 1955. 10.75. Macmillan

ASTRONOMY--STUDY AND TEACHING (520.7)
Shaw, R. W., and S. L. Boothroyd. Manual of astronomy. 1958. pap. 4.00.
    Brown, W. C. (R)
ASTROPHYSICS (523)
Allen, C. W. Astrophysical quantities. 1955. 8.80. Oxford U. P.
Aller, Lawrence H. Astrophysics: Atmospheres of the sun and stars. 1953.
    12.00. Ronald
Aller, Lawrence H. Astrophysics: Nuclear transformations, stellar interiors,
    and nebulae. 1954. 12.00. Ronald
Jastrov, Robert, ed. Exploration of space. 1960. 5.95. Macmillan
Liller, W. Space astrophysics. 1961. 10.00. McGraw
Lyttleton, Raymond A. Modern universe. il. 1957. 3.50. Harper
Woolley, R. v. d. R., and D. W. N. Stibbs. Outer layers of a star. 1953. 8.00.
    Oxford U. P.
ASYLUM, RIGHT OF (341.31)
Garcia-Mora, Manuel R. International law and asylum as a human right. 1956.
    4.50. Pub. Affairs
Organization of American States. Convention on diplomatic asylum, Caracas,
    1954. quadrilingual Spanish, English, French and Portuguese. 0.25. Pan
    American
ATHANASIUS, SAINT, PATRIARCH OF ALEXANDRIA, d. 373 (922.22)
Pelikan, Jaroslay. Light of the world. 1962. 2.50. Harper
ATHEISM (211)
Whitney, Dudley J. Genesis versus evolution. 1961. 2.50. Exposition
ATHENS--ANTIQUITIES (938.5)
Haynes, D. E. L., and W. Forman. Parthenon frieze. il. 1959. 5.95. Tudor
Yalouris, Nikolas. Classical Greece. il. 1961. 8.95. N. Y. Graphic
ATHENS--DESCRIPTION--VIEWS (938)
Hurlimann, Martin. Athens. ed. by Rex Warner. il. 1957. 6.00. Viking
ATHENS--HISTORY (949)
Athens, 478-401 B. C. (Cambridge ancient history. vol 5) 13.50. Cambridge U. P.
Burn, A. R. Pericles and Athens 2.50. Macmillan
Coolidge, Olivia. Men of Athens. il. 1962. 3.50. Houghton
Robinson, Charles A., Jr. Athens in the Age of Pericles. 1959. 2.75. U. of
    Okla.
ATHENS--POLITICS AND GOVERNMENT (938)
Aristotle. Athenian Constitution, Eudemian ethics, Vices and virtues. 1935. 3.50.
    Harvard
Hignett, C. History of the Athenian constitution to the end of the fifth century,
    B C. 1952. 6.10. Oxford U. P.
ATHENS--SOCIAL LIFE AND CUSTOMS (913.38)
Davis, W. S. Day in old Athens. 3.50. Biblo & Tannen
ATHLETES, AMERICAN (920)
Compbell, Gordon. Famous American athletes of today. 3.95. Farrar, Straus
Hirshberg, Al, and Joe McKenney. Famous American athletes of today. 1947.
    3.95. Farrar, Straus
ATHLETICS (796)
Bresnahan, George T., and others. Track and field athletics. il. 1960. 5.50.
    Mosby
Mitchell, E. E. Sports for recreation. 1952. 7.00. Ronald
Mueller, Pat, and Elmer D. Mitchell. Intramural sports. 1960. 6.00. Ronald
Reeder, Red. Pointers on athletics. il. 1962. 3.95. Meredith
Stafford, G. T., and R. O. Duncan. Physical conditioning. 1942. 2.95. Ronald
V-Five Association of America. Conditioning exercises. il. 1959. 4.30. U. S.
    Naval Inst.
ATHLETICS--APPARATUS AND EQUIPMENT (796)
Equipment and supplies for athletics, physical education, and recreation. 1960.
    2.50. Am. Assn. for Health, Phys. Ed. & Rec.

ATHLETICS--HISTORY (796)
Gardiner, E. N. Athletics of the ancient world. il. 1930. 8.80. Oxford U. P.
ATLANTIC COAST (917.4)
Hartog, Jan de. Waters of the new world. il. 1961. 5.95. Atheneum
ATLANTIC OCEAN (940)
De la Croix, Robert. They flew the Atlantic. il. 1959. 3.95. Norton
ATLAS (MISSILE) (623.451)
Chapman, John L. Atlas: The story of a missile. il. 1960. 4.00. Harper
ATLASES (912)
Atlas. (New Cambridge modern history. vol. 14) 9.50. Cambridge U. P.(R)
Atlas of the Arab world and the Middle East. 1960. 9.00. St. Martins (R)
Bartholomew, John. Advanced atlas of modern geography. il. 1956. 11.50; text ed.
    8.50. McGraw (R)
Bartholomew, John. Edinburgh world atlas of modern geography. il. 1962.
    10.00. Warne (R)
Bartholomew, John, ed. Times atlas of the world. vol. 1. il. 1959; vol. 2. 1960;
    vol. 3. il. 1955; vol. 4. 1956; vol. 5. 1957. 25.00 ea. Houghton (R)
Cram's new modern world atlas. 9.95. Cram (R)
Economist Intelligence Unit, and Clarendon Press, Cartographic Department.
    Oxford economic atlas of the world. 1959. 8.00. Oxford U. P. (R)
Encyclopaedia Britannica world atlas. 1962. 29.50. Encycl. Britannica (R)
Fullard, Harold, and H. G. Darby, eds. Library atlas. il. 1961. 10.00. Barnes
    & Noble (R)
Gaustad, Edwin S. Historical atlas of religion in America. 1962. 7.95. Harper
    (R)
Hammond, C. S., and Co. Complete world atlas. il. 1952. 5.95. Hammond (R)
Hammond, C. S., and Co. Diplomat atlas. 9.95. Hammond (R)
Lewis, Clinton, and others, eds. Oxford atlas. 1951. 12.50. Oxford U. P. (R)
Life, and Rand McNally. Life pictorial atlas of world. by the Editors of Life,
    and Rand McNally. il. 1961. 30.00. Rand McNally (R)
Rand McNally. Rand McNally international world atlas. il. 1961. 11.95.
    Rand McNally (R)
Rand McNally and Co. Cosmopolitan world atlas. 1962. 14.95. Rand McNally (R)
Rand McNally and Co. Goode's world atlas. 9th ed. 9.95; 7.50. Rand McNally
    (R)
Williams, Joseph E., ed. Prentice-Hall world atlas. 1958. 9.00. Prentice-Hall
    (R)
ATLASES--BIBLIOGRAPHY(912)
Whyte, Fredrica H. Whyte's Atlas Guide. 4.50. Scarecrow (R)
ATMOSPHERE (551.5)
Cook, J. Gordon. Our astonishing atmosphere. 1957. 3.50 Dial
Gregory, P. H. Microbiology of the atmosphere. 1962. 10.50. Wiley (R)
Hood, Peter. Atmosphere. 1952. 3.00. Oxford U. P.
Orr, Clyde. Between earth and space. il. 1959. 4.95. Macmillan
Wenstrom, William H. Weather and the ocean of air. il. 1942. 5.00. Houghton
ATMOSPHERE, UPPER (523.35)
Goody, R. M. Physics of the stratosphere. 1954. 6.00. Cambridge U. P.
Johnson, Francis S., ed. Satellite environment handbook. 1961. 5.50. Stanford
    (R)
Newell, Homer E., Jr. Window in the sky. 1959. 2.75. McGraw
ATMOSPHERE, UPPER--ROCKET OBSERVATIONS (523)
Burgess, Eric. Frontier to space. 4.95. Macmillan
ATMOSPHERIC ELECTRICITY (621.384)
Chalmers, J. A. Atmospheric electricity. il. 1957. 10.00. Pergamon
ATOMIC BOMB (539.79)
Amrine, Michael. Great Decision. 1959. 3.95. Putnam
Clark, Ronald W. Birth of the bomb. 1962. 3.95. Horizon
Groves, Leslie R. Now it can be told: The story of the Manhattan Project. il.
    1961. 6.95. Harper

Hersey, John. Hiroshima. 1946. 3.00. Knopf

Jungk, Robert. Brighter than a thousand suns. 1958. 5.00. Harcourt

Nagai, Takashi. We of Nagasaki. 1951. 3.50. Duell

Osada, Arata, ed. Children of the A-bomb. il. 1959. 4.50. Int. Pub. Service

Trumbull, Robert. Nine who survived Hiroshima and Nagasaki. il. 1957. 3.00. Dutton

ATOMIC BOMB--SAFETY MEASURES (355. 322)

Kindall, Sylvian G. Total atomic defense. 3.00. Smith, Richard R.

Mawrence, Mel, and Clark Kimball. You can survive the bomb. il. 1961. 3.95. Quadrangle

Severud, F. N., and A. F. Merrill. Bomb, survival and you. 1954. 2.95. technical supplement, 1955. 2.50. Reinhold

ATOMIC BOMB SHELTERS (355)

Brelis, Dean. Run, dig or stay? 1962. 4.50. Beacon

ATOMIC ENERGY (539.7)

American Philosophical Society. Atomic energy and its implications. (Proceedings, vol. 90, no. 1) 1946. 1.00. Am. Philos. Soc.

Fairchild, Johnson E., and David Landman, eds. America faces the nuclear age. 5.00. Sheridan

Fermi, Laura. Atoms for the world. il. 1957. 4.50. U. of Chicago

Gamow, G., and C. L. Critchfield. Theory of atomic nucleus and nuclear energy-sources. il. 1949. 6.40. Oxford U. P.

Glasstone, Samuel. Sourcebook on atomic energy. il. 1958. 4.40. Van Nostrand

Klotz, John W. Challenge of the space age. 1961. pap. 1.00. Concordia

Reinfeld, Fred. Uranium and other miracle metals. il. 1959. 3.95. Sterling

ATOMIC ENERGY--ADDRESSES, ESSAYS, LECTURES (539.04)

Hughes, D. J. On nuclear energy: Its potential for peacetime uses. il. 1957. 4.75. Harvard

ATOMIC ENERGY--DICTIONARIES (539.3)

Carpovich, Eugene A. Atomic dictionary. Russian-English. 1959. 12.00. Tech. Dictionaries (R)

ATOMIC ENERGY--ECONOMIC ASPECTS (621.48)

Fairchild, Johnson E., and David Landman, eds. America faces the nuclear age. 1961. 5.00. Sheridan

Kramish, Arnold, and Eugene M. Zuckert. Atomic energy for your business. 1956. 3.95. McKay'

Rienow, Robert, and L. T. Our new life with the atom. 1959. 3.50. Crowell

Sanders, Ralph. Project ploughshare. 1961. 4.50. Pub. Affairs

ATOMIC ENERGY--PHYSIOLOGICAL EFFECT (539.7)

Haddow, A., ed. Biological hazards of atomic energy. il. 1952. 6.75. Oxford U. P.

ATOMIC ENERGY--POPULAR WORKS (539.7)

Gamow, G. Mr. Thompkins explores the atom. 1945. 2.95. Cambridge U. P.

Jacobowitz, Henry. Fundamentals of nuclear energy and power reactors. il. pap. 2.95. Rider

Lang, Daniel. Man in the thick lead suit. 1954. 4.00. Oxford U. P.

Lapp, Ralph Eugene. Roads to discovery. il. 1960. 3.95; lib. bdg. 3.79. Harper

Sacks, Jacob. Atom at work. 1956. 5.50. Ronald

Teller, Edward, and Albert L. Latter. Our nuclear future: Facts, dangers and opportunities. il. 1958. 3.50. Criterion

ATOMIC MEDICINE (617.124)

Behrens, Charles F., ed. Atomic medicine. il. 1959. 15.00. Williams & Wilkins

Blahd, William H., and others. Practice of nuclear medicine. il. 1958. 12.50. Thomas, C. C

ATOMIC POWER (621.48)

Dean, Gordon. Report on the atom: What you should know about the atomic
   energy program of the United States. 1953. 5.00. Knopf
Hodgson, Peter E. Nuclear physics in peace and war. 1961. 3.50. Hawthorn
Wendt, Gerald. Prospects of nuclear power and technology. il. 1957. 6.00. Van
   Nostrand

ATOMIC SUBMARINES (355)

Baar, James, and William E. Howard. Polaris! il. 1960. 4.50. Harcourt
Beach, Edward L. Around the world submerged: The voyage of the Triton.
   1962. 4.95? Holt, Rinehart & Winston
Rees, Ed. Seas and the subs. il. 1961. 4.50. Duell

ATOMIC THEORY (541.24)

Copeland, Paul L., and William E. Bennett. Elements of modern physics. il.
   1961. 8.50. Oxford U. P.

ATOMIC WARFARE (358.39)

Brodie, Bernard. Strategy in the missile age. 1959. 6.50. Princeton
De Seversky, Alexander P. America: too young to die! 1961. bds. 4.95.
   McGraw
Fryklund, Richard. 100 million lives: Maximum survival in nuclear war. 1962.
   3.95. Macmillan
Hodgson, Peter E. Nuclear physics in peace and war. 1961. 3.50. Hawthorn
Miksche, F. O. Atomic weapons and armies. 1959. 5.00. Praeger
Teller, Edward, and Allen Brown. Legacy of Hiroshima. 1962. 4.95. Doubleday
Turner, Gordon B., and Richard D. Challener, eds. National security in the
   nuclear age. 6.00. Praeger

ATOMIC WARFARE--MORAL AND RELIGIOUS ASPECTS (358.39)

Batchelder, Robert C. Irreversible decision. 1939-1950. 1962. 5.00. Houghton
Bennett, John C., ed. Nuclear weapons and the conflict of conscience. 1961.
   3.95. Scribner
Lang, Daniel. From Hiroshima to the moon. 1959. 5.95. S. and S

ATOMIC WEAPONS (341.67)

Teller, Edward, and Albert L. Latter. Our nuclear future: Facts, dangers, and
   opportunities. il. 1958. 3.50. Criterion

ATOMIC WEAPONS AND DISARMAMENT (341.67)

Brennan, Donald G., ed. Arms control, disarmament, and national security.
   1961. 6.00. Braziller
Cousins, Norman. In place of folly. 1961. 3.50. Harper
Hadley, Arthur T. Nation's safety and arms control. 1961. 3.00. Viking
Pauling, Linus. No more war! il. 1958. 3.50. Dodd
Russell, Bertrand R. Has man a future? 1962. 3.00. S. and S.
Schweitzer, Albert. Peace or atomic war? 1958. 1.50. Holt, Rinehart &
   Winston

ATOMS (539)

Gamow, George. Birth and death of the sun. il. 1940. 4.75. Viking
Hecht, Selig. Explaining the atom. 'by. Eugene Rabinowitch. il. 1954. 4.50; 1960.
   Viking
Semat, Henry. Introduction to atomic and nuclear physics. 1962. 7.50. Holt,
   Rinehart & Winston
Thomson, George. Atom. 1956. 1.70. Oxford U. P.

ATONEMENT (232.3)

Barth, Markus. Was Christ's death a sacrifice? 1961. pap. 2.25. Allenson
Brunner, H. Emil. Mediator. 1947. 7.50. Westminster
Denney, James. Christian doctrine of reconciliation. 1959. 3.50. Allenson
Gockel, H. W. Cross and the common man. 1956. 2.00. Concordia
Knox, John. Death of Christ. 1958. 2.75. Abingdon
Nygren, Anders. Essence of Christianity. 1961. 2.00. Muhlenberg

ATONEMENT--HISTORY (232)
Aulen, Gustaf. Christus victor: An historical study of the three main types of
the idea of atonement. tr. by A. G. Hebert. 2.75. Macmillan
ATTACK AND DEFENSE (MILITARY SCIENCE) (358.42)
Mulley, Frederick W. Politics of western defense. 1962. 6.75. Humanities
ATTAINDER (340)
Chafee, Lechariah, Jr. Three human rights in the constitution. 4.00.
U. of Kans.
ATTENTION (152)
Barbara, Dominick A. Art of listening. il. 1958. 5.50. Thomas, C. C.
Broadbent, D. E. Perception and communication. 8.50. Pergamon
Dumont, Theron Q. Power of cancentration. 2.95. Wehman
Nichols, R., and L. A. Stevens. Are you listening? 1957. 4.95. McGraw
ATTITUDE (PSYCHOLOGY) (136.45)
Adorno, T. W., and others. Authoritarian personality. 1950. 8.75. Harper
Himmelstrand, U. Social pressures, attitudes and democratic processes. pap.
9.50. Humanities
Newcomb, Theodore M. Personality and social change. 1957. 4.25. Holt,
Rinehart & Winston
Rogers, Cyril A., and C. Frantz. Racial themes in Southern Rhodesia. il.
1961. 6.75. Yale
Rokeach, Milton. Open and closed mind. il. 1960. 7.50. Basic Books
Thurstone, Louis L. Measurement of values. il. 1958. 7.50. U. of Chicago
AUDEN, WYSTAN HUGH (920)
Bayley, John. Romantic survival: A study in poetic evolution. 1957. 3.40.
Oxford U. P.
Bloomfield, B. C. Bibliography of W. H. Auden. 5.00. U. of Va. (R)
AUDIO--VISUAL EDUCATION (371.33)
Bachman, John W. How to use audio-visual materials. 1956. 1.00. Assn. Pr.
Brown, James W., and others. A-V instruction: Materials and methods. 1959.
8.50: manual, 3.75. McGraw
Dale, Edgar. Audio-visual methods in teaching. 1954. 8.25. Holt, Rinehart &
Winston
DeKieffer, Robert, and Lee W. Cochran. Manual of audio-visual techniques.
1955. 5.30. 1961. Prentice-Hall
Gerstein, Maurice J. Audio-visual materials for science-math-and general
education. il. 1962. pap. 2.00. N. Y. Pub. Co. (R)
National Education Association, Audio-Visual Instruction Department. School
administrator and his audio-visual program, yearbook. 1954. 3.75. N. E. A.
AUDIO-VISUAL EDUCATION--BIBLIOGRAPHY (371.33)
Rufsvold, Margaret, and Carolyn Guss. Guides to newer educational media.
1961. pap. 1.50. A. L. A. (R)
AUDIO-VISUAL EQUIPMENT (371.33)
Finn, James D. Audio-visual equipment manual. il. 1957. 5.75. Holt, Rinehart
& Winston
AUDITING (657.64)
Holmes, Arthur W. Auditing: Principles and procedure. 1959. 11.35. Irwin
Holmes, Arthur W. Basic auditing principles. il. in prep. Irwin
Johnson, A. W. Auditing, principles and case problems. 1959. 7.50? Rinehart
Kohler, Eric L. Auditing: An introduction to the work of the public accountant.
1954. 10.60. Prentice-Hall
Lasser, Jacob K. Standard handbook for accountants. 1956. 15.00. McGraw (R)
Palen, Jennie M. Report writing for accountants. 1956. 10.60. Prentice-Hall
AUDUBON, JOHN JAMES (925)
Harris, Edward. Up the Missouri with Audubon. il. ed. by John Francis Mc-
Dermott. 1951. 3.75. U. of Okla.
AUGUSTINUS, AURELIUS, SAINT, BP. OF HIPPO (922.22)
Arendt, Hannah. St. Augustine and the concept of love. Collier

Brookes, Edgar H. City of God and the politics of crisis. 1960. 2.00. Oxford U. P.

Fulop-Miller, Rene. Saints that moved the world: Anthony, Augustine, Francis, Ignatius, Theresa. tr. by Alexander Gode and Erika Fulop-Miller. pap. 0.95. Collier

Gilson, Etienne. Christian philosophy of Saint Augustine. 1960. 7.50. Random

Grabowski, Stanislaus J. Church: An introduction to the theology of St. Sugustine. 9.50. Herder

Guitton, Jean. Modernity of Saint Augustine. 1959. 4.00. (Helicon) Taplinger

Henry, Paul. Saint Augustine on personality. 2.25. Macmillan

Polman, A.' D. R. Word of God in the theology of St. Augustine. 1961. 5.00. Eerdmans

Portaliae, Eugene. Guide to the life and thought of St. Augustine. 1960. 6.50. Regnery

AURORAS (538.768)

Chamberlain, J. W. Physics of the aurora and airglow. 1961. 16.50. Academic Press

Stormer, Carl. Polar aurora. 1955. 9.60. Oxford U. P.

AUSTEN, JANE, 1775-1817 (813)

Austen-Leigh, J. E. Memoir of Jane Austen. ed. by Robert W. Chambers. 1926. 2.40. Oxford U. P.

Babb, Howard S. Jane Austen's novels: The fabric of dialogue. 1962. 4.95. Ohio State

Lascelles, Mary. Jane Austen and her art. 1939. 3.40. Oxford U. P.

Wright, Andrew H. Jane Austen's novels: A study in structure. 1953. 2.90. Oxford U. P.

AUSTRALIA (994)

Meinig, Donald W. On the margins of the good earth. 5.00. Rand McNally

Moore, Thrylis, Book of Australia. il. 1962. 2.50. Collins

Pike, D. H. Australia: The quiet continent. 3.95. Cambridge U. P.

AUSTRALIA--DESCRIPTION AND TRAVEL (919.4)

Beatty, B. Here in Australia. il. 5.25. Int. Pub. Service

Glaskin, G. M. Land that sleeps. il. 4.95. Doubleday

Robinson, Ellis O. Australia and New Zealand. 1.25. St. Martins

AUSTRALIA--ECONOMIC CONDITIONS (994)

Davidson, F. G. Industrialization of Australia. 1961. 1.00. Cambridge U. P.

Horsfall, J. C. Australia. 1955. 6.50. Praeger

AUSTRALIA--HISTORY (994)

Clark, Charles M. H. Settlers and convicts. 1953. 3.50. Cambridge U. P.

Scott, Ernest. Short history of Australia. 8th ed. by Herbert Burton. il. 1950. 3.90. Oxford U. P.

Tennant, Kylie. Australia: Her story. 1953. 3.50. St. Martins

AUSTRALIA--POLITICS AND GOVERNMENT (324.25)

Brady, Alexander. Democracy in the Dominions. 1958. 7.95. U. of Toronto

Gollan, R. Radical and working class politics. 1960. 6.50. Cambridge U. P.

Sawer, Geoffrey. Australian government today. 1962. pap. 1.25. (Melbourne U. P.) Cambridge U. P.

AUSTRALIA--SOCIAL CONDITIONS (994)

Gaiger, G. Australian way of life. 1953. 3.00. Columbia

AUSTRALIAN LITERATURE--HISTORY AND CRITICISM (899.6)

Green, H. M. Australian literature. 1951. 0.50. Cambridge U. P.

AUSTRALIAN POETRY (COLLECTIONS)

Wright, Judith, ed. Book of Australian verse. 1956. 2.40. Oxford U. P.

AUSTRIA--DESCRIPTION AND TRAVEL (355)

Clark, Sydney. All the best in Germany and Austria. il. 1961. 5.95. Dodd

Gibbon, Monk. Austria. il. 1962. pap. 1.50. Norton

AUSTRIA--DESCRIPTION AND TRAVEL--GUIDE-BOOKS (943)

Baedeker, Karl. Tyrol and Salzburg. il. 1961. 8.50. Macmillan

Fodor, Eugene, ed. Austria. 4.50. McKay (R)
AUSTRIA--FOREIGN RELATIONS (943)
Jaszi, Oscar. Dissolution of the Habsburg monarchy. 1961. pap. 2.25. U. of
Chicago
AUSTRIA--HISTORY (943.6)
Burghardt, Andrew F. Borderland: A historical and geographical study of
Burgenland, Austria. 1962. 8.00. U. of Wis.
Diamant, Alfred. Austrian Catholics and the First Republic. 1960. 6.50.
Princeton
Kann, Robert A. Study in Austrian intellectual history. il. 1960. 6.00. Praeger
May, Arthur James. Hapsburg monarchy, 1867-1914. 1951. 6.00. Harvard
Rath, R. John. Viennese Revolution of 1848. 6.50. U. of Tex.
Taylor, A. J. P. Hapsburg monarchy, 1809-1918. il. 5.00. Macmillan
AUSTRIA--HISTORY--ALLIED OCCUPATION, 1945-1955 (943)
Hartel, Gunther E. Red herring. 1962. 4.50. Obolensky
AUSTRIA--POLITICS AND GOVERNMENT (943.6)
Gulick, Charles A. Austria from Habsburg to Hitler. 2 vols. vol. 1. Labor's
workshop of democracy; vol. 2. Fascism's subversion of democracy. 1948
10.00. U. of Calif.
Macartney, C. A. Social revolution in Austria. Cambridge U. P.
AUTHORITY (171.1)
Hobbes, Thomas. De cive or the citizen. ed. by Sterling P. Lamprecht.
1949. pap. 1.25. Appleton
Lasswell, Harold, and others. Study of power. 1950. 7.50. Free Press
Peters, Richard S. Authority, responsibility and education. 1960. 3.00. Taplinger
Simon, Yves. Authority. 1962. 5.95. U. of Notre Dame
Simon, Yves. Nature and functions of authority. 1940. 2.50. Marquette
AUTHORITY (RELIGION) (262.8)
Harkness, Georgia. Foundations of Christian knowledge. 1955. 2.75. Abingdon
Todd, John M., ed. Problems of authority. 5.95. Taplinger
AUTHORS (920)
Beach, Sylvia. Shakespeare and Company. il. 1959. 4.50. Harcourt
Cowley, Malcolm, ed. Writers at work: The Paris Review interviews. 1958.
5.00. Viking
Kunitz, S. J., and Howard Haycraft. Junior book of authors. il. 1951. 3.50.
Wilson (R)
Kunitz, S. J., and Howard Haycraft. Twentieth century authors. il. 1942. 8.50.
First suppl. 1955. 8.00. Wilson (R)
Maugham, W. Somerset. Art of fiction. 1955. 4.95. Doubleday
Steinberg, Sigfrid H., ed. Cassell's encyclopedia of world literature. 2 vols.
1953. 25.00. Funk (R)
Wilson, Edmund. Wound and the bow: Seven studies in literature. 1947. 5.50.
Oxford U. P.
AUTHORS--CORRESPONDENCE, REMINISCENCES, ETC. (920)
Brooks, Van Wyck. Days of the Phoenix: The nineteen-twenties I remember.
il. 1957. 3.95. Dutton
Brooks, Van Wyck. From the shadow of the mountain. il. 1961. 4.50 Dutton
Crane, Stephen. Stephen Crane: Letters. ed. by R. W. Stallman, and Lillian
Gilkes. 1960. 6.50. N. Y. U.
Cronin, A. J. Adventures in two worlds. 1956. 6.00. Little
Dickens, Charles. Selected letters. ed. by F. W. Dupee. 1960. 4.75. Farrar,
Straus
Dreiser, Theodore A. Letters of Theodore Dreiser: A selection. 3 vols. ed. by
Robert Elias. 1959. 18.00. U. of Pa.
Emden, Cecil S. Poets in their letters. 1959. 3.40. Oxford U. P.
Kafka, Franz. Letters to Milena. 1954. 4.50. Schocken
Lawrence, D. H. Collected letters of D. H. Lawrence. 2 vols. ed. by Harry T.
Moore. 17.50. Viking

Mann, Thomas. Story of a novel. 1961. 4.00. Knopf

Maugham, W. Somerset. Summing up. 1943. 3.95. il. 1954. 15.00. Doubleday

Sinclair, Upton. My lifetime in letters. 1960. 6.50. U. of Missouri

Stern, Gertrude B. One is only human. il. 1960. 3.50. Regnery

Terry, Ellen, and Bernard Shaw. Shaw-Terry letters. il. 5.00. Theatre Arts

Thoreau, Henry David. Correspondence of Henry David Thoreau. ed. by Walter Harding and Carl Bode. il. 1958. 12.50. N. Y. U.

AUTHORS, AMERICAN (920.073)

Bolton, Sarah K. Famous American authors. by William A. Fahay. 1954. 3.50. Crowell

Brooks, Van Wyck, and Otto L. Bettmann. Our literary heritage: A pictorial history of the writer in America. il. 1956. 8.50. Dutton

Burke, W. J., and Will D. Howe. American authors and books. ed. by Irving Weiss. 8.50. Crown (R)

Burtis, M. E. Recent American literature. 1961. pap. 1.95. Littlefield

Dowley, Malcolm. Exile's return. 1959. 3.25. Smith, Peter

Hubbell, Jay B., ed. American life in literature. 2 vols. il. 1949. 7.25 ea; abr. ed. 1951. 6.75. Harper

Kunitz, Stanley J., and Howard Haycraft. American authors: 1600-1900. il. 1938. 6.00. Wilson (R)

Muir, Jane. Famous modern American women writers. il. 1959. 3.00. Dodd

Saturday Review. Saturday Review gallery. ed. by Jerome Beatty, Jr., and others. 1959. 6.00. S. and S.

AUTHORS, ENGLISH (920.042)

Heppenstall, R. Four absentees: Dylan Thomas, George Orwell, Eric Gill, J. M. Murry. 3.00. Hillary

Kunitz, S. J., and Howard Haycraft. British authors before 1800. il. 1952. 6.00. Wilson (R)

Kunitz, S. J., and Howard Haycraft. British authors of the nineteenth century. il. 1936. 5.00. Wilson (R)

AUTHORS, GREEK (920.038)

Hadas, M. Ancilla to classical reading. 1954. 6.00. Columbia

AUTHORS, NORWEGIAN (920.0481)

McFarland, James W. Ibsen and the temper of Norwegian literature. 1960. 3.40. Oxford U. P.

AUTHORS, RUSSIAN (920.047)

Lavrin, Janko. Russian writers: Their lives and literature. 1954. 6.50. 5.00. Van Nostrand

Muchnic, Helen. Gorky to Pasternak. 1961. 7.50; text ed. 5.60. Random

AUTHORS AND READERS (808)

De Voto, Bernard. World of fiction. 1950. 3.50. Houghton

Morley, Christopher. Ex libris carissimis. 1961. pap. 1.25. Barnes. A. S.

AUTHORSHIP (808)

Allen, Walter E., ed. Writers on writing. 1959. 3.95. Writer

Babcock, Robert W., and John Wilcox. Writing scholarly papers. 1955. pap. 1.00. Wayne

Barzun, Jacques, and Henry F. Graff. Modern researcher. 1957. 6.50. Harcourt

Bird, George L. Article writing and marketing. 1956. 5.50. Rinehart

Blackiston, Elliott. Teach yourself to write. 3.00. Writer

Cox, Sidney. Indirections: For those who want to write. 1947. 3.00. Knopf

Fischer, John, and Robert Silvers, eds. Writing in America. 1960. 3.95. Rutgers

Garrison, Roger H. Creative approach to writing. 1951. 3.75. Holt

Harral, Stewart. Feature writers's handbook. il. 1958. 5.00. U. of Okla. (R)

Lewis, Maxine. Magic key to successful writing. 1956. 4.50. Prentice-Hall

Newsom, Francis W. Writer's technique: A practical guide to creative writing. 1954. 3.00. Coleman-Ross

O'Connor, William Van, ed. Modern prose, form and style. 1959. 4.50. Crowell

Wuiller-Couch, Arthur. On the art of writing. 1961. pap. 1.35. Putnam

Wellborn, G. P., and others. Technical writing. il. 1961. 4.00. Houghton

Widdemer, Margaret. Basic principles of fiction writing. 1953. 3.50. Writer

Wiles, Roy McK. Scholarly reporting in the humanities. 1961. pap. 1.00. U. of Toronto

Writers' and artists' yearbook. 4.50. Writer (R)

AUTHORSHIP--HANDBOOKS, MANUALS, ETC. (802)

Burack, Abraham S., ed. Writer's handbook. 1944. 6.95. Writer

Egri, Lajos. Your key to successful writing. 1952. 3.50. Writer

Iowa State University Press. Editor's handbook. 1957. pap. 0.75. Iowa State

Richter, Anne J., ed. Literary market place 1962-63: The business directory of American book publishing. rev. annually. pap. 7.45. pap. 7.45. Bowker

University of Chicago, Press staff. Manual of style. 1949. 6.00. U. of Chicago (R)

AUTOBIOGRAPHIES (920)

Kaplan, Louis, and others, comps. Bibliography of American autobiographies. 1961. 6.00. U. of Wis. (R)

AUTOBIOGRAPHY--BIBLIOGRAPHY(920)

Lillard, Richard G. American life in autobiography: A descriptive guide. 1956. pap. 3.75. Stanford (R)

AUTOMATIC CONTROL (629.8)

Ahrendt, W. R., and John F. Taplin. Automatic feedback control. il. 1951. 10.50. McGraw

Bibbero, Robert. Dictionary of automatic control. il. 1960. 6.00. Reinhold (R)

Clark, R. N. Introduction to automatic control systems. 5.00. Wiley

AUTOMATION (328.45)

Amber, George H., and Paul S. Anatomy of automation. 1962. 10.60. Prentice-Hall

American Library Association. Recruiting library personnel: Automation in the library. A. C. R. L. monograph no. 17. 1956. pap. 1.25. A. L. A. (R)

Booth, Andrew D., ed. Progress in automation. 1960. 8.50. Academic Press

Brady, Robert A. Organization, automation, and society: The scientific revolution in industry. 1961. 8.00. U. of Calif.

Dreher, Carl. Automation: What it is, how it works, and who can use it. il. 1957. 2.95. Norton

Dunlap, John T., ed. Automation and technological change. 1962. 3.95. Prentice-Hall

Levin, H. S. Office work and automation. 1956. 5.95. Wiley

Weeks, Robert P., ed. Machines and the man. il. 1961. pap. 2.45. Appleton

AUTOMATION--DICTIONARIES (301.243)

Berkeley, Edmund C., and Linda A. Lovett. Glossary of terms in computers and data processing. 1960. pap. 3.95. Berkeley Enterprises (R)

Clason, W. E. Dictionary of automation, computers, control, and measuring. polyglot. 1961. 27.50. Am. Elsevier (R)

AUTOMATION--ECONOMIC ASPECTS (331.45)

Bell, James R., and Lynwood B. Steedman. Personnel problems in converting to automation. 1959. 0.45. U. of Ala.

Einzig, Paul. Economic consequences of automation. 1957. 5.00. Norton

Hoos, Ida R. Automation in the office. 1961. 4.50. Pub. Affairs

Macmillan, R. H. Automation: Friend or foe? 1956. 1.95. Cambridge U. P.

Quinn, Francis X., ed. Ethical aftermath of automation. 1962. 4.25. Newman

Soule, George. Time for living. 1955. 3.00. Viking

Steele, George, and Paul Kirchner. Crisis we face. il. 1960. 4.95. McGraw

AUTOMOBILE DRIVERS (629.28)

American Automobile Association. Sportsmanlike driving. 1960. 4.75.

Brody, Leon, and Herbert J. Stack. Highway safety and driver education. 1954. 9.35. Prentice-Hall

Lauer, A. R. Psychology of driving. il. 1961. 10.50. Thomas C. C.
Sports Illustrated. Sports Illustrated book of safe driving. by the Editors of
   Sports Illustrated. 1962. 2.95. Lippincott
AUTOMOBILE ENGINEERING (629.2)
Glenn, Harold T. Automechanics. il. 1962. 6.96. Bennett
AUTOMOBILE INDUSTRY AND TRADE (338.476)
Anderson, Rudolph E. Story of the American automobile. 1950. 3.75. Pub.
   Affairs
Chinoy, Ely S. Automobile workers and the American dream. 1955. 3.00.
   Random
Pound, Arthur. Automobile and an American city. 1962. pap. 1.25. Wayne
AUTOMOBILE INDUSTRY AND TRADE--DIRECTORIES (338.476)
Doyle, G. R. World's automobiles, 1880-1955: A record of 75 years of car
   building. 4.00. Bentley
AUTOMOBILE RACING (796.72)
Walkerley, Rodney L. Moments that made racing history. 1960. 2.75. Arco
AUTOMOBILE TOURING (388.3)
Byam, Wally. Trailer travel here and abroad. il. 1960. 5.75. McKay
AUTOMOBILES (629)
Crouse, William H. Automotive mechanics. 4th ed. il. 1960. 8.75. il. 1960. 8.75.
   G. 72. McGraw
Doyle, G. R. World's automobiles, 1880-1955: A record of 75 years of car
   building. 4.00. Bentley
AUTOMOBILES--COLLECTORS AND COLLECTING (629)
Buckley, John R. Cars of the connoisseur: A treasury of the years of grace.
   1961. 6.00. Macmillan
AUTOMOBILES--HANDBOOKS, MANUALS, ETC. (629)
Barnard, Charles N., ed. Official automobile handbook. il. 1957. 3.95. Barnes,
   A. S.
Graham, Frank D. Automobile mechanics guide. 6.00. Audel (R)
Toboldt, Bill, and Jud Purvis, eds. Motor Service's automotive encyclopedia.
   1962. 7.95. Goodheart
AUTOMOBILES --HISTORY (629)
Clymer, Floyd. Treasury of early American automobiles, 1877-1925. il.
   1950. 5.95. McGraw (R)
AUTOMOBILES--MOTORS (629.2)
Crouse, William H. Automotive engines. 1959. 8.25; workbook, 1.72. McGraw
AUTOMOBILES--TYPES--FORD (629)
Clymer, Floyd. Henry's wonderful model T, 1908-1927. 1955. 5.95. McGraw
AUXIN (547.473)
Wain, R. L., and F. Wightman, eds. Chemistry and mode of action of plant
   growth substances. 1956. 9.50. Academic Press
AVIATION MEDICINE (616.980)
Caidin, Martin, and Grace. Aviation and space medicine. il. 1962. 3.75.
   Dutton
Ellingson, Harold V. Medical problems of air travel. il. 1960. 2.00. Davis
AZALEA(583.6)
Bowers, Clement G. Rhododendrons and azaleas. 2nd ed. il. 1960. 25.00.
   Macmillan
AZTEC LITERATURE (897.4)
Leon Portilla, Miguel, ed. Broken spears; the Aztec account of the conquest
   of Mexico. tr. by Lysander Kemp. il. 1962. bds. 5.00. Beacon
AZTECS (972.014)
Caso, Alfonso. Aztecs; people of the sun. il. 1959. 7.95. U. of Okla.
Gresham, Elizabeth. World of the Aztecs. 1961. 3.95; lib. bdg. 4.25. with
   Thomas Janvier's In the Aztec treasure house. 6.95; lib. bdg. 7.50. Walker
Madsen, William. Virgin's children: Life in an Aztec village today. il. 1960.
   4.50. U. of Tex.

Vaillant, George C.   Aztecs of Mexico. rev. by Suzannah B. Vaillant. il. 7.50.
   Doubleday
Von Hagen, Victor W.   Ancient sun kingdoms of the Americas. il. 1960. 12.50.
   World Pub.
Wauchope, Robert.. Lost tribes and sunken continents. il. 1962. 3.95. U. of
   Chicago

B

BABY SITTERS (649.1)
Lowndes, Marion.   Manual for baby sitters. 1961. 3.50. Little
BABYLON (935)
Saggs, H. W. F.   Greatness that was Babylon. il. 1962. 9.75. Hawthorn
BABYLONIA (935)
Leemans, W. F.   Foreign trade in the old Babylonian period. 9.50. Humanities
BABYLONIA--ANTIQUITIES (935)
Wiseman, J. P.   New discoveries in Babylonia. 1956. 2.50. Zondervan
BACH, JOHANN SEBASTIAN, 1685-1750 (927)
David, Hans, and Arthur Mendel, eds.   Bach reader. il. 1945. 9.00. Norton
Davison, Archibald Thompson.   Bach and Handel: The consummation of the
   baroque in music. 1951. 2.00. Harvard
Dickinson, A. E. F.   Bach's fugal works. 1956. 6.95. Pitman
Foelber, P. F.   Bach's treatment of the subject of death in his choral music.
   1961. 6.75. Catholic U. of Am. Pr.
Geiringer, Karl.   Bach family: Seven generations of creative genius. 1954.
   12.50. Oxford U. P.
Hindemith, P.   Johann Sebastian Bach. 1952. 2.50. Yale
Kleinhans, Theodore J.   Music master: The story of Johann Sebastian Bach.
   1962. 3.25. Muhlenberg
Neumann, Werner.   Bach: A pictorial biography. il. 1961. 5.95. Viking
Schweitzer, Albert J. S.   Bach. il. 2 vols. tr. by Newman. set, 12.00. Macmillan
Spitta, Philipp.   Johann Sebastian Bach. 3 vols. bd. as 2, 12.50. Dover
Terry, C. S. Bach: A biography. 2nd ed. rev. il. 1933. 7.20. Oxford U. P.
BACON, FRANCIS, VISCOUNT ST. ALBANS, 1561-1626 (923.2)
Anderson, Fulton H.   Francis Bacon: His career and his thought. 1962. 7.50.
   Univ. Pub.
Eiseley, Loren.   Francis Bacon and the modern dilemma. 1961. 3.00.
   U. of Nebr.
BACON'S REBELLION, 1676 (973.2)
Andrews, C. M., ed.   Narratives of the insurrections, 1675-1690. (Original
   narratives of early American history) 1915. 5.75. Barnes and Noble
Warner, Charles W. H.   Road to revolution: Virginia's rebels from Bacon to
   Jefferson, 1675-1776. il. 1961. 3.95. Garrett
BACTERIA (589.9)
Anderson, Cameron G., Introduction to bacteriological chemistry. il. 1946. 5.00.
   Williams & Wilkins
Bisset, Kenneth A.   Bacteria. il. 1962. 7.00. Williams & Wilkins
Clifton, Charles E.   Introduction to bacterial physiology. il. 1957. 9.50. Mc-
   Graw
Dobell, Clifford.   Antony Van Leeuwenhoek and his "Little Animals." 10.00.
   Russell
Skerman, V. B. D.   Guide to the identification of bacteria. 1959. 5.50. Williams
   & Wilkins
BACTERIA, PATHOGENIC (616.92)
Dubos, Rene J., ed.   Bacterial and mycotic infections of man. il. 1958. 8.50.
   Van Nostrand
Frobisher, Martin, and others.. Microbiology and pathology for nurses. il. 1960.
   7.50. Saunders

BACTERIOLOGISTS (920)
Grainger, Thomas H. A guide to the history of bacteriology. 1958. 4.50. Ronald
BACTERIOLOGY (589)
DeKruif, Paul. Microbe hunters. il. 1932. 4.50; by Harry G. Grover. 2.60.
Harcourt
Salle, Anthony J. Fundamental principles of bacteriology. 1961. 11.00. McGraw
BACTERIOLOGY--TECHNIQUE (589.9)
Society of American Bacteriologists. Manual of microbiological methods. ed.
by H. J. Conn and M. W. Jennison. 1957. 5.75. McGraw (R)
BACTERIOLOGY, MEDICAL (616.04)
Fine, Jacob. Bacterial factor in traumatic shock. il. 1954. lexide. 2.75. Thomas,
C. C
BADMINTON (GAME) (790.345)
American Association for Health, Physical Education and Recreation, Division
for Girls' and Women's Sports. Official tennis and badminton rules and
guide. 1.00. Am. Assn. for Health, Phys. Ed. & Rec.
Davidson, K. R. and L. R. Gustavson. Winning badminton. 1953. 4.00. Ronald
National Education Association, American Association for Health, Physical
Education and Recreation. Tennis-badminton: Sports guide. 1.00. N. E. A.
BAHAISM (297.89)
Baha'i World. 6 vols. vol. 5. 1932-1934. 2.50; vol. 6. 1934-1936. 3.00; vol. 9.
1940-1944. 7.50; vol. 10. 1944-1946. 8.50; vol. 11. 1946-1950. 11.00; vol. 12.
1950-1954. 15.00. Baha'i
BAHAMAS--DESCRIPTION AND TRAVEL (972)
Fodor, Eugene, ed. Carribbean, Bahamas, and Bermuda 1960. il. 1960. 5.95.
McKay (R)
Rigg, J. Linton. Bahama Islands. il. 1959. 8.50. Van Nostrand
BAKING (641.71)
Peck, Paula. Art of fine baking. 1961. 6.50. S. and S.
BALANCE OF PAYMENTS (330.151)
Harris, Seymour E., ed. Dollar in crisis. 1962. 4.95. Harcourt
Letiche, John M. Balance of payments and economic growth. 1959. 6.00.
Harper
Triffin, Robert. Gold and the dollar crisis: The future of convertibility. rev.
ed. il. 1961. 5.00. Yale
Vanek, Jaroslave. International trade: Theory and economic policy. il. 1962.
10.00. Irwin
BALANCE OF POWER (327)
Gareau, Frederick H , ed Balance of power and nuclear deterrence. il 1962
pap. 1.95. Houghton
Gulick, Edward V. Europe's classical balance of power. 5.50. Cornell
BALANCE OF TRADE (382)
Aubrey, H. G. United States imports and world trade. 1957. 4.00. Oxford U. P.
Bloomfield, Arthur I. Capital imports and the American balance of payments,
1934-1939. 1950. 6.00. U. of Chicago
Meade, James E. Balance of payments. 5.60. Oxford U. P.
BALCHEN, BERNT, 1899- (920)
Balchen, Bernt. Come north with me: An autobiography. il. 1958. 5.00. Dutton
BALI (ISLAND) (992.3)
Bali: Selected studies on Indonesia by Dutch Scholars. 1960. 7.00. Inst. of Pac
Rel.
Mead, Margaret, and Frances C. Macgregor. Growth and culture. il. 1951. 7.50.
Putnam
BALKAN PENINSULA--HISTORY (949.6)
Wolff, Robert L. Balkans in our time. il. 1956. 8.00. Harvard
BALLADS (398.8)
Gerould, Gordon Hall. Ballad of tradition. 1932. 4.00. Oxford U. P.
Gummere, F. B. Popular ballad. 3.75. Smith, Peter

Pound, Louise. Poetic origins and the ballad. 1961. 6.50. Russell

BALLADS, AMERICAN (811.04)
Beck, Earl Clifton. They knew Paul Bunyan. 1956. 4.75. U. of Mich.
Belden, Henry M., ed. Ballads and songs collected by the Missouri Folk Lore
  Society. 1955. 4.00. U. of Missouri
Davis, E. Cowboy song album. 1.00. Wehman
Doerflinger, William Main. Shantymen and shantyboys. il. 1951. 5.50. Mac-
  millan
Downes, Olin, and Elie Siegmeister, eds. Treasury of American song. 1962. 10.00.
  Knopf
Greenway, John. American folksongs of protest. 4.00. Smith, Peter
Lomax, John A., and Alan. American ballads and folk songs. 8.95.
  Macmillan
Lomax, John A., and Alan. Cowboy songs, and other frontier ballads. rev.
  ed. 8.75. Macmillan
Niles, John J. Ballad book of John Jacob Niles. il. 1961. 6.95. Houghton
Sandburg, Carl. American songbag. il. 1927. 5.95. Harcourt
Seeger, Pete. American favorite ballads. il. 1961. 3.95. Oak
Wells, Evelyn K. Ballad tree. 1950. 6.00. Ronald

BALLADS, ENGLISH (821.04)
Sharp, C. J., comp. English folk songs from the southern Appalachians. 2 vols.
  ed. by Maud Karpeles. 1932. 15.00. Oxford U. P.

BALLADS, ENGLISH--DISCOGRAPHY (821.04)
Friedman, Albert B., ed. Viking book of folk-ballads of the English-speaking
  world. 1956. 4.95. Viking

BALLADS, IRISH (811.104)
Ives, Burl. Irish songs. 1958. 5.00. Duell

BALLADS, NORWEGIAN (839.6)
Blegen, Theodore C., and Martin B. Ruud, eds. Norwegian emigrant songs
  and ballads. il. 1936. 3.00. U. of Minn.

BALLET (792.84)
Ambrose, Kay. Ballet-lover's companion. il. 1949. 2.50. Knopf
Beaumont, Cyril W. Complete book of ballets. 1941. 3.95. Grosset (R)
Bellew, Helene. Ballet in Moscow today. il. 1957. 7.00. N. Y. Graphic
Cohen, S. J., ed. Dictionary of modern ballet. il. 1959. 7.95. Tudor (R)
DeMille, Agnes. Dance to the piper. il. 1952. 5.50. Little
Haskell, Arnold L. How to enjoy ballet. il. 1951. 3.00. Morrow
Maynard, Olga. American ballet. il. 1959. 7.50. Macrae Smith

BALLET--HISTORY (792)
Bastien, Joseph. DeMedici to Markova: Three and one-half centuries of ballet.
  1.00. Humphries
Fokine, Vitale, and Anatole Chujoy. Fokine memoirs of a ballet master. il.
  1961. 7.50. Little
Hall, Fernau. World dance. 1954. 8.00. Wyn

BALLET DANCING (792)
Kirstein, Lincoln. Classic ballet. il. 1952. 6.75. Knopf

BALLETS--STORIES, PLOTS, ETC. (782.95)
Balanchine, George. Balanchine's complete stories of the great ballets. ed.
  by Francis Mason. il. 1954. 5.95. Doubleday
Krokover, Rosalyn. New Borzoi book of ballets. il. 1956. 6.75. Knopf

BALLISTIC MISSILES (623.21)
Burgess, Eric. Long-range ballistic missiles. il. 1962. 7.00. Macmillan
Loosbrock, John E., ed. Space weapons. il. 1959. 5.00. Praeger
Newell, Homer E., Jr. Guide to rockets, missiles, and satellites. il. 1961. 3.25.
  McGraw

BALLISTICS (623.51)
Cummings, Charles S., II. Everyday ballistics. 1950. 3.75. Stackpole
Hall, Alfred R. Ballistics in the 17th century. 1952. 5.00. Cambridge U. P.

Rosser, John Barkley, and others. Mathematical theory of rocket flight. il. 1947. 8.50. McGraw

Whelen, Townsend. Small arms design and ballistics. 2 vols. il. 1955. 6.00 ea. Stackpole

Wimpress, R. N. Internal ballistics of solid-fuel rockets. 1950. 7.50. McGraw

BALLOONS (629.133)
Dollfus, Charles. Orion book of balloons. il. 1961. 6.95. Orion

BALLROOM DANCING (793)
Harris, Jane, and others. Dance a while. 1955. 3.50. Burgess

Hostetler, L. A. Walk your way to better dancing. 1962. 4.50. Ronald

Murray, Arthur. How to become a good dancer. 1954. 3.95. 1959. 3.95. S and S.

Swan, G. Old time popular dances. 1.00. Wehman

Turner, M. J. Dance handbook. 1959. 4.35. Prentice-Hall

BALSAN, CONSUELO VANDERBILT (923.3)
Balsan, Consuelo Vanderbilt. Glitter and the gold. il. 1952. 4.50. Harper

BALZAC, HONORE DE, 1799-1850 (928)
Bowen, Ray P. Dramatic construction of Balzac's novels. 1940. pap. 1.00. U. of Ore.

Hunt, Herbert J. Honore de Balzac: A biography. 1957. 3.40. Oxford U. P.

Oliver, Edward J. Balzac, the European. 1960. 4.25. Sheed

BANCROFT, FREDERIC, 1860-1945 (923.2)
Cooke, Jacob E. Frederic Bancroft, historian. il. 1957. 4.00. U. of Okla.

BANDAGES AND BANDAGING (617.93)
Thorndike, Augustus. Manual of bandaging, strapping and splinting. il. 1959. 2.75. Lea & F.

BANDS (MUSIC) (785.12)
Adkins, Hector E. Treatise on military band. 10.00. Boosey

Hjelmervik, K., and R. C. Berg. Marching bands. 1953. 5.50. Ronald

Loken, N. Cheerleading. 1961. 2.95. Ronald

Marcouiller, D. R. Marching for marching bands. 4.00. Brown, W. C.

Schwartz, H. W. Bands of America. il. 1957. 5.00. Doubleday

BANK HOLDING COMPANIES (332)
Lamb, W. Ralph. Group banking. 1962. 7.50. Rutgers

BANK OF ENGLAND (942)
Clapham, J. H. Bank of England. 2 vols. 1945. set 12.50. Cambridge U. P.

Richards, Richard D. Early history of banking in England. 1929. 7.50. Kelley

BANKING AS A PROFESSION (629)
Beaty, John Y. How to succeed in banking as a career. 1.00. Bankers

BANKING LAW (332.1)
Weyforth, William O. Federal Reserve Board: A study of federal reserve structure and credit control. 1933. 2.25. Johns Hopkins

BANKRUPTCY (332.75)
Warren, Charles. Bankruptcy in United States history. 1935. 2.00. Harvard

BANKS AND BANKING (332)
Beckhart, B. H., ed. Banking systems. 1954. 15.00. Columbia

Boskey, Shirley. Problems and practices of development banks. 1959. pap. 3.50. Johns Hopkins

Chandler, Lester V. Economics of money and banking. 1959. 7.00. Harper

Dahlberg, Arthur O. Money in motion. 1962. pap. 5.95. De Graff

Harriss, C. Lowell. Money and banking. il. 1961. 10.35. Allyn & Bacon

Munn, Glenn G. Encyclopedia of banking and finance. by Ferdinand L. Garcia. in prep. Bankers (R)

Thomas, Rollin G. Our modern banking and monetary system. 1957. 10.00; text ed. 7.50. Prentice-Hall

Whittlesey, Charles R., ed. Readings in money and banking. 1952. 3.35. Norton

BANKS AND BANKING--EUROPE
Mackenzie, Kenneth. Banking systems of Great Britain, France, Germany,
    and United States of America. 1945. 2.50. St. Martins.
BANKS AND BANKING--U. S. (332)
Haines, Walter W. Money, prices and policy. 1961. 7.95. McGraw
Kreps, Clifton H. , Jr. Money, banking, and monetary policy. 1962. 7.50. Ronald
BANKS AND BANKING, COOPERATIVE (332)
Bridewell, David A. Credit unions. 1962. 10.00. Bender
Wilson, Charles M. Common sense credit. 1962. 4.50. Devin
BAPTISM (252.1)
Cullmann, Oscar. Baptism in the New Testament. 1958. pap. 1.75. Allenson
BAR BELLS (620.112)
Gresham, William Lindsay. Book of strength. il. 1961. 3.50. Day
BARKLEY, ALBEN WILLIAM, 1877-1956 (923.2)
Barkley, Jane R. , and Frances S. Leighton. I married the Veep. 3.95. Vanguard
BARNS (631.2)
Sloane, Eric. American barns and covered bridges. il. 1954. 4.50. (Funk,
    Wilfred). Funk
Sloane, Eric. Americana: American barns and covered bridges, American
    yesterday, and Our vanishing landscape. boxed set. 12.50. 12.50. Funk
BARNUM, PHINEAS TAYLOR, 1810-1891 (927)
Wallace, Irving. Fabulous showman: The life and times of P. T. Barnum. il.
    1959. 5.00. Knopf
BAROQUE LITERATURE--HISTORY AND CRITICISM (709.033)
Buffum, Imbric. Studies in the baroque from Montaigne to Rotrou. 1957. 5.00.
    Yale
Nelson, Lowry, Jr. Baroque lyric poetry. 1961. 5.00. Yale
BARRYMORE, ETHEL, 1879-1959 (928)
Barrymore, Ethel. Memories: An autobiography. il. 1955. 4.00. Harper
BARTH, KARL, 1886- (922)
Berkouwer, G. C. Triumph of Grace in the theology of Karl Barth. 1956. 4.95;
    Eerdmans
Hamer, Jerome. Karl Barth. 1962. 4.95. Newman
Klooster, Fred H. Significance of Barth's theology. 1962. 2.95. Baker Bk.
Runia, Klaas. Karl Barth's doctrine of Holy Scripture. 1961. 4.00. Eerdmans
BARTOK, BELA, 1881-1945 (920)
Fassett, Agathe. Naked face of genius. il. 1958. 5.00. Houghton
BARTON, CLARA HARLOWE, 1821-1912 (923.6)
Ross, Ishbel. Angel of the battlefield: The life of Clara Barton. il. 1956. 5.00.
    Harper
BARUCH, BERNARD MANNES, 1870- (923.2)
Baruch, Bernard M. Baruch: My own story. 1957. 5.00. Holt
Baruch, Bernard Mannes. Public years. il. 1960. 6.00. Holt, Rinehart &
    Winston
Coit, Margaret L. Mr. Baruch. 1957. 6.95. Houghton
BASEBALL (796.357)
Allen, Ethan N. Baseball play and strategy. il. 1959. 6.00. Ronald
Allen, Ethan and T. Micoleau. Baseball techniques illustrated. 1951. 2.95.
    Ronald
Campanis, Al. How to play baseball. il. 1954. 3.50. Dutton
Gregory, Paul M. Baseball player: An economic study. 1956. 3.75. Pub.
    Affairs
Mack, Connie. From sandlot to big league. il. 1960. 2.95. Knopf
Official baseball annual. 1.50. Nat. Baseball (R)
Reichler, J. Ronald encyclopedia of baseball. 1962. 10.00. Ronald (R)
Turkin, Hy and Thompson. S. C. Official encyclopedia of baseball. 1956. il. 6.95.
    Barnes, A. S. (R)

BASEBALL--BIOGRAPHY (920)
Daley, Arthur. Kings of the home run. 1962. 3.75. Putnam
Meany, Tom. Baseball's greatest hitters. il. 1950. 3.75. Barnes, A. S.
Meany, Tom. Baseball's greatest pitchers. il. 1951. 4.00. Barnes, A. S.
BASEBALL--HISTORY (796.3)
Buchanan, Lamont. World series and highlights of baseball. il. 4.95. Dutton
Cobb, Ty, and Al Stump. My life in baseball. il. 4.50. Doubleday
Danzig, Allison, and Joe Reichler. History of baseball. 1959. 12.50. Prentice-Hall
Mack, C. Baseball: History of big leagues. 1.00. Wehman
Reichler, Joe and Ben Olan. Baseball's unforgettable games. il. 1960. 5.50. Ronald
Seymour, Harold. Baseball, the early years. 1960. 7.50. Oxford U. P.
Smith, Robert. Baseball. 1947. 3.50. S. and S.
Smith, Robert. Baseball in America. 1961. 10.00. Holt, Rinehart & Winston
BASIC ENGLISH (428.25)
Hogben, Lancelot. Essential world English. 1962. 6.95. Norton
BASKETBALL (796.323)
American Association for Health, Physical Education and Recreation, Division for Girls' and Women's Sports. Official basketball rules and guide. 1.00. Am. Assn. for Health, Phys. Ed. & Rec.
Bunn, John W. Basketball methods. il. 1939. 5.75. Macmillan
Dean, Everett S. Progressive basketball: Methods and philosophy. 1950. 6.00. Prentice-Hall
Garstang. Basketball: The modern way. 1962. 2.95. Sterling
Pinholster, Garland F. Encyclopedia of basketball drills. 5.85. Prentice-Hall
Wilkes, Glenn. Basketball coach's complete handbook! 1962. 6.75. Prentice-Hall
BATRACHIA (597.6)
Barker, Will. Familiar animals of America. il. 1956. 5.95; lib. bdg. 5.11. Harper
Barker, Will. Familiar reptiles and amphibians of America. il. in prep. Harper
Boys, Floyd, and Hobart M. Smith. Poisonous amphibians and reptiles. 1959. 4.75. Thomas, C. C
Cochran, Doris M. Living amphibians of the world. il. 12.50. Doubleday (R)
Conant, Roger. Field guide to reptiles and amphibians. il. 1958. 4.50. Houghton
Kingsley-Noble, G. Biology of the amphibia. il. 5.00. Smith, Peter.
Lee, A., and others. Development and structure of the frog, a photographic' study. 1959. pap. 1.00. Rinehart
Oliver, James A. Natural history of North American amphibians and reptiles. il. 1955. 7.95. Van Nostrand
Smyth, H. Rucker. Amphibians and their ways. il. 1962. 6.50. Macmillan
Wright, Albert Hazen and Anna A. Handbook of frogs and toads of the United States and Canada. 3rd ed. il. 1959. 6.50. Cornell
BATS (599.4)
Griffin, Donald R. Listening in the dark. il. 1958. 7.50. Yale
BATTLES (904)
Armstrong, O. K. Fifteen decisive battles of the United States. 1961. 5.95. McKay
Creasy, Edward S. Fifteen decisive battles of the world. il. 1957. 4.00. Stackpole
Fuller, J. F. C. Military history of the Western world. vol. 1, From the earliest times to the battle of Lepanto, il. 1954; vol. 2. From the defeat of Spanish Armada, 1588, to the Battle of Waterloo, 1815, il. 1955; vol. 3, From the Seven Day's Battle, 1862, to the Battle of Leyte Gulf, 1944, il. 1956. 6.00 ea. 3 vols. 16.50. Funk (R)

Longstreth, Edward. Decisive battles of the Bible. 1962. 4.50. Lippincott
BAUDELAIRE, CHARLES PIERRE, 1821-1867. (927)
Fairlie, Alison. Baudelaire: Les fleurs du mal. 1962. 1.95. Barron's
Sartre, Jean-Paul. Baudlaire. 1950. 1.50. New Directions
BAVARIA--DESCRIPTION AND TRAVEL (943.3)
Baedeker, Karl. Southern Bavaria. il. 1953. 4.75. Macmillan
BAY PSALM BOOK (223)
Haraszti, Zoltan, ed. Bay psalm book. facsimile ed. 1956. 10.00. U. of Chicago
   (R)
BEACONSFIELD, BENJAMIN DISRAELI, 1ST EARL OF, 1804-1881 (923.242)
Graubard, Stephen R. Burke, Disraeli, and Churchill: The politics of perse-
   verance. 1961. 5.00. Harvard
Jerman, B. R. Young Disraeli. 1960. 6.00. Princeton
Maurois, Andre. Disraeli. (46) 1942. 1.65. Modern Lib.
Pearson, Hesketh. Disraeli: His life and Personality. 1960. pap. 1.45. Grosset
BEAGLE EXPEDITION, 1831-1836 (574)
Darwin, Charles Robert. Voyage of the Beagle. 1.95. 1961. Dutton
BEARD, CHARLES AUSTIN, 1874-1948 (923.7)
Benson, Lee. Turner and Beard: American historical writing reconsidered.
   1960. 5.00. Free Press
Borning, Bernard C. Political and social thought of Charles A. Beard. 1962.
   6.75. U. of Wash.
Brown, R. E. Charles Beard and the Constitution. 1956. 4.00. Princeton
BEAUMONT, FRANCIS, 1584-1616 (928)
Danby, John F. Poets on fortune's hill: Studies in Sidney, Shakespeare,
   Beaumont and Fletcher. 4.50. Hillary
BEAUMONT DE LA BOUVINIERE, GUSTAVE AUGUSTE DE, 1802-1866 (920)
Pierson, George W. Tocqueville in America. 1960. 3.50. Smith, Peter
BEAUTY, PERSONAL (646.72)
Archer, Elsie. Let's face it: A guide to good grooming for Negro girls. il.
   1959. 2.95. Lippincott
Baxter, Laura, and others. Our clothing. il. 1952. 3.20. Lippincott
Bergen Polly. Polly Bergen book of beauty, fashion and charm. il. 1962. 4.95.
   Prentice-Hall
Colby, Anita. Anita Colby's beauty book. 1958. 5.95. Prentice-Hall
Cotten, Emmi. Clothes make magic. il. 6.50. Dutton
Davenport, Gwen. Tall girl's handbook. il. 1959. 3.50. Doubleday
Foresman, Ethel. Better health--nicer skin--longer life. 1959. 3.00. Forum
Garland, Madge. The changing face of beauty. 1957. 10.00. Barrows
Hauser, Gayelord. Look younger, live longer. 1951. 3.95. Farrar, Straus
Myerson, Bess. In the feminine manner. 1962. 3.95. Citadel
Powers, John R. How to have model beauty, poise and personality. 1960.
   4.95. Prentice-Hall
Szekely, Edmund. Golden Door beauty and health book. 1961. 4.95. Prentice-Hall
Wingo, Caroline E. Clothes you buy and make. il. 1953. 5.75. McGraw
BECKER, CARL LOTUS, 1873-1945 (923.2)
Wilkins, Burleigh T. Carl Becker: A biographical study in American intellec-
   tual history. il. 1961. 5.50. Harvard
BECKETT, SAMUEL BARCLAY, 1906 (828.914)
Cohn Ruby. Samuel Beckett: The comic gamut. 1962. 6.00. Rutgers
Hoffman, Frederick J. Samuel Beckett: The language of self. 1962. bds. 4.50.
   Southern Ill.
BEECHAM, SIR THOMAS, BART., 1879-1961 (927)
Reid, Charles. Thomas Beecham. il. 1962. 4.50. Dutton
BEEF CATTLE (636)
Snapp, Roscoe R., and A. L. Neuman. Beef cattle. il. 1960. 8.75. Wiley

BEES (638.1)
Butler, Colin G. Honeybee, and introduction to her sense-physiology and behavior. il. 1949. 2.00. Oxford U. P.
Butler, Colin G. World of the honeybee. il. 1954. 5.25. Macmillan
Lindauer, Martin. Communication among social bees. 1961. 4.75. Harvard
Maeterlinck, Maurice. Life of the bee. 3.00. Dodd
BEETHOVEN, LUDWIG VAN, 1770-1827 (927)
Burk, John N. Life and works of Beethoven (241) 1.95. Modern Lib.
James, Burnett. Beethoven and human destiny. 6.50. Roy Pub.
Komroff, Manuel. Beethoven and the world of music. 1961. 3.50. Dodd
Rothschild, Fritz. Musical performance in the times of Mozart and Beethoven. (Lost tradition in music, vol. 2) 4.80. Oxford U. P.
Sullivan, J. W. N. Beethoven: His spiritual development. 1927. 3.50. Knopf
Tovey, Donald F. Beethoven. 1945. 4.00. Oxford U. P.
Valentin, Erich. Beethoven, a pictorial biography. il. 1958. 6.95. Crowell
Vaughan Williams, Ralph. Some thoughts on Beethoven's Choral Symphony, with writings on other musical subjects. 1953. 2.90. Oxford U. P.
BEETLES (595.76)
Dillon, Elizabeth, and Lawrence. Manual of common beetles of eastern North America. 1960. 9.25. Harper
Jaques, Harry E. How to know the beetles. 4.25. Brown, W. C.
Reitter, Ewald. Beetles. il. 1961. 20.00. Putnam
BEHAVIORISM (PSYCHOLOGY) (136.763)
Berlyne, D. E. Conflict, arousal, and curiosity. 1960. 7.95. McGraw
Dulau, Heinz. Behavioral approach. 1962. pap. 1.35? Random
Goodenough, Florence L., and Leona E. Tyler. Developmental psychology. il. 1959. 6.00. Appleton
Mead, George H. Mind, self, and society: From the standpoint of a social behaviorist. ed. by Charles W. Morris. 1934. 6.75. U. of Chicago
Mowrer, Orval H. Learning theory and behavior. 1960. 7.50. Wiley
Pascal, G. R. Behavioral change in the clinic. 1959. 4.75. Grune
BELGIUM (949.3)
Goris, Jan-Albert, ed. Belgium. il. 1946. 5.00. U. of Calif.
Meeus, Adrien de. History of the Belgians. 7.50. Praeger
BELGIUM--DESCRIPTION AND TRAVEL
Edwards, Tudor. Belgium. il. 1955. 4.50. Hastings
Henrot, Therese. Belgium il. 1961. pap. 1.25. Viking
BELIEF AND DOUBT (121.6)
I believe: The personal philosophies of 23 eminent men and women of our time. 5.00. Humanities
James, William. Will to believe, bd. with Human immortality. pap. 1.25. Dover
BELL, ALEXANDER GRAHAM, 1847-1922 (926.2)
Costain, Thomas B. Chord of steel. il. 1960. 3.95. Doubleday
BELLINI, GIOVANNI, d. 1516 (927.45)
Bellini, Giovanni. Bellini. ed. by Philip Hendy, and Ludwig Goldsheider. il. 6.95. N. Y. Graphic
BELLOC, HILAIRE, 1870-1953 (928.44)
Speaight, Robert. Life of Hilaire Belloc. il. 1957. 6.50. Farrar, Straus
BELLS (789.5)
Morrison, Gouverneur. Bells: Their history and romance. il.
BEMELMANS, LUDWIG (928.73)
Bemelmans, Ludwig. My life in art. il. 1958. 6.50. Harper
BENCHLEY, ROBERT CHARLES, 1889-1945 (928.73)
Benchley, Nathaniel. Robert Benchley: A biography. 1955. 3.95. McGraw
BENEDICTINES (271.1)
Benedict, Saint. Rule of St. Bendict. ed. by Justin McCann. 1952. 3.00. Newman
Butler, Cuthbert. Benedictine Monachism. 1961. 7.00. Barnes & Noble

BENEDICTUS, SAINT, ABBOT OF MONTE CASSINO (922)
Van Zeller, Hubert. Holy rule. 1958. 7.50. Sheed
BENET, STEPHEN VINCENT, 1898-1943 (928.73)
Fenton, Charles A. Stephen Vincent Benet. il. 1958. 6,00. Yale
Stroud, Parry E. Stephen Vincent Benet. 1962. 3.50. Twayne
BEN-GURION, DAVID, 1887 (923.1)
Crossman, Richard H. S. Nation reborn. 1960. 3.50. Atheneum
St. John, Robert. Ben-Gurion. 1959. 3.95. Doubleday
BENSON, EZRA TAFT (923.2)
McCune, Wesley. Ezra Taft Benson: Man with a mission. 1958. 2.50. Pub.
    Affairs
BENTHAM, JEREMY, 1748-1832 (923.6)
Davidson, William Leslie. Political thought in England: Utilitarians from
    Bentham to Mill. 1915. 1.70. Oxford U. P.
Mack, Mary P. Jeremy Bentham: An odyssey of ideas. 1962. 7.50. Columbia
Mill, John Stuart. Utilitarianism, on liberty, essay on Bentham. ed. by Mary
    Warnock. 1962. pap. 1.45. Meridian
BENTON, THOMAS HART, 1782-1858 (923.273)
Smith, Elbert B. Magnificent Missourian: The life of Thomas Hart Benton.
    1958. 6.00. Lippincott
BENZENE (547.611.)
Selling, Laurence. Benzol as a leucotoxin. 1913. pap. 1.00. Johns Hopkins
BEOWULF (829.3)
Chambers, Raymond W., ed. Beowulf, an introduction. by Wrenn. 1959. 9.50.
    Cambridge U. P.
Haber, Tom B. Comparative study of the Beowulf and the Aenied. 1931. pap.
    3.00. Hafner
Lawrence, William W. Beowulf and epic tradition. 5.75. Hafner
BERDIAEV, NIKOLAI ALEKSANDROVICH, 1874-1948 (922)
Attwater, Donald, ed. Modern Christian revolutionaries. 4.00. Devin
BERGSON, HENRI LOUIS, 1859-1941 (921.4)
Hanna, Thomas, ed. Bergsonian heritage. 1962. 4.00. Columbia
BERKELEY, GEORGE, BP. OF CLOYNE, 1685-1753 (922)
Armstrong, D. M. Berkeley's theory of vision. 4.50. (Melbourne U. P.)
    Cambridge U. P.
Luce, A. A. Life of Berkeley. 5.00. Humanities
BERLIN--HISTORY--ALLIED OCCUPATION, 1945 (943.155)
Brandt, Willy, and Leo Lania. My road to Berlin. il. 1960. 4.50. Doubleday
Davison, W. P. Berlin blockade. 1958. 7.50. Princeton
Donner, Jorn. Report from Berlin. tr. by Albin T. Anderson. il. 1961. 6.50.
    Indiana
Mander, John. Berlin, hostage to the West. 3.00. Smith, Peter
Mezerik, Avrahm G., ed. Berlin and Germany: Cold war chronology. 1962.
    pap. 2.50. Int. Review Service
Robson, Charles B., ed. Berlin: Pivot of German destiny. 1960. 5.00. U. of N. C.
Klinck, A. Home life in Bible times. 1947. pap. 0.60. Concordia
Price, Ira M., and others. Monuments and the Old Testament. 1959. 6.75.
    Judson
Pritchard, James B., ed. Ancient Near East: An anthology of texts and pic-
    tures. 1958. 6.00. Princeton
Pritchard, J. Archaeology and the Old Testament. 1958. 5.00. Princeton
Thomas, D. Winton, ed. Documents from Old Testament times. 5.00. Nelson
Thompson, J. A. Bible and archaeology. il. 1962. 5.95. Eerdmans
Unger, Merrill, F. Archaeology and the New Testament. 1962. 4.95. Zondervan
BIBLE--APPRECIATION (220.6)
Deitz, Reginald W. What the Bible can mean for you. 1962. 1.00. Muhlenberg
BIBLE--BIOGRAPHY (220.92)
Alexander, George M. Handbook of Biblical personalities. 5.75. Seabury (R)

Deen, Edith. All of the women of the Bible. 1955. 4.95. Harper (R)
Lockyer, Herbert. All the men of the Bible. 4.95. Zondervan (R)
Lundholm, Algot T. Women of the Bible. 1948. 2.50. Augustana
Macartney, Clarence E. Greatest men of the Bible. 2.00. Abingdon
Mead, Frank S. Who's who in the Bible. 1.50. Grosset (R)
BIBLE--BIOGRAPHY--N. T. (220.92)
Rolston, Holmes. Personalities around Paul. 1954. 2.50. John Knox
BIBLE--BIOGRAPHY--O. T. (220.92)
Danielou, Jean. Holy pagans of the Old Testament. 3.00. Taplinger
Hunt, Clark W. Mighty men of God. 1959. 2.50. Abingdon
James, Fleming. Personalities of the Old Testament. 1939. 6.95. Scribner
Kuyper, Abraham. Women of the Old Testament. 1934. 1.95; pap. 1.50.
    Zondervan
BIBLE--CANON (220.12)
Barclay, William. Making of the Bible. 1961. 1.00. Abingdon
BIBLE--CHRONOLOGY (222)
Wardle, W. L. History and religion of Israel. il. 1936. 1.70. Oxford U. P.
BIBLE--COMMENTARIES (220.7)
Interpreter's Bible. 12 vols. 1951-1957. 8.75 ea; set, 89.50. Abingdon (R)
Kretzmann, P. E. Commentary on the Bible. 4 vols. set. 19.55. Concordia (R)
BERLIN CONFERENCE, 1945 (940.53)
Feis, H. Between war and peace: The Potsdam Conference. 1960. 6.50.
    Princeton
BERLIOZ, HECTOR, 1803-1869 (927)
Barzun, Jacques. Berlioz and his century: An introduction to the age of
    romanticism. pap. 1.65. Meridian
Eliot, J. H. Berlioz. 1949. 3.00. Farrar, Straus
BERNADETTE, SAINT (BERNADETTE SOUBIROUS) 1844-1879 (922)
Keyes, Frances Parkinson. Bernadette of Lourdes. il. 1953. 3.50. Hawthorn
BERNARD DE CLAIRVAUX, SAINT, 1091?-1153 (922)
Coulton, G. G. Five centuries of religion. 4 vols. vols. 1-3, o.p; vol. 4, Last
    days of Medieval monarchism. 1950. 13.50. Cambridge U. P.
Merton, Thomas. Last of the fathers. 1954. 3.50. Harcourt
BERNHARDT, SARAH, 1844-1923 (927)
Noble, Iris. Great lady of the theatre: Sarah Bernhardt. 1960. 3.25; lib. ed.
    2.99. Messner
BERNINI, GIOVANNI LORENZO, 1598-1680 (927)
Wittkower, Rudolph. Gian Lorenzo Bernini: Sculptor of the Roman Baroque.
    il. 1955. 12.50. N. Y. Graphic
BERNSTEIN, LEONARD, 1918 (927)
Briggs, John. Leonard Bernstein, the man, his work, and his world. il. 1961.
    4.50. World Pub.
BERRY, MARTHA McCHESNEY, 1866-1942 (923.673)
Kane, Harnett, T., and Inez Henry. Miracle in the mountains. 1956. 3.95.
    Doubleday
BERYLLIUM (546.391)
Nininger, Robert D. Minerals for atomic energy. il. 1956. 8.50. Van Nostrand
BEST SELLERS (655.473)
Mott, Frank L. Golden multitudes. 1947. 8.00. Bowker
BETA RAYS (539.752)
Lipkin, H. J. Beta decay for pedestrians. 1962. 6.00. Wiley
BETROTHAL (392.4)
Burgess, Ernest W., and Paul Wallin. Engagement and marriage. il. 1953.
    7.95. Lippincott
Hansen, Paul G., and others, eds. Engagement and marriage. 1959. 3.00.
    Concordia
Lutheran Church, Missouri Synod, Family Life Committee. Engagement and
    Marriage. 1959. 3.00. Concordia

BIBLE--ADDRESSES, ESSAYS, LECTURES (220)
Kissane, E. J. Word of Life: Essays on the Bible. 1959. pap. 1.75. Newman
Rowley, Harold H., ed. Old Testament and modern study. 1952. 4.50. Oxford U.
P.
Stonehouse, Ned B. Paul before the Areopagus, 1957. 3.50. Eerdmans
BIBLE--ANTIQUITIES (220)
Albright, William Foxwell. Archaeology and the religion of Israel.1941. 3.50.
Johns Hopkins
Bailey, Albert E. Daily life in Bible times. il. 4.50. Scribner
Finegan, Jack. Light from the ancient past. 1959. 10.00. Princeton
Gray, John. Archaeology in the Old Testament world. 6.50. Nelson
Grollenberg, Luc. H. Shorter atlas of the Bible. tr. by Mary F. Hedlund. il.
1959. 3.95. Nelson
Heaton, E. W. Everyday life in Old Testament times. il. 1956. 4.50. Scribner
(R)
BIBLE--COMMENTARIES--N. T. (220.7)
Knox, Ronald, New Testament commentary. vol.1, Commentary on the Gospels.
1952. 3.75; vol. 2, New Testament commentary. 1956. 3.75. Sheed
Lenski, Richard C. H. Commentary on the New Testament. 12 vols. set, 58.25.
Augsburg (R)
BIBLE--COMMENTARIES--N. T. ACTS (226)
Lenski, R. C. H. Interpretation of Acts. 5.45. Augsburg
BIBLE--COMMENTARIES--N. T. COLOSSIANS (225)
Lenski, R. C. H. Interpretation of Colossians, Thessalonians I and II, Timothy
I and II, Titus, and Philemon. 5.45. Augsburg
BIBLE--COMMENTARIES--N. T. EPHESIANS (225)
Lenski, Richard C. H. Interpretation of Galatians, Ephesians, and Philippians.
1937. 4.95. Augsburg
BIBLE--COMMENTARIES--N. T. EPISTLES OF PAUL (227)
Conybeare, W. J. Epistles of St. Paul. 2.50. Baker Bk.
Shepard, John Watson. Life and letters of St. Paul. 1950. 6.00. Eerdmans
BIBLE--COMMENTARIES--N. T. GOSPELS (225)
Lenski, Richard C. H. Interpretation of John. 6.55. Augsburg
Lenski, Richard C. H. Interpretation of Luke. 1943. 6.55. Wartburg
Lenski, Richard C. H. Interpretation of Matthew. 5.45. Augsburg
Luther, Martin. Sermons on the gospel of St. John. (Luther's works, vols. 22
and 24). ed. by Jaroslav Pelikan. tr. by Martin H. Bertram. 6.00 ea. Concor-
dia
Luther, Martin. Works. vol. 23. ed. by Jaroslav Pelikan. tr. by Martin H. Ber-
tram, 1958. 6.00. Concordia
Tenney, Merrill C. John : The Gospel of belief. 1948. 4.00. Eerdmans
BIBLE--COMMENTARIES--O. T. (225)
Pieters, Albertus. Notes on Old Testament history. vol 2. 1950. 3.00.
Eerdmans
BIBLE--CONCORDANCES (220.2)
Cruden, Alexander. Cruden's complete concordance to the Holy Scriptures.(R)
ed. by A. D. Adams, and others. 4.00. Holt, Rinehart, & Winston (R)
Ellison, John W., ed. Nelson's complete concordance of the Revised (R)
standard version of the Bible. 1957. 16.50; lea. 27.50. Nelson (R)
Moulton, W. F., and A. S. Geden. Concordance to the Greek New Testament.
15 00. Kregel
Nelson's concise concordance to the revised standard version Bible. 1961.
2.50. Nelson (R)
Oxford cyclopedic concordance, no. 10. 3.00. Oxford U. P.
Strong, James. Exhaustive concordance of the Bible. 1958. 14.75. thumb
indexed, 16.00. Abingdon (R)
Thompson, Newton, and Raymond Stock. Complete concordance to the Bible:(R)
Douay version. 1945. 16.00. Herder (R)

Young, Robert. Young's analytical concordance to the Bible. 1955. (R) 12.75.
Eerdmans
BIBLE--CRITICISM, INTERPRETATION, ETC. (220.6)
Anderson, Bernhard W. Rediscovering the Bible. 3.50. Assn. Pr.
Arndt, William F. Does the Bible contradict itself? 1931. 1.50. Concordia
Barton, Bruce. Man and Book nobody knows. 1960. 5.00. Bobbs
Daniel, Carey. Bible's seeming contradictions. 1941. 1.95. Zondervan
Moulton, Richard G. Literary study of the Bible. 1894. 6.00. Revell
Smart, James D. Interpretation of Scripture. 1961. 6.00. Westminister
BIBLE--CRITICISM, INTERPRETATION, ETC. --N. T. (225)
Baum, Gregory. Jews and the Gospel. 1961. 4.50. Newman
Loisy, Albert F. Birth of the Christian religion, and Origins of the New
Testament. 1962. 10.00. U. Books
BIBLE--CRITICISM, INTERPRETATION, ETC. --N. T. APOCRYPHA (220)
Goodspeed, Edgar J., ed. Apocrypha. (V163) pap. 1.65. Vintage
Goodspeed, E. Modern Apocrypha. 1956. 2.75. Beacon
BIBLE--CRITICISM, INTERPRETATION, ETC. --N. T. EPISTLES (220)
Scharlemann, Martin H. Qumran and Corinth. 1962. pap. 1.95. Twayne
Schweitzer, Albert. Paul and his interpreters. tr. by Montgomery. 3.50.
Macmillan
Smith, David. Life and letters of St. Paul. 6.00. Harper
Tenney, Merrill C. Galatians, the charter of Christian liberty. 1957. 3.00.
Eerdmans
BIBLE--CRITICISM, INTERPRETATION, ETC. --N. T. GOSPELS (220)
Goodspeed, Edgar J. Twelve: The story of Christ's Apostles. 1957. 3.50.
Winston
Robertson, Archibald T. Studies in Mark's gospel. 1958. 2.50. Broadman
Tenney, Merrill C. Genius of the Gospels. 1951. 2.00. Eerdmans
BIBLE--CRITICISM, INTERPRETATION, ETC. --O. T (220)
Kohler, Ludwig. Hebrew man. 1957. 2.50. Abingdon
Wright, G. Ernest, ed. Bible and the ancient Near East: Essays in honor
of William Foxwell Albright. 7.50. Doubleday
BIBLE--CRITICISM, TEXTUAL(220)
Grant, Frederick C. Translating the Bible. il. 1961. 4.25. Seabury
BIBLE--DICTIONARIES (220.9)
Bridges, Ronald, and Luther A. Weigle. Bible word book, concerning obsolete
or archaic words in the King James version of the Bible. 1960. 5.00. Nelson
(R)
Buttrick, George A., ed. Interpreter's dictionary of the Bible. 4 vols. il. 1962
set, 45.00. Abingdon (R)
Clarke, Adam. Comprehensive Bible concordance. 1960. 3.50. Kregel (R)
Cruden, Alexander. Cruden's dictionary of Bible terms. 3.50. Baker Bk. (R)
Davis, John D., and Henry S. Gehman. Westminster dictionary of the Bible.
1944. 6.00. Westminster
Hastings, James., ed. Dictionary of the Bible. 1927. 12.50. Scribner
Miller, Madeleine S., and J. Lane Miller. Encyclopedia of Bible life. il. 1955.
6.95. Harper (R)
Miller, Madeleine S., and J. Lane. Harper's Bible dictionary. 6th ed. il. 1959.
8.95; indexed, 9.95. Harper (R)
Nave, Orville. Nave's topical Bible. 9.95. Moody (R)
Smith, William. Smith's Bible dictionary. il. 1948. 3.95. Holt, Rinehart &
Winston (R)
BIBLE--GEOGRAPHY--MAPS (220.8)
Grollenberg, L. H., ed. Nelson's atlas of the Bible. il. 1957.15.00. Nelson (R)
Hammond, C. S., and Co. Pictorial atlas of the Bible Lands. 1960. 1.50.
Hammond (R)
Kraeling, Emil G. Rand McNally Bible atlas. il. 1956. 8.95. Rand McNally (R)

Westminster historical maps of Bible lands. 1.00. Westminster (R)

Wright, B. Ernest, and Floyd V. Filson. Westminster historical atlas to the Bible. 1956. 7.50. Westminster (R)

BIBLE--HARMONIES (220)

Burton, Ernest DeWitt, and Edgar J. Goodspeed, eds. Harmony of the Synoptic Gospels in Greek 1920. 5.75. U. of Chicago

BIBLE--HISTORY (220.9)

Bruce, Frederick F. Books and the parchments. 3.50. Revell

Butterworth, Charles C. Literary lineage of the King James Bible, 1340-1611. 1941. 3.50. U. of Pa.

Goodspeed, Edgar J. How came the Bible? 1940. 1.75. pap. 1.00. Abingdon

Kenyon, Frederic. Our Bible and the ancient manuscripts. by A. W. Adams. il. 1958. 6.95. Harper

MacGregor, Geddes. Bible in the making. 1959. 6.00. Lippincott

BIBLE--HISTORY OF BIBLICAL EVENTS (220.9)

Fison, J. E. Understanding the Old Testament. 1953. 1.70. Oxford U. P.

Maus, Cynthia Pearl. Old Testament and the fine arts. 1954. 6.95. Harper (R)

Oursler, Fulton. Greatest book ever written. il. 1951. 3.95. 3.95. Doubleday

Oursler, Fulton, and April O. Armstrong. Greatest faith ever known, il. 1953. 3.95. Doubleday

Rattey, B. K. Short history of the Hebrews from Moses to Herod the Great. 1931. 1.05. Oxford U. P.

Reu, M. Biblical history for school and home. il. 1.85. Augsburg

Sloan, William W. Survey of the new Testament. 1962. pap. 1.95. Littlefield

Sloan, William W. Survey of the Old Testament. 1957. 3.50. Abingdon

Weiss, Johannes. Earliest Christianity, a history of the period A.D. 30-150. 2 vols. ed. by F. C. Grant. 1959. 8.25. Smith, Peter

BIBLE--HISTORY OF CONTEMPORARY EVENTS, ETC. (220.9)

Bouquet, A. C. Everyday life in New Testament times. 1954. 4.50. Scribner

Daniel-Rops, Henri. Daily life in the time of Jesus. 1962. 6.00. Hawthorn

Grant, Frederick C. Roman Hellenism and the New Testament. 1962. 3.95? Scribner*

Keller, Werner. Bible as history: A confirmation of the Book of books. tr. by William Neil. il. 1956. 5.95. Morrow

Pfeiffer, Robert H. History of New Testament times: With an intorduction to the Apocrypha. 1949. 5.00. Harper

Tenney, Merrill C. New Testament survey. il. 1961. 5.95. Eerdmans

BIBLE --HOMILETICAL USE (251)

BIBLE--INDEXES, TOPICAL (220)

Stevenson, Burton. Home book of Bible quotations. 1949. 7.95. Harper (R)

BIBLE--INTRODUCTIONS (220)

Chase, Mary Ellen. Bible and the common reader. 1952. 4.95. Macmillan

Danker, Frederick W. Multi-purpose tools for Bible study. 1959. 3.75. Concordia

Goodspeed, Edgar J. Story of the Bible. 1936. 3.75. U. of Chicago

BIBLE--INTRODUCTIONS--N.T. (225)

Goodspeed, Edgar J. Introduction to the New Testament. il. 1937. 4.00. U. of Chicago

Goodspeed, Edgar J. Story of the New Testament. 1929. 2.75. U. of Chicago

Scott, Ernest F. Literature of the New Testament. 1932. 4.00. Columbia

Tenney, Merrill C. New Testament survey. il. 1961. 5.95. Eerdmans

Thiessen, Henry C. Introduction to the New Testament. 1943. 3.50. Eerdmans

BIBLE--INTRODUCTIONS-- O. T. (221)

Bewer, J. A. Literature of the Old Testament. 3rd ed. 1962. 6.00. Columbia

Goodspeed, Edgar J. Story of the Old Testament. 1934. 2.75. U. of Chicago

Keil, Carl F., and Franz Delitzsch. Introduction to the Old Testament. 2 vols. 1952. 7.00. Eerdmans

Pfeiffer, Robert H. Introduction to the Old Testament. 1948. 6.50. Harper

BIBLE --INTRODUCTIONS--O. T. APOCRYPHA (221)
Goodspeed, Edgar J. Story of the Apocrypha. 1939. 2.75. U. of Chicago
Metzger, Bruce M. Introduction to the Apocrypha. 1957. 3.75. Oxford U. P.
Pfeiffer, Robert H. History of New Testament times: With an introduction to the
  Aprocrypha. 1949. 5.00. Harper
BIBLE--MANUSCRIPTS (220.4)
Kenyon, Frederic. Our Bible and the ancient manuscripts. by A. W. Adams. il.
  1958. 6.95. Harper
Lake, Kirsopp, and Silva New, eds. Six collations of New Testament manuscripts.
  1932. 2.50. Harvard
BIBLE--MEDITATIONS (242)
Coates, Thomas. Proverbs for today. 1960. 2.00. Concordia
Kretzmann, M., and A. Doerffler. Devotional Bible. vol. 1. 1948. 3.50. Con-
  cordia
BIBLE--MUSIC (268.7)
Wellesz, Egon, ed. Ancient and oriental music. (New Oxford history of music.
  vol. 1.) 1957. 12.50. Oxford U. P.
BIBLE--NATURAL HISTORY (220.9)
Walker, Winifred. All the plants of the Bible. il. 1957. 4.95. Harper
BIBLE--PSYCHOLOGY (201.6)
Wise, Carroll A. Psychiatry and the Bible. 1956. 3.50. Harper
BIBLE--READING (264.3)
Goodspeed, Edgar J. How to read the Bible. 1946. 2.50. Winston
Love, Julian P. How to read the Bible. rev. ed. 1959. 3.95. Macmillan
BIBLE--RELATION OF N. T. TO O. T. (220)
Englebert, Omer, and Rene Aigrain. Prophecy fulfilled: The Old Testament
  realized in the New. 1958. 3.95. McKay
BIBLE-SERMONS -- O.T. (252.9)
Redpath, Alan. Victorious Christian living. 1955. 3.00. Revell
BIBLE--THEOLOGY (220)
Burrows, Millar. Outline of Biblical theology. 1946. 4.00. Westminster
Fosdick, Harry Emerson. Guide to understanding the Bible. 1938. 5.00.
  (Torchbks Tb2) 1956. Harper
BIBLE--THEOLOGY--N. T. (220)
Barth, Karl. Christ and Adam. tr. by T. A. Smail. 1957. 2.00. Harper
Smeaton, George. Apostles' doctrine of the atonement. 2.95. Zondervan
BIBLE THEOLOGY--O.T. (220)
Irwin, William A. Old Testament: Keystone of human culture. 1952. 4.00
  Abelard
BIBLE --VERSIONS (220.4)
Bruce, Frederick F. English Bible: A history of translations. il. 1961. 3.75.
  Oxford U. P.
Goodspeed, Edgar J. How came the Bible? 1940. 1.75. pap. 1.00. Abingdon
BIBLE--VERSIONS, ENGLISH (220.4)
Bridges, Ronald, and Luther A. Weigle. Bible word book, concerning obsolete
  or archaic words in the King James version of the Bible. 1960. 5.00. Nelson
Butterworth, Charles C., and Allan Chester. George Joye: A chapter in the
  history of the English Bible and English Reformation. 1962. 6.00. U. of Pa. *
Grant, Frederick C. Translating the Bible. il. 1961. 4.25. Seabury
Pope, Hugh. English versions of the Bible. 1952. 10.00. Herder
Thompson, Newton, and Raymond Stock. Complete concordance to the Bible:
  Douay version. 1945. 16.00. Herder (R)
BIBLE AND SCIENCE (220.85)
DeHaan, M. R. Genesis and evolution. 2.50. Zondervan*
Ramm, Bernard. Christian view of science and scripture. 1954. 4.00. Eerdmans
Rehwinkel, Alfred M. Flood. il. 1957. pap. 1.95. Concordia
Richardson, Alan. Bible in the age of science. 1961. 3.50. Westminster
Rimmer, Harry. Harmony of science and Scripture. 1936. 3.00. Eerdmans

BIBLE AS LITERATURE (220.88)
Goodspeed, Edgar J. How to read the Bible. 1946. 2.50. Winston
Moulton, Richard G. Literary study of the Bible. 1894. 6.00. Heath
BIBLE IN LITERATURE (220.88)
Mueller, William R. Prophetic voice in modern fiction. 1959. 3.50. Assn. Pr.
Thompson, Lawrence. Melville's quarrel with God. 1952. 6.00. Princeton
BIBLE IN LITERATURE--BIBLIOGRAPHY (220.88)
Coleman, Edward D. Bible in English drama. 1931. 1.00. N. Y. P. L.
BIBLE IN THE SCHOOLS (268)
Johnson, Alvin W., and Frank H. Yost. Separation of church and state in the
    United States. 1948. 4.50. U. of Minn.
BIBLIOGRAPHY (010)
Appel, Livia. Bibliographical citation in the social sciences and the humani-
    ties. 3rd ed. 1949. pap. 0.75. U. of Wis. (R)
Bradford, Samuel C. Documentation. 1950. 3.00. Pub. Affairs
Esdaile, Arundell, and Roy Stokes. Student's manual of bibliography. il. 1955. 5.00.
    Barnes & Noble (R)
Hurt, Peyton. Bibliography and footnotes: A style manual for college and univer-
    sity students. ed. by Mary L. Hurt Richmond. 1949. pap. 2.00. U. of Calif.
McKerrow, R. B. Introduction to bibliography for literary students. il. 1927.
    4.80. Oxford U. P.
BIBLIOGRAPHY--BEST BOOKS (010)
American Historical Association. Guide to historical literature. ed. by George
    F. Howe and others. 1961. 16.50. Macmillan (R)
American Library Association. A. L. A. catalog. 1942-1949. 7.00. A. L. A. (R)
American Library Association. Periodicals for small and medium-sized libraries.
    8th ed. 1948. 1.75. A. L. A. (R)
American Library Association. Richer by Asia: Bibliography of books and other
    materials for promoting West-East understanding. 1959. pap. 1.25. A. L. A.
    (R)
A. L. A. Catalog, 1932-1936, 5.00; 1937-1941, 6.00; 1942-1949, 7.00. A. L. A.
    (R)
Coman, Edwin T. Sources of business information. 1949. 5.95. Prentice-Hall
    (R)
Committee on College Reading, National Council of Teachers of English.
    Good Reading. by J. Sherwood Weber. 1960. 4.00. Bowker (R)
Crane, Evan J., and others. Guide to the literature of chemistry. 1957. 8.50.
    Wiley (R)
Dickinson, Asa Don. World's best books: Homer to Hemingway. 1953. 6.00
    Wilson (R)
Downs, Robert. Molders of the modern mind: Books that have shaped western
    civilization. 1961. 6.00. Barnes & Noble (R)
Fadiman, Clifton. Lifetime reading plan. 1960. 3.75. World Pub. (R)
Farber, Evan Ira. Classified list of periodicals for the college library. 1957.
    5.00. Faxon (R)
Graham, Bessie. Bookman's manual. by Hester R. Hoffman. 1960. in prep.
    Bowker
Haines, H. E. Living with books. 1950. 6.00. Columbia (R)
Hoffman, Hester R., ed. Reader's adviser and bookman's manual. 1960. 15.00.
    Bowker (R)
Standard catalog for high school libraries. 1962. also with Catholic suppl. sold
    on service basis. Wilson
Standard catalog for public libraries. Sold on service basis. Wilson (R)
BIBLIOGRAPHY--BIBLIOGRAPHY (010)
Beers, Henry P. Bibliographies in American history. 12.50. Cooper (R)
Besterman, Theodore. World bibliography of bibliographies and of biblio-
    graphical catalogues, calendars, abstracts, digests, indexes and the like.
    2 vols. 49.50. Scarecrow (R)

Bibliographic index. 2 vols. 1951-1955; 1956-1959. Sold on service basis.
 Wilson (R)
Bond, Donald F. Reference guide to English studies. il. 1962. 5.00. pap.
 1.95. U. of Chicago (R)
Downs, Robert B. American library resources. 7.00; suppl. 1950-1961.
 in prep. A.L.A. (R)
Kennedy, Arthur G., and Donald B. Sands. Concise bibliography for students
 of English. Systematically arranged. 1960. pap. 5.00. Stanford (R)
Union list of serials in libraries of the United States and Canada. 2nd suppl. 1944-
 1949. 1954. rates on request. Wilson (R)
Williams, Cecil B., and Allan H. Stevenson. Research manual: For college
 studies and papers. rev. ed. 1951. 2.75. Harper
BIBLIOGRAPHY--BOOKS ISSUED IN SERIES (010)
Orton, Robert M. Catalog of reprints in series. 15.00; suppl. Scarecrow (R)
BIBLIOGRAPHY--DICTIONARIES (019)
Turner, Mary, ed. Bookman's glossary. 1961. 5.00. Bowker (R)
BIBLIOGRAPHY--PAPERBACK EDITIONS (010)
Paperbound books in print. pap. 3.45. 4 issues a year. 10.00. Bowker (R)
Schick, Frank L. Paperbound book in America. il. 1958. 7.50. Bowker
BIBLIOGRAPHY--PERIODICALS (050)
Book review digest, Annuals, 1905-1934. 1905, 1906, 1908, 5.00 ea; 1907,
 1909, 1910, 1912, 6.00 ea; 1911, 1913-1915, 1918, 1919, 1922, 1923,
 7.00 ea; 1916, 1917, 1920, 1921, 1924, 8.00 ea; 1925, 1927, 10.00 ea;
 1928, 11.00; 1926, 12.00;1929, 13.00; 1930, 14.00; 1931-1934, in prep;
 1946-1959, prices on application. sold on service basis. Wilson (R)
Cumulative book index. 5 vols. 1938-1958. 1959-1960. in prep. sold on
 service basis. Wilson (R)
Whitaker's reference catalogue of current literature, 1961. 2 vols. 33.60 plus
 duty. Bowker (R)
BIBLIOGRAPHY--RARE BOOKS (010)
Wemyss, Stanley. General guide to rare Americana. 10.00. Wehman (R)
BIDDLE, NICHOLAS, 1750-1778 (923.373)
Govan, Thomas. Nicholas Biddle. 1959. 7.50. U. of Chicago
BIERCE, AMBROSE, 1842-1914 (928.1)
Fatout, Paul. Ambrose Bierce: The devil's lexicographer. il. 1951. 4.00.
 U. of Okla.
BIG BUSINESS (338.018)
Edwards, Corwin. Big business and the policy of competition. 3.50. Western
 Reserve
Harrington, Alan. Life in the crystal palace. 1959. 4.50. Knopf
Houser, T. V. Big business and human values. 1957. 4.50. McGraw
Quinn, Theodore K. Giant business: Threat to democracy, 1954. 3.75. Exposition

Quinn, Theodore K. Giant corporations: Challenge to freedom. 1956. 3.50.
 Exposition
Quinn, Theodore K. Unconscious public enemies. 1962. 4.95. Citadel
Rosenbluth, G. Concentration in Canadian manufacturing industries. 1957.
 3.50. (Nat. Bureau of Econ. Research) Princeton
Whitney, Simon N. Antitrust policies; American experience in twenty indus-
 tries. 2 vols. 1958. 6.00 ea; set, 10.00. Twentieth Century
BILINGUALISM (425)
Leopold, Werner F. Speech development of a bilingual child. 4 vols. vol. 1,
 Vocabulary growth in the first two years, 1954, 5.00; vol. 2, Sound learn-
 ing in the first two years, 1947, 5.50; vol. 3, Grammar and general problems,
 1949; vol. 4, Diary from age two, 1949, 5.00 ea; set, 20.00. Northwestern U.
BINGHAM, GEORGE CALEB, 1811-1899 (927)
McDermott, John F. George Caleb Bingham, river portraitist. il. 1959. 15.00.
 U. of Okla. (R)

BIOENERGETICS (574)

Asimov, Isaac. Life and energy. il. 1962. bds. 4.95. Doubleday

Kleiber, M. Fire of Life. 1961. 11.50. Wiley

BIOGRAPHY (920)

Bennett, H. S. Six medieval men and women. 1955. 3.25. Cambridge U. P.

Eastman, Max. Great companions, critical memoirs of some famous friends. il. 1959. 4.75. Farrar. Straus

Hyde, Marietta A., and Zuleine Garrett, eds. Modern biography. 1945. 2.48. Harcourt

International yearbook and statesman's who's who. 25.00. Int. Pub. Service (R)

Nelson, James, ed. Wisdom for our time. il. 1961. 4.50. Norton

Phelps, Robert, ed. Men in the news: 1958 personality sketches from The New York Times. 1959. 4.95; 1959 sketches. 1960. 5.95. Lippincott (R)

Plumb, Beatrice, Lives that inspire. 1962. 3.95. Denison

Thomas, Lowell. Vital spark: 101 outstanding lives. il. 1959. 5.75. Doubleday

Untermeyer, Louis. Makers of the modern world. 1955. 7.50; 1962. S. and S. (R)

Wallace, Irving. Square pegs. 1957. 5.00. Knopf

Woolf, Virginia S. Granite and rainbow. 1958. 3.75. Harcourt

BIOGRAPHY--DICTIONARIES, INDEXES, INC. (920)

Barnhart, Clarence, and William D. Halsey, eds. New Century cyclopedia of names. 3 vols. text ed. 39.50. Appleton (R)

Biography index. 4 vols. 1946-1958. vol. 5. 1958-1961. Sold on service basis. Wilson (R)

Current biography. Yearbooks, 1946-1961. 7.00 ea. Cumulate index to Current Biography. gratis. Wilson (R)

DeFord, Miriam A. Who was when? A Dictionary of contemporaries. 1950. 6.00. Wilson (R)

Hyamson, Albert M. Dictionary of universal biography: of all ages and of all people. 1951. 17.50. Dutton (R)

Institute for the Study of the USSR, ed. Who's who in the U.S.S.R. 1961. 21.00. Scarecrow

International Who's who. 22.00. Int. Pub. Service (R)

Kunitz, Stanley J., and Howard Haycraft. American authors: 1600-1900. il. 1938. 6.00. Wilson (R)

Kunitz, Stanley J., and Howard Haycraft. British authors before 1800, il. 1952. 6.00. Wilson (R)

Kunitz, S. J., and Howard Haycraft. British authors of the neneteenth century. il. 1936. 5.00. Wilson (R)

Kunitz, S. J., and Howard Haycraft. Twentieth century authors. il. 1942. 8.50. First suppl. 1955. 8.00. Wilson (R)

Merriam Co., G. and C. Webster's biographical dictionary. 1960. 8.50. Merriam (R)

Thorne, J. O., ed. Chamber's biographical dictionary. 1962. 15.00. St. Martins (R)

Who was who. 1897-1915, with addenda and corrigenda, 11.00; 1916-1928, 11.00; 1929-1950, 15.00; 1951-1960, 17.50. Macmillan (R)

Who's who. 1962. 24.00. St. Martins* (R)

BIOGRAPHY (AS A LITERARY FORM) (920-002)

Bowen, Catherine Drinker. Adventures of a biographer. 1959. 4.00. Little

Merrill, Dana Kinsman. American biography: Its theory and practice. 1957. 5.00. Bowker Press, Portland, Maine

Nicolson, H. Development of English biography. 2.00. Hillary

BIOLOGICAL CHEMISTRY (574.192)

Annual review of biochemistry. 7.00. Annual Reviews

Asimov, Isaac. Chemicals of life. 1962. pap. 0.60. New Am. Lib.

Baldwin, Ernest. Dynamic aspects of biochemistry. 1957. 6.50. Cambridge U. P.

Baldwin, Ernest. Introduction to comparative biochemistry. 8.00. Cambridge U. P.

Butler, John A. V., and others, eds. Progress in biophysics and biophysical chemistry. 12 vols. il. 1950-1960. vols. 1-3, 12.50 ea; vols. 4-7, 12.00 ea; vols. 8-9, 17.50 ea; vol. 10, 15.00; vol. 11, 12.50; vol. 12, 14.00. Pergamon

Ciba Foundation. Biochemistry of human genetics. 1959. 9.50. Little

Downes, Helen R. Chemistry of living cells. 1962. 9.75. Harper

Fearon, William R. Introduction to biochemistry. by William J. E. Jessop. 1961. 8.00. Academic Press

Florkin, Marcel, ed. Aspects of the origin of life. 1960. 5.00. Pergamon

Goodwin, Trevor W. Recent advances in biochemistry. 1960. 11.50. Little

Harris, Harry. Introduction to human biochemical genetics. 1954. 2.75. Cambridge U. P.

Kosower, E. M. Molecular biochemistry. 1962. 12.50. McGraw

White, Abraham, and others. Principles of biochemistry. 1959. 15.00. McGraw

Zamenhof, Stephen. Chemistry of heredity. il. 1959. 4.25. Thomas, C. C

BIOLOGICAL PHYSICS (574.1)

Rashevsky, Nicolas. Mathematical biology of social behavior. 1960. 6.75. U. of Chicago

BIOLOGISTS (920)

Humphrey, Harry B. Makers of North American botany. 1961. 6.00. Ronald

BIOLOGY (574)

Avery, George S., ed. Survey of biological progress. 4 vols. vol. 1, 1949, 8.00; vol. 2, 1952, 8.00; vol. 3, ed. by Bentley Glass, 1957, 7.50; vol. 4, 1962, 10.00. Academic Press

Baitsell, George Alfred. Human biology. il. 1950. 7.95. McGraw

Barnett, Samuel A., ed. Century of Darwin. il. 1958, 5.75. Harvard

Bates, Marston. Nature of natural history. 1962. 4.50. Scribner

Bell, Peter R. Darwin's biological work. 1959. 7.50. Cambridge U. P.

Biot, Rene. What is life? tr. by Eric Earnshaw Smith, 1959. 3.50. Hawthorne

Gamow, G. Mr. Tompkins learns the facts of life. 1953. 2.95. Cambridge U. P.

Graubard, Mark. Foundations of life science. il. 1958. 7.25. Van Nostrand

Hall, T., and F. Moog. Life science. 1955. 6.95. Wiley.

Hardin, Garrett. Biology: Its principles and implications. il. 1961. 8.50. Freeman

Henderson, Lawrence J. Fitness of the environment. 1959. 4.00. Smith, Peter

Hensill, John Samuel. Biology of man. 1954. 6.95. McGraw

Huxley, Julian. New bottles for new wine. il. 1958. 5.00. Harper

Johnson, Willis H., and others. General biology. 1961. 7.95. 3.50. Holt, Rinehart & Winston

Jones, F. Wood. Trends of life. 2.50. St. Martins

Knobloch, Irving W., ed. Readings in biological science. 3.00. Appleton

Life Magazine. Wonders of life on earth. by the Editors of Life and Lincoln Barnett. il. 1960, 12.50; Prentice-Hall

Marshall, A. Milnes. Frog: An introduction to anatomy, histology, and embryology. ed. by H. G. Newth. 1957. 2.25. St. Martins

Marsland, Douglas. Principles of modern biology. 1957. 7.50. Holt, Rinehart & Winston

Mavor, James W. General biology. il. 7.50. Macmillan

Platt, Rutherford. River of life. 1956. 5.00; 1962. S. and S.

Rogers, J. S., and others. Man and the biological world. 1952. 7.95. McGraw

Rostand, Jean. Can man be modified? 1959. 3.00. Basic Books

Simpson, George Gaylord, and others. Life: An introduction to biology. il. 1957. 11.00. Harcourt

Stanford, Ernest E. Man and the living world. il. 6.75. Macmillan

Stauffer, Andrew, ed. Introductory biology. il. 1954. 7.50. Van Nostrand

Waddington, C. H. Strategy of the genes. il. 4.00. Macmillan

Weimer, B. R. Man and the animal world. 1951. 6.50. Wiley

Winchester, A. M. Biology and its relation to mankind. il. 1957. 8.00. Van Nostrand

Woodger, J. H. Biology and language. 1952. 9.50. Cambridge U. P.
Young, Clarence W., and G. Ledyard Stebbins. Human organism and the world
    of life. 1951. 7.00. Harper

BIOLOGY--DICTIONARIES (574)
Abercrombie, M., and others. Dictionary of biology. 5.00. Aldine (R)
Clapper, Russell B. Glossary of genetics and other biological terms. 1960.
    3.95. Vantage (R)
Gray, Peter. Encyclopedia of biological sciences. il. 1961. 20.00. Reinhold
    (R)
Henderson, I. F., and W. D. Dictionary of scientific terms. by John H. Kenneth.
    1961. 12.50. Van Nostrand (R)
Jaeger, Edmund C. Biologist's handbook of pronunciations. il. 1960. 6.75.
    Thomas, C. C (R)

BIOLOGY--HISTORY (574)
Bodenheimer, F. S. History of biology. 1958. 10.00. Bentley
Dawes, Ben. Hundred years of biology. il. 1952. 5.00. Macmillan
Gabriel, Mordecai, and S. Fogel, eds. Great experiments in biology. 1955.
    3.95. Prentice-Hall
Gardner, Eldon J. History of life science. il. 1960. pap. 4.75. Burgess
Locy, William A. Biology and its makers. il. 1915. 6.95. Holt
Moore, Ruth, Coil of life. il. 1960. 5.95. Knopf

BIOLOGY--PHILOSOPHY (574)
Agar, W. E. Contribution to the theory of the living organism. 1952. 5.50. Cam-
    bridge U. P.
Arber, Agnes. Mind and the eye. 1954. 3.75. Cambridge U. P.
Beck, William S. Modern science and the nature of life. 1957. 5.75. Harcourt
Beckner, Morton. Biological way of thought. 1959. 6.00. Columbia
Elsasser, Walter M. Physical foundation of biology: An analytical study. 4.75.
    Pergamon
MacIver, Robert M. Life: Its dimensions and its bounds. 1960. 3.50. Harper
Sinnott, Edmund W. Matter, mind and man. 1957. 3.50. Harper

BIOLOGY--TABLES, ETC. (574)
National Academy of Science. Handbook of biological data. 1956. 7.50. Saunders
    (R)

BIOLOGY--TERMINOLOGY (574)
Jaeger, Edmund C. Source book of biological names and terms. il. 1959. 5.75.
    Thomas, C. C. (R)

BIOMATHEMATICS (510)
Rashevsky, Nicolas. Mathematical principles in biology and their applications.
    1961. 6.00. Thomas, C. C.

BIRDS
Allen, Arthur A. Book of bird life. 1961. il. 9.75. 7.50. Van Nostrand
Allen, G. M. Birds and their attributes. 4.00. Smith, Peter
Audubon, J. J. Audubon and his journals. 2 vols. ed. by Maria Audubon. il.
    8.00. Smith, Peter
Austin, Oliver L., Jr. Birds of the world. il. 1961. 14.95; lib. bdg. 11.98
    net. 16.95. Golden Press
Collins, Henry. Bird watcher's guide. il. 1961. 2.95. Golden Press.
Cruickshank, Allan and Helen. 1001 questions answered about birds. il. 1958.
    5.00. Dodd (R)
Gilliard, E. Thomas. Living birds of the world. il. 1958. 6.95. Doubleday
Peterson, Roger Tory. How to know the birds. il. 1962. 3.50. Houghton
Wallace, George J. Introduction to ornithology. il. 1955. 6.00. Macmillan

BIRDS--ANATOMY (598.2)
Worden, A. N. Functional anatomy of birds. il. 1957. 2.25. All-Pets

BIRDS--EGGS AND NESTS (598.25)
Headstrom, Richard. Birds' nests: A field guide. il. 1961. 3.95. Washburn

BIRDS--HABITS AND BEHAVIOR (598.2)
Bent, Arthur C. Bent's life histories of North American birds. ed. by Henry
  H. Collins, Jr. 2 vols. vol. 1. Water birds. vol. 2. Land birds. il.
  1960. 5.95 ea. Harper (R)
Bent, Arthur C. Life histories of North American birds of prey. 2 vols. il.
  1961. 2.35 ea. Dover (R)
Edminster, Frank C. American game birds of field and forest. il. 1954. 12.50.
  Scribner
BIRDS--MIGRATION (598.252)
Dorst, Jean. Migration of birds. il. 1962. 6.75. Houghton*
BIRDS--PICTORIAL WORKS (598.2)
Gilliard, E. Thomas. Living birds of the world. il. 1958. 6.95. Doubleday
Murphy, Robert C., and Dean Amadon. Land birds of America. il. 1953. 7.95.
BIRDS--AMERICA (598.2)
Griscom, Ludlow, and others. Warblers of America. il. 1957. 15.00. Devin
BIRDS--AUSTRALIA AND NEW ZEALAND (598.2)
Chisholm Alec H. Bird wonders of Australia. 1958. 5.00. Mich State
BIRDS--EUROPE (598.2)
Peterson, Roger Tory, and others. Field guide to birds of Britain and Europe.
  il. 1954. 4.95. Houghton
BIRDS--NORTH AMERICA (598.2)
Audubon, John James. Birds of America. il. 11.95. Macmillan (R)
Bent, Arthur C. Life histories of North American cuckoos, goatsuckers, hum-
  mingbirds, and their allies. in prep. Dover
Bent, Arthur C. Life histories of North American jays, crows, and titmice
  in prep. Dover
Bent, Arthur C. Life histories of North American woodpeckers. in prep.
  Dover
Cruickshank, Allan D. Cruickshank's pocket guide to the birds. il. 1953.
  2.95. Dodd
Day, Albert M. North American waterfowl. il. 1959. 5.75. Stackpole
Forbush, Edward H. Natural history of American birds of eastern and central
  North America. ed. by John R. May. 1939. il. 12.50. Houghton
Kortright, Francis H. Ducks, geese and swans of North America. il. 1953.
  7.50. Stackpole
Pearson, T. Gilbert. Brids of America. il. 1936. 6.95. Doubleday (R)
Peterson, Roger Tory. Field guide to the birds. il. 1947. 4.95. Houghton
BIRDS--U.S. (598.297)
Fisher, James, and R. M. Lockley. Sea-birds. il. 1954. 6.00. Houghton
Forbush, Edward H. Natural history of American birds of eastern and central
  North America ed. by John R. May. 1939. il. 12.50. Houghton
Headstrom, Richard. Bird's nests of the West: A field guide. il 1951. 3.00.
  Washburn
Peterson, Roger Tory. Field guide to western birds. il. 1961. 4.95. Houghton
  (R)
Pough, Richard H. Audubon water bird guide. il 1951. 3.95. Doubleday
Pough, Richard H. Audubon Western bird guide. il. 1957. 3.95. Doubleday (R)
Saunders, Aretas A. Guide to bird songs. il. 1959. 3.50 . Doubleday
BIRDS--PROTECTION OF (598.201)
Welker, R. H. Birds and men: American birds in science, art, literature, and
  conservation, 1800-1900. il. 1955. Harvard
BIRTH CONTROL(613.943)
Bates, Marston. Prevalence of people. 1955. 3.95: Scribner
Freedman, R., and others. Family planning, sterility and population growth.
  1959. 9.50. McGraw
Guttmacher, Alan F. Babies by choice or by chance. 1959. 3.95. Doubleday
Vogt, William. People? Challenge to survival. 1960. 4.50. Sloane

BIRTH CONTROL--RELIGIOUS ASPECTS (232. 921)

Fagley, Richard M. Population explosion and Christian responsibility. 1960.
4. 25. Oxford U. P.

Lestapis, Stanislas. Family planning and modern problems. 1961. 6 50.
Herder & Herder, N. Y. C.

Narramore, Clyde M. Christian view of birth control. 1961. pap. 0. 50.
Zondervan

Rehwinkel, Alfred M. Planned parenthood and birth control in the light of
Christian ethics. 1959. 2. 25. Concorida

BISHOPS (262. 12)

Urtasun, Josef. What is a bishop? 1962. 3. 50. Hawthorn

BISON, AMERICAN (799. 277)

Sandoz, Mari. Buffalo hunters. il. 1954. 4. 95. Hastings

BIZET, GEORGES, 1838-1875 (927)

Curtiss, Mina K. Bizet and his world. il. 1958. 7. 50. Knopf

BLAKE, WILLIAM, 1757-1827 (821. 79)

Blunt, Anthony F. Art of William Blake. il. 1959. 6. 95. Columbia

Damon, S. Foster. William Blake, his philosophy and symbols. 12. 50. Smith,
Peter

Rudd, Margaret. Divided image: A study of Blake and Yeats 5. 00. Hillary

BLANSHARD, PAUL, 1892- (920)

O'Neill, James M. Catholicism and American freedom. 1952. 3. 75. Harper

BLIND (655. 38)

Carroll, Thomas J. Blindness: What it is, what it does, and how to live with
it. 1961. 6. 50. Little

Farrell, Gabriel. Story of blindness. 1956. 4. 50. Harvard

Hartwell, Dickson. Dogs against darkness. il. 1960. 3. 50. Dodd

BLIND--PERSONAL NARRATIVES (920. 7)

Keller, Helen. Story of my life. il. 1954. 3. 95. Doubleday

BLIND--PRINTING AND WRITING SYSTEMS (655. 38)

Loomis, Madeleine Seymour. Standard English braille. 1934. 1. 25. Harper

BLOOD (612. 11)

Asimov, Isaac. Living river. 1959. 3. 95. Abelard

Dreyfus, Camille. Some milestones in the history of hematology. il. 1957.
4. 75. Grune

Glynn, John H. Story of blood. 3. 00. Wyn

Henderson, Lawrence J. Blood: A story in general physiology. 1928. 5. 00.
Yale

Kato, K. Atlas of clinical hematology. il. 1960. 25. 00. Grune (R)

Macfarlane, R. G., and A. H. T. Robb-Smith, eds. Functions of the blood. 1961.
16. 80. Academic Press

Seeman, Bernard. River of life. il. 1961. 4. 50. Norton

BLOOD--ANALYSIS AND CHEMISTRY (616. 075)

Gray, Charles H., and Alfred L. Bacharach, eds. Hormones in blood. il. 1961.
20. 00. Academic Press

Kugelmass, I. Newton. Biochemistry of blood in health and disease. il. 1959.
15. 75. Thomas C. C

Pollak, Otaker, Jeroslav. Grouping, typing, and banking of blood. il. 1951. 5. 75.
Thomas, C. C.

BLOOD--CIRCULATION (612. 11)

Doby, Tibor. Discoverers of blood circulation. il. 1962. 6. 50. Abelard

Gregg, Donald E. Coronary circulation in health and disease. il. 1950. 4. 50.
Lea & F

Harvey, William. Motion of the heart and blood. 1. 95. Dutton

Montagna, W., and others, eds. Blood vessels and circulation. 1961. 10. 00.
Pergamon

National Academy of Science. Handbook of circulation. 1959. pap. 7. 50.
Saunders (R)

BLOOD--CIRCULATION, DISORDERS OF (616.15)

National Academy of Science. Handbook of circulation. 1959. 7.50. Saunders

Wood, Paul. Diseases of the heart and circulation. il. 1952. 17.50. Lippincott

BLOOD--COAGULATION (615.718)

Morawitz, Paul. Chemistry of blood coagulation. il. 1958. 4.50. Thomas, C. C

BLOOD--DISEASES (616.15)

Meulengracht, E., and others. Symposium on the blood and blood-forming organs. il. 1946. 3.50. U. of Wis.

Whitby, Lionel E. H., and C. J. C. Britton. Disorders of the blood. il. 1957. 12.00. Grune

BLOOD PRESSURE (612.14)

Burch, George E., and Nicholas P. DePasquale. Primer of the clinical measurement of blood pressure. il. 1962. 5.50. Mosby

D'Alonzo, Constance A. Heart disease, blood pressure and strokes. il. 1960. 3.50. Gulf

Master, Arthur M., and others. Normal blood pressure and hypertension: New definitions. il. 1952. 4.00. Lea & F

BLUE-PRINTS (744.5)

Coover, Shriver L. Drawing, sketching, and blueprint reading. il. 1954. 5.60. McGraw

Coover, Shriver L. Industrial arts drawing and blueprint reading. 1961. 4.80. McGraw

Daizell, James R. Blueprint reading for home builders. 1955. 7.50. McGraw

Heine, Gilbert M., and others. How to read electrical blueprints. il. 1954. 4.75; study guide, 1.25. Am. Tech. Soc.

Ihne, Russel W., and Walter E. Streeter. Machine trades blueprint reading. 4th ed. il. 3.50. Am. Tech. Soc.

Nicholson, Fred, and others. Blueprint reading. il. 1959. 4.20. Van Nostrand

Spencer, Henry C., and Hiram E. Grant. Blueprint language. il. 1947. 5.75. Macmillan

BOARD GAMES (794.2)

Bell, Robert C. Board and table games from many civilizations. il. 1960. half cl. 5.00. Oxford U. P.

BOAS, FRANZ, 1858-1942 (572.081)

Goldschmidt, Walter, ed. Anthropology of Franz Boas. 1959. 3.50. Chandler Pub.

BOAT-BUILDING (623.822)

Baay, Henry Van L. Boats, boat yards, and yachtsmen. il. 1961. 6.50. Van Nostrand

Chapelle, Howard I. American small sailing craft. il. 1951. 10.00. Norton

Crockett, V. B. Designing small boats for fun and profit. il. 1953. 10.00. Van Nostrand

Verney, Michael. Complete amateur boat building. 3.95. Macmillan

BOATS AND BOATING (797.1)

Aymar, Brandt, and John Marshall. Guide to boatmanship, seamanship, and safe boat handling. il. 1960. 2.95. Chilton

Brindze, R., ed. Expert's book of boating. 1959. 5.95. Prentice-Hall

De Fontaine, Wade H. 1001 questions answered about boats and boating. il. 1962. 6.00. Dodd

Hutchinson, James. All about boats. il. 1958. 2.95. Hawthorn

Lane, Carl D. Boatman's manual. il. 1962. 6.95. Norton

McKeown, William T., ed. Boating in America. il. 1960. 3.95. Barnes, A. S.

Scharff, Robert A. Complete boating handbook. 1955. 6.95. McGraw (R)

Stanford, Alfred. Boatman's handbook. 1959. 1.50. DeGraff

BODY FLUIDS (612.017)

Gaunt, Robert, and James Birnie. Hormones and body water. il. 1951. 2.25. Thomas, C. C

Snively, William D., Jr. Sea within: Story of our body fluid. il. 1960. 3.95. Lippincott

Strauss, Maurice. Body water in man. 1957. 7. 00. Little
BODY SIZE (573. 6)
Weyl, Peter. Men, ants and elephants: Size in the animal world. il. 1959.
   3. 00. Viking
BODY TEMPERATURE (612. 5)
Selle, W. A. Body temperature. il. 1952. lexide. 3. 50. Thomas, C. C
BOERS (968)
Patterson, S. Last trek: A study of the Boer people and the Afrikaner
   nation. 5. 50. Hillary
BOHEMIANISM (301. 15)
Parkinson, Thomas F., ed. Casebook on the beat. 1961. 3. 95. Crowell
Parry, Albert. Garrets and pretenders, a history of Bohemianism in America.
   il. 4. 00. Smith, Peter
BOHR, NIELS HENRIK DAVID, 1885- (925)
Pauli, W., ed. Niels Bohr and the development of physics. 1955. 4. 50.
   Pergamon
BOLIVAR, SIMON, 1783-1830 (923. 198)
Masur, Gerhard. Simon Bolivar. 5. 00. U. of N. Mex.
Van Loon, Hendrik Willem. Fighters for freedom: Jefferson and Bolivar. il.
   4. 00. Dodd
BOLIVIA (918. 4)
Arnade, Charles W. Emergence of the Republic of Bolivia. 1957. 6. 50. U. of
   Fla.
Osborne, Harold. Bolivia. 1955. 2. 90. Oxford U. P.
BOMBING, AERIAL (358. 42)
Ikle, Fred C. Social impact of bomb destruction. il. 1958. 3. 95. U. of Okla.
Saundby, Robert. Air bombardment. il. 1961. 5. 00. Harper
BONDS (332. 6)'
Robinson, Roland I. Postwar market for State and loval government securities.
   il. 1960. 5. 00. Princeton
BONE (611)
Ciba Foundation. Bone structure and metabolism. 1956. 9. 00. Little
McLean, Franklin C., and Marshall R. Urist. Bone: An introduction to the
   physiology of skeletal tissue. 1961. 6. 00. U. of Chicago
BONES--DISEASES (616. 41)
Aegerter, Ernest E., and John A. Kirkpatrick, Jr. Orthopedic diseases:'
   Physiology, pathology, radiology. il. 1958. 12. 50. Saunders
Luck, J. Vernon. Bone and joint diseases: Pathology correlated with roent-
   genological and clinical features. il. 1950. 18. 50. Thomas C. C
Snapper, I. Bone diseases in medical practice. 1957. 15. 75. Grune
BONN--DESCRIPTION--GUIDEBOOKS (914. 3)
Baedeker, Karl. Cologne and Bonn, with environs. 1961. 3. 50. Macmillan (R)
BONNARD, PIERRE, 1867-1947 (927)
Rewald, John, Pierre Bonnard. il. 3. 00. Doubleday
BOOK COLLECTING (010)
Bradley, Van Allen. Gold in your attic. 1958. 5. 95. Fleet
Bradley, Van Allen. More gold in your attic. il. 1961. 5. 95. Fleet
Everitt, Charles P. Adventures of a treasure hunter: A rare book dealer in
   search of American history. 1951. 5. 00. Little
BOOK INDUSTRIES AND TRADE (655. 5)
UNESCO. Books for all: A study of international book trade. 3. 00. Int.
   Doc. Service-Columbia
Wright, Wyllis E., and Phyllis Steckler, eds. Bowker annual of library and
   book trade information. 6. 95. Bowker
BOOK OF THE DEAD (893)
Massey, Gerald. Egyptian book of the dead. 3. 00. Borden
BOOK SELECTION (025. 21)
Fiske, Marjorie. Book selection and censorshipL A study of school and public
   libraries in California; 1959. 3. 75. U. of Calif.

Haines, H. E. Living with books. 1950. 6.00. Columbia
Smith, Lillian H. Unreluctant years: a critical approach to children's literature. 1953. 4.50. A. L. A.
BOOKBINDING--REPAIRING (025.7)
Lydenberg, Harry M., and John Archer. Care and repair of books. by John
    Alden. 1960. 6.15. Bowker
BOOKKEEPING (657.2)
Breidenbaugh, Vachel E., and others. Bookkeeping principles. 1958. 3.40. '
    Pitman
Hammond, W. R. How to solve introductory accounting problems. 2.95.
    Prentice-Hall
BOOKS (002)
McMurtrie, D. C. Book: Story of printing and bookmaking. rev. il. 1943. 11.00.
    Oxford U. P.
BOOKS--HISTORY (002)
Dahl, Svend. History of the book. il. 1958. 6.00. Scarecrow
Rogers, Frances. Painted rock to printed page. il. 1960. 3.50. Lippincott
BOOKS--REVIEWING AND REVIEWS (028.1)
Book review digest. Annuals
Davies, Robertson. Voice from the attic. 1960. 4.75. Knopf
Haydn, Hiram, and Edmund Fuller, eds. Thesaurus of book digests. 1949.
    pap. 1.95. Crown (R)
Highet, Gilbert. People, places, and books. 1953. 3.50. Oxford U. P.
James, Henry. Literary reviews and essays. ed. by Albert Mordell. 10.00.
    Twayne
James, Henry. Literary reviews and essays on American, English, and French
    literature. ed. by Albert Mordell. 1962. 2.95. College & Univ.
Keller, Helen R. Reader's digest of books. 7.50. Macmillan (R)
Lawrence, David Herbert. Selected literary criticism. ed. by Anthony Beal.
    1956. 5.00. Viking
Mansfield, K. Novels and novelists. 1959. pap. 1.65. Beacon
Merritt, LeRoy C., and others. Reviews in library book selection. 1958. pap.
    2.50. Wayne
Oppenheimer, Evelyn. Book reviewing for an audience. 1962. 3.50. Chilton
Schorer, Mark, ed. Modern British fiction. 1961. 2.25. Oxford U. P.
Schorer, Mark, ed. Modern British fiction, essays in criticism. 1962. 4.25.
    Smith, Peter (R)
Walker, Elinor, ed. Book bait: Detailed notes on adult books popular with
    young people. 1957. 1.25. A. L. A.
BOOKS AND READING (028)
Adler, Mortimer J. How to read a book. 1956. 1.75. S. and S.
Altick, Richard D. English common reader: A social history of the mass
    reading public. 1800-1900. 1957. 6.00. U. of Chicago
Bauer, Harry C. Seasoned to taste. 1961. 4.75. U. of Wash.
Bennett, James O'Donnell. Much loved books. 3.95. Liveright
Berenson, Bernard. One year's reading for fun. il. 1960. 5.00. Knopf
Cook, Margaret G. New library key. Wilson
Cowley, Malcolm, and Bernard Smith. Books that changed our minds. 3.50.
    Russell (R)
Downs, Robert B. Books that changed the world. 1956. 2.25. A. L. A.
Duff, Annis. Bequest of wings: A family's pleasures with books. 1944. 3.00.
    Viking
Duff, Annis. Longer flight: A family grows up with books. il. 1955. 3.00.
    Viking
Haines, H. E. Living with books. 1950. 6.00. Columbia
Hirschberg, Cornelius. Priceless gift. 1960. 4.95. S. and S.
Mersand, Joseph E. Attitudes toward English teaching. 1961. 4.00. Chilton
Price, Jacob M., ed. Reading for life: Developing the college student's life-
    time reading interest. 1959. 6.00. U. of Mich.

Stefferud, Alfred, ed. Wonderful world of books. 1953. 2.00. Houghton

BOOKSELLERS AND BOOKSELLING (016)

Hoffman, Hester R., ed. Reader's adviser and bookman's manual. 1960. 15.00. Bowker (R)

O. P. market 1962: Reference directory of antiquarian and specialist booksellers. pap. 1.00. Antiquarian Bookman

Steiner-Prag, Elenor F., ed. American book trade directory. 1961. 25.00. net postpaid. Bowker (R)

BOOTH, EDWIN, 1833-1893 (927.92)

Ruggles, Eleanor. Prince of players: Edwin Booth il. 1953. 5.00. Norton

BORAH, WILLIAM EDGAR, 1865-1940 (923.2)

McKenna, Marian C. Borah. il. 1961. 7.50. U. of Mich.

BORGIA, LUCREZIA, 1480-1519 (945.06)

Bellonci, Maria. Life and times of Lucrezia Borgia. 1957. 1.65. Grossett

BORGLUM, JOHN GUTZON DE LA MOTHE, 1867-1941 (927)

Fite, Gilbert C. Mount Rushmore. il. 1952. 3.75. U. of Okla.

Price, Willadene. Gutzon Borglum: Artist and patriot. il. 1961. 3.50. Rand

BOSCH, HIERONYMUS VAN AKEN, KNOWN AS, d. 1516 (927)

Delevoy, Robert L. Bosch. il. 1960. 5.75. World Pub.

BOSTON (974.46)

Chiang Yee. Silent travelier in Boston. il. 1959. 6.95. Norton

Handlin, Oscar. Boston's immigrants: A study of acculturation. il. 1959. 6.75. Harvard

Ross, Marjorie. Book of Boston: Colonial Period. il. 1960. 3.50. Hastings

BOSTON--SOCIAL LIFE AND CUSTOMS (974.46)

Amory, Cleveland. Proper Bostonians. 5.00; (D2) Dutton

Grund, Francis J. Aristocracy in America. 1959. 3.75. Smith, Peter

BOSWELL, JAMES, 1740-1795 (928.2)

Carlyle, T. Essays. English and other critical essays. 1.95. Dutton

Pearson, Hesketh. Johnson and Boswell. il. 1958. 5.50. Harper

BOTANICAL CHEMISTRY (581.19)

Davies, D. D., and others. Plant biochemistry. il. 1962. 7.95? Davis

Foster, Jackson W. Chemical activities of fungi. 1949. 12.00. Academic Press

BOTANY (580)

Bold, Harold C. Plant kingdom. il. 1960. 8.75. Prentice-Hall

Botanical Society of America. Fifty years of botany, ed. by W. C. Steere. 1958. 10.50. McGraw

Braungart, Dale C., and Ross H. Arnett, Jr. Introduction to plant biology. il. 1962. 7.00. Mosby

Brown, William Henry. Plant kingdom. 8.75. Ginn

Clarkson, Quentin D. Handbook of field botany. il. 1961. 2.00. Binfords (R)

Coulter, Merle Crowe. Story of the plant kingdom. rev. ed. by Howard J. Dittmer. 1959. 5.00. U. of Chicago

Darlington, C. D. Chromosome botany. il. 2.75. Macmillan

Dodd, John D. Form and function in plants. 1961. 6.50. Iowa State

Fuller, Harry J., and Oswald Tippo. College botany. il. 1954. 8.95. Holt

Godwin, H. Plant biology. 1945. 3.25. Cambridge U. P.

Harrington, H. D. How to identify plants. il. by L. W. Durrell. 1957. 3.00. Swallow, A.

Johansen, Donald. Plant microtechnique. 1940. 9.90. McGraw

Platt, Rutherford. This green world. il. 6.00. Dodd

Sinnott, Edmund W., and Katherine S. Wilson. Botany. 1955. 7.95; laboratory manual, 3.95. McGraw

BOTANY--ANATOMY (581.4)

Carlquist, Sherwin. Comparative plant anatomy. 1961. 5.00. Holt, Rinehart & Winston

Eames, Arthur, and Laurence MacDaniels. An introduction to plant anatomy. 1947. 8.50. McGraw

Esau, Katherine. Anatomy of seed plants. il. 1960. 6.95. Wiley
Esau, K. Plant anatomy. 1953. 9.75. Wiley'
Metcalfe, Charles R. Anatomy of the monocotyledons. vol. 1. Gramineae. il.
    1960. 14.40; vol. 2. Palmae. by T. B. Tomlinson. 1961. 10.10. Oxford U. P.
Metcalfe, C. R., and L. Chalk. Anatomy of the dicotyledons. il. 2 vols. 1950.
    set. 30.25. Oxford U. P.
Sass, John E. Botanical microtechnique. il. 1958. 4.50. Iowa State

BOTANY--CLASSIFICATION (580.12)

Benson, Lyman. Plant classification. il. 1956. 11.50. Heath
Core, Earl L. Plant taxonomy. 1955. 10.65. Prentice-Hall
Jaques, Harry E. Plant families, how to know them. 1949. 2.50. Brown, W. C.
Lawrence, George H. M. Introduction to plant taxonomy. il. 1955. 4.25.
    Macmillan
Lawrence, George H. M. Taxonomy of vascular plants. il. 1951. 9.75.
    Macmillan
Porter, Cedric L. Taxonomy of flowering plants. 1960. 6.75. Freeman
Rendle, A. B. Classification of flowering plants. 2 vols. vol. 1, Gymnosperms
    and monocotyledons; vol. 2, Dicotyledons. 8.50 ea. Cambridge U. P.

BOTANY--DICTIONARIES (580.3)

Bailey, Liberty H., and Ethel Z. Bailey. Hortus second. 13.50. Macmillan (R)
Davydov, A. Russian-English-French-German-Latin botanical dictionary. 5.00.
    San Francisco (R)
Featherly, H. I. Taxonomic terminology of the higher plants. 1954. 3.95. Iowa
    State (R)
Jackson, Benjamin D. Glossary of botanic terms. 1953. 4.50. Hafner (R)
Willis, J. C. Flowering plants and ferns. 1931. 5.50. Cambridge U. P.

BOTANY--ECOLOGY (581.5)

Ashby, Maurice. Introduction to plant ecology. il. 1961. 5.75. St. Martins
Clements, Edith S. Adventures in ecology. 1960. 5.00. Pageant
Daubenmire, Rexford F. Plants and environment. il. 1957. 6.95. Wiley
Hylander, Clarence J. Flowers of field and forest. il. 1962. 4.50. Macmillan (R)
Leach, W. Plant ecology. 1957. 2.00. Wiley
Munz, Philip A., and David D. Keck. California flora. il. 1959. 11.50. U. of
    Calif.
Newbigin, Marion I. Plant and animal geography. by H. J. Fleure. 5.50. Dutton
Polunin, Nicholas. Introduction to plant geography. 1960. 10.50. McGraw
UNESCO. Plant ecology: Review of research. 8.00. Int. Doc. Service-Columbia

BOTANY--MORPHOLOGY (581.4)

Bold, Harold C. Morphology of plants. 1957. 9.25. Harper
Eames, Arthur J. Morphology of the angiosperms. il. 1961. 13.50. McGraw
Eames, Arthur. Morphology of vascular plants - lower groups. 1936. 10.00.
    McGraw
Haupt, A. W. Plant morphology. il. 1953. 9.00. McGraw
Sass, John E. Botanical microtechnique. il. 1958. 4.50. Iowa State

BOTANY--NOMENCLATURE (580.1)

American Joint Committee on Horticultural Nomenclature. Standardized plant
    names. 2nd ed. 1942. 10.50. McFarland, J. Horace (R)
Johnson, Arthur T. Plant names simplified. il. 1951. 2.00. Transatlantic
St. John, H. Nomenclature of plants. 1958. 3.00. Ronald (R)

BOTANY--U.S. (581.973)

Abrams, LeRoy. Illustrated flora of the Pacific States. 4 vols. vol. 1. Ferns
    to birthworts. 1923. 17.50; vol. 2. Buckwheats to kramerias. 1944. 17.50;
    vol. 3. Geraniums to figworts. 1951. 17.50; vol. 4. Ferris, Roxanna S. Big-
    nonias to Sunflowers. 1960. 17.50. Stanford
Bailey, Liberty H. Manual of cultivated plants. il. 1949. 19.50. Macmillan
Clements, Edith S. Adventures in ecology. 1960. 5.00. Pageant
Coon, Nelson. Using wayside plants. il. 1960. 3.95. Hearthside
Dutton, Joan P. Enjoying America's gardens. il. 1958. 5.00. Reynal

Gray, Asa. Manual of botany. il. 15.00. Am. Bk. Co. (R)
Hylander, Clarence J. World of plant life. il. 1956. 10.95. Macmillan (R)
Jaeger, Edmund C. Desert wild flowers. 1941. 5.00. Stanford
Martin, Alexander C., and others. American wildlife and plants, a guide to
    wildlife food habits. 4.00. Smith, Peter
Medsger, Oliver P. Edible wild plants. il. 1939. 6.50. Macmillan
Muenscher, W. C. Poisonous plants of the United States. rev. ed. il. 5.95.
    Macmillan
Small, John K. Manual of the southeastern flora. 1953. 12.50. U. of N.C.

BOTANY, ECONOMIC (581.6)
Balls, Edward K. Early uses of California plants. il. 1962. 1.75. U. of Calif.
Hill, Albert Frederick. Economic botany. il. 1952. 9.50. McGraw
Marx, David S. American book of the woods. 1940. 2.50. Botanic
Stanford, Ernest Elwood. Economic plants. il. 5.50. Appleton
Uphof, J. C. T. Dictionary of economic plants. 1959. 10.00. Hafner (R)

BOTANY, MEDICAL (581)
Culpeper, Nicholas. Culpeper's complete herbal. il. 1959. 4.50. Sterling
Nelson, Alexander. Medical botany. il. 1951. 6.50. Williams & Wilkins
Wren, R. C. Potter's New cyclopaedia of botanical drugs and preparations. 7th
    ed. 1956. 10.00. Pitman (R)

BOTTICELLI, SANDRO, 1447?-1510 (927)
Argan, Guilio Carlo. Botticelli. il. 1957. 5.75. in English, French, or
    German. World Pub.
Botticelli, Sandro. Botticelli. ed. by Lionello Venturi. il. 1961. 5.95. N. Y.
    Graphic
Chastel, Andre. Botticelli. il. 1958. 22.50. N. Y. Graphic

BOWEN, ELIZABETH (MRS. ALAN CHARLES CAMERON) 1899- (813)
Heath, William. Elizabeth Bowen: An introduction to her novels. 1961. 4.50.
    U. of Wis.

BOWIE, JAMES, 1805-1836 (923.9)
Baugh, Virgil E. Rendezvous at the Alamo. il. 1960. 3.50. Pageant

BOWLING (794.6)
Carter, Don. Ten secrets of bowling. il. 1958. 2.95. Viking
Fraley, Oscar, and Charles Yerkow. Complete handbook of bowling. 1958. 3.50.
    Prentice-Hall

BOXING (796.83)
Durant, John. Heavyweight champions. il. 1960. 3.95. Hastings
Fleisher, Nat. Fifty years at ringside. il. 1958. 4.95. Fleet
Haislet, E. L. Boxing. 1940. 2.95. Ronald

BOY SCOUTS (369.43)
Grant, Bruce, and others. Boy Scout encyclopedia. 2.95. Rand McNally
Reynolds, Ernest E. Baden-Powell: A biography of Lord Baden-Powell of
    Gilwell. 1957. 2.90. Oxford U. P.
Smith, Charles F. Games and recreational methods for clubs, camps, and
    scouts. il. 4.75. Dodd

BOYLE, ROBERT, 1627-1691 (925)
Boas, Marie. Robert Boyle and seventeenth century chemistry. 1958. 5.50.
    Cambridge U. P.

BOYS' CLUBS OF AMERICA (369.42)
Hall, William E. One hundred years and millions of boys: The dynamic story
    of the Boys' Clubs of America. il. 1961. 3.75. Farrar, Straus

BRADDOCK'S CAMPAIGN, 1755 (923.5)
Hamilton, Charles, ed. Braddock's defeat. il. 1959. 3.95. U. of Okla.

BRADFORD, WILLIAM, 1588-1657 (923.2)
Smith, Bradford. Bradford of Plymouth. 1951. 5.00. Lippincott

BRAHMANISM (181.4)
Radhakrishman, Sarvepalli. Indian philosophy. 2 vols. 1923-27. 12.00.
    Macmillan

BRAHMS, JOHANNES, 1833-1897 (927)
Geiringer, Karl. Brahms, his life and work. il. 1947. 7.50. Oxford U. P.
Latham, Peter, Brahms. 1949. 3.50. Farrar, Straus
BRAILLE, LOUIS, 1809-1852 (923.7)
DeGering, E. Seeing fingers: The story of Louis Braille. il. 1962. 2.95. McKay
BRAIN (612.821)
Angevine, Jay B., and others. Atlas of the human cerebellum. 1961. 15.00.
    Little (R)
Lassek, A. M. Human brain: From primitive to modern. 1957. 4.75. Thomas,
    C. C
Pfeifer, John. Human brain. 1955. 4.95. Harper
Rubinstein, Hyman S. Study of the brain. il. 1953. 10.00. Grune
Russell, W. Ritchie. Brain, memory, learning: A neurologist's view. 1959.
    5.00. Oxford U. P.
Stelmasiak, M. Anatomical atlas of the human brain and spinal cord. il. 1958.
    12.50. Hafner (R)
BRAIN--DISEASES (612.821)
Blackwood, William, and others. Atlas of neuropathology. in prep. Williams & Wilkins
Pickworth, F. A. New outlook on mental diseases. il. 1952. 12.00. Williams
    & Wilkins
BRAIN - WASHING (131.33)
Hunter, Edward. Brainwashing: Pavlov to Powers. 5.00. Bookmailer
Hutton, J. Bernard. Frogman spy. il. 1960. 3.50. Obolensky
Huxley, Aldous. Brave new world revisited. 1958. 3.50. Harper
Sargant, William. Battle for the mind. il. 1957. 4.50. Doubleday
Schein, Edgar H., and others. Coercive persuasion. 6.75. Norton
Winance, Eleutherius. Communist persuasion. 1959. 3.95. Kenedy
BRANDEIS, LOUIS DEMBITZ, 1856-1941 (923)
Mason, Alpheus Thomas. Brandeis: A free man's life. il. 1956. 7.50. Viking
BRANDYWINE, BATTLE OF, 1777 (973.341)
Canby, Henry Seidel. Brandywine. il. 1941. 4.00. Rinehart
BRAQUE, GEORGES, 1882- (921)
Flanner, Janet. Men and monuments. il. 1957. 5.00. Harper
Leymarie, Jean. Braque. 5.75. World Pub.
BRAZIL (981)
Hunnicutt, Benjamin Harris. Brazil: World frontier. il. 1949. 6.50. Van
    Nostrand
Kelsey, Vera. Seven Keys to Brazil. il. 1944. 3.00. Funk
BRAZIL--CIVILIZATION (981.1)
Freyre, Gilberto. New world in the Tropics: The culture of modern Brazil.
    1959. 5.00. Knopf
BRAZIL--DESCRIPTION AND TRAVEL (918.11)
Foster, Mulford B., and Racine S. Brazil: Orchid of the tropics. 1946. 5.00.
    Ronald
BRAZIL--FOREIGN RELATIONS (981.06)
Hill, Lawrence F. Diplomatic relations between the United States and Brazil.
    1932. 5.00. Duke
BRAZIL--HISTORY (981.01)
Haring, C. H. Empire in Brazil. il. 1958. 4.00. Harvard
Kelsey, Vera. Seven keys to Brazil. il. 1944. 3.00. Funk
BRAZIL--POLITICS AND GOVERNMENT--1930 (981)
Gunther, John. Inside Latin America. 1941. 6.00. Harper
BRAZIL--SOCIAL CONDITIONS (981.06)
Freyre, Gilberto. Masters and the slaves. 1956. 8.50. Knopf
Ramos, Arthur. Negro in Brazil. 4.25. Assoc. Publishers
Smith, T. Lynn. Brazil: People and institutions. il. 7.50. La. State
BRAZILIAN LITERATURE--HISTORY AND CRITICISM (981)
Ellison, Fred P. Brazil's new novel: Four Northeastern masters. Jose Lins

do Rego, Jorge Amado, Graciliano Ramos, Rachel de Queiroz. 1954. 3. 75.
U. of Calif.
BRAZILIAN LITERATURE--TRANSLATIONS INTO ENGLISH (860)
Onis, Harriet de, ed. Golden land: An anthology of Latin American folklore.
1948. 5. 75. Knopf
BREAD (664. 75)
Bennion, Edmund B. Breadmaking: Its principles and practice. 1954. 8. 00.
Oxford U. P.
BREAKAGE, SHRINKAGE, ETC. (COMMERCE) (343. 6)
Edwards, Loren E. Shoplifting and shrinkage protection for stores. 1958. 7. 50.
Thomas, C. C
BRECHT, BERTOLT, 1898-1956 (832. 912)
Demetz, Peter, ed. Brecht: A collection of critical essays: 1962. 3. 95. Prentice-
Hall
Esslin, Martin. Brecht: The man and his work. 1960. 4. 50. Doubleday
Willett, John. Theatre of Bertolt Brecht. 1958. 8. 00. New Directions
BRIDGER, JAMES, 1804-1881 (929)
Caesar, Gene. King of the mountain men. il. 1961. 4. 95. Dutton
BRIDGES, ROBERT SEYMOUR, 1844-1930 (928)
Wright, Elizabeth Cox. Metaphor, sound and meaning: A study of Robert
Bridges' The testament of beauty. 1951. 6. 50. U. of Pa.
BRIDGES (624. 2)
Jacoby, Henry Sylvester, and Roland Davis. Foundations of bridges and
buildings. 1941. 8. 95. McGraw
Smith, H. Shirley. World's great bridges. il. 1954. 3. 95. Harper
BRISTOL, ENGLAND (942. 41)
Carus-Wilson, Eleanora. Medieval merchant venturers. 6. 00. Humanities
BRITAIN, BATTLE OF, 1940 (942. 084)
Collier, Basil. Battle of Britain. il. 1962. 4. 50. Macmillan
McKee, Alexander. Strike from the sky. il. 1961. 4. 75. Little
Wood, Derek, and Derek Dempster. Narrow margin: The Battle of Britain
and the rise of air power 1930-40. il. 1961. 6. 50. McGraw
BRITISH GUIANA (988. 1)
Guppy, Nicholas. Wai-Wai: Through the forests north of the Amazon. il.
1958. 5. 95. Dutton
Smith, Raymond T. British Guiana. 1962. 4. 00. Oxford U. P.
Swan, M. Marches of El Dorado. 1958. 2. 50. Beacon
BRITISH HONDURAS (972. 82)
Waddell, D. A. G. British Honduras: A historical and contemporary survey.
1962. 2. 90. Oxford U. P.
BRITISH IN THE U. S. (973)
Berthoff, Rowland Tappan. British immigrants in industrial America, 1790-
1950. 1953. 5. 00. Harvard
BRITISH NORTH BORNEO (991. 15)
Keith, Agnes Newton. Land below the wind. il. 1939. 6. 00. Little
Keith, Agnes Newton. White man returns. il. 1951. 6. 00. Little
BRITTANY (944. 1)
Deruenn, Claude. Brittany. il. 4. 95. Tudor
Giot, P. R. Brittany. il. 1960. 6. 95. Praeger
BRONCHI (611. 23)
Brock, R. C. Anatomy of the bronchial tree. il. 1954. 11. 50. Oxford U. P.
Kassay, D. Clinical applications of bronchology. 1960. 15. 00. McGraw
BRONTE, ANNE 1820-1849 (928. 2)
Gerin, Winifred. Anne Bronte, a biography. 1959. 7. 50. Nelson
Harrison, Ada, and Derek Stanford. Anne Bronte. 1959. 6. 50. Day
BRONTE, CHARLOTTE, 1816-1855 (928. 2)
Gaskell, Mrs. Elizabeth C. Life of Charlotte Bronte. 1. 95. Dutton

BRONTE, EMILY JANE, 1818-1848 (928. 2)
Grandall, Norma. Emily Brontë: A psychological portrait. 3. 50. Smith,
    Richard R.
Visick, Mary. Genesis of Wuthering Heights. 1958. 2. 00. Oxford U. P.
BRONTE, PATRICK BRANWELL, 1817-1848 (928. 2)
Du Maurier, Daphne. Infernal world of Branwell Bronte. 1961. 4. 50. Doubleday
Gerin, Winifred. Branwell Bronte. 1961. 7. 50. Nelson
BRONTE FAMILY (928. 2)
Bentley, Phyllis. Bronte sisters. pap. 0. 50. British Bk.
BRONZE AGE (571. 3)
Fox, Cyril. Life and death in the Bronze Age. il. 1959. 8. 50. Humanities
BROOK FARM (335. 9)
Curtis, Edith R. Season in Utopia. 1961. 6. 95. Nelson
Swift, Lindsay. Brook Farm. 4. 00. Smith, Peter
BROUN, HEYWOOD CAMPBELL, 1888-1939 (928)
Kramer, Dale. Heywood Broun. 3. 50. Wyn
BROWN, CHARLES BROCKDEN, 1771-1810 (928. 2)
Clark, David Lee. Charles Brockden Brown: Pioneer voice of America. 1952.
    6. 00. Duke
Warfel, Harry R. Charles Brockden Brown: American Gothic novelist.
    1949. 4. 50. U. of Fla.
BROWN, JOHN, 1800-1859 (920)
Keller, Allan. Thunder at Harper's ferry. 1958. 4. 95. Prentice-Hall
Nelson, Truman J. Surveyor. il. 1960. 5. 95. Doubleday
Ruchames, Louis, ed. John Brown reader. 1959. 7. 50. Abelard
BROWNE, SIR THOMAS, 1605-1682 (929)
Finch, Jeremiah S. Sir Thomas Browne: A doctor's life of science and faith.
    il. 1950. 3. 50. Abelard
Merton, E. S. Science and imagination in Sir Thomas Browne. 1949. 2. 50.
    Columbia
BROWNING, ELIZABETH (BARRETT) 1806-1861 (928)
Porter, Katherine H. Through a glass darkly: Spiritualism in the Browning
    circle. 1958. 3. 50. U. of Kans.
Taplin, G. B. Life of Elizabeth Barrett Browning. 1957. 6. 50. Yale
Winwar, Frances. Immortal lovers. 1950. 5. 00. Harper
Besier, Rudolph. Barretts of Wimpole Street. il. 1930. 3. 75. Little
BROWNING, ROBERT, 1812-1889 (928)
Berdoe, Edward. Browning cyclopaedia. 4. 75. Macmillan (R)
Crowell, Norton B. Triple soul: Browning's theory of knowledge. U. of N. Mex.
De Vane, William C. Browning handbook. 1955. 6. 00. Appleton
Kenmare, Dallas. Browning love story. il. 5. 25. Transatlantic
BRUCELLOSIS IN CATTLE (636. 2)
Huddleson, I. Forest, and others. Brucellosis in man and animals. il. 1943. 3. 50.
    Harvard
BRUEGHEL, PEETER, THE ELDER, 1528-1569 (927)
Bruegel, Peter. Paintings of Bruegel. ed. by Fritz Grossman. il. 1955. 8. 50.
    (Phaidon) N. Y. Graphic
Delevoy, Robert L. Bruegel. il. 1959. in English, French or German. 5. 75.
    (Skira) World Pub.
BRUMMELL, GEORGE BRYAN, 1778-1840 (920. 8)
Franzero, Charles M. Beau Brummell, his life and times. il. 1958. 4. 50. Day
BRUSH DRAWING (741. 29)
Brooks, Leonard. Course in wash drawing. il. 1961. 4. 95. Reinhold
Carlson, C. X. Ink, pen, and brush. 1. 00. Sentinel
Fei Cheng-wu. Brush drawing in the Chinese manner. il. 1958. 6. 50. Viking
BRYAN, WILLIAM JENNINGS, 1860-1925 (923. 273)
Glad, Paul W. Trumpet soundeth: William Jennings Bryan and his democracy,
    1896-1912. il. 1960. 4. 75. U. of Nebr.

BUCCANEERS (923.41)
Burney, James. History of the buccaneers of America. 1951. 3.75. Norton
Kemp, Peter K., and Christopher Lloyd. Brethren of the coast. il. 1961.
4.95. St. Martins
MacLiesh, Fleming, and Martin L. Krieger. Privateers. 1962. 4.95. Random
BUCHANAN, JAMES, PRES. U.S., 1791-1868 (923.173)
Klein, Philip S. President James Buchanan. il. 1962. 7.50. Penn. State
BUCHENWALD (CONCENTRATION CAMP) (355)
Poller, Walter. Medical block Buchenwald. 1961. 4.95. Stuart, Lyle
BUDDHA AND BUDDHISM (294.3)
Arvon, Henri. Buddhism. 1962. 3.50. Walker
Asoka. Edicts of Asoka. ed. by N. A. Nikam and Richard P. McKeown. 1958.
1.75. U. of Chicago
Beck, L. Adams. Life of the Buddha. 1.85. Collins
Conze, Edward. Buddhism, its essence and development. 3.35. Smith, Peter
David-Neel, Alexandra. Magic and mystery in Tibet. 1958. 6.00. U. Books
Eliot, Charles. Hinduism and Buddhism: An historical sketch. 3 vols. 1954.
17.50. Barnes & Noble
Fausset, Hugh. Flame and the light: Meanings in Vedanta and Buddhism.
1958. 5.00. Abelard
Gard, Richard A. Buddhism. 1961. 4.00. Braziller
Humphreys, Christmas. Buddhism. pap. 0.95. Penguin
Humphreys, Christmas, ed. Wisdom of Buddhism. 1961. 4.95. Random
Linssen, Robert. Living Zen. il. 1959. 2.25. Grove
Schweitzer, Albert. Indian thought and its development. tr. by Mrs. Charles
E. B. Russell. 1962. 3.60. Smith, Peter
Suzuki, Beatrice L. Mahayana Buddhism. 1959. 3.25. Macmillan
Suzuki, D. T. Manual of Zen Buddhism. 1960. pap. 1.95. Grove
Thomas, Edward J. History of Buddhist thought. il. 1951. 7.50. Barnes & Noble
Weber, Max. Religion of India. 1958. 6.50. Free Press
BUDGET (351.72)
Kimmel, Lewis H. Federal budget and fiscal policy, 1789-1958. 1959. 5.00.
Brookings
BUDGET IN BUSINESS (339.42)
Dearden, John. Cost and budget analysis. il. 1962. 6.00. Prentice-Hall
Heckert, J. B., and J. D. Willson. Business budgeting and control. 2nd ed.
1955. 8.00. Ronald
Wellington, C. Oliver. Primer on budgeting. 1953. 3.50. Van Nostrand
BUILDING (690)
Architectural Record. Architectural engineering: New concepts, methods,
materials, applications. by the Editors of Architectural Record. 1955. 12.75.
McGraw
Arnold, Pauline, and Percival White. Homes: Americas building business. il.
1960. 4.50. Holiday
Dietz, Albert G. H. Dwelling house construction. 2nd ed. il. 1954. 8.00;
Van Nostrand
Emery, Arthur S. Advanced building craft. 1.35. St. Martins
Michaels, L. Contemporary structure in architecture. 1950. 12.00. Reinhold
Parker, Harry E. Simplified engineering for architects and builders. 1961. 6.25.
Wiley
BUILDING--DICTIONARIES (690)
Siegele, Herman H. Siegele's building trades dictionary. 4.00. Drake, F. J. (R)
Van Mansum, C. J., ed. Dictionary of building construction. 1959. 15.75.
Am. Elsevier (R)
BUILDING--HANDBOOKS, MANUALS, ETC. (690)
Architectural Record. Time-saver standards. by the Editors of Architectural
Record. 1954. 13.75. McGraw (R)
Drury, Evelyn, and R. H. Gould, eds. Builder's and decorator's reference book
1959. 25.00. Transatlantic (R)

BUILDING MATERIALS (691)
Hornbostel, Caleb. Materials for architecture: An enoyclopedia guide. 1961.
20.00. Reinhold (R)
Mills, A. P., and others. Materials of construction. 1955. 7.95. Wiley
Withey, Morton O., and G. W. Washa. Materials of construction. 1954. 9.50.
Wiley
BULBS (635.944)
Rockwell, Frederick Frye, and Esther C. Grayson. Complete book of bulbs.
il. 1959. 4.95. Doubleday
BULGARIA (949.77)
Jelavich, Charles. Tsarist Russia and Balkan nationalism. il. 1958. 6.50. U. of
Calif.
Macdermott, Mercia. History of Bulgaria, 1393-1885. 1962. 8.75. Praeger
BULL-FIGHTS (791.82)
Conrad, Barnaby. Barnaby Conrad's encyclopedia of bullfighting. il. 1961.
6.95. Houghton (R)
Conrad, Barnaby. Gates of fear. il. 1957. 7.50. Crowell
Hemingway, Ernest. Death in the afternoon. il. 1932. 10.00. Scribner
Miller, Ann D. Matadors of Mexico. il. 1961. 6.75. King, Dale Stuart
Smith, Rex. Biography of the bulls: An anthology of Spanish bullfighting. il.
1957. 7.95. Rinehart
BULL RUN, 1ST BATTLE OF, 1861 (973.731)
Beatie, Russel H. Road to Manassas. il. 1961. 3.95. Cooper
BULL RUN, 2ND BATTLE, 1862 (973.732)
Stackpole, Edward J. From Cedar Mountain to Antietam. il. 1959. 5.95.
Stackpole
BUNKER HILL, BATTLE OF, 1775 (973.3312)
Fleming, Thomas. Now we are enemies. 1960. 5.00. St. Martins
BUNYAN, JOHN, 1628-1688 (922)
Winslow, Ola E. John Bunyan. 1961. 5.00. Macmillan
BUNYAN, PAUL (398.2)
McCormick, Dell J. Tall timber tales. il. 1956. 3.50. Caxton
Stevens, James. Paul Bunyan. il. 1948. 4.00. Knopf
BUREAUCRACY (351.1)
Dimock, Marshall E. Administrative vitality: The conflict with bureaucracy.
1959. 5.75. Harper
Strauss, Erich. Ruling servants: Bureaucracy in Russia, France, and Britain.
6.75. Praeger
Thompson, Victor A. Modern organization. 1961. 3.75. Knopf
BURIAL LAWS (393)
Jackson, Percival. Law of cadavers. 1950. 12.50. Prentice-Hall
BURKE, EDMUND, 1720?-1797 (923)
Canavan, Francis P. Political reason of Edmund Burke. 1960. 5.00. Duke
Lucas, F. L. Art of living: Four eighteenth century minds, Hume, Horace
Walpole, Burke, Benjamin Franklin. il. 1959. 5.50. Macmillan
Oliver, Robert T. Four who spoke out: Burke, Fox, Sheridan, Pitt. 1946. 2.50.
Syracuse
Paine, Thomas. Rights of man. il. 1961. 6.00. Heritage
Stanlis, Peter. Edmund Burke and the natural law. 1958. 5.75. U. of Mich.
BURLINGTON STRIKE, 1888 (331.89)
McMurry, D. L. Great Burlington strike of 1888: A case history in labor
relations. 1956. 6.00. Harvard
BURMA (959.1)
Khaing, Mi Mi. Burmese family. il. 1962. 3.95. Indiana
Tinker, Hugh. Union of Burma. 1961. 6.75. Oxford U. P.
Trager, Frank N. Building a welfare state in Burma. 1958. 4.00. Inst. of
Pac. Rel.
Trager, Frank N. Burma and the United States. 1959. 4.50. Harper

Cady, John F. History of modern Burma. il. 1958. 7.50. Cornell

Pye, Lucian W. Politics, personality, and nation building: Burma's search for identity. 1962. 7.50. Yale

BURNS, ROBERT, 1759-1796 (928)

Carlyle, T. Essays. Scottish and other miscellanies. 1.95. Dutton

Crawford, Thomas. Burns: A study of the poems and songs. 1960. 6.50. Stanford

Daiches, David. Robert Burns. 1951. pap. 3.00. Holt, Rinehart & Winston

Lindsey, John. Robert Burns: Rantin' dog, poet extraordinary. il. 3.95. Liveright

Lockhart, J. G. Life of Burns. 1959. 1.95. Dutton

Snyder, Franklyn Bliss. Robert Burns, his personality, his reputation and his art. 1936. 2.50. U. of Toronto

BURR, AARON, 1756-1836 (929)

Abernethy, Thomas P. Burr conspiracy. 1954. 6.50. Oxford U. P.

Beirne, Francis F. Shout treason: The trial of Aaron Burr. 1959. 5.00. Hastings

Schachner, Nathan. Aaron Burr. il. 1961. 2.25. Barnes, A. S.

Seton, Anya. My Theodosia. 4.95. Houghton

BUSHMEN (916)

Thomas, Elizabeth M. Harmless people. il. 1959. 4.75. Knopf

Van der Post, Laurens. Lost world of the Kalahari. 1958. 4.00. Morrow

BUSINESS (658)

Beard, Miriam. History of business: From Babylon to the monopolists. 1962. 4.40; (Ann Arbor bks. AA62) pap. 2.95. U. of Mich.

Brown, Stanley M., and Lillian Doris. Business executive's handbook. 1953. 9.50 Prentice-Hall

Janis, J. Harold. Business communication reader. 1958. 6.00. Harper

Lasser, Jacob K. Executive's guide to business procedures. ed. by Prerau. 1960. 6.00. McGraw

Lasser, J. K. How to start and build a successful business. 1962. pap. 1.00. Grosset

Spengler, Edwin H., and Jacob Klein. Introduction to business. 1955. 7.50; workbook, 2.75; instructor's manual. 2.00. McGraw

Tver, David F. Dictionary of business and scientific terms. 1961. 10.00. Gulf

BUSINESS--DICTIONARIES (658.03)

Clark, Donald T., and Bert A. Gottfried. Dictionary of business and finance. 1957. 6.95. Crowell (R)

Miller, B. M., ed. Private secretary's encyclopedic dictionary. 5.95. Prentice-Hall (R)

Prentice-Hall Editorial Staff. Encyclopedic dictionary of business. 1952. 10.00. Prentice-Hall (R)

Prentice-Hall, inc. Encyclopedic dictionary of business finance. by the editorial staff of Prentice-Hall. il. 1961. 19.50. Prentice-Hall

BUSINESS--HANDBOOKS, MANUALS, ETC. (658.04)

Lasser, Jacob K. Business management handbook. by Prerau. 1960. 12.50. McGraw (R)

Lawrence, Nelda, ed. Secretary's business review. 1960. 10.60. Prentice-Hall

Pelo, William Joseph, ed. Executive's desk book. il. 1934. 9.95. Winston (R)

BUSINESS CYCLES (338.54)

Alt, George T. Our economic dilemma. il. 1959. 2.95. Ramfre

Chambers, Edward J. Economic fluctuations and forecasting. il. 1961. 8.95. Prentice-Hall

Duesenberry, James S. Business cycles and economic growth. 1958. 6.50. McGraw

Estey, James A. Business cycles: Their nature, cause and control. 1950. 10.00. Prentice-Hall

Fels, Rendigs. American business cycles, 1865-1897. 1959. 6.00. U. of N.C.

Gordon, Robert A. Business fluctuations. 1961. 7.50. Harper

Haberler, Gottfried. Prosperity and depression. il. 1958. 6.00. Harvard

Hansen, Alvin H. Business cycles and national income. 1951. 6.90. Norton

Hicks, J. R. Contribution to the theory of the trade cycle. il. 1950. 2.90. Oxford U. P.

Lee, Maurice W. Economic fluctuations. rev. ed. 1959. 10.60. Irwin

Matthews, Robert C. O. Business cycle. 1959. pap. 1.95. U. of Chicago

Merlin, S. Theory of fluctuations in contemporary economic thought. 1949. 2.75. Columbia

Morgenstern, Oskar. International financial transactions and business cycles. 1958. 12.00. Princeton

Smith, Edgar L. Common stocks and business cycles. il. 1959. 10.00. William-Frederick

BUSINESS EDUCATION (658.07)

Dame, J. Frank, and Albert R. Brinkman. Guidance in business education. 3rd ed. 1961. 4.00. South-Western Pub.

Douglas, Lloyd V., and others. Teaching business subjects. 1958. 9.00. 6.75. Prentice-Hall

National Education Association, American Business Education Association. One hundred years in business education. 1957. 2.00. N. E. A.

Pierson, Frank C. Education of American businessmen. 1959. 7.75. McGraw

BUSINESS ETHICS (174)

Braun, Carl F. Fair thought and speech. 1957. 1.75. Braun

Bursk, Edward C., ed. Business and religion. 1959. 4.75. Harper

Johnston, Herbert. Business ethics. 1961. 5.50. Pitman

Selekman, Benjamin. Moral philosophy for management. 1959. 6.00. McGraw

Selekman, Sylvia, and Benjamin. Power and morality in a business society. 1956. 4.00. McGraw

Spurrier, William A. Ethics and business. 1962. 3.50. Scribner

BUSINESS ETIQUETTE (395.4)

Becker, Esther R., and Richard L. Lawrence. Success and satisfaction in your office job. 1954. 3.00. Harper

MacGibbon, Elizabeth Gregg. Manners in business. 1954. 3.50. Macmillan

Wilson, Everett B., and Sylvia B. Wright. Getting along with people in business. 1950. 3.00. Funk

BUSINESS FORECASTING (338.544)

Bratt, Elmer C. Business cycles and forecasting. 5th ed. 1961. 10.60. Irwin

BUSINESS LAW (347.7)

Savage, W. G., and others. Business review for professional secretaries. 1959. 6.00. Pitman

BUSINESS MATHEMATICS (511.8)

Curry, O. J., and John E. Pearson. Basic mathematics for business analysis. 1961. 6.60. Irwin

Daus, Paul H., and W. M. Whyburn. Algebra with applications to business and economics. 1961. 6.75. Addison-Wesley

Grazda, Edward E., and Martin E. Jansson. Handbook of applied mathematics. 3rd ed. il. 1955. 7.95. Van Nostrand (R)

Hilborn, Claire E. Mathematics for use in business. 1946. 6.00. Houghton

Lasley, Sidney J., and Myrtle F. Mudd. New applied mathematics. 5th ed. 1957. 4.16. Prentice-Hall

Lowenstein, Lloyd L. Mathematics in business. il. 1958. 4.95; 1.95. Wiley

Meier, R. C., and S. H. Archer. Introduction to mathematics for business analysis. 1960. 6.95. McGraw

Parker, Commercial algebra. 5.00. Am. Bk. Co.

Rosenberg, R. Robert. College business mathematics. 1961. 5.75. McGraw

Smith, Franklin C. Mathematics of finance. 1951. 5.25. Appleton

Snyder, Llewellyn R. Essential business mathematics. 1958. 6.50. McGraw

BUSINESSMEN (650)
Baumer, William H., and Donald G. Herzberg. Politics is your business. 1960.
3.50. Dial
Greenewalt, Crawford H. Uncommon man: The individual in the organization.
1959. 4.00. McGraw
Worthy, James C. Big business and free men. 1959. 4.00. Harper
BUTLER, BENJAMIN FRANKLIN, 1818-1893 (923.273)
Holzman, Robert S. Stormy Ben Butler. il. 1954. 5.00. Macmillan
BUTTERFLIES (595.789)
Ehrlich, P. R. How to know the butterflies. ed. by H. E. Jaques. 1960. 3.25;
Brown, W. C.
Holland, William J. Butterfly book. il. 1931. 12.50. Doubleday
Klots, Alexander B. Field guide to the butterflies. il. 1951. 4.50. Houghton (R)
Klots, Alexander B. World of butterflies and moths. il. boxed. 1958. 15.00.
McGraw
Werner, Alfred, ed. Butterflies and moths. il. 1956. 10.00. Random
BYRD ANTARCTIC EXPEDITIONS (919.9)
Byrd, Richard E. Alone. 4.50. Putnam
BYRNES, JAMES F., 1879 (923.273)
Byrnes, James F. All in one lifetime. il. 1958. 5.00. Harper
BYRON, GEORGE GORDON NOEL BYRON, 6th BARON, 1788-1824 (821)
Boyd, Elizabeth F. Byron's Don Juan: A critical study. 5.00. Humanities
Calvert, William J. Byron, romantic paradox. 1962. 6.50. Russell
Cline, C. L. Byron, Shelley and their Pisan circle. il. 1952. 5.00. Harvard
Marchand, Leslie A. Byron: Autobiography. 3 vols. il. 1957. 20.00. Knopf
Marshall, William H. Byron, Shelley, Hunt, and the Liberal. 1960. 5.00. U. of
Pa.
Moore, Doris Langley. Late Lord Byron. il. 1961. 8.50. Lippincott
Quennell, Peter. Byron in Italy. il. 1941. 3.50; 1957. Viking
Rutherford, Andrew. Byron, a critical study. 1961. 5.00. Stanford
Thorslev, Peter L., Jr. Byronic hero: Types and prototypes. 1962. 5.00. U.
of Minn.
West, Paul. Byron and the spoiler's art. 1960. 4.00. St. Martins
BYZANTINE EMPIRE (949.5)
Baynes, N. H. Byzantine Empire. 1926. 1.70. Oxford U. P.
Baynes, N. H., and H. St. L. B. Moss, eds. Byzantium: Introduction to East
Roman civilization. 1948. 5.60. Oxford U. P.
Diehl, Charles. Etudes Byzantines. il. 1905. 18.50. Franklin, B.
Hussey, J. M. Byzantine world. 2.50. Hillary
Runciman, Steven. Byzantine civilization. 5.50. St. Martins
Talbot Rice, David. Byzantines. 1962. 6.95. Praeger
BYZANTINE EMPIRE--HISTORY (949.5)
Chubb, Thomas C. Byzantines. 1959. 3.50. World Pub.
Diehl, Charles. Byzantium: Greatness and decline. 1956. 8.50. Rutgers
Gordon, C. C. Age of Attila: Fifth-century Byzantium and the barbarians.
1960. 3.95. U. of Mich.
Lamb, Harold. Constantinople: Birth of an empire. il. 1957. 5.75. Knopf
Ostrogorsky, George. History of the Byzantine State. 1957. 12.50. Rutgers
BYZANTINE POETRY (COLLECTIONS) (808.1)
Trypanis, C. A. Medieval and modern Greek poetry: An anthology. 1951. 4.50.
Oxford U. P.

C

CABELL, JAMES BRANCH, 1879- (928)
David, Joe Lee. James Branch Cabell. 1962. 3.50. Twayne
CABINET OFFICERS (353)
De Conde, Alexander. American Secretary of State. 1962. 4.50? 1.75. Praeger

Fenno, Richard F., Jr. President's cabinet. 1959. 5.50. Harvard

Graebner, Norman A. Uncertain tradition: American Secretaries of State in
the twentieth century. 1961. 6.95. McGraw

Hendrick, Burton J. Lincoln's war cabinet. 3.50. Smith, Peter

Horn, Stephen. Cabinet and Congress. 1960. 6.00. Columbia

Tanzer, Lester, ed. Kennedy circle. 1961. 4.95. McKay

CABINET SYSTEM (353)

Ehrman, John. Cabinet government and war: 1890-1940. 1958. 3.00. Cambridge
U. P.

Jennings, Ivor. Cabinet government. 1959. 9.50. Cambridge U. P.

Patterson, C. Perry. Presidential government in the United States. 1947.
4.00. U. of N.C.

CABINET --WORK (684.2)

Hjorth, Herman, and William Holtrop. Principles of woodworking. rev. ed.
1961. 5.40. Bruce

Hoard, F. E., and Andrew W. Marlow. Cabinetmaker's treasury. il. 1952.
8.00. Macmillan

Hooper, John. Modern cabinet work. il. 1953. 12.50. Lippincott

Pelton, B. W. Furniture making and cabinet work. il. 1961. 7.95. Van Nostrand

CABLE, GEORGE WASHINGTON, 1844-1925 (928)

Butcher, Philip. George W. Cable: The Northampton years. il. 1959. 6.00.
Columbia

Turner, Arlin. George W. Cable. 1956. 6.00. Duke

CABLES, SUBMARINE (621.3828)

Clarke, Arthur C. Voice across the sea. il. 1958. 3.75. Harper

CACTUS (583.47)

Chidamian, Claude. Book of cacti and other succulents. il. 4.50. Doubleday

Cutak, Ladislaus. Cactus guide. il. 1956. 3.95. Van Nostrand (R)

Marsden, C. Grow cacti, a practical handbook. 1959. 4.50. St. Martins

CAESAR, C. JULIUS (923.145)

Brady, Sidney G. Caesar's Gallic campaigns. il. 1960. 3.25. Stackpole

Duggan, Alfred. Julius Caesar. 1955. 3.00. Knopf

Holmes, T. R. E. Caesar's conquest of Gaul. il. 1911. 8.80. Oxford U. P.

CAFFEIN (615.711)

Nash, Harvey. Alcohol and caffeine: a study of their psychological effects.
il. 1962. 7.25. Thomas, C. C

CAILLAUX, JOSEPH, 1863-1944 (923.242)

Binion, Rufolph. Defeated leaders. 1960. 7.50. Columbia

CAKE (641.631)

Amendola, Joseph. Bakers' manual. il. 1960. 6.00. Ahrens

Hoffman, Louis. Housewives' treasury of baking delicacies. 1960. 3.00.
Pageant

Norwak, Mary. Five o'clock cookbook. il. 1960. 2.00. Transatlantic

CAKE DECORATING (641.85)

Chelmo, Harriet, It's fun to bake and decorate with sugar. il. 1961. 2.00.
Exposition

Murphy, Esther. Art of creative cake decorating. il. 1953; 1958. suppl. Party
and holiday cakes. 15.00. Am. Trade

CALCULATING--MACHINES (651.264)

Meehan, J. R. How to use the calculator and comptometer. 1959. 2.50.
McGraw

Walker, Arthur L., and others. How to use adding and calculating machines.
2nd ed. il. 1960. 3.16; teacher's manual and key, 1.50. McGraw

CALCULUS (517)

Ayres, Frank. Outline of theory and problems of calculus. il. 1950. 2.50.
Schaum

Bacon, Harold M. Differential and integral calculus. 2nd ed. il. 1955. 7.95;
McGraw

Cogan, Edward, and Robert Norman. Handbook of calculus, difference and differential equations. 1958. 6.60. Prentice-Hall

De Morgan, Augustus. Elementary illustrations of the differential and integral calculus. 3.00. Open Ct.

Evans, Trevor, and Bevan Youse. How to solve problems in calculus and analytic geometry, vol. 1. il. 1961. pap. 2.95. Prentice-Hall

Franklin, Philip. Differential and integral calculus. 1953. 7.95. McGraw

Gay, Harold J. Analytic geometry and calculus. 1950. 6.75. McGraw

Gibson, George A. Advanced calculus. 1931. 4.00. St. Martins

Granville, William A. Differential and integral calculus. 7.00. Ginn

Granville, William A., and others. Elements of differential and integral calculus. 1957. 7.00. Ginn

Kent, James R. F. Differential and integral calculus. il. 1960. 6.75. Houghton

Klaf, A. Albert. Calculus refresher for technical men. 1957. pap. 2.00. Dover

Love, Clyde E., and Earl D. Rainville. Differential and integral calculus. 6th ed. il. 1962. 7.50. Macmillan

Miller, Frederic H. Analytic geometry and calculus: A unified treatment. 1949. 6.75. Wiley

Osgood, William F. Introduction to the calculus. il. 5.90. Macmillan

Peterson, Thurman S. Calculus with analytic geometry. 1960. 7.50. Harper

Rainville, Earl D. Unified calculus and analytic geometry. il. 8.50. Macmillan

Richmond, Donald E. Introductory calculus. 1959. 6.75. Addison-Wesley

Sawyer, W. W. What is calculus about? 1961. pap. 1.95. Random

Sherwood, George E. F., and Angus E. Taylor. Calculus. 1954. 13.35; text ed. 10.00. Elementary differential equations, in combination with Calculus by Sherwood and Taylor. 1.50. Prentice-Hall

Smail, Lloyd L. Calculus. 1949. 6.00. Appleton

Taylor, Angus E. Edvanced calculus. 1955. 9.25. Ginn

Thomas, G. B., Jr. Calculus. 1961. 9.75. Addison-Wesley

Thomas, G. B., Jr. Elements of calculus and analytic geometry. 1959. 7.50. Addison-Wesley

Thompson, James E. Calculus for the practical man. 3rd ed. 8.00. Van Nostrand

Thompson, Silvanus P. Calculus made easy. 1946. 2.95. St. Martins

Westwater, F. L. Simplified calculus. il. 3.50. Macmillan

Young, W. H. Fundamental theorems of the differential calculus. 1910. 3.00.

CALENDARS (529.3)

Farjeon, Eleanor. New book of days. il. 1961. 4.50. Walck (R)

Lipkind, William. Days to remember--an almanac. 1960. 3.95. Obolensky (R)

Mirkin, Stanford. When did it happen? 1957. 5.75. Washburn (R)

CALHOUN, JOHN CALDWELL, 1782-1850 (923.273)

Capers, Gerald M. John C. Calhoun, opportunist. 1960. 6.75. U. of Fla.

Coit, Margaret L. John C. Calhoun. 1950. 7.50; (Sentry 5) 1961. pap. 2.45. Houghton

CALIFORNIA (917.94)

Jacobson, Dan. No further west. 1961. 3.50. Macmillan

Jaeger, Edmund C. California deserts. il. 1955. 5.00. Stanford

Marryat, Frank. Mountains and molehills. 1962. 3.95. Lippincott

Writers' Project, California. rev. ed. 1954. 6.50. Hastings

CALIFORNIA--HISTORY (979.4)

Bidwell, John. Echoes of the past: An account of the first emigrant train to California. 3.25. Smith, Peter

CALIFORNIA, LOWER (979.4)

Baegert, Johann Jakob. Observations in Lower California. tr. by Magda Brandenburg, and Carl L. Baumann. il. 1952. 5.00. U. of Calif.

Gardner, Erle Stanley. Hunting the desert whale: Personal adventures in Baja California. il. 1960. 6.00. Morrow

Krutch, Joseph W. Forgotten peninsula. il. 1961. 5.00. Sloane

CALIFORNIA STATE PRISON, SAN QUENTIN (979.4)
Duffy, Clinton T., and Al Hirshberg. 88 men and 2 women. 4.50. Doubleday
Lamott, Kenneth. Chronicles of San Quentin: Biography of a prison. il. 1961.
    4.95. McKay
CALLAS, MARIA, 1923- (927)
Callas, Evangelia. My daughter, Maria Callas. il. 1960. 4.50. Fleet
Jellinek, George. Callas, portrait of a prima donna. il. 1960. 1.95.
    Barnes, A. S.
CALVIN, JEAN, 1509-1564 (922)
Bratt, John H. Rise and development of calvinism. 1959. 2.75. Eerdmans
Hoogstra, Jacob T., ed. John Calvin, contemporary prophet. 4.50. Baker Bk.
Van Halsema, Thea B. This was John Calvin. 2.95. Zondervan
CAMBODIA (959.6)
Briggs, Lawrence P. Ancient Khmer empire. 1951. 6.00. Am. Philos. Soc.
Pym, Christopher. Road to Angkor. il. 1959. 4.50. Int. Pub. Service
CAMELLIA (635.93)
Hume, H. Harold. Azaleas and camellias.
CAMERAS (978.9)
Wagg, Alfred. Know your camera. il. 1956. 3.95.
CAMINO REAL
Moorhead, Max L. New Mexico's royal road. il. 1958. 4.00. U. of Okla.
CAMOES, LUTZ DE, 1524?- 1580 (928)
Hart, Henry H. Luis de Camoens and the Epic of the Lusiads. 1962. 5.00. U.
    of Okla.
CAMOUFLAGE (MILITARY SCIENCE) (355.42)
Chesney, Clement H. R. Art of camouflage. il. 1952. 2.75. Transatlantic
Sloane, Eric. Camouflage simplified. il. 1942. 2.50. Devin
CAMP COUNSELORS (796.54)
Hartwig, Marie, and Bettye Myers. Children are human, if the counselors
    really know them. 1962. 2.25. Burgess
Ledlie, John A., and Francis W. Holbein. Camp counselor's manual. 1958. 1.25.
    Assn. Pr.
Mitchell, A. Viola, and Ida B. Crawford. Camp counseling. 1961. pap. 6.25.
    Saunders
Ott, Elmer F. So you want to be a camp counselor. 1946. 1.25. Assn. Pr.
CAMP-MEETINGS (269.2)
Johnson, Charles A. Frontier camp meeting: Religion's harvest time. il. 1955.
    5.00. S. M. U.
CAMPAIGN LITERATURE (329.01)
Brown, William B. People's choice. il. 1960. 4.00. La. State
Sevareid, Eric, ed. Candidates 1960: Behind the headlines in the Presidential
    race. 1959. 4.95. Basic Books
Wilson, Woodrow. Crossroads of freedom: The 1912 campaign speeches of
    Woodrow Wilson. ed. by J. W. Davidson. 1956. 6.00. Yale
CAMPBELL, ROY 1901- (920)
Campbell, Roy. Light on a dark horse. il. 1952. 4.00. Regnery
CAMPING (796.54)
Handel, C. W. Canoe camping. 1953. 4.00. Ronald
Jaeger, Ellsworth. Woodsmoke. il. 1953. 3.95. Macmillan
Macfarlan, Allan. Living like Indians. 1961. 6.95. Assn. Pr.
Merrill, W. K. All about camping. 1962. 3.95. Stackpole
Miracle, Leonard, and Maurice Decker. Complete book of camping. 1962.
    4.95. Pop. Science. order from Harper
Rutstrum, Calvin. New way of the wilderness. il. 4.50. Macmillan
Whelen, Townsend, and Bradford Angier. On your own in the wilderness. il.
    5.00. Stackpole
CAMPS (796.54)
Sargent, Porter. Guide to summer camps and summer schools. 4.40. 2.20. Sargent

CAMUS, ALBERT, 1913-1960 (840.8.)
Bree, Germaine. Camus. 1961. 5.00. Rutgers
Cruickshank, John. Albert Camus and the literature of revolt. 1959. (Galaxy BG43) pap. 1.50. Oxford U. P.
Hanna, Thomas. Thought and art of Albert Camus. 1959. 1.25. Regnery
Maquet, Albert. Albert Camus: An invincible summer. 1958. 3.75. Braziller
CANADA (971)
Brown, George W., ed. Canada. il. 1950. 6.50. U. of Calif.
Horne, Alistair. Canada and the Canadians. 1962. 7.00. St. Martins
Lang, Gladys E. Canada. 1959. 2.50. Wilson
CANADA--BIOGRAPHY (920)
Greene, B. M. Who's who in Canada. 1963. 25.00. McKay (R)
CANADA--ECONOMIC CONDITIONS (971)
Aitken, Hugh G. J., and others. American economic impact on Canada. 1959. 4.50. Duke
Easterbrook, W. T., and H. G. T. Aitken, Canadian economic history. 1960. 8.00. St. Martins
Innis, Harold A. Fur trade in Canada. 1956. 8.50. U. of Toronto
Safarian, A. E. Canadian economy in the great depression. il. 1959. 3.50. U. of Toronto
Wright, Alfred J. United States and Canada: A regional geography. 2nd ed. il. 7.00. Appleton
CANADA--HISTORY (971)
Allen, Ralph. Ordeal by fire: Canada, 1910-1945. 1961. 5.95. Doubleday
Brebner, John B. Canada: A modern history. il. 1960. 10.00. U. of Mich.
Brown, George W. Canada in the making. 1953. 3.00. U. of Wash.
Creighton, Donald Grant. History of Canada: Dominion of the North. 1958. 7.50. Houghton
Creighton, Donald G. Story of Canada. il. 1960. 5.00. Houghton
Glazebrook, G. P. de T. Short history of Canada. il. 1950. 2.40. Oxford U. P.
Hardy, William G. From sea unto sea: Road of nationhood, 1850 to 1910. 1960. 4.95. Doubleday
McInnis, Edgar. Canada, a political and social history. il. 1959. 10.90. text ed. 7.50. Holt, Rinehart & Winston
Peck, A. M. Pageant of Canadian history. 1943. 6.50. McKay
CANADIAN LITERATURE--HISTORY AND CRITICISM (810)
Whalley, A. Writings in Canada. 1955. 4.50. St. Martins
CANADIAN POETRY (COLLECTIONS) (819.1)
Smith, Arthur J. M., ed. Oxford book of Canadian verse. bilingual. in English and French. 1960. 7.50. Oxford U. P.
CANADIAN POETRY--HISTORY AND CRITICISM (819.1)
Matthews, John T. Tradition in exile. 1962. 5.00. U. of Toronto
CANALS (627.52)
Goodrich, Carter. Government promotion of American canals and railroads, 1800-1890. 1960. 7.50. Columbia
Payne, Robert. Canal builders. il. 1959. 5.50. Macmillan
Waggoner, Madeline S. Long haul west: The great canal era, 1817-1850. il. 5.75. Putnam
CANARY ISLANDS (964.9)
Eldridge, Paul. Tales of the Fortunate Isles. 1959. 4.95. Yoseloff
Gordon-Brown, Alfred. Madeira and the Canary Islands. il. 1959. 4.50. Int. Pub. Service
CANCER (616.9)
Boesch, Mark. Long search for the truth about cancer. 1960. 4.95. Putnam
Cameron, Charles. S. Truth about cancer. il. 1956. 4.95. Prentice-Hall
Crile, George, Jr. Cancer and common sense. 1955. 2.75. Viking
Goldman, Leonard B. There is an answer to cancer. 1958. 3.50. Harper
Kenigsberg, Alexander H. Origin and nature of cancer. 4.00. Twayne

Ochsner, Alton. Smoking and health. 1954. 3.00. Messner
Sokoloff, Boris. Cancer: New approaches, new hope. 1952. 3.95. Devin
CANDLES (665.1)
Faraday, Michael. Chemical history of a candle. il. 1957. 2.75. Crowell
CANNON, JOSEPH GURNEY, 1836-1926 (923.273)
Gwinn, William R. Uncle Joe Cannon. 5.00. Twayne
CANOES AND CANOEING (797.122)
Handel, C. W. Canoeing. 1956. 2.95. Ronald
CANT (427.09)
Goldin, Hyman E., and others, ed. Dictionary of American underworld lingo.
    1962. pap. 1.95. Citadel
Partridge, Eric. Dictionary of the underworld. 1961. 12.75. Macmillan (R)
CAPE COD (974.49)
Beston, Henry. Outermost house: A year of life on the great beach of Cape
    Cod. 1949. 3.00. Rinehart
Thoreau, Henry David. Cape Cod. il. 1951. 5.50. Norton
Thoreau, Henry D. Walden, Week on the Concord and Merrimack Rivers,
    Maine Woods, and Cape Cod. il. 1961. set, 12.50. Crowell
CAPITAL (339)
Keirstead, Burton S. Capital, interest, and profits. il. 1959. 4.00. Wiley
Marx, Karl. Capital. 2 vols. 1.95 ea. Dutton
Marx, Karl. Capital. 2.95. Modern Lib.
Marx, Karl. Das Kapital. ed. by Levitsky. 1960. Regnery
Meyer, F. V. Inflation and capital. 3.75. Saifer
Veblen, Thorstein. Theory of business enterprise. 0.50. New Am. Lib.
CAPITAL PUNISHMENT (343.22)
Koestler, Arthur. Reflections on hanging. in prep. Collier
McClellan, Grant S. Capital punishment. 1961. 2.50. Wilson
Playfair, Giles, and Derrick Sington. Offenders: The case against legal
    vengeance. 1957. 3.95. S. and S.
Tuttle, Elizabeth O. Crusade against capital punishment in Great Britain.
    1961. 5.75. Quadrangle
CAPITALISM (330.15)
Arnold, Thurman W. Folklore of capitalism. 1937. 4.50. Yale
Chamberlain, John R. Roots of capitalism. 1959. 5.50. Van Nostrand
Crosser, Paul K. State capitalism in the economy of the U.S. 1960. 4.00.
    Twayne
Ebenstein, W. Today's isms: Communism, Fascism, Socialism, Capitalism.
    3rd ed. 4.35. Prentice-Hall
Fanfani, Amintore. Catholicism, Protestantism, and capitalism. 1955. 3.00.
    Sheed
Hoover, Calvin B. Economy, liberty, and the state. 1959. 5.00. Twentieth
    Century
Kelso, Louis O., and Mortimer J. Adler. Capitalist manifesto. 1958. 3.75.
    Random
Kelso, Louis O., and Mortimer J. Adler. New capitalists. il. 1961. 3.50.
    Random
Schumpeter, Joseph A. Capitalism, socialism and democracy. 1950. 6.50. Harper
Wallich, Henry C. Cost of freedom. 1960. 3.75. Harper
CAPITALISTS AND FINANCIERS (923.3)
Holbrook, Stewart H. Age of the moguls. il. 1953. 5.75. Doubleday
Jennings, Walter Wilson. Twenty giants of American business. 1952. 5.00.
    Exposition
Josephson, Matthew. Robber barons. 1934. 4.75. Harcourt
Rees, Goronwy. Multimillionaires: Six studies in wealth. 1961. 3.50. Macmillan
Tebbel, John. Inheritors. 1961. 5.00. Putnam
Wall Street Journal. New millionaires and how they made their fortunes. 1961.
    4.95. Random

CAPITULATIONS, MILITARY (327)
Armstrong, Anne. Unconditional surrender: The impact of the Casablanca
policy upon World War II. 1961. 6.00. Rutgers
Kecskemeti, Paul. Strategic surrender. 5.00. Stanford
CARBOHYDRATES (547.78)
Pigman, W. W., ed. Carbohydrates: Chemistry, biochemistry, physiology.
1957. 20.00. Academic Press
CARBURETORS (629.253)
Judge, Arthur W. Motor manuals. 5 vols. vol. 1. Automobile engines; vol. 2.
Carburetors and fuel systems: vol. 3. Mechanisms of the car; vol. 4. Car
Maintenance and repair. vol. 5. Modern transmission systems. 1952. 6.50
ea; set, 27.50. Bentley
CARD TRICKS (795)
Blackstone, Harry. Blackstone's modern card tricks. 1958. 2.50. Doubleday

Hugard, Jean. Encyclopedia of card tricks. il. 1961. 6.00. Wehman (R)
CARDINALS (922.2)
Kittler, Glenn D. Papal princes: A history of the Sacred College of Cardinals.
Reynolds, Ernest Edwin. Three cardinals: Newman, Wiseman, Manning. il.
1958. 5.50. Kenedy
CARDIOVASCULAR SYSTEM (612.1)
National Academy of Science. Handbook of circulation. 1959. pap. 7.50.
Saunders
Singer, Charles. Discovery of the circulation of the blood. il. 1956. 3.00.
Bentley
CARDS (795.4)
Foster, Robert F. Foster's complete Hoyle. 4.95. Lippincott (R)
Frey, Richard L., and others, eds. New complete Hoyle. 1956. 3.95. Doubleday (R)

Goren, Charles H., and others. Goren's Hoyle encyclopedia of games. il.
1960. 5.95. Hawthorn
CARIBBEAN AREA (972.9)
Wilgus, A. Curtis, ed. Caribbean: British, Dutch, French, United States.
1958. 6.50. U. of Fla.
CARIBBEAN AREA--DESCRIPTION AND TRAVEL--GUIDEBOOKS (917.29)
Gellhorn, Eleanor Cowles. McKay's guide to Bermuda, the Bahamas, and the
Caribbean. rev. ed. 1958. 5.75. McKay
Henle, Fritz, and P. E. Knapp. Caribbean. il. 1961. 6.95. Viking
CARIBBEAN SEA (972.9)
Arciniegas, German. Caribbean: Sea of the New World. il. 1946. 6.75. Knopf
Clark, Sydney. All the best in the Caribbean, including Bermuda and the
Bahamas. rev. ed. il. 1959. 4.95. Dodd
CARICATURE (741.5)
Becker, Stephen. Comic art in America. 1959. 7.50. S. and S.
Darvas, Lou. You can draw cartoons. il. 4.50. Doubleday
Fraydas, Stan. Graphic humor: A course in professional cartooning. 1961.
7.50. Reinhold
Nelson, Roy P. Fell's guide to the art of cartooning. 1962. 4.95. Fell
Seligman, Janet. Figures of fun. 1957. 3.40. Oxford U. P.
CARICATURES AND CARTOONS (741.5)
Chase, John C. Today's cartoon. il. 10.00. Hauser
Hofmann, Werner. Caricature from Leonardo to Picasso. 1957. 5.95. Crown
Lariar, Lawrence, ed. Best cartoons of the year. 2.95. Crown
Murrell, William. History of American graphic humor. 2 vols. vol. 1, 1747-
1865. il. 5.00. Praeger
Thurber, James. Thurber's dogs. 1955. 3.95. S. and S.
CARLYLE, THOMAS, 1795-1881 (923.6)
Bentley, Eric. Century of hero-worship. 3.75. Smith, Peter
Lehman, B. H. Carlyle's theory of the hero. 1928. 3.50. Duke

CARNEGIE, ANDREW, 1835-1919 (923.3)
Carnegie, Andrew. Autobiography of Andrew Carnegie. 5.00. Houghton
McCloskey, Robert Green. American conservatism in the age of enterprise:
    A study of William Graham Sumner, Stephen J. Field, and Andrew Carnegie.
    1951. 3.25. Harvard
CARNEGIE HALL, NEW YORK (780.974)
Schickel, Richard. World of Carnegie Hall. il. 1960. 8.50. Messner
CAROLS (783.6)
Simon, Henry. Treasury of Christmas songs and carols. il. 1955. 5.95.
    Houghton
CARPACCIO, VITTORE, 1455-1525 (927)
Pignatti, Terisio. Carpaccio. 1958. 5.75. World Pub.
CARPENTRY (694)
Burbank, Nelson, L., and Charles Phelps. House carpentry simplified. 5.95.
    Simmons-Boardman
Durbahn, Walter E. Fundamentals of carpentry. 2 vols. il. vol. 1, Tools,
    materials, practice. 3rd ed. 4.75, study guide. 1.25; vol. 2, Practical
    construction. 2nd ed. 4.95; study guide. 1.25. Am. Tech. Soc.
Hayward, Charles. Carpentry book. il. 1955. 5.95. Van Nostrand
Mix, Floyd, and Ernest Cirou. Practical carpentry. il. 1958. 5.00. Goodheart
Wilson, John Douglas. Practical house carpentry. 1957. 7.95. McGraw
CARTHAGE (930)
Charles-Picard, Gilbert and Colette. Daily life in Carthage at the time of
    Hannibal. il. 1961. 4.00. Macmillan
Warmington, B. H. Carthage. 1960. 4.95. Praeger
CARTOGRAPHY (526.8)
Brown, Lloyd A. Story of maps. il. 1949. 12.50. Little
Crone, G. R. Maps and their makers: An introduction to the history of
    cartography. 1953. 2.50. Hillary
Robinson, Arthur H. Elements of cartography. il. 1960. 8.75. Wiley
Skelton, Raleigh A. Explorers' maps. il. 1958. 12.50. Praeger
CARUSO, ENRICO, 1873-1921 (927)
Drummond, H. J., and J. Freestone. Enrico Caruso: His recorded legacy.
    1961. 7.50. Denison
CARVER, GEORGE WASHINGTON, 1864? - 1943 (925)
Holt, Rackham. George Washington Carver: An American biography. il. 1943.
    4.00. Doubleday
CARY, JOYCE, 1888-1957 (820.81)
Wright, Andrew H. Joyce Cary, a preface to his novels. il. 1959. 4.50. Harper
CASANOVA DE SEINGALT, GIACOMO GIROLAMO, 1725-1798 (920.9)
Dobrée, Bonamy. Three eighteenth century figures: Sarah Churchill, John
    Wesley and Giacomo Casanova. 1962. 4.80. Oxford U. P.
CASCADE RANGE (979.75)
Douglas, William O. Of men and mountains. 1950. 6.00. Harper
CASTE (301.44)
Cox, Oliver Cromwell. Caste, class and race: A study in social dynamics. il.
    1959. 7.50. Monthly Review
CASTLES (728.81)
Cruden, Stewart. Scottish castle. 1961. 10.00. Nelson
Dutton, Ralph. Chateaux of France. 1957. 7.50. Hastings
Edwards, J. G. Edward I's castle-building in Wales. 1944. 1.15. Oxford U. P.
CATALAN POETRY (SELECTIONS: EXTRACTS, ETC.) (849.91)
Gili, Joan, Anthology of Catalan lyric poetry. 1953. 5.00. U. of Calif.
CATALOGING (025.3)
Akers, Susan G. Simple library cataloging. 1954. 5.00. A. L. A. (R)
American Library Association. A. L. A. cataloging rules for author and title
    entries. 1949. 5.00. A. L. A. (R)
American Library Association. Code for cataloging music and phono-records.
    1958. 2.25. A. L. A. (R)

Mann, Margaret. Introduction to cataloging and the classification of books. 1943. 3.25. A. L. A.

Tauber, Maurice F. Cataloguing and classification (vol. 1, pt. 1) . bd. with Frarey, Carlyle J. Subject headings (vol. 1, pt. 2). 1960. 8.00. Rutgers

CATALOGS, CLASSIFIED (DEWEY DECIMAL) (016)

Standard catalog for high school libraries. 1962. also with Catholic suppl. sold on service basis. Wilson (R)

Standard catalog for public libraries. Sold on service basis. Wilson (R)

CATALOGS, PUBLISHERS' (015.73)

Pollock, Muriel, comp. Publishers' trade list annual 3 vols. 8.50. Bowker (R)

Prakken, Sarah L., ed. Books in print. An index to the Publishers' trade list annual. 18.00. Bowker (R)

CATALOGS, SUBJECT (016)

American Library Association. Subject and title index to short stories for children. 1955. 5.00. A. L. A. (R)

Prakken, Sarah L., ed. Subject guide to Books in Print. 17.50. Bowker (R)

CATERERS AND CATERING (642.47)

Emery, W. H. Manual of catering. il. 1962. 6.50. Williams & Wilkins

Lange, Howard. Catering. il. 1955. 3.50. Ahrens

CATESBY, MARK, 1679-1749 (925)

Frick, George, and Raymond P. Stearns. Mark Catesby: The colonial Audubon. il. 1960. 5.00. U. of Ill.

CATHARINE HOWARD, CONSORT OF HENRY VIII, KING OF ENGLAND d. 1542. (923.142)

Smith, Lacey B. Tudor tragedy: The life and times of Catherine Howard. il. 1961. 4.50. Pantheon

Westcott, Jan. Queen's grace. 1959. 4.50. Crown

CATHEDRALS (726.6)

Aubert, Marcel, and Simone Gaubet. Gothic cathedrals of France. il. 1960. 17.95. British Bk.

Batsford, Harry, and Charles Fry. Cathedrals of England. il. 3.75. Macmillan

Gimpel, Jean. Cathedral builders. tr. by Carl F. Barnes, Jr. 3.35. Smith, Peter

Harvey, John. Cathedrals of Spain 1957. 7.50. Hastings

Harvey, John H. English cathedrals. rev. ed. il. 1961. pap. 1.50. Norton

Howgrave-Graham, R. P. Cathedrals of France. 1959. 7.50. Hastings

Hurlimann, Martin. English cathedrals. il. 1962. 12.00. Viking

Hirlimann, Martin. French cathedrals. il. 1961. 12.00. Viking

Prentice, Sartell. Heritage of the cathedral. il. 1936. 5.00. Morrow

Simson, Otto von. Gothic cathedral il. 1962. 7.50. Pantheon

CATHER, WILLA SIBERT, 1875-1947 (813.52)

Bennett, Mildred R. World of Willa Cather. il.1961. pap. 1.50. U. of Neb.

Bloom, Edward A., and Lillian D. Willa Cather's gift of sympathy. 1962. 4.50. Southern Ill.

Brown, Edward K., and Leon Edel. Willa Cather. 1953. 4.50. Knopf

Daiches, David. Willa Cather: A critical introduction. pap. 0.95. Collier

Randall, John H. Landscape and the looking glass. il. 1960. 5.75. Houghton

CATHERINE OF ARAGON, CONSORT OF HENRY VIII, 1485-1536 (923.142)

Mattingly, Garrett. Catherine of Aragon. 1960. pap. 1.45. Vintage

CATHERINE II, EMPRESS OF RUSSIA, 1729-1796 (923.1)

Almedingen, E. M. Catherine, Empress of Russia. 1961. 5.00. Dodd

Grey, Ian. Catherine the Great. il. 1962. 6.00. Lippincott

CATHOLIC CHURCH--ADDRESSES, ESSAYS, LECTURES (271)

Ong, Walter J. American Catholic crossroads. 3.50. Macmillan

Sheen, Fulton J. Life is worth living. il. 1953. 3.75. McGraw

CATHOLIC CHURCH (271)

Francis of Assisi, Saint. St. Francis of Assisi. ed. by Leo Sherley-Price. il. 1960. 4.50. Harper

Thomas Aquinas, Saint. Selected writings. 1939. 2.95. Dutton

CATHOLIC CHURCH--DICTIONARIES (271.03)
Addis, William E., and others. Catholic dictionary. 1951. 10.00. Herder (R)

Attwater, Donald, ed. Catholic dictionary. 5.95. Macmillan (R)

Broderick, Robert C. Catholic concise encyclopedia. 1957. 3.95. S. and S. (R)

CATHOLIC CHURCH--HISTORY (271.09)
Baldwin, Summerfield. Organization of Medieval Christianity. 3.00. Smith, Peter.

De Wohl, Louis. Founded on a rock: A history of the Catholic Church. 1961. 3.95. Lippincott

Ellis, John Tracy. Documents of American Catholic history. 1956. 8.75. Bruce

Hughes, Philip. Popular history of the Catholic Church. 5.95. Macmillan

Pichon, Charles. Vatican and its role in world affairs. il. 1950. 5.00. Dutton

CATHOLIC LITERATURE (271)
Caponigri, A. Robert, ed. Modern Catholic thinkers. 1960. 10.00. Harper

Chapin, John, ed. Book of Catholic quotations. 1956. 8.50. Farrar, Straus

Chapin, John, ed. Treasury of Catholic reading. 1957. 7.50. Farrar, Straus

Woods, Ralph L., ed. Catholic companion to the Bible. 1956. 3.95. Lippincott

CATS (636.8)
Denlinger, Milo G. Complete book of the cat. il. 1947. 3.75. Howell Bk.

Soderberg, P. M. Care of your cat. il. 1958. 4.95. Harper

Whitney, Leon F. Complete book of cat care. il. 1953. 3.95. Doubleday

Wilson, Kit. Cat encyclopedia. il. 1941. 1.75. All-Pets

CATS--ANATOMY (599.744)
Bigelow, Robert P. Directions for the dissection of the cat. il. 3.00. Macmillan

Campbell, John D. Dissection of the dogfish and the cat. 1950. 3.50. Educ. Pubs. Inc.

Eddy, Samuel, and others. Atlas of outline drawings for vertebrate anatomy. il. 1955. 3.50. Wiley

Eddy, S., and others. Guide to the study of the anatomy of the shark, necturus, and the cat. 1960. 3.50. Wiley

Harrison, Bruce M. Dissection of the cat. 4th ed. il. 1962. 3.75. Mosby

Leach, William J. Functional anatomy: Mammalian and comparative. 1961. 6.50. McGraw

Reighard, Jacob, and others. Anatomy of the cat. il. 1935. 7.00. Holt, Rinehart & Winston

CATS (IN RELIGION, FOLK-LORE, ETC.) (398)
Howey, M. O. Cat in magic and religion. 5.00. Wehman

CATTLE (636.2)
Bailey, J. W. Veterinary handbook for cattlemen. il. 1958. 5.50. Springer

Dobie, J. Frank. Longhorns. il. 1941. 6.75. Little

Salisbury, Glenn W., and Noland L. Van Demark. Physiology of reproduction and artificial insemination of cattle. il. 1961. 12.50. Freeman

Towne, Charles W., and Edward N. Wentworth. Cattle and men. il. 1955. 4.00. U. of Okla.

CATTLE BREEDING
Asdell, Sidney A. Cattle fertility and sterility. 1955. 5.50. Little

Johansson, Ivar. Genetic aspects of dairy cattle breeding. il. 1961. 7.50. U. of Ill.

CATTLE TRADE (636.2)
Atherton, Lewis. Cattle kings. il. 1961. 6.95. Indiana

Frink, Maurice, and others. When grass was king. 1956. 8.50. U. of Colo.

Gard, Wayne. Chisholm trail. il. 1954. 5.00. U. of Okla.

Henlein, Paul C. Cattle kingdom in the Ohio valley. 1959. 6.50. U. of Ky.

Leakey, John, and Nellie S. Yost. West that was: From Texas to Montana. il. 1958. 5.00. S. M. U.

McCoy, Joseph G. Historic sketches of the cattle trade of the West and Southwest. 1952. 8.50. Long's College Bk.

Mercer, A. S. Banditti of the plains. il. 1959. 2.00. U. of Okla.

Nordyke, Lewis. Great roundup: The story of Texas and Southwestern cowmen. il. 1955. 5.00. Morrow

Oliver, Herman. Gold and cattle country. il. 1962. 4.50. Binfords

Osgood, Ernest Staples. Day of the cattlemen. il. 1957. pap. 1.50. U. of Chicago

Sandoz, Mari. Cattlemen. 1958. 6.50. Hastings

Schmitt, Martin F., and Dee Brown. Trail driving days. il. 1952. 10.00. Scribner

Sheller, Roscoe. Ben Snipes: Northwest cattle king. il. 1959. 3.75. Binfords

Wilhelm, Stephen R. Cavalcade of hooves and horns. il. 1958. 5.00. Naylor

CAUCASUS (947.9)

Dumas, Alexandre. Adventures in Caucasia. 1962. 3.50. Chilton

Mummery, Albert F. My climbs in the Alps and the Caucasus. il. 1951. 2.75. Transatlantic

CAULFIELD, GENEVIEVE (921)

Caulfield, Genevieve. Kingdom within. ed. by Ed Fitzgerald. 1960. 4.50. Harper

CAUSATION (122)

Cassirer, Ernst. Determinism and indeterminism in modern physics. tr. by O. Theodor Benfey. 1956. 5.00. Yale

Kant, Immanuel. Critique of pure reason. tr. by Norman Kemp Smith. 5.50. St. Martins

Lenzen, Victor F. Causality in natural science. 1954. 3.00. Thomas, C. C.

CAVALRY (357)

Lunt, James D. Charge to glory! il. 1960. 4.50. Harcourt

CAVE-DRAWINGS (571.7)

Bandi, Hans-Georg. Art of the Stone Age. il. 5.95. Crown

Bataille, Georges. Lascaux: Prehistoric painting. il. 1955. in English, French, or German. 17.50. World Pub.

Raphael, Max. Prehistoric cave paintings. tr. by Norbert Guterman. il. 1945. 7.50. Pantheon

CAVES (551.4)

Coon, Carleton S. Seven caves. il. 1957. 5.75. Knopf

Lubke, Anton. World of caves. il. 1959. 5.00. Coward

Pinney, Roy. Complete book of cave exploration. il. 1962. 4.50. Coward

CAVES--U.S. (551.4)

Folsom, Franklin. Exploring American caves. il. 5.00. Crown

Halliday, William R. Adventure is underground. il. 1959. 4.50. Harper

Mohr, Charles E., and Howard N. Sloane, eds. Celebrated American caves. il. 1955. 5.00. Rutgers

CAXTON, WILLIAM, 1422-1491 (928)

Buhler, Curt F. William Caxton and his critics. 1959. 2.50. Syracuse

CAYLEY, SIR GEORGE, BART., 1773-1857 (925)

Pritchard, John L. Sir George Cayley, the inventor of the aeroplane. il. 1962. 6.50. Horizon

CELLINI, BENVENUTO, 1500-1571 (927)

Cellini, Benvenuto. Autobiography. 1.95. Dutton

Cellini, Benvenuto. Life of Benvenuto Cellini. ed. by John Pope-Hennessy. tr. by John A. Symonds. il. 1960. 3.50. N. Y. Graphic

CELLS (574.87)

Andrew, Warren. Cellular changes with age. il. 1952. 2.50. Thomas, C. C.

Bourne, Geoffrey H. Introduction to functional histology. 1960. 8.50. Little

Bowen, V. T., ed. Chemistry and physiology of the nucleus. 1952. 12.00. Academic Press

Brachet, Jean. Biochemical cytology. 1958. 8.80. Academic Press

Butler, John A. V. Inside the living cell. il. 1959. 3.50. Basic Books

Cells and tissues. 1956. 16.50. Academic Press
Downes, Helen R. Chemistry of living cells. 1962. 9.75. Harper
Gerard, Ralph W. Unresting cells. 2.25. Harper
Harris, R. J. C., ed. Biological applications of freezing and drying. 1954.
 10.00. Academic Press
Kuyper, C. M. A. Organization of cellular activity. 1962. 7.00. Am. Elsevier
Paul, John. Cell and tissue culture. il. 1960. 7.50. Williams & Wilkins
White, Philip R. Cultivation of animal and plant cells. 1954. 7.00. Ronald
Wilson, Edmund B. Cell in development and heredity. il. 1925. 16.00. Macmillan
CELTS (936.4)
Dunn, Charles W. Highland settler. 1953. 4.00. U. of Toronto
Powell, T. G. E. Celts. il. 1958. 6.95. Praeger
CENCI, BEATRICE, 1577-1599 (822)
Hicks, Arthur C., and Milton Clarke. Stage version of Shelley's Cenci. 1945.
 3.50. Caxton
CENSORSHIP (323.4)
Downs, Robert B., ed. First freedom: Liberty and justice in the world of
 books and reading. 1960. 8.50. A. L. A.
McKeon, Richard, and others. Freedom to read: Perspective and program.
 1957. 3.00. Bowker
Widmer, Kingsley, and Eleanor. Literary censorship. 1961. 1.95. Wadsworth
Wittenberg, Phillip. Law of literary property. 1957. 5.00. World Pub.
CENTRAL AMERICA (972.8)
Colvin, Gerard. Central America. il. 1962. 1.75. Macmillan
CENTRAL AMERICA--ANTIQUITIES (972.8)
Covarrubias, Miguel. Indian art of Mexico and Central America. il. 1957.
 17.50. Knopf
Mason, J. A. American collections of the University Museum: The ancient
 civilizations of Middle America. 1943. 1.00. U. Museum
Von Hagen, Victor W. Maya explorer: John Lloyd Stephens and the lost
 cities of Central America and Yucatan. il. 1954. 5.75. U. of Okla.
CENTRAL AMERICA--DESCRIPTION AND TRAVEL (917.28)
Butler, G. Paul, and Erica. Butlers' Caribbean and Central America. 1960.
 il. 5.95. Van Nostrand
Gage, Thomas. Travels in the new world. ed. by J. Eric S. Thompson. il.
 1958. 5.00. U. of Okla.
CENTRAL AMERICA--HISTORY (972.8)
Peck, A. M. Pageant of Middle American history. 1947. 6.50. McKay
CENTRAL AMERICA--POLITICS (972.8)
Karnes, Thomas L. Failure of union: Central America, 1824-1960. 1961. 6.00.
 U. of N. C.
Martz, John D. Central America: The crisis and the challenge. 1959. 7.50.
 U. of N. C.
CENTRIFUGAL PUMPS (621.67)
Allen, E. Using centrifugal pumps. il. 1960. 4.80. Oxford U. P.
Stepanoff, A. J. Centrifugal and axial flow pumps. 1957. 12.50. Wiley
CEPHALOPODA (594.56)
Lane, Frank W. Kingdom of the Octopus: The life-history of the cephalopoda.
 il. 7.50. Sheridan
CERAMICS (738)
Kingery, W. D. Introduction to ceramics. 1960. 14.00. Wiley
Lee, P. William. Ceramics. il. 1961. 5.95. Reinhold
Norton, F. H. Ceramics. il. 2.95. Doubleday
Roy, Vincent A. Ceramics. 1959. 7.75. McGraw
Witty, M. B., and others. Dictionary of plastics and ceramics abbreviations.
 15.00. Seti (R)
CEREBRAL PALSY (616.836)
Allen, Robert M., and Thomas W. Jefferson. Psychological evaluation of the
 cerebral palsied person. il. 1962. 5.00. Thomas C. C.

Crothers, Bronson, and Richmond S. Paine. Natural history of cerebral palsy.
il. 1959. 6.75. Harvard
Cruickshank, William M., and George M. Raus, eds. Cerebral palsy: Its
individual and community problems. 1955. 7.50. Syracuse
Cruickshank, William M., and others. Perception and cerebral palsy. 1957.
5.00. Syracuse
Hopkins, Thomas W. Cerebral-palsied child. 1958. 3.95. S. and S.
Levitt, Sophie. Physiotherapy in cerebral palsy. il. 1961. 6.50. Thomas C. C.
CEREBRAL PALSY--PERSONAL NARRATIVES (616.836)
Killilea, Marie L. Karen. 1952. 3.95. Prentice-Hall
CERVANTES SAAVEDRA, MIGUEL DE. 1547-1616 (860)
Arbo, Sebastien Juan. Cervantes: The man and his times. il. 1955. 4.00.
Vanguard
Busoni, Rafaello, Man who was Don Quixote. 1958. 3.95. Prentice-Hall
Croft-Cooke, Rupert. Through Spain with Don Quixote. il. 1960. 5.00. Knopf
Krutch, Joseph W. Five masters, a study in the mutations of the novel. 1959.
3.75. Smith, Peter
CEYLON (954.89)
Blaze, Ray. Ceylon: Its peoples and its homes. il. 1962. 2.00. Transatlantic
Brown, W. Norman, ed. India, Pakistan, Ceylon. il. 1961. 5.00. U. of Pa.
Guylenburg, Reg van. Image of an island: A portrait of Ceylon. 1961. 8.50.
Orion
Tresidder, Argus J. Ceylon. 1960. 4.25. Van Nostrand
Vijaya-Tunga, J. Grass for my feet. 1935. 3.00. St. Martins
Wriggins, W. H. Ceylon: Dilemmas of a new nation. 1960. 10.00. Princeton
CEZANNE, PAUL. 1839-1906 (927)
De Beucken, Jean. Cezanne: A pictorial biography. il. 1961. 5.95. Viking
Biederman, Charles. New Cezanne. 5.50. Art History
Cezanne, Paul. Cezanne. ed. by Meyer Shapiro. il. 1952. 15.00. Abrams
Cezanne, Paul. Cezanne. ed. by Fritz Novotny. il. 1961. 5.95. (Phaidon)
N. Y. Graphic
Cezanne, Paul. Cezanne drawings. ed. by Alfred Neumeyer. 7.50. Yoseloff
Fry, Roger. Cezanne. il. 1952. 3.75. Macmillan
Loran, Erle. Cezanne's composition: Analysis of his form with diagrams
and photographs of his motifs. il. 1959. 7.50. U. of Calif.
Raynal, Maurice. Cezanne. il. 1954. in English, French or German. 5.75.
(Skira) World Pub.
Venturi, L. Four steps toward modern art. il. 1956. 3.00. Columbia
CHAGALL, MARC. 1887- (927)
Chagall, Marc. Chagall: Portfolio with text. il. 1960. 1.50. World Pub.
Venturi, Lionello. Chagall. il. 1956. 5.75. World Pub.
CHAIRS (749)
Iverson, Marion D. American chair: 1630-1890. il. by Ernest Donnelly.
1957. 10.00. Hastings
Ormsbee, Thomas H. Windsor chair. 7.95. Hearthside
CHALK-TALKS (741.2)
Barnett, Stella O. Better chalk talks. 2.25. Revell
Tarbell, Harlan. Chalk talk stunts. il. 1926. 1.00. Denison
CHAMBER MUSIC (785.7)
Ulrich, Homer. Chamber music. 1948. 6.75. Columbia
CHAMBERLAIN, JOSEPH 1836-1914 (923.242)
Garvin, James L. Life of Joseph Chamberlain. 4 vols. vol. 1. 1836-1885;
Chamberlain and democracy. 5.00. vol. 2. 1885-1895: Disruption and combat.
4.00. vol. 3. 1895-1900: Empire and world policy. o.p; vol. 4. 1901-1903: At
the height of his power. Amery, Julian. 6.00. St. Martins
CHAMBERLAIN, NEVILLE, 1869-1940 (923.242)
Macleod, Iain. Neville Chamberlain. il. 1962. 5.75. Atheneum

CHAMPLAIN, SAMUEL DE, 1567-1635 (923. 9)
Ritchie, C. T. First Canadian: The story of Champlain. il. 2. 95. St. Martins
CHANCE (795. 01)
Figgis, Eric. Gambling: Challenge to chance. 5. 00. Wehman
Venn, J. Logic of chance. 4th ed. 4. 50. Chelsea
CHANCELLORSVILLE, BATTLE OF, 1863 (973. 734)
Stackpole, Edward J. Chancellorsville: Lee's greatest battle. il. 1958. 5. 75.
  Stackpole
CHANG, HENG, 78-139 (895)
Hughes, Ernest R. Two Chinese poets: Vignettes of Han life and thought. 1960.
CHANNING, WILLIAM ELLERY, 1780-1842. (922. 8173)
Rice, Madeleine H. Federal Street pastor: Life of William Ellery Channing.
  6. 00. Twayne
CHANTS (783. 5)
Apel, Willi. Gregorian chant. il. 1957. 15. 00. Indiana
Werner, E. Sacred bridge. 1956. 15. 00. Columbia
CHAPMAN, JOHN, 1774-1845 (923. 6)
Price, Robert. Johnny Appleseed: Man and myth. il. 1954. 5. 00. Indiana
CHAPMAN, JOHN JAY, 1862-1933 (923. 4)
Hovey, Richard B. John Jay Chapman: An American mind. 1959. 6. 50.
  Columbia
CHARACTER (137)
Abbott, Andrew. Key to character reading. 1959. bds. 1. 00. Ottenheimer
Eddy, Edward D. College influence on student character. 1959. 3. 00. A. C. E.
Kunkel, Fritz. What it means to grow up. 1955. 3. 00. Scribner
Peck, R. F., and R. J. Havighurst. Psychology of character development.
  1960. 6. 50. Wiley
Riesman, D. Faces in the crowd. 1952. 10. 00. Yale
CHARACTERS AND CHARACTERISTICS (137)
Allport, Gordon W. Pattern and growth in personality. 1961. 7. 50. Holt,
  Rinehart & Winston
Dingwall, Eric J. Some human oddities. il. 1962. 6. 00. U. Books
Frederick, J. George. What is your emotional age? 1928. 3. 00. Bus. Bourse
Jung, C. G. Psychological types. 1959. 7. 50. Pantheon
Kunkel, Fritz. In search of maturity. 1943. 3. 95. Scribner
Wallace, Irving. Square pegs. 1957. 5. 00. Knopf
CHARACTERS AND CHARACTERISTICS IN LITERATURE (809)
Boyce, Benjamin. Character-sketches in Pope's poems. il. 1962. 5. 00. Duke
Elwood, Maren. Characters make your story. 4. 50. Writer
Wallace, Irving. Fabulous originals. 1955. 4. 50. Knopf
CHARCOAL-DRAWING (741. 22)
Fitzgerald, Edmond J. Painting and drawing in charcoal and oil. 1959. 4. 95.
  Reinhold
CHARITABLE USES, TRUSTS AND FOUNDATIONS (347. 65)
Simes, Lewis M. Public policy and the dead hand. 1955. 5. 50. U. of Mich.
CHARITIES (361)
Laubach, Frank C. World is learning compassion. 3. 50. Revell
Mandeville, Bernard. Fable of the bees. 3. 50. 1962. Putnam
CHARITIES--U.S. (361)
Bornet, Vaughn D. Welfare in America. il. 1960. 4. 95. U. of Okla.
Bremmer, Robert H. American philanthropy. 1960. 4. 50; pap. 1. 75. U. of
  Chicago
Bremner, Robert H. From the depths: The discovery of poverty in the United
  States. il. 1956. 5. 50. N. Y. U.
Cohen. Social work in the American tradition. 5. 00. Holt, Rinehart & Winston
Kurtz, Russell H., ed. Social work year book. vol. 14, 1960. 8. 50. Nat. Assn.
  of Social Workers
CHARLEMAGNE, 742-814) (398. 22)
Einhard. Life of Charlemagne. 1960. 4. 40. U. of Mich.

Lamb, Harold. Charlemagne: The legend and the man. 1954. 4.50. Doubleday
Wallach, Luitpold. Alcuin and Charlemagne: Studies in Carolingian history
   and literature. 1959. 6.50. Cornell
CHARLES II, KING OF ENGLAND, 1630-1685 (923.142)
Pearson, Hesketh. Merry monarch: The life and likeness of Charles II. il.
   1960. 5.00. Harper
CHARM (646.7)
Cornell, Betty. Betty Cornell's teen-age popularity guide. 1953. 3.95.
   Prentice-Hall
Dumont, Theron Q. Personal magnetism. 2.95. Wehman
Francis, Arlene. That certain something. 1960. bds. 3.00. Messner
King, Eleanore. Eleanore King's guide to glamor. 1957. 4.95. Prentice-Hall
MacFadyen, Mary. Beauty plus. il. 1947. 3.95. Emerson
Powers, and Partington. John Robert Powers way to teenage beauty, charm and
   popularity. 1962. 3.95. Prentice-Hall
Powers, John R., and Mary S. Miller. Secrets of charm. il. 1954. 4.50. Winston
CHARTISM (342.4)
Briggs, Asa. Chartist studies. 1959. 9.00. St. Martins
Hammond, John L., and Barbara. Age of the Chartists, 1832-1854. 1930. 8.50.
   Shoe String
Mather, F. C. Public order in the age of the Chartists. 1959. 6.50. Barnes &
   Noble
CHARTRES, FRANCE--NOTRE-DAME (CATHEDRAL) (726.6)
Adams, Henry. Mont Saint Michel and Chartres. il. 6.00. Houghton
Dierick, Alfons. Stained glass at Chartres. il. 1960. 2.00. Taplinger
Kidson, Peter, and Ursula Pariser. Sculpture at Chartres. il. 1959. 6.50.
   Transatlantic
CHASE, SALMON PORTLAND, 1808-1873 (923.4)
Belden, Thomas G., and Marva R. So fell the angels. 1956. 6.50. Little
CHATTANOOGA, BATTLE OF, 1863 (973.7359)
Downey, Fairfax. Storming of the gateway: Chattanooga, 1863. il. 1960. 5.50.
   McKay
CHATTANOOGA RAILROAD EXPEDITION, 1862 (973.73)
O'Neill, Charles. Wild train: The story of the Andrews Raiders. 1956. 6.00.
   Random
CHAUCER, GEOFFREY, d. 1400 (821.17)
Baum, Paull F. Chaucer, a critical appreciation. 6.00. Duke
Baum, Paull F. Chaucer's verse. 1961. 6.00. Duke
Bennett, Henry Stanley. Chaucer and the fifteenth century. 1947. 6.00.
   Oxford U. P.
Bennett, J. A. W. Parlement of foules: An Interpretation. 1957. 5.60. Oxford
   U. P.
Bowden, Muriel. Commentary on the general prologue to the Canterbury tales.
   1948. 6.00. Macmillan
Bronson, Bertrand H. In search of Chaucer. 1960. 3.50. U. of Toronto
Bryan, William F., and G. C. Dempster, eds. Sources and analogues of
   Chaucer's Canterbury tales. 15.00. Humanities
Chute, Marchette. Geoffrey Chaucer of England. il. 1951. 5.00. pap. 1.55. Dutton
Coghill, Nevill. Poet Chaucer. 1949. 1.70. Oxford U. P.
Coulton, G. G. Chaucer and his England. il. 5.00. Dutton
Curry, Walter C. Chaucer and the medieval sciences. 1959. 4.50. Barnes &
   Noble
Dempster, Germaine. Dramatic irony in Chaucer. 1959. 3.75. Humanities
Dodd, William G. Courtly love in Gower and Chaucer. 1958. 4.00. Smith,
   Peter
Eisner, Sigmund. A tale of wonder: A source study of Chaucer's The wife of
   Bath's tale. 1957. 6.50. Franklin, B.
French, R. D. Chaucer handbook. il. 1947. 4.00. Appleton

Gerould, G. H. Chaucerian essays. 1952. 2.00. Princeton
Griffith, Dudley D. Bibliography of Chaucer, 1908-1953. 1955. 5.00. U. of Wash.
Kittredge, George Lyman. Chaucer and his poetry. 1915. 3.50. Harvard
Kokeritz, H. Guide to Chaucer's pronunciation. 1962. pap. 1.00. Holt, Rinehart
   & Winston
Lawrence, William W. Chaucer and the Canterbury tales. 1950. 4.00.
   Columbia
Legouis, Emile. Geoffrey Chaucer. 6.50. Russell
Lounsbury, Thomas R. Studies in Chaucer. His life and writings. 3 vols. 1962.
   30.00. Russell
Lowes, J. L. Geoffrey Chaucer. 1934. 3.50. Oxford U. P.
Lumiansky, R. M. Of sondry folk: The aramatic principle in the Canterbury
   Tales. il. 1955. 5.00. U. of Tex.
Magoun, Francis P., Jr. Chaucer gazetteer. 1961. 3.50. U. of Chicago
Manly, J. M. Some new light on Chaucer. il. 4.00. Smith, Peter
Manly, John M, and Edith Rickert. Text of the Canterbury tales. 8 vols. il.
   1940. 75.00. U. of Chicago
Muscatine, Charles. Chaucer and the French tradition. 1960. 6.00. U. of Calif.
Owen, Charles A., Jr., ed. Discussions of the Canterbury tales. 1961. pap.
   1.40. Heath
Preston, R. Chaucer. 5.00. Humanities
Root, R. K. Poetry of Chaucer. 4.00. Smith, Peter
Schoeck, Richard, and Jerome Taylor, eds. Chaucer criticism: The Canter-
   bury tales. 1960. 1.45. U. of Notre Dame
Schoeck, Richard, and Jerome Taylor, eds. Chaucer criticism: Troilus and
   Criseyde and the minor poems. 1961. 1.95. U. of Notre Dame
Spurgeon, Caroline F. E. Five hundred years of Chaucer criticism and
   allusion. 3 vols. 1960. 35.00. Russell
Tatlock, John S. P. Mind and art of Chaucer. 1950. 2.50. Syracuse
Wagenknecht, Edward C., ed. Chaucer: Modern essays in criticism. 4.75.
   Smith, Peter

CHATAUQUAS (790)
Gould, Joseph E. Chautauqua movement. il. 1961. 4.50. Univ. Pub.
Harrison, Harry P. Culture under canvas: The story of tent Chautauqua. ed.
   by Karl Detzer. 1957. 6.50. Hastings

CHECKERS (794.2)
Grover, Kenneth M., and Thomas Wiswell. Let's play checkers. 1940. 2.50.
   McKay
Reinfeld, Fred. How to be a winner at checkers. il. 1960. 2.95. Doubleday
Wiswell, Thomas, and Millard F. Hopper. Checker kings in action. il. 1952.
   2.75. McKay

CHECKS (332.76)
Sternitzky, Julius L, Forgery and fictitious checks. il. 1955. 4.75. Thomas
   C. C.

CHEERS (371.898)
Brings, Lawrence M. Master pep book. 1957. 4.50. Denison
Loken, N. Cheerleading. 1961. 2.95. Ronald

CHEESE (637)
Van Slyke, Lucius L., and Walter V. Price. Cheese. 6.95. Judd

CHEKHOV, ANTON PAVLOVICH, 1860-1904 (928)
Bruford, W. H. Chekhov and his Russia. 3.75. Humanities
Magarshack, David. Chekhov: A life. il. 1953. 6.00. Grove
Simmons, Ernest J. Chekhov. il. 1962. 10.00. Little

CHEMICAL ELEMENTS (661.1)
Aller, Lawrence H. Abundance of the elements. 1961. 10.00. Wiley
Latimer, Wendell M. Oxidation potentials. 1952. 12.00. Prentice-Hall
Sidgwick, N. V. Chemical elements and their compounds. 2 vols. il. 1950.
   18.00. Oxford U. P.

CHEMICAL ENGINEERING (660.28)
Anderson, L. B., and Wenzel. Introduction to chemical engineering. 1961.
9.50. McGraw
Carr, E., ed. Chemical engineering processes and equipment. 1955. 5.50.
Transatlantic
Hesse, Herman C., and John H. Rushton. Process equipment design. il. 1945.
9.50. Van Nostrand
Perry, John H. Chemical engineers' handbook. 1963. 25.00. McGraw

Rumford, Frank. Chemical engineering operations. 1952. 7.50. Tudor
Taylor, F. Sherwood. History of industrial chemistry. il. 1957. 7.50. Abelard
CHEMICAL ENGINEERING--DICTIONARIES (660.2803)
Carpovich, Eugene A. Chemical dictionary. Russian-English. 1961. 14.00.
Tech. Dictionaries (R)
Ernst, Richard, and Ingeborg E. von Morgenstern. Concise German-English
chemical dictionary. 1962. 7.95. Crowell (R)
CHEMICAL ENGINEERING AS A PROFESSION (660.069)
Feder, Raymond L. Your future in chemical engineering. 1961. 2.95. Richards
Rosen
CHEMICAL EQUILIBRUIM (541.392)
Hogness, Thorfin R., and Warren C. Johnson. Introduction to qualitative
analysis. 1957. 5.00. Holt, Rinehart & Winston
Moelwyn-Hughes, Emyr A. States of matter. il. 1961. 3.50. Wiley
CHEMICAL INDUSTRIES (660)
Happel, John. Chemical process economics. il. 1958. 7.50. Wiley
Perry, John H. Chemical business handbook. 1955. 22.00. McGraw
CHEMICAL MODELS (660.078)
Sanderson, Robert T. Teaching chemistry with models. il. 1962. 5.75. Van
Nostrand
CHEMICAL REACTION--CONDITIONS AND LAWS (541.39)
Ketelaar, J. A. A. Chemical constitution: An introduction to the theory of the
chemical bond. il. 8.95. Am. Elsevier
CHEMICAL REACTION, RATE OF (541.39)
Eyring, H., and E. M. Modern chemical kinetics. 1962. 1.95. Reinhold
Melander, Lars C. S. Isotope effects on reaction rates. 1960. 6.00. Ronald
Penner, Stanford S. Introduction to the study of chemical reactions in flow
systems. 3.00. Pergamon
CHEMICAL REACTIONS (541.39)
Barnett, E. de Barry. Mechanism of organic chemical reactions. il. 1956.
6.50. Wiley
Kosower, Edward M. Molecular biochemistry. 1962. 12.50. McGraw
Slater, Noel B. Theory of unimolecular reactions. 1959. 4.75. Cornell
Vander Werf, Calvin A. Acids, bases, and the chemistry of the covalent bond.
il. 1961. 1.95. Reinhold
CHEMICAL TESTS AND REAGENTS (543.01)
Busev, A. A., and N. G. Polyanskii. Use of organic reagents in inorganic
analysis. 1960. 3.50. Pergamon
International Union of Chemistry. Reagents for qualitative inorganic analysis.
ed. by Paul E. Wenger and R. Duckert. il. 1948. 9.50. Am Elsevier
Rosin, Joseph. Reagent chemicals and standards. 1961. 14.50. Van Nostrand
Welcher, Frank. Organic analytical reagents. 4 vols. 48.50. Van Nostrand
CHEMICAL WARFARE (358.34)
Medical manual of chemical warfare. il. 1956. 4.00. Tudor
CHEMICALS (661)
Foulger, John H. Chemicals, drugs, and health. 1959. 4.25. Thomas C. C.
Mellan, Ibert, and Eleanor. Encyclopedia of chemical labeling. 1961. 8.50?
Tudor
Thomas, Edward. Chemical inventions and chemical patents. 1950. 16.50.
Boardman, Clark

Young, J. A. Elements of general chemistry. 1960. 6.95. Prentice-Hall
CHEMISTRY--DICTIONARIES (540.03)
Clark, George L., and G. G. Hawley, eds. Encyclopedia of chemistry. 1957.
19.50 10.00. Reinhold (R)
Hackh, Ingo W. D. Chemical dictionary. 1963. 22.50. McGraw (R)
Kingzett, C. T. Chemical encyclopaedia. 8th ed. 1952. 18.50. Van Nostrand (R)
Rose, Arthur, and Elizabeth G. eds. Condensed chemical dictionary. 1961. 17.50.
Reinhold (R)
Van Nostrand. Van Nostrand's chemist's dictionary. ed. by George W. Murphy,
and others. il. 1953. 12.00. Van Nostrand
Witty, M. B., and others. Dictionary of chemical abbreviations. lib. bdg. 18.50.
Seti
CHEMISTRY--HISTORY (540)
Berry, A. J. From classical to modern chemistry. 1954. 5.50. Cambridge U. P.
Boas, Marie. Robert Boyle and seventeenth century chemistry. 1958. 5.50.
Cambridge U. P.
Clements, Richard. Modern chemical discoveries. il. 1954. 5.00. Dutton
Farber, E. Evolution of chemistry. 1952. 6.00. Ronald
Farber, Eduard. Great chemists. il. 1961. 29.50. Wiley
Findlay, Alexander. Hundred years of chemistry. 3.25. Macmillan
Friend, John Newton. Man and the chemical elements. il. 1961. 6.00. Scribner
Irwin, Keith Gordon. Romance of chemistry: From ancient alchemy to
nuclear fissions. il. 1959. 3.75. Viking
Jaffe, Barnard. Crucibles: The story of chemistry. abridged. 1960. pap. 0.50.
Fawcett
Leicester, H. M., and H. S. Klickstein. Source book in chemistry, 1400-1900.
il. 1956. 7.50. Harvard
Moore, Farris J. History of chemistry. il. 1939. 7.95. McGraw
Newcomb, Ellsworth, and Hugh Kenny. Alchemy to atoms. il. 1961. 2.95.
Putnam
Partington, James R. Short history of chemistry. 1957. 4.25. St. Martins
Stillman, J. M. Story of alchemy and early chemistry. 4.50. Smith, Peter
CHEMISTRY--PROBLEMS, EXERCISES, ETC. (540)
Anderson, H. V. Chemical calculations. 1955. 4.95. McGraw
Babor, Joseph A., and Chester B. Kremer. How to solve problems in general
chemistry. 1955. pap. 1.75. Crowell
Babor, Joseph A., and J. Kenneth W. Macalpine. How to solve problems in
qualitative analysis. 1943. pap. 1.25. Crowell
CHEMISTRY--STUDY AND TEACHING (540.07)
Sanderson, Robert T. Teaching chemistry with models. il. 1962. 5.75. Van
Nostrand
CHEMISTRY--TABLES, ETC. (540)
Atack, F. W. Handbook of chemical data. 1957. 6.75. Reinhold (R)
Bauer, Edward L. Statistical manual for chemists. 1960. 4.75. Academic
Press
Bruce, James, and Harry Harper. Tables for qualitative analysis. 1949. 0.35.
St. Martins
Kaye, George W. C., and T. H. Laby. Tables of physical and chemical con-
stants. 1959. 5.00. Wiley
CHEMISTRY--TERMINOLOGY (540.014)
Fieser, Louis F., and Mary. Style guide for chemists. il. 1960. 2.95.
Reinhold (R)
CHEMISTRY, ANALYTIC (543)
Briscoe, Henry V. A., and Peter F. Holt. Inorganic micro-analysis. 1950.
3.00. St. Martins
Ewing, Galen W. Instrumental methods for chemical analysis. 1960. 9.50.
McGraw
Griffin, Roger Castle. Technical methods of analysis. il. 1927. 14.50. McGraw

Jacobs, Morris B. Chemical analysis of foods and food products. il. 1958. 15.75. Van Nostrand

Jones, A. G. Analytical chemistry: Some new techniques. 1958. 7.50. Academic Press

Meites, Louis, and Henry C. Thomas. Advanced analytical chemistry. 1958. 9.50. McGraw

Swift, Ernest H. System of chemical analysis. 1939. 6.50. Freeman

Treadwell, F. P., and William T. Hall. Qualitative analysis. 1937. 8.75. Wiley

Walton, Harold F. Principles and methods of chemical analysis. 10.35. Prentice-Hall

Willard, Hobart H., and others. Instrumental methods of analysis. 1958. 8.25. Van Nostrand

CHEMISTRY, ANALYTIC--QUALITATIVE (544)

Clifford, Alan F. Inorganic chemistry of qualitative analysis. 1961. 6.95. Prentice-Hall

Feigl, Fritz. Spot tests in inorganic analysis. tr. by Ralph E. Oesper. 1960. 13.25. Am. Elsevier

Hogness, Thorfin R., and Warren C. Johnson. Introduction to qualitative analysis. 1957. 5.00. Holt, Rinehart & Winston

Hogness, Thorfin R., and Warren C. Johnson. Ionic equilibrium as applied to qualitative analysis. 1954. 5.00. Holt, Rinehart & Winston

Hogness, Thorfin R., and Warren C. Johnson. Qualitative analysis and chemical equilibrium. 1954. 6.25. Holt

Nordmann, J. B. Qualitative testing and inorganic chemistry. 1957. 6.50. Wiley

Noyes, Arthur A., and Ernest H. Swift. Course of instruction in the qualitative chemical analysis of inorganic substances. 1942. 5.90. Macmillan

Sorum, Clarence H. Introduction to semimicro qualitative analysis. il. 1953. 3.95. Prentice-Hall

Swift, Ernest H., and William P. Schaefer. Qualitative elemental analysis. il. 1962. 6.75. Freeman

CHEMISTRY, ANALYTIC--QUANTITATIVE (545)

Arenson, S. B. How to solve problems in quantitative analysis. 1959. pap. 1.75. Crowell

Benedetti-Pichler, A. A. Essentials of quantitative analysis. 1956. 12.50. Ronald

Charlot, Gaston, and Denise Bezier. Quantitative inorganic analysis. 1957. 16.50. Wiley

Daggett, Albert F., and William B. Meldrum. Quantitative analysis. 1955. 6.50. Heath

Engelder, C. J. Calculations of quantitative analysis. 1939. 2.90. Wiley

Fales, Harold A., and Frederic Kenny. Inorganic quantitative analysis. il. 6.50. Appleton

Fischer, Robert B. Quantitative chemical analysis. il. 1961. 6.75. Saunders

Kolthoff, Izaak M., and E. B. Sandell. Textbook of quantitative inorganic analysis. 1952. 7.50. Macmillan

Olson, Axel R., and others. Introductory quantitative chemistry. il. 1956. 5.75. Freeman

Peters, John P., and Donald D. Van Slyke. Quantitative clinical chemistry. vol. 1, Interpretations. il. 1946. 7.00; vol. 2, Methods. il. 1932. 10.00. Williams & Wilkins

Pierce, W. C., and others. Qualtitative analysis. 1958. 5.75. Wiley

Smith, W. T., and Ralph L. Shriner. Examination of new organic compounds. 1956. 3.75. Wiley

Vogel, A. I. Textbook of quantitative inorganic analysis. 1961. 12.00. Wiley

Walton, H. F. Elementary quantitative analysis. 1958. 7.90. Prentice-Hall

Willard, Hobart H., and others. Elements of quantitative analysis. il. 1956. 6.25. Van Nostrand

CHEMISTRY, INORGANIC (546)

Busev, A. A., and N. G. Polyanskii. Use of organic reagents in inorganic analysis. 1960. 3.50. Pergamon

Cavell, Alexander C. Inorganic chemistry. 2.50. St. Martins

Caven, R. M., and others. Systematic inorganic chemistry. il. 1946. 8.00. Van Nostrand

Day, Marion C., Jr., and Joel Selbin. Theoretical inorganic chemistry. il. 1962. 12.00. Reinhold

Gilreath, Esmarch S. Fundamental concepts of inorganic chemistry. 1958. 8.50. McGraw

Gould, Edwin S. Inorganic reactions and structure. 1962. 8.50. Holt, Rinehart & Winston

Griffin, Carroll W. Inorganic quantitative analysis. 1954. 5.95. McGraw

Heslop, R. B., and P. L. Robinson. Inorganic chemistry. il. 1959. 9.00. Am. Elsevier

Latimer, Wendell M., and Joel H. Hildebrand. Reference book of inorganic chemistry. il. 6.25. Principles of chemistry. 9.50. Macmillan

Moeller, Therald. Inorganic chemistry. 1952. 10.75. Wiley

Partington, James R. General and inorganic chemistry for university students. il. 10.00. St. Martins

Pollard, F. H., and J. F. W. McOmie. Chromatographic methods of inorganic analysis. 1953. 5.50. Academic Press

Tyree, S. Young, Jr., and Kerro Knox. Textbook of inorganic chemistry. 1961. 7.00. Macmillan

CHEMISTRY, MEDICAL AND PHARMACEUTICAL (615.19)

Barlow, R. B. Introduction to chemical pharmacology. 1955. 6.50. Wiley

Burger, Alfred. Medicinal chemistry. il. 1960. 35.00. Wiley

Evers, Norman, and Dennis Caldwell. Chemistry of drugs. il. 1959. 12.75. Wiley

Jenkins, Glenn L., and others. Chemistry of organic medicinal products. 1957. 10.75. Wiley

CHEMISTRY, ORGANIC (547)

Alexander, E. R. Principles of ionic organic reactions. 1950. 6.50. Wiley

Barnett, E. de Barry. Mechanism of organic chemical reactions. il. 1956. 6.50. Wiley

Beynon, J. H. Mass spectrometry and its use in organic chemistry. il. 1960. 24.00. Am. Elsevier

Campbell, Neil. Qualitative organic chemistry. 2.00. St. Martins

Cason, J. Essential principles of organic chemistry. 11.00. 8.25. Prentice-Hall

Conant, James B., and Albert Harold Blatt. Chemistry of organic compounds. 7.95. Macmillan

Cram, Donald, and George S. Hammond. Organic chemistry. 1959. 9.75; instructor's manual, 1.50. McGraw

Day, Allan R., and Madeleine R. Joullie. Organic chemistry. 1960. 9.50. Van Nostrand

English, James, Jr., and Harold G. Cassidy, Jr. Principles of organic chemistry. 1961. 8.95. McGraw

Fieser, Louis F., and Mary. Basic organic chemistry. 1959. 6.25. Heath

Fieser, Louis F., and Mary. Introduction to organic chemistry. 1957. 8.75. Heath

Fieser, Louis F., and M. Organic chemistry. 1956. 10.00. Reinhold

Hart, Harold, and Robert D. Schuetz. Short course in organic chemistry. 6.50. 1961. Houghton

Leffler, John E. Short course of organic chemistry. il. 1959. 5.75. Macmillan

Morrison, Robert T., and Robert N. Boyd. Organic chemistry. 1959. 14.35; 10.75. Allyn & Bacon

Noller, Carl R. Chemistry of organic compounds. il. 1957. 9.00. Saunders
Noller, Carl R. Structure and properties of organic compounds: A brief
    survey. il. 1962. 6.00. Saunders
Robertson, J. Monteath. Organic crystals and molecules: Theory of x-ray
    structure analysis, with applications to organic chemistry. il. 1953. 5.00.
    Cornell
Sykes, P. Guidebook to mechanism in organic chemistry. 1961. 3.95. Wiley
Wertheim, Edgar. Practical organic chemistry. il. 1953. 5.25. McGraw
Wheland, George W. Advanced organic chemistry. 1960. 16.00. Wiley
CHEMISTRY, PHYSICAL AND THEORETICAL (541)
Brey, Wallace, S., Jr. Principles of physical chemistry. il. 1958. 7.00.
    Appleton
Daniels, Farrington. Mathematical preparation for physical chemistry. 1928.
    4.90; 1959. McGraw
Daniels, Farrington, and R. A. Alberty. Physical chemistry. 1961. 8.95. Wiley
Glasstone, Samuel, and David Lewis. Elements of physical chemistry. il. 1960.
    8.50. Van Nostrand
Glasstone, Samuel. Textbook of physical chemistry. il. 1946. 12.95. Van Nos-
    trand
Gold, V., ed. Advances in physical organic chemistry. vol. 1. in prep.
    Academic Press
Hamill, W., and R. R. Williams. Principles of physical chemistry. 1959.
    8.95. Prentice-Hall
Hutchinson, Eric. Electrons, elements and compounds. il. 1959. 6.00.
    Saunders
Klotz, I. M. Some principles of energetics in biochemical reactions. il. 1957.
    3.00. Academic Press
Margenau, Henry, and George Moseley Murphy. Mathematics of physics and
    chemistry. il. 1956. 9.25. Van Nostrand
Moelwyn-Hughes, E. A. Physical chemistry. 1940. 11.00. Cambridge U. P.
Moore, Walter John. Physical chemistry. 2nd ed. 1955. 11.65. 8.75. 1962. 14.65.
    Prentice-Hall
Oparin, A. I. Origin of life on the earth. 1957. 7.50. Academic Press
Rice, F. O., and Edward Teller. Structure of matter. 1949. 7.75. Wiley
CHEMISTRY, TECHNICAL (660)
Findlay, Alexander. Chemistry in the service of man. il. 1960. pap. 1.75.
    Harper
Lange, Norbert A. Handbook of chemistry. 1961. 11.00. McGraw
Leighou, Robert B. Chemistry of engineering materials. il. 1942. 9.50. McGraw
Pyke, Magnus. About chemistry. il. 1960. 4.50. Macmillan
Riegel, Emil R. Industrial chemistry. ed. by J. A. Kent. 1962. 20.00. Reinhold
Snell, Foster D. and Cornelia T. Dictionary of commercial chemicals. il.
    1962. 12.50. Van Nostrand (R)
Haynes, Williams. Chemical trade names and commercial synonyms. 1955.
    8.50. Van Nostrand (R)
CHEMISTRY, TECHNICAL--RESEARCH (660)
Griffith, R. H. Practice of research in the chemical industries. 1949. 2.40.
    Oxford
CHEMISTRY AS A PROFESSION (540.069)
Pollack, Philip. Careers and opportunities in chemistry. il. 1960. 3.50.
    Dutton
CHEMISTS (925.4)
Farber, Eduard. Great chemists. il. 1961. 29.50. (Interscience) Wiley
Farber, Eduard. Nobel Prize winners in chemistry: 1901-1961. il. 1962. 6.50.
    Abelard
Findlay, Alexander. Hundred years of chemistry. 3.25. Macmillan
Jaffe, Barnard. Crucibles: The story of chemistry. abridged. 1960. pap. 0.50.
    Fawcett

Smith, Henry Monmouth. Torchbearers of chemistry. 1949. 8.50. Academic
Press
CHEMOTHERAPY (616.8918)
Battista, Orlando. Mental drugs: Chemistry's challenge to psychotherapy.
1960. 3.95. Chilton
McIlwain. Chemotherapy and the central nervous system. 1957. 10.00. Little
Reinfeld, Fred. Miracle drugs and the new age of medicine. 1959. 3.95. Sterling
CHENNAULT, CLAIRE LEE, 1890-1958 (923.5)
Scott, Robert L., Jr. Flying Tiger: Chennault of China. 1959. 3.95. Doubleday
CHESAPEAKE AND OHIO CANAL (386.4)
Sanderlin, W. S. Great national project: A history of the Chesapeake and
Ohio Canal. 1946. 4.00. Johns Hopkins
CHESS (794.1)
Alexander, C. H. O. Chess. 3.75. Pitman
Assiac. Delights of chess. il. 1961. 4.95. Barnes, A. S.
Capablanca, J. R. Primer of chess. il. 4.50. Harcourt
Chernev, Irving, and Fred Reinfeld. Fireside book of chess. 1949. 5.95.
S. and S.
Chernev, Irving. Logical chess, move by move. 1957. 3.95. S. and S.
Horowitz, I. A., and Fred Reinfeld. How to improve your chess. il. 1962. 4.00.
Harvey
Horowitz, I. A., and Fred Reinfeld. Macmillan handbook of chess. il. 1956.
4.95. Macmillan
Reinfeld, Fred. Complete chess course. il. 1959. 5.95. Doubleday
CHESSMAN, CARYL, 1921-1960 (923)
Machlin, Milton, and William R. Woodfield. Ninth life. il. 1961. 4.95. Putnam
CHEST--SURGERY (617.54)
Bordicks, Kathrine J. Nursing care of patients having chest surgery. 1962.
3.00. Macmillan
Collis, J. Leigh, and L. E. Mabbitt. Handbook of chest surgery for nurses. il. 1956
3.75. Williams & Wilkins
CHESTER PLAYS (822)
Salter, F. M. Mediaeval drama in Chester. il. 1955. 4.50. U. of Toronto
CHESTERFIELD, PHILIP DORMER STANHOPE, 4th EARL OF, 1694-1773 (923.242)
Shellabarger, Samuel. Lord Chesterfield and his world. 1951. 5.00. Little
CHESTERTON, GILBERT KEITH, 1874-1936 (928)
Chesterton, Gilbert K. Autobiography. 4.00. Sheed
Ward, Maisie. Gilbert Keith Chesterton. il. 3.00. Sheed
Wills, Garry. Chesterton, man and mask. 1961. 4.50. Sheed
CHEVREUL, MICHEL EUGENE, 1786-1889 (925)
Costa, Albert B. Michel Eugene Chevreul: Pioneer of organic chemistry. 1962
3.50. Wis. State Hist. Soc.
CHIANG KAI-SHEK, 1886- (923.151)
Paneth, P. Chiang Kai Shek. il. 2.00. Transatlantic
CHICAGO--HAYMARKET SQUARE RIOT, 1886 (977.311)
David, Henry. History of the Haymarket affair. 6.75. Russell
CHICAGO--SOCIAL CONDITIONS (917.7311)
Abrahamson, Julia H. Neighborhood finds itself. 1959. 5.00. Harper
Addams, Jane. Twenty years at Hull-House. il. 1923. 6.00. Macmillan
Anderson, Nels. Hobo: The sociology of the homeless man. il. 1961. pap. 1.95.
U. of Chicago
Thrasher, Frederic M. Gang: A study of 1313 gangs in Chicago. 1936. 7.50. U.
of Chicago
CHICAGO STRIKE, 1894
Manning, Thomas G. Chicago strike of 1894: Industrial labor in the nineteenth
century. pap. 1.00. Holt, Rinehart & Winston
Warne, Colston E., ed. Pullman boycott of 1894: The problem of federal
intervention. 1955. pap. 1.50. Heath

<u>CHICKAMAUGA, BATTLE OF,</u> 1863 (978.09)
Tucker, Glenn. Chickamauga: Bloody battle of the West. 1961. 6.00. Bobbs
<u>CHILD PSYCHIATRY</u> (618.92)
Bender, Lauretts. Dynamic psychopathology of childhood. il. 1954. 7.50.
    Thomas, C. C
Bettelheim, Bruno. Truants from life: The rehabilitation of emotionally dis-
    turbed children. 1955. 6.00. Free Press
Bovet, L. Psychiatric aspects of juvenile delinquency. 1951. 1.00. Int. Doc.
    Service-Columbia
Burns, Charles. Mental health in childhood. 1956. 2.75. Fides
Caplan, Gerald, ed. Emotional problems of early childhood. 1955. 10.00. Basic
    Books
Cruickshank, W., ed. Psychology of exceptional children and youth. 1955.
    10.35. 7.50. Prentice-Hall
Delacato, Carl H. Treatment and prevention of reading problems. il. 1961.
    4.75. Thomas, C. C
Finch, Stuart M. Fundamentals of child psychiatry. 1960. 6.50. Norton
Freud, Anna. Psychoanalysis for teachers and parents. 1935. 2.25. Emerson
Freud, Anna. Psychoanalytical treatment of children. 1960. 2.50. Int. Univs.
Getz, Steven. Environment and the deaf child. 1956. 3.75. Thomas, C. C.
Gondor, Emery I. Art and play therapy. 1954. pap. 0.95. Random
Greenberg, Harold A. Child psychology in the community. 1950. 4.25. Putnam
Kanner, Leo. Child psychiatry. 1960. 10.50. Thomas, C. C
Klein, Melanie. Psychoanalysis of children. 5.00. Hillary
Kramer, Edith. Art terapy in a children's community. il. 1958. 6.75?
    Thomas, C. C
Lippman, Hyman S. Treatment of the child in emotional conflict. 1962. 9.50.
    McGraw
Moustakas, Clark E. Children in play therapy. 1953. 4.75. McGraw
Riese, Bertha. Heal the hurt child. 1962. 8.50. U. of Chicago
<u>CHILD PSYCHIATRY--CASES, CLINICAL REPORTS, STATISTICS</u> (618.92)
Baruch, Dorothy W. One little boy. 3.50. Julian
Bennett, Ivy. Delinquent and neurotic children. 1960. 10.00. Basic Books
Pearson, Gerald H. J. Emotional disorders of children. 1949. 6.50. Norton
Soddy, Kenneth. Clinical child psychiatry. 1961. 8.50. Williams & Wilkins
<u>CHILD STUDY</u> (136.7)
American Council on Education, Division on Child Development and Teacher
    Personnel. Helping teachers understand children. 3.50. A. C. E.
Ausubel, D. P. Theory and problems of child development. 1958. 11.75. Grune
Baker, Harry J. Introduction to exceptional children. il. 1959. 6.90. Macmillan
Baldwin, Alfred L. Behavior and development in childhood. 1955. 7.25. Holt,
    Rinehart & Winston
Barclay, Dorothy. Understanding the city child. 1959. 4.95. Watts
Bender, Lauretta. Aggression, hostility and anxiety in children. il. 1953.
    5.50. Thomas, C. C
Bettelheim, Bruno. Love is not enough: The treatment of emotionally dis-
    turbed children. 1950. 5.00. Free Press
Blair, Arthur Witt, and William H. Burton. Growth and development of the
    pre-adolescent. 1951. 2.75. Appleton
Bossard, James H. S., and Eleanor S. Boll. Sociology of child development.
    1960. 8.50. Harper
Breckenridge, Marian E., and E. Lee Vincent. Child development. il. 1960.
    6.50. Saunders
Buhler, Charlotte, and others. Childhood problems and the teacher. il. 1952.
    4.75. Holt
Buhler, Charlotte. From birth to maturity. 4.00. Humanities
Buhler, Karl. Mental development of the child. 1954. 3.00. Humanities
Carmichael. Leonard. Manual of child psychology . 1954. 13.50. Wiley

Cole, Luella, and J. J. B. Morgan. Psychology of childhood and adolescence. 1947. 5.50. Holt, Rinehart & Winston

Cox, Catharine M. Early mental traits of three hundred geniuses. 10.00. Stanford

Crow, Lester D., and Alice. Child development and adjustment. il. 1962. 6.50. Macmillan

Davis, W. Allison, and Robert J. Havighurst. Father of the man. 4.00. Houghton

Dennis, Wayne, ed. Readings in child psychology. 1951. 5.95. Prentice-Hall

D'Evelyn, Katherine E. Meeting children"s emotional needs: A guide for teachers. 1957. 7.00. 5.25. Prentice-Hall

Driscoll, Gertrude P. Child guidance in the classroom. 1955. pap. 1.25. T. C.

Eng, Helga. Psychology of children's drawings. 5.00. Humanities

Erikson, Erik. Childhood and society. 1950. 5.95. Norton

Forest, Isle. Child development. il. 1954. 5.95. McGraw

Fraiberg, Selma. Magic Years. 1959. 4.50. Scribner

Freud, Anna, and Dorothy T. Burlingham. War and children. ed. by Philip R. Lehrman. 1943. 1.50. Int. Univs.

Garrison, Karl C. Growth and development. 1959. 5.50. McKay

Gesell, Arnold, and Frances L. Ilg. Child development. 1949. 6.50. Harper

Gesell, Arnold, and Frances L. Ilg. Child from five to ten. il. 1946. 5.95. Harper

Gesell, Arnold. First five years of life. il. 1940. 5.95. Harper

Gesell, Arnold. How a baby grows. il. 1945. 3.95. Harper

Gesell, Arnold, and Frances Ilg. Infant and child in the culture of today. il. 1943. 5.95. Harper

Gesell, Arnold. Studies in child development. il. 1948. 4.00. Harper

Gesell, Arnold, and others. Youth: The years from ten to sixteen. 1956. 5.95; Harper

Gillham, Helen L. Helping children accept themselves and others. 1959. pap. 1.25. T. C.

Goodenough, Florence L. Exceptional children. il. 4.50. Appleton

Hardy, Martha C., and Carolyn Hoefer. Healthy growth: A study of the influence of health education on growth and development of school children. il. 1936. 6.00. U. of Chicago

Hartley, Ruth E., and others. Understanding children's play. 1952. 5.00. Columbia

Hawkes, Glenn R. and Damaris Pease. Behavior and development from 5 to 12. 1962. 5.75. Harper

Hymes, James L., Jr. Child development point of view. 1955. 3.75. Prentice-Hall

Ilg, Frances L., and Louise Bates Ames. Child behavior. 1955. 5.50. Harper

Ing, Frances L., and Louise B. Ames. Parents ask. 1962. 5.50? Harper

Isaacs, Susan. Intellectual growth in young children. 1930. 5.50. Humanities

Isaacs, Susan. Social development in young children. 1933. 6.00. Humanities

Iscoe, Ira, and Harold W. Stevenson, eds. Personality development in children. 1960. 4.00. U. of Tex.

Jenkins, Gladys G. Helping children reach their potential. 1961. softbound, 2.25. Scott

Jersild, Arthur T. Child psychology. 1960. 10.60. Prentice-Hall

Jersild, Arthur T. In search of self: An exploration of the role of the school in promoting self-understanding. 1952. pap. 1.75. T. C.

Josselyn, Irene M. Happy child: A psychoanalytic guide to emotional and social growth. 1955. 3.95. Random

Justin, Florence, and M. E. Snyder. Directed observation in child development. 3.00. Houghton

Kepler, Hazel. Child and his play. 1952. 3.75. Funk

Kugelmass, I. Newton. Complete child care in body and mind. 1959. 6.95. Twayne

Lamoreaux, Lillian A., and Dorris May Lee. Learning to read through experience. il. 1943. 2.50. Appleton

Laughlin, Frances. Peer status of sixth and seventh grade children. 1955. 2.75. T. C.

Lee, J. Murray, and Dorris May Lee. Child and his development. il. 1958. 6.50. Appleton

Levy, D. M. Maternal overprotection. 6.00. Columbia

Loomis, Mary Jane. Preadolescent: Three major concerns. il. 1959. 4.00. Appleton

Lowenfeld, Viktor. Your child and his art. il. 1954. 5.95. Macmillan

Luria, A. R. Role of speech in the regulation of normal and abnormal behavior. il. 1961. 5.00. Liveright

Manwell, Elizabeth, and Sophia L. Fahs. Consider the children: How they grow. 1951. 3.50. Beacon

Merry, Frieda K., and Ralph. First two decades of life. 1958. 6.75. Harper

Millard, Cecil V. Child growth and development in the elementary school years. 1958. 6.75. Heath

Mussen, Paul Henry, and John Janeway Conger. Child development and personality. 1956. 6.00. Harper

Olson, Willard C. Child development. 1959. 6.75. Heath

Page, Hilary. Playtime in the first five years. il. 1954. 3.50. Lippincott

Peck, R. F., and R. J. Havighurst. Psychology of character development. 1960. 6.50. Wiley

Piaget, J. Child's conception of the world. 5.00. Humanities

Piaget, Jean. Construction of reality in the child. 1954. 7.50. Basic Books

Piaget, Jean. Judgment and reasoning in the child. 1947. 5.00. Humanities

Piaget, Jean. Language and thought of the child. rev. 1959. 5.00. Humanities

Piaget, Jean. Moral judgment of the child. 6.00. Free Press

Piaget, Jean. Origins of intelligence in children. tr. by Margaret Cook. 1952. 6.00. Int. Univs.

Prescott, D. A. Child in the educative process. 1957. 6.95. McGraw

Reeves, Katherine. Children: Their ways and wants. 1959. 2.95. Teacher's Pub.

Ribble, M. Personality of the young child. 1955. 2.75. Columbia

Spoerl, Dorothy, ed. Tensions our children live with; stories for discussion. 1959. 3.50. Beacon

Strang, Ruth M. Introduction to child study. 4th ed. il. 1959. 6.75. Macmillan

Walsh, Ann Marie. Self-concepts of bright boys with learning difficulties. 1956. 2.75. T. C.

White, Verna. Studying the individual pupil. 1958. 4.00. Harper

White House Conference on Child Health and Protection. Growth and development of the child. 2 vols. vol. 3. Nutrition, 4.00; vol. 4, Appraisement of the Child, 2.75. Appleton

Wolf, Anna. Parents' manual. 1961. 5.00. Ungar

CHILD WELFARE--U.S. (362.7)

Kammerer, Gladys M. British and American child welfare services. 1962. 8.50. Wayne

Lundberg, Emma Octavia. Unto the least of these: Social services for children. 3.75. Appleton

Organization for the care of handicapped children: National, state, and local. (Publications of White House Conference on Child Health and Protection) 2.75. Appleton

Zietz, Dorothy. Child welfare. 1959. 5.50. Wiley

CHILDBIRTH (618.4)

Gilbert, Charles R. A. Childbirth: The modern guide for expectant mothers. il. 1960. 3.95. Hawthorn

CHILDBIRTH--PSYCHOLOGY (618.4)

Dick-Read, Grantly. Introduction to motherhood. il. 1951. 1.95. Harper

Kroger, William S., and Jules Steinberg. Childbirth with hypnosis. il. 1961.
  3.95. Doubleday
<u>CHILDREN</u> (136.7)
Jenkins, Gladys G., and others. These are your children. 1953. 3.50. Whitman

Mead, Margaret, and Martha Wolfenstein, eds. Childhood in contemporary
  cultures. 1955. 7.50. U. of Chicago
Moss, Arthur J., and Forrest H. Adams. Problems of blood pressure in
  childhood. il. 1962. 5.50. Thomas, C. C
<u>CHILDREN--CARE AND HYGIENE</u> (649.1)
American Public Health Association. Health supervision of young children.
  19601 3.00. Am. Public Health
Benz, Gladys S. Pediatric nursing. il. 1960. 6.25. Mosby
Better Homes and Gardens. Baby book. by the Editors of Better Homes and
  Gardens. 1943. 3.95. Meredith
Blake, Florence G. Child, his parents and the nurse. 1954. 6.00. Lippincott
Bradbury, Dorothy E., and Edna P. Amidon. Learning to care for children. il.
  1946. 1.80. Appleton
Patri, Angelo. How to help your child grow up. 1948. 4.00. Rand McNally
Schlesinger, Edward R. Health services for the child. il. 1953. 9.00. McGraw
Spock, Benjamin. Common sense book of baby and child care. il. 1946. 5.95.
  Meredith
Spock, Benjamin, and others. Every woman's standard guide to home and
  child care. il. 1959. 10.00. Hawthorn
Witmer, Helen Leland, ed. Pediatrics and the emotional needs of the child:
  The report of the Pediatric-Psychiatric Conference, Hershey, Pennsylvania.
  il. 1948. pap. 2.00. Harvard
<u>CHILDREN--DISEASES</u> (618.92)
Allen, Frederick M. B., and I. J. Carre. Aids to diagnosis and treatment of
  diseases of children. 1961. 3.75. Williams & Wilkins
English, Oliver S., and G. H. J. Pearson. Common neuroses of children and
  adults. 1937. 6.50. Norton
Henderson, John. Parents' guide to children's illnesses. il. 1958. 4.75. Duell
Kessel, I. Essentials of pediatrics for nurses. 1957. 4.75. Williams & Wilkins
Wenar, Charles. Origins of psychosomatic and emotional disturbances. 1962.
  4.50. Hoeber
Williamson, Bruce. Handbook on diseases of children. il. 1958. 6.00. Williams
  & Wilkins
<u>CHILDREN--LANGUAGE</u> (372.6)
Anderson, Virgil A. Improving the child's speech. 1953 4.75. Oxford
Beasley, Jane. Slow to talk: A guide for teachers and parents of children with
  delayed language development. 1956. 3.00. T. C.
Eisenson, Jon and Ogilvie, Mardel. Speech correction in the schools. il. 1957.
  4.95. Macmillan
Herrick, Virgil E., and L. B. Jacobs, eds. Children and the language arts.
  1955. 7.50. Prentice-Hall
Mackintosh, Helen K., ed. Language arts for today's children. 1954. 4.50.
  Appleton
Piaget, Jean. Language and thought of the child. rev. 1959. 5.00. Humanities
Rinsland, Henry D. Basic vocabulary of elementary school children. 1953.
  5.75. Macmillan
Slitz, Rene A. No and yes: On the genesis of human communication. 1957.
  4.00? Int. Univs.
<u>CHILDREN--MANAGEMENT</u> (136.7)
Baruch, Dorothy W. New ways in discipline. 1949. 4.95. McGraw
Baruch, Dorothy W. Understanding young children. 1949. pap. 0.75. T. C.
Bro Margueritte Harmon. When children ask. 1956. 3.50. Harper
Chittenden, Gertrude E. Living with children. il. 1944. 4.25. Macmillan

DeLys, Claudia. Treasury of parenthood and its folklore. 5.00. Speller

Despert, J. Louise. Children of divorce. 1953. 3.95. Doubleday

Fishbein, Morris, and R. J. R. Kennedy. Modern marriage and family living. 1957. 5.50. Oxford U. P.

Gruenberg, Sidonie Matsner, ed. Encyclopedia of child care and guidance. il. 1954. 5.95. Doubleday (R)

Healy, Edwin F. Marriage guidance. 1958. 4.00. Loyola

Hohman, Leslie B. As the twig is bent. 1940. 3.75. Macmillan

Hymes, James L., Jr. Understanding your child. 1952. 3.50. Prentice-Hall

Jones, G. Curtis. Parents deserve to know. 3.95. Macmillan

Langdon, Grace, and Irving W. Stout. Teaching moral and spiritual values. 1962. 3.00. Day

Menninger, William C., and others. How to help your children. il. 1959. 4.95. Sterling

Patri, Angelo. How to help your child grow up. 1948. 4.00. Rand McNally

Post, Emily. Children are people. il. 1959. 3.50. Funk

Spock, Benjamin. Problems of parents. 1962. 5.00. Houghton

Shyte, Dorothy K. Teaching your child right from wrong. 1961. 3.50. Bobbs

CHILDREN IN THE SAMOAN ISLANDS (136.799)
Mead, Margaret. Coming of age in Samoa. 3.75. Smith, Peter

Mead, Margaret. From the South Seas: Studies of adolescence and sex in primitive societies. 1939. 5.00. Morrow

CHILDREN IN THE U. S. (301.43.)
Earle, Alice M. Child life in colonial days. il. 1899. 4.95. Macmillan

Ginzberg, Eli, ed. Nation's children. 1960. 7.50.

White House Conference on Children and Youth, 1960. Values and ideals of American youth. ed. by E. Ginzbert. 1961. 6.00. Columbia

CHILDREN'S LITERATURE--BIBLIOGRAPHY (028.5)
American Library Association. Subject and title index to short stories for children. 1955. 5.00. A. L. A.

Arbuthnot, May Hill, and others. Children's books too good to miss. rev. ed. pap. 1.25. Western Reserve

Frank, Josette. Your child's reading today. 1960. half cl. 3.95. Doubleday

Strang, Ruth, and others. Gateways to readable books. 1958. 3.00. Wilson

CHILDREN'S LITERATURE--HISTORY AND CRITICISM (028.5)
Adams, Bess Porter. About books and children. il. 1953. 8.75; Holt, Rinehart & Winston

Arbuthnot, May Hill. Children and books. 1957. 6.75. Scott

Kunitz, S. J., and Howard Haycraft. Junior book of authors. rev. il. 1951. 3.50. Wilson (R)

Meigs, Cornelia, and others, eds. Critical history of children's literature. 1953. 7.95. Macmillan

Moore, Annie E. Literature old and new for children. 5.00. Houghton

Smith, Lillian H. Unreluctant years: a critical approach to children's literature. 1953. 4.50. A. L. A.

CHILDREN'S LITERATURE--STUDY AND TEACHING (028.5)
Huck, Charlotte S., and Doris A. Young. Children's literature in the elementary school. 1961. 6.75 Holt, Rinehart & Winston

CHILE (983)
Bowers, Claude. Chile through embassy windows. 1958. 5.00. S. and S.

Butland, G. J. Chile. 1956. 2.90. Oxford U. P.

Pike, Fredrick B., ed. Chile and the United States, 1880-1962. 1962. 7.50. U. of Notre Dame

CHILE--HISTORY (983)
Davis, William C. Last conquistadores. 1950. 5.00. U. of Ga.

CHINA (951)
China Handbook Editorial Board, ed. China handbook, 1957-1958. 7.50? Tuttle

Hu, Chang-tu and others. China: Its people, its society, its culture. il. 1959. 10.00. Taplinger

Latourette, Kenneth Scott. Chinese: Their history and culture. rev. 2 vols. in 1, 9.75. Macmillan

Lattimore, Owen. Inner Asian frontiers of China. pap. 2.95. Beacon

MacLure, Millar, ed. Far East: China and Japan. 1961. 2.50. U. of Toronto

MacNair, Harley Farnsworth, ed. China. il. 1951. 6.50. U. of Calif.

CHINA--CIVILIZATION (951)

Bodde, Derk. China's cultural tradition. 1957. pap. 1.25. Holt, Rinehart & Winston

Creel, H. G. Birth of China. 1954. 7.50. Ungar

Fitzgerald, Charles P. China, a short cultural history. il. 1954. 12.50. Praeger

Hsu, Francis L. K. Americans and Chinese: Two ways of life. 1953. 6.00. Abelard

Levenson, Joseph R. Confucian China and its modern fate. 1958. 5.00. U. of Calif.

Wright, Arthur F., ed. Studies in Chinese thought. il. 1953. 4.50. U. of Chicago

CHINA--DESCRIPTION AND TRAVEL (915.1)

Beauvoir, Simone de. Long march. 7.50. World Pub.

Clark, Gerald. Impatient giant-Red China today. il. 1959. 5.50. McKay

Cressey, George B. Land of the 500 million: A geography of China. 1955. 12.75. 9.50. McGraw

Greene, Felix. Awakened China. 5.95. Doubleday

Stevenson, William H. Yellow wind. il. 1959. 6.00. Houghton

CHINA--FOREIGN RELATIONS (951)

Ballantine, Joseph W. Formosa. 1953. 2.75. Brookings

Chakravarti, Prithwis C. India's China policy. il. 1962. 4.95. Indiana

Cheng, Tien Fong. History of Sino-Russian relations. 1957. 6.00. Pub. Affairs

Chiang, Kai-Shek. Soviet Russia in China. 1958. 6.00. Farrar, Straus

Fairbank, John King. United States and China. il. 1958. 5.50. Harvard

Hsu, Immanuel C. Y. China's entrance into the family of nations: The diplomatic phase, 1858-1880. 1960. 5.50. Harvard

Kalb, Marvin L. Dragon in the Kremlin. 1961. 4.50. Dutton

Kiernan, E. V. G. British diplomacy in China. 1939. 8.50. Cambridge U. P.

Luard, Evan. Britain and China. 1962. 5.00. Johns Hopkins

McLane, Charles B. Soviet policy and the Chinese Communists, 1931-1946. 1958. 5.50. Columbia

Morse, H. B. International relations of the Chinese empire. 3 vols. 20.00. Paragon

Rostow, W. W. Prospects for Communist China. 1954. 5.00. Wiley

CHINA--HISTORY (951)

Beckmann, George M. Modernization of China and Japan. 1962. 7.50. Harper

Eberhard, Wolfram. History of China. rev. 1960. 5.00. U. of Calif.

Goodrich, Luther Carrington. Short history of the Chinese people. il. 1959. 4.50. Harper

Grousset, Rene. Rise and splendour of the Chinese empire. il. 1953. pap. 1.95. U. of Calif.

Li, Chien-Nung. Political history of China, 1840-1928. 1956. 7.50; Van Nostrand

Seeger, Elizabeth. Pageant of Chinese history. 1962. 6.50. McKay

Wint, Guy. Common sense about China. 1960. 2.95. Macmillan

CHINA--POLITICS AND GOVERNMENT (951)

Brunnert, H. S., and V. Hagelstrom. Present day political organization of China. 9.00. Paragon

Ch'ien, Tuan-sheng. Government and politics of China. 1950. 10.00. Harvard

Linebarger, Paul M. A., and others. Far Eastern governments and politics. il. 1956. 7.25. Van Nostrand

Quigley, Harold S. China's politics in perspective. il. 1962. 4.50. U. of Minn.

Tang, P. Communist China today. 1958. vol. 2, 3.75. Praeger
CHINA--SOCIAL LIFE AND CUSTOMS (951)
Ch'ti, T'ung-tsu. Law and society in traditional China. 1961. 13.50. Inst. of
Pac. Rel.
Lin, Yutang. Chinese way of life. 1959. 3.50. World Pub.
CHINESE LITERATURE--TRANSLATIONS INTO ENGLISH (890)
Legge, James. Chinese classics. 5 vols. 1960. 80.00; rev. suppl. material bd.
alone. pap. 2.00. Oxford U. P.
Lin, Yutang, ed. and tr. Importance of understanding. 1960. 6.00. World
Pub.
Waley, Arthur. Translations from the Chinese. il. 1955. 7.50. Knopf
Wisdom of China and India. 2.95. Modern Lib.
CHINESE POETRY--HISTORY AND CRITICISM (895)
Liu, James J. Y. Art of Chinese poetry. 1962. 4.50. U. of Chicago
CHINESE POETRY--TRANSLATIONS INTO ENGLISH (895.1)
Kiang, Kang-hu, and Witter Bynner. Jade mountain: A Chinese anthology.
1929. 4.50. Knopf
Payne, Robert, ed. White pony: An anthology of Chinese poetry. (Mentor
MT301) pap. 0.75. New Am. Lib.
Rexroth, Kenneth, ed. 100 poems from the Chinese. 1956. 3.50. New
Directions
CHISHOLM TRAIL (917)
Gard, Wayne. Chisholm trail. il. 1954. 5.00. U. of Okla.
CHIVALRY (394.7)

Ferguson, Arthur B. Indian summer of English chivalry. 1960. 6.00. Duke
Painter, Sidney. French chivalry: Chivalrie ideas and practices in Medieva.
France. 1940. 3.50. Johns Hopkins
CHLORINE (665.83)
Sconce, J. S. Chlorine: Its manufacture, properties and uses. 5.00.
Reinhold
CHLOROFORM (615.781)
Waters, Ralph M., ed. Chloroform: A study after 100 years. 1951. 2.75.
U. of Wis.
CHOIRS (MUSIC) (784)
Finn, William J. Art of the choral conductor. 2 vols. 1960. 4.50 ea. Summy
Heaton, Charles H. How to build a church choir. 1958. 1.00. Bethany
Hume, Paul. Catholic church music. 1956. 4.00. Dodd
Ingram, Madeline D. Organizing and directing children's choirs. 1959. 2.50.
Abingdon
CHOLERA, ASIATIC (614.514)
Rosenberg, Charles E. Cholera years. 1962. 7.50. U. of Chicago
Snow, John. Snow on cholera: A reprint of two papers. Biographical memoir
by B. W. Richardson. 1936. 3.00. Harvard
CHOLESTEROL (547.73)
Cook, R. P., ed. Cholesterol: Its chemistry, biochemistry, and pathology. 1958.
15.00. Academic Press
Revell, Dorothy. Cholesterol control cookery. 1.95. Carlton
CHOPIN, FRYDERYK FRANCISZEK, 1810-1849 (927)
Abraham, Gerald. Chopin's musical style. 1939. 3.00. Oxford U. P.
Hedley, Arthur. Chopin. 1949. 3.50. Farrar, Straus
Weinstock, Herbert. Chopin. il. 1949. 6.00. Knopf
Wierzynski, Casimir. Life and death of Frederic Chopin. tr. by Norbert'
Guterman. 1949. 3.95. S. And S.
CHORAL MUSIC (784.1)
Davison, Archibald Thompson. Choral conducting. 1940. 2.00. Harvard
Davison, Archibald Thompson. Technique of choral composition. il. 1945.
4.00. Harvard

Young, Percy M. Choral tradition. 1962. 7.95. Norton

CHORAL SPEAKING (808.55)

DeWitt, Marguerite E. Practical methods in choral speaking. 2.25. Expression

Gullan, Marjorie. Choral speaking. 1.75. Expression

Gullan, Marjorie. Speech choir. 1937. 3.50. Harper

Keppie, Elizabeth E. Choral verse speaking. 3.25. Expression

Keppie, Elizabeth E. Teaching of choric speech. 2.25. Expression

Swann, Mona. Approach to choral speech. 1.75. Expression

CHORDATA (596)

Eddy, S. Atlas of drawings for chordate anatomy. 1949. 5.50. Wiley

Smith, Hobart M. Evolution of chordate structure: An introduction to comparative anatomy. 1960. 7.00. Holt, Rinehart & Winston

Weichert, Charles K. Elements of chordate anatomy. 1959. 7.50. McGraw

CHOREOGRAPHY (792.8)

Hayes, E. R. Dance composition and production for high schools and colleges. 1955. 5.00. Ronald

Humphrey, Doris, ed. Art of making dances. ed. by Barbara Pollack. il. 1959. 6.50. Holt, Rinehart & Winston

CHRETIEN DE TROYES, 12TH CENTURY (928)

Guyer, Foster. Chretien de Troyes: Inventor of the modern novel. 4.00. Twayne

Loomis, R. S. Arthurian tradition and Chretien de Troyes. 1949. 6.75. Columbia

CHRISTIAN ANTIQUITIES (220.93)

Finegan, Jack. Light from the ancient past. 1959. 10.00. Princeton

Marucchi, Ozario, and Hubert Vecchierello. Christian archeology. 1935. 4.25. St. Anthony

Meer, F. van der, and Christine Mohrmann. Atlas of the early Christian world. 1959. 15.00. Nelson

CHRISTIAN ART AND SYMBOLISM (246)

Appleton, Leroy H., and Stephen Bridges. Symbolism in liturgical art. 1959. 3.50. Scribner

Cetto, Anna Maria. Ravenna mosaics. il. 1960. 2.00. Taplinger

Croft, Aloysius, and Carl van Treeck. Symbols of the church. 1960. 3.00. Bruce

Espinosa, Jose E. Saints in the valleys. 6.50. U. of N. Mex.

Ferguson, George. Signs and symbols in Christian art. il. 1959. 7.50. Oxford U. P.

Fleming, Daniel Johnson. Christian symbols in a world community. il. 1940. 3.00. Friendship

Frankenstein, Alfred, and Norman Carlson. Angels over the alter: Christian folk art in Hawaii and the south seas. 12.00. U. of Hawaii

Getlein, Frank, and Dorothy. Christianity in art. 1959. 4.50. Bruce

Getlein, Frank, and Dorothy. Christianity in modern art. il. 1961. 5.00. Bruce

Gough, Michael. Early Christians. il. 6.95. Praeger

Grodecki, Louis, and Roar Hauglid. Norway, paintings from stave churches. il. 1955. half cl. boxed. 18.00. N. Y. Graphic

Kretzmann, P. E. Christian art. 3.50. Concordia

McClinton, Katherine. Christian church art through the ages. il. 1962. 6.50. Macmillan

Male, Emile. Gothic image. Religious art in France in the thirteenth century. 1958. 4.00. Smith, Peter

Maus, Cynthia Pearl. Church and the fine arts. il. 1960. 6.95. Harper

Morey, C. R. Christian art. il. 1958. 2.95. pap. 1.25. Norton

Nathan, Walter L. Art and the message of the church. il. 1961. 5.00. Westminster

Ouspensky, Leonid, and Wladimir Lossky. Meaning of icons. il. 20.00. Boston Bk.

Regamey, Raymond. Religious art in the twentieth century. in prep. Herder & Herder, N. Y. C.
Ritter, Richard H. Arts of the church. 1947. 3.50. Pilgrim
Van Zeller, Hubert, Dom. Approach to Christian sculpture. il. 1959. 3.75. Sheed
Watts, Alan W. Myth and ritual in Christianity. il. 1954. 5.50. Vanguard
CHRISTIAN BIOGRAPHY (922)
Bach, Marcus. Adventures in faith. 3.50. Denison
Bainton, Roland H. Travail of religious liberty. 1951. 4.00. Westminster
Barrois, Georges. Pathways of the inner life. 1956. 5.00. Bobbs
Bowie, Walter R. Men of fire. 1961. 3.95. Harper
Davidson, H. Martin P. Good Christian men. 1940. 4.50. Scribner
Deen, Edith. Great women of the Christian faith. 1959. 4.95. Harper (R)
McLeister, Clara. Men and women of deep piety. 3.50. Newby
Payne, Robert. Fathers of the Western church. il. 1951. 5.00. Viking
Potter, Charles Francis. Great religious leaders. 1958. 7.50. S. and S.
CHRISTIAN ETHICS (171.1)
Beach, W., and H. R. Niebuhr. Christian ethics. 1955. 5.50. Ronald
Beach, Waldo. Conscience on campus. 1958. 2.50. pap. 1.00. Assn. Pr.
Bennett, John C. Christian ethics and social policy. 2.50. Scribner
Berdyaev, Nikolai. Destiny of man. 6.00. Hillary
Bonhoeffer, Bietrich. Ethics. ed. by Eberhard Bethge. 1955. 4.95. Macmillan
Carpenter, Edward F. Common sense about Christian ethics. 1962. 2.95. Macmillan
Elert, Werner. Christian ethos. 1957. 6.00. Muhlenberg
Gardner, E. Clinton. Biblical faith and social ethics. 1960. 4.75. Harper
Gilson, Etienne H. Moral values and the moral life. tr. by Leo. R. Ward. 1961. 7.00. Shoe String
Harkness, Georgia. Christian ethics. 1957. 3.75. Abingdon
Harvey, John F. Moral theology of the Confessions of St. Augustine. 1951. 3.00. Catholic U. of Am. Pr.
Heick, Otto W. Guide to Christian living. 1954. 3.00. Muhlenberg
Henry, Carl F. H. Christian personal ethics. 1957. 6.95. Eerdmans
Kenny, John P. Principles of medical ethics. 1962. 4.50. Newman
Knudson, Albert C. Principles of Christian ethics. 1943. 4.00. Abingdon
Micklem, Nathaniel. Is there a Christian ethic? 1959. 0.50. Oxford U. P.
Pike, James A. Beyond anxiety. 1953. 2.95. Scribner
Pike, James A. Doing the truth: A summary of Christian ethics. 1955. 2.95. Doubleday
Quanbeck, W. A., ed. God and Caesar. 1959. 3.95. Augsburg
Rasmussen, A. T. Christian social ethics: Exerting Christian influence. 1956. 7.95; text ed. 5.95. Prentice-Hall
Sittler, Joseph A.. Structure of Christian ethics. 1958. 2.50. La. State
Thomas, George F. Christian ethics and moral philosophy. 1955. 5.00. Scribner
Thompson, Kenneth W. Christian ethics and the dilemmas of foreign policy. 1959. 3.50. Duke
Von Hildebrand, Dietrich. Christian ethics. 1953. 6.00. McKay
Weber, Max. Protestant ethic and the spirit of capitalism. 1948. 3.95; pap. 1.45. Scribner
Weber, Max. Protestant ethic and the spirit of capitalism. 3.50. Smith, Peter
CHRISTIAN LIFE (248.4)
Allen, Charles L. God's psychiatry. 1954. 2.50. Revell
Bonhoeffer, Dietrich. Life together. 1954. 2.00. Harper
Clark, Glenn. Way, the truth and the life. 1946. 2.50. Harper
Cliffe, A. E. Lessons in successful living. 1952. 2.95. Prentice-Hall
Drummond, Henry. Changed life. 1956. 1.00. Revell
Dulles, John Foster. Spiritual legacy. ed. by Henry P. VanDusen. 1960. 3.95. Westminster

Ferre, Nels F. S. Making religion real. 1955. 2.50. Harper

Fosdick, Harry Edmerson. Meaning of service. 3.50. Assn. Pr.

Heick, Otto W. Guide to Christian living. 1954. 3.00. Muhlenberg

Price, Eugenia. Discoveries. 1953. 1.95; pap. 1.00. Zondervan

Riess, Oswald. Secret of beautiful living. 1953. 1.75. Concordia

Sangster, W. E. Secret of radiant life. 1957. 3.00. Abingdon

Shoemaker, Samuel M. How to become a Christian. 1953. 2.50. Harper

Smith, Hannah Whitall. Christian's secret of a happy life. 1.95; pap. 0.95.
   Revell

Sockman, Ralph W. Whole armor of God. 1955. 1.00. Abingdon

Trueblood, Elton. Your other vocation. 1952. 2.00. Harper

Wuest, Kenneth S. Great truths to live by (Word studies in the Greek New
   Testament. vol. 11) 1952. 2.25. Eerdmans'

CHRISTIAN LITERATURE, EARLY (COLLECTIONS) (281.1)

Ante-Nicene Fathers. Writings. 1951. 10 vols. ed. by Alexander Roberts, and
   James Donaldson. vols. 1-8, 6.00 ea. vol. 9. 3.00; vol. 10. 5.00; set, 55.00.
   Eerdmans

Apostolic Fathers. Works. (Loeb nos. 24-25) 2 vols. vol. 1, Clement, Ignatius, Polycarp, Didache, Barnabas; vol. 2, Shepherd of Hermas, Martyrdom
   of Polycarp, Epistle to Diognetus. 3.50 ea. Harvard

Augustine, Saint. Earlier writings. ed. by J. H. S. Burleigh. 1953. 5.00.
   Westminster

Augustine, Saint. Later works. ed. by John Burnaby. 1955. 5.00. Westminster

Bettenson, Henry, ed. Early Christian fathers: A selection from the writings
   of the fathers from St. Clement of Rome to St. Athanasius. 1956. 4.50.
   Oxford U. P.

Fremantle, Anne, ed. Treasury of early Christianity. pap. 0.75. New Am. Lib.

Goodspeed, Edgar J., ed. Apostolic Fathers: An American translation. 1950.
   5.00. Harper

CHRISTIAN LITERATURE, EARLY--HISTORY AND CRITICISM (281.1)

Goodspeed, Edgar J. Twelve: The story of Christ's Apostles. 1957. 6.00.
   Winston

Leclercq, Jean, Dom. Love of learning and the desire for God. 1961. 5.50.
   Fordham

CHRISTIAN UNION (280)

Latourette, K. S. Emergence of a world Christian community. 1949. 2.00.
   Yale

Lee, Robert. Social sources of church unity. 1960. 4.50. Abingdon

Pittenger, W. Norman. Church, the ministry, and reunion. 1957. pap. 2.75.
   Seabury

Spinka, Matthew. Quest for church unity. 1960. 2.50. Macmillan

Trueblood, Elton. Common ventures of life. 1949. 2.00. Harper

Van Dusen, Henry P. One great ground of hope. 1961. 3.95. Westminster

CHRISTIANITY (200)

Baker, Frank S., ed. Christian perspectives in contemporary culture. 1962.
   3.50. Twayne

Bethune-Baker, J. F. Christian religion. 2.50 ea. Cambridge U. P.

Klotsche, E. H. Christian symbolics. 4.00. Muhlenberg

Kraemer, Hendrik. Why Christianity of all religions? 1962. 2.75. Westminster

Locke, John. Reasonableness of Christianity, and Discourse of miracles.
   ed. by I. T. Ramsey. 2.50. Stanford

Pittenger, William Norman. Principles and practice of the Christian faith.
   1955. 3.00. Allenson

Tolstoy, Leo. On life, and Essays on relition. (W. C. 426) tr. by Aylmer
   Maude. 2.75. Oxford U. P.

CHRISTIANITY--ADDRESSES, ESSAYS, LECTURES (204)

Barth, Karl. Word of God and the word of man. (Torchbks Tb13) 1957. pap.
   1.65. Harper

Lewis, C. S. Case for Christianity. 1.95. Macmillan
Lewis, C. S. Mere Christianity. 3.50; pap. 1.25. Macmillan
Lewis, C. S. World's last night, and other essays. 1960. 3.50. Harcourt
Luccock, H. E. Living without gloves: More letters of Simeon Stylites. 1957.
   3.00. Oxford U. P.
Niebuhr, Reinhold. Essays in applied Christianity. pap. 1.55. Meridian
Phillips, J. B. Plain Christianity: And other broadcast talks. 1954. 2.50.
   Macmillan
Pitts, Mildred R. In my Father's house are many mansions. 3.00. Carlton
CHRISTIANITY--ESSENCE, GENIUS, NATURE (201)
Aulen, Gustaf. Church, law and society. 1948. 2.95. Scribner
Carnell, Edward J. Case for orthodox theology. 1959. 3.50. Westminster
Ferre, Gustave A. Layman examines his faith. 1960. 1.95. Bethany
Ferre, Nels F. S. Know your faith. 1959. 2.50. Harper
Harnack, Adolph. What is Christianity. 1958. 3.50. Smith, Peter
Loew, Cornelius. Modern rivals to Christian faith. 1956. 1.00. Westminster
Miegge, Giovanni. Christian affirmations in a secular age. 1958. 3.75. Oxford
   U. P.
Nygren, Anders. Essence of Christianity. 1961. 2.00. Muhlenberg
Phillips, J. B. New Testament Christianity. 1956. 0.95. Macmillan
CHRISTIANITY--ORIGIN (209)
Coneybeare, Frederic C. Origins of Christianity. 1958. 6.00. U. Books
Davies, W. D. Christian origins and Judaism. 1962. 5.00. Westminster
Graystone, Geoffrey. Dead sea scrolls and the originaltiy of Christ. 1956.
   2.50. Sheed
Parkes, James. Foundations of Judaism and Christianity. 1960. 6.00. Quad-
   rangle
Robertson, Archibald. Origins of Christianity. 1962. 3.75. Int. Pubs.
Wikgren, Allen, ed. Early Christian origins. 1961. 5.00. Quadrangle
CHRISTIANITY--PHILOSOPHY (201)
Butterfield, Herbert. Christianity and history. 1950. 2.95; pap. 1.25. Scribner
Ferre, Nels F. S. Return to Christianity. 1943. 1.25. Harper
Hazelton, Roger. New accents in contemporary theology. 1960. 3.00.
   Harper
Keyser, L. S. Philosophy of Christianity. 1928. 2.50. Muhlenberg
Kierkegaard, Soren. Fear and trembling. tr. by Walter Lowrie. 1941. 3.00.
   Princeton
Kierkegaard, Soren. Thoughts on crucial situations in human life. tr. by David
   F. Swenson. 1941. 2.50. Augsburg
Kierkegaard, Soren. Training in Christianity. tr. by Walter Lowrie. 1944.
   6.00. Princeton
Macquarrie, John. Existentialist theology. 1955. 4.75. Macmillan
Marney, Carlyle. Faith in conflict. il. 1957. 2.50. Abingdon
Niebuhr, Reinhold. Beyond tragedy. 1937. 3.95; pap. 1.45. Scribner
Niebuhr, Reinhold. Faith and history. 1949. 3.95. Scribner
Sayers, Dorothy L. Mind of the maker. 1941. 3.50. Harcourt
Teihard de Chardin, Pierre. Divine milleu. 1960. 3.00. Harper
Tillich, Paul. Biblical religion and the search for ultimate reality. 1955. 2.50.
   U. of Chicago
Tillich, Paul. Protestant era. 1948. 5.75. abridged. ed. pap. 1.50. U. of Chicago
CHRISTIANITY--PSYCHOLOGY (201.6)
Michalson, Carl. Faith for personal crisis. 1958. 3.50. Scribner
Neill, Stephen C. Genuinely human existence, towards a Christian psychology.
   1959. 4.50. Doubleday
Oates, Wayne E. Anxiety in Christian experience. 1955. 3.00. Westminster
CHRISTIANITY--EARLY CHURCH (200)
Gough, Michael. Early Christians. il. 6.95. Praeger

CHRISTIANITY--19th CENTURY (200)
Tolstoy, Leo. Kingdom of God is within you. 1905. 4.50. pap. 1.95. Farrar, Straus
CHRISTIANITY--20th CENTURY (200)
Garbett, Cyril. In an age of revolution. 1952. 3.20. Oxford U. P.
Lewis, C. S. Screwtape letters. bd. with Screwtape proposes a toast. 1944. 3.50. Macmillan
Phillips, J. B. God our contemporary. 1960. 2.50; pap. 1.25. Macmillan
Phillips, J. B. Making men whole. 1953. 2.50. Macmillan
Trueblood, Elton. Alternative to futility. 1948. 2.00. Harper
Trueblood, Elton. Company of the committed. 1961. 2.50. Harper
Trueblood, Elton. Predicament of modern man. 1.50. Harper
Youngs, Robert W. What it means to be a Christian. 1960. 3.50. Farrar, Straus
CHRISTIANITY AND ECONOMICS (261)
Childs, Marquis W., and Douglass Cater. Ethics in a business society. 1954. 3.50. Harper
Green, Robert W., ed. Protestantism and capitalism: The Weber thesis and its critics. 1959. pap. 1.50. Heath
Obenhaus, Victor. Responsible Christian: A Protestant interpretation. 1957. 4.00. U. of Chicago
Weber, Max. Protestant ethic and the spirit of capitalism. 3.50. Smith, Peter
CHRISTIANITY AND INTERNATIONAL AFFAIRS (261.6)
Butterfield, Herbert. International conflict in the twentieth century. 1960. 3.00. Harper
Dulles, John Foster. Spiritual legacy. ed. by Henry P. Van Dusen. 1960. 3.95. Westminster
Malik, Charles H. Christ and crisis. 1962. 3.00. Eerdmans
CHRISTIANITY AND OTHER RELIGIONS (290)
Allen, E. L. Christianity among the religions. 1961. pap. 1.45. Beacon
Bouquet, Alan C. Christian faith and non-Christian religions. 1959. 7.00. Harper
Braden, Charles S. Jesus compared: A comparative study of Jesus and the other great founders of religion. 1957. 6.60. 4.95. Prentice-Hall
Dewick, E. C. Christian attitude to other religions. 1953. 5.50. Cambridge U. P.
Hume, Robert E. World's living religions. 1959. 3.50. Scribner
Kellogg, S. H. Handbook of comparative religion. 1951. 2.50. Eerdmans
Kraemer, Hendrik. Religion and the Christian faith. 1957. 6.00. Westminster
Kraemer, Hendrik. World cultures and world religions. 1961. 6.50. Westminster
Neill, Stephen. Christian faith and other faiths. 1961. 4.25. Oxford U. P.
Newbigin, Lesslie. Faith for this one world. 1962. 2.75. Harper
Ohm, Thomas. Asia looks at western Christianity. 1959. 4.75. Herder & Herder
Perry, Edmund. Gospel in dispute. 1958. 3.95. Doubleday
Schweitzer, Albert. Christianity and the religions of the world. tr. by Johanna Powers. 1.75. Macmillan
Toynbee, Arnold. Christianity among the religions of the world. 1957. 2.95. Scribner
CHRISTIANITY AND OTHER RELIGIONS--BUDDHISM (294.3)
Carus, Paul. Gospel of Buddha. 3.00; pap. 1.45. il. 4.50. Open Ct.
King, Winston L. Buddhism and Christianity. 1962. 5.00. Westminster
Thomas, Edward J. Life of Buddha as legend and history. rev. 1949. 6.50. Barnes & Noble
CHRISTIANITY AND OTHER RELIGIONS--GREEK (292)
Jaeger, Werner W. Early Christianity and Greek paideia. 1961. 3.25. Harvard
CHRISTIANITY AND OTHER RELIGIONS--HINDUISM (294.5)
Pitt, Malcom. Introducing Hinduism. 1955. pap. 0.90. Friendship
Soper, Edmund D. Inevitable choice: Vedanta philosophy or Christian gospel. 1957. 2.50. Abingdon

CHRISTIANITY AND OTHER RELIGIONS--JUDAISM (296)
Baeck, Leo. Judaism and Christianity. 1958. 4.00. Jewish Pub. Soc.
Davies, W. D. Christian origins and Judaism. 1962. 5.00. Westminster
Jocz, Jacob. Theology of election. 1958. 5.00. (S. P. C. K.) Seabury
Katz, Jacob. Exclusiveness and tolerance: Studies in Jewish-Gentile relations
  in medieval and modern times. 1961. 3.40. Oxford U. P.
Silver, Hillel Abba. Where Judaism differed: An inquiry into the distinctiveness
  of Judaism. 4.95. Macmillan
CHRISTIANITY AND POLITICS (261.7)
Bennett, John C. Christian as citizen. 1955. 1.25. Assn. Pr.
Maritain, Jacques. Christianity and democracy. 1.50. Hillary
Muehl, William. Politics for Christians. 1956. 3.00. Assn. Pr.
Niebuhr, Reinhold. Christian realism and political problems. 1953. 3.00.
  Scribner
Niebuhr, Reinhold. Self and the dramas of history. 1955. 3.75. Scribner
Thompson, Kenneth W. Christian ethics and the dilemmas of foreign policy.
  1959. 3.50. Duke
Ward, Barbara. Faith and freedom. 1954. 5.50. Norton
CHRISTIANITY IN LITERATURE (808.89)
Huppe, Bernard F. Doctrine and poetry: Augustine's influence on Old English
  poetry. 1959. 6.00. Univ. Pub.
Stewart, Randall. American literature and Christian doctrine. 1958. 3.50.
  La. State
CHRISTMAS (394.268)
Baur, John E. Christmas on the American frontier. il. 1961. 5.00. Caxton
Becker, May Lamberton, ed. Home book of Christmas. 5.00. Dodd
Gardner, H. J. Let's celebrate Christmas. 1940. 3.50. Ronald
Haugan, Randolph, ed. Christmas: An annual of Christmas literature and art.
  3.50; pap. 1.50. Augsburg
Hole, Christina. Christmas and its customs. il. 1958. 2.50. Barrows
Thomas, Dylan. Child's Christmas in Wales. 1959. pap. 1.00. New Directions
Watts, Franklin, ed. Complete Christmas book. 1958. 4.95. Watts
Weiser, Francis X. Christmas book. 1952. 3.00. Harcourt
Wernecke, H. H. Celebrating Christmas around the world. 1962. 3.95.
  Westminster
Wernecke, Herbert H. Christmas customs around the world. 1959. 3.50.
  Westminster
CHRISTMAS MUSIC (783.28)
Reed, W. L., ed. Treasury of Christmas music. 1961. 4.95. Emerson
CHRISTMAS PLAYS (808.25)
Brings, Lawrence M. Modern treasury of Christmas plays. 1955. 4.50.
  Denison
Fisher, Aileen L. Christmas plays and programs. 1960. 5.00. Plays
CHRISTMAS SERMONS (252.61)
Marshall, Peter. Let's keep Christmas. il. 1953. 2.00. McGraw
CHRISTMAS STORIES (394.26)
Lohan, Robert, ed. Christmas tales for reading aloud. 3.75. Ungar
Van Dyke, Henry. Spirit of Christmas. il. 1957. 1.50. Scribner
CHROMATOGRAPHIC ANALYSIS (544.92)
Dal Nogare, S., and R. S. Juvet. Gas-liquid chromatography. 1962. 13.95.
  Wiley
Weissberger, Arnold, ed. Adsorption and chromatography. il. 1951. 8.50. Wiley
Weissberger, Arnold, ed. Fundamentals of chromatography. il. 1957. 12.00.
  Wiley
CHROMIUM (546.532)
Sully, A. H. Chromium. 1954. 7.50. Academic Press
Udy, Marvin J. Chromium. 2 vols. 1956. 11.00 ea. Reinhold

CHROMOSOMES (581. 87)
Macleish, John, and Brian Snoad. Looking at chromosomes. 1958. 3.75. St.
  Martins
Schrader, Franz. Mitosis. 1953. 5.00. Columbia
White, Michael J. D. Chromosomes. 1961. 3.25. Wiley
CHRONIC DISEASES (616)
Commission on Chronic Illness. Chronic illness in the United States. 4 vols.
  vol. 1. Prevention of chronic illness. 1957. 6.00; vol. 2. Care of the long-term
  patient. 1956. 8.50; vol. 3. Chronic illness in a rural area. by Ray E.
  Trussell and Jack Elinson. 1959. 7.50; vol. 4. Chronic illness in a large city.
  1957. 8.00. Harvard
Harrower, Molly R., ed. Medical and psychological teamwork in the care of
  the chronically ill. il. 1955. 5.75. Thomas, C. C.
Travis, Georgia. Chronic disease and disability: A basic medical-social guide.
  1961. 6.00. U. of Calif.
Wohl, Michael G., ed. Long term illness. il. 1959. 17.00. Saunders
CHRYSANTHEMUMS (635.93355)
Ackerson, Cornelius. Complete book of chrysanthemums. il. 1957. 4.95.
  Doubleday
CHURCH (254)
Brown, Robert McAfee. Significance of the church. 1956. 1.00. Westminster
Homrighausen, Elmer G. I believe in the church. 1959. 1.50. Abingdon
Hudson, Winthorp S., ed. Baptist concepts of the church. 1959. 3.00. Judson
Lubac, Henri de. Splendor of the church. 1956. 3.50. Sheed
Miller, Samuel H. Life of the church. 1953. 2.50. Harper
Newbigin, Lesslie. Household of God. 1954. 2.95. Friendship
Niebuhr, H. Richard, and others. Purpose of the church and its ministry.
  1956. 2.50. Harper
Van Dusen, Henry P. Reality and religion. 0.75. Assn. Press
Visser't Hooft, W. A. Renewal of the church. 1957. 2.50. Westminster
Vogt, Von Ogden. Art and religion. 1960. pap. 1.75. Beacon
CHURCH AND EDUCATION (377.1)
Adams, Herbert B. Church and popular education. 1900. 1.50. Johns Hopkins
Blum, Virgil C. Freedom of choice in education. 1958. 3.95. Macmillan
Brickman, William W., and Stanley Lehrer, eds. Religion, government, and
  education. 1961. 5.25. Soc. for the Advancement of Educ.
Dierenfield, R. B. Religion in American public schools. 1962. 3.25. Pub.
  Affairs
Healey, Robert M. Jefferson on religion in public education. 1962. 6.50? Yale
Johnson, Alvin W., and Frank H. Yost. Separation of church and state in the
  United States. 1948. 4.50. U. of Minn.
Rushdoony, Rousas J. Intellectual schizophrenia. 1961. 2.75. Presbyterian &
  Reformed
CHURCH AND SOCIAL PROBLEMS (261.83)
Auien, Gustaf. Church, law and society. 1948. 2.95. Scribner
Bennett, John C. Christian ethics and social policy. 2.50. Scribner
Childs, Marquis W., and Douglass Cater. Ethics in a business society. 1954.
  3.50. Harper
Clark, Dennis. Cities in crisis: The Christian response. 1960. 3.50. Sheed
Duff, Edward. Social thought of the World Council of Churches. 1956. 7.50.
  Assn. Pr.
George, Charles, and Katharine. Protestant mind of the English Reformation,
  1570-1640. 1961. 8.50. Princeton
McNeill, Robert B. Prophet, speak now! 1961. 2.50. John Knox
Mason, Phillip. Christianity and race. 2.50. St. Martins
Maston, T. B. Christianity and world issues. 1957. 5.00. Macmillan
Obenhaus, Victor. Responsible Christian: A Protestant interpretation. 1957.
  4.00. U. of Chicago

Pike, Esther, ed. Who is my neighbor? 1960. 3.50. Seabury

Yinger, J. Milton. Religion in the struggle for power. 1962. 6.50. Russell

CHURCH AND SOCIAL PROBLEMS--U.S. (261.83)

Kloetzli, Walter. Church and the urban challange. 1961. 2.00. Muhlenberg

Lee, Robert. Social sources of church unity. 1960. 4.50. Abingdon

Lipman, Eugene J., and Albert Vorspan. Tale of ten cities. 1962. 4.95. Union

Smith, Timothy L. Revivalism and social reform 1957. 4.00. Abingdon

CHURCH AND STATE (322)

Bennett, John C. Christians and the state. 4.50. Scribner

Brose, Olive J. Church and Parliament: The reshaping of the Church of England, 1828-1860. 1959. 5.00. Stanford

Murray, A. Victor. State and the church in a free society. 1958. 4.50. Cambridge U. P.

Wood, James E., Jr., and others. Church and state in scripture, history and constitutional law. 1958. 3.00; pap. 1.75. Baylor

CHURCH AND STATE IN THE U.S. (261.73)

Beth, Loren P. American theory of Church and State. 1958 4.50. U. of Fla.

Blanshard, Paul. American freedom and Catholic power. 1958. 4.50. Beacon

Blanshard, Paul. God and man in Washington. 1960. 3.50. Beacon

Dawson, Joseph M. Separate church and state now. 3.00. Smith, Richard R.

Howe, Mark DeWolfe, ed. Cases on church and state in the United States. 1952. pap. 6.00. Harvard

Johnson, Alvin W., and Frank H. Yost. Separation of church and state in the United States. 1948. 4.50. U. of Minn.

McGrath, John J. Church and state in American law. in prep. Bruce

Murray, John C. We hold these truths. 1961. 5.00. Sheed

Nichols, Roy F. Religion and American democracy. 1959. 2.50. La. State

O'Neill, James M. Catholicism and American freedom. 1952. 3.75. Harper

Powell, Theodore. School bus law. 1960. 5.00. Wesleyan U. P.

Shields, C. Democracy and Catholicism in America. 1958. 5.50. McGraw

Tussman, Joseph, ed. Supreme Court on church and state. 1961. pap. 1.95. Oxford U. P.

Walter, Erich A., ed. Religion and the state university. 1958. 6.50. U. of Mich.

CHURCH ARCHITECTURE (726)

Guy, Christian. Modern church architecture. il. 1962. 12.50. Orion

Hamilton, J. Arnott. Byzantine architecture and decoration. il. 8.50. Boston Bk.

Henze, Anton. Contemporary church art. il. 1956. 7.50. Sheed

O'Connell, J. B. Church building and furnishing. il. 1956. 6.00. U. of Notre Dame

CHURCH HISTORY (270)

Bainton, Roland H. Christian attitudes toward war and peace. il. 1960. 4.75. Abingdon

Bevan, Edwyn. Christianity. 1932. 1.70. Oxford U. P.

Bowie, Walter Russell. Story of the church. 1955. 2.95. Abingdon

Cairns, E. E. Christianity through the centuries. 1954. 5.95. Zondervan

Foxe, John. Christian martyrs of the world. 3.95. Moody

Foxe, John. Foxe's book of martyrs. 3.00. Holt, Rinehart & Winston

Guignebert, Charles A. H. Ancient, medieval, and modern Christianity. 1961. 7.50. U. Books

Hughes, Philip. History of the church? 1947. 3 vols. 5.00 ea; set. 15.00. Sheed

Hughes, Philip. Popular history of the Catholic Church. 5.95. Macmillan

Hutchinson, Paul and Winfred E. Garrison. 20 centuries of Christianity. 1959. 6.00. Harcourt

Jacobs, Charles M. Story of the church. 1947. 3.75. Muhlenberg

Latourette, Kenneth Scott. History of Christianity. 1953. 11.00. Harper

Latourette, Kenneth S. History of the expansion of Christianity: 7 vols. vol. 1, First five centuries, 1937. vol. 2, Thousand years of uncertainty, A.D. 500-1500. 1938. vol. 3, Three centuries of advance: A. D. 1500-1800. 1939. vol.

4, Great century in Europe and the United States, A.D. 1800-1914. 1941;
vol. 5. Great century in the Americas, Australasia and Africa. 1943; vol. 6,
Great century in Northern Africa and Asia. 1944; vol. 7, Advance through
storm, A.D. 1914 and after with concluding generalizations. 1945. 6.00 ea;
set. 37.50. Harper

Maus, Cynthia Pearl. Church and the fine arts. il. 1960. 6.95. Harper

Purinton, C. E. Christianity, and its Judaic heritage. 1961. 6.00. Ronald

Schaff, Philip. History of the Christian church. 8 vols. vol. 1, Apostolic
Christianity; vol. 2, Anti-Nicene, vol. 3, Nicene and Post-Nicene, vol. 4,
Medieval Christianity; vols. 5 and 6, Middle ages; vol. 7, German Reform-
ation; vol. 8, Swiss Reformation. 1960. 6.00 ea. set 45.00. Eerdmans

Stuber, Stanley I. How we got our denominations. 1959. 3.50. Assn. Pr.

Walker, Williston. History of the Christian Church. 1959. 6.75. Scribner

CHURCH HISTORY--PRIMITIVE AND EARLY CHURCH (270.1)

Alfoldi, Andrew. Conversion of Constantine and pagan Rome. tr. by Harold
Mattingly. 1948. 4.00. Oxford U. P.

Bainton, Roland H. Early and medieval Christianity. 1962. 6.00. Beacon

Bihlmeyer, Karl. Church history: Christian antiquity. 1958. 8.50. Newman

Coneybeare, Frederic C. Origins of Christianity. 1958. 6.00. U. Books

Daniel-Rops, H. Church of the apoltles and martyrs. tr. by Audrey Butler. il.
1960. 10.00. Dutton

Guignebert, Charles A. H. Early history of Christianity. 1962. 4.50. Twayne

Hatch, Edwin. Influence of Greek ideas on Christianity 1957. 1.45. Harper

Jones, Arnold H. M. Constantine and the conversion of Europe. pap. 0.95. Collier

Latourette, Kenneth Scott. First five centuries (History of the expansion of
Christianity, vol. 1) 6.00. Harper

Purves, George T. Christianity in the Apostolic Age. 1955. 3.00. Baker Bk. (R)

Ramsay, William M. Luke the physician. 4.50. Baker Bk.

Schaff, Philip. Nicene and Post-Nicene. 311-600. (History of the Christian church, vo
3) 6.00. Eerdmans

Wright, Robert R. Church's first thousand years. 1960. pap. 1.00. Abingdon

CHURCH HISTORY--MIDDLE AGES (270.5)

Bainton, Roland H. Early and medieval Christianity. 1962. 6.00. Beacon

Coulton, G. G. Five centuries of religion. 4 vols. vol. 1-3, o.p; vol. 4, Last
days of Medieval monachism. 1950. 13.50. Cambridge U. P.

Coulton, George G. Ten medieval studies. 1959. 3.75. Smith, Peter

Daniel-Rops, H. Church in the Dark Ages. il. 1959. 10.00. Dutton

Daniel-Rops, Henri. Protestant Reformation. tr. by Audrey Butler. 1961.
10.00. Dutton

Dawson, Christopher. Making of Europe. 1946. 4.50. Sheed

Latourette, Kenneth Scott. Thousand years of uncertainty, A. D. 500-1500
(History of the expansion of Christianity, vol. 2) 6.00. Harper

Schaff, Philip. Middle Ages 1049-1294. (History of the Christian church, vol.
5) 6.00. Eerdmans

Schaff, Philip. Middle Ages 1294-1517. (History of the Christian church, vol.
6) 6.00. Eerdmans

CHURCH HISTORY--MODERN PERIOD (270.8)

Cragg, Gerald R. Church and the age of reason, 1648-1789. 1961. 4.50.
Atheneum

Daniel-Rops, Henri. Catholic Reformation. tr. by John Warrington. 10.00
Dutton

Hales, E. E. Y. Catholic church in the modern world. 1958. 4.50; (Image D95)
pap. 0.95. Doubleday

Latourette, Kenneth S. Christianity in a revolutionary age. 5 vols. vol. 1. Nineteenth century in Europe: Background and the Roman Catholic phase. 1958.
7.00; vol. 2. Nineteenth century in Europe: The Protestant and Eastern
Churches. 1959. 7.00; vol. 3. Nineteenth century outside Europe. 1961. 7.50,
vol. 4. Twentieth century in Europe. 1961. 8.50; vol. 5. Twentieth century outside Europe. 1962. 8.50. Harper

Latourette, Kenneth Scott. Great century in Europe and the United States, A. D. 1800-1914 (History of the expansion of Christianity, vol. 4) 6.00. Harper

Latourette, Kenneth Scott. Great century in Northern Africa and Asia (History of the expansion of Christianity, vol. 6) 6.00. Harper

Latourette, Kenneth Scott. Great century in the Americas, Australasia and Africa (History of the expansion of Christianity, vol. 5) 6.00. Harper

Norwood, Frederick A. Development of modern Christianity. 1956. 3.75. Abingdon

Wand, John W. C. History of the modern church, from 1500 to the present day. 1952. 3.95. British Bk.

CHURCH HISTORY--20TH CENTURY (270)

Latourette, Kenneth Scott. Advance through storm, A. D. 1914 and after with concluding generalizations (History of the expansion of Christianity, vol. 7) 6.00. Harper

Latourette, Kenneth S. Twentieth Century in Europe. (Christianity in a revolutionary age, vol. 4) 1961. 8.50. Harper

Miller, Robert M. American Protestantism and social issues, 1919-1939. 1958. 6.00. U. of N. C.

CHURCH MUSIC (783)

Douglas, Winfred. Church music in history and practice. 1962. 5.95. Scribner

Moerner, O. W. Better music in the church. pap. 1.00. Abingdon

Sowerby, Leo. Ideals in church music. pap. 0.75. Seabury

CHURCHILL, SIR WINSTON LEONARD SPENCER, 1874- (923.242)

Birkenhead, Frederick W. F. Smith, Earl of. Professor and the prime minister. 1962. 5.95. Houghton

Bocca, Geoffrey. Adventurous life of Winston Churchill. 1958. 5.00. Messner

Broad, Lewis. Winston Churchill: The years of preparation. il. 1959. 6.00. Hawthorn

Broad, Lewis. Winston Churchill: The years of preparation. il. 1959. 6.00. Hawthorn

Cowles, Virginia. Winston Churchill: The era and the man. 1960. pap. 1.65. Grosset

Graubard, Stephen R. Burke, Disraeli, and Churchill: The politics of perseverance. 1961. 5.00. Harvard

Harrity, Richard, and Ralph G. Martin. Man of the century: Churchill. il. 1962. 6.95. Meredith

Hughes, Emrys. Winston Churchill: British bulldog. il. 1955. 5.00. Exposition

Le Vien, Jack, and John Lord, eds. Winston Churchill: The valiant years. 1961. 7.50. Random

Miller, Tatlock H. , and Loudon Sainthill, eds. Churchill: The walk with destiny. il. 7.95. Macmillan

Moorehead, Alan. Winston Churchill. il. 1960. 6.50. Viking

CICERO, MARCUS TULLIUS, 106-43 B. C. (923.2)

Haight, E. H. Roman use of anecdote in Cicero, Livy and the Satirists. 1940. 2.50. McKay

Lightfoot, G. C. Cicero and Catiline. 1960. 1.75. St. Martins

Plutarch. Lives: Life stories of men who shaped history. by Edward C. Lindeman. pap. 0.60. New. Am. Lib.

EL CID CAMPEADORE (398.22)

Sherwood, M. , ed. Tale of the warrior lord: The Cid. 1957. 3.75. McKay

CILIA AND CILIARY MOTION (593.172)

Sleigh, M. A. Biology of cilia and flagella. 6.00. Pergamon

CILIATA (593.172)

Corliss, J. O. Ciliated protozoa. 1961. 12.00. Pergamon

CIPHERS (652.8)

Ball, W. W. Rouse. Mathematical recreations and essays. il. 1960. 3.95. Macmillan

D'Agapeyeff, Alexander. Codes and ciphers. il. 1939. 1.40. Oxford U. P.
CIRCUS--HISTORY (791.3)
Chindahl, George L. History of the circus in America. 1958. 5.00. Caxton
Murray, Marian. Circus: From Rome to Ringling. il. 1956. 7.95. Meredith
CITIES AND TOWNS (301.36)
Bergel, Egon Ernest. Urban sociology. 1955. 7.25. McGraw
Boskoff, Alvin. Sociology of urban regions. il. 1962. 6.00. Appleton
Clark, Dennis. Cities in crisis: The Christian response. 1960. 3.50. Sheed
Ericksen, E. Gordon. Urban behavior. il. 1954. 6.25. Macmillan
Gist, Noel P., and L. A. Halbert. Urban society. il. 1956. 6.00. Crowell
Greer, Scott. Emerging City. 1962. 5.75. Free Press.
Grodzins, Morton. Metropolitan area as a racial problem. il. 1958. pap. 0.50.
    U. of Pittsburgh
Gutkind, E. A. Twilight of cities. 1962. 5.00. Free Press
Mayer, Harold M., and Clyde F. Kohn. Readings in urban geography. 1959.
    8.50. U. of Chicago
Mumford, Lewis. Culture of cities. il. 1938. 7.50. 5.00. Harcourt
Park, Robert E. Human communities. 1952. 5.00. Free Press
Quinn, James A. Urban sociology. 6.50. Am. Bk. Co.
Robson, William A., and others, eds. Great cities of the world. il. 1955. 11.00.
    Macmillan
Taylor, Griffith. Urban geography: A study of site, evolution, pattern and
    classification in villages, towns and cities. il. 1949. 6.75. Dutton
Vereker, C. H., and J. B. Mays. Urban re-development and social change.
    1960. 5.00. Lounz
Weber, Max. City. 4.00. Free Press
CITIES AND TOWNS--GROWTH (301.36)
McKelvey, Blake. Urbanization of America, 1865-1915. 1962. 10.00. Rutgers
Self, Peter. Cities in flood: The problems of urban growth. il. 5.25. Trans-
    atlantic
Wibberley, G. P. Agriculture and urban growth. il. 1960. 5.25. Int. Pub.
CITIES AND TOWNS--HISTORY (301.36)
Golden ages of the great cities. il. 6.00. Vanguard
Hilberseimer, L. Nature of cities. 1955. 8.75. Theobald
Mumford, Lewis. City in history. il. 1961. 11.50. 8.50. Harcourt
CITIES AND TOWNS--PLANNING (301.36)
Abercrombie, Patrick. Town and country planning. by D. Rigby Childs. 1959.
    1.70. Oxford U. P.
Breese, G., and D. E. Whitman, eds. Approach to urban planning. 1953. pap.
    2.00. Princeton
Grimm, Sergei N. Physical urban planning. 1961. pap. 2.00. Syracuse
Perloff, Harvey S. Education for planning: City, state, and regional. 1957.
    3.50. Johns Hopkins
Perloff, Harvey S., ed. Planning and the urban community. 1961. 4.00.
    U. of Pittsburgh
Woodbury, Coleman, ed. Future of cities and urban redevelopment. 1953.
    11.50. U. of Chicago
Wright, Frank Lloyd. Living city. il. 7.50. Horizon
CITIES AND TOWNS--PLANNING--U.S. (301.36)
Dyckman, F., and R. Isaacs. Capital requirements for urban development
    and renewal. il. 1961. 11.50. McGraw
Futterman, Robert A. Future of our cities. 4.95. Doubleday'
Higbee, Edward. Squeeze: Cities without space. 1960. 5.95. Morrow
Jacobs, Jane. Death and life of American cities. 1961. 5.95; text ed. 5.60.
    Random
Johnson, Thomas F., and others. Renewing America's cities. 1962. 5.00. Inst.
    for Soc. Sci. Res.

CITIES AND TOWNS--U.S. (301.36)
Bridenbaugh, Carl. Cities in revolt. il. 1955. 7.50. Knopf
Dobriner, William Mann, ed. Suburban community. il. 1958. 6.50. Putnam
Duncan, O. D., and A. J. Reiss. Social characteristics of urban and rural
    communities-1950. 1956. 7.95. Wiley
Fortune. Exploding metropolis. 1958. by the Editors of Fortune. 3.95. pap. 0.95.
    Doubleday
Gallaher, Art, Jr. Plainville fifteen years later. 1961. 5.00. Columbia
Griffith, E. S. History of American city government: The Colonial period.
    1938. 4.50. Oxford U. P.
Kammerer, Gladys, and others. City managers in politics. 1962. pap. 2.00.
    U. of Fla.
Macdonald, Austin F. American city government and administration. 1956. 6.50.
    Crowell
Queen, Stuart A., and D. B. Carpenter. American city. 1953. 6.95. McGraw
Schlesinger, Arthur M. Rise of the city. 1878-1898. il. 6.75. Macmillan
Wade, Richard C. Urban frontier: The rise of western cities, 1780-1830.
    1959. 6.00. Harvard
West, J. Plainville, U.S.A. 1945. 3.75; pap. 1.55. Columbia
Whyte, William Foote. Street-corner society: The social structure of an
    Italian slum. il. 1955. 6.00. U. of Chicago
Wolle, Muriel S. Bonanza Trail: Ghost towns and mining camps of the West.
    il. 1953. 10.00. Indiana
CITIES AND TOWNS, ANCIENT (930)
Fowler, William Warde. City state of the Greeks and Romans. 2.75. St. Martins
Fustel de Coulanges, Numa Denis. Ancient city. 1959. 3.00. Smith, Peter
Turner, Ralph E. Great cultural traditions. vol. 2, Classical empires. 1941. 9.50.
    McGraw
CITIES AND TOWNS, MEDIEVAL (930)
Pirenne, Henri. Medieval cities, their origins and the revival of trade. 3.00.
    Smith, Peter
CITIES AND TOWNS, RUINED, EXTINCT, ETC. (913)
Cottrell, Leonard. Lost cities. il. 4.50. Rinehart
Schreiber, Hermann, and Georg. Vanished cities. 1957. 5.75. Knopf
Silverberg, Robert. Lost cities and vanished civilizations. il. 1962. 3.95.
    Chilton
CITIES AND TOWNS IN ART (741.24
Watson, Ernest W. Buildings and streets (Vol. 1. Course in pencil sketching).
    1956. 2.95. Reinhold
CITIZENSHIP (323.6)
Brogan, D. W. Citizenship today: England-France-The United States. 1960.
    3.00. U. of N.C.
Hagedorn, Hermann, ed. Americanism of Theodore Roosevelt. 1923. 2.04.
    Houghton
National Education Association, National Council for the Social Studies.
    Citizenship and a free society: Education for the future, yearbook. 1960.
    5.00. N. E. A.
Port, Weimar. How to become an American citizen. 1962. 1.00. Judy Pub.
Roche, John P. Early development of United States citizenship. 1949. pap. 0.50.
    Cornell
CITY AND TOWN LIFE (301.36)
Atherton, Lewis. Main Street on the Middle Border. il. 1954. 6.00. Indiana
Ericksen, E. Gordon. Urban behavior. il. 1954. 6.25. Macmillan
Glazer, Nathan, and Robert Gutman. City life: A reader 6.00. Random
Oeser, O. A., and S. B. Hammond. Social structure and personality in a city.
    6.00. Humanities
CIVIL ENGINEERING (624)
Abbett, R. W. American civil engineering practice. 3 vols. 1956. vols. 1 and 2,
    18.00 ea; vol. 3. 1957. 25.00. Wiley

Condit, Carl W. American building art: The twentieth century. il. 1961. 15.00.
Oxford U. P.
Hammond, Rolt. Civil engineering today. il. 1960. 3.40. Oxford U. P.
Urquhart, Leonard C. Civil engineering handbook. 1959. 20.00. McGraw
CIVIL PROCEDURE (347.9)
Blume, William. American civil procedure. 1955. 6.75. Little
Bradway, John Saeger. History of a law-suit. 1958. pap. 3.50. Duke
Scott, Austin W., and Sidney P. Simpson. Cases and other materials on civil
procedure. 1950. 9.75. Little
CIVIL RIGHTS (323.4)
Becker, Carl L., and others. Safeguarding civil liberty today. 2.50. Smith,
Peter
Douglas, William O. Living Bill of rights. 1961. 1.50. Doubleday
Trueblood, Elton. Declaration of freedom. 1955. 1.50. Harper
Truman, Harry S. Freedom and equality. ed. by David Horton. 1960. 2.95.
U. of Missouri
CIVIL RIGHTS--U.S. (323.473)
Barnett, Richard. Where the states stand on civil rights. 2.95. Sterling
Caughey, John W. In clear and present danger. 1958. 4.00. U. of Chicago
Chafee, Zechariah, Jr. Blessings of liberty. 1956. 5.00. Lippincott
Commager, Henry Steele. Freedom, loyalty, dissent. 1954. 3.75. Oxford U. P.
Douglas, William O. Almanac of liberty. 1954. 5.95. pap. 1.45. Doubleday
Douglas, William O. Right of the people. 1958. 4.00. Doubleday
Dowden, Wilfred S., and T. N. Marsh, eds. Heritage of freedom: Essays on
the rights of free men. 1962. pap. 2.95. Harper
Fellman, David. Limits of freedom. 1959. 2.75. Rutgers
Gellhorn, Walter. American rights. 1960. 4.50. Macmillan
Hand, Learned. The Bill of Rights. 1958. 2.50. Harvard
Kauper, Paul G. Civil liberties and the Constitution. 1962. 6.00. U. of Mich.
Konvitz, Milton R., ed. Bill of Rights reader: Leading constitutional cases.
1960. 8.25. Cornell
Konvitz, Milton R. Fundamental liberties of a free people: Religion, speech,
press, assembly. 1958. 5.00. Cornell
Morison, Samuel Eliot. Freedom in contemporary society. 1956. 3.50.
Little
O'Brian, J. L. National security and individual freedom. 1955. 2.00. Harvard
Perry, Richard L., ed. Sources of our liberties. 1959. 5.00. N. Y. U.
Pound, Roscoe. Development of constitutional guarantees of liberty. 1957.
4.00. Yale
Rutland, Robert A. Birth of the Bill of Rights: 1776-1791. 1955. 5.00. U. of
N. C.
CIVIL SERVICE--U.S. (351.1)
Baum, Bernard H. Decentralization of authority in a bureaucracy. il. 1961.
4.50. Prentice-Hall
David, Paul T., and Ross Pollock. Executives for government: Central issues
of federal personnel administration. 1957. pap. 1.50. Bookings
Kaplan, Herman E. Law of Civil Service. 1958. 11.00. Bender
Turner, David R. Civil service handbook. 1958. pap. 1.00. Arco (R)
Van Riper, Paul P. History of the United States Civil Service. 1958. 7.50.
Harper
CIVILIZATION (901.9)
Clough, Shepard B. Basic values of western civilization. 1960. 3.00. Columbia
Collingwood, R. G. New leviathan; or, Man, society, civilization and barbar-
ism. 1942. 6.10. Oxford U. P.
Columbia College, Contemporary Civilization Staff. Man in contemporary
society. 2 vols. 1955. 7.50 ea. Columbia
Cunningham, William. Western civilization. pt. 1. Ancient times. 1898. 3.50.

Frued, Sigmund. Civilization and its discontents. 1961. 3.75. Norton
Fromm, Erich. Sane society. 1955. 5.00. Rinehart
Koestler, Arthur. Lotus and the robot. 1960. 3.95. Macmillan
Kohn, C., and D. Drummond. World: Its regions and cultures. in prep.
   McGraw
Linton, Ralph, ed. Most of the world. 1949. 6.50. Columbia
Lowie, R. H. Culture and ethnology. 3.00. Smith, Peter
Mannheim, Karl. Man and society in an age of reconstruction. 4.50. Harcourt
Marcuse, Herbert. Eros and civilization. 1956. 3.95. Beacon
Ortegay Gasset, Jose. Revolt of the masses. 1932. 3.75. Norton
Sarton, George. Ancient science and modern civilization. 1954. 2.50. U. of
   Nebr.
Toynbee, Arnold J. Study of history. abridgement of vols. 1-10, in 2 vols. ed.
   by D. C. Somervell. vols. 1-6, 1947, 6.00; vols, 7-10, 1957. 5.00. Oxford
   U. P.
Trueblood, Elton. Predicament of modern man. 1.50. Harper
White, Leslie A. Science of culture. 1949. 6.00. Farrar, Straus
CIVILIZATION--HISTORY (901.9)
Bowie, John. ed. Concise encyclopedia of world history. il. 1958. 15.00.
   Hawthorn (R)
Breasted, James Henry. Conquest of civilization. il. 1938. 7.50. Harper
Brinton, Crane. Ideas and men: The story of western thought. 1950. 9.00;
   6.75. Prentice-Hall
Clough, Shepard B. Rise and fall of civilization. 1961. pap. 1.95. Columbia
Columbia College, Contemporary Civilization Staff. Chapters in Western
   civilization. 2 vols. 1962. 6.00. Columbia
De Burgh, William G. Legacy of the ancient world. 1960. 5.00. Barnes & Noble
Durant, Will. Story of civilization. 7 vols. il. vol. 1, Our oriental heritage,
   1935, 12.00; vol. 2, Life of Greece, 1939, 10.00; vol. 3, Caesar and Christ,
   1944, 10.00; vol. 4, Age of faith, 1950, 12.00; vol. 5, Renaissance, 1953,
   10.00; vol. 6, Reformation, 1957, 12.00; vol. 7, Age of reason begins, with
   Ariel Durant, 1961, 10.00? S. and S.
Hawkes, Jacquetta. Man on earth. il. 1955. 3.75. Random
Jamieson, Elizabeth M., and others. Trends in nursing history. 5th ed. il.
   1959. 5.00. Saunders
Kahler, Erich. Man the measure. 1956. 6.50. Braziller
Linton, Ralph. Tree of culture. il. 1955. 9.75. 7.25. Knopf
Muller, Herbert K. Uses of the past. 1952. 6.00. Oxford U. P.
Mumford, Lewis. Condition of man. il. 7.50. Harcourt
Mumford, Lewis. Technics and civilization. 1934. 6.00. Harcourt
Mumford, Lewis. Transformations of man. 1956. 4.00. Harper
Nef, John U. Cultural foundations of industrial civilization. 1958. 4.00.
   Cambridge U. P.
Ortega, Gasset, Jose. Man and crisis. 1958. pap. 1.55. Norton
Raleigh, J. H. History and the individual: A college reader. 1962. 6.95. Holt,
   Rinehart & Winston
Randall, John H., Jr. Making of the modern mind. 1940. 6.00. Houghton
Ries, Estelle H. Ingenuity of man. il. 1962. 4.00. Exposition
Smith, Preserved. History of modern culture. 2 vols. vol. 1. Origins of
   modern culture, 1543-1687. vol. 2, Enlightenment, 1687-1776. pap. 1.95 ea.
   Collier
Smith, Preserved. History of modern cultures. 2 vols. 15.00. Smith, Peter
Spengler, Oswald. Decline of the West. 2 vols. 1945. 16.50. 1962. 6.95. Knopf
Stevens, Henry Bailey. Recovery of culture. 1949. 3.00. Harper
Thorndike, Lynn. Short history of civilization. 1926. 5.00. Appleton
Toynbee, Arnold. Civilization on trial, and The world and the West. pap. 1.55.
   Meridian
Toynbee, Arnold. Historian's approach to religion. 1956. 5.00. Oxford U. P.

Toynbee, Arnold J.   World and the West. 1953. 3.00. Oxford U. P.
Whitehead, Alfred N.   Adventures of ideas. 1933. 5.00. Macmillan

CIVILIZATION--HISTORY--OUTLINES, SYLLABI, ETC. (901.9)

Hyma, Albert.   Outline of Far Eastern civilizations. 0.75. Long's College Bk.
Hyma, Albert.   Outline of the growth of Western civilization. 2 pts. 1938. 1.00.
  ea. Long's College Bk.
McNeill, William H.   History handbook of Western civilization. il. 1958. pap. 4.50.
  U. of Chicago (R)

CIVILIZATION--HISTORY--SOURCES (901.9)

Beatty, John, and Oliver Johnson.   Heritage of western civilization: Select
  readings. 1958. 7.95; Renaissance to the present. pap. 4.75. Prentice-Hall
Columbia College, Contemporary Civilization Staff.   Introduction to contemporary civilization in the west; Source book. 2 vols. 1960-1. 7.50 ea. Columbia

CIVILIZATION--PHILOSOPHY (901)

Barr, Stringfellow.   Pilgrimage of western man. 1962. 5.95; pap. 1.95. Lippincott

Beard, Charles A., and Mary R.   American spirit. pap. 1.50. Collier
Becker, Carl L.   Progress and power. 1949. 3.00. Knopf
Berdyaev, Nicolas.   Fate of man in the modern world. 1935. 4.40. U. of Mich.

Cassirer, Ernst.   Essay on man. 1944. 5.00; pap. 1.65. Yale
Dixon, William M.   Human situation. 4.50. St. Martins
Northrop, F. S. C., ed.   Ideological differences and world order. 1949. 5.00.
  Yale
Northrop, F. S. C.   Meeting of East and West: An inquiry concerning world
  understanding. il. 1946. 6.00. Macmillan
Schwietzer, Albert.   Philosophy of civilization. tr. by Campion. 2 vols. in 1.
  6.00. Macmillan
Sorokin, P. A.   Crisis of our age: The social and cultural outlook. il. 5.00;
  Dutton
Sorokin, Pitirim A.   Social and cultural dynamics. 4 vols. 1962. 11.00 ea; set,
  boxed, 40.00. Bedminster
Sorokin, Pitirim A.   Social and cultural dynamics. 1957. 7.50. Sargent
Wilson, Colin.   Outsider. 1956. 5.00. Houghton
Wilson, Colin.   Religion and the rebel. 1957. 4.00. Houghton
Wilson, Colin.   Stature of man. 1959. 3.00. Houghton

CIVILIZATION, ANCIENT (930)

Bibby, Geoffrey.   Four thousand years ago. 1961. 6.95. Knopf
Frankfort, Henri.   Birth of civilization in the Near East. il. 1951. 4.50. Indiana
Frankfort, Henri, and others.   Intellectual adventure of ancient man: An essay
  on speculative thought in the ancient Near East. 1946. 7.50. U. of Chicago
Hall, H. R.   Ancient history of the Near East. 8.50. Macmillan
Lissner, Ivar.   Man, God and magic. 1961. 5.95. Putnam
Lissner, Ivar.   Silent past. il. 1962. 6.95. Putnam
Peake, Harold, and H. J. Fleure.   Horse and the sword. 1933. 2.40. Oxford
  U. P.
Peake, Harold, and H. J. Fleure.   Law and the Prophets. 1936. 2.40. Oxford
  U. P.
Peake, Harold, and H. J. Fleure.   Priests and kings. 1927. 2.40. Oxford U. P.
Peake, Harold, and H. J. Fleure.   Steppe and the sown. 1928. 2.40. Oxford
  U. P.
Peake, Harold, and H. J. Fleure.   Peasants and potters. 1927. 2.40. Oxford
  U. P.
Peake, Harold, and H. J. Fleure.   Times and places. 1956. 6.75. Oxford U. P.
Peake, Harold, and H. J. Fleure.   Way of the sea. 1929. 2.40. Oxford U. P.
Piggott, Stuart, ed.   Dawn of civilization. il. 1961. 28.50. McGraw
Sarton, George A.   History of science: Ancient science through the Golden Age
  of Greece. il. 1952. 11.00. Harvard

Smith, Charles E., and Paul G. Moorhead. Short history of the ancient world. 1939. 5.75. Appleton

Suhr, Elmer G. Ancient mind and its heritage. vol. 1, Exploring the Primitive, Egyptian and Mesopotamian cultures,1959. 3.50; vol. 2, Exploring the Hebrew, Hindu, Greek and Chinese cultures, 1960. 5.00. Exposition

White, Leslie A. Evolution of culture. 1959. 7.95; pap. 2.25. McGraw

CIVILIZATION, ANGLO-SAXON (935.32)

Martin-Clarke, D. Elizabeth. Culture in early Anglo-Saxon England. il. 1947. 2.25. Johns Hopkins

CIVILIZATION, ARABIC (939.47)

Hitti, Philip Khuri. History of the Arabs. rev. 9.00. St. Martins

CIVILIZATION, CHRISTIAN (261.6)

Agar, Herbert. Declaration of faith. 1952. 3.00. Houghton

Belloc, Hilaire. Crisis of civilization. 1937. 2.50. Fordham

Cochrane, Charles Norris. Christianity and classical culture. 1944. 7.00. pap. 2.45. Oxford U. P.

Dawson, Christopher. Medieval essays. pap. 0.95. Doubleday

Dawson, Christopher H. Movement of world revolution. 1959. 3.00. Sheed

Dawson, Christopher. Religion and the rise of Western culture. 3.50. Sheed

Hayes, Carleton J. H. Christianity and Western civilization. 1954. 2.50. Stanford

Olsson, Karl A. Things common and preferred. 1959. 2.75. Augsburg

Smith, William E. Holy Spirit, state, church, and school. 1959. 5.00. Forum

Taylor, Henry Osborn. Classical heritage of the Middle Ages. 4.50. Ungar

CIVILIZATION, GRECO-ROMAN (938)

Taylor, Henry Osborn. Classical heritage of the Middle Ages. 4.50. Ungar

CIVILIZATION, GREEK (938)

Agard, Walter R. Greek mind. 1957. pap. 1.25. Van Nostrand

Bonnard, Andre. Greek civilization. 3 vols. il. tr. by Lytton Sells. vol. 1, From Ilaid to the Parthenon. 1957. 6.00; vol. 2. From Antigone to Socrates. 1959. 6.00; vol. 3. From Euripides to Alexandria. tr. by R. C. Knight. 1962. 7.00. Macmillan

Bowra, Maurice. Great Greek experience. 6.00. World Pub.

Cary, M., and T. J. Haarhoff. Life and thought in the Greek and Roman world. 4.00. Barnes & Noble

Dickinson, G. Lowes. Greek view of life. 3.00. Smith, Peter

Dodds, E. R. Greeks and the irrational. 1960. 6.50. U. of Calif.

Durant, Will. Life of Greece (Story of civilization. vol. 2) 10.00. S. and S.

Geer, Russel M. Classical civilization: Rome. 1950. 7.50. Prentice-Hall

Gittler, Joseph B. Social thought among the early Greeks. 1941. 3.00. U. of Ga.

Hadas, Moses. Hellenistic culture fusion and diffusion. 1959. 6.00. Columbia

Hamilton, Edith. Greek way. (320) 1.95. Modern Lib.

Hamilton, Edith. Greek way. 1930. 4.50. Norton

Jaeger, Werner. Paideia: Ideals of Greek culture. vol. 1, Archaic Greece, and Mind of Athens. 1945. vol. 2, In search of the divine center. 1943. vol. 3, Conflict of cultural ideals in the age of Plato. 1944. 7.50 ea. tr. by Gilbert Highet. Oxford U. P.

Kluckhohn, Clyde K. M. Anthropology and the classics. 1961. 2.00. Brown U.

Livingstone, R. W. Greek genius and its meaning to us. 1915. 2.40. Oxford U. P.

Livingstone, Richard W. Greek ideals and modern life. 1935. 2.00. Oxford U. P.

Livingstone, Richard W., ed. Legacy of Greece. il. 1921. 5.75. Oxford U. P.

Messinesi, Xenophon L. Meet the ancient Greeks. il. 1959. 5.00. Caxton

Murray, Gilbert. Greek studies. 1946. 3.40. Oxford U. P.

Stobart, John C. Glory that was Greece. by F. N. Pryce. il. 1962. pap. 3.95. Grove

Suhr, Elmer G. Exploring the Hebrew, Hindu, Greek and Chinese cultures
     (Ancient mind and its heritage. vol. 2) 5.00. Exposition
Van Hook, La Rue. Greek life and thought. 1923. 4.00. Columbia
Voegelin, Eric. Plato and Aristotle. 1957. 6.00. La. State
Voegelin, Eric. World of the polis. 1957. 6.00. La. State
Webster, T. B. L. Art and literature in fourth century Athens. 1956. 4.00.
     Oxford U. P.
Zschietzschmann, Willy. Hellas and Rome. tr. by Hedi Schanabl. il. 1959. 7.50.
     Universe

CIVILIZATION, HOMERIC (883.1)

Finley, Moses. World of Odysseus. il. 1954. 3.00. Viking
Mireaux, Emile. Daily life in the time of Homer. 1959. 5.00. Macmillan

CIVILIZATION, MEDIEVAL (940.1)

Artz, Frederick B. Mind of the Middle Ages. il. 1954. 6.50. Knopf
Coulton, George G. Medieval panorama. il. 1955. pap. 2.45. Meridian
Coulton, George G. Medieval scene. il. 3.75. Smith, Peter
Coulton, George G. Medieval village, manor and monastery. 4.50. Smith,
     Peter
Crump, C. G., and E. F. Jacob, ed. Legacy of the Middle Ages. il. 1926. 6.00.
     Oxford U. P.
Davis, William Stearns. Life on a medieval barony. 1928. 5.00. Harper
Dawson, Christopher. Making of Europe. 1946. 4.50. Sheed
Gierke, Otto. Political theories of the Middle Age. tr. by Frederic W. Maitland.
     1900. 6.50. Cambridge U. P.
Haskins, Charles. Renaissance of the twelfth century. 3.75. Smith, Peter
Havighurst, Alfred F., ed. Pirenne thesis: Analysis, criticism, and revision.
     1958. pap. 1.50. Heath
Holmes, Urban T., Jr. Daily living in the Twelfth Century: Based on the
     observations of Alexander Neckam in London and Paris. il. 1952. 3.85. U. of
     Wis.
Huizinga, Johan. Waning of the Middle Ages. 4.75. St. Martins
Painter, Sidney. French chivlary: Chivlaric ideas and practices in Medieval
     France. 1940. 3.50. Johns Hopkins
Power, Eileen. Medieval people. 3.00. Smith, Peter
Rand, Edward K. Founders of the Middle Ages. 3.75. Smith, Peter
Taylor, Henry Osborn. Mediaeval mind: A history of the development of
     thought and emotion in the Middle Ages. 2 vols. 1949. 10.00. Harvard

CIVILIZATION, MODERN (901.94)

Ayres, C. E. Toward a reasonable society. 1961. 4.75. U. of Tex.
Brinton, Crane, and others. Modern civilization: A history of the last five
     centuries. 1957. 9.50. Prentice-Hall
Bronowski, Jacob, and Bruce Mazlish. Western intellectual tradition: From
     Leonardo to Hegel. 1960. 7.50. Harper
Commager, Henry Steele, ed. Contemporary civilization, no. 2. 1961. soft-
     bound. 2.50. Scott
Dawson, Christopher H. Movement of world revolution. 1959. 3.00. Sheed
Garbett, Cyril. In an age of revolution. 1952. 3.20. Oxford U. P.
Greene, Theodore M. Our cultural heritage. 1956. 4.75. Van Nostrand
Jaspers, Karl. Man in the modern age. 3.00. Humanities
Krutc Joseph W. Human nature and the human condition. 1959. 3.95. Random
Krutch, Joseph Wood. Measure of man. pap. 1.75. Bobbs
Pearson, L. B. Democracy in world politics. 1955. 2.75. Princeton
Peckham, Morse. Beyond the tragic vision. 1962. 7.50. Braziller
Ritner, Peter. Society of space. 1961. 3.75. Macmillan
Schurz, William L. American foreign affairs. 1959. 4.50. Dutton
Wishy, Bernard, ed. Western world in the twentieth century. 1961. 5.00.
     Columbia

CIVILIZATION, MODERN--ADDRESSES, ESSAYS, LECTURES (901.94)

Baruch, Bernard. Philosophy for our time. 1954. 2.00. S. and S.

Huxley, Julian S., ed. Humanist frame. 1962. 6.50. Harper

Mumford, Lewis. Human prospect. 1955. pap. 1.45. Beacon

Saturday Evening Post. Adventures of the mind. by Richard Thruelsen, and John Kobler. 1959. 4.50. 1961. 6.50. Knopf

Toynbee, Arnold, and others. New frontiers of knowledge. 1957. 2.75. Pub. Affairs

CIVILIZATION, MOHAMMEDAN (950)

Arnold, T. W., and Alfred Guillaume, eds. Legacy of Islam. il. 1931. 6.00. Oxford U. P.

Gibb, Hamilton A. R. Studies on the civilization of Islam. ed. by Stanford J. Shaw and William R. Folk. 1962. 7.50. Beacon

Landau, Rom. Islam and the Arabs. 1959. 4.95. Macmillan

Smith, W. C. Islam in modern history. 1957. 6.00. Princeton

CIVILIZATION, MYCENAEAN (913.391)

Cottrell, Leonard. Bull of Minos. il. 1958. 4.50. Rinehart

CIVILIZATION, OCCIDENTAL (901)

Agar, Herbert. Declaration of faith. 1952. 4.50. Vanguard

Brinton, Crane. Ideas and men: The story of western thought. 1950. 9.00; Prentice-Hall

Carr, Edward H. Soviet impact on the western world. 1947. 3.50. Macmillan

Dawson, Christopher. Religion and the rise of Western culture. 3.50. Sheed

Hayes, Carlton J. H. Christianity and Western civilization. 1954. 2.50. Stanford

McNeill, William H. History handbook of Western civilization. il. 1958. pap. 4.50. U. of Chicago

Neill, Thomas P., ed. Readings in the history of western civilization. vol. 1. 1957; vol. 2. 1958. pap. 2.25 ea. Newman

Niebuhr, H. Richard. Radical monotheism and Western culture. 1950. 2.75. Harper

Salvadori, Massimo. Western roots in Europe. 5.25. Roy Pub.

Van Der Meer, Frederic. Atlas of western civilization. il. 1960. 15.00. Van Nostrand

Webb, Walter Prescott. Great frontier. 1952. 6.00. Houghton

Weber, Eugen. Western tradition: 4 vols. vol. 1, From the ancient world to the atomic age, 1959, 7.75; vol. 2, From the ancient world to Louis 14, 1959, pap. 2.95; vol. 3, From the renaissance to the atomic age, 1959, pap. 3.95; vol. 4, From the enlightenment to the atomic age, 1959, pap. 2.95. Heath

CIVILIZATION, OCCIDENTAL--HISTORY--SOURCES (901)

Baumer, Franklin Le Van, ed. Main currents of Western thought: Readings in western European intellectual history from the Middle Ages to the present. 1952. 6.50. Knopf

Knoles, George S., and Rixford K. Snyder. Readings in western civilization. 1960. 7.50. Lippincott

CIVILIZATION, ORIENTAL (901)

Dean, Vera Micheles. American student and the non-western world. 1956. 1.50. Harvard

Dean, Vera Micheles. Nature of the non-western world. pap. 0.60. New Am. Lib.

Beischauer, Edwin O., and John K. Fairbank. East Asia: The great tradition. (History of East Asian civilization. vol. 1). il. 12.50. Houghton

CIVILIZATION, ROMAN (901)

Durant, Will. Caesar and Christ. (Story of civilization, vol. 3) 10.00. S. and S.

CLAIBORNE, WILLIAM, 1600-1677 (923.473)

Hale, Nathaniel C. Virginia venturer. 1951. 5.00. Dietz

CLAIRVOYANCE (133.8)

Sugrue, Thomas. There is a river. 5.00. Holt

Williams, Sophia. You are psychic. 1961. 2.49. Clark Pub.

CLARK, HARRY HAYDEN, 1901- (921)
Paine, Thomas. Thomas Paine : Representative selections. by Harry H. Clark.
1962. 4.00. Smith, Peter
CLARKE, HANS THACHER, 1887- (921)
Graff, S. Essays in biochemistry. 1956. 7.50. Wiley
CLARKE, JOHN HESSIN, 1857-1945 (923.4)
Warner, Hoyt L. Life of Mr. Justice Clarke. 1959. 5.00. Western Reserve
CLASSICAL BIOGRAPHY (920)
Plutarch. Lives. 2.95. Modern Lib.
CLASSICAL DICTIONARIES (913.38)
Avery, Catherine B., ed. New Century classical handbook. 1962. 15.00.
    Meredith
Cary, M., and others. Oxford classical dictionary. 13.50. Oxford U. P.
Harvey, Paul, ed. Oxford companion to classical literature. il. 1937. 4.50.
    Oxford U. P. (R)
Lempriere, J. Lempriere's Classical dictionary of proper names mentioned
    in ancient authors, with a chronological table. rev. ed. 3.75. Dutton (R)
Peck, Harry T., ed. Harper's dictionary of classical literature and antiqui-
    ties. 19.95. Cooper
CLASSICAL GEOGRAPHY (911.3)
Cary, M. Geographic background of Greek and Roman history. 1949. 7.20.
    Oxford U. P.
Heyden, A. A. M. van der, and R. H. Scullard, eds. Atlas of the classical
    world. il. 1960. 15.00. Nelson
Muir, Ramsey. Muir's atlas of ancient and classical history. by George Goodall,
    and R. F. Treharne. 1956. 2.75. Barnes & Noble
Shorter atlas of the classical world. 1962. 3.95. Nelson
CLASSICAL LITERATURE--HISTORY AND CRITICISM (880)
Hadas, Moses. Ancilla to classical reading. 1954. 6.00; pap. 1.95. Columbia
Musurillo, Herbert. Symbol and myth in ancient poetry. 1960. 5.00. Fordham
Reinhold, Meyer. Classical drama, Greek and Roman. 1959. 3.50; pap. 1.95.
    Barron's
Thomson, James A. K. Classical background of English literature. 1948. 3.50.
    Macmillan
CLASSICAL LITERATURE--TRANSLATIONS INTO ENGLISH (880)
MacKendrick, Paul L., and Herbert M. Howe, eds. Classics in translation.
    vol. 1. Greek literature; vol. 2. Latin literature. 1952. 5.00 ea; set, 9.00;
    pap. 3.00 ea. U. of Wis.
CLASSICISM (759.03)
Bate, Walter J. From Classic to Romantic. 3.35. Smith, Peter
Borgerhoff, E. B. O. Freedom of French classicism. 1950. 4.00. Princeton
CLASSIFICATION--BOOKS (025)
Bliss, Henry E. Organization of knowledge in libraries. 1939. 4.00. Wilson
CLASSIFICATION, DECIMAL (025.33)
Dewey, Melvil. Dewey decimal classification and relative index. 2 vols. 1958.
    30.00. Forest
Sears, Minnie E. Sears list of subject headings. by Bertha M. Frick. 1959.
    6.00. Wilson
CLAUDEL, PAUL, 1868-1955 (928)
Chaigne, Louis. Paul Claudel: The man and the mystic. 1961. 4.95. Meredith
CLAUDIUS, EMPEROR OF ROME, B. C. 10-A. D. 54 (923.145)
Momigilano, Arnaldo D. Claudius the emperor and his achievements. 1962.
    3.25. Barnes & Noble
Scramuzza, Vincent Mary. Emperor Claudius. il. 1940. 3.75. Harvard
CLAY, HENRY, 1777-1852 (923.273)
Eaton, Clement. Henry Clay and the art of American politics. 1957. 3.75.
    Little

CLEMENCEAU, GEORGES EUGENE BENJAMIN, 1841-1929 (923.242)
Jackson, J. Hampden. Clemenceau and the Third Republic. 1948. 2.50.
  Macmillan
CLEMENS, SAMUEL LANGHORNE, 1835-1910 (813.4)
Allen, Jerry. Adventures of Mark Twain. 1954. 6.00. Little
Bellamy, Gladys Carmen. Mark Twain as a literary artist. il. 1950. 5.00.
  U. of Okla.
Blair, Walter. Mark Twain and Huck Finn. il. 1960. 7.50. U. of Calif.
Brooks, Van Wyck. Ordeal of Mark Twain. pap. 1.45. Meridian
Budd, Louis J. Mark Twain: Social philosopher. il. 1962. 6.95. Indiana
Clemens, Samuel Langhorne. Autobiography of Mark Twain. ed. by Charles
  Neider. 1961. pap. 0.90. Washington Square
Clemens, Samuel Langhorne. Mark Twain and the Government. ed. by Svend
  Petersen. 1960. 3.50. Caxton
Covici, Pascal, Jr. Mark Twain's humor: The image of a world. 1962. 4.50.
  S. M. U.
De Voto, Bernard. Mark Twain's America. 1951. 5.00. Houghton
Fatout, Paul. Mark Twain on the lecture circuit. il. 1960. 6.00. Indiana
Foner, Philip S. Mark Twain: Social critic. 1958. 4.50. Int. Pubs.
Harnsberger, Caroline T. Mark Twain's views of religion. 1961. 5.00. Schori
Howells, William Dean. Selected writings. ed. by Henry Steele Commager.
  1950. 5.00. Random
Scott, Arthur L., ed. Mark Twain: Selected criticism. 1955. 5.00. S.M.U.
Wagenknecht, Edward C. Mark Twain, the man and his work. 1961. 4.50. U. of
  Okla.
CLEVELAND, GROVER, PRES. U.S., 1837-1908 (923.273)
Merrill, Horace Samuel. Bourbon leader: Grover Cleveland and the Demo-
  cratic party. 1957. 3.75. Little
Nevins, Allan, ed. Grover Cleveland: A study in courage. il. 1932. 10.00. Dodd
CLIMATOLOGY (551.5)
Hare, F. K. Restless atmosphers. 2.50. Hillary
Kendrew, Wilfred George. Climates of the continents. 1961. il. 8.80. Oxford
  U. P.
Koeppe, Clarence E., and George C. DeLong. Weather and climate. 1958. 7.95.
  McGraw
Shapley, Harlow, ed. Climatic change: Evidence, causes, and effects. 1954.
  7.00. Harvard
Trewartha, Glenn T. Earth's problem climates. il. 1961. 7.50. U. of Wis.
Trewartha, Glenn T. Introduction to climate. il. 1954. 8.25. McGraw
CLINICAL PSYCHOLOGY (132.075)
Alexander, Franz, and Helen Ross, eds. Impact of Freudian psychiatry.
  pap. 1.75. U. of Chicago
Andry, Robert G. Delinquency and parental pathology. il. 1960. 5.50. Thomas,
  C. C.
Davis, D. R. Introduction to psychopathology. 1957. 7.50. Oxford U. P.
Engel, George L. Psychological development in health and disease. 1962.
  7.50. Saunders
Hadley, John M. Clinical and counseling psychology. 1958. 7.00. Knopf
Louttit, C. M., and others. Clinical psychology of exceptional children. 1957.
  7.00. Harper
Michal-Smith, Harold. Mentally retarded patient. 1956. 4.00. Lippincott
Zisking, Eugene. Psychophysiologic medicine. 1954. 7.00. Lea & F
CLIPPER-SHIPS (387.22)
Carse, Robert. Moonrakers: The story of the clipper ship men. il. 1961.
  4.00. Harper
Villiers, Alan. Falmouth for orders. 1952. 4.50. Scribner
CLOSED-CIRCUIT TELEVISION (371.3358)
Mayers, Morris A., and R. D. Chipp. Closed circuit TV system planning. il.
  1957. 10.00. Rider

Zworykin, V. K. and others. Television in science and industry. il. 1958.
10.00. Wiley

CLOTHING AND DRESS (646)

Bergen, Polly. Polly Bergen book of beauty, fashion, and charm. il. 1962. 4.95.
Prentice-Hall

Doten, Hazel, and Constance Boulard. Fashion drawing: How to do it. il. 1953.
7.50. Harper

Flugel, J. C. Psychology of clothes. 5.00. Hillary

Goldstein, Harriet, and Vetta. Art in everyday life. il. 1954. 7.50. Macmillan

McCardell, Claire. What shall I wear? 1956. 3.50. S. and S.

Morton, Grace M. Arts of costume and personal appearance. 1955. 6.95. Wiley

Pepin, Harriet. Modern pattern design. il. 1942. 6.00. Funk

Powers, John R., and Mary S. Miller. Secrets of charm. il. 1954. 4.50.
Winston

Rathbone, Lucy, and others. Fashions and fabrics. 5.32. Houghton

Spears, Charleszine. How to wear colors. 1959. 2.00. Burgess

CLOTHING TRADE (338.476)

Fried, Eleanor L. Is the fashion business your business? 1961. 5.50. Fairchild

Richards, Florence S. Ready-to-wear industry. 1951. 2.00. Fairchild

CLOUD CHAMBER (530)

Wilson, John G. Principles of cloud chamber technique. 1951. 4.00.
Cambridge U. P.

CLOUDS (551.572)

Fletcher, N. H. Physics of rain clouds. 1962. 11.50. Cambridge U. P.

Ludlam, F. H. and R. S. Scorer. Cloud study. il. 3.95. Macmillan

Mason, B. J. Physics of clouds. 1957. 12.80. Oxford U. P.

CLOUGH, ARTHUR HUGH 1819-1861 (928.142)

Chorley, Katharine C. Arthur Hugh Clough, the uncommitted mind. il. 1962.
7.20. Oxford U. P.

COACHING (ATHLETICS) (796.077)

American Association for Health, Physical Education, and Recreation.
Coaches handbook. 1959. pap. 1.50. Am. Assn. for Health, Phys. Ed. & Rec.

Bonder, James B. How to be a successful coach. 1959. 4.95. Prentice-Hall

Miller, Richard I. Fundamentals of track and field coaching. 1952. 5.25.
McGraw

National Education Association, American Association for Health, Physical
Education and Recreation. Coaches handbook . 1959. 1.50. N. E. A.

COAL (553.2)

Francis, Wilfrid. Coal: Its formation and composition. 1961. 27.50. St. Martins

Greene, Homer. Coal and the coal mines. 1928. 2.40. Houghton

Parker, Glen. Coal industry: Study in social control. 1940. 3.00. Pub. Affairs

Sharpley, Forbes W., ed. Chemical engineering in the coal industry. 1957.
8.50. Pergamon

COAL-MINERS (622.33)

Goodrich, Carter. Miner's freedom. il. 1925. 2.00. Jones, Marshall

Lantz, H. R. People of Coal Town. 1958. 5.75. Columbia

COAL-TAR PRODUCTS (668.7)

Wilson, Philip J., and Joseph H. Wells. Coal, coke, and coal chemicals. 1950.
12.50. McGraw

COASTS (355.45)

Guilcher, Andre. Coastal and submarine morphology. il. 1958. 6.50. Wiley

COBALT (669.733)

Young, Roland S. Cobalt. il. 1960. 15.00. Reinhold

COCTEAU, JEAN, 1889- (928.841)

Crosland, Margaret. Jean Cocteau. il. 1956. 5.00. Knopf

Oxenhandler, Neal. Scandal and parade: The theater of Jean Cocteau. 1957.
5.00. Rutgers

CODY, WILLIAM FREDERICK, 1846-1917 (923.9)

Russell, Donald B. Lives and legends of Buffalo Bill. 1960. 5.95. U. of Okla.

Baker, James V. Sacred River: Coleridge's theory of imagination. 1957. 4.50.
  La. State
Beer, John B. Coleridge the visionary. 1959. 6.00. Macmillan
Boulger, James D. Coleridge as religious thinker. 1961. 5.00. Yale
Brett, R. L. Reason and imagination. 1959. 2.90. Oxford U. P.
Chambers, E. K. Samuel Taylor Coleridge: A biographical study. 1938.
  6.60. Oxford U. P.
Cobban, Alfred. Edmund Burke and the revolt against the eighteenth century.
  1961. 3.75. Barnes & Noble
Coburn, Kathleen, ed. Inquiring spirit: A new presentation of Coleridge.
  1951. 5.00. Pantheon
Colmer, John. Coleridge: Critic of society. 1959. 4.80. Oxford U. P.
Fogle, Richard H. Idea of Coleridge's criticism (Perspectives in criticism 9)
  1962. 4.25. U. of Calif.
Gettmann, Royal A. Rime of the Ancient Mariner handbook. 1961. 1.95.
  Wadsworth
Griggs, Earl, ed. Wordsworth and Coleridge. 6.50? Russell
Lowes, John L. Road to Xanadu. in prep. Houghton
Lowes, John L. Road to Xanadu. 1959. pap. 1.65. Vintage
Mill, John Stuart. On Bentham and Coleridge. pap. 0.95. Harper
Muirhead, J. H. Coleridge as philosopher. 5.00. Humanities
Nethercot, Arthur H. Road to Tryermaine: A study of the history, background,
  and purposes of Coleridge's Christobel. 6.50? Russell
Richards, I. A. Coleridge on imagination. 1960. pap. 1.75 Indiana
Suther, Marshall E. Dark night of Samuel Taylor Coleridge. 1960. 5.00.
  Columbia
COFFEE-HOUSES (647.94)
Old English coffee houses. 0.95. Yoseloff
COGNITION (153)
Gattell, R. B. Subjective character of cognition. 1930. 2.75. Cambridge U. P.
Gardner, Riley W., and others. Personality organization in cognitive controls
  and intellectual abilities. 1961. 4.00. Int. Univs.
COHESION (531.7)
Jaswon, M. A. Theory of cohesion. il. 1954. 7.50. Pergamon
COINAGE (737.4)
Brooke, George C. English coins: From the 7th century to the present day.
  8.50. Humanities
Mattingly, Harold. Roman coins: From the earliest times to the fall of the
  western Empire. il. 1960. 12.50. Quadrangle (R)
COINS (737.4)
Carson, R. A. G. Coins of the world: Ancient, medival, modern. il. 1962.
  15.00? Harper
Del Monte, Jacques. Fell's international coin book. pap. 1.00. Cornerstone
Liebers, Arthur. Guide to North American coins. 1961. 3.00. Arco (R)
Reinfeld, Fred. Catalog of world coins. 1956. 5.95. Sterling (R)
Reinfeld, Fred. Treasure of the world's coins. il. 1955. 3.95. Sterling
COINS, AMERICAN (737.4)
Del Monte, Jacques. Fell's United States coin book. 1959. 1.98. Fell
Knight, Hugh M. Simplified guide to collecting American coins. 1959. 2.95.
  Doubleday (R)
Reinfeld, Fred. Treasury of American coins. il. 1961. 3.95. Doubleday
Yeoman, Richard S. Guide book of U. S. coins. 1.75. Wehman
COLD--PHYSIOLOGICAL EFFECT (616.989)
Smith, Audrey U. Biological effects of freezing and supercooling. il. 1961.
  11.00. Williams & Wilkins
Virtue, Robert W. Hypothermic anesthesia. il. 1955. 1exide. 2.50. Thomas, C. C.
COLERIDGE, SAMUEL TAYLOR, 1772-1834 (821)
Armour, Richard W., and Raymond F. Howes, eds. Coleridge the talker: A
  series of contemporary descriptions and comments. il. 4.00. Cornell

COLET, LOUISE (REVOIL), 1810-1876 (928.144)
Steegmuller, Francis. Flaubert, and Madame Bovary. pap. 1.25. Vintage
COLETTE, SIDONIE GABRIELLE, 1873-1954 (928.344)
Davies, Margaret. Colette. 3.00. Smith, Peter
COLLECTIVE BARGAINING (331.116)
American Management Association. Understanding collective bargaining. ed.
    by Elizabeth Marting. 1958. 7.50. Am. Management Assn.
Bonnett, Clarence E. Labor-management relations. il. 1958. 10.00. Exposition
Chamberlain, Neil W. Collective bargaining. il. 1951. 7.50. McGraw
Dunlop, John T., and James J. Healy. Collective bargaining: Principles and
    cases. 1953. 9.95. 7.25. Irwin
Dunlop, John T. Wage determination under trade unions. 1950. 3.00. Kelley
Garbarino, Joseph W. Health plans and collective bargaining. 1960. 5.00. U.
    of Calif.
Hart, Wilson. Collective bargaining in the federal civil service. 1961. 6.50.
    Harper
Kuhn, James W. Bargaining in grievance settlement: The power of industrial
    work groups. 1961. 4.50. Columbia
National Education Association, Research Division. Public-school (teachers
    and collective bargaining. 1958. 0.25. N. E. A.
Selekman, Benjamin. Labor relations and human relations. 1947. 5.95.
    McGraw
Selekman, Benjamin M., and others. Problems in labor relations. 2nd ed. 1958.
    8.95. McGraw
Slichter, Sumner H., and others. Impact of collective bargaining on manage-
    ment. 1960. 8.75. Brookings
Sturmthal, Adolph, ed. Comparative collective bargaining. 1957. 4.50. N. Y. State
    School of Ind. and Labor Rel.
Weber, Arnold R., ed. Structure of collective bargaining. 1961. 8.50. Free Press
COLLECTIVE SETTLEMENTS (331.116)
Hinds, William A. American communities. 3.25. Smith, Peter
Spiro, M. E. Kibbutz: Venture in Utopia. 1956. 4.50. Harvard
Webber, Everett. Escape to Utopia. 1958. 5.50. Hastings
COLLECTIVISM (335)
Berdyaev, Nicolas. Fate of man in the modern world. 1935. 4.40. 1961. pap. 1.75.
    U. of Mich.
Chodorov, Frank. Rise and fall of society. 1959. 3.95. Devin
Lippmann, Walter. Good society. 1943. 5.00. Little
Wittmer, Felix. Conquest of the American mind. 1956. 5.00. Forum
COLLECTORS AND COLLECTING (703)
Bernasconi, J. R. Collector's glossary of antiques and fine arts. il. 1959. 9.25.
    Int. Pub. Service
Bricker, William P. Complete book of collecting hobbies. il. 1952. 5.00. Sheridan
Drepperd, Carl. Dictionary of American antiques. 5.95. Branford
COLLEGE AND SCHOOL JOURNALISM (371.805)
English, Earl E., and Clarence W. Hach. Scholastic journalism. il. 1962. 3.95.
    Iowa State
Julian, James L. Practical news assignments for student reporters. 1951. pap.
    4.25. Brown, W. C.
Melin, C. J. School yearbook editing and management. il. 1956. 5.00. Iowa State
Staudenmayer, Maude Shanks. Reading and writing the news. 1941. 2.56.
    Harcourt
COLLEGE COSTS (378.24)
Craig, W. Bradford. How to finance a college education. 1959. pap. 1.95. Holt,
    Rinehart & Winston
King, Francis P. Financing the college education of faculty children. 1954.
    1.75. Holt
Lansing, John B., and others. How people pay for college. il. 1960. 3.00. U. of
    Mich., Inst. for Soc. Res.

COLLEGE SPORTS (796.4)
Mitchell, E. D. Sports for recreation. 1952. 7.00. Ronald
Mueller, Pat, and Elmer D. Mitchell. Intramural sports. 1960. 6.00. Ronald
Thorndike, Augustus. Athletic injuries. il. 1962. 5.00. Lea & F
COLLEGE STORIES (808)
Burnett, Whit, and Hallie, eds. Best college writing, 1961. 3.95. Random
COLLEGE TEACHERS (378.12)
Axelrod, Joseph, ed. Graduate study for future college teachers. 1959. 1.50.
    A. C. E.
Bunnell, Kevin. Faculty work load. 1960. pap. 2.00. A. C. E.
Caplow, Theodore, and Reece J. McGee. Academic marketplace. 1958.4.95.
    Basic Books
Greenough, William C., and Francis P. King. Retirement and insurance plans
    in American colleges. 1959. 8.50. Columbia
Longenecker, Herbert E. University faculty compensation policies and practices
    in the United States. 1956. pap. 1.50. U. of Ill.
McGrath, Earl J. Quantity and quality of college teachers. 1961. pap. 1.00.
    T. C.
National Education Association, Association for Higher Education. Compensation
    on the campus. 1961. 3.00. N. E. A.
National Education Association, Public School Adult Educators Department.
    Teacher Supply and demand in universities, colleges, and junior colleges,
    1957-58 and 1958-1959. 1 copy gratis; 2-9 copies, 0.50 ea; 10 or more, 0.45
    ea. N. E. A.
National Education Association, Research Division. Salaries paid and salary prac-
    tices in universities, colleges, and junior colleges, 1961-62. 1962. 1.00.
    N. E. A.
National Education Association, Research Division. Teacher supply and demand
    in universities, colleges, and junior colleges, 1959-60 and 1960-61. in prep.
    N. E. A.
Stecklein, John E. How to measure faculty load. 1961. 1.50. A. C. E.
COLLEGE TEACHING (371)
Buxton, Claude E. Guide to college teaching. 1957. 4.95. Harcourt
Cooper, Russell, ed. The two ends of the log: Learning and teaching in today's
    college. 1958. 4.00. U. of Minn.
Deferrari, R. J., ed. Quality of college teaching and staff. 1961. 3.75. Catholic
    U. of Am. Pr.
LeFevre, Perry Deyo. Christian teacher, 1958. 2.75. Abingdon
Meshke, Edna. Analysis of college classroom teaching and a form for recording
    evidence of quality. 1959. pap. 1.50. Burgess
Millett, Fred B. Professor: Problems and regards in college teaching. 1961.
    3.50. Macmillan
COLLIER, JEREMY, 1650-1726 (928.942)
Krutch, Joseph Wood. Comedy and conscience after the Restoration. 1949. 5.00.
    pap. 1.85. Columbia
COLLISIONS (NUCLEAR PHYSICS) (530)
Bates, D. R., ed. Atomic and molecular processes. 1962. 19.50. Academic
    Press*
Bruining, H. Physics and applications of secondary electron emission. il. 1954.
    5.50. Pergamon
Zucker, Alexander, and others. Reactions between complex nuclei. il. 1960.
    8.50. Wiley
COLLOIDS (660.294)
Alexander, A. E., and P. Johnson. Colloid science. 2 vols. 1949. 10.40.
    Oxford U. P.
Gronwall, Anders. Dextran and its use in colloidal infusion solutions. il. 1957.
    5.00. Academic Press
Jirgensons, Bruno. Organic colloids. il. 1958. 16.75. Am. Elsevier

Kruyt, Hugo R., ed. Colloid science. 2 vols. vol. 1, Irreversible systems. il.
    1952. 15.00; vol. 2. Reversible systems. il. 16.50. Am. Elsevier
Mysels, K. J. Introduction to colloid chemistry. il. 1959. 9.50. (Interscience)
    Wiley

COLOMBIA (986.1)
Fals-Borda, Orlando. Peasant society in the Colombian Andes: A sociological
    study of Saucio. 1955. 5.00. U. of Fla.
Fluharty, Vernon L. Dance of the millions: Military rule and the social revolu-
    tion in Colombia, 1930-1956. 1957. 6.00. U. of Pittsburgh
Henao, J. M., and G. Arrubla. History of Colombia. tr. by J. F. Rippy. 1938.
    5.00. U. of N. C.
Parks, E. Taylor. Colombia and the United States, 1765-1934. 1935. il. 6.00.
    Duke
Wilgus, A. Curtis, ed. Caribbean: Contemporary Colombia. 1962. 7.50.
    U. of Fla.

COLONIAL COMPANIES (942.325)
Williamson, James A. Short history of British expansion. 2 vols. il. vol. 1
    Old colonial empire. 1945. 5.00; vol. 2. Modern empire and commonwealth.
    1951. 5.00. St. Martins

COLONIES (325.3)
Easton, Stewart C. Twilight of European colonialism. 1960. 10.90. 7.50. Holt,
    Rinehart & Winston
Emerson, Rupert. From empire to nation. 1960. 7.75. Harvard
Langer, William L. Diplomacy of imperialism. 1935. 9.75. Knopf
Nowell, Charles E. Great discoveries and the first colonial empires. 1961. 4.50;
    pap. 1.25. Cornell
Sady, Emil J. United Nations and dependent peoples. 1956. pap. 1.50. Brookings.
Strausz-Hupe, Robert, and Harry W. Hazard. Idea of colonialism. 5.50. Praeger
Syme, Ronald. Colonial elites, Rome, Spain and the Americas. 1958. 1.20.
    Oxford U. P.
Ward, Barbara. Five ideas that change the world. il. 1959. 3.95; text ed. 1960.
    ?.95. Norton
Wright, Harrison M., ed. New imperialism: Analysis of late nineteenth-century
    expansion. 1961. pap. 1.50. Heath

COLONIZATION (325.3)
Frankel, S. H. Economic impact on underdeveloped societies. 1953. 3.25.
    Harvard
Hussey, William D. Discovery, expansion and empire. 1954. 1.25. Cambridge U. P
Maunier, Rene. Sociology of colonies. 2 vols. 1949. 12.50. Humanities

COLOR (152.1)
Birren, Faber. Color, form and space. il. 1961. 11.50. Reinhold
Birren, Faber. Color: From ancient mysticism to modern science. il. 1962. 12.50.
    U. Books*
Birren, Faber. Creative color. il. 1961. 10.00. Reinhold
Birren, Faber. New horizons in color. 1955. 10.00. Reinhold
Bragg, William. Universe of light. 4.00. Smith, Peter
Evans, Ralph M. Introduction to color. 1948. 15.00. Wiley
Graves, Maitland E. Art of color and design. il. 1951. 8.50. McGraw
Graves, Maitland E. Color fundamentals. il. 1952. 10.00. McGraw
Guptill, Arthur L. Color manual for artists. 1962. 6.50. Reinhold
Luckiesh, Matthew. Color and colors. 1938. 5.00. Van Nostrand
Optical Society of America, Committee on Colorimetry. Science of color. il.
    1953. 8.65. Crowell
Taylor, Frank A. Colour technology for artists, craftsmen, and industrial designer
    il. 1962. bds. 4.80. Oxford U. P.

COLOR - PSYCHOLOGY (152.1)
Birren, Faber. Color psychology and color therapy. 1961. 7.50. U. Books
Kargere, Audrey. Color and personality. 3.00. Wehman

COLOR - BLINDNESS (617.795)
Teevan, Richard C., and Robert C. Birney, eds. Color vision. il. 1961. pap.
    1.45. Van Nostrand
COLOR PHOTOGRAPHY (778.6)
Popular Photography. Color photography, 1960. by the Editors of Popular
    Photography. 1959. 3.95. S. and S.
COLOR TELEVISION (621.388)
Kaufman, and Thomas. Introduction to color TV. 2nd ed. il. pap. 2.70. Rider
Kiver, Milton S. Color television fundamentals. 1955. 6.00. McGraw
National Television System Committee. Color television standards. ed. by
    D. Fink. 1955. 5.75. McGraw
Sams, Howard W., and Co. Color TV training manual. il. pap. 6.95. (Sams)
    Bobbs
COLORADO - DESCRIPTION AND TRAVEL (917.97)
Ormes, Robert M. Guide to Colorado Mountains. 3.50. Swallow, A.
Writer's Project. Colorado. rev. ed. 1951. 6.50. Hastings
COLORADO RIVER AND VALLEY (978.811)
Powell, John Wesley. Exploration of the Colorado River. il. 1957. 3.75.
    U. of Chicago
COLORIMETRY (545.812)
Allport, Noel L., and J. W. Keyser. Colorimetric analysis. vol. 1. Determina-
    tions of clinical and biochemical significance. il. 1957. 9.00. Macmillan
Boltz, David F., ed. Colorimetric determination of nonmetals. il. 1958. 10.50.
    Wiley
COLORS (752)
Reinhold color atlas. 1962. 8.75. Reinhold
Vanderwalker, Fred N. Mixing colors and paints. 1957. 3.50. Drake, F. J.
COLT, SAMUEL, 1814-1892 (925)
Mitchell, James L. Colt: The man, the arms, the company. il. 1959. 10.00.
    Stackpole
COLUMBIA RIVER AND VALLEY (979.73)
De Voto, Bernard. Journals of Lewis and Clark. 1953. 6.50. Houghton
Lewis, Meriwether. Lewis and Clark Expedition. 3 vols. il. 1961. set, 12.50;
    pap. 1.95 ea; set, pap. 5.85. Lippincott
Strong, Emory. Stone age on the Columbia River. il. 1960. 4.50. Binfords
COLUMBUS, CHRISTOPHER (CRISTOFORO COLOMBO) (923.9)
Adams, Herbert B., and H. Wood. Columbus and his discovery of America. 1492.
    1.50. Johns Hopkins
Columbus, Ferdinand. Life of the Admiral Christopher Columbus. ed. by Benjamin
    Keen. 1959. 7.50. Rutgers
Morison, Samuel Eliot. Admiral of the ocean sea. il. 1942. 8.50. (Atlantic
    Monthly Press) Little
Morison, Samuel Eliot. Christopher Columbus, mariner. il. 1955. 3.75.
    Little
Morison, Samuel E. Route of Columbus along the north coast of Haiti, and the
    site of Navidad. 1940. 1.00. Am. Philos. Soc.
Olson, J. E., and E. G. Bourne, ed. Northmen, Columbus and Cabot, 985-1503.
    1906. 5.75. Barnes & Noble.
COMBUSTION (541.362)
Ducarme, J., and others, eds. Progress in combustion science and technology.
    1961. 10.00. Pergamon
Griswold, John. Fuels, combustion and furnaces. 1946. 11.00. McGraw
Lewis, Bernard, and others, eds. Combustion processes. 1956. 17.50. Prince-
    ton
Penner, S. S. Chemistry problems in jet propulsion. 1957. 12.50. Pergamon
COMEDY (808.2)
Bergson, Henri. Laughter bd. with George Meredith's Essay on comedy. 3.00.
    Smith, Peter

Cooper, Lane. Aristotelian theory of comedy, with an adaptation of the Poetics and a translation of the Tractatus Coislinianus. 1922. 3.00. Cornell

Feibleman, James. In praise of comedy: A study in its theory and practice. 1962. 7.50. Russell

Meredith, George. Essay on comedy and the uses of the comic spirit. ed. by Lane Cooper. 2.50. Cornell

Perry, Henry T. E. Comic spirit in Restoration drama: Studies in the comedy of Etherege, Wycherly, Congreve, Vanbrugh and Farquhar. 1962. 6.00. Russell

Potts, Leonard J. Comedy. 2.50. Hillary

Seyler, Athene, and Stephen Haggard. Craft of comedy. 2.50. Theatre Arts

COMETS (533.6)

Kuiper, G. P., and B. M. Middlehurst, eds. Moon, meteorites, and comets (solar system, vol. 4) 8.50. U. of Chicago

Lyttleton, Raymond A. Comets and their origin. 1953. 3.50. Cambridge U. P.

Watson, Fletcher G. Between the planets. il. 1956. 5.00. Harvard

Williams, Kenneth P. Calculation of the orbits of asteroids and comets. 5.75. Principia Press of Trinity U.

COMMERCE (382)

American Management Association. Challenge of export expansion. il. 1962. pap. 2.25. Am. Management Assn.

Caves, Richard E. Trade and economic structure. il. 1960. 6.00. Harvard

Enke, Stephen, and Virgil Salera. International economics. 1957. 10.35. Prentice-Hall

Gordon, Wendell C. International trade: Goods, people, and ideas. il. 1958. 6.75. Knopf

Gregg, Josiah. Commerce of the prairies. 2 vols. ed. by Archibald Hanna. 1962. boxed, 7.95; pap. 1.95 ea. Lippincott*

Marshall, Alfred. Money credit and commerce. 1923. 8.50. Kelley

National Education Association, National Council for the Social Studies. Teachers guide to world trade. il. 1960. 1.00. N. E. A.

Rosenthal, Morris S. Techniques of international trade. il. 1950. 8.50. McGraw

Shaterian, William S. Export-import banking. 1956. 7.50. Ronald

Viner, Jacob. International trade and economic development. 1952. 3.00. Free Press

Woytinsky, W. S., and E. S. World commerce and governments: Trends and outlook. 1955. 10.00. Twentieth Century.

Zook, Paul D., ed. Foreign trade and human capital. 1962. 3.00. S. M. U. *

COMMERCE - DICTIONARIES (382.03)

Nanassy, L. C., and W. Selden. Business dictionary. 1959. 3.90. 3.12. Prentice-Hall

COMMERCE - HISTORY (382.09)

Cheyney, E. P. European background of American history, 1300-1600. 3.00. Smith, Peter

Condliffe, John B. Commerce of nations. 1950. 7.50. Norton

Lopez, R. S., and I. W. Raymond, eds. Medieval trade in the Mediterranean World. 1955. 6.75. Columbia

Pirenne, Henri. Medieval cities, their origins and the revival of trade. 3.00. Smith, Peter

COMMERCIAL ART (741.6)

Baker, S. Advertising layout and art direction. 1959. 13.50. McGraw

Byrnes, Gene, and A. Thornton Bishop. Commercial art: Complete guide to drawing, illustration, cartooning, and painting. 1948. 7.50. S. and S.

Ernst, James A. Drawing the line: Fine and commercial art. 1962. 10.00. Reinhold

Feirer, John L. Drawing and planning for the industrial arts. 1956. 4.52. Bennett

Rand, Paul. Thoughts on design. il. 1951. 15.00. Wittenborn

Rodewald, Fred, and Edward M. Gottschall. Commercial art as a business. 1960. 4.95. Viking

Sutnar, Ladislav. Visual design in action. il. 1961. 17.50. Hastings

COMMERCIAL CORRESPONDENCE (647.962)

Aurner, Robert R. Effective communication in business. 1958. 6.75. South-Western Pub.

Aurner, Robert R. Practical business English. 1960. 3.20. South-Western Pub.

Bender, James F. Make your business letters make friends. 1952. 4.95. McGraw

Brennan, Lawrence Business communication. 1960. pap. 1.95. Littlefield

Butterfield, William H. Credit letters that win friends. 1944. 1.75. U. of Okla.

Frailey, L. E. Handbook of business letters. 1948. 12.50. Prentice-Hall

Frailey, L. E. Sales manager's letter book. 1951. 6.95. Prentice-Hall

Gruber, Edward. Grammar and spelling simplified. 1957. pap. 1.00. Arco

Himstreet, William C., and Wayne M. Baty, Business communications. 1961. 6.50. Wadsworth

Kramer, Edward. How to punctuate a business letter.. 1955. pap. 0.25. Pitman

Opdycke, John B. Take a letter please! il. 1944. 3.00. Funk

Parkhurst, Charles C. Modern executive's guide to effective communication. 1962. 10.00. Prentice-Hall (R)

Sigband, Norman B. Effective report writing. 1960. 6.75. Harper

COMMERCIAL LAW (347.7)

Bergh, L. O., and T. Conyngton. Business law. 1956. 8.00. Ronald

Committee on College Business Law. College business law. 1960. 6.00. Pitman

Cook, Franklin H. Principles of business and the federal law. 1951. 7.00. Macmillan

Goodman, Kennard E., and W. L. Moore. Today's business law. 1961. 3.80. Pitman

Lewis, R. Duffy, and J. Norman. What every retailer should know about the law. 1951. 2.50. Fairchild

Prentice-Hall Editorial Staff. Encyclopedic dictionary of business law. 1961. 19.50. Prentice-Hall (R)

COMMERCIAL LAW - CASES (347.7)

Anderson, Ronald A., and Walter A. Kumpf. Business law principles and cases. 1958. 7.95. South-Western Pub.

Beutel, Frederick K. Beutel's Cases and materials on interpretation of uniform commercial laws. 1950. with suppl. 7.00. Bobbs

Spencer, William H., and Cornelius W. Gillam. Casebook of law and business. 1953. 9.50. McGraw

Stimson, C. W., and J. Lazar. Recent cases and materials in business law. 1955. 1.95. Houghton

COMMERCIAL POLICY (382)

Brown, William Adams, Jr. United States and the restoration of world trade. 1950. 5.00. Brookings

Frank, Isaiah. European common market. 1961. 7.50. Praeger

Heilperin, Michael A. Trade of nations. 1952. 4.50. Knopf

Isaacs, Asher. International trade: Tariff and commercial policies. 1948. 10.00. 7.50. Irwin

Proehl, Paul O., ed. Legal problems of international trade. 1959. 6.50. U. of Ill.

COMMERCIAL PRODUCTS (387)

Chisholm, G. G. Handbook of commercial geography. ed. by L. Dudley Stamp, and S. C. Gilmour. 6.50. Wiley (R)

Commodity survey, 1960. 1961. 3.00. U.N. (R)

Commodity yearbook. rev. annually. 14.95. Commodity Res. Bur.

COMMERCIAL STATISTICS (330)

Yates, P. Lamartine. Forty years of foreign trade. 1959. 9.00. Macmillan (R)

COMMON LAW (347)
Blackstone, William. Ehrlich's Blackstone. ed. by Jacob W. Ehrlich. 1959.
    15.00. Nourse
Holmes, Oliver Wendell, Jr. Common law. 5.00. Little
Plucknett, Theodore F. T. Concise history of the common law. 1956. 12.50.
    Little
Pound, Roscoe. Spirit of the common law. 1931. 2.50. Jones, Marshall
COMMONWEALTH OF NATIONS (942)
Attlee, Earl. Empire into Commonwealth. 1961. 1.20. Oxford U. P.
Jennings, Ivor. Problems of the new commonwealth. 1958. 2.50. Duke
Mansergh, Nicholas, and others. Commonwealth perspectives. 1958. 4.50. Duke
Menzies, R. G. Changing Commonwealth. 1960. 0.75. Cambridge U. P.
Miller, J. D. B. Commonwealth in the world. il. 1959. 5.00. Harvard
Simnett, W. E. Emergent Commonwealth: The British Colonies. 2.50. (HUL)
    Hillary
Strachey, John. End of empire. 1960. 5.00. Random
Underhill, Frank H. British commonwealth: An experiment in co-operation
    among nations. 1956. 3.00. Duke
Wheare, Kenneth C. Constitutional structure of the Commonwealth. 1960.
    4.00. Oxford U. P.
COMMUNICABLE DISEASES (616.9)
Anderson, W. Gaylor, and others. Communicable disease control. 1962. 11.00.
    Macmillan
American Public Health Association. Control of communicable diseases in
    man. 1955. 0.60. Am. Public Health
Banks, H. Stanley. Common infectious disease. il. 1949. 4.50. Williams &
    Wilkins
Baron, A. L. Man against germs. 1957. 4.50. Dutton
Bower, Albert G., and others. Communicable diseases for nurses. il. 1958.
    7.50. Saunders
Burnet, F. McFarlane, Natural history of infectious disease. 1962. 6.00.
    Cambridge U. P.
Greenberg, Morris, and Anna V. Matz. Modern concepts of communicable
    disease. 1953. 5.50. Putnam
Hull, Thomas G. Diseases transmitted from animals to man. Thomas, C. C.
Williams, R. E. O., and others. Hospital infection: Causes and prevention.
    1961. 7.50. Year Bk.
COMMUNICABLE DISEASES IN ANIMALS (636.089)
Hagan, W. A., and D. W. Bruner. Infectious diseases of domestic animals.
    il. 1961. 11.50. Cornell
COMMUNICATION (651.7)
American Academy of Arts and Sciences. Mass culture and mass media. 1960.
    1.75. Am. Acad. of Arts & Sci.
American Library Association. Youth, Communication and libraries. 1949.
    3.50. A. L. A.
Barnouw, Erik. Mass communication: Television, radio, film and press.
    1956. 5.10. Rinehart
Bereday, George, and Joseph Lauwerys. Communication media and the school.
    1960. 8.50. Harcourt
Berelson, Bernard, and Morris Janowitz, eds. Reader in public opinion and
    communication. 1953. 7.50. Free Press
Carpenter, Edmund, and Marshall McLuhan, eds. Explorations in communication.
    1960. 4.00. Beacon
Chase, Stuart. Power of words. 1954. 3.95. 3.00. Harcourt
Clark, Wesley C., ed. Journalism tomorrow. 1948. 4.00. Syracuse
Dale, Edgar. Mass media and education. NSSE, 53rd yrbk. pt.2. 1954. 4.50;
    pap. 3.75. U. of Chicago

Dean, Howard H. , and Bryson. Effective communication. 1961. 5.25. Prentice-Hall

Duncan, Hugh D. Communication and social order. 1961. 10.00. Bedminster

Hackett, Herbert, and others. Understanding and being understood. 1957. 4.75. McKay

Henle, Paul, ed. Language, thought, and culture. 1958. 4.95. U. of Mich.

Hovland, Carl Iver, and others. Communication and persuasion. 1953. 6.75. Yale

Hovland, Carl I., ed. Order of presentation in persuasion. 4.00. Yale

Ingram, Karl C. Talk that gets results. 1957. 3.95. McGraw

Jacobs, Norman, ed. Culture for the millions? 1961. 4.95. Van Nostrand

Klapper, Joseph T. Effects of mass communication. 1960. 5.00. Free Press

Lacy, Dan M. Freedom and communications. 1961. 3.00. U. of Ill.

Macrorie, Ken. Perceptive writer, reader, and speaker. 1959. 4.50. Harcourt

Marty, Martin E. Improper opinion: Mass media and the Christian faith. 1961. 3.50. Westminster

Morrin, H. C. Communication for nurses. 1960. pap. 1.95. Littlefield

National Education Association, Educational Policies Commission. Mass communication and education. 1958. 1.50. N.E.A.

Riesman, David. Oral tradition, the written word, and the screen image. pap. 0.50. Antioch

Schramm, Wilbur. Process and effects of mass communication. 1954. 6.00. U. of Ill.

Schramm, Wilbur. Responsibility in mass communication. 1957. 5.50. Harper

Siebert, Fredrick S. , and others. Four theories of the press. 1956. 3.50. U. of Ill.

Witty, M. B. , and others. Dictionary of communications abbreviations. lib. bdg. 20.00. Seti (R)

COMMUNISM (335)

Bowen, Robert O. Truth about communism. 1962. 3.00. Colonial Press

Budenz, Louis F. Techniques of Communism. 1962. 2.00. Regnery

Cannon, James P. Struggle for a proletarian party. 2.75. Pioneer Publishers N. Y. C.

Chambre, Henri. From Karl Marx to Mao Tse-Tung. 4.95. Kenedy

Cohen, Carl. Communism, fascism, and democracy. 1961. pap. 3.95. Random

Cole, George D. H. Communism and social democracy, 1914-1931. 14.50. St. Martins

Colegrove, Kenneth. Democracy versus communism. il. 1961. 5.75. Van Nostrand

Cook, Thomas I. , and Malcolm C. Moos. Power through purpose. 1954. 4.00. Johns Hopkins

Daniels, Robert N. Nature of Communism. 1962. 6.50. Random

Djilas, Milovan. Anatomy of a moral. 1959. 2.95. Praeger

Djilas, Milovan. New class. 1957. 3.95. Praeger

Goodman, Elliot R. Soviet design for a world state. 1960. 6.75. Columbia

McFadden, C. J. Philosophy of Communism. 1939. 4.75. Benziger

Marx, Karl. Critique of the Gotha Programme. 1933. 2.00. Int. Pubs.

Nagy, Imre. Imre Nagy on Communism. 1957. 5.50. Praeger

Osanka, Franklin M. Modern guerilla warfare: Fighting Communist guerilla movements, 1941-1961. 1962. 7.50. Free Press

Rossiter, Clinton. Marxism: The view from America. 1960. 6.75. Harcourt

Schlesinger, Arthur, Jr. Vital center. 3.50. 1962. Houghton

Schwarz, Frederick C. You can trust the Communists. 1960. 2.95. Prentice-Hall

Slocomb, Whitney H. Communist Constitution vs. United States Constitution. 1955. 3.00. Forum

Strausz-Hupe, Robert, and others. Protracted conflict. 1959. 4.50. Harper

Trotsky, Leon. Third international after Lenin. 4.00. Pioneer Publishers, N. Y. C.

Utley, T. E. , and J. Stuart Maclure. Documents of modern political thought. 1958. 3.75. Cambridge U. P.

Almond, G. A. Appeals of Communism. 1954. 6.00. Princeton

Bouscaren, Anthony T. Guide to anti-communist action. 1958. 4.00. Regnery

Brzezinski, Zbigniew K. Idealogy and power in Soviet politics. 1962. 4.50.
  Praeger

Daniels, Robert V. Documentary history of communism. 1960. 8.75. Random

Hunt, Robert N. Carew. Marxism: Past and present. 1955. 3.95. Macmillan

Hunt, Robert N. Carew. Theory and practice of communism. 1957. 5.00.
  Macmillan

Lichteim, George. Marxism: A historical and critical study. 8.50. Praeger

Overstreet, Harry A., and Bonaro. What we must know about Communism. 1958.
  4.50. Norton

Salvadori, Massimo. Rise of modern communism. 1952. 2.55. Holt, Rinehart
  & Winston

Seton-Watson, Hugh. From Lenin to Khrushchev. 1960. 6.00. Praeger

Ulam, Adam Bruno. Titoism and the Cominform. 1952. 4.50. Harvard

Ulam, Adam B. Unfinished revolution. 1960. 5.00. Random

Swearingen, Rodger. World of communism. by Howard R. Anderson. il. 1962.
  3.25. Houghton

Mintz, Jeanne, and others. Marxism in Southeast Asia; a study of four countries.
  by Frank N. Trager. 1959. 7.50. Stanford

Wolff, Robert L. Balkans in our time. il. 1956. 8.00. Harvard

Bodde, Derk. Peking diary: A year of revolution. il. 1950. 3.75. Abelard

Brandt, Conrad, and others. Documentary history of Chinese communism. 1952.
  7.50. Harvard

Chandrasekhar, Sripati. Red China: An Asian view. 4.00. Praeger

Clark, Gerald. Impatient giant-Red China today. il. 1959. 5.50. McKay

Croft, Michael. Red carpet to China. 1960. 5.00. St. Martins

Guillain, Robert. 600 million Chinese. 1957. 5.00. Criterion

Hunter, Edward. Brain-washing in Red China: The calculated destruction of
  men's minds. 1951. 4.95. Vanguard

Isaacs, Harold R. Tragedy of the Chinese revolution. 1961. 7.50. Stanford

Lindsay, Lord. China and the cold war. 1955. 3.75. Cambridge U. P.

Mao, Tse-tung. On the protracted war. 1960. 1.00. China

Mao, Tse-tung. Selected works. 4 vols. 3.00 ea. Int. Pubs.

Mende, Tibor. China and her shadow. il. 1962. 5.00. Coward

Smedley, Agnes. Great road: The life and times of Chu Teh. 6.75. Monthly
  Review

Snow, Edgar. Red star over China. 3.00. Smith, Peter

Trotsky, Leon. Problems of the Chinese Revolution. 1962. 7.50. Paragon

Walker, Richard L. China under communism: The first five years. il. 1955.
  5.00. Yale

Walker, Richard L. Continuing struggle. 2.00. Bookmailer

Winance, Eleutherius. Communist persuasion. 1959. 3.95. Kenedy

Zagoria, Donald S. Sino-Soviet conflict, 1956-1961. 1962. 8.50. Princeton

Draper, Theodore. Castro's revolution. 1962. 4.50. Praeger

Tang, Peter S. H. Chinese communist impact on Cuba. 1962. 2.50. Res. Inst.
  on Sino-Soviet Bloc

Weyl, Nathaniel. Red star over Cuba. 1960. 4.50. Devin

Reisky de Dubnic, Vladimir. Communist propaganda methods. 1961. 6.00. Praeger

Borkenau, Franz. European communism. 1953. 6.50. Harper

Ilok, S. Brotherhood of silence: The story of an anti-communist underground. 1962
  4.95. McKay

Owen, Robert. New view of society, etc. 1.95. Dutton

Shuster, George N. In silence I speak. il. 4.50. Farrar, Straus

Harrison, Selig S. India: The most dangerous decades. il. 1960. 6.50. Princeton

Alexander, Robert J. Communism in Latin America. 1957. 9.00. Rutgers

Rivero, Nicolas. Castro's Cuba: An American dilemma. 1962. 4.50. McKay

Bauer, Raymond A., and others. How the Soviet system works: Cultural, psycholo
  gical, and social themes. 1956. 5.25. Harvard

Berdyaev, Nicolas. Origin of Russian communism. 1955. 3.00. Allenson

Berdyaev, Nicolas. Russian Revolution. 1960. 4.40. U. of Mich.

Cadwell, Roy E. Communism and the modern world. 1962. 4.95. Dorrance

Dallin, David J. Changing world of Soviet Russia. 1956. 6.00. Yale

Kulski, Wladyslav W. Peaceful co-existence: An analysis of Soviet foreign policy. 1959. 12.50. Regnery

Lenin, Vladimir I., and Joseph Stalin. Russian Revolution. 1938. 2.50. Int. Pubs.

Marx, Karl. Marx vs. Russia. by J. A. Doerig. 3.50. Ungar

Mead, Margaret. Soviet attitudes toward authority. 1955. 5.00. Morrow

Overstreet, Harry A., and Bonard. War called peace: Khrushchev's communism. 1961. 4.50. Norton

Schapiro, Leonard. U.S.S.R. and the future. 1962. 6.00. Praeger

Stalin, Joseph. Selected writings. 2.75. Int. Pubs.

Trotsky, Leon. Terrorism and communism. 4.40. 1961. U. of Mich.

Buckley, William F., and L. Brent Bozell. McCarthy and his enemies. 1954. pap. 2.00. Regnery

Budenz, Louis F. Men without faces: The communist conspiracy in the U.S.A. 3.95. Harper

Cannon, James P. History of American Trotskyism. 2.75. Pioneer Publishers, N. Y. C.

Chambers, Whittaker. Witness. 1952. 2.95. Random

Draper, Theodore. American communism and Soviet Russia. 1960. 8.50. Viking

Draper, Theodore. Roots of American communism. il. 1957. 6.75. Viking

Ginzburg, Benjamin. Rededication to freedom. 1959. 3.50. S. and S.

Hoover, J. Edgar. Masters of deceit. 1958. 5.00. Holt

Howe, I., and L. Coser. American Communist party. 1958. 6.75. Beacon

Johnson, Oakley. Day is coming: The biography of Charles E Ruthenberg. 1957. 3.00. Int. Pubs.

Kirk, Russell. American cause. 1957. 3.50. Regnery

Musmanno, Michael A. Across the street from the courthouse. il. 1954. 4.00. Dorrance

Philbrick, Herbert A. I led three lives. 1952. 2.49. Grosset

Root, E. Merrill. Collectivism on the campus. 5.00. Devin

Roy, Ralph L. Communism and the churches. 1960. 7.50. Harcourt

Saposs, David J. Communism in American politics. 1960. 5.00. Pub. Affairs

Saposs, David J. Communism in American unions. 1959. 7.50. McGraw

Thomas, Norman. Test of freedom. 1954. 5.50. Norton

Truman, Harry S. Freedom and equality. by David Horton. 1960. 2.95. U. of Missouri

Voros, Sandor. American commissar. 1961. 4.95. Chilton

Giap, Vo Nguyen. Peoples' war, people's army: The Viet Cong insurrection manual for underdeveloped countries. il. 1962. 5.00. Praeger

Bennett, John C. Christianity and Communism today. 1960. 3.50. Assn. Pr.

Cuninggim, Merrimon. Christianity and Communism. 1958. 4.00. S. M. U.

Iverson, Robert W. Communists and the schools. 1959. 7.50. Harcourt

Brzezinski, Zbigniew K. Soviet bloc: Unity and conflict. 1960. 7.75. Harvard

Djilas, Milovan. Conversations with Stalin. 1962. 3.95. Harcourt

Bereday, George Z. F., and Jaan Pennar. Politics of Soviet education. 1960. 6.00. Praeger

Trotsky, Leon. First five years of the Communist International. 2 vols. 7.00. Pioneer Publishers, N. Y. C.

Trotsky, Leon. Third international after Lenin. 4.00. Pioneer Publishers, N. Y. U.

COMMUNITY AND SCHOOL (370.193)

Burns, Norman, and Cyril O. Houle. Community responsibilities of institutions of higher learning. 1948. pap. 3.00. U. of Chicago

Grinnel, J. E., and R. J. Young. School and the community. 1955. 6.50. Ronald

Morphet, Edgar L. Citizens co-operation for better public schools. 1954. 4.50. pap. 3.75. U. of Chicago

Olsen, Edward G. School and community. 1954. 8.65. Prentice-Hall

Pierce, Truman M. Controllable community characteristics related to the
quality of education. 1947. pap. 2.25. T. C.
Seay, Maurice F. Community school. NSSE, 52nd yrbk. pt. 2. 1953. 4.50;
pap. 3.75. U. of Chicago

COMMUNITY DEVELOPMENT (301.34)

Arndt, Christian O., ed. Community education. 1959. NSSE, 58th yrbk. pt. 1.
4.50; pap. 3.75. U. of Chicago
Batten, T. R. Communities and their development. 1957. 2.40. Oxford U. P.
Batten, T. R. Training for community development. il. 1962. 3.60. Oxford
U. P.
King, Clarence W. Working with people in small communities. 1959. 2.50.
Harper
National Education Association, Adult Education Service, and National
Association of Public School Adult Educators. Forces in community develop-
ment. 1961. 2.00. N.E.A.*
Nelson, Lowry, and others. Community structure and change. 1960. 6.75.
Macmillan

COMMUNITY LIFE (323.35)

Angell, Robert Cooley. Free Society and moral crisis. 1958. 6.00. U. of Mich.
Banfield, Edward C. Moral basis of a backward society. 4.00. Free Press
Biddle, William W. Cultivation of community leaders. 1953. 3.00. Harper
Elliott, Mabel A., and Francis E. Merrill. Social disorganization. 1961. 8.50.
Harper
Fordham, Jefferson B. Larger concept of community. 1956. 3.00. La. State
Gruener, Jennette R., and Deborah M. Jensen. Community problems. il.
1954. 4.00. Mosby
Kinneman, J. A. Community in American society. il. 4.00. Appleton
Lynd, Robert and Helen Merrell. Middletown 1959. pap. 2.25. Harcourt
Lynd, Robert S., and Helen Merrell. Middletown in transition: A study in
cultural conflicts. il. 1939. 4.50. Harcourt
Morgan, Arthur E. Community of the future. 3.00; pap. 1.50. Community
Service
Stein, Maurice R. Eclipse of community: An interpretation of American studies.
1960. 6.00. Princeton
Sussman, Marvin B., ed. Community structure and analysis. il. 1959. 6.50.
Crowell
Warner, W. Lloyd, and others. Democracy in Jonesville, 1949. 4.50. Harper

COMMUNITY ORGANIZATION (323.35)

Abrahamson, Julia H. Neighborhood finds itself. 1959. 5.00. Harper
Buell, B. Community planning for human services. 1952. 6.75. Columbia
Dillick, Sidney. Community organization for neighborhood development--past
and present. 1953. 4.00. Whiteside
Green, Helen D. Social work practice in community organization. 1955. 4.50.
Whiteside
Harper, Ernest B., and Arthur C. Dunham. Community organization in action.
1959. 7.50. Assn. Pr.
Murphy, C. Community organization practice. 1954. 5.75. Houghton
National Conference of Social Work. Group work and community organization,
1953-54, 2.25; 1955, 2.25; 1956, 2.50. Columbia
National Conference of Social Work. Planning social services for urban needs.
1957. 2.50. Columbia
Poston, Richard Waverly. Democracy is you: A guide to citizen action. 1953,
3.50. Harper
Ross, Murray G. Case histories in community organization. 1958. 4.00.
Harper
Sanders, Irwin T. Making good communities better. 1953. 2.50. U. of Ky.

COMPARATIVE ECONOMICS (338.016)

Adams, G. P., Jr. Competitive economic systems. 1959. 6.00. Crowell

Blodgett, Ralph H., and D. L. Kemmerer. Comparative economic development. 1956. 7.75. McGraw
Blodgett, Ralph H. Comparative economic systems. 7.75. Macmillan
Burns, Arthur R. Comparative economic organization. 1955. 10.60. Prentice-Hall
Hubbard, Bela. Political and economic structures. 1956. 4.00. Caxton
Loucks, William N. Comparative economic systems. 6th ed. 1961. 8.00. Harper

COMPARATIVE EDUCATION (370)
Hans, Nicholas. Comparative education. 1950. 4.50. Humanities
Mallinson, Vernon. Introduction to the study of comparative education. 1957. 3.50. Macmillan
Moehlman, Arthur, and Joseph Roucek. Comparative education. 1952. 6.25. Holt, Rinehart & Winston

COMPARATIVE GOVERNMENT (342.4)
Beer, Samuel H., and others, eds. Patterns of government: The major political systems of Europe. 1962. 6.75. Random
Brewster, R. Wallace. Government in modern society. il. 1958. 7.25. Houghton
Brown, Bernard E. New directions in comparative politics. 1962. 4.50. Taplinger
Brown, Delbert F. Growth of democratic government. 1959. 3.25. Pub. Affairs
Burmeister, Werner. Democratic institutions in the world today. 5.00. Praeger
Butz, Otto. Of man and politics: An introduction to political science. 1960. 4.00. Holt, Rinehart & Winston
Dragnich, Alex N. Major European governments. 1961. 9.35. Dorsey
Field, George Lowell. Governments in modern society. il. 1951. 6.95. McGraw
Finer, Herman. Theory and practice of modern government. 1949. 9.00. Holt
Hermens, Ferdinand A. Representative Republic. 1958. 7.50. U. of Notre Dame
Macridis, Roy C., and Bernard E. Brown, eds. Comparative politics. 1961. 7.00. Dorsey
Neumann, Robert G. European and comparative government. il. 1960. 8.75. McGraw
Spiro, Herbert J. Government by constitution. 1959. 6.75. Random
Stewart, Michael. Modern forms of government. 1960. 4.00. Holt, Rinehart & Winston
Zink, Harold. Modern governments. il. 5.00. Van Nostrand

COMPARATIVE LAW (342)
Maine, Henry J. S. Ancient law: Its connection with the early history of society and its relation to modern ideas. 1931. 2.25. Oxford U. P.
Weber, Max. Max Weber on law in economy and society. ed. by Max Rheinstein. tr. by E. Shils. 1954. 6.00. Harvard

COMPETITION (338.522)
Abbott, Lawrence. Quality and competition. 1955. 3.75. Columbia
Anderson, Thomas J. Our competitive system and public policy. 1958. 7.50. South-Western Pub. *
Baldwin, William L. Antitrust and the changing corporation. il. 1961. 8.75. Duke
Bober, Mandell M. Intermediate price and income theory. 1962. 6.95. Norton
Chamberlin, Edward H. Theory of monopolistic competition. 1934. 6.00. Harvard
Chamberlin, E. H. Towards a more general theory of value. 1957. 5.00. Oxford U. P.
Clark, J. M. Competition as a dynamic process. 1961. 7.50. Brookings
Lauterbach, Albert. Man, motives, and money. 1959. 5.00. Cornell
Massel, Mark S. Competition and monopoly: Legal and economic issues. 1962. 6.75. Brookings
Mead, Margaret. Cooperation and competition among primitive peoples. 5.00. Smith, Peter
Reck, Dickson. Government purchasing and competition. il. 1954. 5.00. U. of Calif.

Triffin, Robert Adolphe. Monopolistic competition and general equilbrium theory. 1940. 3.50. Harvard

COMPETITION, UNFAIR (338.522)

Hoover, Edgar M., Jr., and Joel Dean, eds. Readings in the social control of industry. 1942. 5.50. Irwin

Machlup, Fritz. Political economy of monopoly. 1952. 5.50. Economics of sellers' competition. 1952. 6.50. Combined price for both books. 10.00. Johns Hopkins

Pilpel, Harriet F., and Theodora Zavin. Rights and writers. 1960. 7.50. Dutton

Sharp, Frank Chapman, and Philip G. Fox. Business ethics. 3.50. Appleton

COMPOSERS (780.92)

Brockway, Wallace, and Herbert Weinstock. Men of music. 1950. 6.95. 1958. S. and S.

Cardus, Neville. Composers eleven. il. 1959. 4.00. Braziller

Cross, Milton J., and David Ewen. Encyclopedia of the great composers and their music. 2 vols. 1962 boxed, 5.95. Doubleday (R)

Ewen, David. Composers of yesterday. il. 1937. 5.00. Wilson

Ewen, David. Lighter classics in music. 1961. 5.00. Arco

Ewen, David. ed. New book of modern composers. 1961. 7.50. Knopf (R)

Ewen, David. World of great composers. 1962. 10.00. Prentice-Hall. (R)

Hodeir, Andre. Since Debussy, view of contemporary music. 5.00. Smith, Peter

Horton, John. Some nineteenth century composers. 1950. 1.40. Oxford U. P.

Hughes, Gervase. Composers of operetta. 1962. 8.00. St. Martins (R)

Machlis, Joseph. Introduction to contemporary music. il. 1961. 10.00. Norton

Smith, Delos. Music in your life. 1957. 3.95. Harper

Thomas, Henry, and Dana Lee. Living biographies of great composers. 1959. 2.50. Doubleday (R)

Zoff, Otto, ed. Great composers: Through the eyes of their contemporaries. 6.50. Dutton

COMPOSERS, AMERICAN (780.92)

Burton, J. Blue book of Tin Pan Alley. il. 1951. 10.00. Century House

Cohn, Arthur. Collector's twentieth-century music in the western hemisphere. 1961. pap. 1.95. Lippincott

Composers of the Americas. bilingual English and Spanish. 7 vols. vols. 1-6 1955-1960; vol. 7, 1962. 1.00 ea. Pan American (R)

Ewen, David. American composers today. il. 1949. 4.00. Wilson (R)

Ewen, David. Complete book of the American musical theater. rev. ed. il. 1959. 7.50; with Book of European light opera, in slip case. 13.95. Holt, Rinehart & Winston (R)

Ewen, David. Popular American composers. 1962. 7.00. Wilson

COMPOSERS, EUROPEAN (780.92)

Ewen, David. European composers today. il. 1954. 4.00. Wilson (R)

COMPOSITION (ART) (751.4)

Ghyka, Matila. Practical handbook of geometric composition and design. il. 1952. 2.75. Transatlantic

Rasmusen, H. M. Art structure. 1950. 7.95. McGraw

Watson, Ernest W. Composition in landscape and still life. in prep. Collier

Watson, Ernest W. Composition in landscape and still life. 12.50. Watson

Wolchonok, Louis. Art of pictorial composition. 1961. 7.50. Harper

COMPOSITION (MUSIC) (781.61)

Abraham, Gerald, Design in music. 1949. 0.80. Oxford U. P.

Dallin, L. Techniques of twentieth century composition. 1958. pap. 3.50. Brown, W. C.

Davison, Archibald T. Technique of choral composition. il. 1945. 4.00. Harvard

Jacob, Gordon. Composer and his art. 1955. 1.70. Oxford U. P.

Orrey, Leslie. Foundations of harmony and composition. 1948. 3.95. Pitman

Stanford, Charles V. Musical composition. 2.00. St. Martins

COMPRESSIBILITY (533.2)
Bridgman, P. W. Physics of high pressure, il. with suppl. 1950. 8.00. Macmillan
Mises, Richard von. Mathematical theory of compressible flow. rev. and ed. by Hilda Geiringer and G. S. S. Ludford. 1958. 15.00. Academic Press
Pai, Shih-i. Introduction to the theory of compressible flow. il. 1959. 10.75. Van Nostrand
Rosenhead, L., and others. Selection of tables for use in calculations of compressible airflow. 1952. 6.40. Oxford U. P.

COMTE, AUGUSTE, 1798-1857 (194.8)
Hawkins, Richmond Laurin. Positivism in the United States, 1853-1861. il. 1938. 3.00. Harvard.
Mill, John Stuart. Auguste Comte and positivism. 4.40. 1961. U. of Mich.

CONCENTRATION CAMPS (364)
Bettelheim, Bruno. Informed heart: Autonomy in a mass age. 1960. 5.00. Free Press
Cohen, Elie A. Human behavior in the concentration camp. 1953. 7.50. Norton
Frankl, V. From death-camp to existentialism. 1959. 3.00. Beacon
Keith, Agnes Newton. Three came home. il. 1947. 6.00. Little

CONCORD RIVER - DESCRIPTION AND TRAVEL (917)
Thoreau, Henry David. Concord and the Merrimack. ed. by Dudley C. Lunt. il. 1954. 4.75. Little
Thoreau, Henry D. Walden, Week on the Concord and Merrimack Rivers, Maine Woods, and Cape Cod. il. 1961. 4.00 ea; set, 12.50; pap. 7.50. Crowell
Thoreau, Henry D. Week on the Concord and Merrimack Rivers. il. 1961. 4.00; boxed with Walden, Maine woods, and Cape Cod. set, 12.50; set, pap. 7.50. Crowell

CONCRETE (691.3)
Lea, F. M., and Desch, C. H. Chemistry of cement and concrete. 1956. 15.00. St. Martins
Moore, Herbert F., and Mark B. Textbook of the materials of engineering. 8th ed. il. 1953. 7.95. McGraw
Mulligan, John A. Handbook of brick masonry construction. il. 1942. 12.50. McGraw (R)

CONCRETE CONSTRUCTION (693.5)
Concrete handbook. il. 2.00. Hawthorn
La Londe, William S., and Milo Janes, eds. Concrete engineering handbook. 1961. 25.00. McGraw (R)

CONDENSERS (ELECTRICITY) (537.242)
Bloomquist, W. C., and others. Capacitors for industry. 1950. 6.00. Wiley
Dummer, Geoffery W. A., and H. M. Nordenberg. Fixed and variable capacitors. 1960. 10.00. McGraw
Mark, David. R-L-C components handbook. il. pap. 3.50. Rider (R)
Mullin, William F. Understanding capacitors and their uses. il. 1961. pap. 1.95. Bobbs

CONDITIONED RESPONSE (158.423)
Hilgard, Ernest R., and Donald G. Marquis. Conditioning and learning. il. 2nd ed. by Gregory Kimble. 1960. 6.75. Appleton
Pavlov, Ivan P. Conditioned reflexes. tr. and ed. by G. V. Anrep. il. 4.25. Smith, Peter
Salter, Andrew. Conditioned reflex therapy. 1949. 4.25. Farrar, Straus
Spence, K. Behavior theory and conditioning. 1956. 6.00. Yale

CONDUCT OF LIFE (150)
Armstrong, Edith. Make the most of life. 1.50. DeVorss
Bennett, Arnold. How to live on 24 hours a day. 1.95. Doubleday
Bennett, Margaret E. College and life. 1952. 4.95. McGraw
Chesterfield, Lord. Letters to his son. 1.95. Dutton

Hulme, William E. Face your life with confidence: Counsels for youth. 3.50.
   Prentice-Hall
Maurois, Andre. Art of living. 1959. 3.50. Harper
Menninger, William C. and others. How to understand the opposite sex. 1956.
   2.95. Sterling
Mumford, Lewis. Conduct of life. 1951. 6.75. Harcourt
Osler, William. Way of life and other selected writings. 3.50. Smith, Peter
Overstreet, Harry, and Bonaro. Mind alive. 1954. 4.50. Norton
Overstreet, Harry, and Bonaro. Mind goes forth. 1956. 4.50. Norton
Schopenhauer, Arthur. On human nature: Essays partly posthumous in ethics
   and politics. 1957. 2.50. Barnes & Noble
Seneca. Moral letters. 3 vols. 3.50 ea. Harvard

CONDUCTING (781.63)

Braithwaite, Warwick. Conductor's art. 1952. 4.50. De Graff
Grosbayne, B. Techniques of modern orchestral conducting. il. 1956. 10.00.
   Harvard
Noyes, Frank. Anthology of musical examples for instrumental conducting. pap.
   6.50. Brown, W. C.
Noyes, F. Fundamentals of conducting. 1954. 2.50. Brown, W. C.
Scherchen, Hermann. Handbook of conducting. tr. by M. D. Calvocoressi, 1933.
   5.50. Oxford U. P.
Van Hoesen, Karl. Handbook of conducting. il. 3.50. Appleton

CONDUCTING (CHORAL) (784.6)

Coleman, Henry. Amateur choir trainer. 1932. 2.00. Oxford U. P.
Finn, William J. Art of the choral conductor. 2 vols. il. 1960. 4.50 ea. Summy

CONFORMITY (301.152)

Douglas, William O. America challenged. 1960. 2.50. Princeton
Lindner, Robert. Must you conform? 3.50. Rinehart
Walker, Edward L., and Roger W. Heyns. Anatomy for conformity. il. 1962.
   3.95; pap. 1.95. Prentice-Hall
White, Winston. Beyond conformity. 1961. 5.00. Free Press

CONFUCIUS AND CONFUCIANISM (181)

Creel, H. G. Confucius and the Chinese way. 3.85. Smith, Peter
Herbert, Edward, Confucian notebook 1.50. Taplinger
Soothill, W. E. Three religions of China. 1930. 2.40. Oxford U. P.
Weber, Max. Religion of China. 1951. 6.00. Free Press

CONGO (967)

Davidson, Basil. Black mother: The years of the African slave trade. 1961.
   6.50. Little

CONGO, BELGIAN (967.5)

Brausch, Georges. Belgian administration in the Congo. 1961. 1.75. Oxford
   U. P.
Calder, R. Agony of the Congo. 4.00. Int. Pub. Service
Legum, Colin. Congo disaster. 1961. 2.85. Smith, Peter
Lumumba, Patrice. Congo, my country. 1962. 6.50. Praeger
Merriam, Alan P. Congo, background of conflict. 1961. 6.00. Northwestern U.
Schuyler, Philippa. Who killed the Congo? 1962. 5.00. Devin

CONGREGATIONAL CHURCHES (285.8)

Edwards, Johnathan. Representative selections. by Clarence Faust, and
   Thomas Johnson. 4.25. Smith, Peter
Forsyth, Peter T. Congregationalism and reunion. 1952. 1.25. Allenson
Mather, Cotton. Selections from Cotton Mather. by Kenneth B. Murdock.
   1960. 2.45. Hafner
Miller, Perry. Orthodoxy in Massachusetts, 1630-1650. 4.00. Smith, Peter
Oberholzer, E., Jr. Delinquent saints. 1956. 6.00. Columbia
Jacobs, Charles F. Dignity of the undefeated. 1958. 3.00. Christopher
Robinson, Wade. Sermons. 1.95. Dutton

CONGRESSES AND CONVENTIONS (060)
Capes, Mary. Communication or conflict: Conferences, their nature, dynamics
and purpose. 1960. 4.00. Assn. Pr.
Herbert, Jean. Conference terminology. polyglot. 5..00. Am. Elsevier
CONGREVE, WILLIAM, 1670-1729 (822)
Holland, Norman F. First modern comedies: The significance of Etherege,
Wycherley, and Congreve. 1959. 5.50. Harvard
CONIC SECTIONS (516)
Bailey, John H. S. Elementary analytical conics. 1950. 2.00. Oxford U. P.
Salmon, George. Conic sections. 3.50. Chelsea
Smith, Charles. Elementary treatise on conic sections by the methods of
coordinate geometry. 1948. 2.00. St. Martins
Spain, Barry. Analytic conics. 1957. 5.00. Pergamon
CONIFERAE (585.2)
Dallimore, William, and Albert B. Jackson. Handbook of the coniferae and
ginkgoaceae. 17.50. St. Martins
Jackson, Albert B. Identification of conifers. 1946. 2.50. St. Martins.
CONJURING (793.8)
Dexter, W. Everybody's book of magic. 2.50. Wehman
Dunninger, Joseph. How to make a ghost walk. 3.00. Wehman
Hunter, Norman. Successful magic for amateurs. 1957. 3.50. Arco
CONNECTICUT (974.6)
Beals, Carleton. Our Yankee heritage. 1954. 4.00. McKay
Destler, Chester M. Joshua Coit, American Federalist, 1758-1798. 1962.
5.75. Wesleyan U. P.
Hard, Walter. Connecticut. 1947. 4.00. Rinehart
Lee, W. Storrs. Yankees of Connecticut. 1957. 5.00. Holt
Zeichner, Oscar. Connecticut's years of controversy, 1750-1776. 1949. 6.00.
U. of N. C.
CONNECTIVE TISSUES (616.77)
McKusick, Victor A. Heritable disorders of connective tissue. 1960. 12.00.
Mosby
Page, Irvine H., ed. Connective tissue, thrombosis, and atherosclerosis.
1959. 9.50. Academic Press
CONRAD, JOSEPH, 1857-1924 (823.91)
Curle, Richard. Joseph Conrad and his characters. 1957. 3.40. Oxford U. P.
Cushwa, F. W. Introduction to Conrad. 1933. 2.50. Odyssey
Gillon, Adam. Eternal solitary: A study of Joseph Conrad. 4.00. Twayne
Guerard, Albert J. Conrad the novelist. 1958. 5.50. Harvard
Gurko, Leo. Joseph Conrad: Giant in exile. 1962. 5.00. Macmillan
Harkness, Bruce. Conrad's Heart of darkness and the critics. 1960. 1.95.
Wadsworth
Haugh, Robert F. Joseph Conrad: Discovery in design. 1957. 3.75. U. of Okla.
Hewitt, Douglas. Joseph Conrad: A reassessment. 1952. 2.95. Dufour
Karl, Frederick R. Reader's guide to Joseph Conrad. 1959. 5.00. Farrar,
Straus
Moser, Thomas. Joseph Conrad: Achievement and decline. 1957. 4.50. Harvard
Visiak, E. H. Mirror of Conrad. 3.50. Hillary
Wiley, Paul L. Conrad's measure of man. 1953. 3.85. U. of Wis.
CONSCIENCE (171)
Hallesby, O. Conscience. tr. by Clarence J. Carlsen. 1933. 2.00. Augsburg
Lasswell, Harold, and others. Study of power. 1950. 7.50. Free Press
Rehwinkel, Alfred M. Voice of conscience. 1956. 2.75. Concordia
Reik, Theodor. Myth and guilt. 1957. 5.75. Braziller
CONSCIENTIOUS OBJECTORS (940)
Sibley, Mulford, and Philip Jacob. Conscription of conscience: The American
state and the conscientious objector, 1940-1947. 6.50. Cornell

CONSCIOUSNESS (153.7)

Bergson, Henri. Time and free will. tr. by F. L. Pogson. 1913. 3.75. Macmillan
Broad, C. D. Mind and its place in nature. 7.00. Humanities
Bucke, Richard M. Cosmic consciousness. 1961. 5.95. U. Books
Hartmann, Edward, von. Philosophy of the unconscious. 6.50. Humanities
Kroner, Richard. Culture and faith. 1951. 6.00. U. of Chicago
Marcel, Gabriel. Mystery of being. 2 vols. 1960. vol. 1. Reflection and mystery; vol. 2. Faith and reality. 1.45. ea. Regnery
Neumann, Erich. Origins and history of consciousness. il. 1954. 5.00. Pantheon
Russell, Bertrand. Analysis of mind. 1921. 3.50. Macmillan
Sartre, Jean-Paul. Transcendence of the ego. 1957. 3.00. 1.25. Farrar, Straus
Schaefer, Karl. Environmental effects on consciousness. 1962. 5.50. Macmillan
Smith, Homer W. From fish to philosopher. 1953. 4.75. Little
Von Hartmann, Edward. Philosophy of the unconscious. 6.50. Humanities

CONSERVATISM (320.1)

Auerbach, M. Morton. Conservative illusion. 1959. 6.75. Columbia
Chamberlin, William H. Evolution of a conservative. 1959. 5.50. Regnery
Evans, Medford S. Revolt on the campus. 1961 . 4.50. Regnery
Kirk, Russell. Conservative mind. 1954. 6.50. Regnery
Rossiter, Clinton. Conservatism in America. 1962. 5.00. Knopf

CONSERVATIVE PARTY (GT. BRIT.) (329.942)

McKenzie, R. T. British political parties. 5.95. St. Martins
Vicker, Ray. How an election is won. 1962. 4.50. Regnery
White, R. J., ed. Conservative tradition. 1957. 3.75. N. Y. U.

CONSOLATION (242.4)

Luther, Martin. Letters of spiritual counsel. by Theodore G. Tapperty. 1955. 5.00. Westminister
More, Sir Thomas. Utopia, and Dialogue of comfort against tribulation. 1951. 1.95. Dutton
Morrison, James Dalton. Let not your heart be troubled. 1938. 1.00. Harper
Peale, Norman Vincent. Not death at all. 1949. 1.75. Prentice-Hall

CONSOLIDATION AND MERGER OF CORPORATIONS (658.16)

Martin, David D. Mergers and the Clayton Act. 1960. 6.00. U. of Calif.
Nelson, Ralph L. Merger movements in American industry, 1895-1956. 1959. 5.00. Princeton
Weston, J. Fred. Role of mergers in the growth of large firms. 1953. 3.50. U. of Calif.

CONSTANTINE I, THE GREAT EMPEROR OF ROME, d. 337 (949.501)

Alfoldi, Andrew. Conversion of Constantine and pagan Rome. tr. by Harold Mattingly. 1948. 4.00. Oxford U. P.
Doerries, Hermann. Constantine and religious liberty. 1960. 4.00. Yale

CONSTELLATIONS (523.8)

Olcott, William T. Field book of the stars. 1907. 3.00. Putnam
Pickering, James Sayre. Stars are yours. rev. ed. 4.95. Macmillan
Sidgwick, J. B. Introducing astronomy. 1957. 3.95. Macmillan

CONSTITUTIONAL HISTORY (342)

Friedrich, Carl J. Constitutional government and democracy. 1950. 8.75; in prep. Ginn
Livingston, W. S. Federalism and constitutional change. 1956. 7.20. Oxford U. P.
McLaughlin, Andrew C. Constitutional history of the United States. 5.50. Appleton
Palmer, Robert R. Age of the democratic revolution: A political history of Europe and America, 1760-1800. 1959. 7.50. Princeton

CONSTITUTIONAL LAW (342)

Asad, Muhammad. Principles of state and government in Islam. 1961. 3.00. U. of Calif.
Barker, Ernest. Essays on government. 1951. 4.80. Oxford U. P.

Iwi, E. F. Laws and flaws: Lapses of the legislators. 1956. 3.40. Oxford U. P.

Jennings, Ivor. Approach to self-government. 1956. 3.50. Cambridge U. P.

Kauper, Paul G. Frontiers of constitutional liberty. 1956. 6.00. U. of Mich.

Sharma, I. D. Modern constitutions at work. 1962. 8.50. Taplinger

Wheare, K. C. Modern constitutions. 1951. 1.70. Oxford U. P.

CONSTITUTIONS--COLLECTIONS (342)

Wight, Martin. British colonial constitutions, 1947. 1952. 7.70. Oxford U. P.

CONSTRUCTION INDUSTRY (692)

Architectural Forum. Building, U. S. A. by the Editors of Architectural Forum. 1957. 3.95. McGraw

Dunlop, John Thomas, and Arthur D. Hill. Wage Adjustment Board: Wartime stabilization in the building and construction industry. 1950. 3.50. Harvard

Kelly, Burnham. Design and the production of houses. 1959. 12.00. McGraw

Meyerson, Martin, and others. Housing, people, and cities. il. 1962. 9.75. McGraw

Voss, Walter C. Construction management and superintendence. 1958. 6.95. Van Nostrand

CONSTRUCTION INDUSTRY--ACCOUNTING (657. 869)

Coombs, W. E. Construction accounting and financial management. 1958. 12.85. McGraw

Walker, F. R. Practical accounting and cost keeping for contractors. 1956. 5.00. Walker, F. R.

CONSUMER CREDIT (658. 883)

Barnes, E. H. Barnes on credit and collection. 1961. bds. 12.50. Prentice-Hall

Black, Hillel. Buy now, pay later. 1961. 3.95. Morrow

Cole, Robert H., and Robert S. Hancock. Consumer and commercial credit management. 1960. 10.60; 7.95. Irwin

CONSUMER EDUCATION (647.1)

Fitzsimmons, Cleo. Consumer buying. 1961. 8.95. Wiley

Logan, William B., and Helen M. Moon. Facts about merchandise. 1962. 7.25? 5.80? Prentice-Hall

National Education Association, Home Economics Department. Consumer education for family life. 1962. 0.50. N. E. A.

Troelstrup, Arch W. Consumer problems and personal finance. 1957. 6.75; instructor's manual, 1.50. McGraw

Wilson, W. Harmon, and Elvin S. Eyster. Consumer economic problems. 1961. 4.48. South-Western Pub.

Wingate, Isabel B., and others. Know your merchandise. 1953. 6.32. in prep. McGraw

Wingo, Caroling E. Clothes you buy and make. 1953. 5.75. McGraw

CONSUMERS (647.1)

Clark, Lincoln H., and Nelson N. Foote, Consumer behavior. vol 1, Dynamics of consumer reaction. 1954. 4.00; vol. 2, Life cycle and consumer behavior. 1955. 5.00; vol. 4, Household decision making. 1961. 6.50. N. Y. U.

Clark, Lincoln, Consumer behavior: Research on consumer reactions. 1958. 7.50. Harper

Cochrane, Willard W., and C. S. Bell. Economics of consumption. 1956. 7.50. McGraw

Gilbert, Eugene. Advertising and marketing to young people. 1957. 7.50. Printers' Ink

Hamilton, David B. Consumer in our economy. 1962. 6.50. Houghton

Jonassen, C. T. Shopping center versus downtown. 1955. 3.50. Bur. of Bus. Res., O. S. U.

Juster, Francis T. Consumer expectations, plans, and purchases. 1959. pap. 2.50. Nat. Bur. of Economic Research

Katona, George. Powerful consumer. 1960. 6.50. McGraw

Lippitt, Vernon G. Determinants of consumer demand for house furnishings and equipment. 1959. 6.00. Harvard

Williston, Samuel. Cases on contracts. William T. Laube. 1954. 10.00. Little

CONTROLLED FUSION (621.48)

Allis, William P. Nuclear fusion. 1960. 12.50. Van Nostrand

Glasstone, S., and Ralph C. Lovberg. Controlled thermonuclear reactions: An introduction to theory and experiment. 1960. 5.60. Van Nostrand

Saxe, Raymond F. Approaches to thermonuclear power. 1960. 2.75. Simmons-Boardman

Simon, A. Introduction to thermonuclear research. 1959. 5.50. Pergamon

CONTROLLERSHIP (657)

Anderson, David R., and Leo A. Schmidt. Practical controllership. 1961. 10.65. Irwin

Heckert, Josiah B., and J. D. Willson. Controllership. 1952. 8.50. Ronald

Thomas, William E., ed. Readings in cost accounting, budgeting, and control. 1960. 7.00. South-Western Pub.

CONVERSATION (808.5)

Dahlquist, Albert. Conversation today: Its art and techniques. 6.95. Nelson-Hall

Huston, Alfred D., and others. Effective speaking in business. 1955. 9.00. 6.75. Prentice-Hall

Lee, Irving J. How to talk with people. 1952. 2.95. Harper

Oliver, Robert T. Conversation. 1962. 5.00. Thomas, C. C.

Prochnow, Herbert V. 1001 ways to improve your conversation and speeches. 1952. 4.95. Harper

Wright, Milton. Art of conversation. 1936. 4.95. McGraw

CONVERSION (248)

Brandon, Owen. Battle for the soul. 1960. 1.25. Westminster

Ferm, Robert O. Psychology of Christian conversion. 1959. 4.00. Revell

James, William. Varieties of religious experience. 1.95. Modern Lib.

Nock, A. D. Conversion: The old and the new in religion from Alexander the Great to Augustine of Hippo. 1933. 6.10. Oxford U P.

White, Ernest. Christian life and the unconscious. 1956. 3.00. Harper

CONVERTS (248)

Lin, Yutang. From pagan to Christian. 1959. 3.50. World Pub.

CONVEX BODIES (513)

Eggleston, H. G. Problems of Euclidean space: Application of convexity. 6.50. Pergamon

CONVICT LABOR (331.51)

Dallin, D. J., and B. I. Nicolaevsky. Forced labor in Soviet Russia. 1947. 6.50. Yale

Parvilahti, Unto. Beria's Gardens: A slave laborer's experiences in the Soviet Utopia. 5.00. Dutton

COOK, JAMES, 1728-1779 (923.9)

Chickering, William H. Within the sound of these waves. 1956. 5.00. Harcourt

Gwyther, John. Captian Cook and the South Pacific. 1955. 3.50. Houghton

COOKERY (641.5)

Adams, Charlotte. Old Original Bookbinder's Restaurant cookbook. 1961. 3.95. Crowell

Allen, Jean. Budget cook book. il. 1957. 2.50. Arco

Crocker, Betty. Betty Crocker's guide to easy entertaining. 1959. 1.89. Golden Press

Crocker, Betty. Betty Crocker's new good and easy cook book. 1962. 2.99. Golden Press

Farmer, Fannie M. Fannie Merritt Farmer Boston Cooking School cook book. by Wilma Lord Perkins. 1959. 5.95. Little

Rombauer, Irma S., and Marion R. Becker. Joy of cooking. 1951. 5.95. Bobbs

Vanderbilt, Amy. Amy Vanderbilt's complete cookbook. 5.50; thumb index, 6.00. Doubleday

West, Betty M.   Diabetic menus, meals and recipes. 1959. 3. 95. Doubleday
Shannon, Ellen.   American dictionary of culinary terms. 1961. 6. 95. Barnes,
   A. S. (R)
McLean, Beth B. , and Thora H. Campbell. Complete meat cookbook. 1953.
   6. 75. Bennett
Beard, James, and Isabel E. Callver.   James Beard cookbook. il. 1961. 4. 95.
   Dutton
Berolzheimer, Ruth, United States regional cook book. 1947. 3. 50. Doubleday
Brown, Marion.   Southern cook book. 1951. 2. 75. U. of N. C.
Cranwell, John P.   Fast and fancy cookery. 1959. 3. 75. Doubleday
Dietz, F. Meredith, and August A. , Jr.   Gay Nineties cookbook. 1946. 3. 00.
   Dietz
Early, Eleanor.   New England cookbook. 1954. 3. 95. Random
Hunt, Peter.   Peter Hunt's Cape Cod cookbook. 1962. 3. 95. Greene
Hutchinson, Ruth.   New Pennsylvania Dutch cookbook. 1958. 3. 95. Harper
COOKERY, OUTDOOR (641. 578)
Crocker, Betty.   Betty Crocker's outdoor cook book. 1961. 1. 00. Golden Press
COOKERY FOR INSTITUTIONS, ETC. (641. 57)
Smith, E. Evelyn.   Handbook on quantity food management. 1955. 3. 50. Burgess
Stokes, J. W.   Food service in industry and institutions. 1960. 8. 00. Brown,
   W. C.
Terrell, Margaret E.   Large quantity recipes. 1951. 7. 00. Lippincott
West, Bessie B. , and LeVelle Wood.   Food service in institutions. 1955.
   7. 75. Wiley
COOKIES (641. 631)
Pasley, Virginia.   Christmas cookie book. 1949. 3. 50. Little
Sumption, Lois, and Marguerite L. Ashbrook.   Cookies and more cookies.
   1948. 2. 95. Bennett
COOLIDGE, CALVIN, PRES. U. S. 1872-1933 (923.173)
Lathem, Edward C. , ed.   Meet Calvin Coolidge. 4. 50. Greene
COOPER, JAMES FENIMORE, 1789-1851. (813. 24)
Grossman, James.   James Fenimore Cooper. 4. 00. Sloane
Philbrick, Thomas L.   James Fenimore Cooper and the development of
   American sea fiction. 1962. 6. 25. Harvard
Ringe, Donald A.   James Fenimore Cooper. 3. 50. Twayne
Walker, Warren S.   James Fenimore Cooper. 1962. 2. 95. Barnes & Noble
COOPERATION (334)
Childs, Marquis W.   Sweden: The middle way. 1960. 5. 00. Yale
Cooperatives in the Caribbean. 2 vols. pap. 1. 00 ea. U. of Fla.
Digby, Margaret.   World co-operative movement. 2. 50. Hillary
Kropotkin, Petr.   Mutual aid. 1955. 3. 00. Sargent
Mead, Margaret.   Cooperation and competition among primitive peoples. 5. 00.
   Smith, Peter
Parker, Florence E.   First 125 years: A history of distributive and service
   cooperation in U. S. , 1829-1954. 1956. 5. 00. Coop. League
Woorhis, Jerry.   American cooperatives. 1961. 4. 75. Coop. League, or Harper
COOPERATIVE COMMONWEALTH FEDERATION (334)
McHenry, Dean E.   Third force in Canada: The Cooperative Commonwealth
   Federation, 1932-1948. 1950. 3. 50. U. of Calif.
COOPERATIVE SOCIETIES (334)
Packel, Israel.   Organization and operation of cooperatives. 1956. 12. 00.
   Bender
Voorhis, Jerry.   American cooperatives. 1961. 4. 75. Coop. League, or Harper
COORDINATES (516)
Gerrish, F.   Algebra, trigonometry, coordinate geometry. 6. 50. Cambridge U. P.
Maxwell, Edwin Arthur.   Coordinate geometry with vectors and tensors. 1958.
   4. 50. Oxford U. P.
Maxwell, Edwin A.   Elementary coordinate geometry. 1958. 4. 50. Oxford U. P.

COORDINATION COMPOUNDS (541.396)
Bailar, J. C. Chemistry of the co-ordination compounds. 1958. 15.00.
   Pergamon
Graddon, D. P. Introduction to coordination chemistry. 1961. 4.00. Pergamon
Lewis, Jack, and R. G. Wilkins. Modern coordination chemistry. 1960. 13.50.
   Wiley
COPELAND, CHARLES TOWNSEND, 1860-1952 (923.7)
Adams, J. Donald Copey of Harvard. 1960. 5.00. Houghton
COPERNICUS, NICOLAUS, 1473-1543 (925)
Armitage, Angus. Copernicus: The founder of modern astronomy. 1962. pap.
   1.95. Barnes A. S.
Kesten, Hermann. Copernicus and his world. 3.50. Roy Pub.
COPLAND, AARON 1900- (927)
Smith, Julia. Aaron Copland: His works and contribution to American music.
   1955. 5.95. Dutton
COPPER (669.3)
Butts, Allison. Copper. 1954. 22.50. Reinhold
COPPER AGE (571.3)
Burkitt, M. C. Our early ancestors. 1926. 4.50. Cambridge U.P.
COPPER ALLOYS (669.953)
Versagi, F. J. Routine analysis of copper base alloys. 1960. 5.00. Tudor
COPPERHEAD (NICKNAME) (973.718)
Klement, Frank L. Copperheads in the Middle West. 1960. 7.50. U. of Chicago
COPPERWORK (673.3)
Kramer, Karl, and Nora. Coppercraft and silver made at home. 1959. 3.00.
   Chilton
COPY-READING (070.41)
Cranford, Robert J. Copy editing. pap. 3.50. Holt, Rinehart & Winston

Lasky, Joseph. Proofreading and copy-preparation. 1954. 7.50. Mentor Pr.
COPYING PROCESSES (652.4)
Herrmann, Irvin A. Manual of office reproduction. 1956. 3.25. Office Pubns.
Wiseman, Maxine, and others. Producing the duplicated school newspaper.
   1959. 1.00. Iowa State
COPYRIGHT (655.6)
Copyright protection in the Americas. 1950. with 1954 suppl. 2.00. Pan American
Nicholson, Margaret. Manual of copyright practice for writers, publishers,
   and agents. 1956. 7.00. Oxford U.P.
Amdur, Leon H. Copyright law and practice, with forms. 1936. 20.00.
   Boardman, Clark
Berle, Alf K., and L. Sprague de Camp. Inventions, patents and their manage-
   ment. 1959. 12.50. Van Nostrand
Pilpel, Harriet F., and Morton D. Goldberg. Copyright guide. 1960. pap. 3.00.
   Bowker
Pilpel, Harriet, and Theodora Zavin. Rights and writers. 1960. 7.50. Dutton
Rothenberg, Stanley. Copyright law: Basic and related materials. 1956. with
   1958 suppl. 20.00. Boardman, Clark
Rothenberg, Stanley. Legal protection of literature, art and music. 1960.
   10.00. Boardman, Clark
Wittenberg, Phillip. Law of literary property. 1957. 5.00. World Pub.
Larus, Joel. Development of international copyright. 1962. 4.50. Pub. Affairs
CORAL REEFS AND ISLANDS (551.96)
Darwin, Charles. Structure and distribution of coral reefs. 4.00. Smith, Peter
Wiens, Herold J. Atoll environment and ecology. 1962. 15.00. Yale
CORK (634.9)
Cooke, G. B. Cork and the cork tree. 1961. 7.50. Pergamon
CORN (633.1)
Mosher, M. L. Early corn yield tests and related later programs. 1962. 3.95.
   Iowa State

Sprague, G. F. Corn and corn improvement. 1955. 11.50. Academic Press

CORN LAW LEAGUE (337)

McCord, N. Anti-corn law league 1838-1846. 5.00. Humanities

CORN LAWS (337)

Barnes, Donald G. History of the English Corn Laws from 1660-1846. 1930.
   8.50. Kelley

Malthus, Thomas R. Observations on the effects of the corn laws and of a
   rise or fall in the price of corn on the agriculture and general wealth of
   the country. 1932. pap. 1.00. Johns Hopkins

CORNEA (617.7)

Thomas, Charles I. Cornea. il. 1956. 30.00. Thomas C. C

CORNELL, KATHARINE, 1898- (927)

McClintic, Guthrie. Me and Kit. 1955. 5.00. Little

CORONARY ARTERIES (616.123)

Brams, William A. Managing your coronary. 1960. 3.50. Lippincott

Gofman, John W. What we do know about heart attacks. 1958. 3.50. Putnam

CORONERS (340.6)

Havard, J. D. J. Detection of secret homicide. 1960. 8.00. St. Martins

LeBrun, George P., and Edward D. Radin. It's time to tell. 1962. 3.75.
   Morrow

CORPORATION LAW (338.74)

Berle, Adolph A., Jr., and G. C. Means. Modern corporation and private
   property. 1937. 6.50. Macmillan

Carter, W. A., and M. Lindahl. Corporate concentration and public policy.
   1959. 8.00. Prentice-Hall

Cherrington, Homer. Investor and the securities act. 1942. 2.50. Pub. Affairs

Crowley, Joseph R., ed. Role of corporate counsel. 1959. 3.75. Fordham

Frey, Alexander H. Cases and materials on corporations and partnerships.
   1951. 9.75. Little

Latty, Elvin R. Introduction to business associations: Cases and materials.
   1951. 8.50. Little

Owens, Richard N. Business organization and combination. 1951. 7.00.
   Prentice-Hall

Prentice-Hall Editorial Staff. Corporate secretary's encyclopedia. 4 vols.
   39.95. Prentice-Hall

Rohrlich. Organizing corporate and other business enterprises. 1958. with
   suppl. 15.00. Bender

Wormser, I. M., and J. A. Crane. Cases on private corporations. 8.00.
   Bobbs

CORPORATION REPORTS (338.74)

Floyd, Elizabeth R. Preparing the annual report. 1960. 4.50. Am. Management
   Assn.

Foster, Louis O. Understanding financial statements and corporate annual
   reports. 1961. 3.95. Chilton

Winfrey, Robley. Technical and business report preparation. 1961. 5.95.
   Iowa State

CORPORATIONS (338.74)

Berie, Adolf A., Jr. 20th century capitalist revolution. 1954. 3.50. Harcourt

Branch, Melville C. Corporate planning process. 1962. 6.75. Am. Management
   Assn.

Buchanan, Norman S. Economics of corporate enterprise. 1940. 6.50. Holt

Drucker, Peter F. Concept of the corporation. 1946. 5.00. Day

Eells, Richard. Government of corporations. 1962. 7.50. Free Press

Eells, Richard. Meaning of modern business. 1960. 7.50. Columbia

Eldot, Leon D. Getting and holding your executive position. 1960. 4.95.
   Prentice-Hall

Ewing, David W. Long-range planning for management. 1958. 6.50. Harper

Florence, P. Sargant. Ownership, control and success of large companies.
  an analysis of English industrial structure and policy, 1936-1951. 1961.
  12.50. Quadrangle

CORPORATIONS--ACCOUNTING (657)

Foulke, Roy A. Practical financial statement analysis. 1961. 12.50. McGraw
Guthmann, Harry G. Analysis of financial statements. 1953. 1.00. Prentice-
  Hall
Murphy, M. C. Internal check and control for small companies. 1940. 1.00.
  Pub. Affairs
Paton, William A., and William A., Jr. Corporation accounts and statements.
  1955. 7.25; problems and cases. 3.40. Macmillan

CORPORATIONS--DIRECTORIES (338.74)

Directory of American firms operating in foreign countries, 1962-63. Annual.
  17.50. World Trade Academy (R)

CORPORATIONS--FINANCE (338.74)

American Management Association. New responsibilities in corporate finance.
  1962. 3.00. Am. Management Assn.
Bradley, Joseph F. Fundamentals of corporation finance. 1959. 7.00. Rinehart
Burtchett, F. F., and others. Corporation finance. 1959. 6.95. Johnsen
Gerstenberg, Charles W. Financial organization and management of business.
  1959. 10.60. Prentice-Hall
Gordon, Myron J. Investment, financing, and valuation of the corporation. 1962.
  6.50; text ed. 6.50. Irwin
Gross, Harry, and Maxwell J. Mangold. Guide to current techniques in
  financing. 1961. pap. 2.00. Pilot
Husband, William H., and James C. Dockeray. Modern corporation finance.
  1962. 11.00. Irwin
Osborn, Richards C. Corporation finance. 1959. 7.00. Harper
Schwartz, Eli. Corporation finance. 1962. 9.50. St. Martins
Solomon, Ezra, Management of corporate capital. 1959. 7.50. Free Press
Tew, J. H. B., and R. F. Henderson. Studies in company finance. 1959. 6.50.
  Cambridge U. P.
Walker, Ernest W., and William H. Baughn. Financial planning and policy.
  1961. 8.00. Harper
Wessell, Robert H. Principles of financial analysis. 1961. 7.50. Macmillan

CORPORATIONS--U.S. (338.74)

American Management Association. Applying financial controls in foreign
  operations. 1957. 3.75. Am. Management Assn.
American Management Association. Increasing profits from foreign operations.
  1957. 5.25. Am. Management Assn.
Baldwin, William L. Antitrust and the changing corporation. 1961. 8.75.
  Duke
Berle, Adolph A., Jr., and G. C. Means. Modern corporation and private
  property. 1937. 6.50. Macmillan
Bittker, Boris I. Federal income taxation of corporations and shareholders.
  1959. with 1961 supplement. 12.50. Federal Tax
Blough, Roger M. Free man and the corporation. 1959. 4.50. McGraw
Chandler, Alfred D., Jr. Strategy and structure: Chapters in the history of the
  industrial enterprise. 1962. 10.00. M.I.T.
Childs, John F. Long term financing. 1961. 15.00. Prentice-Hall
Dewing, A. S. Corporate promotions and reorganizations. 1914. 6.00. Harvard
Gaa, Charles J. Taxation of corporate income. 1944. 4.00. U. of Ill.
Guthmann, Harry G., and H. E. Dougall. Corporate financial policy. 1955.
  8.25. Prentice-Hall
Holden, Paul E., and others. Top-management organization and control. 1951.
  6.50. McGraw
Kamm, Jacob O. Investor's handbook. 4.95. World Pub.
Mason, Edward S. Corporation in modern society. 1960. 6.75. Harvard

Oleck, Howard L. Non-profit corporations and associations: Organization, management and dissolution. 1956. 12.50. Prentice-Hall
Owens, Richard N. Business organization and combination. 1951. 7.00. Prentice-Hall
Robinson, Richard D. Cases in international business. 1962. pap. 2.50. Holt, Rinehart & Winston
Shockey, Houstin, and Henry W. Sweeney. Tax effects of operating as a corporation or partnership. 1957. 8.50. Prentice-Hall
Silverstein, Nathan L. Corporation finance simplified. 1949. 4.50. Am. Tech. Soc.

Stein, Eric, and Thomas L. Nicholson. American enterprise in the European common market. 2 vols. 30.00. U. of Mich.
Warner, W. Lloyd. Corporation in the emergent American society. 1962. 3.00. Harper
Worthy, James C. Big business and free men. 1959. 4.00. Harper

CORPORATIONS, GOVERNMENT (338.74)
Hanson, Albert H. Parliament and public ownership. 1961. 4.80. Oxford U. P.
Hanson, Albert H. Public enterprise and economic development. 1959. 8.50. Humanities

CORPULENCE (613.2)
Cantor, Alfred J. How to lose weight the doctor's way. 1959. 2.95. Fell
George, Alfred L. Your weight and your life. 1951. 3.95. Norton
Peale, Robert C. Live longer and better. 1961. 3.95. Prentice-Hall

CORREGIO, ANTONIO ALLEGRI, KNOWN AS, 1494-1534 (927)
Popham, Arthur E. Correggio's drawings. 1957. 19.35. Oxford U. P.

CORRELATION (STATISTICS) (311.25)
Kendall, Maurice G. Rank correlation methods. 1955. 6.50. Hafner

CORRESPONDENCE SCHOOLS AND COURSES (374.1)
White, Alex S. Correspondence colleges revisited. 1962. 3.95. Aurea
White A. Sandri. Vocations for all. 1962. 5.75. Aurea

CORROSION AND ANTI--CORROSIVES (620.112)
De Paul, D. J. Corrosion and wear handbook. 1957. 7.00. McGraw
Evans, Ulick R. Corrosion and oxidation of metals. 1960. 27.50. St. Martins
Molloy, E. Electro-plating and corrosion prevention. 1954. 4.50. Transatlantic
Speller, Frank. Corrosion: Causes and prevention. 1951. 14.00. McGraw
Uhlig, Herbert H. Corrosion handbook. 1948. 21.00. Wiley

CORRUPTION (IN POLITICS) (324.27)
Allen, Robert S. Our sovereign state. 5.00. Vanguard
Douglas, Paul H. Ethics in government. 1952. 2.25. Harvard
Regier, C. C. Era of the muckrakers. 4.25. Smith, Peter
Steffens, Joseph Lincoln. Shame of the cities. 1959. 3.50. Smith, Peter
Weinberg, Arthur, and Lila. Muckrakers. 1961. 7.50. S. and S.

CORTES, HERNANDO, 1485-1547 (972)
Braden, Charles S. Religious aspects of the conquest of Mexico. 1930. 6.00. Duke
Gardiner, C. Harvey. Naval power in the conquest of Mexico. 1956. 4.95. U. of Tex.
Prescott, W. H. Conquest of Mexico. 2 vols. Dutton
Prescott, William H. Conquest of Mexico and Conquest of Peru. Modern Lib.

CORTISONE (615.364)
Ingle, Dwight J. and Burton L. Baker. Physiological and therapeutic effects of corticotropin and cortisone. 1953. 5.50. Thomas C. C

COSMETICS (646.72)
Consumers Report. Medicine show. by the Editors of Consumers' Report. 1961. 3.95. pap. 1.50. S. and S.
Wall, Florence E. Principles and practice of beauty culture. 7.50. Sheridan

COSMIC PHYSICS (539.7223)
Boyd, R. L. F. Space research by rocket and satellite. 1961. 2.25. Harper

Campbell, Paul. Medical and biological aspects of the energies of space. 1961. 10.00. Columbia

Dungey, J. W. Cosmic electrodynamics. 1958. 6.00. Cambridge U. P.

Jastrov, Robert. Exploration of space. 1960. 5.95. Macmillan

Van Allen, James A. Scientific uses of earth satellites. 1958. 10.00. U. of Mich.

COSMIC RAYS (539.7223)

Galbraith, William. Extensive air showers. 7.50. 1958. Academic Press

Hooper, J. E., and M. Scharff. Cosmic radiation. 1958. 2.75. Wiley

COSMOGONY (523.1)

Beau, Georges. Springtime of the stars. 1961. 3.95. Criterion

Berrill, N. J. You and the universe. 1958. 3.50. Dodd

Ernst, and E. DeVries. Atlas of the universe. 1961. 9.95. Nelson (R)

Gamow, George. Biography of the earth. 1959. 4.95. pap. 1.35. Viking

Gamow, George. Creation of the universe. 1961. 4.50. Viking

Gamow, George. Matter, earth and sky. 1958. 10.60. 7.95. Prentice-Hall

Heim, Karl. World: Its creation and consummation. 1962. 3.00. Muhlenberg

Heuer, Kenneth. Next fifty billion years. 6.00. Collier

Jeans, James. Astronomy and cosmogony. 4.50. Smith, Peter

Jeans, J. H. Universe around us. 1944. 5.00. Cambridge U. P.

Lamplugh, Jesse R. Rational universe. 1962. 6.50. Livingston

Lovell, A. C. B. Individual and the universe. pap. 0.50. New Am. Lib.

Opik, Ernst J. Oscillating universe. 1960. pap. 0.50. New Am. Lib.

Shapley, H. Of stars and men. 1958. 3.50. Beacon

COSMOLOGY (523.1)

Broms, Allan. Our emerging universe. 1961. 4.95. Doubleday

Eddington, A. S. Expanding universe. 1933. 2.50. Cambridge U. P.

Eddington, A. S. Fundamental theory. 1946. 8.50. Cambridge U. P.

Foley, Leo. Cosmology: Philosophical and scientific. 5.00. Bruce

Haber, Heinz. Stars, men and stoms. 1962. 3.99. Golden Press

Jones, G. O., and others. Atoms and the universe. 1957. 4.50. Scribner

Kahn, Charles H. Anaximander and the origins of Greek cosmology. 1960. 6.50. Columbia

Koyre, Alexandre. From the closed world to the infinite universe. 1956. 5.00. Johns Hopkins

Kuhn, Thomas S. Copernican revolution: Planetary astronomy in the development of western thought. 1957. 5.50. Harvard

Lehrs, Ernest. Man or matter. 1958. 6.00. Harper

McVittie, G. C. Fact and theory in cosmology. 1962. 3.95. Macmillan

Milne, E. A. Modern cosmology and the Christian idea of God. 1952. 3.40. Oxford U. P.

Munitz, Milton K. Space, time and creation. 1957. 4.00. Free Press

Munitz, Milton K. Theories of the universe. 1957. 7.50. Free Press

Scientific American. Universe. by the Editors of Scientific American. 1957. 1.45. S. and S.

Teilhard de Chardin, Pierre. Phenomenon of man. 1959. 5.00. 1961. Harper

Tillyard, E. M. W. Elizabethan world picture. 1946. 2.25. Macmillan

Whitehead, Alfred North. Process and reality. 1960. 6.50. Macmillan

Whitehead, Alfred N. Adventures of ideas. 1933. 5.00. Macmillan

Wood, Nathan R. Secret of the Universe, 1955. 2.50. Eerdmans

COST (338.522)

Clark, John M. Studies in the economics of overhead costs. 1923. 8.50. U. of Chicago

Rostas, L. Productivity, prices and distribution. 1948. 5.50. Cambridge U. P.

Stigler, George J., and Kenneth E. Boulding. Readings in price theory. 1952. 6.75. Irwin

COST ACCOUNTING (657.4)

Burton, Norman L. Introduction to accounting cost. 1959. pap. 1.50. Littlefield

Cassidy, Mary, and George Woll. Introductory cost accounting. 1961. spiral bdg. 7.50. Allenson

Crowningshield, Gerald. Cost accounting: Principles and managerial applications. 7.75. Houghton

Devine, Carl Thomas. Cost accounting and analysis. 1950. 7.75. Macmillan

Dickey, Robert I. Accountants' cost handbook. 1960. 15.00. Ronald

Grant, E. L. Basic accounting and cost accounting. 1956. 6.95; student's workbook, 3.50; teacher's manual, 2.00. McGraw

Keller, I. Wayne. Management accounting for profit control. 1957. 7.75. McGraw

Lasser, J. K. Handbook of cost accounting methods. 1949. 17.50. Van Nostrand

Reitell, C., and G. L. Harris. Cost accounting. 1949. 8.00. Int. Textbook

Thomas, William E. Readings in cost accounting, budgeting, and control. 1960. 7.00. South-Western Pub.

COST AND STANDARD OF LIVING (339.42)

Clark, Colin. Conditions of economic progress. 1957. 14.00. St. Martins

Fourastie, Jean. Causes of wealth. 1959. 5.00. Free Press

Zimmerman, Carle C. Consumption and standards of living. 1936. 6.50. Van Nostrand

COST AND STANDARD OF LIVING--U.S. (339.42)

Bigelow, Howard F. Family finance. 1953. 9.25. Lippincott

COSTS, INDUSTRIAL (657.4)

Carroll, Phil. How to control production costs. 1953. 6.50. McGraw

Gillespie, Cecil. Accounting systems, procedures and methods. 1961. 12.65; text ed. 9.50. Prentice-Hall

Johnston, John. Statistical cost analysis. 1960. 6.75. McGraw

Stedry, Andrew C. Budget control and cost behavior. il. 1960. 4.50. Prentice-Hall

COSTUME (391.09)

Downs, Harold. Theatre and stage. 2 vols. 1951. 25.00. Pitman

Monro, Isabel S., and Kate M. Costume index supplement. il. 1957. 6.00. Wilson

Paterek, Josephine D. Costuming for the theatre. 1959. 3.50. Crown

Zirner, Laura. Costuming for the modern stage. il. 1957. pap. 3.00. U. of Ill.

Bradley, Carolyn G. Western world costume: An outline history. il. 4.75. Appleton

Bruhn, Wolfgang, and M. Tilke. Pictorial history of costume. il. 1956. 25.00. Praeger

Calthrop, D. C. English costume, 1066-1830. 4.50. Hillary

Davenport, Millia. Book of costume. il. 12.95. Crown

Evans, Mary. Costume throughout the ages. il. 1950. 6.00. Lippincott

Garland, Madge. Changing face of beauty. 1957. 10.00. Barrows

Gorsline, Douglas. What people wore. il. 1952. 10.00. Viking

Hansen, Henry Harald. Costumes and styles: The evolution of fashion from early Egypt to the present. il. 1956. 7.50. Dutton

Lester, Katherine M. Historic costume. 1956. 4.50. Bennett

Tilke, M. Costume patterns and designs. il. 1957. 25.00. Praeger

Bhushan, J. B. Costumes and textiles of India. il. 16.50. Int. Pub. Service

Rue, L. Costumes of the Orient. 1.00. Wehman

Anderson, Ruth M. Spanish costume: Estremadura. il. 1951. 11.00. Hispanic

Bradfield, Nancy. Historical costumes of England, 1066-1956. 1956. 6.00. Barnes & Noble

Brooke, Iris. English costume, 1900-1950. 2.50. Hillary

Brooke, Iris. English costume of the Early Middle Ages, 10th to the 13th centuries. il. 1936. 2.75. Macmillan

Brooke, Iris. English costume of the 18th century. il. 2.75. Macmillan

Brooke, Iris. English costume of the Later Middle Ages, 14th and 15th centuries. il. 1935. 2.75. Macmillan

Brooke, Iris. History of English costume. 3.00. Hillary

Semple, William. Scottish tartans. il. 3.00. Transatlantic

Solier, W. du. Ancient Mexican costume. 7.50. Rogers
Hope, Thomas. Costumes of the Greeks and Romans. 2 vols. il. 4.00.
    Smith, Peter
Wilson, Lillian M. Roman toga. 1924. 5.00. Johns Hopkins
COSTUME DESIGN (646.01)
Doten, Hazel, and Constance Boulard. Fashion drawing: How to do it. il. 1953.
    7.50. Harper
Lapick, Gaetan J. Scientific designing of women's clothes. 1949. 6.00. Fairchild
McJimsey, Harriet T. Costume selection. 1956. 3.00. Burgess
Picken, Mary Brooks, and Dora Loues Miller. Dressmakers of France. il.
    1956. 5.00. Harper
COTTON (633.51)
Brown, Harry B., and J. O. Ware. Cotton. 1958. 13.00. McGraw
COTTON GROWING (633.51)
Cardozier, V. R. Growing cotton. il. 1956. 6.20. McGraw
Cohn, D. L. Life and times of King Cotton. 1956. 5.50. Oxford U. P.
Kent, Kate Peck. Cultivation and weaving of cotton in the prehistoric south-
    western United States. 1957. 4.00. Am. Philos. Soc.
Street, James H. New revolution in the cotton economy: Mechanization and its
    consequences. 1956. 5.00. U. of N. C.
COTTON MANUFACTURE (677.21)
Merrill, G. R. Cotton carding. 2.50. Textile Bk.
Smelser, Neil. Social change in the industrial revolution. 1959. 6.00. U. of
    Chicago
COTTONSEED (665.323)
Bailey, Alton E. Cottonseed and cottonseed products (Fats and Oils). il. 1948.
    18.00. Wiley
COUNCIL, EUROPEAN (341)
Robertson, A. H. Council of Europe. 9.00. Praeger
COUNCILS AND SYNODS (262.5)
Fairweather, Eugene R., and Edward R. Hardy. Voice of the church: The
    ecumenical council. 1962. bds. 3.00. Seabury
Dvornik, Francis. Ecumenical councils. 1961. 3.50. Hawthorn
Hughes, Philip. Church in crisis: A history of the general councils, 325-1870.
    1961. 4.95. Doubleday
Jedin, Hubert. Ecumenical councils of the Catholic Church. tr. by Ernest
    Graf. 1960. 3.95. Herder & Herder, N. Y. C.
Thielen, Thoralf T. What is an ecumenical council? 1960. 2.95. Newman
COUNSELING (371.4)
Aptekar, H. H. Dynamics of casework and counseling. 1955. 4.50. Houghton
Arbuckle, Dugald. Counseling: An introduction. il. 1961. 6.25. Allyn & Bacon
Bordin, Edward S. Psychological counseling. 1955. 6.00. Appleton
Brammer, Lawrence M., and Everett L. Shostrom. Therapeutic psychology.
    Fundamentals of counseling and psychotherapy. il. 1960. 7.50. Prentice-Hall
Buchheimer, Arnold, and Sarah Balogh. Counseling relationship. il. 1962. 4.75.
    Sci. Res. Assoc.
Callis, Robert, and others. Casebook of counseling. il. 1955. 5.00. Appleton
Cottle, William C., and N. M. Downie. Procedures and preparation for
    counseling. il. 1960. 8.00. Prentice-Hall
Curran, Charles A. Personality factors in counseling. il. 1945. 6.00. Grune
Hamrin, Shirley A., and Blanche B. Paulson. Counseling adolescents. 1950.
    4.75. Sci. Res. Assoc.
Kidd, J. W. Residence hall guidance. 1956. 1.75. Brown, W. C.
McGowan, J. F., and L. D. Schmidt. Counseling: Readings in theory and
    practice. 4.75. Holt, Rinehart & Winston
McKinney, Fred. Counseling for personal adjustment. 6.75. Houghton
May, Rollo. Art of counseling. 2.50. Abingdon
Oates, Wayne E. Where to go for help. 1957. 2.00. Westminster

Rogers, Carl R. Client-centered therapy. 1951. 6.00. Houghton
Snyder, William U. Casebook of non-directive counseling. 1947. 5.75. Houghton
Tyler, Leona E. Work of the counselor. 4.75. Appleton
Wrenn, C. G. Student personnel work in college. 1951. 6.75. Ronald
COUNTERFEITS AND COUNTERFEITING (332.9)
Pirie, Anthony. Operation Bernhard. il. 1962. 5.00. Morrow
COUNTERPOINT (781.4)
Atkisson, Harold F. Basic counterpoint. 1957. 5.95. McGraw
Bairstow, Edward C. Counterpoint and harmony. 1945. 4.25. St. Martins
COUNTRY LIFE (630.1)
Bromfield, Louis. Malabar Farm. il. 1948. 6.95. Harper
Kolb, John H., and Edmund de S. Brunner. Study of rural society. 7.50. Houghton
Oeser, O. A., and F. E. Emery. Social structure and personality in a rural community. 5.00. Humanities
Rich, Louise Dickinson. My neck of the woods. 1950. 4.50. Lippincott
Spectorsky, A. C. Exurbanities. il. 1955. 4.95. Lippincott
Woodson, Carter G. Rural Negro. 1930. 3.25. Assoc. Publishers
COUNTRY LIFE--AFRICA (916.762)
Dinesen, Isak. Shadows on the grass. 1961. 3.75. Random
COUNTRY LIFE--ASIA (915.2)
Japan Travel Bureau. Rural life in Japan. il. pap. 2.50. Tuttle
COUNTRY LIFE--GT. BRIT. (914.2)
Maxwell, Gavin. Ring of bright water. il. 1961. 5.95. Dutton
Orwin, C. S. Problems of the countryside. 1945. 1.50. Cambridge U. P.
COUNTRY LIFE--LATIN AMERICA (917.2)
Nelson, Lowry. Rural Cuba 1950. 3.50. U. of Minn.
Whetten, Nathan L. Rural Mexico. il. 1948. 11.50. U. of Chicago
COUNTY GOVERNMENT (352)
Wager, Paul W. County government across the nation. 1950. 7.50. U. of N. C.
COURAGE (179.6)
Kennedy, John F. Profiles in courage. il. 1961. 3.95. Harper
Mackenzie, Compton. Certain aspects of moral courage. 4.50. Doubleday
Tillich, Paul. Courage to be. 1952. 3.75. Yale
COURBET, GUSTAVE, 1819-1877 (927)
Mack, Gerstle. Courbet. il. 6.75. Boston Bk.
Mack, Gerstle. Gustave Courbet. il. 1951. 6.75. Knopf
COURT RULES (347.9)
Federal code annotated. Rules of the various federal courts. 1 vol. 1952. 10.00. Bobbs (R)
COURTS (351.95)
Abraham, Henry J. Courts and judges. 1959. pap. 1.00. Oxford U. P.
Abraham, Henry J. Judicial process: An introductory analysis of the courts of the United States, England, and France. 1962. pap. 2.25. Oxford U. P.
Frank, Jerome. Courts on trial. 1949. 6.00. Princeton
Hazard, John N. Settling disputes in Soviet society. 1960. 9.50. Columbia
Jaffe, Louis L. Judicial aspects of foreign relations. 1933. 3.50. Harvard
Jackson, Richard M. Machinery of justice in England. 1960. 8.50. Cambridge U. P.
Mayers, Lewis. American legal system. 1955. 8.50. Harper
Moore, James W. Commentary of judicial code and federal procedural rules. 1949. 12.00. Bender
Parks, E. Patrick. Roman rhetorical schools as a preparation for the courts under the early empire. 1945. 1.50. Johns Hopkins
Wagner, W. J. Federal states and their judiciary. 9.50. Humanities
COURTS AND COURTIERS (909)
Castiglione, Baldassare. Book of the courtier. ed. by Friench Simpson. 1959. 2.25. Ungar

COURTS-MARTIAL AND COURTS OF INQUIRY (344)
Aycock, William B., and Seymour W. Wurfel. Military law under the uniform
    code of military justice. 1955. 7.50. U. of N. C.
Everett, Robinson O. Military justice in the armed forces of the United States.
    il. 1956. 5.00. Military Service
Mayers, Lewis. American legal system. 1955. 8.50. Harper
Spratt, James L. Military trial techniques. 5.50. Am. Guild
COURTSHIP (177.6)
Burgess, Ernest W., and others. Courtship, engagement and marriage. 1954.
    6.00. text ed. 5.00. Lippincott
Constance, Kate. How to get and keep a husband. 1957. 3.50. Dorrance
Duvall, Evelyn M., and Joy D. Johnson. Art of dating. 1958. 2.50. Assn. Pr.
Fielding, William. Strange customs of courtship and marriage. 2.95. Doubleday
Gould, Sandra. Always say maybe. il. 1960. 3.50. Golden Press
Klemer, Richard H. Man for every woman. 1959. 4.95. Macmillan
LeMasters, E. E. Modern courtship and marriage. il. 5.75. Macmillan
Mayer, John E. Jewish-Gentile courtships. 1961. 5.00. Free Press
Merrill, Francis E. Courtship and marriage. 1959. 5.50. Holt, Rinehart &
    Winston
Murray, Alfred L. Youth's courtship problems. 1945. 1.95. Zondervan
Small, Dwight H. Design for Christian marriage. 1959. 3.50. Revell
COVERED BRIDGES (388.1)
Congdon, Herbert W. Covered bridge. 6.00. Vermont
Sloane, Eric. Americana: American barns and covered bridges, American
    yesterday, and Our vanishing landscape. 12.50. Funk
COWBOYS (917.8)
Adams, Ramon F. Best of the American cowboy. il. 1957. 4.95. U. of Okla.
Frantz, Joe B., and Julian E. Choate, Jr. American cowboy. 1955. 3.75 U.
    of Okla.
COWBOYS--SONGS AND MUSIC (784.4)
Dobie, J. Frank. Texas and Southwestern lore. 1927. 2.50. S. M. U.
COWPER, WILLIAM, 1731-1800 (821)
Golden, Morris. In search of stability: The poetry of William Cowper. 1960.
    bds. 4.50. Twayne
Hartley, Lodwick. William Cowper. 1960. 5.00. U. of N. C.
Huang, Roderick. William Cowper: Nature poet. 1957. 2.90. Oxford U. P.
Thomas, G. William Cowper and the 18th century. 3.50. Hillary
COZZENS, JAMES GOULD, 1903- (813.5)
Bracher, Frederick G. Novels of James Gould Cozzens. 1959. 5.75. Harcourt
CRACKING PROCESS (665.533)
Enos, John L. Petroleum progress and profits. il. 1962. 9.50. M. I. T.
CRANE, HART, 1899-1932 (811)
Dembo, L. S. Hart Crane's Sanskrit charge: A study of The bridge. 1960.
    2.85. Cornell
Hazo, Samuel. Hart Crane. 2.95. Barnes & Noble
Horton, Philip. Hart Crane: The life of an American poet. 1957. 3.75. Viking
CRANE, STEPHEN, 1871-1900 (813.4)
Ahnebrink, Lars. Beginnings of naturalism in American fiction. 1961. 10.00.
    Russell
Berryman, John. Stephen Crane. 4.00. Sloane
Cady, Edwin. Stephen Crane. 1962. 3.50. Twayne
Colvert, James B. Stephen Crane. il. 1962. 2.95; pap. Barnes & Noble
Hoffman, D. G. Poetry of Stephen Crane. 1957. 5.75. Columbia
Linson, Corwin K. My Stephen Crane. il. 3.50. Syracuse
CRANES (BIRDS) (598.3)
Walkinshaw, Lawrence H. Sandhill cranes. il. 1949. 3.50. Univ. Pub.
CRASHAW, RICHARD, 1613-?1649 (821)
Bennett, Joan. Four metaphysical poets. 1953. 3.00. Cambridge U. P.

Wallerstein, Ruth. Richard Crashaw: A study in style and poetic development. 1959. 4.00. U. of Wis.

CRAYON DRAWING (741.2)
Boylston, Elise R. Creative expression with crayons. 1953. 3.95. Davis Pubns.

CREATION (213)
Garrigou-Lagrange, Reginald. Trinity and God the Creator. 1952. 7.50. Herder
Rimmer, Harry. Modern science and the Genesis record. 1937. 3.00. Eerdmans
Thomas Aquinas, Saint. Creation (On the truth of the Catholic faith. bk. 2) pap. 0.95. Doubleday

CREATION (LITERARY, ARTISTIC, ETC.) (700)
Anderson, Harold H. Creativity and its cultivation. il. 1959. 5.75. Harper
Art Directors Club of New York. Creativity. by Paul Smith. 1958. 6.95. Hastings
Block, Haskell M., and Herman Salinger. Creative vision. 1960. 4.00. Smith, Peter
Cary, Joyce. Art and reality. 1958. 3.50. Harper
Copland, Aaron. Music and imagination. 1952. 2.75. Harvard
Foundation for Research on Human Behavior. Creativity and conformity: A problem for organizations. 1958. pap. 3.00. Foundation for Res. on Human Behavior
Ghiselin, Brewster. Creative process. pap. 0.60. New Am. Lib.
Heywood, Robert B. Works of the mind. 1947. 4.50. U. of Chicago
Le Corbusier. Creation is a patient search. il. 1960. 15.00. Praeger
Lehman, Harvey C. Age and achievement. 1953. 7.50. Am. Philos. Soc.
Lowenfeld, Viktor. Nature of creative activity. 6.50. Humanities
Maritain, Jacques. Creative intuition in art and poetry. il. 1953. 7.50. Pantheon
Sachs, Hanns. Creative unconscious. 1951. 6.00. Sci-Art
Whiting, Charles S. Creative thinking. il. 1958. 3.95. Reinhold

CREATIVE ABILITY (155.3)
Getzels, J. W., and P. W. Jackson. Creativity and intelligence. 1962. 5.95. Wiley
Lowenfeld, Viktor. Creative and mental growth. il. 6.50. Macmillan
McKellar, Peter. Imagination and thinking. 5.00. Basic Books
Reed, E. G. Developing creative talent. 3.50. Vantage
Stein, Morris I., and Shirley J. Heinze. Creativity and the individual. 1960. 10.00. Free Press

CREATIVE ACTIVITIES AND SEAT WORK (371.36)
Batterberry, Hilda, and Phyllis Van Dyke. Trails in kindergarten. 1958. 2.50. Exposition
Batterberry, Hilda, and Phyllis Van Dyke. Wonderland in kindergarten. 1957. 3.00. Exposition
Benson, Kenneth R. Creative crafts for children. 1958. 6.00; text ed. 4.50. Prentice-Hall
Wilt, Miriam E. Creativity in the elementary school. il. 1959. pap. 0.95. Appleton

CREDIT (332.7)
Batchker, Nathan A. Instalment credit computations for yields, charges, rebates and earnings. 1958. 5.00. Bankers
Beckman, Theodore N., and Robert Bartels. Credits and collections in theory and practice. 1955. 7.50. McGraw
Chapman, J. M., and others. Commercial banks and consumer instalment credit. 1940. 3.00. Princeton
Commission on Money and Credit. Money and credit. 1961. 3.95. Prentice-Hall

Credit Research Foundation. Credit management handbook. 1958. 12.00. Irwin
Curtis, Edward T. Credit department organization and operation. il. 1958. pap. 3.75. Am. Management Assn.
Irons, W. H., and D. H. Bellemore. Commercial credit and collection practice. 1957. 7.50. Ronald

Jacoby, N. H., and R. J. Saulnier. Business finance and banking. 1947. 3.50. Princeton

Little, John D. Complete credit and collection litter book. 1953. 5.95. Prentice-Hall

Marshall, Alfred. Money and commerce. 1923. 8.50. Kelley

Murad, Anatol. Private credit and public debt. 1954. 3.75. Pub. Affairs

Nadler, M., and others. Money market and its institutions. 1955. 6.50. Ronald

Prather, Charles L. Money and banking. 1961. 10.00. Irwin

Schwartz, Robert, and Allyn Schiffer. Credit and collection know-how. 1953. 5.00. Fairchild

Ward, W., and H. Harfield. Bank credits and acceptances. 1958. 7.00. Ronald

Weyforth, William O. Federal Reserve Board: A study of federal reserve structure and credit control. 1933. 2.25. Johns Hopkins

CREEDS (238)

Algermissen, Konrad. Christian denominations. 1945. 8.50. Herder

Callahan, Daniel J. Christianity divided: Protestant and Roman Catholic theological issues. 1961. 6.00. Sheed

Forell, George W. Protestant faith. 1960. 7.35. Prentice-Hall

Fuhrmann, Paul T. Introduction to the great creeds of the church. 1960. 3.00. Westminster

Kelly, John N. D. Early Christian creeds. 1960. 11.00. McKay

Mayer, Frederick E. Religious bodies of America. by A. C. Piepkorn. 1961. 8.50. Concordia

Neve, J. L. Churches and sects of Christendom. 1952. 5.00. Augsburg

CRETE (949.98)

Allbaugh, L. G. Crete. 1953. 7.50. Princeton

Willetts, R. F. Cretan cults and festivals. 1962. 8.75. Barnes & Noble

CRETE--ANTIQUITIES (939.18)

Cottrell, Leonard. Bull of Minos. il. 1958. 4.50. Rinehart

Graham, James W. Palaces of Crete. 1962. 7.50. Princeton

Nilsson, M. P. History of Greek religion. by F. J. Fielden. 1949. 4.50. Oxford U. P.

Palmer, Leonard R. Mycenaens and Minoans. il. 1962. 6.00. Knopf

Honour, Alan. Secrets of Minos: Sir Arthur Evans' discoveries at Crete. il. 1961. 3.25. McGraw

CRIME AND CRIMINALS (364)

Alexander, Franz, and Hugo Staub. Criminal, the judge, and the public. 1957. 4.00. Free Press

Barnes, Harry Elmer, and N. K. Teeters. New horizons in criminology. 1959. 7.95. Prentice-Hall

Bell, Josephine. Crime in our time. 1962. 4.50. Abelard

Bloch, Herbert A., and Gilbert Geis. Man, crime, and society: The forms of criminal behavior. 1962. 9.95. Random

Caldwell, R. G. Criminology. 1956. 7.50. Ronald

Cavan, Ruth S. Criminology. il. 1962. 6.75. Crowell

Clinard, Marshall B. Sociology of deviant behavior. 1957. 6.50. Rinehart

Cissler, K. R. Searchlights on delinquency. 1956. 10.00. Int. Univs.

Elliott, Mabel A. Crime in modern society. 1952. 7.50. Harper

Glueck, Sheldon, and Eleanor. After-conduct of discharged offenders. 1945. 1.75. St. Martins

Glueck, Sheldon, and Eleanor. Predicting delinquency and crime. 1959. 6.00. Harvard

Hynd, Alan. Sleuths, slayers, and swindlers: A casebook of crime. 1959. 3.95. Barnes A. S.

Johnston, N., and others. Sociology of punishment and correction. 1962. 6.50. Wiley

McLoughlin, Emmett. Crime and immorality in the Catholic church. 1962. 4.95. Stuart, Lyle

Pezet, A. W., and Bradford Chambers. Greatest crimes of the century. 1954. 2.00. Stravon

Playfair, Giles, and Derrick Sington. Offenders: The case against legal vengeance. 1957. 3.95. S. and S.

Sutherland, Edwin H., and Donald R. Cressey. Principles of criminology. 1960. 9.50. Lippincott

Tappan, Paul W. Crime, justice and correction. 1960. 10.95. McGraw

Tyler, Gus. Organized crime in America. 1962. 7.50. U. of Mich.

Vedder, Clyde B., and others. Criminology: A book of readings. 1963. 6.50. Holt, Rinehart & Winston

Wolfgang, Marvin E., and others. Sociology of crime and delinquency. 1962. 6.75; pap. 4.45. Wiley

CRIME AND CRIMINALS--GT. BRIT. (364)

Laurence, John. History of capital punishment. 5.00. Citadel

Rolph, C. H. Common sense about crime and punishment. 1961. 2.95. Macmillan

CRIME AND CRIMINALS--U.S. (364)

Allsop, Kenneth. Bootleggers and their era. 4.95. Doubleday

Bowen, Walter S., and Harry E. Neal. United States secret service. 1960. 4.95. Chilton

Chessman, Caryl. Cell 2455 - Death Row. 1960. 4.50. Prentice-Hall

Lewis, Jerry D. Crusade against crime. 1961. 4.95. Random

McClellan, John L. Crime without punishment. 1962. 4.95. Meredith

Millspaugh, A. C. Local democracy and crime control. 1936. 2.00. Brookings

Ness, Eliot, and Oscar Fraley. Untouchables. 1957. 3.95. Messner

O'Connor, Richard. Hell's kitchen. 4.95. Lippincott

St. Charles, Alwyn J. Narcotics menace. 3.00. Borden

Sondern, Frederic. Brotherhood of evil, the Mafia. il. 1959. 3.95. Farrar, Straus

Sutherland, Edwin H. Professional thief. 1937. 5.00. U. of Chicago

CRIME AND CRIMINALS--THE WEST (364)

Horan, James D., and Paul Sann. Pictorial history of the wild West. il. 1954. 5.95. Crown

CRIMINAL ANTHROPOLOGY (364.33)

Godwin, George. Criminal man. 1960. 4.00. Braziller

McCord, Joan, and others. Origins of crime. 1959. 6.00. Columbia

Pakenham, Francis A. Causes of crime. 1959. 4.75. Thomas C. C.

Walder, Hans. Drive structure and criminality. by Lipot Szondi. tr. by Marvin W. Webb. il. 1959. 7.50. Thomas C. C.

CRIMINAL INVESTIGATION (364.12)

Barth, Alan. Price of liberty. 4.50. Viking

Bliss, Edward N., Jr. Defense investigation. 1956. 6.50. Thomas, C. C.

Fricke, Charles W., and Kolbrek. Criminal investigation. 1962. 5.00. Legal Bk.

Gardner, Erle Stanley. Court of last resort. 3.50. Sloane

Houts, Marshall. From evidence to proof: A searching analysis of methods to establish fact. il. 1956. 7.50. Thomas C. C.

Jones, Leland V. Scientific investigation and physical evidence. by E. Caroline Gabard. il. 1959. 8.50. Thomas, C. C.

Reik, Theodor. Compulsion to confess. 1959. 7.50. Farrar, Straus

CRIMINAL LAW (343)

Bedford, Sybille. Faces of justice. 1961. 4.50. S. and S.

Devlin, Patrick. Criminal prosecution in England. 1958. 3.50. Yale

Fricke, Charles W. 5,000 criminal definitions, terms and phrases. 1961. 2.50. Legal Bk.

Hall, Jerome. General principles of criminal law. 1947. 8.50. 1960. 9.50. Bobbs

Hall, Jerome. Cases and readings on criminal law and procedure. 1949. 9.00. Bobbs

CRIMINAL LIABILITY (364)

Hoch, Paul H., and Joseph Zubin. Psychiatry and the law. 1955. 6.00. Grune

Roche, Philip Q. Criminal mind. 1958. 5.00. Farrar, Straus
CRIMINAL PSYCHOLOGY (364.34)
Abrahamsen, David. Psychology of crime. 1960. 6.00. Columbia
Lindner, Robert M. Rebel without a cause. 1944. 6.00. Grune
Macdonald, John M. Psychiatry and the criminal. 1957. 5.50. Thomas, C. C.
Sheldon, William H. Varieties of delinquent youth. il. 1949. 10.00. Harper
CRITICISM (801.9)
Arnold, Matthew. Essays in criticism, first series. by Sister Thomas Marion
    Hochter. 1962. 10.00. Univ. Pub.
Beaver, Harold L. American critical essays. 1961. 2.25. Oxford U. P.
Boas, George. Primer for critics. 1937. 2.00. Johns Hopkins
Bowers, Fredson. Textual and literary criticism. 1959. 3.75. Cambridge U. P.
Burke, Kenneth. Philosophy of literary form. 1959. 3.25. Smith, Peter
Coleridge, Samuel Taylor. Bilgraphia literaria. by John Shawcross. 2 vols.
    1907. 4.80. Oxford U. P.
Crane, R. S. Languages of criticism and the structure of poetry. il. 1953. 5.50.
    U. of Toronto
Daiches, David. Critical approaches to literature. 1956. 9.00. Prentice-Hall
D'Alton, J. F. Roman literary theory and criticism. 1962. 10.00. Russell
Dryden, John. Essay of dramatic poesy. by Thomas Arnold. by W. T. Arnold.
    1.00. Oxford U. P.
Dryden, John. Of dramatic poesy, and other critical essays. 2 vols. 1.95 ea.
    Dutton
Eliot, T. S. Sacred wood. 1950. 2.50. Barnes & Noble
Eliot, T. S. Selected essays. 1950. 5.75. Harcourt
Foerster, Norman. American criticism: A study in literary theory from Poe
    to the present day. 1962. 7.50? Russell
Foster, Richard J. New romantics. 1962. 5.75. Indiana
Fry, Christopher, and others. Experience of critics. by Kaye Webb. il. by
    Ronald Searle. 1953. 2.25. Oxford U. P.
Frye, N. Anatomy of criticism. 1957. 6.00. Princeton
Goldberg, Gerald J., and Nancy M. Goldberg. Modern critical spectrum. 1962.
    9.25. Prentice-Hall
Howe, Irving. Modern literary criticism. 1959. 6.50. Beacon
Howells, William Dean. Criticism and fiction, and other essays. by Clara
    Marburg Kirk and Rudolf. 1959. 6.00. N. Y. U.
Hyman, Stanley. Armed vision: A study in the method of modern literary
    criticism. 1955. pap. 1.45. Vintage
Johnson, Samuel. Critical opinions of Samuel Johnson. by Joseph E. Brown.
    1960. 10.00. Russell
Jordan, Elijah. Essays in criticism. 1952. 7.00. U. of Chicago
Lamborn, E. A. G. Rudiments of criticism. 1.40. Oxford U. P.
Lewis, C. S. Experiment in criticism. 1961. 2.95. Cambridge U. P.
Leider, Paul R., and Robert Withington. Art of literary criticism. 1941. 4.00.
    Appleton
McKean, Keith F. Moral measure of literature. 1961. 3.00. Swallow A.
Matthiessen, F. O. Responsibilities of the critic. 1952. 5.00. Oxford U. P.
Moulton, Charles W. Library of literary criticism of English and American
    authors. 8 vols. 10.00 ea. Smith, Peter
Muller, Herbert J. Science and criticism. 1956. 3.00. Braziller
Murry, John M. Problem of style. 1922. pap. 1.25. Oxford U. P.
Peacock, Markham, Jr. Critical opinions of William Wordsworth. 1950. 6.00.
    Johns Hopkins
Pepper, Stephen Coburn. Basis of criticism in the arts. 1945. 3.50. Harvard
Pope, Alexander. Essay on criticism. by J. Churton Collins. 1.00. St. Martins
Richards, Ivor A. Practical criticism. pap. 1.45. Harcourt
Schneider, Elisabeth. Aesthetics of William Hazlitt. 1952. 3.50. U. of Pa.
Schorer, Mark and others. Criticism: The foundations of modern literary
    judgment. 1958. 9.75. Harcourt

Smith, George G. Elizabethan critical essays. 2 vols. 1904. 8.00. Oxford U. P.
Smith, James Harry, and E. W. Parks. Great critics. 1951. 7.25. Norton
Spingarn, J. E. Critical essays of the seventeenth century. 3 vols. 1957. 5.75.
ea; set, 15.00. Indiana
Spingarn, J. E. History of literary criticism in the Renaissance. 1938. 3.50.
Columbia
Stallman, Robert W. Critiques and essays in criticism, 1920-1948. 1949.
7.50. Ronald
Stallman, Robert W. Houses that James built, and other literary studies. 1961.
5.00. Mich. State
Walker, Robert H. Poet and the gilded age. il. 1962. 7.50. U. of Pa.
Wellek, Rene, and Austin Warren. Theory of literature. 1956. pap. 1.65. Harcourt
West, Ray B., Jr. Essays in modern literary criticism. 1952. 9.45. Holt, Rine-
hart & Winston
Winters, Yvor. Function of criticism: Problems and exercises. 1956. 3.00.
Swallow A.
Zola, Emile. Experimental novel, and other essays. in prep. Russell

CRITICISM--ADDRESSES, ESSAYS, LECTURES (801.9)

Dunsany, Lord, and others. Essays in the arts. pap. 0.50. Humphries
Eliot, T. S. Use of poetry and the use of criticism. 1955. 3.00. Barnes &
Noble
Gilbert, Allan H. Principles and practice of criticism: Othello, Merry wives,
Hamlet. 1959. 4.50. Wayne
Read, Herbert. Tenth muse: Essays in criticism. 1959. pap. 2.45. Grove
Shapiro, Karl J. In defense of ignorance. 1960. 4.00. Random

CRITICISM--BIBLIOGRAPHY (801)

Hefling, Helen, and Jesse W. Dyde. Index to contemporary biography and
criticism. 1934. 5.00 net. Faxon (R)

CRITICISM--HISTORY (801.9)

Allen, Gay W., and Harry H. Clark. Literary criticism: Pope to Croce. 1962.
6.50. Wayne
Atkins, John W. H. Literary criticism in antiquity; vol 1. Greek, 3.50; vol. 2
Graeco-Roman, 6.00. Smith, Peter
Campbell, Oscar J., and others. Poetry and criticism of the Romantic movement.
6.50. Appleton
Charvat, William. Origins of American critical thought: 1810-1835. 1961. pap.
1.65. Barnes, A. S.
English Institute. Critical approaches to medieval literature. by Dorothy
Bethurum. 1960. 4.50. Columbia
Gilbert, Allan H. Literary criticism: Plato to Dryden. 1962. 6.50. Wayne
Wayne
Hall, Vernon. Renaissance literary criticism, a study of its social content.
1959. 4.00. Smith, Peter
Hyman, Stanley E. Poetry and criticism: Four revolutions in literary taste.
1961. 4.00. Atheneum
Logan, James V. Wordsworthian criticism: A guide and bibliography. 5.00.
Ohio State
Saintsbury, George. History of criticism and literary taste in Europe. 3 vols.
17.50. Humanities
Schutze, Martin. Academic illusions in the field of letters and the arts. 1933.
7.50. Shoe String
Weinberg, Bernard. History of literary criticism in the Italian Renaissance.
2 vols. 1961. 20.00. U. of Chicago
Wellek, Rene. History of modern criticism. 2 vols. 1955. vol. 1. Later 18th
century. 5.50; vol. 2. Romantic age. 6.50. Yale
Wimsatt, William K., Jr., and Cleanth Brooks. Literary criticism. il. 1957.
9.75. Knopf

CRITICISM--FRANCE (801, 9)
Elledge, Scott, and Donald S. Schier. Continental model: Selected French
  critical essays of the seventeenth century. in English. 7.75. U. of Minn.
Iknayan, Marguerite M. Idea of the novel in France. 6.00. Lounz
Weinberg, Bernard. Critical prefaces of the French Renaissance. 1950. 5.00.
  Northwestern U.
CRITICISM--GT. BRIT. (801.9)
Atkins, John W. H. English literary criticism: 17th and 18th centuries. 1952.
  6.00. Barnes & Noble
Atkins, J. W. H. English literary criticism: The Medieval phase. 3.50. Smith,
  Peter
Decker, Clarnece R. Victorial conscience. 3.00. Twayne
Elledge, Scott. Eighteenth century critical essays. 2 vols. 1961. 12.50 set.
  Cornell
Foerster, Donald M. Fortunes of epic poetry: A study of English and American
  criticism 1750-1950. 1962. 4.95. Catholic U. of Am. Pr.
Holmes, Charles S., and others. Major critics: The development of English
  literary criticism. 1957. 3.00. Knopf
Marks, Emerson. Relativist and absolutist. 1955. 3.50. Rutgers
CRITICISM--ITALY (801.9)
Hathaway, Baxter. Age of criticism: The late Renaissance in Italy. 1962. 7.50.
  Cornell
CRITICISM--RUSSIA (801.9)
Neider, Charles. Mark Twain and the Russians: An exchange of views. 1960.
  pap. 0.50. Hill & Wang
CRITICISM--SWEDEN (801.9)
Anderson, Carl L. Swedish acceptance of American literature. 1956. 5.00.
  U. of Pa.
CRITICISM--U.S. (801.9)
Brooks, Van Wyck. Makers and finders. 5 vols. vol. 1, World of Washington
  Irving; vol. 2, Flowering of New England; vol. 3, Times of Melville and Whitman;
  vol. 4, New England: Indian Summer: vol. 5, Confident years, 1885-1915. 2.95
  ea; boxed. 12.50. Dutton
Brown, Clarence Arthur. Achievement of American criticism. 1954. 8.00.
  Ronald
Foerster, Donald M. Fortunes of epic poetry: A study in English and American
  criticism 1750-1950. 1962. 4.95. Catholic U. of Am. Pr.
Fraiberg, Louis. Psychoanalysis and American literary criticism. 1960. 5.95.
  Wayne
Leary, Lewis. Contemporary literary scholarship. 1958. 5.00. Appleton
McMahon, Helen. Criticism of fiotion. 3.50. Twayne
Miller, Perry. Raven and the whale. 1962. pap. 1.95. Harcourt
O'Connor, William Van. Age of criticism, 1900-1950. 1952. 3.00. Regnery
Oldsey, Bernard S., and Arthur O. Lewis, Jr. Visions and revisions in modern
  American literary criticism. pap. 1.95. Dutton
Pritchard, John Paul. Criticism in America: An account of the development
  of critical techniques from the early period of the republic to the middle years
  of the twentieth century. 1956. 5.00. U. of Okla.
Stovall, Floyd. Development of literary criticism in America. 1955. 4.00. U.
  of N. C.
Van Nostrand, Albert D. Literary criticism in America. 1957. 4.50. Bobbs
CRITICISM, TEXTUAL (801.9)
Dearing, Vinton A. Manual of textual analysis. 1958. 3.75. U. of Calif.
Maas, Paul. Textual criticism. il. 1958. 2.40. Oxford U. P.
CROCE, BENEDETTO, 1866-1952 (928)
Orsini, Gian N. G. Benedetto Croce: Philosopher of art and literary critic.
  1961. 10.00. Southern Ill.

CROMWELL, OLIVER, 1599-1658 (923. 2)
Ashley, M. Cromwell's generals. 1955. 4. 50. St. Martins
Ashley, Maurice. Greatness of Oliver Cromwell. il. 5. 00. Macmillan
Ashley, Maurice. Oliver Cromwell and the rule of the Puritans in England.
    2. 75. Oxford U. P.
Wedgwood, C. V. Oliver Cromwell. il. 1. 95. Macmillan
CROMWELL, THOMAS, EARL OF ESSEX, 1485-1540 (923. 2)
Dickens, Arthur G. Thomas Cromwell and the English Reformation. 1960.
    2. 50. Macmillan
CRONIN, ARCHIBALD JOSEPH, 1896- (928)
Cronin, A. J. Adventures in two worlds. 1956. 6. 00. Little
CROSSES (247. 92)
Troyer, Johannes. Cross as symbol and ornament. il. 1961. 4. 50. Westminster
CROWDS (301.158)
Curry, Jesse E. , and Glen D. King. Race tensions and the police. 1962. 5. 50.
    Thomas, C. C.
Le Bon, Gustave. Crowd: A study of the popular mind. 1925. 1. 75. Macmillan
Rude, George. Crowd in the French Revolution. 1959. 5. 60. Oxford U. P.
Smelser, Neil J. Theory of collective behavior. 6. 50. Free Press
CRUSADES (940. 18)
Atiya, Aziz S. Crusade, commerce and culture. 1962. 6. 00; with Crusade:
    historiography and bibliography. 10. 00. Indiana
Dubois, Pierre. Recovery of the Holy Land. by W. I. Brandt. 1956. 5. 00.
    Columbia
Lamb, Harold. Crusades. il. 1945. 6. 00. Doubleday
Runciman, Steven. History of the Crusades. 3 vols. 9. 50 ea. Cambridge U. P.
CRUSTACEA (565. 3)
Carlisle, D. B. , and Francis Knowles. Endocrine control in crustaceans. 1959.
    3. 75. Cambridge U. P.
Green, J. Biology of crustacea. il. 1961. 5. 75. Quadrangle
Hobbs, H. H. , Jr. Crayfishes of Florida. il. 1942. pap. 2. 50. U. of Fla.
Thimann, K. V. Action of hormones in plants and invertebrates. 1952. 7. 00.
    Academic Press
CRYPTOGAMS (586)
Bower, Frederick O. Primitive land plants. 1959. 10. 00. Hafner
Eames, Arthur. Morphology of vascular plants - lower groups. 1936. 10. 00.
    McGraw
Smith, Gilbert M. Cryptogamic botany. vol. 1. Algae and fungi. 1955. 10. 75;
    vol. 2, Bryophytes and pteridophytes. 1955. 9. 50. McGraw
CRYPTOGRAPHY (652. 8)
Ball, W. W. Rouse. Mathematical recreations and essays. 1960. 3. 95. Mac-
    millan
CRYSTALLOGRAPHY (548)
Arkel, Anton E. van. Molecules and crystals in inorganic chemistry. il. 1957.
    6. 50. Wiley
Azaroff, L. V. Introduction to solids. 1960. 9. 95. McGraw
Buerger, M. J. Elementary crystallography. 1956. 8. 95. Wiley
Dana, E. S. , and Cornelius S. Hurlbut. Minerals and how to study them. 1949.
    6. 50. Wiley
De Jong, W. F.. General crystallography. 6. 00. Freeman
Evans, Robert C. Introduction to crystal chemistry. 5. 50. Cambridge U. P.
Kraus, Edward H. , and Walter F. Hunt. Mineralogy. il. 1959. 9. 25. McGraw
Pauling, Linus. Nature of the chemical bond and the structure of molecules
    and crystals: An introduction to modern structural chemistry. il. 1960. 8. 85.
    Cornell
Wade, Franklin A. , and Richard B. Mattox. Elements of crystallography and
    mineralogy. il. 1960. 7. 50. Harper
Buerger, Martin J. Vector Space: And its application in crystal-structure
    investigation. 1959. 12. 00. Wiley

Buerger, Martin J. Crystal-structure analysis. 1960. 18.50. Wiley
Nye, J. F. Physical properties of crystals. 1957. 8.80. Oxford U. P.

CUBA (972.91)
Barnett, C. R., and others. Cuba. 1962. 8.75. Taplinger
Miller, Warren. 90 miles from home. il. 1961. 3.95. Little

CUBA--FOREIGN RELATIONS--U.S. (972.91)
Phillips, R. Hart. Cuban dilemma. 1962. 4.95. Obolensky
Smith, Robert. United States and Cuba. 5.00. Twayne
Smith, Robert F. What happened in Cuba? 1962. 6.00. Twayne

CUBA--HISTORY (972.91)
Foner, Philip S. History of Cuba and its relation with the United States. vol. 1,
    1492-1845. From the Conquest of Cuba to La Escalera. 3.75. Int. Pubs.
Huberman, Leo, and Paul M. Sweezy. Cuba: Anatomy of a revolution. il. 1960.
    3.50. Monthly Review
Manch, Jorge. Marti, apostle of freedom. il. 1950. 4.50. Devin
Matthews, Herbert L. Cuban story. 4.50. Braziller
Meyer, Karl E., and Tad Szulc. Cuban invasion. 1962. 3.95. Praeger
Rivero, N. Castro's Cuba: An American dilemma. 1962. 4.50. McKay
Taber, Robert. M26; biography of a revolution. 1961. 4.95. Stuart, Lyle

CUBA--POLITICS AND GOVERNMENT (972.91)
Casuso, Theresa. Cuba. 1961. 5.00. Random
Draper, Theodore. Castro's revolution. 1962. 4.50. Praeger
Weyl, Nathaniel. Red star over Cuba. 1960. 4.50. Devin

CUBISM (709.04)
Appolonio, Umbro. Fauves and Cubists. il. 1959. 7.95. Crown
Gray, Christopher. Cubist aesthetic theories. 1953. 4.50. Johns Hopkins
Habasque, Guy. Cubism. 1959. 6.50. (also available at same price with French
    or German text) World Pub.
Picasso, Pablo. Picasso cubism to present. il. collectors ed. 3.95. Abrams
Rosenblum, Robert. Cubism and twentieth century art. il. 1960. 25.00. Abrams

CULTURAL PROPERTY, PROTECTION OF (341)
Hollander, Barnett. International law of art. 1959. 12.50. Hillary

CULTURAL RELATIONS (301.2)
Barghoorn, Frederick C. Soviet cultural offensive. 1960. 7.50. Princeton
Humphrey, Richard A. Education without boundaries. 1959. 1.00. A. C. E.
Oliver, Robert T. Culture and communication. 1962. 6.50. Thomas, C. C.
Redfield, Robert. Human nature and the study of society. by Margaret P.
    Redfield. 1962. 10.00. U. of Chicago
Rose, Peter I. Race and culture contacts in the United States. 6.00. Random
Seward, Georgene H. Clinical studies in culture conflict. il. 1958. 8.00. Ronald
Snyder, Harold E. When peoples speak to peoples. 1953. 3.00. A. C. E.

CULTURE (301.2)
Arnold, Matthew. Culture and anarchy. 1932. 2.75; pap. 1.45. Cambridge U. P.
Ashley Montagu, M. F. Cultured man. 3.95. World Pub.
Bagby, Philip. Culture and history. Prolegomena to the comparative study of
    civilizations. 1960. 5.00. U. of Calif.
Cowell, Frank R. Culture in private and public life. 1959. 6.50. Praeger
Eliot, T. S. Christianity and culture. 1940. pap. 1.95. Harcourt
Eliot, T. S. Notes towards the definition of culture. 3.00. Harcourt
Huxley, Aldous. Brave new world revisited. 1958. 3.50. Harper
Kroeber, Alfred L. Nature of culture. il. 1952. 10.00. U. of Chicago
Leavis, F. R. Culture and environment. 2.00. Hillary
Linton, Ralph. Cultural background of personality. 1945. pap. 1.95. Appleton
Malinowski, Bronislaw. Scientific theory of culture. 1944. 3.00. U. of N. C.
Mannheim, Karl. Essays on the sociology of culture. by Ernest Manheim, and
    Paul Kecskemeti. 1956. 5.60. Oxford U. P.
Niebuhr, H. Richard. Christ and culture. 1956. pap. 1.65. Harper
Pieper, Josef. Leisure, the basis of culture. 1952. 3.00. Pantheon

Robertson, S. Crafts and culture in the world today. 3.50. Int. Doc. Service-Columbia

Sapir, Edward. Selected writings of Edward Sapir in language, culture, and personality. by David G. Mandelbaum. 1951. 6.50. U. of Calif.

Shapiro, Harry L. Aspects of culture. 1957. 2.75. Rutgers

Sorokin, P. A. Crisis of our age: The social and cultural outlook. il. 5.00. 1.55. Dutton

Sorokin, Pitirim A. Society, culture and personality. 5.50. Cooper

Steward, Julian H. Theory of culture change. 1955. 4.00. U. of Ill.

Tillich, Paul. Theology of culture. by Robert C. Kimball. 1959. 4.00. Oxford U. P.

CULTURE CONFLICT (301.23)

Stonequist, Everett V. Marginal man: A study in personality and culture conflict. 1962. 6.50. Russell

CUMMINGS, EDWARD ESTLIN, 1894-1962 (811)

Baum, S. V., EETI: e e c. E. E. Cummings and the critics. 1961. 7.50. Mich. State

Friedman, Norman. E. E. Cummings: The art of his poetry. 1960. 4.00. Johns Hopkins

Norman, Charles. Magic-maker: E. E. Cummings. 1959. 5.95. Macmillan

CUNEIFORM INSCRIPTIONS (490)

Burrows, Eric R. Archaic texts. 1935. 10.00. U. Museum

Chiera, Edward. They wrote on clay: The babylonian tablets speak today. il. by George G. Cameron. 1938. 5.00; 1955. U. of Chicago

Clay, A. T. Documents from the temple archives of Nippur dated in the reigns of Cassite rulers. 3 pts. 1906-12. 10.00. U. Museum

CURIE, MARIE (MME. PIERRE CURIE), 1867-1934 (925)

Curie, Eve. Madame Curie. il. 1949. 5.00. Doubleday

Thorne, Alice D. Story of Madame Curie. il. 1959. 1.95. Grosset

CURIOSITIES (030)

McWhirter, Norris D. Book of world records. il. 1959. 3.50. Sterling

CURRENCY QUESTION (332.9)

Aschheim, Joseph. Techniques of monetary control. 4.50. Johns Hopkins

Halm, George N. International monetary cooperation. 1945. 1.30. U. of N. C.

Hansen, A. H. Monetary theory and fiscal policy. 1949. 5.95. McGraw

Kurihara, Kenneth K. Monetary theory and public policy. 1950. 5.50. Norton

Lindholm, Richard W., and others. Principles of money and banking related to national income and fiscal policy. 1954. 6.50. Norton

Mellon, Helen. Credit control. 1941. 2.00. Pub. Affairs

Schneider, Erich, Money, income, and employment. tr. by Kurt Klappholz. il. 1962. 6.00. Macmillan

Smith, Lawrence. Money, credit, and public policy. il. 1959. 7.25. Houghton

Soddy, Frederick. Wealth, virtual wealth and debt. il. 4.50. Omni

Thomas, Rollin G. Our modern banking and monetary system. 1957. 9.35. 7.00. Prentice-Hall

Triffin, Robert. Gold and the dollar crisis: The future of convertibility. il. 1961. 5.00. Yale

CURRENCY QUESTION--U.S. (332.9)

American Assembly. United States monetary policy. il. by Neil Jacoby. 1959. 2.00. Am. Assembly.

Bell, James W., and Walter E. Spahr. Proper monetary and banking system for the United States. 1960. 6.00. Ronald

Blum, John M. From the diaries of Henry Morgenthau, Jr. il. 1959. 7.50. Houghton

Dwinell, Olive Cushing. Story of our money. 1945. 3.00. Forum

Fisher, Irving. Mastering the crisis. 3.50. Franklin, B.

Hanks, J. Whitney, and Roland Stucki. Money, banking, and national income. 1956. 6.00. Knopf

Harris, Seymour E. Dollar in cirsis. 1962. 4.95. Harcourt
Kreps, Clifton H., Jr. Money, banking, and monetary policy. 1962. 7.50. Ronald
McCaleb, Walter F. How much is a $. 1959. 2.00. Naylor
Vennard, Wickliffe B., Sr. Federal Reserve hoax. 1955. 2.00. Forum
Welch, Edgar B. Progress and a new system. 1960. 3.00. Forum
CURRENT EVENTS (375)
Kimball, R. S. Current events instruction. 4.50. Houghton
CURRIER AND IVES (769)
Conningham, Frederic A. Currier and Ives prints. il. 10.00. Crown
CURVES (513)
Baker, Henry F. Analytical principles of the theory of curves. 6.50. Ungar
Hilbert, David, and Stephen Cohn-Vossen. Geometry and the imagination. 1952.
    6.00. Chelsea
Salmon, G. Higher plane curves. 4.95. Chelsea
CURVES, ALGEBRAIC (512)
Primrose, E. J. Plane algebraic curves. 1955. 3.00. St. Martins
CURVES, PLANE (513.1)
Yates, Robert C. Handbook on curves and their properites. 1959. 4.00. Edwards
CUSHING, HARVEY WILLIAMS, 1869-1939 (925)
Thomson, Elizabeth. Harvey Cushing: Surgeon, author, artist. il. 1950. 4.00.
    Abelard
CUSTER, GEORGE ARMSTRONG, 1839-1876 (923.9)
Brininstool, Earl A. Troopers with Custer. 1952. 5.00. Stackpole
Custer, Elizabeth B. Boots and saddles; or Life in Dakota with General Custer.
    il. 1961. 2.00. U. of Okla.
Harpers Weekly. Massacre of General Custer and his men, Montana, 1876. by
    the Editors of Harpers Weekly. 1959. 3.95. Bloch & Co.
Monaghan, Jay. Custer: The life of General George Armstrong Custer. il. 1959.
    6.00. Little
CUSTOMS ADMINISTRATION (336.262)
Elliott, G. A. Tariff procedures and trade barriers. 1955. 5.95. U. of Toronto
CYBERNETICS (006)
Ashby, W. Introduction to cybernetics. 1956. 6.95. Wiley
George, Frank H. Brain as a computer. il. 1962. 9.00? Addison-Wesley
Greniewski, H. Cybernetics without mathematics. 1960. 6.00. Pergamon
Guilbaud, G. T. What is cybernetics? il. 1959. 3.50. Criterion
Hook, Sidney. Dimensions of mind. 1960. 5.00. N. Y. U.
Neumann, John von. Computer and the brain. 1958. 4.00. Yale
Pask, Gordon. Approach to cybernetics. il. 1962. 2.50. Harper
Scientific American. Automatic control. by the Editors of Scientific American.
    1956. 1.45. S. and S.
Taube, Mortimer. Computers and common sense. 1961. 3.75. Columbia
Weiner, Norbert. Human use of human beings. 1950. 3.50. Houghton
CYCADACEAE (585.9)
Desikachary, T. V. Cyanophyta. 1959. 15.00. Academic Press
CYCLING (796.6)
Frankel, Lillian, and Godfrey. 101 things to do with a bike. 2.50. Sterling
CYPRUS (956.45)
Durrell, Lawrence. Bitter lemons. 3.75; 1959. Dutton
Home, Gordon C. Cyprus then and now. il. 1960. 5.25. Int. Pub. Service
CYRANO DE BERGERAC, SAVINIEN, 1619-1655 - DRAMA (842)
Rostand, Edmond. Cyrano de Bergerac. tr. by Brian Hooker. 1951. 3.95. Holt,
    Rinehart & Winston
CYRUS, THE GREAT, KING OF PERSIA d. B.C. 529 (923)
Lamb, Harold. Cyrus the Great. 1960. 4.50. Doubleday
CYRUS, THE YOUNGER, d 401 B.C. (923)
Xenophon. Anabasis by W. Welch, and C. G. Duffield. 1.50. St. Martins
Xenophon. March up country. tr. by W. H. D. Rouse. 1958. 3.95. U. of Mich.

CYTOGENETICS (574.87)
Elliott, Fred C. Plant breeding and cytogenetics. il. 1958. 9.50. McGraw
Raven, Christian P. Oogenesis: The storage of developmental information. il. 1962. 8.50. Pergamon
Sager, Ruth, and Francis J. Ryan. Cell heredity. 1961. 7.50. Wiley
Swanson, Carl P. Cytology and cytogenetics. 1957. 13.35. Prentice-Hall

CYTOLOGY (574.87)
Allen, John M. Molecular control of cellular activity. il. 1962. 10.50. McGraw
Baker, John B. Cytological technique. 1960. 2.90. Wiley
Bourne, Geoffrey, H. Cytology and cell physiology. il. 1951. 9.60. Oxford U. P.
Brachet, Jean, and A. E. Mirsky. Cell: Morphology, physiology, biochemistry. 3 vols. 8.00 ea. Academic Press (R)
Chambers, Robert, and Edward. Explorations into the nature of the living cell. 1961. 8.00. Harvard
Chayen, J. Modern research in plant cytology. 8.00. Academic Press
Frey-Wyssling, A. Macromolecules in cell structure. 1958. 5.00. Harvard
Giese, Arthur C. Cell physiology. il. 10.00. Saunders
Hoffman, Joseph G. Life and death of cells. il. 1957. pap. 0.95. Doubleday
Hughes, Arthur. History of cytology. il. 1959. 5.00. Abelard
Kasdon, S. Charles, and Sophia B. Bamford. Atlas of in situ cytology. 1961. 17.50. Little
Langley, L. L. Cell function. 1961. 7.50. Reinhold
Mellors, Robert C. Analytical cytology. 1959. 17.50. McGraw
Picken, Laurence E. R. Organization of cells and other organisms. il. 1960. 13.45. Oxford U. P.
Ramsay, James A., and V. B. Wigglesworth. Cell and the organism. 1961. 9.50. Cambridge U. P.
Robertis, E. D. P. de, and others. General cytology. il. 1960. 10.00. Saunders
Society for Endocrinology. Cell mechanisms in hormone production and action. by C. R. Austin and P. C. Williams. 7.50. Cambridge U. P.
Walker, P. M. B. New approaches in cell biology. 1960. 6.00. Academic Press

CZECHOSLOVAK REPUBLIC--HISTORY (943.7)
Glaser, Kurt. Czecho-Slovakia: A critical history. il. 1961. 5.50. Caxton
Kerner, Robert Joseph. Czechoslovakia. il. 1945. 5.00. U. of Calif.

D

DDT (INSECTICIDE) (632.954)
West, T. F., and G. A. Campbell. DDT and newer persistent insecticides. 1952. 8.50. Tudor

DADAISM (759.06)
Motherwell, Robert B. Dada painters and poets. il. 1951. 15.00. Wittenborn
Verkauf, Willy. Dada: Monograph of a movement. bilingual, in English and German. il. 1961. 6.95. Hastings

DAIRY CATTLE (637.12)
Davis, Richard F. Modern dairy cattle management. 1962. 7.00. Prentice-Hall
Eckles, Clarence H., and others. Dairy cattle and milk production. by Ernest L. Anthony. il. 6.75. Macmillan
Eckles, Clarence Henry, and others. Milk and milk products. il. 1951. 7.95. McGraw
Gilmore, Lester D. Dairy cattle breeding. il. 1952. 7.95. Lippincott
Hammer, Bernard W., and F. J. Babel. Dairy bacteriology. 1957. 9.50. Wiley

Harrison, E. S. Judging dairy cattle. 1940. 5.95. Wiley'
Henderson, H. O., and P. M. Reaves. Dairy cattle feeding and management. 1954. 6.75. Wiley

Whittier, Earle O., and B. H. Webb. Byproducts from milk. 1950. 6.00. Reinhold
Yapp, William W. Dairy cattle judging and selection. 1959. 5.95. Wiley
Yapp, William W., and W. B. Nevens. Dairy cattle: Selection, feeding and
    management. 1955. 4.75. Wiley
DALI, SALVADOR, 1904- (927)
Cowles, Fleur, Case of Salvador Dali. il. 1959. 6.50. Little
Morse, A. Reynolds, and Michel Tapie. Dali: A study of his life and work. il.
    1958. bds. 15.00. N. Y. Graphic
DAMS (627.8)
Cullen, Allen H. Rivers in harness: The story of dams. 1962. 3.95. Chilton
DANCE MUSIC (781.55)
Fox, Grace I., and K. G. Merrill. Folk dancing. 1957. 4.50. Ronald
Gilbert, Pia, and Aileene Lockhart. Music for the modern dance. 1960. 4.50.
    Brown, W. C.
Knorr, Frederick, and Lloyd Shaw. Cowboy dance tunes. 1939. Caxton
Ryan, G. L. Dances of our pioneers. 1939. 4.00. Ronald
DANCERS (927)
DeMille, Agnes. Dance to the piper. il. 1952. 5.50. Little
DeMille, Agnes. Promenade home. il. 1958. 5.50. Little
DANCING (793.3)
Gilbert, Pia, and Aileene Lochart. Music for the modern dance. il. 1960. 4.50.
    Brown W. C.
H'Doubler, Margaret. Dance: A creative art experience. il. 1959. pap. 1.25. U.
    of Wis.
La Salle, D. Rhythms and dances for elementary schools. 1951. 5.00. Ronald
National Education Association, American Association for Health, Physical
    Education and Recreation. Focus on dance. 1960. 2.00. N. E. A.
Pierre. Latin and American dances for students and teachers. 5.00. Soccer
    Assoc.
Rogers, Frederick R. Dance: A basic educational technique. il. 1941. 6.75.
    Macmillan
Sachs, Curt. Commonwealth of art. il. 1946. 7.95. Norton
Sachs, Curt. World history of the dance. il. 1957. 7.50. Norton
Seldes, Gilbert. Seven lively arts. 1957. 4.95. Sagamore
Turner, Margery J. Modern dance for high school and college. 1957. 4.25.
    Prentice-Hall
Terry, Walter. Dance in America. il. 1956. 4.00. Harper
DANTE ALIGHIERI, 1265-1321 (851.15)
Auerbach, Erich. Dante, poet of the secular world. tr. by Ralph Manheim.
    1961. 5.00. U. of Chicago
Barbi, Michele. Life of Dante. tr. by Paul Ruggiers. 3.25. Smith, Peter
D'Entreves, A. P. Dante as a political thinker. 1952. 2.40. Oxford U. P.
Dunbar, H. Flanders. Symbolism in medieval thought. 1960. 12.50. Russell
Mazzeo, Joseph A. Medieval cultural tradition in Dante's Comedy. 1960. 4.50.
    Cornell
Mazzeo, Joseph A. Structure and thought in the Paradiso. 1958. 4.50. Cornell
Santayana, George. Three philosophical poets. 1953. pap. 0.95. Doubleday
Vittorini, Domenico. Age of Dante. il. 1957. 6.00. Syracuse
Vossler, Karl. Mediaval culture: An introduction to Dante and his times. 2
    vols. 1958. 9.00. Ungar
Williams, Charles. Figure of Beatrice: A study in Dante. 3.95. Farrar, Straus
DARIUS I, 521 B. C. - 486 B. C. (930)
Rowley, Harold Henry. Darius the Mede. 1959. 5.00. Allenson
Whitcomb, John C. Darius the Mede. 1949. 2.75. Eerdmans
DARROW, CLARENCE SEWARD, 1857-1938 (923.4)
Darrow, Clarence. Story of my life. 1957. pap. 1.95. Grosset
Ravitz, Abe C. Clarence Darrow and the American literary tradition. 1962. 4.50.
    Western Reserve

Stone, Irving. Clarence Darrow for the defense. il. 1949. 5.00. Doubleday

DARWIN, CHARLES ROBERT, 1809-1882 (925)

Barnett, Samuel A. Century of Darwin. il. 1958. 5.75. Harvard

Barzun, Jacques. Darwin, Marx, Wagner: Critique of a heritage. 3.00. Smith, Peter

Darwin, Charles R. Autobiography. by Nora Barlow. il. 1959. 4.50. Harcourt

Ellegard, Alvar. Darwin and the general reader. 1958. 7.75. Humanities

Huxley, Julian S., and others. Book that shook the world. 1958. pap. 1.50. U. of Pittsburgh

Irvine, William. Apes, angels, and Victorians. pap. 1.55. Meridian

Keith, A. Darwin revalued. 5.00. Humanities

DATING (SOCIAL CUSTOMS) (392.4)

Datebook. Datebook's complete guide to dating. by Art Unger. il. 1961. bds. 3.95. Prentice-Hall

Jackson, Joyce. Joyce Jackson's guide to dating. 1955. 3.95. Prentice-Hall

DAVID, KING OF ISRAEL (922)

Maclaren, Alexander. Life of David as reflected in his psalms. 1955. 2.75. Baker Bk.

Meyer, F. B. David. 2.50. Christian Lit. Crusade

Slaughter, Frank G. David, warrior and king. 1962. 5.95. World Pub.

DAVIS, JEFFERSON, 1808-1889 (923.2)

Patrick, Rembert W. Jefferson Davis and his cabinet. 1961. 6.00. La. State

Strode, Hudson. Jefferson Davis: American Patriot, 1808-1861. il. 1955. 6.75. Harcourt

Strode, Hudson. Jefferson Davis: Confederate president. 1959. 6.75. Harcourt

DAVY, SIR HUMPHREY, BART., 1778-1829 (925)

Cartwright, F. F. English pioneers of anesthesia. il. 1952. 4.50. Williams & Wilkins

Kendall, James. Humphry Davy. 3.00. Roy Pub.

DAY NURSERIES (362.71)

Allen, Winifred Y., and Doris Campbell. Creative nursery center. 1948. 2.00. Family Service Assn.

Beer, Ethel S. Working mothers and the day nursery. 1957. 3.50. Whiteside

DAYLIGHT (525.35)

Walsh, John W. T. Science of daylight. il. 1961. 7.75. Pitman

DEAD SEA SCROLLS (221.4)

Allegro, John M. Dead Sea scrolls, and Origins of Christianity. 1957. 4.50. Criterion

Allegro, John M. People of the Dead Sea Scrolls. 1958. 5.00. Doubleday

Bruce, F. F. Second thoughts on the Dead Sea Scrolls. 1961. 3.00. Eerdmans

Burrows, Millar. Dead sea scrolls. il. 1955. 6.50. Viking

Burrows, Millar. More light on the Dead Sea Scrolls: New Scrolls and new interpretations. 1958. 6.50. Viking

Schonfield, Hugh J. Secrets of the Dead Sea scrolls. 1957. pap. 1.45. Barnes, A. S.

Schubert, Kurt. Dead Sea Community. 1959. 3.75. Harper

Wilson, Edmund. Scrolls from the Dead Sea. 1955. 3.50. Oxford U. P.

DEAF--EDUCATION (371.912)

Bender, Ruth E. Conquest of deafness. il. 1960. 6.00. Western Reserve

Ewing, Irene R., and Alex W. G. New opportunities for deaf children. il. 4.95. Thomas, C. C.

Fiedler, M. F. Deaf children in a hearing world. 1952. 5.50. Ronald

Lack, Agnes. Teaching of language to deaf children. 1955. 3.40. Oxford U. P.

National Education Association, Council for Exceptional Children. Children with impaired hearing: Administration of special education in small school systems. 1960. 2.00. N. E. A.

Morkovin, Boris V. Through the barriers of deaf and dumb. 1960. 4.50. Macmillan

<u>DEAFNESS</u> (617.89)
Davis, Hallowell. Hearing and deafness: A guide for layman. il. 1957. 7.50.
  Holt, Rinehart & Winston
Levine, Edna S. Psychology of deafness. 1960. 7.50. Columbia
<u>DEATH</u> (236.1)
Covey, Cyclone. American pilgrimage, the roots of American history, religion
  and culture. 3.00. Smith, Peter
Feifel, Herman. Meaning of death. il. 1959. 6.95. McGraw
Freud, Sigmund. Civilization, war, death. 2.00. Hillary
Hocking, William Ernest. Meaning of immortality in human experience. 1957.
  3.50. Harper
<u>DEBATES AND DEBATING</u> (808.53)
Baird, A. Craig. Argumentation, discussion and debate. 1950. 5.95. McGraw
Behl, W. A. Discussion and debate. 1953. 4.50. Ronald
Bogardus, Emory. Democracy by discussion. 1942. 1.00. Pub. Affairs
Braden, Waldo W., and Earnest S. Brandneburg. Oral decision-making; Prin-
  ciples of discussion and debate. 1955. 5.50. Harper
Clark, Glenn. World's greatest debate. 3.50. Macalester
Ehninger, Douglas, and Wayne Brockriede. Decision by debate. 5.50. Dodd
Ewbank, Henry L., and J. Jeffrey Auer. Discussion and debate. 1951. 4.50.
  Appleton
Foster, William T. Argumentation and debating. 1917. 5.00. Houghton
Freeley, Austin J. Argumentation and debate: Rational decision making. 1961.
  6.50. Wadsworth
Garland, J. V. Discussion methods: Explained and illustrated. 1951. 3.00.
  Wilson
Gulley, Halbert E. Essentials of discussion and debate. 1955. pap. 2.00. Holt,
  Rinehart & Winston
Huber, R. Argumentation. 1962. 4.75. McKay
McBurney, James H., and Kenneth G. Hance. Discussion in human affairs.
  1950. 4.50. Harper
McBurney, James R., and others. Argumentation and debate. 4.75. Macmillan
Musgrave, George M. Competitive debate, rules and techniques. 1957. 2.50.
  Wilson
Potter, David. Argumentation and debate. 1954. 5.50. Holt, Rinehart & Winston
Reference shelf. Sold on subscription basis. H. W. Wilson (R)
Shepard, David W., and Paul H. Cashman. Handbook for beginning debaters.
  1961. spiral bdg. 2.00. Burgess
<u>DEBS, EUGENE VICTOR, 1855-1926</u> (923.2)
Ginger, Ray. Eugene V. Debs. pap. 1.50. Collier
Morgan, H. Wayne. Eugene V. Debs. Socialist for president. il. 1962. 5.75.
  Syracuse
<u>DEBT</u> (336.34)
Cooke, Helen J. Role of debt in the national economy. 1961. 3.25. Pub. Affairs
Abbott, Charles Cortez. Federal debt: Structure and impact. 1953. 4.00.
  Twentieth Century
Buchanan, James M. Public principles of public debt. 1958. 5.00; text ed. 5.00.
  Irwin
Castetter, William B. Public school debt administration. 1957. 5.00. U. of Pa.
Copeland, Morris I. Trends in government financing. 1961. 5.00. Princeton
Hamilton, Alexander. Papers on public credit, commerce and finance. 1957.
  3.50. pap. 1.45. Bobbs
Kuczynski, Robert R. Bankers' profits from German loans. 1932. 1.75.
  Brookings
Murad, Anatol. Private credit and public debt. 1954. 3.75. Pub. Affairs
<u>DEBUSSY, CLAUDE, 1862-1918</u> (927)
Dumesnil, Maurice. Claude Debussy: Master of dreams. 1940. 3.50. Washburn
Shera, Frank H. Debussy and Ravel. 1925. 0.60. Oxford U. P.

DECENTRALIZATION IN GOVERNMENT (351)
Baum, Bernard H. Decentralization of authority in a bureaucracy. il. 1961.
4.50. Prentice-Hall
Metcalf, E. S. Esau's children. 1960. 3.00. Augustana
DECISION-MAKING (159.1)
Ackoff, Russell L. Scientific method: Optimizing applied research decisions.
1962. 9.50. Wiley
Blake, R. R., and J. S. Mouton. Group dynamics: Key to decision making. il.
1961. 3.50. Gulf
Cooper, Joseph D. Art of decision making. 4.95. Doubleday
Melman, Seymour. Decision making and productivity. il. 1959. 7.00. Wiley
Vroom, Victor H. Some personality determinants of the effects of participation.
il. 1960. 4.50. Prentice-Hall
DECORATION AND ORNAMENT (745)
Coffey, Ernestine S., and Dorothy F. Minton. Leader's guide to nature and
garden fun. 2.75. Hearthside
Meyer, Franz S. Handbook of ornament. il. 1957. pap. 2.25. Dover
Palestrant, S. Hand decorating projects 3.95. Wehman
Priolo, Joan B. Designs--and how to use them. il. 1956. 5.95. Sterling
Waugh, Dorothy. Festive decoration the year around. il. 1962. 3.95. Macmillan
Whiton, Sherrill. Elements of interior design and decoration. il. 1957. 10.50;
text ed. 7.95. Lippincott
Irwin, John, and Mme. Pupul Jayaker. Textiles and ornaments of India. by
Monroe Wheeler. 4.00. Mus. of Mod. Art
Lee, Sherman E. Japanese decorative style. il. 1961. 9.50. Abrams
Strange, T. A. English furniture, decoration, woodwork and allied arts. il.
1950. 15.00. Museum Bks.
Detroit Institute of Arts. Decorative arts of the Italian Renaissance, 1400-
1600. il. 1959. 4.00. Detroit Inst. or Wayne
Sitwell, Sacheverell. British architects and craftsmen. il. 1948. 5.25. British
Bk.
Brazer, Esther S. Early American decoration. il. 16.50. Pond-Ekberg
Christensen, Erwin O. Early American designs: Ceramics. 1952. 1.00. Pitman
Cramer, Edith. Handbook of early American decoration. 3.95. Branford
Hallett, C. Furniture decoration made easy. 1952. 5.95. Branford
Lipman, Jean. American folk decoration. 1952. 12.50. Oxford U. P.
Sabine, Ellen S. American folk art. il. 1958. 6.95. Van Nostrand
Pain, William, and James. Decorative details. il. 2.25. Transatlantic
Bossert, Helmuth T. Folk art of primitive peoples. il. 1956. 12.50. Praeger
DEER (599.735)
Rue, Leonard Lee, III. World of the white-tailed deer. il. 1962. 4.95. Lippincott
Taylor, Walter P. Deer of North America. il. 1956. 12.50. Stackpole
DEER HUNTING (799.277)
Anderson, L. A. How to hunt deer and small game. 1959. 3.50. Ronald
DEFENSE (CRIMINAL PROCEDURE) (343.1)
Beaney, William M. Right to counsel in American courts. 1955. 4.50. U. of
Mich.
DEFICIENCY DISEASES (616.39)
American Public Health Association. Control of malnutrition in man. 1960. 1.50.
Am. Public Health
Follis, Richard H., Jr. Deficiency disease. il. 1958. 14.75. Thomas C. C.
Goldsmith, Grace A. Nutritional diagnosis. il. 1959. 5.50. Thomas C. C.
DEFICIENCY DISEASES IN PLANTS (581.21)
Gilbert, Frank A. Mineral nutrition and the balance of life. il. 1957. 5.95. U.
of Okla.
Gilbert, Frank A. Mineral nutrition of plants and animals. il. 1953. 2.75. U.
of Okla.
Wallace, T. Diagnosis of mineral deficiencies in plants. 1961. 14.50. Tudor

DEFOE, DANIEL, 1661?-1731 (823)
Moore, John R. Daniel Defoe. 1958. 7.50. U. of Chicago
Watt, Ian. Rise of the novel: Studies in Defoe, Richardson, and Fielding. 1957.
  pap. 1.95. U. of Calif.
DEFORMATIONS (MECHANICS) (620.11)
Planck, Max. Mechanics of deformable bodies. 6.25. Macmillan
Sommerfeld, Arnold. Mechanics of deformable bodies. 7.50. Academic Press
DEFORMITIES (611.012)
Association for the Aid of Crippled Children. Prematurity, congenital mal-
  formation and birth injury. by L. Emmett Holt, Jr., and Others. il. 1953.
  4.00. Williams & Wilkins
Ciba Foundation. Congenital malformations. 1960. 9.00. Little
Gordon, Gavin C. Congenital deformities. 1960. 8.50. Williams & Wilkins
DEGAS, HILAIRE GERMAIN EDGAR, 1834-1917 (759.4)
Browse, Lillian. Degas dancers. il. 15.00. Boston Bk.
Degas, Hilaire. Degas. by Daniel Catton Rich. il. 1951. 15.00. Abrams
Degas, Hilaire. Women as seen by Degas. il. collectors ed. 3.95. Abrams
Fosca, Francois. Degas. il. 1954. 5.75. World Pub.
DEISM (211.5)
Aldridge, Alfred O. Shaftesbury and the Deist manifesto: 1951. 1.50. Am. Philos.
  Soc.
Morais, Herbert M. Deism in eighteenth century America. 1943. 5.00. Russell
DE KOONING, WILLEM, 1904- (759.13)
Hess, Thomas B. Willem de Kooning. il. 1959. 4.95. Braziller
DE LA MARE, WALTER JOHN, 1873- (927)
Sackville-West, V. Walter de la Mare, and The traveller. 1953. 0.85. Oxford
  U. P.
DELEGATION OF POWERS (321.8)
Macmahon, Arthur W. Delegation and autonomy. 1962. 3.75. Taplinger
DELINQUENTS (364.2)
Clinard, Marshall B. Sociology of deviant behavior. 1957. 6.50. Rinehart
Healy, William, and A. Bronner. New light on delinquency and its treatment.
  1936. 3.50. Yale
Lemert, Edwin M. Social pathology. il. 1951. 6.95. McGraw
McCord, W., and J. Psychopathy and delinquency. 1956. 6.75. Grune
Wootton, Barbara, and others. Social science and social pathology. 1959. 6.00.
  Macmillan
DELPHIAN ORACLE (292.32)
Parke, Herbert W., and D. E. W. Wormell. Delphic Oracle. 2 vols. vol. 1,
  History. vol. 2, Oracular responses. 17.50. Humanities
DELSARTE SYSTEM
Delsarte, F. Delsarte system of expression. by G. Stebbins. 4.50. Wehman
DEMOCRACY (321.4)
Agard, Walter R. What democracy meant to the Greeks. 1960. pap. 1.75. U. of
  Wis.
Babbitt, Irving. Democracy and leadership. 1924. 3.50. Houghton
Becker, Carl L. Modern democracy. 1941. 3.50. Yale
Blaich, T. P., and J. C. Baumgartner. Challenge of democracy. 1960. 5.96;
  McGraw
Bowers, Claude G. Jefferson and Hamilton. il. 1929. 7.50; sold with Young
  Jefferson, and Jefferson in power, 3 vols. 21.00. Houghton
Brady, R. A. Business as a system of power. 1943. 3.75. Columbia
Buchanan, James M., and Gordon Tullock. Calculus of consent: Logical foun-
  dations of constitutional democracy. 1962. 6.95. U. of Mich.
Cahn, Edmond. Predicament of democratic man. 1961. 3.95. Macmillan
Cassinelli, C. W. Politics of freedom: An analysis of the modern democratic
  state. 1961. 4.75. U. of Wash.
Coker, Francis W. Recent political thought. 1934. 5.50. Appleton
Colegrove, Kenneth. Democracy versus communism. il. 1961. 5.75. Van Nostrand

Coleman, P. Evans. Challenge of democracy inside and outside the U.S.A. 3.00. Pageant

Commager, Henry Steele. Majority rule and minority rights. 2.50. Smith, Peter

Curti, Merle E. Making of an American community. 1959. 8.50. Stanford

Dahl, Robert A. Preface to democratic theory. 1956. 3.50. U. of Chicago

Dewey, John. Public and its problems. 1957. 2.50. Swallow, A.

Donald, David H. Excess of democracy: The American Civil War and the social process. 1960. pap. 0.60. Oxford U. P.

Emden, Cecil S. People and the Constitution. 1956. 7.20. Oxford U. P.

Faulkner, Harold V., and others. History of the American way. il. 1950. 4.80. McGraw

Fromm, Erich. Escape from freedom. 3.75. 1941. Rinehart

Gabriel, Ralph H. Course of American democratic thought. 1956. 6.50. Ronald

Gooch, G. P. English democratic ideas in the 17th century. 1955. 3.50. Cambridge U. P.

Hallowell, John H. Moral foundation of democracy. 1954. 3.50. U. of Chicago

Hook, Sidney. Political power and personal freedom. 1959. 7.50. Criterion

Hook, Sidney. Reason, social myths and democracy. 4.00. Humanities

Ketchum, Richard M. What is democracy? il. 1955. 3.95. Dutton

Kornhauser, William. Politics of mass society. 1959. 5.00. Free Press

Lerner, Max. Democracy in America. 5.00. Collier

Lindsay, Alexander D. Modern democratic state. 1st American ed. 1947. 3.25. Oxford U. P.

Lippmann, Walter. Public philosophy. 1955. 4.00. Little

McCutchen, Samuel P., and others. Goals of democracy: A problems approach. il. 5.32. Macmillan

McGuire, Edna, and Don C. Rogers. Growth of democracy. il. 1941. 3.72. Macmillan

Mannheim, Karl. Freedom, power and democratic planning. 1950. 6.50. Oxford U. P.

Maritain, Jacques. Man and the state. 1951. 4.00. U. of Chicago

Mayo, Henry B. Introduction to democratic theory. 1960. 6.50. Oxford U. P.

Michels, Robert. Political parties. 1960. 3.75. Smith, Peter

Niebuhr, Reinhold. Children of light and the children of darkness. 1944. 3.00; pap. 1.25. Scribner

Ostrander, Gilman. Rights of man in America, 1607-1861. 6.00? U. of Missouri

Peek, George A., and Karl A. Lamb. Democracy in a world of conflict. 1962. 5.50? Random

Riemer, Neal. Revival of democratic theory. 1962. pap. 1.95. Appleton

Riker, William H. Democracy in the United States. 1953. pap. 2.65. Macmillan

Rossiter, Clinton. Marxism: The view from America. 1960. 6.75. Harcourt

Ryan, John A., and others. Democracy: Should it survive? 1943. 2.00. Catholic U. of Am. Pr.

Salvadori, Massimo. Liberal democracy. 1957. 3.00. Doubleday

Spitz, David. Democracy and the challenge of power. 1958. 5.00. Columbia

Stamps, Norman L. Why Democracies fall: A critical evaluation of the causes for modern dictatorships. 1957. 5.75. U. of Notre Dame

Streit, Clarence K. Union now: A proposal for an Atlantic federal union of the free. postwar ed. 3.00. Harper

Swabey, Marie. Theory of the democratic state. 1937. 2.50. Harvard

Thorson, T. L. Logic of democracy. 1962. pap. 2.25. Holt, Rinehart & Winston

Tocqueville, Alexis de. Democracy in America. 2 vols. tr. by Phillips Bradley. 1944. 7.50. Knopf (R)

Utley, T. E., and J. Stuart Maclure. Documents of modern political thought. 1958. 3.75. Cambridge U. P.

Verney, Douglas V. Analysis of political systems. 1959. 5.75. Free Press

Warner, W. Lloyd, and others. Democracy in Jonesville. 1949. 4.50. Harper

Wiltse, Charles. Jeffersonian tradition in American democracy. 1960. 4.50. Hill & Wang

Wright, David McCord. Democracy and progress. 4.65. Macmillan

DEMOCRATIC PARTY (329.3)
Acheson, Dean. Democrat looks at his party. 1955. 3.00. Harper
Brown, Stuart Gerry. First Republicans: Political philosophy and public policy in the party of Jefferson and Madison. 1954. 3.00. Syracuse
Clancy, Herbert J. Democratic Party: Jefferson to Jackson. 1961. 5.00. Fordham
Cohn, David. Fabulous democrats. 1956. 5.95. Putnam
Cunningham, Noble E., Jr. Jeffersonian Republicans: The formation of party organization, 1789-1801. 1958. 6.00. U. of N. C.
Harris, Seymour E. Economics of the political parties. 1962. 7.00. Macmillan
Hoyt, Edwin P., Jr. Jumbos and jackasses: A popular history of the political wars. 5.95. Doubleday
Remini, Robert V. Martin Van Buren and the making of the Democratic Party. 1959. 5.00. Columbia
Stevens, Harry R. Early Jackson party in Ohio. 1957. 4.50. Duke

DEMOGRAPHY (312)
Blanc, Robert. Handbook of demographic research in underdeveloped countries. 5.00. Int. Pub. Service (R)
Cox, Peter R. Demography. 1960. 5.00. Cambridge U. P.
Demographic yearbook, 1961. bilingual, in English and French. 1962. 11.50. U. N. (R)
Eversley, David E. C. Social theories of fertility and the Malthusian debate. il. 1959. 5.60. Oxford U. P.
Hauser, Philip M. and Otis Dudley Duncan. Study of population. il. 1959. 15.00. U of Chicago

DENMARK--ANTIQUITIES (948.9)
Klindt-Jensen, Ole. Denmark. il. 1957. 6.95. Praeger
Manniche, Peter. Denmark, a social laboratory. il. 1939. 2.00. Oxford U. P.
Starcke, Viggo. Denmark in world history. il. 1962. 10.00. U. of Pa.

DENTAL HYGIENISTS (617.6)
Bregstein, Samuel J. Handbook for dental assistants, hygienists, and secretaries. il. 1961. 6.95. Prentice-Hall
Peterson, Shailer. Clinical dental hygiene. il. 1959. 6.75. Mosby

DENTISTRY (617.6)
Cranin. Modern family guide to dental health. 1962. 2.95. Prentice-Hall
Clark, J. Stanley. Open wider, please. il. 1955. 5.00. U. of Okla.

DENTISTRY AS A PROFESSION (617.069)
Cohen, Raymond. Your future in dentistry. 1960. 2.95. 2.65. Richards Rosen

DEPARTMENT STORES (658.871)
Cumming, James C. Keys to selling department stores. 1953. 3.00. Fairchild
Ferry, John W. History of the department store. il. 1960. 7.95. Macmillan
Lombard, George F. F. Behavior in a selling group. 1955. 4.00. Harv. Bus. School
McNair, Malcolm P. Operating results of department and specialty stores in 1961. 1962. 6.00. Harv. Bus. School
Mayfield, Frank. Department store story. 1949. 5.00. Fairchile

DEPRESSION, MENTAL (132.195)
Grinker, Roy R. Phenomena of depression. 1961. 6.50. Hoeber
Mendelson, Myer. Psychoanalytic concepts of depression. 1960. 6.50. Thomas, C. C

DEPRESSIONS (338.54)
Galbraith, John K. Great crash, 1929. 1955. 3.50. Houghton
Warren, Harris G. Herbert Hoover and the great depression. 1959. 7.00. Oxford U. P.

DERMATOLOGY (616.5)
Goldsmith, Norman R. You and your skin. il. 1953. 3.75. Thomas, C. C.
Greenberg, Leon, and David Lester. Handbook of cosmetic materials. 1954. 14.50. Wiley

Sutton, Richard L., Jr. Skin. 4.95. Doubleday
DESCARTES, RENE, 1596-1650. (194)
Beck, L. J. Method of Descartes. 1952. 5.60. Oxford U. P.
Popkin, R. H. History of scepticism from Erasmus to Descartes. 6.00.
   Humanities
Roth, Leonard. Descartes' Discourse on method. 1937. 2.40. Oxford U. P.
Spinoza, Benedictus de. Principles of Descartes' philosophy. tr. by Halbert
   Hains Britan. 2.00. Open Ct.
DESERT FAUNA (591.9)
Jaeger, Edmund C. Desert wildlife. il. 1961. 5.95. Stanford
Jaeger, Edmund C. North American deserts. 5.95. Stanford
Krutch, Joseph Wood. Desert year. 1952. 3.75. Sloane
Krutch, Joseph Wood. Voice of the desert. il. 1955. 3.75. Sloane
Olin, George, and Jerry Cannon. Mammals of the southwest deserts. il. 1959.
   1.00. Southwestern
DESERT FLORA (581.9)
Dodge, Natt N., and Jeanne R. Janish. Flowers of the Southwest deserts. il.
   1960. 1.00. Southwestern
Huntington, Harriet E. Let's go to the desert. il. 1949. 3.00. Doubleday
Jaeger, Edmund C. North American deserts. 5.95. Stanford
Leese, Oliver, and Margaret. Desert plants, cacti and succulents. il. 7.50.
   Transatlantic
Munz, Philip A. California desert wildflowers. il. 4.75; pap. 2.95. U. of Calif.
Rigby, Douglas. Desert happy. il. 1957. 5.50. Lippincott
DESERTS (551.45)
Corle, Edwin. Desert country. 1941. 4.95. Duell
White, Gilbert F. Future of the arid lands. 1956. 6.75. A.A.A.S.
DESIGN (745.4)
Anderson, Donald M. Elements of design. pap. 5.00. Holt, Rinehart & Winston
Bates, Kenneth F. Basic design. il. 1960. 4.95. World Pub.
Beitler, B. C., and E. J. Lockhart. Design for you. 1961. 7.95. Wiley
Caskey, Lacey Davis. Geometry of Greek vases. il. 1922. 5.00. Harvard
Downer, Marion. Discovering design. 1947. 3.50. Lothrop
Drexler, Arthur, and Greta Daniel. Introduction to twentieth century design.
   il. 1959. pap. 2.95. Mus. of Mod. Art
Feldsted, Carol J. Design fundamentals. 1958. 6.50. Pitman
Graves, Maitland E. Art of color and design. il. 1951. 8.50. McGraw
Scott, Robert G. Design fundamentals. il. 1951. 8.95. McGraw
Wedd, J. A. Dunkin. Sources of design. 5.00. Boston Bk.
Wolchonok, Louis. Art of three dimensional design. il. 1959. 8.50. Harper
Baranski, Matthew. Graphic design. il. 1960. 9.00. Int. Textbook
Best-Maugard, Adolfo. Method for creative design. il. 1926. 3.95. Knopf
Estrin, Michael. 2,000 designs and ornaments. il. 3.50; pap. 1.95. Tudor
Lang, John. Geometric designs for artists and craftsmen. il. 1959. 3.50.
   Exposition
Sabine, Ellen S. American folk art. il. 1958. 6.95. Van Nostrand
DESIGN, INDUSTRIAL (745.2)
Buhl, Harold. Creative engineering design. il. 1960. 4.95. Iowa State
Dreyfuss, Henry. Designing for people. 1958. pap. 1.95. S. and S.
Greenwood, Douglas C. Engineering data for product design. 1961. 10.00.
   McGraw
Greenwood, Douglas C. Product engineering design manual. 1959. 11.00.
   McGraw
Gump, Richard. Good taste costs no more. il. 1951. 5.00. Doubleday
DESPOTISM (321.62)
Beloff, Max. Age of absolutism, 1660-1815. 1954. 2.00. Hillary
Wittfogel, Karl A. Oriental despotism. 1957. 8.50. Yale
DETECTIVE AND MYSTERY STORIES--HISTORY AND CRITICISM (801.9)
Haycraft, Howard. Art of the mystery story. pap. 2.25. Grosset

DETECTIVES (364.12)

Soderman, Harry, and John J. O'Connell. Modern criminal investigation. by Charles E. O'Hara. il. 1962. 7.50. Funk

Ward, Milburn Robert, Jr. Story behind private investigation. il. 1957. 3.50. Vantage

DETERMINANTS (512.83)

Aitken, Alexander C. Determinants and matrices. 1956. 1.75. Wiley

Browne, Edward Tankard. Introduction to the theory of determinants and matrices. 1958. 7.50. U. of N. C.

Turnbull, H. W. Theory of determinants, matrices, and invariants. pap. 2.00. Dover

DETERRENCE (STRATEGY) (355.4)

Kahn, Herman. Thinking about the unthinkable. 1962. 4.50. Horizon

Liddell Hart, B. H. Deterrent or defense. 1960 . 4.95. Praeger

DEVIL (235.47)

Bounds, Edward M. Satan: His personality, power and overthrow. 1962. 2.50. Kregel

Woolf, Mildred E. Origin of Satan. 3.50. Royal

DEVOTION (242)

Steere, Douglas V. On beginning from within. 1943. 2.50. Harper

Burton, Joe W. Altar fires for family worship. 1955. 2.50. Broadman

Chambers, Oswald. My utmost for His Highest: The golden book of Oswald Chambers. 1935. 3.00. Dodd

Clark, Thomas Curtis. Today is mine. 1950. 2.00. Harper

Lindsell, Harold. Daily Bible readings from the Revised Standard Version. 1957. 2.00; deluxe lea. ed. 5.00. Harper

Spurgeon, C. H. Check book on the bank of faith. 1957. 3.00. Christian Lit. Crusade

Fenelon, Francois. Reflections for every day of the month. 0.35. Templegate

Jones, E. Stanley. Growing spiritually. 1954. 2.00. Abingdon

Jones, E. Stanley. Mastery. 1955. 1.75. Abingdon

Luther, Martin. Day by day we magnify Thee. 3.50. Muhlenberg

Spurgeon, Charles H. Spurgeon's morning and evening. by D. O. Fuller. 1955. complete, 3.95; small, 3.00; deluxe, 7.50. Zondervan

Kepler, Thomas S. Fellowship of the saints: An anthology. 1949. 7.50. Abingdon

Thurman, Howard. Meditations of the heart. 1953. 2.75. Harper

Traherne, Thomas. Centuries, poems, and thanksgivings. by H. M. Margoliouth. 2 vols. 1958. 13.45. Oxford U. P.

DEWEY, JOHN, 1859-1952 (191.9)

Blewett, John. John Dewey: His thought and influence. 1960. 5.00. Fordham

Dewey, John. Intelligence in the modern world: John Dewey's philosophy. 1939. 2.95. Modern Lib.

Geiger, George R. John Dewey in perspective. 1958. 5.50. Oxford U. P.

Handlin, Oscar. John Dewey's challenge to education. 1959. 2.50. Harper

Hendel, Charles W. John Dewey and the experimental spirit in philosophy. 1959. 3.00. Bobbs

Horne, Herman H. Democratic philosophy of education. 6.25. Macmillan

McCluskey, Neil G. Public schools and moral education, the influence of Horace Mann, William Torrey Harris, and John Dewey. 1958. 6.00. Columbia

Schilpp, Paul A. Philosophy of John Dewey. 1951. 6.95. Tudor

DIABETES (616.46)

Colwell, Arthur R. Types of deabetes mellitus and their treatment. il. 1950. lexide. 2.50. Thomas, C. C.

Dolger, Henry, and Bernard Seeman. How to live with diabetes. 1958. 3.95. Norton

Duncan, Garfield G. Modern pilgrim's progress for diabetics. il. 1956. bds. 2.50. Saunders

Joslin, Elliott P. Diabetic manual. il. 1959. 3.75. Lea & F

Marble, Alexander, and George F. Cahill. Chemistry and chemotherapy of
    diabetes mellitus. il. 1962. 7.75. Thomas, C. C.
Pollack, Herbert, and Marie V. Krause. Your diabetes. 1952. 3.00. Harper
Sindoni, Anthony M. Diabetic's handbook. 1959. 5.00. Ronald
DIAGNOSIS (616.075)
Merck manual of diagnosis and therapy. 7.50. Merck
Stokes, E. Joan. Clinical bacteriology. il. 1960. 7.00. Williams & Wilkins
Hyman, Harold Thomas. Handbook of differential diagnosis. 1957. 9.00.
    Lippincott
McLaren, John W. Modern trends in diagnostic radiology. il. 1961. 16.00.
    Hoeber
Middlemiss, Howard. Radiology as a diagnostic aid in clinical surgery. il.
    1960. 7.50. Thomas, C. C.
Owen, Charles A. Diagnostic radioisotopes. il. 1959. 15.75. Thomas, C. C
DIALECTIC (160)
Friedman, Maurice S. Martin Buber: The life of dialogue. 1955. 6.00. U. of
    Chicago
Hook, Sidney. Reason, social myths and democracy. 4.00. Humanities
DIALECTICAL MATERIALISM (146.3)
Engels, Friedrich. Dialectics of nature. 1940. 5.00. Int. Pubs.
Wetter, Gustavo A. Dialectical materialism 1959. 10.00. Praeger
DIALOGUES (808.54)
Ireland, Norma Olin. Index to monologs and dialogs. 1949. 6.00 net; supplement.
    1959. 6.00. Faxon
DIAMONDS (549)
Gemological Institute of America Staff. Diamond dictionary. il. 1960. 8.75.
    Gemological Inst. (R)
DICKENS, CHARLES, 1812-1870 (823.83)
Engel, Monroe. Maturity of Dickens. 1959. 4.00. Harvard
Fielding, K. J. Charles Dickens: A critical introduction. 1958. 4.00. McKay
Ford, G. H. Dickens and his readers. 1956. 6.00. Princeton
Forster, John. Life of Charles Dickens. 2 vols. 1.95 ea. Dutton
Miller, Joseph H., Jr. Charles Dickens: The world of his novels. 1958. 6.00.
    Harvard
Priestley, John B. Charles Dickens: A pictorial biography. il. 1962. 6.50.
    Viking
DICKINSON, EMILY NORCROSS, 1830-1886 (928.1)
Anderson, Charles R. Emily Dickinson's poetry: Stairway of surprise. 1960.
    5.95. Holt, Rinehart & Winston
Bingham, Millicent Todd. Emily Dickinson: A revelation. 1954. 3.00. Harper
Johnson, T. H. Emily Dickinson: An interpretive biography. il. 1955. 4.50.
    Harvard
Ransom, John C. Emily Dickinson. 5.00. U. of Minn.
Ward, Theodora V. W. Capsule of the mind: Chapters in the life of Emily
    Dickinson. 1961. 4.50. Harvard
Whicher, George F. This was a poet: Emily Dickinson. 1957. 4.40. U. of Mich.
DICOTYLEDONS (583)
Gundersen, A. Families of dictyledons. 1950. 5.00. Ronald
Rendle, A. B. Dicotyledons. (Classification of flowering plants. vol. 2) 8.50.
    Cambridge U. P.
DICTATORS (321.62)
Gilbert, Gustave M. Psychology of dictatorship. 1950. 5.50. Ronald
Hallgarten, G. W. F. Devils or saviors: A history of dictatorships since 600
    B.C. 6.00. Humanities
Porter, Charles O., and Robert J. Alexander. Struggle for democracy in Latin
    America. 4.50. Macmillan
Stamps, Norman L. Why Democracies fall: A critical evaluation of the causes
    for modern dictatorships. 1957. 5.75. U. of Notre Dame

DICTION (808.52)
Barfield, O. Poetic diction, a study in meaning. 3.75. Hillary
Hanley, Theodore D., and W. L. Thurman. Developing vocal skills. 1962. 4.00.
  Holt, Rinehart & Winston
Mayer, Lyle V. Notebook for voice and diction. 1953. pap. 3.25. Brown, W. C.
DICTIONARIES, POLYGLOT (413)
Davydov, A. Russian-English-French-German-Latin botanical dictionary. 5.00.
  San Francisco
Duden, Konrad. Pictorial encyclopedia in five languages: English, French, German,
  Italian, Spanish. 2 vols. il. 40.00. Ungar (R)
Kleczek, Josip. Astronomical dictionary. polyglot. 1962. 25.00. Academic
World language dictionary. 1962. 35.00. Encycl. Britannica (R)
DIDEROT, DENIS, 1718-1784 (194)
Crocker, Lester G. Two Diderot studios: Ethics and esthetics. 1952. pap. 2.50.
  Johns Hopkins
Vartanian, A. Diderot and Descartes. 1953. 6.00. Princeton
DIESEL LOCOMOTIVES (621.436)
Hinde, Douglas W., and M. Electric and diesel-electric locomotives. 1948. 7.50.
  St. Martins
Graham, Frank D. Diesel engine manual. 4.00. Audel
Molloy, E. Diesel engine manual. 5.50. Transatlantic
Smith, Donald H. Modern diesel. 1954. 5.00. Chilton
DIET (613.2)
Alexander, Dan D. Good health and common sense. 3.95. Crown
Colby, Anita. Anita Colby's beauty book. 1958. 5.95. Prentice-Hall
Rose, Mary Swartz. Feeding the family. il. 5.75. Macmillan
DIET IN DISEASE (613.2)
Harris, Catherine F. Handbook of dietetics for nurses. il. 1953. 4.00.
  Williams & Wilkins
Iowa State Department of Health. Simplified diet manual. il. 1961. 2.50.
  Iowa State
Krause, Marie V. Food, nutrition and diet therapy. 1961. 6.75. Saunders
Turner, Dorothea. Handbook of diet therapy. il. 1959. 5.00. U. of Chicago
DIFFERENCE (PSYCHOLOGY) (136)
Anastasi, Anne. Differential psychology. il. 7.50. Macmillan
Cutts, Norma E., and Nicholas Moseley. Providing for individual differences
  in the elementary school. il. 1960. 7.95; text ed. 5.95. Prentice-Hall
Tyler, Leona E. Psychology of human differences. 6.00. Appleton
Willner, Corothy. Decisions, values and groups. vol. 1. 1960. 12.50. Pergamon
DIFFERENCE EQUATIONS (517.38)
Batchelder, Paul Mason. Introduction to linear difference equations. 1928.
  4.00. Harvard
Boole, George. Treatise on the calculus of finite differences. 3.75. Smith,
  Peter
Goldberg, Samuel. Introduction to difference equations. il. 1958. 6.75. Wiley
Kunz, K. L. Numerical analysis. 1957. 8.75. McGraw
Milne, William E. Numerical calculus. 1949. 6.00. Princeton
Richardson, Clarence H. Introduction to the calculus of the finite differences.
  il. 1954. 4.00. Van Nostrand
DIFFERENTIAL EQUATIONS (517.38)
Agnew, Ralph P. Differential equations. il. 1960. 7.50. McGraw
Ayres, Frank. Outline of theory and problems of differential equations. il. 1952.
  2.95. Schaum
Bellman, Richard. Stability theory of differential equations. il. 1953. 6.95.
  McGraw
Betz, Herman, and others. Differential equations with applications. 1954. 5.25.
  Harper
Birkhoff, Garrett, and Glan-Carlo Rota. Ordinary differential equations. il.
  1962. 8.50. Ginn

Golomb, Michael, and M. E. Shanks. Elements of ordinary differential equations. 1950. 6.50. McGraw

Greenspan, Donald. Theory and solution of ordinary differential equations. il. 1960. 5.50. Macmillan

Hildebrand, Francis B. Introduction to numerical analysis. 1956. 9.75. McGraw

Kells, Lyman M. Elementary differential equations. 1960. 6.75. McGraw

Ku, Y. H. Analysis and control of nonlinear systems. 1958. 10.00. Ronald

Miller, Frederic H. Partial differential equations. 1941. 4.75. Wiley

Warren, A. G. Mathematics applied to electrical engineering. il. 1959. 11.50. Consultants Bureau

DIFFERENTIAL EQUATIONS, LINEAR (517.382)

Cheng, D. K. Analysis of linear systems. 1959. 9.75. Addison-Wesley

Frazer, Robert A., and others. Elementary matrices. 7.50. Cambridge U. P.

Lanczos, Cornelius. Linear differential operators. il. 1961. 13.50. Van Nostrand

DIFFERENTIAL EQUATIONS, PARTIAL (517.383)

Bateman, H. Partial differential equations of mathematical physics. 1959. 7.50. Cambridge U. P.

Courant, Richard and D. Hilbert. Partial differential equations. 1962. 17.50. Wiley

Forsythe, George E., and P. C. Rosenbloom. Numerical analysis and partial differential equations. 1958. 7.50. Wiley

Greenspan, Donald. Introduction to partial differential equations. 1961. 7.50. McGraw

Sneddon, Ian N. Elements of partial differential equations. 1957. 8.75. McGraw

DIFFUSION (544.5)

Crank, J. Mathematics of diffusion. 1956. 8.80. Oxford U. P.

Grew, K. E., and T. L. Ibbs. Thermal diffusion in gases. 1952. 5.00. Cambridge U. P.

Jost, Wilhelm. Diffusion in solids, liquids, gases. 1960. 16.00. Academic Press

DIGESTION (612.3)

Beaumont, William. Experiments and observations on the gastric juice and the physiology of digestion. 3.50. Smith, Peter

Young, John R. Experimental inquiry into the principles of nutrition and the digestive system. Facsimile of 1803. by William C. Rose. 1959. 2.50. U. of Ill.

DIGESTIVE ORGANS (611.3)

Davenport, Horace W. Physiology of the digestive tract. 1961. 8.50. Year Bk.

DIODATI, CHARLES. 1608-1638 (928)

Milton, John. Milton's Lycidas: The tradition and the poem. by C. A. Patrides. 1961. pap. 2.75. Holt, Rinehart & Winston

DIPLOMACY (327)

Beard, Charles A. Cross currents in Europe today. 2.50. Jones, Marshall

Fitzsimons, Matthew A., and Stephen D. Kertesz. Diplomacy in a changing world. 1959. 7.50. U. of Notre Dame

McKenna, Joseph C. Diplomatic protest in foreign policy. 1962. 6.00. Loyola

Pearson, Lester B. Diplomacy in the nuclear age. 1959. 2.75. Harvard

Webster, Charles K. Art and practice of diplomacy. 1962. 6.00. Barnes & Noble

DIPLOMATIC AND CONSULAR SERVICE (341.8)

Buck, Philip W., and Martin Travis, Jr. Control of foreign relations in modern nations. 1957. 7.25. Norton

Cardozo, Michael H. Diplomats in international cooperation. 1962. 3.50. Cornell

Radlovic, I. Monte. Etiquette and protocol. 1956. 3.95. Harcourt

Spaulding, Ernest Wilder. Ambassadors ordinary and extraordinary. 1960. 5.00. Pub. Affairs

Strang, William. Diplomatic career. 7.50. Praeger

Stuart, Graham H. American diplomatic and consular practice. 1952. 6.50. Appleton

Wriston, Henry M. Diplomacy in a democracy. 1956. 2.50. Harper
DISARMAMENT (341.67)
American Assembly. Arms control: Issues for the public. by Louis Henkin.
    1961. 3.50. Prentice-Hall
Brennan, Donald G. Arms control, disarmament, and national security. 1961.
    6.00. Braziller
Bull, Hedley. Control of the arms race. 4.00. Praeger
Forbes, Henry W. Strategy of disarmament. 1962. 4.50. Pub. Affairs
Henkin, Louis. Arms cortrol and inspection in American law. 1958. 5.50.
    Columbia
Kennedy, John F. Why England slept. 1961. 3.50. Funk
Khrushchev, Nikita S. Disarmament and colonial freedom. 2.25. Int. Pub.
    Service
Melman, Seymour. Peace race. 1962. bds. 3.95. Braziller
Mezerik, Avrahm G. Disarmament: Impact on underdeveloped countries. 1961.
    pap. 2.50. Int. Review Service
Morray, J. P. From Yalta to Disarmament: Cold war debate. 1961. 8.50.
    Monthly Review
Osgood, Charles E. Alternative to war or surrender. 1962. pap. 1.45. U. of
    Ill.
Pauling, Linus: No more war. il. 1958. 3.50. Dodd
Russell, Bertrand. Common sense and nuclear warfare. 1959. 2.50. S. and S.
Spanier, John W., and Joseph Nogee. Politics of disarmament: A study in
    Soviet-American gamesmanship. 1962. 5.00. Praeger
Warburg, James P. Disarmament. 4.50. Doubleday
DISASTERS (361.5)
Baker, George W., and Dwight W. Chapman. Man and society in disaster. 1962.
    10.00. Basic Books
Bixby, William. Havoc: The story of natural disasters. il. 1961. 3.50. McKay
Buckingham, Clyde. Red Cross disaster relief: Its origin and development.
    1956. 1.00. Pub. Affairs
Ikle, Fred C. Social impact of bomb destruction. il. 1958. 3.95. U. of Okla.
Sorokin, P. A. Man and society in calamity. 1942. 5.00. Dutton
Sutton, Ann, and Myron. Nature on the rampage. 1962. 6.00. Lippincott
DISCOVERIES (GEOGRAPHY) (910)
Beazley, Charles R. Dawn of modern geography. 3 vols. 35.00. Smith, Peter
Cheyney, E. P. European background of American history, 1300-1600. 3.00.
    Smith, Peter
Debenham, Frank. Discovery and exploration. il. 1960. 9.95. Doubleday
Golder, F. A. Russian expansion on the Pacific: 1641-1850. 6.00. Smith, Peter
Hakluyt, Richard. Hakluyt's voyages. vols. 1 and 2 only. 1.95 ea. Dutton
Hermann, Paul. Great age of discovery. il. 1958. 6.50. Harper
Nowell, Charles E. Great discoveries and the first colonial empires. 1961.
    4.50. Cornell
Stefansson, Vilhjalmur. Great adventures and explorations. 1947. 6.00. Dial
Sykes, Percy. History of exploration. 1961. pap. 2.75. Harper
Williamson, James A. Age of Drake. il. 1961. 5.75. Macmillan
DISCRIMINATION (177.5)
Adorno, T. W., and others. Authoritarian personality. 1950. 8.75. Harper
Barton, Rebecca C. Our human rights: A study in the art of persuasion. 1955.
    2.50. Pub. Affairs
Berger, M. Equality by statute. 1952. 3.25. Columbia
Epstein, Benjamin R., and Arnold Forster. Some of my best friends. 1962.
    4.50. Farrar, Straus
Javits, Jacob K. Discrimination, U.S.A. 1962. pap. 0.60. Washington Square
DISCRIMINATION IN EDUCATION (371.96)
Rosenblum, Victor G. Law as a political instrument. 1955. pap. 0.95. Random
Sexton, Patricia. Education and income: Inequalities of opportunity in our
    public schools. il. 1961. 6.00. Viking

Williams, Robin M., Jr., and Margaret W. Ryan. Schools in transition. 1954. 3.00. U. of N. C.

DISCRIMINATION IN EMPLOYMENT (331.113)

Becker, Gary S. Economics of discrimination. 1957. 3.50. U. of Chicago

Hope, John. Equality of opportunity: A union approach to fair employment. 1956. 3.25. Pub. Affairs

Ruchames, L. Race, jobs, and politics. 1953. 3.75. Columbia

DISCRIMINATION IN HOUSING (331.113)

Abrams, Charles. Forbidden neighbors: A study of prejudice in housing. 1955. 5.00. Harper

Rosen, Harry, and David. But not next door. 1962. 3.95. Obolensky

Vose, Clement. Caucasians only: The supreme court, the N. A. A. C. P., and the restrictive covenants. il. 1959. 6.00. U. of Calif.

Wilner, Daniel M., and others. Human relations in interracial housing. 1955. 4.00. U. of Minn.

DISCUSSION (808.53)

Auer, J. Jeffery, and Henry Lee Ewbank. Handbook for discussion leaders. 1954. 2.95. Harper

Braden, Waldo W., and Earnest S. Brandenburg. Oral decision-making. Principles of discussion and debate. 1955. 5.50. Harper

Howell, William S., and Donald K. Smith. Discussion. 4.75. Macmillan

Lee, Irving J. Customs and crises in communication. 1954. 4.00. Harper

McBurney, James H., and Kenneth G. Hance. Discussion in human affairs. 1950. 4.50. Harper

Matlaw, Myron, and James B. Stronks. Pro and con. 1960. 4.75. Houghton

Utterback, William E. Group thinking and conference leadership. 1950. 3.50. Holt, Rinehart & Winston

Zapf, Rosalind M. Democratic processes in the secondary classroom. il. 1959. 5.95. Prentice-Hall

Zelko, H. P. Successful conference and discussion techniques. 1957. 5.00; McGraw

DISEASES (610)

Brahdy, Leopold. Disease and injury. 1961. 12.50. Lippincott

Buchner, F. Personality and nature in modern medicine. 1958. 1.50. Grune

Hemming, James. Mankind against the killers. 1956. 4.75. Mckay

Royal College of Physicians. Smoking and health. 1962. pap. 1.00. Pitman

Stambul, Joseph. Mechanisms of disease: A study of the autonomic nervous system, the endocrine system and the electrolytes, in their relationship to clinical medicine. 1952. 10.00. Froben

Winter, Origins of illness and anxiety. 4.95. Julian

DISINFECTION AND DISINFECTANTS (614.48)

Reddish, George F. Antiseptics, disinfectants, fungicides and chemical and physical sterilization. il. 1957. 15.00. Lea & F

Sykes, George. Disinfection and sterilization. il. 1958. 11.75. Van Nostrand

DISLOCATIONS (617.16)

Perkins, George. Fractures and dislocations. 1958. 9.20. Oxford U. P.

Wiles, Philip. Fractures, dislocations, and sprains. 1960. 8.50. Little

DISPLAY OF MERCHANDISE (659.15)

Gardner, and Heller. Exhibition and display. 1960. 13.75. McGraw

DISSECTION (591)

Bigelow, Robert P. Directions for the dissection of the cat. il. 3.00. Macmillan

Eddy, S., and others. Guide to the study of the anatomy of the shark, necturus, and the cat. 1960. 3.50. Wiley

Harrison, Bruce M. Dissection of the cat. il. 1962. 3.75. Mosby

Lassek, Arthur M. Human dissection: Its drama and struggle. 1958. 6.50. Thomas C. C.

DISSENTERS (274.2)

Cowherd, R. G. Politics of English dissent: The religious aspects of liberal and humanitarian reform movements from 1815 to 1848. 1956. 5.00. N. Y. U.

Hall, Thomas Cuming. Religious background of American culture. 1959. 5.75.
Ungar

Thomas, Norman. Great dissenters. 1961. 5.00. Norton

DISTANCES--MEASUREMENT (523.4)

Lee, Oliver J. Measuring our universe. 1950. 4.50. Ronald

DITHYRAMB (880)

Pickard-Cambridge, A. W. Dithyramb, tragedy and comedy. il. 1927. 4.89.
Oxford U. P.

DIVINATION (133.3)

Manas, J. H. Divination: Ancient and modern. 1947. 3.00. Wehman

DIVING (797.23)

Beebe, William. Half mile down. 1951. 7.95. Duell

De Borhegyi, Suzanne. Ships, shoals, and amphoras: The story of underwater
archaeology. 1961. 3.95. Holt, Rinehart & Winston

Dugan, James. Man under the sea. il. 1956. 7.50. Harper

Ellsberg, Edward. Men under the sea. il. 1939. 4.00. Dodd

Link, Marian C. Sea diver, a quest for history under the sea. il. 1959. 4.95.
Rinehart

Piccard, Auguste. Earth, sky and sea. tr. by Christina Stead. 1956. 4.50.
Oxford U. P.

Blair, Clay, Jr. Diving for pleasure and treasure. il. 1960. 4.95. World Pub.

Bronson-Howard, G. Handbook for skin divers. il. 1958. 2.50. Arco

Cousteau, Jacques Uves and James Dugan. Captain Cousteau's underwater
treasury. 1959. 6.50. Harper

Cousteau, Jacques-Yves, and others. Complete manual of free diving. il. 1957.
4.00. Putnam

DIVINING-ROD (133.323)

Roberts, Kenneth. Seventh sense. il. 1953. 4.00. Doubleday

DIVISION OF LABOR (331.87)

Durkheim, Emile. Division of labor in society. 1952. 6.00. Free Press

DIVORCE (301.428)

Bergler, Edmund. Divorce won't help. 1948. 3.95. Harper

Blaine, Tom R. Marriage happiness or unhappiness. 1955. 2.50. Dorrance

Blake, Nelson M. Road to Reno. il. 1962. 5.00. Macmillan

Emerson, James G., Jr. Divorce, the church, and remarriage. 1961. 3.95.
Westminster

Fishman, Nathaniel. Marriage: This business of living together. 1946. 4.00.
Liveright

Goode, William J. After divorce. 1955. 7.50. Free Press

Haussamen, Florence, and Mary A. Guitar. Divorce handbook. 1960. 3.95.
Putnam

Jacobson, Paul. American marriage and divorce. 1959. 12.00? Rinehart

Kal, Frederick M., and Harry A. Frumess. Divorce problems handbook. 1961.
4.95. Fell

O'Mahony, Patrick J. Catholics and divorce. 1960. 2.95. Nelson

DOCUMENTATION (010)

Bradford, Samuel C. Documentation. 1950. 3.00. Pub. Affairs

Perry, James W. Documentation and information retrieval. il. 1957. 5.00.
Wiley

Shera, Jesse H., and others. Information resources. 1958. 5.00. Wiley

DODGSON, CHARLES LUTWIDGE, 1832-1898 (823)

Green, Roger L. Lewis Carroll. 1962. 2.50. Walck

Greenacre, Phyllis. Swift and Carroll: A psychoanalytic study of two lives. il.
1955. 5.00. Int. Univs.

DOGS (636.7)

American Kennel Club. Complete dog book. il. 1956. 3.95. Doubleday

Davis, Henry P. Modern dog encyclopedia. il. 13.50. Stackpole (R)

DOLPHINS (599.53)

Alpers, Anthony. Dolphins: The myth and the mammal. 1961. 5.00. Houghton

Lilly, John C. Man and dolphin. il. 4.95. Doubleday

DOMESTIC ANIMALS (636)

Dukes, H. H., and others. Physiology of domestic animals. il. 1955. 9.75. Cornell

DOMESTIC RELATIONS (301.42)

Clarke, Helen I. Social legislation. 1957. 6.90. Appleton

Harper, Fowler V. Problems of the family. 1952. 10.00. Bobbs

DONNE, JOHN, 1573-1631 (821)

Alvarez, Alfred. School of Donne. 1961. 3.75. Pantheon

Bennett, Joan. Four metaphysical poets. 1953. 3.00. Cambridge U. P.

Coffin, Charles M. John Donne and the new philosophy. 6.00. Humanities

Gosse, Edmund. Life and letters of John Donne. 2 vols. 12.00. Smith, Peter

Legouis, Pierre. Donne the craftsman: An essay upon the structure of the songs and sonnets. 1962. 5.00. Russell

Louthan, Doniphan. Poetry of John Donne. 3.50. Twayne

Rugoff, Milton. Donne's imagery: A study in creative sources. 1961. 7.50. Russell

Simpson, E. M. Study of the prose works of John Donne. 1948. 4.80. Oxford U. P.

Ungar, Leonard. Donne's poetry and modern criticism. 1962. 5.00. Russell

Williamson, George. Donne tradition, study in English poetry from Donne to the death of Cowley. 1959. 3.50. Smith, Peter

DORMITORIES (371.87)

Augustine, G. M. Some aspects of management of college residence halls for women. il. 3.25. Appleton

National Education Association, National Association of Women Deans and Counselors. Residence hall for students. 1959. 1.25. N. E. A.

DOS PASSOS, JOHN RODERIGO, 1896- (813.5)

Wrenn, John H. John Dos Passos. 3.50. Twayne

DOSTOEVSKII, FEDOR MIKHAILOVICH, 1821-1881 (893)

Carr, Edward Hallett. Dostoevsky, 1821-1881. 3.50. Macmillan

Gide, Andre. Dostoevsky. 1949. 2.50. New Directions

Hubben, William. Four prophets of our destiny: Kiekegaard, Dostoevsky, Nietzsche, Kafka. 1952. 3.25. Macmillan

Masaryk, Thomas G. Spirit of Russia. 2 vols. by Slavik. 1955. vol. 1, 4.25; vol. 2, 6.00; 2 vol. set 16.00. Macmillan

Matlaw, R. E. Brothers Karamazov, novelistic technique. 1.25. Humanities

Steiner, George. Tolstoy or Dostoevsky. 1959. 5.75. Knopf

Wasiolek, Edward. Crime and Punishment and the critics. 1961. 1.95. Wadsworth

Yarmolinsky, Avrahm. Dostoevsky, his life and art. il. 1957. 7.50. Criterion

DOUGLAS, STEPHEN ARNOLD, 1831-1861 (923.273)

Capers, Gerald M. Stephen A. Douglas, defender of the Union. 1959. 3.75. Little

Jaffe, Harry V. Crisis of the house divided. 1959. 6.50. Doubleday

DOUGLASS, FREDERICK, 1817?-1895 (928.973)

Foner, Philip S. Life and writings of Frederick Douglass. 4 vols. vol. 1, Early years. 4.50; vol. 2, Pre-Civil War decade. 5.00; vol. 3, Civil War. 4.50; vol. 4, Reconstruction and after. 5.00; set 15.00. Int. Pubs.

Quarles, Benjamin. Frederick Douglass. il. 1948. 4.00. Assoc. Publishers

DOYLE, SIR ARTHUR CONAN, 1859-1930 (823)

Baring-Gould, William S. Sherlock Holmes of Baker Street. 5.00. Potter, C. N.

Carr, John Dickson. Life of Sir Arthur Conan Doyle. 1949. 4.95. Harper

Starrett, Vincent. Private life of Sherlock Holmes. il. 1960. 4.75. U. of Chicago

DRAGON-FLIES (595.733)

Corbet, Philip S. Biology of dragonflies. il. 1962. 5.75. Quadrangle

DRAINAGE (631.6)

Ayres, Quincy C., and Daniels Scoates. Land drainage and reclamation. 1939. 9.50. McGraw

Darby, Henry C. Draining of the fens. 1957. 6.50. Cambridge U. P.

DRAKE, SIR FRANCIS, 1540?-1596 (923.942)
Drake, Francis, the Younger. World encompassed by Sir Francis Drake.
   by Wm. S. W. Vaux. price on request. Franklin, B.
Williamson, James A. Age of Drake. il. 1961. 5.75. Macmillan
DRAMA (808.2)
Barnet, Sylvan, and others. Aspects of the drama. il. 1962. pap. 2.75. Little
Cooper, Charles W. Preface to drama. 1955. 5.50. Ronald
Eliot, T. S. Poetry and drama. 1951. 1.50. Harvard
Ellis-Fermor, Una. Shakespeare the dramatist. il. 1961. 5.00. Barnes & Noble
Fergusson, Francis. Human image in dramatic literature. 1957. pap. 0.95.
   Doubleday
Gassner, John, and Ralph Allen. Theatre and drama in the making. in prep.
   Houghton
Granville-Barker, Harley. On dramatic method. 1960. 3.00. Smith, Peter
Nathan, George Jean. Magic mirror. 1960. 5.00. Knopf
Nicoll, Allardyce. Theatre and dramatic theory. 1962. 3.75. Barnes & Noble
O'Hara, Frank Hurburt, and Margueritte H. Bro. Invitation to the theater. 1951.
   3.00. Harper
Peacock, R. Art of the drama. 5.00. Hillary
Rosenheim, Edward. What happens in literature: A student's guide to poetry,
   drama, and fiction. 1960. pap. 1.25. U. of Chicago
Saint-Denis, Michel. Theatre: The rediscovery of style. 3.00. Theatre Arts
Selden, Samuel. Man in his theatre. 1957. 3.00. U. of N. C.
Shaw, George Bernard. Shaw on theatre. by E. J. West. 1959. 3.95. Hill & Wang
Walley, Harold R. Book of the play. 1950. 5.00. Scribner
DRAMA--BIBLIOGRAPHY (808.2)
Logasa, Hannah, and Winifred Ver Nooy. Index to one-act plays, 1900-1924.
   1924. 7.50; net; supplement, 1924-1931. 1932. 7.50; net; 2nd supplement, 1932-
   1940. 1941. 7.50 net; 3rd supplement, 1941-1948. 1950. 7.50 net; 4th supplement,
   1948-1957. 7.50. Faxon
Mantle, Burns. Best plays of 1894-1961. 45 vols. vol. 1. 5.00; vols. 2 to 29,
   6.00 ea; vols. 30-40, by John Chapman, 6.00 ea; vols. 35-44, by Louis
   Kronenberger, 6.00 ea; vol. 44, index for 1949-1960. 5.00; vol. 45, by
   Henry Hewes, 6.00. For complete list see Dodd Catalog (R)
Mersand, Joseph. Guide to play selection. 1959. 3.50. Appleton
Thomson, Ruth G. Index to full-length plays 1895-1925. 1956. 7.00 net; 1926-
   1944. 1946. 6.00 net. Faxon
West, Dorothy H., and Dorothy M. Peake. Play index: 1949-1952. 1953. 5.00.
   Wilson
DRAMA--COLLECTIONS (808.82)
Allison, Alexander W., and others. Masterpieces of the drama. pap. 3.25.
   Macmillan
Bentley, Eric. Classic theatre. 3 vols. vol. 1, Six Italian plays, 3.25; vol. 2,
   Five German plays; vol. 3, Six Spanish plays. 3.50 ea. Smith, Peter
Bentley, Eric. From the modern repertoire. 3 ser. ser. 1, 1949. 6.00; ser.
   2, il. 1952. 6.75; ser. 3, il. 1956. 7.95; set, 17.95. Indiana
Bentley, Eric. Modern theater: An anthology. 6 vols. vols. 1-3, 1955. pap. 0.95
   ea; vol. 4, 1956. pap. 1.45; vols. 5-6, 1957, 1960. pap. 0.95 ea. Doubleday
Bentley, Eric. Modern theatre. 6 vols. vols. 1-3, and 5-6, 3.00 ea; vol. 4,
   3.50. Smith, Peter
Bentley, Eric. Play: A critical anthology. 1951. 6.60. Prentice-Hall
Block, Haskell, and Robert Shedd. Masters of modern drama. 1962. 12.95. Random
   (R)
Brooks, Cleanth, and Robert B. Heilman. Understanding drama: Twelve plays.
   1948. 7.50. Holt
Brown, Edmund R. Five modern plays. 1962. pap. 0.50. Humphries
Clark, B. H. World drama. 2 vols. 4.00 ea. Smith, Peter
Clark, William Smith. Chief patterns of world drama. 1946. 8.50. Houghton

Cubeta, Paul M. Modern drama for analysis. 6.50. Holt, Rinehart & Winston
Dean, Leonard F. Nine great plays. 1956. pap. 3.50. Harcourt
Dickinson, Thomas H. Chief contemporary dramatists. First and third series.
  8.00 ea. Houghton
Downer, Alan S. Art of the play. 1955. 8.65. Holt, Rinehart & Winston
Gassner, John. Treasury of the Theatre. 1951. 3. vols. vol. 1 (Aeschylus to
  Turgenev) vol. 2 (Ibsen to Sartre) vol. 3 (Wilde to Arthur Miller) 7.50 ea;
  set, 22.50. S. and S.
Gassner, John. Twenty best European plays on the American stage. 5.95. Crown
Griffin, Alice V. Living theatre. 6.95. Twayne
Hatcher, Harlan. Modern Continental dramas. 1941. 5.95. Harcourt
Hatcher, Harlan. Modern dramas. 1948. 3.50. Harcourt
Matthews, Brander. Chief European dramatists. 1916. 7.50. Houghton
Mayorga, Margaret. Best short plays. 1957-58, 5.95. 1958-59, 3.95. 1959-60,
  3.95. 1960-61, 3.95. Beacon
Millett, Fred B., and Gerald Eades Bentley. Play's the thing. 5.50. Appleton
Nathan, George Jean. World's great plays. 1957. 3.75. World Pub.
Tucker, S. Marion, and Alan S. Downer. Twenty-five modern plays. 1953. 7.50.
  Harper
Whitman, Charles H. Representative modern dramas. 6.75. Macmillan
Whitman, Charles H. Seven contemporary plays. 1931. 3.20. Houghton

DRAMA--COLLECTIONS--20TH CENTURY (808.82)

Clurman, Harold. Seven plays of the modern theater. 1962. 8.50. Grove
Cordell, Richard A. Twentieth century plays - British, American, continental.
  1947. 3.50. Ronald
Gassner, John. From Ibsen to Ionesco. 10.50. Holt, Rinehart & Winston
Moon, Samuel. One act short plays of the modern theatre. 5.00. Smith, Peter
Reinert, Otto. Modern drama. 1962. pap. 3.50. Little
Ulanov, Barry. Makers of the modern theater. 1961. 8.95. McGraw
Watson, Ernest B., and Benfield Pressey. Contemporary drama, eleven plays.
  1956. pap. 3.00. Scribner
Watson, Ernest B., and Benfield Pressey. Contemporary drama: European,
  English, and Irish, American plays. 1941. 7.25. Scribner
Watson, Ernest B., and Benfield Pressey. Contemporary drama: Fifteen plays.
  1959. pap. 3.25. Scribner
Watson, Ernest B., and Benfield Pressey. Contemporary drama: Nine plays.
  1941. pap. 2.75. Scribner

DRAMA--DICTIONARIES, INDEXES, ETC. (808.2)

Barnet, Sylvan, and others. Aspects of the drama. il. 1962. pap. 2.75. Little
  (R)
Bowman, Walter P., and Robert H. Ball. Theater language, a dictionary. 1961.
  6.95. Theatre Arts (R)
Sobel, Bernard. New theatre handbook and digest of plays. 1948. 5.95. Crown
West, Dorothy H., and Dorothy M. Peake. Play index: 1949-1952. 1953. 5.00.
  Wilson

DRAMA--HISTORY AND CRITICISM (809.2)

Beerbohm, Max. Selection from Around theatres. pap. 1.45. Doubleday
Bentley, Eric R. What is theatre? 1955. pap. 1.75. Beacon
Boulton, Marjorie. Anatomy of drama. 3.00. Hillary
Brooks, Cleanth. Tragic themes in Western literature. 1955. 4.00. Yale
Brooks, Cleanth, and Robert B. Heilman. Understanding drama: Twelve plays.
  1948. 7.50. Holt
Cheney, Sheldon. Theatre. 1959. 9.50. McKay
Clark, Barrett H. European theories of the drama. 5.00. Crown
Coggin, Philip A. Uses of drama. 1956. 5.00. Braziller
Dryden, John. Of dramatic poesy, and other critical essays. 2 vols. 1.95 ea.
  Dutton
Fergusson, Francis. Human image in dramatic literature. 3.00. Smith, Peter

Fry, Christopher, and others. Experience of critics. by Kaye Webb. il. 1953. 2.25. Oxford U. P.

Gassner, John. Form and idea in modern theatre. 1956. 4.90. Holt, Rinehart & Winston

Gassner, John. Masters of the drama. il. 6.95. Dover

James, Henry. Scenic art. by Allen Wade. 1948. 6.00. Rutgers

Kerr, Walter. How not to write a play. 3.95. Writer

Langner, Lawrence. Play's the thing. 1960. 4.00. Putnam

Nicoll, Allardyce. Development of the theatre. 10.75. Harcourt

Nicoll, Allardyce. World drama. il. 1949. 9.00. Harcourt

Shaw, Bernard. Plays and players: Essays on the theatre. 1954. 2.25. Oxford U. P.

Shaw, George Bernard. Shaw's dramatic criticism from the Saturday Review (1895-1898) by John F. Matthews. 1960. 3.50. Smith, Peter

Shipley, Joseph T. Guide to great plays. 1956. 10.00. Pub. Affairs

Steiner, George. Death of tragedy. 1961. 5.00. Knopf

Stoll, Elmer E. Shakespeare and other masters. 8.50. Russell

Stuart, Donald Clive. Development of dramatic art. 4.75. Smith, Peter

Whitfield, G. J. N. Introduction to drama. 1938. 1.40. Oxford U. P.

Whiting, Frank M. Introduction to the theatre. 1961. il. 8.00. Harper

Young, Stark. Immortal shadows. 3.95. Scribner

DRAMA--HISTORY AND CRITICISM--19TH CENTURY (809.2)

Bentley, Eric. Playwright as thinker. 1955. pap. 1.55. Meridian

Krutch, Joseph W. Modernism in modern drama. 1962. 5.00. Russell

Williams, Raymond. Drama from Ibsen to Eliot. 1953. 3.80. Oxford U. P.

DRAMA--HISTORY AND CRITICISM--20TH CENTURY (809.2)

Clark, Barrett H., and George Freedley. History of modern drama. 1947. text ed. 7.00. Appleton

Clark, Barrett H., and George Freedley. History of modern drama. 1947. 9.50. Meredith

Corrigan, Robert. Theatre in the twentieth century. 1962. 5.75. Grove

Gassner, John. Theatre at the crossroads: Plays and playwrights on the mid-century American stage. 1960. 5.95. Holt, Rinehart & Winston

Krutch, Joseph W. Modernism in modern drama. 1962. 5.00. Russell

Lumley, Frederick. Trends in twentieth century drama: A survey since Ibsen and Shaw. 1960. 7.00. Oxford U. P.

Williams, Raymond. Drama from Ibsen to Eliot. 1953. 3.80. Oxford U. P.

DRAMA--STORIES, PLOTS, ETC. (808.2)

Lovell, John, Jr. Digests of great American plays. il. 1961. 5.95. Crowell

Reinhold, Meyer. Classical drama. 1959. 3.50. Barron's

Shipley, Joseph T. Guide to great plays. 1956. 10.00. Pub. Affairs

DRAMA--TECHNIQUE (808.2)

Archer, William. Play-making, a manual of craftsmanship. 3.75. Smith, Peter

Baker, George P. Dramatic technique. 8.00. Houghton

Egri, Lajos. Art of dramatic writing. 3.95. Writer

Jewkes, Wilfred T. Act division in Elizabethan and Jacobean plays. 1958. 6.50. Shoe String

Kinne, W. P. George Pierce Baker and the American theatre. il. 1954. 6.00. Harvard

Macgowan, Kenneth. Primer of playwriting. 2.95. Random

Millett, Fred B., and Gerald E. Bentley. Art of the Drama. il. 3.25. Appleton

Selden, Samuel. Introduction to playwriting. 2.50. Appleton

Van Druten, John. Playwright at work. 3.50. Writer

DRAMA, MEDIEVAL (808.2)

Chambers, Edmund K. Mediaeval stage. il. 2 vols. 1903. 12.00. Oxford U. P.

Hunningher, Benjamin. Origin of the theater. il. 1961. 3.75. Hill & Wang

DRAMA IN EDUCATION (372.5)

Coggin, Philip A. Uses of drama. 1956. 5.00. Braziller

Durland, Frances C. Creative dramatics for children. 1952. 2.75. Antioch

Ellis, Mary J. Finger play approach to dramatization. 1961. 3.50. Denison

Kerman, Gertrude L. Plays and creative ways with children. il. 1961. 6.95.
Harvey

Siks, Geraldine, and Hazel B. Dunnington. Children's theatre and creative
dramatics. il. 1961. 5.00. U. of Wash.

Simos, Jack. Social growth through play production. 1957. 3.75. Assn. Pr.

DRAMATISTS (927)
Gilder, Rosamond. Enter the actress. pap. 1.95. Theatre Arts

DRAPERY (747.5)
Hardy, Kay. Beauty treatments for the home. il. 1945. 3.00. Funk

Singer home decorations sewing book. 4.95. Grosset

DRAWING (741)
Cooper, Hal. Art for everyone. 4.95. Watson

Doten, Hazel R., and Constance Boulard. Costume drawing. 1956. pap. 1.00.
Pitman

Eng, Helga. Psychology of children's drawings. 5.00. Humanities

Fawcett, Robert. On the art of drawing. 10.00. Watson

Lowenfeld, Viktor. Your child and his art. il. 1954. 5.95. Macmillan

Piaget, Jean. Child's conception of space. 1948. 8.00. Humanities

Pope, Arthur. Language of drawing and painting. il. 1949. 5.50. Harvard

Rasmusen, H. M. Art structure. 1950. 7.95. McGraw

Rosenberg, Jakob. Great draughtsmen from Pisanello to Picasso. il. 1959.
12.50. Harvard

Watrous, James. Craft of old master drawings. 1957. 10.00. U. of Wis.

Zipprich, A. E. Freehand drafting for technical sketching. 1954. 3.60. Van
Nostrand

DRAWING--INSTRUCTION (740)
Anderson, Doug. How to draw with the light touch. 3.50. Watson

Anderson, Doug. New things to draw and how to draw them. 1958. 2.75. Dodd

Arestein, Jean. How to draw people and animals. 1958. 2.95. Sterling

Bradshaw, Percy V., and Rowland Hilder. Sketching and painting indoors.
il. 1957. 6.00. Viking

Clifton, Jack. Manual of drawing and painting. 5.95. Watson

Fitzgerald, Edmond J. Painting and drawing in charcoal and oil. 1959. 4.95.
Reinhold

Gollwitzer, Gerhard. Express yourself in drawing. 2.95. Sterling

Guptill, Arthur L. Drawing with pen and ink. 1961. 8.95. Reinhold

Guptill, Arthur L. Freehand drawing self-taught. il. 1933. 7.00. Harper

Hill, Adrian. Sketching and painting out of doors. 1961. 2.75. Pitman

Hill, Adrian. What shall we draw? Beginner's book of drawing. il. 1959. 2.50.
Emerson

Morehead, James C., and James C., Jr. Handbook of perspective drawing. il.
1952. 6.50. Van Nostrand

Mullin, William F. You can draw anything! 1947. 2.50. Winston

Nicolaides, Kimon. Natural way to draw. il. 1941. 5.00. Houghton

Norling, Ernest R. Perspective made easy. il. 4.50. Macmillan

Perard, Victor Drawing faces and expressions. 1956. pap. 1.00. Pitman

Perard, Victor, and others. How to draw. 1957. 3.95. Pitman

Watson, E., and A. Watson drawing book. in prep. Reinhold

Wolchonok, Louis. Art of pictorial composition. 1961. 7.50. Harper

Wolchonok, Louis. Design for artists and craftsmen. il. 1953. 4.95. Dover

Zaidenberg, Arthur. Anyone can draw. il. 1947. 4.45. Doubleday

Zaidenberg, Arthur. New encyclopedia of drawing, painting, and the graphic
arts. 5.95. Barnes, A. S. (R)

Zaidenberg, Arthur. Seeing with pencil and brush. il. 1962. 4.95. Harper

DRAWING-ROOM PRACTICE (744)
Carini, L. F. D. Drafting for electronics. il. 1946. 5.00. McGraw

Feirer, John L. Drawing and planning for the industrial arts. 1956. 4.52. Bennett

Healy, W. L., and A. H. Rau. Simplified drafting practice. 1953. 6.50. Wiley
Higbee, Frederic G., and John M. Russ. Engineering drawing problems. 1955.
3.50. Johnsen
Lombardo, Josef V., and others. Engineering drawing. 1956. pap. 2.50. Barnes
& Noble
Sahag, Leon M., and Joseph A. Bennett. Engineering drawing. 1962. 6.50.
Colonial Pr.

DRAWINGS (741.9)
Mongan, Agnes. One hundred master drawings. il. 1949. 7.50. Harvard
Moskowitz, Ira. Great drawings of all time. 4 vols. 1962. boxed, 160.00;
after Jan. 1, 1963, 175.00. Tudor
Sachs, Paul J. Modern prints and drawings. il. 1954. 7.50. Knopf

DRAWINGS--EXHIBITIONS (606.4)
Hayes, Bartlett H. American line. 1959. 2.50. Addison Gallery

DRAWINGS, EUROPEAN (741.940)
Drobna, Z. Gothic drawing. il. 1960. 9.80. Vanous

DREAMS (135.3)
Bonime, Walter. Clinical use of dreams. 1962. 8.50. Basic Books
Diamond, Edwin. Science of dreams. il. 1962. 4.50. Doubleday
Fodor, Nandor. New approaches to dream interpretation. 1962. pap. 1.95.
Citadel
Freud, Sigmund. Interpretation of dreams. by James Strachey. 1955. 8.50.
Basic Books
Freud, Sigmund. Interpretation of dreams. 1.95. Modern Lib.
Freud, Sigmund. On dreams. 1952. 3.00. Norton
Fromm, Erich. Forgotten language: An introduction to the understanding of
dreams, myths and fairy tales. 1951. 3.75. Rinehart
Jones, Ernest. On the nightmare. 1951. 4.95. Liveright
Sharpe, Ella F. Dream analysis. 3.50. Hillary

DREISER, THEODORE, 1871-1945 (813.5)
Kazin, Alfred, and Charles Shapiro. Stature of Theodore Dreiser. 1955. 5.00.
Indiana
Matthiessen, F. O. Theodore Dreiser. 1951. 4.75. Sloane
Shapiro, Charles. Theodore Dreiser: Our bitter patroit. 1962. 4.50. Southern
Ill.

DRESSMAKING (646.4)
Bane, Allyne. Creative sewing. 1956. 7.95. McGraw
Baxter, Laura, and others. Our clothing. il. 1952. 3.20. Lippincott
Baxter, Laura, and Alpha Latzke. Today's clothing. il. 1949, with supplement
by Gertrude A. Lathrop and Elizabeth F. Thomas. Today's manmade fibers.
4.84. Lippincott
Better Homes and Gardens. Sewing book. by the Editors of Better Homes and
Gardens. 3.95. Meredith
Butler, Margaret G. Clothes, their choosing, making and care. il. 6.50.
Textile Bk.
Erwin, Mabel D. Clothing for moderns. 1949. 6.25. Macmillan
Erwin, Mabel D. Practical dress design. 5.75. Macmillan
Hillhouse, Marion S., and Evelyn A. Mansfield. Dress design: Draping and
flat pattern making. 1948. 7.00. Houghton
Iowa Home Economics Association. Unit method of sewing. 1959. 2.25. Iowa
State
Lewis, Dora S., and others. Clothing construction and wardrobe planning. il.
1960. 4.60. Macmillan
Lynch, Mary, and Dorothy Sara. Sewing made easy. 1960. 3.95. Doubleday
Mansfield, Evelyn A. Clothing construction. 1953. 9.75. Houghton
Meshke, Edna D. Textiles and clothing analysis and synthesis. il. 1961. 4.00.
Burgess
Picken, Mary B. Modern dressmaking made easy. il. 1949. 4.50. Funk

Picken, Mary Brooks. Sewing for everyone. 1944. 2.95. World Pub.

Picken, Mary B. Singer dressmaking course in eight easy steps. 4.95. Grosset

Rathbone, Lucy, and Elizabeth Tarpley. Fabrics and dress. il. 1948. 6.25; Houghton

DRESSMAKING--PATTERN DESIGN (646.4)

Hollen, Norma R. Flat pattern methods with selected sewing suggestions. il. 1961. spiral bdg. 3.60. Burgess

Margolis, Adele P. How to design your own dress patterns. il. 1959. 4.95. Doubleday

Picken, Mary Brooks, and Dora Loues Miller. Dressmakers of France. il. 1956. 5.00. Harper

Sonneland, Yvonne E. Let's alter your pattern. 1959. 2.75. Burgess

DREYFUS, ALFRED, 1859-1935 (923.5)

Halasz, Nocholas. Captain Dreyfus. 1955. 3.50. S. and S.

DRIFT (551.41)

Du Toit, Alexander L. Our wandering continents: An hypothesis of continental drifting. il. 1957. 5.50. Hafner

DRIFTWOOD ARRANGEMENT (635.96)

Ishimoto, Tatsuo. Treasury of driftwood arrangements. 2.95. Crown

Thompson, Mary E. Driftwood book. 1960. 5.95. Van Nostrand

DRILL AND MINOR TACTICS (355.5)

Essentials of military training. 1959. 6.50. Stackpole

Glasgow, William M., Jr. Exhibition drills. il. 1958. pap. 2.50. Stackpole

DRINKING CUSTOMS (394.1)

Fukukita, Yasunosuke. Tea cult of Japan. il. 1955. 3.00. Tuttle

DRINKING WATER (641)

Hutchinson, R. C. Food for survival. 1959. 2.75. Cambridge U. P.

DROSOPHILA (575.1)

Haskell, Gordon. Practical heredity with Drosophila. 1961. 1.95. Scholar's Lib.

Patterson, John Thomas, and Wilson S. Stone. Evolution in the genus Drosophila. il. 1952. 12.00. Macmillan

DRUGS (615.1)

Alexander, Harry L. Reactions with drug therapy. il. 1955. 7.50. Saunders

American Medical Association. New and nonofficial drugs, 1962. 1962. 4.00. Lippincott

Beckman, Harry. Pharmacology: The nature, action and use of drugs. 1961. 15.50. Saunders

Burn, Harold. Drugs, medicines, and man. 1962. 4.50. Scribner

Modell, Walter. Drugs in current use. flexible bdg. 2.25. Springer

Cook, James. Remedies and rackets. 1958. 3.95. Norton

Foulger, John H. Chemicals, drugs, and health. 1959. 4.25. Thomas C. C.

DRUM MAJORS (785.1207)

Lee, Roger L. Baton: Twirling made easy. 1.50. Boosey

DRYDEN, JOHN, 1631-1700 (821)

Beljame, Alexandre. Men of letters and the English public in the eighteenth century. 1948. 6.50. Humanities

Bredvold, Louis I. Intellectural milieu of John Dryden. 1956. 4.40. U. of Mich.

Hoffman, Arthur W. John Dryden's imagery. 1962. 5.00. U. of Fla.

Myers, R. M. Handel, Dryden, and Milton. 5.00. Hillary

Schilling, Bernard W. Dryden and the conservative myth. 1961. 6.00. Yale

Van Doren, Mark. John Dryden: A study of his poetry. 1960. 3.75. Smith, Peter

Ward, Charles E. Life of John Dryden. 1961. 7.50. U. of N. C.

DUALISM (273.2)

Lovejoy, Arthur O. Revolt against dualism. 1930. 6.00. Open Ct.

DUBINSKY, DAVID, 1892- (923.31)

Danish, Max D. World of David Dubinsky. il. 4.75. World Pub.

DU BOIS, WILLIAM EDWARD BURGHARDT, 1868- (923.6)

Broderick, Francis L. W. E. B. Du Bois, Negro leader in a time of crisis. il. 1959. 5.00. Stanford

Rudwick, Elliott M. W. E. B. Du Bois: A study in minority group leadership.
1961. 6.00. U. of Pa.
DUE PROCESS OF LAW (342)
Grant, James A. C. Our common law constitution. 1960. 3.00. Boston U.
DUELING (394.8)
Kane, Harnett T. Gentlemen, swords and pistols. 1951. 3.50. Morrow
DURER, ALBRECHT, 1471-1528 (927.943)
Brion, Marcel. Durer, his life and work. il. 1960. 5.95. Tudor
Panofsky, Erwin. Life and art of Albrecht Durer. 1955. 10.00. Princeton
Ripley, Elizabeth. Durer, a biography. il. 1958. 3.50. Lippincott
DUFY, RAOUL, 1877-1953 (927.944)
Cogniat, Raymond, Dufy. il. 3.50. Crown
Dufy, Roaul. Dufy. by Marcel Brion. il. 1958. 3.95. N. Y. Graphic
Lassaigne, Jacques. Dufy. il. 1954. 5.75. World Pub.
DULLES, JOHN FOSTER, 1888-1959 (923.2)
Beal, John R. John Foster Dulles: 1888-1959. 1959. 6.00. Harper
Comfort, Mildred H. John Foster Dulles, peacemaker. 3.00. Denison
Goold-Adams, Richard. John Foster Dulles: A reappraisal. 1962. 5.50. Meredith
Heller, Deane, and David. John Foster Dulles, soldier for peace. il. 1960. 4.50.
   Holt, Rinehart & Winston
DUMAS, ALEXANDRE, 1802-1870 (843.7)
Maurois, Andre. Titans. il. 1958. 5.95. Harper
Maurois, Andre. Alexandre Dumas. 1955. 3.00. Knopf
DUNBAR, PAUL LAWRENCE, 1872-1906 (811.)
Lawson, Victor F. Dunbar critically examined. 2.15. Assoc. Publishers
DUNCAN, ISADORA, 1878-1927 (927)
Duncan, Isadora. My life. il. 3.95. Liveright
DUNKIRK, FRANCE, BATTLE OF, 1940 (940.5421)
Divine, David. Nine days of Dunkirk. il. 1959. 4.50. Norton
DUNS, JOANNES, SCOTUS, 1265?-1308? (922.941)
Harris, Charles R. S. Duns Scotus. 2 vols. 15.00. Humanities
DUODENUM (616.34)
Crohn, Burrill B. Understand your ulcer. 1950. 3.75. Sheridan
DU PONT FAMILY (PIERRE SAMUEL DU PONT DE NEMOURS, 1739-1817) (923.3)
Dorian, Max. Du Ponts: From gunpowder to nylon. il. 1962. 6.50. Little
DUPORTAIL, LOUIS LEBEGNE DE PRESLE, 1743-1802 (923.5)
Kite, Elizabeth S. Brigadier-General Louis Lebegue Duportail: Commandant
   of engineers in the Continental Army, 1777-1783. 1933. 2.50. Johns Hopkins
DURBAN, NATAL (968.4)
Kuper, Leo, and others. Durban; a study in racial ecology. 1958. 3.75.
   Columbia
DURKHEIM, EMILE 1858-1917 (923.6)
Alpert, Harry. Emile Durkheim and his sociology. 1961. 6.00. Russell
DURRELL, LAWRENCE, 1912- (928)
Moore, Harry T. World of Lawrence Durrell. 1962. 4.50. Southern Ill.
DUST STORMS (551.559)
Tannehill, Ivan Ray. Drought. 1947. 5.00. Princeton
DUTCH IN THE EAST (FAR EAST) (325.91)
Hyma, Albert. History of the Dutch in the Far East. 1953. 3.95. Wahr
DUTCH IN THE U.S. (325.73)
Lucas, Henry S. Netherlanders in America. il. 1955. 10.00. U. of Mich.
DUTCH WAR, 1672-1678 (942.068)
Haley, K. H. D. William of Orange and the English opposition: 1672-4. 1953.
   4.80. Oxford U. P.
DUTY (170)
Prichard, Harold A. Moral obligation. 1949. 4.00. Oxford U. P.
Ross, W. D. Right and the good. 1930. 3.40. Oxford U. P.
Werkmeister, William H. Theories of ethics. 1961. 5.50. Johnsen

DVORAK, ANTONIN, 1841-1904 (927)
Robertson, Alec. Dvorak. 1949. 3.50. Farrar, Straus
Sourek, Otakar. Chamber music of Dvorak. 3.00. Boosey
Sourek, Otakar. Orchestral music of Dvorak. 4.50. Boosey
DWELLINGS (728)
Agan, Tessie. House, its plan and use. 1956. 6.95. Lippincott
Burbank, Nelson L., and Oscar Shaftel. House construction details. 5.95.
    Simmons-Boardman
Carter, D. G., and K. H. Hinchcliff. Family housing. 1949. 5.75. Wiley.
Dietz, Albert G. H. Dwelling house construction. 1954. 8.00; text ed. 6.50.
    Van Nostrand
Duncan, Kenneth. Home builder's handbook. il. 1948. 6.95. Van Nostrand
Lewis, Dora S., and others. Housing and home management. 1961. 4.60.
    Macmillan
Shortney, Joan R. How to live on nothing. 1961. 4.95. Doubleday
Sleeper, H. R., and C. Sleeper. House for you. 1948. 7.50. Wiley
Underwood, George. House construction costs. il. 1950. 6.50. McGraw
Conklin, Groff. Weather conditioned house. 1958. 4.95. Reinhold
Better Homes and Gradens. Handyman's book. by the Editors of Better Homes
    and Gardens. 1951. 4.95. Meredith
Bradman, W. A. G. Taking care of your home. il. 3.25. Transatlantic
Schaefer, Carl J. Home mechanics. 1961. 3.75. Bruce
Whitman, Roger C. First aid for the ailing house. 1958. 5.95. McGraw
American Builder. How to remodel your home. by the Editors of American
    Builder. 1959. 2.95. Simmons-Boardman
Highland, Harold J. How to double the living space in your home. 1955. 5.95.
    Harper
DYES AND DYEING (667.2)
Hall, Archibald John. Handbook of textile dyeing and printing. 5.50. Textile Bk.
DYNAMICS (621.81)
Atkin, R. H. Classical dynamics. 1960. 5.75. Wiley
Barnard, Robert J. A. Elementary dyanmics. 2.00. St. Martins
Crossley, F. R. E. Dynamics in machines. 1954. 7.50. Ronald
Frazer, Robert A., and others. Elementary matrices. 7.50. Camoriuge U. P.

Gray, Robert C. Elementary dynamics for students of science and engineering.
    2.00. St. Martins
Hartman, J. B. Dynamics of machinery. 1956. 8.00. McGraw
Karman, Theodore von, and Maurice A. Biot. Mathematical methods in engi-
    neering. 1940. 8.95. McGraw
Loney, S. L. Elements of dynamics. 1.50. Cambridge U. P.
Maxwell, Robert L. Kinematics and dynamics in machinery. 1960. 9.75.
    Prentice-Hall
Shames, Irving. Dynamics (Engineering mechanics vol. 2) 6.75. Prentice-Hall
Timoshenko, Stephen, and D. H. Young. Dynamics. (Engineering mechanics.
    vol. 2) il. 1956. 5.25; solutions, 1.00. McGraw
Younger, J. E. Advanced dynamics. 1958. 8.50. Ronald
DYNAMOS (621.3132)
Kloeffler, Royce G., and others. Direct-current machinery. 1948. 6.75.
    Macmillan

E

EAR (612.85)
Bast, Theodore H., and Barry J. Anson. Temporal bone and the ear. il. 1949.
    12.00. Thomas C. C.
Wever, G., and M. Lawrence. Physiological acoustics. 1954. 10.00. Princeton

EAR--DISEASES (617.8)

Reading, Phillip. Common diseases of the ear, nose and throat. 1961. 8.00. Little

EAR TRAINING (784.94)

Lieberman, Maurice. Ear training and sight singing. 1959. 5.25. Norton

EARHART, AMELIA, 1898-1937 (926)

Briand, Paul L., Jr. Daughter of the sky: The story of Amelia Earhart. il. 1960. 3.95. Duell

EARP, ALVIRA PACKINGHAM (SULLIVAN), 1847-1947 (923.9)

Waters, Frank. Earp Brothers of Tombstone. il. 1960. 5.00. Potter, C. N.

EARTH (550)

Bascom, Willard. Hole in the bottom of the sea. il. 4.95. Doubleday

Beiser, Arthur. Our earth. il. 1959. 2.95. Dutton

Carrington, Richard. Story of our earth. il. 1956. 3.50. Harper

Edgeworth, Kenneth E. Earth, the planets, and the stars. il. 1961. bds. 5.75. Macmillan

Gamov, George. Biography of the earth. 1959. 4.95. Viking

Gutenberg, Beno. Internal constitution of the earth. 1957. pap. 2.45. Dover

Gutenberg, Beno. Physics of the earth's interior. 1959. 8.50. Academic Press

Kahn, Fritz. Design of the universe: The heavens and the earth. il. 1954. 6.95. Crown

Kuiper, Gerard P. Earth as a planet. il. 1954. 12.50. U. of Chicago

Kummel, Bernhard. History of the earth: An introduction to historical geology. il. 1961. 8.75. Freeman

Larousse. Larousse encyclopedia of the earth: Geology, paleontology and prehistory. il. 1961. 15.00. Putnam (R)

Pounds, Norman. Earth and you. 6.95. Rand McNally

Scientific American. Planet earth. by the Editors of Scientific American. 1957. 1.45. S. and S.

Velikovsky, Immanuel. Earth in upheaval. 1955. 3.95. Doubleday

Whipple, Fred L. Earth, moon and planets. 2.95. Grosset

EARTH--AGE (551.7)

Haber, Francis C. Age of the world: Moses to Darwin. 1959. 5.00. Johns Hopkins

EARTHQUAKES (551.22)

Davison, C. Origin of earthquakes. 1912 1.75 Cambridge U. P.

Eiby, G. A. About earthquakes. il. 1957. 3.00. Harper

EAST (FAR EAST)--DESCRIPTION AND TRAVEL (950)

Rama, Rau, Santha. East of home. 1950. 4.50. Harper

Stucki, Lorenz. East Asia in danger. tr. by Peter Jacobsohn. 1961. 5.00. Walker

Thielicke, Helmut. Voyage to the Far East. 1962. 4.25. Muhlenberg

EAST (FAR EAST--DESCRIPTION AND TRAVEL--GUIDEBOOKS (950)

Fodor, Eugene, ed. Japan and East Asia. 1962. rev. annually. il. 6.95. McKay (R)

Gellhorn, Eleanor C. McKay's guide to the Far East and Middle East. rev. 1956. 5.00. McKay (R)

Olson, Harvey S. Olson's Orient guide. il. 1962. 6.95. Lippincott

EAST (FAR EAST)--ECONOMIC CONDITIONS (950)

Problems of economic reconstruction in the Far East. 1949. 2.00. Inst. of Pac. Rel.

Thompson, Warren S. Population and progress in the Far East. 1959. 7.50. U. of Chicago

EAST (FAR EAST)--HISTORY (950)

Buss, Claude A. Far East: A history of recent and contemporary international relations in East Asia. 1955. 7.95. Macmillan

Cameron, Meribeth E., and others. China, Japan and the powers. 2nd ed. 1960. 8.00. Ronald

Hyma, Albert. Outline of Far Eastern civilizations. 1946. 0.75. Long's College Bk.

Latourette, Kenneth Scott. Short history of the Far East. 3rd ed. 6.40. Macmillan

Peffer, Nathaniel. Far East: A modern history. il. 1958. 7.50. U. of Mich.

Vinacke, Harold M. History of the Far East in modern times. 6th ed. il. 1959. 7.00. Appleton

EAST (FAR EAST)--HISTORY--SOURCES (950)

Maki, John M., ed. Conflict and tension in the Far East: Key documents. 1894-1960. 1961. 5.00. U. of Wash.

EAST (FAR EAST)--POLITICS (950)

Battistini, Lawrence H. Rise of American influence in Asia and the Pacific. 1960. 5.00. Mich. State

Dutt, Vidya P., ed. East Asia: China, Korea, Japan, 1947-50. 1958, 7.95. Oxford U. P.

Vinacke, Harold M. Far Eastern politics in the postwar period. il. 1956. 6.50. Appleton

EAST (FAR EAST)--SOCIAL CONDITIONS (950)

Heiser, Victor G. American doctor's odyssey. il. 1936. 7.95. Norton

Thompson, Warren S. Population and progress in the Far East. 1959. 7.50. U. of Chicago

EAST (FAR EAST)--SOCIAL LIFE AND CUSTOMS (950)

Copland, Margaret L. Fun and festival from the rim of East Asia: Korea, Okinawa, Taiwan, Hong Kong. 1962. pap. 0.75. Friendship

Keith, Agnes Newton. Bare feet in the palace. 1955. 6.00. Little

EAST AND WEST (909)

Brown, Benjamin H. ed. East and West must meet. 1959. 3.00. Mich. State

Gulick, Sidney L. East and West: A study of their psychic and cultural characteristics. 5.00. Tuttle

Moore, Charles A., ed. Philosophy and culture, east and west. 10.00. U. of Hawaii

Toynbee, Arnold J. World and the West. 1953. 3.00. Oxford U. P.

Ward, Barbara. Interplay of East and West. 1957. 3.75. Norton

EASTER (394.268)

Adams, Charlotte. Easter idea book. il. 1954. 4.50. Barrows

Franke, Hermann. Lent and Easter. 1955. 1.75. Newman

Hazeltine, Alice, I., ed. Easter book of legends and stories. il. 1947. 3.50. Lothrop

Hole, Christina. Easter and its customs. il. 1961. bds. 2.50. Barrows

Shepherd, Massey H., Jr. Paschal liturgy and the Apocalypse. 1960. pap. 1.75. John Knox

Wallis, Charles L., ed. Lenten-Easter sourcebook. 1961. 2.95. Abingdon

Watts, Alan W. Easter: Its story and meaning. il. 1950. 2.50. Abelard

EASTER ISLAND (919.7)

Heyerdahl, Thor. Aku-Aku. 6.95. Rand McNally

Heyerdahl, Thor, and Edwin N. Ferdon, Jr. Archaeology of Easter Island. 25.00. Rand McNally

Metraux, Alfred. Easter Island. 1957. 6.00. Oxford U. P.

EASTERN QUESTION (950)

American Assembly. United States and the Far East. 2nd ed. by Willard Thorp. il. 1962. 3.95. Prentice-Hall

Gunther, John. Inside Asia. 1942. 6.95. Harper

Hurewitz, J. C. Diplomacy in the Near and Middle East. vol. 1. Documentary record 1535-1914. 1956. 7.50. vol. 2. Documentary record 1914-1956. 9.50. Van Nostrand

Marriott, John A. R. Eastern question: An historical study in European diplomacy. il. 4th ed. 1950. 4.50. Oxford U. P.

EASTERN QUESTION (FAR EAST) (950)

Beloff, Max. Soviet policy in the Far East, 1944-1951. 1953. 4.00. Oxford U. P.

Curry, Roy W. Woodrow Wilson and Far Eastern policy. 6.00. Twayne
Dennett, Tyler. Roosevelt and the Russo-Japanese War. 1958. 5.00. Smith,
   Peter
Dewey, Thomas E. Journey to the far Pacific. il. 1952. 4.00. Doubleday
Flynn, John T. While you slept. 1951. 3.00. Devin
Griswold, A. Whitney. Far Eastern policy of the United States. 1938. 10.00.
   Yale
Kent, Percy H. B. Twentieth century in the Far East. 1937. 3.50. St. Martins
Latourette, Kenneth S. American record in the Far East. 1952. 3.00. Inst. of
   Pac. Rel.
Michener, James A. Voice of Asia. 1951. 3.95. Random
Vinacke, Harold M. United States and the Far East. 1952. 3.00. Inst. of Pac.
   Rel.

ECCLESIATICAL LAW (348)

Brand, Norton F., and Vernon M. Ingram. Pastor's legal adviser. 1942. 2.50.
   Abingdon
Tussman, Joseph, ed. Supreme court on church and state. 1961. pap. 1.95.
   Oxford U. P.

ECOLOGY (574.5)

Bates, Marston. Forest and the sea. 1960. 3.95. Random
Benton, Allen H., and William E. Werner. Manual of field biology and ecology.
   1961. 3.00. Burgess
Benton, A. H., and W. E. Werner. Principles of field biology and ecology. 1958.
   7.25. McGraw
Bonner, J. T. Cells and societies. 1955. 4.50. Princeton
Buchsbaum, Ralph, and Mildred. Basic ecology. 1957. 3.50; Boxwood
Carpenter, Richard J. Ecological glossary. 1938. 5.75. Hafner (R)
Clarke, G. L. Elements of ecology. 1954. 7.95. Wiley (R)
Dansereau, P. Biogeography. 1957. 8.50. Ronald
Darling, Frank F. Wild life in an African territory. il. 1960. 4.00. Oxford U. P.
Dasmann, Raymond F. Environmental conservation. il. 1959. 6.50. Wiley
Moore, Hilary B. Marine ecology. il. 1958. 9.75. Wiley
Odum, Eugene P., and Howard T. Fundamentals of ecology. 2nd ed. il. 1959.
   7.50. Saunders
Reid, George K. Ecology of inland waters and estuaries. 1961. 7.50. Reinhold
Storer, John H. Web of life. il. 3.50. Devin

ECONOMIC ASSISTANCE (338.91)

Benham, Frederic. Economic aid to underdeveloped countries. 1961. 2.00.
   Oxford U. P.
Black, Eugene R. Diplomacy of economic development. 1960. 3.00. Harvard
Kenen, Peter B. Giant among nations: Problems in United States foreign
   economic policy. 1960. 5.00. Harcourt
Pentony, DeVere E. Underdeveloped lands: A dilemma of the international
   economy. 1960. pap. 1.50. Chandler Pub.
Shonfield, Andrew. Attack on world poverty. 1960. 5.00. Random

ECONOMIC ASSISTANCE, AMERICAN (309.2)

Curti, Merle. American philanthropy abroad. 1962. 12.50. Rutgers
Krause, Walter. Economic development: The underdeveloped world and the
   American interest. 1961. 8.50. Wadsworth
Loeber, Thomas S. Foreign aid, our tragic experiment. 1961. 3.50. Norton
McClellan, G. S. U. S. foreign aid. 1957. 2.00. Wilson
Price, Harry B. Marshall Plan and its meaning. il. 1955. 5.00. Cornell

ECONOMIC DEVELOPMENT (338.91)

Adelman, Irma. Theories of economic growth and development. il. 1961. 5.00.
   Stanford
Asher, Robert E., and others. Development of the emerging countries. 1962.
   3.75. Brookings
Bauer, Peter T. Economic analysis and policy in underdeveloped countries.
   1957. 3.00. Duke

Belshaw, Horace. Population growth and levels of consumption. 1956. 6.00. Inst. of Pac. Rel.

Black, Eugene R. Diplomacy of economic development. 1960. 3.40. Oxford U. P.

Brand, Willem. Struggle for a higher standard of living. 7.50. Free Press

Cairncross, A. K. Factors in economic development. 6.50. Praeger

Coale, Ansley J., and E. M. Hoover. Population growth and economic development in low-income countries. 1958. 8.50. Princeton

Galbraith, John Kenneth. Economic development in perspective. 1962. 2.50. Harvard

Kindelberger, C. P. Economic development. 1958. 6.95. McGraw

Knorr, Klaus, and William Baumol. What price economic growth? il. 1961. 3.95. Prentice-Hall

Kurihara, Kenneth K. Keynesian theory of economic development. 1959. 5.50. Columbia

Myrdal, Gunnar. Rich lands and poor. 1958. 3.00. Harper

National Educational Association, Educational Finance Committee. Education and economic growth. il. 1961. pap. 1.00. N. E. A.

Rostow, Walt W. Process of economic growth. rev. ed. 1960. 6.90. Norton

Rostow, W. W. Stages of economic growth. 1960. 3.75. Cambridge U. P.

Villard, Henry H. Economic development. il. 1959. pap. 2.75. Holt, Rinehart & Winston

Ward, Barbara. Rich nations and the poor nations. 1962. bds. 3.75. Norton

ECONOMIC FORECASTING (330)

Bean, L. How to predict the stock market. 1962. 2.95. (Luce) McKay

Chambers, Edward J. Economic fluctuations and forecasting. il. 1961. 8.95. Prentice-Hall

ECONOMIC HISTORY (330.9)

Clough, S. Economic development of western civilization. 1959. 7.90. McGraw

Fortune. Readings in economic geography. ed. by Richard J. Ward, and Lawrence A. Hoffman. il. 1960. pap. 2.20. Holt, Rinehart & Winston

Henderson, W. O. Industrial Revolution in Europe. 1961. 6.00. Quadrangle

Levy, Lester S., and Roy J. Sampson. American economic development. il. 1962. 10.60. Allyn & Bacon

Schumpeter, Joseph. Business cycles. 2 vols. 1939. 18.00. McGraw

Schumpeter, Joseph A. Theory of economic development. (Galaxy GB55) 1961. pap. 1.50. Oxford U. P.

ECONOMIC HISTORY--TWENTIETH CENTURY (330.9)

National Bureau Committee for Economic Research. Demographic and economic change in developed countries. 1960. 12.00. Princeton

Sternberg, Fritz. Military and industrial revolution of our time. 1959. 5.75. Praeger

Trotsky, Leon. Europe and America. 0.50. Pioneer Publishers. N. Y. C.

ECONOMIC HISTORY--1945- (330.9)

Douglas, William O. Democracy's manifesto. 2.00. Doubleday

Woytinsky, W. S., and E. S. World population and production: Trends and outlook. 1953. 12.00. Twentieth Century

ECONOMIC POLICY (336)

Boulding, Kenneth. Principles of economic policy. 1958. 10.60. Prentice-Hall

Grayson, Henry. Economic planning under free enterprise. 1954. 2.00. Pub. Affairs

Hayek, Friedrich A. Road to serfdom. 1944. 5.75. U. of Chicago

Knight, Frank H. Intelligence and democratic action. 1960. 3.75. Harvard

Lauterbach, Albert. Economic security and individual freedom: Can we have both? 2.50. text ed. 2.00. Cornell

Myrdal, Gunnar. Beyond the welfare state. 1960. 4.50. Yale

Myrdal, G. Political element in the development of economic theory. 1954. 5.00. Harvard

National Bureau Committee for Economic Research. Capital formation and
economic growth. 1955. 12. 00. Princeton
Paton, William A. Shirtsleeve economics: A commonsense survey. 1952.
4. 50. (Appleton) Meredith
Robbins, Lionel. Economic problem in peace and war. 1. 25. St. Martins
Ropke, Wilhelm T. Humane economy: The social framework of the free
market. tr. by Elizabeth Henderson. 1960. 5. 00. Regnery
Slocomb, Whitney H. Communist Constitution vs. United States Constitution.
1955. 3. 00. Forum
Smithies, Arthur, and others. Economics and public policy: Brookings
lectures 1954. 1955. 2. 00. Brookings
Staley, Eugene. Future of underdeveloped countries. rev. ed. 1961. 6. 00?
Harper
Theobald, Robert. Challenge of abundance. 1961. 4. 50. Potter, C. N.
Wallich, Henry C. Cost of freedom. 1960. 3. 75. Harper
Williams, John Henry. Economic stability in a changing world. 1953. 6. 00.
Oxford U. P.
Wootton, Barbara. Freedom under planning. 1945. 2. 50. U. of N. C.
Wright, David McCord. Democracy and progress. 4. 25. Macmillan
Wright, David McC., ed. Impact of the labor union. 1956. 5. 00. Kelley
ECONOMICS (330)
Arendt, Hannah. Human condition. 1958. 5. 50. U. of Chicago
Aristotle. Politics and economics: Politica, Oeconomica, Atheniensium repub-
lica. (Aristotle's works: The Oxford translation. vol. 10) ed. by J. A. Smith,
and W. D. Ross. 4. 80. Oxford U. P.
Bagley, William C., Jr., and Richard M. Perdew. Understanding economics.
1951. 5. 48. Macmillan
Bentham, Jeremy. Bentham's economic writings. 3 vols. ed. by W. Stark.
8. 00 ea. set, 22. 50. Franklin B.
Brainard, Harry G. Economics in action. 1959. 5. 50. Oxford U. P.
Brems, Hans. Output, employment, capital, and growth. 1959. 6. 00. Harper
Brown, A. J. Introduction to the world economy. 1959. 3. 50. Holt, Rinehart
& Winston
Brown, Harry Gunnison. Basic principles of economics. 4. 00. Lucas Bros.
Bye, Raymond T., and William W. Hewett. Applied economics. 5th ed. il. 1960.
6. 50. Appleton
Chamberlain, Neil W. General theory of economic process. 1955. 5. 00. Harper
Committee on Economics. Principles of economics. 1960. 7. 25. Pitman
Dillard, Dudley. Economics of John Maynard Keynes. 1948. 9. 00. Prentice-Hall
Dobb, Maurice. Economic theory and socialism. 1955. 4. 00. Int. Pubs.
Dodd, J. Harvey, and others. Applied economics. 6th ed. 1962. 4. 48. South-
Western Pub.
Dowd, Douglas F. Modern economic problems in historical perspective. in
prep. Heath
Ferguson, C. E., and J. M. Kreps. Principles of economics. 1962. 7. 95. Holt,
Rinehart & Winston
Galbraith, John Kenneth. Affluent society. 1958. 5. 00. Houghton
Galbraith, John K. Economics and the art of controversy. 1955. 2. 75. Rutgers
Gemmill, Paul F. Fundamentals of economics. 6th ed. 1960. 6. 75. Harper
George, Henry. Progress and poverty. (36) 1938. 1. 95. Modern Lib.
Heilbroner, Robert. Worldly philosophers. rev. ed. 1961. 5. 00. S. and S.
Hicks, J. R., and others. Social framework of the American economy: An
introduction to economics. 2nd ed. 1955. 4. 75. Oxford U. P.
Hicks, J. R. Value and capital: An inquiry into some fundamental principles
of economic theory. 2nd ed. il. 1946. 5. 00. Oxford U. P.
Keynes, John Maynard. General theory of employment, interest, and money.
1936. 6. 00. Harcourt
Kiekhofer, William Henry. Economic principles, problems, and policies.
4th ed. 1951. 5. 50. Appleton

Lauterbach, Albert. Man, motives, and money. 2nd ed. 1959. 5.00. Cornell

Lerner, Abba P. Economics of employment. il. 1951. 6.75. McGraw

Malthus, Thomas R. Definitions in political economy. 1827. 7.50. Kelley

Malthus, Thomas R. Principles of political economy. 2nd ed. 6.00. Kelley

Marx, Karl. Capital. 2.95. Modern Lib.

Mill, John Stuart. Principles of political economy. ed. by W. J. Ashley. 10.00. Kelley

Oxenfeldt, Alfred R. Economic principles and public issues. 1959. pap. 4.25. Holt, Rinehart & Winston

Paton, William A. Shirtsleeve economics: A commonsense survey. 1952. 4.50. Meredith

Pigou, Arthur C. Economics of welfare. 1920. 7.50. St. Martins

Polak, Jacques J. International economic system. il. 1954. 4.75. U. of Chicago

Polanyi, Karl, and others, eds. Trade and market in the early empires. 1957. 6.00. Free Press

Ricardo, David. Principles of political economy and taxation. 1933. 1.95. Dutton

Robinson, Marshall A., and others. Introduction to economic reasoning. rev. ed. 1960. 3.00. Brookings

Rowan, Leslie. Arms and economics: The changing challenge. 1961. 0.95. Cambridge U. P.

Samuelson, Paul A. Economics: An introductory analysis. 1961. 7.95. McGraw

Seligman, Edwin. Econimic interpretation of history. 1924. 3.00. Columbia

Sievers, Allen M. Revolution, evolution, and the economic order. 1962. 3.95; Prentice-Hall

Smith, Adam. Wealth of nations. (G32) 2.95. Modern Lib.

Soule, George. Economics: Measurement, theories, case studies. 1961. 5.75. Holt, Rinehart & Winston

Taussig, Frank W. Principles of economics. 4th ed. 2 vols. 1961. 6.50. ea. Macmillan

Tawney, R. H. Acquisitive society. 1946. 3.00. Harcourt

Walras, Leon. Elements of pure economics. tr. by William Jaffe. 1954. 7.75;' Irwin

Ward, A. Dudley, ed. Goals of economic life. 1953. 4.00. Harper

Weisskopf, Walter. Psychology of economics. 1955. 4.00. U. of Chicago

ECONOMICS--ADDRESSES, ESSAYS, LECTURES (330.18)

Buchanan, James M. Fiscal theory and political economy: Selected essays. 1960. 5.00. U. of N. C.

Burns, A. F. Frontiers of economic knowledge. 1954. 5.00. Princeton

Carnegie, Andrew. Gospel of wealth and other timely essays. ed. by Edward C. Kirkland. 1962. 4.50. Harvard

Friedman, Milton. Essays in positive economics. 1953. 6.25. U. of Chicago

Taylor, O. H. Economics and liberalism. 1955. 5.00. Harvard

Veblen, Thorstein B. Place of science in modern civilization. 1961. 7.50. Russell

ECONOMICS--BIBLIOGRAPHY (330.016)

Coman, Edwin T. Sources of business information. 1949. 5.95. Prentice-Hall

Sigband, Norman B. Effective report writing. 1960. 6.75. Harper

ECONOMICS--COLLECTIONS (330)

Bowditch, John, and Clement Ramsland, eds. Voices of the Industrial Revolution. 1961. 4.40. U. of Mich.

Harriss, Clement L., ed. Selected readings in economics. 1962. 3.95. Prentice-Hall

Hess, Arleigh P., Jr., and others. Outside readings in economics. 1956. 2.75. Crowell

Samuelson, Paul A., and others. Readings in economics. 1953. 4.50. McGraw

Spengler, Joseph J., and William R. Allen, eds. Essays in economic thought: Aristotle to Marshall. 8.50. Rand McNally

Veblen, Thorstein. Portable Veblen. by Max Lerner. 1948. 2.95. Viking

ECONOMICS--DICTIONARIES (330.03)
Horton, Byrne, and Julian Ripley. Dictionary of modern economics. 1948.
  5.00. Pub. Affairs (R)
Sloan, Harold S., and Arnold J. Zurcher. Dictionary of economics. 4th ed. rev.
  1961. 3.75. Barnes & Noble (R)
Wilson, Howard. Glossary of economic terms. 2nd ed rev. 1957. 0.50. Admin.
  Res. Associates (R)
ECONOMICS--HISTORY (330.9)
Dorfman, Joseph. Economic mind in American civilization. 5 vols. vols. 1-2
  (1606-1865) o.p. vol. 3 (1865-1918) 1949. 7.50; vol. 4-5 (1918-1933) 1959.
  12.50. Viking
Ellis, Howard S., ed. Survey of contemporary economics. vol. 1. 1948. 6.50;
  Irwin
Harris, Abram L. Economics and social reform. 1958. 5.00. Harper
Hazlitt, Henry. Failure of the new economics: An analysis of the Keynesian
  fallacies. 1959. 7.50. Van Nostrand

Knight, Frank H. On the history and method of economics. 1956. 6.00. U. of
  Chicago
Lekachman, Robert. History of economic ideas. 1959. 6.00. Harper
Levy, Lester S., and Roy J. Sampson. American economic development. il.
  1962. 10.60. Allyn & Bacon
Michell, Humfrey. Economics of ancient Greece. 1958. 8.50. Barnes & Noble
Schumpeter, Joseph. Ten great economists, from Marx to Keynes. 1951. 5.00.
  Oxford U. P.
Stigler, George J. Production and distribution theories. 1941. 5.75. Macmillan
Taylor, Overton H. History of economic thought. 1960. 7.95. McGraw
Toynbee, Arnold. Industrial Revolution. 1959. 3.25. Smith, Peter
Whittaker, Edmund. Schools and streams of economic thought. 6.50. Rand
  McNally
ECONOMICS--HISTORY--U.S. (330.9)
Galbraith, John Kenneth. Affluent society. 1958. 5.00. Houghton
Spiegel, Henry W. Rise of American economic thought. 1960. 5.00. Chilton
ECUADOR (986.6)
Linke, Lilo. Ecuador. 3rd ed. 1960. 4.00. Oxford U. P.
ECUMENICAL MOVEMENT (280.1)
Bradshaw, Marion J. Free churches and Christian unity. 1954. 3.50. Beacon
Cavert, Samuel M. On the road to Christian unity. 1961. 3.75? Harper
Garrison, Winfred E. Quest and character of a united church. 1957. 3.50.
  Abingdon
Goodall, Norman. Ecumenical movement. 1961. 4.50. Oxford U. P.
Hogg, W. Richey. One world, one mission. 1960. 2.95. study guide, 0.50.
  Friendship
Nelson, J. Robert. One Lord, one church. 1958. 1.25. Assn. Pr.
Outler, A. C. Christian tradition and the unity we seek. 1957. 3.25. Oxford U. P.
Visser't Hooft, Willem A. Pressure of our common calling. 1959. 2.50.
  Doubleday
EDICT OF NANTES (944)
Stankiewicz, Wladyslaw J. Politics and religion in seventeenth-century France.
  1960. 6.00. U. of Calif.
EDISON, THOMAS ALVA, 1847-1931 (923.573)
Josephson, Matthew. Edison. 1959. 6.95. McGraw
EDUCATION (370)
Adler, Mortimer J., and Milton Mayer. Revolution in education. 1958. 3.75.
  U. of Chicago
Alcott, Amos B. Essays on education, 1830-1862. 7.50. Scholars' Facs.
American Academy of Arts and Sciences. Education in the age of science. 1959.
  1.75. Am. Acad. of Arts & Sci.

American Council on Education, Executive Committee, and National Education
Association, American Association of School Administrators. Education and
national security. 1951. 0.50. A. C. E.
Buber, Martin. Between man and man. 1955. pap. 1.25. Beacon
Commager, Henry Steele. Our schools have kept us free. 1962. 0.25. N. E. A.
Conant, James Bryant. Education and liberty: The role of the schools in a
modern democracy. 1953. 3.50. Harvard
Dewey, John. Democracy and education. 5.25. Macmillan
Foff, Arthur, and Jean D. Grambs. Readings in education. 1956. 5.00. Harper
Foshay. Handbook of education. 5.00. Rand McNally
Gruber, Frederick C., ed. Quality and quantity in American education. 1960.
3.75. U. of Pa.
Harvard Committee. General education in a free society. 1945. 4.00. Harvard
International Conference on World Education Problems, Vassar College, 1961.
Education in world perspective. ed. by Emmet J. Hughes. 1962. 4.75. Harper
Kandel, I. L. New era in education. 1955. 5.00. Houghton
Kelley, Earl C., and Marie I. Rasey. Education and the nature of man. 1952.
3.75. Harper
King, Edmund J. Other schools and ours. il. 1959. 5.75. Holt, Rinehart &
Winston
King, Edmund. World perspectives in education. 1962. 6.00? Bobbs
Locke, John. On politics and education. 1947. 1.75. Van Nostrand
Mann, Horace. Republic and the school: The education of free men. ed. by
Lawrence A. Cremin. 1959. 2.50. T. C.
Maritain, Jacques. Education at the crossroads. 1943. 3.00; 1960. Yale
Mayer, Frederick. New perspectives for education. 1962. 3.25. Pub. Affairs
Molnar, Thomas S. Future of education. 1961. 3.95. Fleet
Mursell, James. Principles of democratic education. 1955. 4.95. Norton
National Education Association, Educational Policies Commission. Essay on
quality in public education. 1959. 0.35. N. E. A.
National Education Association, Educational Policies Commission. Mass
communication and education. 1958. 1.50. N. E. A.
Russell, Bertrand. Education and the good life. 1931. 3.50. Liveright
Russell, Wylie H. Student guide to the study of education. 1959. 3.00. Educ.
Pubs. Inc.
Traxler, Arthur E., ed. Improving the efficiency and quality of learning. 1962.
pap. 2.50. A. C. E.
Traxler, Arthur E., ed. Vital issues in education. 1957. 2.00. A. C. E.
Ward, William E. F. Educating young nations. 1960. 2.70. Oxford U. P.
EDUCATION--ADDRESSES, ESSAYS, LECTURES (370.4)
Commager, Henry Steele, and others. Education in a free society, vol. 2. 1960.
3.00. U. of Pittsburgh
Day, Edmund Ezra. Education for freedom and responsibility: Selected essays
by Edmund Ezra Day. ed. by Milton R. Konvitz. 1952. 2.50. Cornell
Dewey, John. Philosophy of education. 1956. pap. 1.50. Littlefield
Dewey, John. Sources of a science of education. 2.00. Liveright
Eliot, Charles W. Education for efficiency. 1906. 1.50. Houghton
Eliot, Charles W. Tendency to the concrete and practical in modern education.
1.50. Houghton
Hutchins, Robert M. Education for freedom. 1943. 2.50. La. State
Phelps, William Lyon. Excitement of teaching. 1931. 2.00. Liveright
Spencer, Herbert. Essays on education. 1.95. Dutton
Van Til, William. Making of a modern educator. 1961. pap. 1.95. Bobbs
Walsh, William. Use of imagination. 1961. 5.00. Barnes & Noble
Whitehead, Alfred North. Aims of education. 5.00. Macmillan
EDUCATION--AIMS AND OBJECTIVES (370.1)
Adams, Fay G. Educating America's children. 2nd ed. 1954. 5.75. Ronald

Cook, Lloyd A., and Elaine F. Cook. Sociological approach to education. 3rd ed. 1960. 6.95. McGraw

Kilpatrick, W. H. Education and the social crisis. 1932. 2.00. Liveright

Mayer, Frederick. Goals of education. 1959. 3.25. Pub. Affairs

Tead, Ordway. Equalizing educational opportunities beyond the secondary school. 1947. 1.00. Harvard

Tyler, Fred T., ed. Individualizing instruction. (NSSE yearbk. 1961 pt. 1). 1962. 4.50. U. of Chicago

Woelfel, Norman. Educational goals for America. 1962. 3.75. Pub. Affairs

EDUCATION--BIBLIOGRAPHY (370.016)

Alexander, Carter, and Arvid J. Burke. How to locate educational information and data. 4th ed. 1958. 6.25. T. C.

National Education Association, International Relations Committee. American dissertations on foreign education. 1959. 1.00. N. E. A.

EDUCATION--CURRICULA (371)

Faunce, Roland C., and Nelson L. Bossing. Developing the core curriculum. 2nd ed. 1958. 6.95. Prentice-Hall

General education in school and college: A committee report by members of the faculties of Andover, Exeter, Lawrenceville, Harvard, Princeton, and Yale. 1952. 2.50. Harvard

Kandel, Isaac L., and others. International understanding through the public-school curriculum. NSSE, 36th yearbook pt. 2. 2.50. U. of Chicago

Krug, Edward A. Curriculum planning. rev. ed. 1957. 4.00. Harper

Leese, Joseph, and others. Teacher in curriculum making. 1961. 5.50. Harper

National Education Association, Association for Supervision and Curriculum Development. Balance in the curriculum, yearbk. 1961. 4.00. N. E. A.

National Education Association, Association for Supervision and Curriculum Development. New dimensions in learning: A multidisciplinary approach. 1962. 1.50. N. E. A.

National Education Association, Association for Supervision and Curriculum Development. Perceiving, behaving, becoming. 1962. 4.50. N. E. A.

National Education Association, Association for Supervision and Curriculum Development. Self-contained classroom. 1960. 1.25. N. E. A.

National Education Association, Association for Supervision and Curriculum Development. What are the sources of the curriculum? 1962. 1.50. N. E. A.

National Education Association, National School Public Relations Association. Who should plan the curriculum? 1962. 0.50. N. E. A.

National Education Association, Supervision and Curriculum Development Department. Forces affecting American education, yearbook. 1953. 3.50. N. E. A.

Parker, J. Cecil, and others. Curriculum in America. 1962. 6.75. Crowell

Traxler, Arthur E., ed. Curriculum planning to meet tomorrow's needs. 1960. pap. 2.00. A. C. E.

Whitehead, Alfred North. Aims of education. 5.00. Macmillan

EDUCATION--DICTIONARIES (370.3)

Good, Carter. Dictionary of education. 2nd ed. 1959. 10.75. McGraw (R)

Harris, Chester, ed. Encyclopedia of educational research. 3rd ed. 1960. 25.00. Macmillan (R)

Smith, Edward. W., and others. Educator's encyclopedia. 1961. 19.50. Prentice-Hall (R)

EDUCATION--EARLY WORKS TO 1800 (371.3)

Comenius, John A. School of infancy. ed. by Ernest M. Eller. 1957. 1.00. U. of N. C.

Kant, Immanuel. Education. 1960. 4.40. U. of Mich.

Rousseau, J. J. Emile,or education. 1.95. Dutton

EDUCATION--EXPERIMENTAL METHODS (371.3)

Morse, A. D. Schools of tomorrow - today. 3.50. Smith, Peter

Rusk, Robert R. Outline of experimental education. 1961. 3.50. St. Martins

EDUCATION--HISTORY (370.9)

Boyd, William. History of western education. 6th ed. 4.50. Macmillan

Brubacher, John S. History of the problems of education. 1947. 7.50. McGraw

Butts, R. F. Cultural history of western education. 2nd ed. 1955. 7.50. McGraw

Cole, Luella. History of education: From Socrates to Montessori. 1950. 7.50. Holt, Rinehart & Winston

Cubberley, Ellwood P. History of education. 1922. 7.25. Houghton

Eby, Frederick. Development of modern education. 2nd ed. 1952. 7.75. Prentice-Hall

Eby, Frederick, and Charles F. Arrowood. History and philosophy of education ancient and medieval. 1940. 11.65. Prentice-Hall

Good, Harry G. History of western education. il. 1960. 6.50; 2nd ed. 1962. 6.75. Macmillan

Graves, Frank P. Student's history of education. rev. ed. 6.50. Macmillan

Mayer, Frederick. History of educational thought. il. 1960. 7.50. Merrill, C. E.

Mulhern, J. History of education. 2nd ed. 1959. 7.50. Ronald

Myers, Edward DeL. Education in the perspective of history. 1960. 6.00. Harper

Power, E. J. Main currents in the history of education. 1962. 7.50. McGraw

Thompson, Merritt M. History of education. 3rd ed. 1951. pap. 1.25. Barnes & Noble

Thut, I. N. Story of education. 1957. 6.75. McGraw

Ulich, Robert, ed. Education of nations. 1961. 6.75. Harvard

Ulich, Robert, ed. Three thousand years of educational wisdom: Selections from great documents. 2nd ed. 1954. 7.00. Harvard

EDUCATION--PERIODICALS--INDEXES (370.050)

Education index. 5 vols. 1947-1959. vol. 12. 1959-1961. Sold on service basis. Wilson (R)

EDUCATION--PHILOSOPHY (370.1)

Bell, Terrell H. Philosophy of education for the space age. 1962. 2.75. Exposition

Brackenbury, Robert L. Getting down to cases. 1958. 4.00. Putnam

Brameld, Theodore B. H. Education for the emerging age. 1961. 3.75. Harper

Brubacher, John S. Eclectic philosophy of education. 1962. 7.50. Prentice-Hall

Brubacher, John S. Modern philosophies and education. NSSE, 54th yrbk. pt. 1. 1955. 4.50. U. of Chicago

Brubacher, John S. Modern philosophies of education. 2nd ed. 1950. 6.75. McGraw

Brubacher, John S. Philosophies of education. NSSE, 41st yrbk. pt. 1. 1942. 3.00. U. of Chicago

Byrne, Herbert W. Christian approach to education. il. 1961. 4.95. Zondervan

Curti, Merle E. Social ideas of American educators. 4.95. Cooper

Dewey, John. Dewey on education. ed. by Martin S. Dworkin. il. 1959. 2.50; T. C.

Fuller, Edmund, ed. Christian idea of education. 2 pts. pt. 1. 1957. 4.00; 1960. pap. 1.45; pt. 2, Schools and scholarship. 1962. 6.50. Yale

Gruber, Frederick C. Foundations for a philosophy of education. il. 1961. 5.75. Crowell

Hansen, Kenneth H. Philosophy for American education. 1960. 6.25. Prentice-Hall

Henderson, Stella Van Petten. Introduction to the phiolsophy of education. 1947. 5.75. U. of Chicago

Hutchins, Robert M. Conflict in education: In a democratic society. 1953. 3.00. Harper

Jefferson, Thomas. Crusade against ignorance: Thomas Jefferson on education. ed. by Gordon C. Lee. 1961. 2.50. T. C.

Jones, Howard Mumford. Reflections on learning. 1958. 2.75. Rutgers
Kilpatrick, William Heard. Philosophy of education. 1951. 5.75. Macmillan
Lerner, Max. Education and a radical humanism. 1962. 2.50. Ohio State
Lewis, C. S. Abolition of man. 1947. 2.50. Macmillan
Mayer, Frederick, and Frank E. Brower. Education for maturity. 1956. 3.25.
    Pub. Affairs
National Education Association, American Educational Research Association.
    Philosophical and social framework of education. 1958. 2.00; 1961. 2.00.
    N. E. A.
Park, Joe, ed. Selected readings in the philosophy of education. 5.50.
    Macmillan
Riesman, David. Constraint and variety in American education. 1958. pap. 0.95.
    Doubleday
Smith, Mortimer. And madly teach. 1949. 2.75. Regnery
Thelen, Herbert A. Education and the human quest. 1960. 4.75. Harper

EDUCATION--SOCIETIES, ETC. (371.104)

Dale, Edgar. Mass media and education. NSSE, 53rd yrbk. pt. 2. 1954. 4.50;
    J. of Chicago
Terman, Lewis M. Nature and nurture. pt. 1: Their influence upon intelligence;
    pt. 2; Their influence upon achievement. NSSE, 27th yrbk. pts. 1 and 2. 1928.
    pap. 1.75 ea. U. of Chicago

EDUCATION--STATISTICS (311)

Blommers, Paul J., and E. F. Lindquist. Elementary statistical methods in
    psychology and education. il. 1960. 6.00. Houghton
David, Martin, and others. Educational achievement: Its causes and effects.
    1961. pap. 2.00. U. of Mich.
Garrett, Henry E. Statistics in psychology and education. 5th ed. 1958. 5.75.
    McKay
Guilford, J. P. Fundamental statistics in psychology and education. 3rd ed.
    1956. 7.25. McGraw
Ruch, Floyd and others. Intermediate statistics in psychology and education.
    3.50. Lucas Bros.
Wert, James E., and others. Statistical methods in educational and psy-
    chological research. il. 1954. 6.00. Appleton

EDUCATION--YEAR-BOOKS (370.58)

Kirk, Samuel A. Education of exceptional children. NSSE, 49th yrbk. pt. 2.
    1950. 4.50. U. of Chicago
National Education Association, National Council of Teachers of Mathematics.
    Growth of mathematical ideas, yearbook. 1959. 5.00. N. E. A.
National Education Association, Supervision and Curriculum Development
    Department. Forces affecting American education, yearbook. 1953. 3.50.
    N. E. A.

EDUCATION--EAST (FAR EAST) (378.4)

Vining, Elizabeth Gray. Windows for the crown prince. il. 1952. 6.00.
    Lippincott

EDUCATION--EUROPE (378.4)

Rickover, Hyman G. Swiss schools and ours. il. 1962. bds. 3.95. (Atlantic
    Monthly Press) Little
Samuel, Richard H., and R. Hinton Thomas. Education and society in modern
    Germany. 1949. 3.50. Humanities

EDUCATION--RUSSIA (378.4)

Bereday, George Z. F., and others. Changing Soviet school. 1960. 6.50;
    Houghton
Counts, George S. Challenge of soviet education. 1957. 6.50. McGraw
Harnwell, Gaylord P. Russian diary. 1959. 3.75. U. of Pa.
Hechinger, Fred M. Big red schoolhouse. 1959. 3.95. Doubleday
Kline, George L., ed. Soviet education. 1957. 4.00. Columbia
Korol, A. G. Soviet education for science and technology. 1957. 8.50 Wiley

Levin, Deana. Soviet education today. 1959. 3.00. De Graff

Trace, Arthur S., Jr. What Ivan knows that Johnny doesn't. 1961. 3.95.
Random

Vigdorova, F. Diary of a Russian schoolteacher. tr. by Rose Prokofieva.
1960. 5.00. Grove

EDUCATION--U.S. (378.4)

Adler, Irving. What we want of our schools. 1957. 3.75 Day

Bent, Rudyard K., and Henry H. Kronenberg. Principles of secondary education.
4th ed. il. 1961. 6.75. McGraw

Bereday, George Z. F., and Luigi Volpicelli. Public education in America: A
new interpretation of purpose and practice. 1958. 4.50. Harper

Bestor, Arthur. Restoration of learning. 1955. 6.75. Knopf

Brubacher; John S. Eclectic philosophy of education. 1962. 7.50. Prentice-Hall

Buttrick, George A. Faith and education. 1952. 2.00. Abingdon

Callahan, Raymond E. Introduction to education in American society. 1956.
5.75. Knopf

Conant, James B. Slums and suburbs: A commentary on schools in metropolitan areas. 1961. bds. 3.95. McGraw

Coulter, E. Merton. College life in the old South. 4.50. U. of Ga.

Counts, George S. Education and American civilization. 1952. 4.00. T. C.

Covello, Leonard, and Guido D'Agostino. Heart is the teacher. 1958. 4.75.
McGraw

Crow, Lester D., and Alice. Introduction to education. rev. ed. 1960. 6.25. Am.
Bk. Co.

Dewey, John, and Evelyn. Schools of tomorrow. pap. 1.65. Dutton

De Young, Chris A., and R. Wynn. American education. 4th ed. 1960. 6.75;
McGraw

Dunn, Joan. Retreat from learning: Why teachers can't teach...A case history.
1955. 3.75. McKay

Fine, Benjamin. Modern family guide to education. 7.50. Doubleday (R)

Fletcher, Cyril S., ed. Education: The challenge ahead. 1962. bds. 4.50.
Norton

Gilchrist, Robert S., and others. Secondary education for American democracy. rev. ed. 1957. 5.00. Rinehart

Gruber, Frederick, C. Education in transition. 1960. 3.75. U. of Pa.

Harvard Committee. General education in a free society. 1945. 4.00. Harvard

Haskew, Laurence D. F. Discipline of education and America's future. 1959.
1.50. U. of Pittsburgh

Haskew, L. D. This is teaching. rev. ed. 1962. 5.75. Scott

Henry, David D. What priority for education? The American people must
soon decide. 1961. 2.50. U. of Ill.

Hillway, Tyrus. Education in American society. il. 1961. 6.00. Houghton

Hutchins, Robert M. Conflict in education: In a democratic society. 1953.
3.00. Harper

Hutchins, Robert M. Some observations on American education. 1956. 2.75.
Cambridge U. P.

Kandel, I. L. American education in the twentieth century. 1957. 5.00. Harvard

Kandel, Isaac L. Impact of the war on American education. 1949. 4.25. U. of
N. C.

Knight, Edgar W. Education in the South. 1924. 0.50. U. of N. C.

McClellan, Grant S., ed. America's educational needs. 1958. 2.00. Wilson

Mayer, Martin. Schools. 1961. 5.50. Harper

Mort, Paul R., and W. S. Vincent. Modern education practice: A handbook
for teachers. 1950. 6.50. McGraw

National Education Association, Educational Policies Commission. Contemporary issues in elementary education. 1960. 0.35. N. E. A.

Perkins, John A. Plain talk from a campus. 1959. 4.00. Univ. Pub.

Reeder, Ward G. First course in education. 4th ed. 6.25. Macmillan

Reinhardt, Emma. American education, rev. ed. 1960. 5.50. Harper
Rickover, Hyman G. Education and freedom. 1959. 3.50. Dutton
Rockefeller Brothers Fund. Pursuit of excellence: Manpower and education.
    1959. pap. 0.75. Doubleday
Rudd, Augustin G. Bending the twig. 3.95. Bookmailer
Rugg, Harold. Foundations for American education. 7.50. Harcourt
Rugg, Harold, and B. Marian Brooks. Teacher in school and society. 5.50.
    Harcourt
Russell, J. D., and C. H. Judd. American educational system. 1940. 5.00.
    Houghton
Still, Joseph W. Science and education at the crossroads. 1958. 3.75. Pub.
    Affairs
Traxler, Arthur E., ed. Education in a free world. 1.75. A. C. E.
Traxler, Arthur E., ed. Long-range planning for education. 1958. 2.00. A. C. E.
Traxler, Arthur E., ed. Positive values in the American educational system.
    1959. 2.00. A. C. E.
Tyler, Ralph W., ed. Social forces influencing American education. 1961. 4.50;
    pap. 3.75. U. of Chicago
Warner, W. Lloyd, and others. Who shall be educated? 1944. 3.50. Harper
Wilson, Charles. Teacher is a person. 1956. 3.75. Holt
Woodring, Paul. Fourth of a nation. 1957. 4.95. McGraw
Woodring, Paul. Let's talk sense about our schools. 1953. 3.75. McGraw
Woodrow Wilson Foundation. Education in the nation's service. 1960. 4.75.
    Praeger

EDUCATION--U.S.--FINANCE (378.4)
Mort, Paul R., and others. Public school finance. 3rd ed. 1960. 7.50. McGraw
Rivlin, Alice M. Role of the Federal Government in financing higher education.
    1961. 3.00. Brookings
Steel, Ronald, ed. Federal aid to education. 1961. 2.50. Wilson

EDUCATION--U.S.--HISTORY (379.4)
Butts, R. Freeman, and Lawrence A. Cremin. History of education in American
    culture. 1953. 6.75. Holt
Conant, James B. Thomas Jefferson and the development of American public
    education. 1960. 5.50. U. of Calif.
Cubberley, Ellwood P. Public education in the United States. 1919. 7.75.
    Houghton
Good, Harry G. History of American education. 2nd ed. il. 1956. 6.50.
    Macmillan'
Hofstadter, Richard. Academic freedom in the age of the college. 1961. Columbia

EDUCATION, COOPERATIVE (378)
Wilson, James W., and Edward H. Lyons. Work-study college programs. 1961.
    3.50. Harper

EDUCATION, ELEMENTARY (372)
Brogan, Peggy, and Lorene K. Fox. Helping children learn. 4.50. Harcourt
Crow, Lester D., and others, eds. Teaching in the elementary school. 1961.
    McKay
Cutts, Norma E., and Nicholas Moseley. Providing for individual differences
    in the elementary school. il. 1960. 7.95. Prentice-Hall
Hofstadter, R., and W. P. Metzger. Development of academic freedom in the
    United States. 1955. 6.50. Columbia
Knight Edgar W., ed. Documentary history of education in the South before
    1860. 5 vols. vols. 2-5, 5.00 ea; vol. 1, available only in set; set, 25.00.
    U. of N. C.
Knight, Edgar Wallace. Fifty years of American education, 1900=1950. 1952.
    6.00. Ronald
Knight, Edgar W., and Clifton L. Hall. Readings in American educational
    history. 1951. 6.00. Appleton
Meyer, A. E. Educational history of the American people. 1957. 6.95. McGraw
Morison, Samuel E. Intellectual life of colonial New England. pap. 1.95. Cornell

Meeker, Alice. Teachers at work in the elementary school. 1962. pap. 2.00?
 Bobbs
Otto, Henry J. Elementary school organization and administration. 3rd ed. il.
 1954. 6.00. Appleton

EDUCATION, ELEMENTARY--CURRICULA (372.2)

Beck, Robert H., and others. Curriculum in the modern elementary school.
 2nd ed. 1960. 7.25. Prentice-Hall
Hurley, B. D. Curriculum for elementary school children. 1957. 6.00. Ronald
National Education Association, American Educational Research Association.
 Educational program: Early and middle childhood. 1959. 2.00. N. E. A.
Rucker, W. Ray. Curriculum development in the elementary school. 1960.
 5.00. Harper

EDUCATION, HIGHER (378)

American Council on Education, Executive Committee on the Cooperative
 Study in General Education. Cooperation in general education. 3.00. A. C. E.
Barzun, Jacques. Teacher in America. 1945. 5.00. Little
Bellman, Samuel I., ed. College experience. 1962. pap. 2.25. Chandler Pub.
Brickman, William W., and Stanley Lehrer, eds. Century of higher education.
 1962. 4.95. Soc. for the Advancement of Educ.
Brubacher, John S., and Willis Rudy. Higher education in transition: An
 American history, 1636-1956. 1958. 8.50. Harper
Carmichael, Oliver C. Universities: Commonwealth and American. 1959. 6.00.
 Harper
Conant, James Bryant. Citadel of learning. 1956. 2.50. Yale
Cronkhite, Bernice B., ed. Handbook for college teachers. 1950. 3.75. Harvard
Dressel, Paul L., and Lewis B. Mayhew, eds. General education: Explorations
 in evaluation. 1954. 3.50. A. C. E.
Educational Records Bureau. College freshmen speak out. ed. by Agatha
 Townsend. 1956. 5.00. Harper
Eurich, Alvin C. General education in the American college. NSSE, 38th yrbk.
 pt. 2. 1939. 2.75. U. of Chicago
Fisher, Margaret B., and Jeanne L. Noble. College education as personal
 development. 1960. 4.95. Prentice-Hall
Garrison, Roger H. Adventure of learning in college. 1959. 3.50. Harper
General education in school and college: A committee report by members of
 the faculties of Andover, Exeter, Lawrenceville, Harvard, Princeton and
 Yale. 1952. 2.50. Harvard
Griswold, A. W. In the university tradition. 1957. 3.00. Yale
Harris, M. Lafayette. Voice in the wilderness. 1941. 1.50. Christopher
Havighurst, Robert J. American higher education in the 1960's il. 1960.
 2.50. Ohio State
Henderson, Algo D. Policies and practices in higher education. 1960. 5.75.
 Harper
Hofstadter, Richard, and Wilson Smith. American higher education. 2 vols.
 15.00. U. of Chicago
Hopkins, Ernest Martin. College mind. 1930. 1.00. Dartmouth
Houle, Cyril O., and Charles A. Nelson. University, the citizen, and world
 affairs. 1956. 3.00. A. C. E.
Hutchines, Robert M. Higher learning in America. 1936. 7.50. Yale
Jacob, Philip E. Changing values in college. 1958. 3.50. Harper
Knight, Edgar W. What college presidents say. 1940. 1.30. U. of N. C.
McConnell, Thomas R. General pattern for American public higher education.
 il. 1962. 4.95. McGraw
Mayer, Frederick. Creative universities. 3.50. Twayne
Millett, John D. Liberating arts. 1957. 2.25. Allen, Howard
Newman, John Henry. Idea of a university. by Martin Svaglic. 1959. pap. 1.25.
 Rinehart.
Newman, John H. Select discourses from Idea of a university. ed. by May
 Yardley. 1.75. Cambridge U. P.

Sanford, R. Nevitt. American college: A psychological and social interpretation of higher learning. 1962. 8.75. Wiley
Tead, Ordway. Climate of learning. 1958. 2.50. Harper
Tead, O. College teaching and college learning. 1949. 2.75. Yale
Trueblood, Elton. Idea of a college. 1959. 4.00. Harper
Veblen, Thorstein. Higher learning in America. 3.25. Smith, Peter
Williams, George. Some of my best friends are professors. 1958. 3.95. Abelard
Workman, John R. New horizons of higher education. 1959. 2.50. Pub. Affairs

EDUCATION, HIGHER--ADDRESSES, ESSAYS, LECTURES (378)
Gould, Samuel B. Knowledge is not enough. 1959. 3.50. Antioch
Hutchins, Robert M., and others. What's a college for? 1961. 2.50. Pub. Affairs

EDUCATION, HUMANISTIC (378)
Burkhardt, Frederick H. Science and the humanities. 1959. pap. 0.50. Antioch
Dressel, Paul L. Evaluation of general education programs. 1954. pap. 4.25. Brown, W. C.
Dressel, Paul L., and Lewis B. Mayhew, eds. General education: Explorations in evaluation. 1954. 3.50. A. C. E.
Fisher, James A. Humanities in general education. 1960. 4.50. Brown, W. C.
Greene, Theodore M. Liberal education reconsidered. 1953. 1.50. Harvard
Griswold, A. Whitney. Liberal education and the democratic ideal. 1959. pap. 1.25. Yale
McGrath, Earl J. Liberal education in the professions. 1959. pap. 1.50. T. C.
McGrath, Earl J., and others. Toward general education. 1948. 5.50. Macmillan
Thomas, Russell B. Search for a common learning. 1962. 6.95. McGraw
Van Doren, Mark. Liberal education. 1959. pap. 1.75. Beacon
Woody, Thomas. Liberal education for free men. 1951. 4.00. U. of Pa.

EDUCATION, MEDIEVAL (378.09)
Haskins, Charles Homer. Rise of universities. 1957. pap. 1.25. Cornell
Schachner, Nathan. Mediaeval universities. 1962. pap. 2.45. Barnes, A. S.
Thompson, James Westfall. Literacy of the laity in the Middle Ages. 1960. 9.50. Franklin, B.
Thorndike, L. University records and life in the Middle Ages. 1944. 5.75. Columbia

EDUCATION, PRIMARY (372)
Lambert, Hazel M. Early childhood education. il. 1961. 8.65. Allyn & Bacon

EDUCATION, RURAL (379.173)
Strang, Ruth. Education in rural communities. NSSE, 51st yearbook. pt. 2. 1952. 4.50. U. of Chicago

EDUCATION, SECONDARY (373)
Beatley, B. Achievement in the junior high school. 1932. 2.00. Harvard
Bossing, Nelson L. Principles of secondary education. 2nd ed. 1955. 9.25. Prentice-Hall
Butler, Frank A. Improvement of teaching in secondary schools. 3rd ed. 1954. 5.50. U. of Chicago
Carter, L. William, and others. Learning to teach in the secondary school. il. 1962. 6.50. Macmillan
Conant, James B. American high school today. il. 1959. 2.95. McGraw
Conant, James Bryant. Child, the parent, and the state. 1959. 3.50. Harvard
Douglass, Harl R. Modern administration of secondary schools. 1954. 7.25; rev. ed. in prep. Ginn
Educational Records Bureau. High school students speak out. ed. by David Mallery. 1962. 3.75. Harper
French, William M. American secondary education. 4.25. Odyssey
Halverson, Paul M., ed. Frontiers of secondary education. vol. 1, 1956; vol. 2, 1957; vol. 3, 1958; vol. 4, 1959; pap. 2.25 ea; vol. 5, 1960; pap. 1.75. Syracuse

Koerner, James D., ed. Case for basic education. 1959. 4.00. Little

Mills, H. H., and H. R. Douglass. Teaching in high school. 2nd ed. 1957. 6.25. Ronald

National Education Association, Association for Supervision and Curriculum Development. High school we need. 1959. 0.50. N. E. A.

Wellington, Charles B., and Jean. Teaching for critical thinking. 1960. 6.50. McGraw

EDUCATION AND STATE--U.S. (379)

American Assembly. Federal Government and higher education. ed. by Douglas Knight. 1960. 3.50. Prentice-Hall

Babbidge, Homer D.; and R. M. Rosenzweig. Federal interest in higher education. 1962. 5.95. McGraw

Blum, Virgil C. Freedom of choice in education. 1958. 3.95. Macmillan

Gruber, Frederick C., ed. Education and the state. 1960. 2.75. U. of Pa.

Moos, Malcolm, and Francis E. Rourke. Campus and the state. 1959. 6.00. Johns Hopkins

Orlans, Harold. Effects of Federal programs on higher education. 1962. 5.00; Brookings

EDUCATION OF ADULTS (374)

American Library Association. Studying the community: A basis for planning library adult services. 1960. pap. 2.50. A. L. A.

Grattan, C. Hartley. In quest of knowledge. 1955. 4.75. Assn. Pr.

Houle, Cyril O. Inquiring mind: A study of the adult who continues to learn. 1961. pap. 1.50. U. of Wis.

Knowles, M. S. Adult education movement in the United States. 5.00. Holt, Rinehart & Winston

EDUCATION OF CHILDREN (371.92)

California School Supervisors Association. Guiding the young child, kindergarten to grade three. 2nd ed. by Helen Heffernan. il. 1959. 6.00. Heath

Dewey, John. Child and the curriculum. 1902. 1.50. U. of Chicago

Dewey, John. School and society. 2nd ed. il. 1915. 4.00. U. of Chicago

Featherstone, William B. Teaching the slow learner. rev. ed. 1951. pap. 1.25. T. C.

Fine, Lillian, and Benjamin. How to get the best education for your child. 1959. 3.95. Putnam

Frasier, George Willard. Introduction to the study of education. rev. ed. 1956. 6.00. Harper

Hathaway, Winifred. Education and health of the partially seeing child. 4th ed. 1959. 5.00. Columbia

Hildreth, Gertrude. Readiness for school beginners. 5.00. Harcourt

National Education Association, American Educational Research Association. Educational program: Early and middle childhood. 1959. 2.00. N. E. A.

National Education Association, Educational Research Service. Help for the underachiever in 59 school districts. 1961. 1.00. N. E. A.

Otto, Henry J., and others. Principles of elementary education. rev. ed. 1955. 5.50. Rinehart

Pechstein, L. A., and Frances Jenkins. Psychology of the kindergarten-primary child. 1927. 4.00. Houghton

Pintner, Rudolph, and others. Psychology of the physically handicapped. il. 1941. 3.50. Appleton

Sherry, Richard. Treatise of schemes and tropes, 1550, bd. with Desiderius Erasmus' Education of children. tr. by Richard Sherry. 7.50. Scholars' Facs.

EDUCATION OF WOMEN (376)

Cirautas, Kazys C. American college girl. 1962. 3.95. Citadel

Mueller, Kate Hevner. Education women for a changing world. 1954. 4.75. U. of Minn.

Muller, Leo C., and Ouida G. College for coeds. 1960. 3.95. Pitman

National Education Association, National Association of Women Deans and
Counselors. Changing patterns in the higher education of women. 1962.
1.25. N. E. A.
Newcomer, Mabel. Century of higher education for American women. 1959.
5.00. Harper

EDUCATIONAL PSYCHOLOGY (370.15)

Baller, W. R. Readings in the psychology of human growth and development.
1962. pap. 4.75. Holt, Rinehart & Winston
Blair, Glenn M., and others. Educational psychology. il. 1954. 6.25; 2nd ed. il.
1962. 7.00. Macmillan
Cole, Lawrence E., and William F. Bruce. Educational psychology. rev. ed.
6.95. Harcourt
Cronbach, Lee J. Educational psychology. il. 1954. 10.00; instructor's manual
gratis. Harcourt
Crow, Lester D., and Alice. Educational psychology. rev. ed. 1959. 6.25; tests
and problems, 0.75. Am. Bk. Co.
Crow, Lester D., and Alice. Readings in educational psychology. 1956. pap.
1.95. Littlefield
Dewey, John. How we think. 1933. 5.00. Heath
Dreikurs, Rudolf. Psychology in the classroom. 1957. 4.50. Harper
Edwards, A. S. Psychology of elementary education. 1925. 4.50. Houghton
Frandsen, Arden N. How children learn: An educational psychology. il. 1957.
6.75; instructor's manual, 1.00. McGraw
Fullager, William A., and others. Readings for educational psychology. 1956.
bds. 3.50. Crowell
Garrison, K. C., and D. G. Force, Jr. Psychology of exceptional children. 3rd
ed. 1959. 6.50. Ronald
Gates, Arthur I., and others. Educational psychology. 3rd ed. il. 6.25.
Macmillan
Harris, Irving D. Emotional blocks to learning. 1961. 4.00. Free Press
James, William. Talks to teachers. 1962. pap. 1.00. Dover
James, William. Talks to teachers on psychology and to students on some of
life's ideals. 1958. pap. 1.25. Norton
Jones, Ernest. Papers on psychoanalysis. 1961. pap. 2.65. Beacon
Lane, Howard, and Mary Beauchamp. Human relations in teaching. 1955. 6.75.
Prentice-Hall
Levine, Albert J. Fundamentals of psychological guidance. 2.00. Sci-Art
Mead, Margaret. School in American culture. 1951. 1.50. Harvard
Morse, William C., and G. Max Wingo. Psychology and teaching. rev. ed.
1962. 6.75. Scott
Murray, A. L. Psychology for Christian teachers. 1943. 2.50. Zondervan
Pintner, Rudolf, and others. Educational psychology. 1936. pap. 1.50. Barnes
& Noble
Pressey, S. L., and Francis Robinson. Laboratory workbook in applied
educational psychology. 1.00. Harper
Seidman, J. Readings in educational psychology. 3.75. Houghton
Skinner, Charles E., ed. Educational psychology. 4th ed. 1959. 7.95. Prentice-
Hall
Skinner, Charles E., ed. Essentials of educational psychology. 3rd ed. of
Elementary educational psychology. 1958. 9.00. Prentice-Hall
Stephens, John M. Educational psychology: Study of educational growth. 1956.
rev. ed. 7.25. Holt, Rinehart & Winston
Symonds, Percival M. What education has to learn from psychology. 3rd ed.
1960. pap. 1.50. T. C.
Thelen, Herbert A. Education and the human quest. 1960. 4.75. Harper
Trow, William C. Psychology in teaching and learning. il. 1960. 5.75. Houghton
Waddell, Charles W. Introduction to child psychology. 4.00. Houghton
Witty, Paul A. Mental health in modern education. NSSE, 54th yearbook. pt. 2.
1955. 4.50; pap. 3.75. U. of Chicago

EDUCATIONAL RESEARCH (370. 78)

Dressel, Paul L., and others. Evaluation in higher education. il. 1961. 6.25. Houghton

Encyclopedia of educational research. 25.00. Collier-Macmillan (R)

Good, Carter V. Introduction to educational research. 2nd ed. 1962. 6.00. Appleton

Hunnicutt, C. W., and William J. Iverson. Research in the three r's. 1958. 6.00. Harper

Lindquist, E. F. Statistical analysis in educational research. 6.00. Houghton

Traxler, Arthur E., ed. Measurement and research in today's schools. 1961. 2.50. A. C. E.

Van Dalen, Deobold B. Understanding educational research. 1962. 6.95. McGraw

EDUCATIONAL SOCIOLOGY (370.193)

Bell, Robert R., ed. Sociology of education, a source book. il. 1962. 8.65. Dorsey

Collier, Kenneth G. Social purposes of education. 4.50. Humanities

Cook, Lloyd A., and Elaine F. Cook. Sociological approach to education. 3rd ed. 1960. 6.95. McGraw

Davis, Allison. Social-class influences upon learning. 1948. pap. 1.00. Harvard

Gross, Carl H., and others. School and society: Readings in the social and philosophical foundations of education. 1962. 7.25. Heath

Halsey, A. H. and others, ed. Education, economy, and society. 1961. 7.50. Free Press

Havighurst, Robert J., and Bernice L. Neugarten. Society and education. 2nd ed. 1961. 9.25. Allyn & Bacon

Hodgkin, R. A. Education and change. 1957. 1.60. Oxford U. P.

Hodgkinson, Harold L. Education in social and cultural perspectives. il. 1962. 3.95. Prentice-Hall

Howes, Raymond F., ed. Higher education and the society it serves. 1957. 1.00. A. C. E.

Moore, C. H., and W. E. Cole. Sociology in educational practice. 5.50. Houghton

National Education Association, Educational Finance Committee. Education and economic growth. il. 1961. pap. 1.00. N. E. A.

National Education Association, Elementary School Principals Department. Education and society: Kindergarten limitations on learning. 1962. 0.75. N. E. A.

Redl, Fritz, and William Wattenberg. Mental hygiene in teaching. 2nd ed. 1959. 5.95. Harcourt

Rodehaver, Myles W., and others. Sociology of the school. 1957. 4.00. Crowell

Rugg, Harold, and William Withers. Social foundations of education. 1955. 7.25. Prentice-Hall

Thayer, V. T. Role of the school in American society. 1960. 6.50. Dodd

EDUCATIONAL TESTS AND MEASUREMENTS (371.26)

Ahmann, J. Stanley, and others. Evaluating elementary school pupils. 1960. 8.65. Allyn & Bacon

Baron, Denis, and H. W. Bernard. Evaluation techniques for classroom teachers. 1958. 6.25. McGraw

Bean, Kenneth L. Construction of educational and personnel tests: A guide for teachers and personnel workers. il. 1953. 5.95. McGraw

Beride, Ralph F., and others. Counseling, and the use of tests. 1962. pap. 2.00 ea. U. of Minn.

Dressel, Paul., and others. Evaluation to higher education. il. 1961. 6.25. Houghton

Gilbaugh, John W. Teacher's guide for test construction and percentage tables for computing test scores. 1960. pap. 1.00. Modern Educ. Pub.

Latchaw, Marjorie, and Camille Brown. Evaluation process in health education, physical education and recreation. 1962. 7.65. Prentice-Hall

Lindquist, Everet F., ed. Educational measurement. 1951. 6.00. A. C. E.

Manuel, Herschel T. Taking a test: How to do your best. 1956. 1.00. Harcourt

Mouly, G. J., and L. E. Walton. Outline of theory and problems of test items in education. 1962. pap. 2.50. Schaum

National Education Association, American Educational Research Association Department. Educational and psychological testing. 1959. 2.00. N. E. A.

National Education Association, American Educational Research Association. Educational and psychological testing. 1961. 2.00. N. E. A.

National Education Association, Elementary School Principals Department. Educational measurement: Interpreting and using the result. 1961. 0.75. N. E. A.

Odell, Charles W. How to improve classroom testing. 1953. pap. 4.00. Brown, W. C.

Remmers, Hermann H., and Nathaniel L. Gage. Educational measurement and evaluation. rev. ed. 1955. 6.50. Harper

Remmers, Hermann H., and others. Practical introduction to measurement and evaluation. il. 1960. 4.75. Harper

Ross, Clay C. Measurement in today's schools. 1954. 6.95. Prentice-Hall

Thomas, Robert M. Judging student progress. 2nd ed. 1960. 5.50. McKay

Travers, Robert M. W. Educational measurement. il. 1955. 5.95. Macmillan

Traxler, Arthur E., and others. Introduction to testing and the use of test results in public schools. 1953. 3.00. Harper

Wandt, Edwin, and Gerald W. Brown. Essentials of educational evaluation. 1957. pap. 1.60. Holt, Rinehart & Winston

Wrightstone, J. Wayne, and others. Evaluation in modern education. 7.00. Am. Bk. Co.

EDUCATORS (371.1)

Curti, Merle E. Social ideas of American educators. 4.95. Cooper

Meyer, Adolph E. Development of education in the twentieth century. 2nd ed. 1949. 8.35. Prentice-Hall

Rusk, Robert R. Doctrines of the great educators. 2nd ed. 1954. 3.00. St. Martins

EDUCATORS--DIRECTORIES (371.1)

Cattell, Jacques, ed. Directory of American scholars. 3rd ed. 1957. 20.00. Bowker

EDWARD I, KING OF ENGLAND, 1239-1307 (923.142)

Costain, Thomas B. Three Edwards. 1958. 4.75. Doubleday

EDWARD VI, KING OF ENGLAND, 1537-1553 (923.142)

Chapman, Hester W. Last tudor king. il. 4.95. Macmillan

EDWARD VII, KING OF GT. BRIT. 1841-1910 (923.142)

Cowles, Virginia. Gay monarch: The life and pleasures of Edward VII. il. 1956. 5.00. Harper

Fulford, Roger. Hanover to Windsor. il. 1960. 5.00. Macmillan

EDWARD VIII, KING OF GREAT BRITAIN, 1894- (923.142)

Windsor, Edward, Duke of. Windsor revisited. il. 1960. 6.00. Houghton

EDWARD, PRINCE OF WALES, called the BLACK PRINCE, 1330-1376 (923.142)

Hewitt, H. J. Black Prince's Expedition, 1355-1357. 1958. 6.50. Barnes & Noble

EDWARDS, JONATHAN, 1703-1758 (922.73)

Jones, Adam Leroy. Early American philosophers. 1958. 2.50. Ungar

Miller, Perry. Jonathan Edwards. pap. 1.55. Meridian

Turnbull, Ralph G. Jonathan Edwards the preacher. 3.95. Baker Bk.

Winslow, Ola E. Jonathan Edwards, 1703-1758. pap. 1.50. Collier

EFFICIENCY, INDUSTRIAL (658.01)

Close, Guy C., Jr. Work improvement. il. 1960. 6.75. Wiley

Laird, Donald A., and Eleanor C. Dynamics of personal efficiency. il. 1961. 4.95. Harper

Zinck, W. Clements. Dynamic work simplification. il. 1962. 7.95. Reinhold

EGYPT--ANTIQUITIES (913.32)
Cottrell, Leonard. Lost pharaohs. il. 1961. 5.00. Holt, Rinehart & Winston
Frankfort, Henri. Birth of Civilization in the Near East il. 1951. 4.50. Indiana
Hayes, William C. Scepter of Egypt. 2 vols. il. 1959. 15.00 ea. Harvard
Leclant, Jean. In the steps of the pharoahs. 1958. 8.50. Hastings
Randall-MacIver, D., and Leonard Woolley. Buhen. 1911. pap. 14.00. U.
    Museum
Raphael, Max. Prehistoric pottery and civilization in Egypt. tr. by Norbert
    Guterman. il. 1947. 7.50. Pantheon
Zehren, Erich. Crescent and the bull. il. 1962. 6.95. Hawthorn
EGYPT--CIVILIZATION (913.32)
Aldred, Cyril. Egyptians. il. 1961. 6.95. Praeger
Breasted, James H. Dawn of conscience. il. 1933. 5.95. Scribner
Glanville, Stephen R. K., ed. Legacy of Egypt. il. 1942. 6.00. Oxford U. P.
Lucas, A. Ancient Egyptian materials and industries. 3rd ed. 1962. 7.50. St.
    Martins
Noerdlinger, Henry S. Moses and Egypt. il. pap. 1.95. U. S. C.
Save-Soderbergh, Torgny. Pharoahs and mortals. 1961. 7.50. Bobbs
Steindorff, George, and Keith C. Seele. When Egypt ruled the East. rev. ed. il.
    1957. 6.50. U. of Chicago
Suhr, Elmer G. Exploring the primitive, Egyptian and Mesopotamian cultures
    3.50. Exposition
Wilson, John A. Burden of Egypt: An interpretation of ancient Egyptian culture.
    il. 1951. 6.00. U. of Chicago
Wilson, John A. Culture of Ancient Egypt. il. 1956. pap. 1.95. U. of Chicago
EGYPT--FOREIGN RELATIONS (962)
Lengyel, Emil. Egypt's role in world affairs. 1957. 2.50. Pub. Affairs
EGYPT--HISTORY (962)
Hesseltine, William B., and Hazel C. Wolf. Blue and the Gray on the Nile. il.
    1961. 5.00. U. of Chicago
Mellersh, H. E. L. Finding out about Ancient Egypt. 1961. 3.00. Lothrop
Nasser, Gamal Abdel. Egypt's liberation: Philosophy of the revolution. 1955.
    2.50. Pub. Affairs
Rowlatt, Mary. Founders of modern Egypt. 1962. 11.75. Taplinger
Smith, William Stevenson. Ancient Egypt as represented in the Museum of
    Fine Arts. 4th ed. rev. il. 1960. pap. 2.00. Harvard
EGYPT--HISTORY--ANCIENT TO 640 (932)
Bell, H. I. Egypt from Alexander the Great to the Arab conquest. 1948. 2.90.
    Oxford U. P.
Breasted, James H. History of Egypt. il. 12.50. Scribner
Dimick, M. T. Memphis: The city of the white wall. 1956. 0.50. Museum
Egypt and Babylonia to 1580 B.C. rev. ed. 6.50. Cambridge U. P.
Gardiner, Alan H. Egypt of the Pharaohs. il. 1961. 5.60. Oxford U. P.
Hall, H. R. Ancient history of the Near East. 11th ed. 8.50. Macmillan
Steindorff, George, and Keith C. Seele. When Egypt ruled the East. rev. ed. il.
    1957. 6.50. U. of Chicago
EGYPT--HISTORY--1882-1952 (932)
Sadat, Anwar El. Revolt on the Nile. 1957. 3.00. Day
EGYPT--HISTORY--1952 (932)
Whellock, Keith. Nasser's new Egypt. 1960. 6.00. Praeger
EGYPT--KINGS AND RULERS (962)
Elgood, P. G. Later dynasties of Egypt. 3.50. Humanities
EGYPT--POLITICS AND GOVERNMENT (962)
Nasser, Gamal Abdel. Egypt's liberation: Philosophy of the revolution. 1955.
    2.50. Pub. Affairs
EGYPT--RELIGION (209)
Breasted, James H. Development of religion and thought in ancient Egypt.
    1959. 4.00. Smith, Peter

Budge, Wallis. Egyptian religion. il. 1959. 5.00. U. Books
Cerny, Jaroslav. Ancient Egyptian religion. 1957. 2.50. (HUL) Hillary
Drioton, Etienne, and others. Religions of the Ancient East. tr. by M. B.
  Loraine. 1959. 3.50. Hawthorn
EGYPT--SOCIAL CONDITIONS (962)
Gadalla, Saad M. Land reform in relation to social development, Egypt.
  1962. 3.75. U. of Missouri
EGYPT--SOCIAL LIFE AND CUSTOMS (962)
Cottrell, Leonard. Life under the pharoahs. il. 1960. 5.00. Holt, Rinehart &
  Winston
Montet, Pierre. Everyday life in Egypt to the days of Ramesses the Great. il.
  1958. 8.00. St. Martins
EGYPTIAN LANGUAGE--WRITING, HIEROGLYPHIC (493.1)
Davies, Nina M. Picture writing in ancient Egypt. 1958. 4.80. Oxford U. P.
EICHMANN, ADOLF, 1906-1962 (923.5)
Reynolds, Quentin J., and others. Minister of death: The Adolf Eichmann
  story. il. 1960. 5.00. Viking
Zeiger, Henry A., ed. Case against Adolf Eichmann. 1960. pap. 0.50. New Am.
  Lib.

EIGHTEENTH CENTURY (909.7)
Becker, Carl L. Heavenly city of the eighteenth century philosophers. 1932.
  3.50; 1959. Yale
Nicolson, Harold G. Age of reason, the eighteenth century. 1961. 5.95.
  Doubleday
Snyder, Louis L. Age of reason. 1955. pap. 1.25. Van Nostrand
EINSTEIN, ALBERT, 1879-1955 (925.1)
Barnett, Lincoln. Universe and Dr. Einstein. rev. ed. 1957. 3.50. Sloane
Frank, Philipp. Einstein: His life and times. il. 1953. 5.00. Knopf
Infeld, Leopold. Albert Einstein. 1950. 3.00. Scribner
Lieber, Lillian R. Einstein theory of relativity. il. 1945. 3.95. Rinehart
Schilpp, Paul A., ed. Albert Einstein. 2 vols. 1959. 1.95 ea. Harper
Schilpp, Paul A., ed. Albert Einstein: Philosopher-sceintist. 1951. 6.95. Tudor
EISENHOWER, DWIGHT DAVID, PRES. U.S. 1890- (923.173)
Adams, Sherman. First-hand report. il. 1961. 6.50. Harper
Childs, Marquis, W. Eisenhower, captive hero. il. 1958. 4.75. Harcourt
Donovan, Robert J. Eisenhower: The inside story. il. 1956. 6.00. Harper
Gunther, John. Eisenhower. 1952. 3.50. Harper
Pusey, Merlo J. Eisenhower, the president. 1956. 4.50. Macmillan
Rosamond, Robert. Crusade for Peace. 1962. 5.00. Lexington
Shoemaker, Ralph J. President's words. 7 vols. vol. 1, Eisenhower, June
  1952-May 1954. 1954. 3.00; vol. 2, Eisenhower, June 1954. December 1955.
  1956. vol. 3, Eisenhower, 1956. 1957. vol. 4, Eisenhower, 1957. 1958. vol.
  5, Eisenhower, 1958. 1959. vol. 6, Eisenhower, 1959. 1960; vol. 7, Eisenhower
  1960-January 20, 1961. 1961. vols. 2-7. 5.00 ea. Shoemaker
Smith, A. Merriman. President's odyssey. 1961. 3.95. Harper
Smith, W. B. Eisenhower's six great decisions: Europe 1944-45. 1956. 3.95.
  McKay
ELASTICITY (624.171)
Borg, Sidney F. Fundamentals of engineering elasticity. il. 1962. 7.95. Van
  Nostrand
Godfrey, D. E. R. Theoretical elasticity and plasticity for engineers. il. 1960.
  10.00. Macmillan
Lightfoot, Edgar. Moment distribution. il. 1961. 11.00. Wiley
ELEANOR, OF AQUITAINE, CONSORT OF HENRY II, 1122?-1204 (923.142)
Kelly, Amy. Eleanor of Aquitaine and the four kings. il. 1950. 5.50. Harvard
ELECTIONS (324.24)
Baker, Gordon E. Rural versus urban political power. 1955. pap. 0.95.
  Random

Lakeman, Emid, and J. D. Lambert. Voting in democracies. rev. ed. 5.00. Hillary

Lipset, Seymour M. Political man: The social bases of politics. 1959. 4.95. Doubleday

Mackenzie, W. J. M. Free elections. 1958. 3.85. Praeger

Smith, T. E. Elections in developing countries. 1960. 6.75. St. Martins

ELECTIONS--GT. BRIT. (942)

Butler, David Edgeworth. Electoral system in Britain, 1918-1951. 1953. 4.00. Oxford U. P.

ELECTIONS--U.S. (324)

Berelson, Bernard R., and others. Voting: A study of opinion formation in a presidential campaign. il. 1954. 7.50. U. of Chicago

Buchanan, Lamont. Ballot for Americans: A pictorial history of American elections and electioneering, 1789-1956. il. 1956. 4.95. Dutton

Campbell, Angus, and others. American voter. 1960. 6.95. Wiley

Ernst, Morris, and David Loth. People know best. 1949. 2.50. Pub. Affairs

Heard, Alexander. Costs of democracy. 1960. 6.00. U. of N. C.

Heard, Alexander, and Donald S. Strong. Southern primaries and elections. 1950. pap. 3.50. U. of Ala.

Kelley, Stanley, Jr. Political campaigning. 1960. 3.50. Brookings

Sait, Edward McC. Sait's American parties and elections. ed. by Howard R. Penniman. 5th ed. 1952. 5.50. Appleton

Shannon, Jasper B. Money and politics. 1959. pap. 0.95. Random

ELECTIONS--U.S.--STATISTICS (310)

Seammon, Richard M., ed. America votes. 3 vols. vol. 1, 1956; vol. 2, 1958; vol. 3, 1959; vol. 4, 1962. 7.50 ea; set. 25.00. U. of Pittsburgh

ELECTRIC CIRCUITS (621.31)

Fitzgerald, Arthur E., and David E. Higginbotham. Basic electrical engineering. 2nd ed. il. 1957. 8.95. McGraw

Frazier, R. H. Elementary electric-circuit theory. 1945. 6.50. Ronald

ELECTRIC ENGINEERING (621.3)

Cook, Arthur L., and C. C. Carr. Elements of electrical engineering. 6th ed. 1954. 7.75. Wiley

Dawes, Chester L. Course in electrical engineering. 2 vols. vol. 1, Direcet currents, 4th ed., 1952, 8.95. vol. 2, Alternating currents, 4th ed. 1947, 8.95. McGraw

Gray, Alexander, and G. A. Wallace. Principles and practice of electrical engineering. 8th ed. 1962. 9.50. McGraw

Singer, B. B. Basic mathematics for electricity, radio, and television. 1957. 8.25. answers, 6.50. McGraw

Timbie, William H., and V. Bush. Principles of electrical engineering. 4th ed. 1951. 7.50. Wiley

ELECTRIC ENGINEERING--HANDBOOKS, MANUALS, ETC. (620.2)

Abbott, A. L., and F. Stetka. National electrical code handbook. 10th ed. 12.00 McGraw (R)

Croft, Terrell, and Clifford C. Carr. American electrician's handbook. 8th ed. 1961. 17.50; N. J   '?}

Graham, Frank Duncan. Handy book of electricity. 5.00. Audel

Pender, Harold, and others, eds. Electrical engineers' handbook. 4th ed. vol. 1, Electric power, ed. by Harold Pender, and William A. Del Mar, 1949; vol. 2, Communication-electronics, ed. by Harold Pender, and Knox McIlwai 1950. 11.00 ea. Wiley

ELECTRIC MACHINERY (621)

Adkins, Bernard. General theory of electrical machines. 1958. 8.75. Wiley

Fitzgerald, Arthur E., and David E. Higginbotham. Basic electrical engineering. 2nd ed. il. 1957. 8.95. McGraw

Loew, E. A., and F. R. Bergseth. Direct and alternating currents. 4th ed. il. 1954. 9.50. McGraw

Skilling, Hugh. Electromechanics 1962. 10.00. Wiley

ELECTRIC RELAYS (621)
Chute, George M. Electronics in industry. 2nd ed. il. 1956. 8.50. McGraw
ELECTRIC TRANSFORMERS (621.319)
Gibbs, J. B. Transformer principles and practice. 2nd ed. il. 1950. 8.50.
  McGraw
ELECTRIC WAVES (537.12)
Adler, Richard, and others. Electromagnetic energy transmission and radiation.
  1960. 12.50. Wiley
Brown, R. G., and others. Lines, waves, and antennas. 1961. 10.00. Ronald
ELECTRIC WELDING (671.521)
Lincoln Electric Co. Procedure handbook of arc welding design and practice.
  il. 1957. 3.00. Lincoln Electric
Sacks, Raymond J. Theory and practice of arc welding. 2nd ed. il. 1960. 5.95.
  Van Nostrand
ELECTRICITY (537.2)
Bishop, Calvin C. Fundamentals of electricity. il. 1960. 6.95. Chilton
Dawes, Chester L. Industrial electricity. 2 vols. vol. 1. 1956. 6.00; vol. 2.
  1960. 7.50. McGraw
Fink, Donald G., and David M. Lutyers. Physics of television. il. 1960. pap. 0.95.
  Doubleday
Gillie, Angelo C. Electrical principles of electronics. il. 1961. 10.00. McGraw
Planck, Max. Theory of electricity and magnetism. (Introduction to theoretical
  physics. vol. 3) 6.25. Macmillan
ELECTROCHEMISTRY (541.37)
Potter, Edmund C. Electrochemistry: Principles and applications. il. 11.00.
  Macmillan
ELECTROLYTES (541.37)
King, Edward J. Qualitative analysis and electrolytic solutions. 7.50. 1959.
  Harcourt
ELECTRON TUBES (621.381)
Millman, Jacob. Vacuum-tube and semiconductory electronics. 1958. 11.50;
  McGraw
ELECTRONIC APPARATUS AND APPLIANCES (621.315)
Bair, Edward J. Introduction to chemical instrumentation. 1962. 10.75.
  McGraw
Greenwood, Ivan A., and others, eds. Electronic instruments. 1948. 13.50.
  McGraw
Johnson, J. R. How to build electronic equipment. 6.95. Rider
ELECTRONIC CALCULATING-MACHINES (651.26)
Adler, Irving. Thinking machines. il. 1961. 4.00. Day
Clason, W. E. Dictionary of automation, computers, control, and measuring.
  ployglot. 1961. 27.50. Am. Elsevier (R)
ELECTRONIC CIRCUITS (621.381)
Markus, John, and Vin Zeluff. Handbook of industrial electronic control
  circuits. 1956. 11.00; with Handbook of electronic control circuits, and
  Handbook of industrial electronic circuits, set, 30.50. McGraw
Richter, Walther. Fundamentals of industrial electronic circuits. 1947. 6.95.
  McGraw
ELECTRONICS (537.5)
Albert, Arthur L. Electronics and electron devices. il. 8.75. Macmillan
Cooke, Nelson M. Basic mathematics for electronics. 2nd ed. il. 10.75. McGraw
Gillie, Angelo C. Electrical principles of electronics. 1961. 10.00. McGraw
Grob, Bernard. Basic electronics. 1959. 9.25. McGraw
Mandl, Matthew. Fundamentals of electronics. il. 1960. 10.60. Prentice-Hall
Mann, Martin. Revolution in electricity. il. 1962. 5.00. Viking
Timbie, William H., and F. J. Ricker. Basic electricity for communications.
  1958. 6.75. Wiley
Williams, Arthur O. Electronics. 1953. 4.50. Van Nostrand

ELECTRONICS--DICTIONARIES (537.03)
Carter, Harley. Dictionary of electronics. 1960. 8.50. Pitman (R)
International dictionary of physics and electronics. 2nd ed. il. 1961. 27.85.
   Van Nostrand (R)
Manly, Harold P. Radio-television-electronic dictionary. 1960. 5.00. Drake,
   F. J. (R)
Oldfield, R. L. Practical dictionary of electricity and electronics. il. 1959.
   5.95. Am. Tech. Soc.
ELECTRONICS--LABORATORY MANUALS'(537)
Zbar, P. B., and S. Schildkraut. Basic electronics. 2nd ed. 1958. 2.25.
   McGraw
ELECTRONICS AS A PROFESSION (537.069)
Levine, Sol. Your future in electronic engineering. 1961. 2.95. Richards Rosen
ELECTRONS (539.73)
Blackwood, O. H., and others. Outline of atomic physics. 3rd ed. 1955. 7.50.
   Wiley
Crowther, James A. Ions, electrons and ionizing radiations. 8th ed. 1949.
   5.25. (Arnold) St. Martins
Jauch, Josef M., and F. Rohrlich. Theory of photons and electrons. 1955. 12.50.
   Addison-Wesley
Langmuir, David B., and W. D. Hershberger. Foundations of future electron-
   ics. il. 1961. 10.75. McGraw
Thomson, John, and E. B. Callick, Electron physics and technology. il. 1959.
   10.00. Macmillan
ELEGIAC POETRY--HISTORY AND CRITICISM (808.14)
Bowra, Cecil Maurice. Early Greek elegists. 1960. 4.00? Barnes & Noble
Wallerstein, Ruth. Studies in seventeenth-century poetic. il. 1950. 6.50. U. of
   Wis.
EL GRECO (DOMINICO THEOTOCOPULI) d. 1614 (92?)
Guinard, Paul. El Greco. il. 1956. 5.75. (also available at same price with
   French or German text) (Skira) World Pub.
ELIJAH, THE PROPHET (922)
Bothwell, Jean. Flame in the sky: The story of the prophet Elijah. il. 1954.
   3.00. Vanguard
Wallace, Ronald S. Elijah and Elisha. 1957. 3.00. Eerdmans
ELIOT, GEORGE PSEUD., i.e. MARIAN EVANS, AFTERWARDS CROSS,
   1819-1880 (928)
Bennett, Joan. George Eliot: Her mind and her art. 1948. 3.50.   ridge U. P.
Daiches, David. George Eliot: Middlemarch. in prep. Barron's
Hardy, Barbara. Novels of George Eliot: A study in form. 1959. 4.00. Oxford
   U. P.
ELIOT, THOMAS STEARNS, 1888- (811.5)
Drew, Elizabeth. T. S. Eliot: The design of his poetry. 3.25. Smith, Peter
Gardner, Helen L. Art of T. S. Eliot. 1959. Dutton
Jones, David E. Plays of T. S. Eliot. 1960. 4.00. U. of Toronto
Kenner, Hugh, ed. T. S. Eliot: A collection of critical essays. 1962. 3.95;
   Prentice- all
Leavis, Frank R. New bearings in English poetry. 1960. 4.40. U. of Mich.
Lucy, Sean. T. S. Eliot and the idea of tradition. 1960. 5.00. Barnes & Noble
Matthiessen, Francis O. Achievement of T. S. Eliot: An essay on the nature
   of poetry. Oxford U. P.
Maxwell, D. E. S. Poetry of T. S. Eliot. 5.00. Hillary
Williamson, George. Reader's guide to T. S. Eliot. 1955. 4.50. Farrar Straus
ELIZABETH, QUEEN OF ENGLAND, 1533-1603 (923.142)
Chidsey, Donald Barr. Elizabeth I. 1955. 3.00. Knopf
Jenkins, Elizabeth. Elizabeth and Leicester. il. 1952. 5.75. Coward
Jenkins, Elizabeth. Elizabeth the Great. il. 1959. 5.75. Coward
Neale, John E. Queen Elizabeth I. 1959. 7.00. St. Martins

Strachey, Lytton. Elizabeth and Essex. il. 1928. 3.25. Harcourt
ELIZABETH II, QUEEN OF GT. BRITAIN, 1926- (923.142)
Cathcart, Helen. Her Majesty the Queen, the story of Elizabeth II. il. 1962.
    4.00. Dodd
Crawford, Marion. Little princesses. il. 1950. 4.95. Harcourt
Laird, Dorothy. How the queen reigns. 6.00. World Pub.
EMBLEMS, NATIONAL (929.8)
Lehner, Ernst, ed. American symbols: A pictorial history. 1957. 3.50. Tudor
EMBRYOLOGY (574.3)
Anderson, John G. Graphic aids to embryology. il. 1959. Scientific Il. & Pubs. (R)
Arey, Leslie Brainerd. Developmental anatomy. 6th ed. il. 1954. 9.50.
    Saunders
Balinsky, B. I. Introduction to embryology. il. 1960. 7.75. Saunders
Barth, Lester G. Embryology. rev. ed. 1953. 7.95. Holt, Rinehart & Winston
Berrill, N. J. Growth, development, and pattern. il. 1961. 10.00. Freeman
De Beer, Gavin R. Embryos and ancestors: il. 1958. 4.50. Oxford U. P.
McElroy, William, and Bentley Glass. Chemical basis of development. 1958.
    15.00. Johns Hopkins
Mintz, Beatrice, ed. Enviromental influences on prenatal development. 1958.
    3.00. U. of Chicago
Needham, Joseph. History of embryology. 2nd ed. il. 1959. 7.50. Abelard (R)
Patten, Bradley M. Foundations of embryology. 1958. 9.75. McGraw
Raven, C. P. Outline of developmental physiology. tr. by L. De Ruiter. 1959.
    5.00. Pergamon
Rugh, Roberts. Experimental embryology, techniques and procedures.
    1962. 9.25. Burgess
Spemann, Hans. Embryonic development and induction. il. 1938. 10.00. Hafner
Sussman, Maurice. Animal growth and development. 1960. 3.75. Prentice-Hall
Waddington, C. H. Principles of embryology. il. 1956. 7.50. Macmillan
Wardlaw, C. W. Embryogenesis in plants. 1955. 7.95. Wiley
Willier, Benjamin H., and others. Analysis of development. il. 1955. 15.00.
    Saunders
EMBRYOLOGY--BIRDS (591.33)
Lillie, Frank R., and Howard L. Hamilton. Lillie's development of the chick:
    Introduction to embryology. 3rd ed. il. 1952. 9.50. Holt. Rine... & Winston
Patten, Bradley M. Early embryology of the chick. 4th ed. 1951. 4.95.
    McGraw
EMBRYOLOGY--INSECTS (591.33)
Campbell, Frank L., ed. Physiology of insect development. 1959. 4.00. U. of
    Chicago
EMBRYOLOGY--MAMMALS (591.33)
Patten, Bradley M. Embryology of the pig. 3rd ed. 1948. 5.75. McGraw
EMBRYOLOGY--VERTEBRATES (591.33)
Huettner, Alfred F. Fundamentals of comparative embryology of the verte-
    brates. il. 1949. 5.50. Macmillan
McEwen, Robert S. Vertebrate embryology. 4th ed. 1957. 7.95. Holt, Rinehart &
    Winston
Nelson, Olin E. Comparative embryology of the vertebrates. 1953. 10.75. McGraw
Witschi, Emil. Development of vertebrates. il. 1956. 8.50. Saunders
EMBRYOLOGY, HUMAN (612.64)
Allan, Frank D. Essentials of human embryology. 1960. 5.75. Oxford U. P.
Beck, Lester F. Human growth. il. 1949. 2.95. Harcourt
Blechschmidt, Erich. Stages of human development before birth. il. 1961.
    23.00. Saunders
Brash, James C. Human embryology. 1956. 2.00. Oxford U. P.
Flanagan, Geraldine. First nine months of life. 1962. 3.95. S. and S.
Hamilton, William J., and others. Human embryology. in prep. Williams
    Wilkins

Martin, Phyllis C., and Elizabeth L. Vincent. Human biological development. il. 1960. 6.50. Ronald
Patten, Bradley M. Human embryology. 2nd ed. il. 1953. 13.50. McGraw

EMERSON RALPH WALDO, 1803-1882
Kenvitz, Milton R., and Stephen E. Whicher. Emerson: A collection of critical essays. 1962. 3.95. Prentice-Hall
Keyes, Charlotte. Experimenter: The life of Ralph Waldo Emerson. 1962. 3.50. College & Univ.
Matthiessen, F. O. American renaissance: Art and expression in the age of Emerson and Whitman. il. 1941. 10.00. Oxford U. P.

EMIGRATION AND IMMIGRATION (325.1)
Hansen, Marcus L. Atlantic migration, 1607-1860. il. 1962. 4.25. Smith, Peter
Kulischer, E. M. Europe on the move. 1948. 5.00. Columbia
Thomas, Brinley. Migration and economic growth. 1954. 9.00. Cambridge U. P.

EMIGRATION AND IMMIGRATION LAW (364.42)
Auerbach, Frank L. Immigration laws of the United States. 2nd ed. 1961. 15.00. Bobbs
Konvitz, Milton R. Civil rights in immigration. 1953. 3.50. Cornell
Paul, Rodman Wilson. Abrogation of the gentlemen's agreement. 1936. 1.25. Harvard

EMOTIONAL MATURITY (157.2)
Abrahamsen, David. Road to emotional maturity. 1958. 4.95. Prentice-Hall

EMOTIONS (157)
Arnold, Magda B. Emotion and personality. 2 vols. 1960. 7.50 ea. Columbia
Bennett, Edward M. Search for emotional security. 1959. 4.50. Ronald
Blatz, William E., and others. Emotional episodes in the child of school age. il. 1937. pap. 0.25. U. of Toronto
Candland, Douglas K. Emotion: Bodily change. il. 1962. 1.95. Van Nostrand
Caplan, Gerald, ed. Emotional problems of early childhood. 1955. 10.00. Basic Books
Cobb, Stanley. Emotions and clinical medicine. 1950. 4.00. Norton
Foote, Gaston. Living in four dimensions. 1954. 2.00. Revell
Frank, Lawrence K. Feelings and emotions. 1954. pap. 0.85. Random
Haring, Norris G., and Ewing L. Phillips. Education of emotionally disturbed children. 1962. 6.50. McGraw
Harris, Irving D. Emotional blocks to learning. 1961. 4.00. Free Press
Mac Murray, John. Reason and emotion. 1962. 3.50. Barnes & Noble
O'Brien, Patrick. Emotions and morals. 1950. 4.00. Grune
Prescott, Daniel Alfred. Emotion and the educative process. 1938. 2.50. A. C. E.
Robertiello, Richard C. Handbook of emotional illness and treatment. 1961. 3.95. Citadel
Simon, Alexander, and others, eds. Physiology of emotions. 1961. 8.50. Thomas C. C.
Spoerl, Dorothy, ed. Tensions our children live with; stories for discussion. 1959. 3.50. Beacon
Werner, Hazen G. Live with your emotions. 1951. 2.50. Abingdon

ENCYCLOPEDIAS AND DICTIONARIES (030)
Americana annual. il. 12.00. Americana Corp.
Bell, Raymond M., ed. New century book of facts. 1962. 32.50. Continental Pub. Co. Continental Pub. Co.
Bridgwater, William and Elizabeth J. Sherwood, eds. Columbia encyclopedia. with 1959 suppl. il. 1959. 35.00; suppl. alone 2.00. Columbia Columbia
Chase, Stuart. Some things worth knowing. 1958. 4.50. Harper
Collier's encyclopedia. 20 vols. 1960. lib. bdg. 299.50. Collier-Macmillan
Columbia-Viking desk encyclopedia. 2nd ed. 1960. 8.95. Viking Viking

Encyclopedia Americana. 1962 ed. 30 vols. 329.50-475.00. Americana Corp.
Encyclopedia Britannica. 1962. 398.00 and up. Encycl. Britannica
Kane, Joseph N. Famous first facts. rev. ed. 1950. 7.00. Wilson
Lincoln library of essential information. rev. ed. il. 1961. 1 or 2 vols. single
  vols. 28.50 and 34.50; 2 vol. sets 32.50. and 39.50. Frontier Pr.
Petit Larousse; All French encyclopedia. rev. ed. il. 6.95. Tudor
Stimpson, George. Book about a thousand things. 1946. 5.95. Harper
Weideman, Hugh, ed. Rapid fact finder. 1958. 4.95. Crowell

ENGINEERING (620)
Canfield, D. T., and J. H. Bowman. Business, legal and ethical phases of
  engineering. 2nd ed. 1954. 7.75. McGraw
Howell, A. C. Handbook of English in engineering usage. 2nd ed. 1940. 4.50.
  Wiley
Young, C. R., and others. Engineering and society. pap. 2.25. U. of Toronto
Young, Clarence R. Introduction to engineering economics. il. 1949. 3.95. U.
  of Toronto

ENGINEERING--ADDRESSES, ESSAYS, LECTURES (620.04)
Cross, Hardy, and R. C. Goodpasture. Engineers and ivory towers. 1959. pap.
  1.50. McGraw
Jones, Everett L., and Philip Durham. Readings in science and engineering.
  1961. 4.50. Holt, Rinehart & Winston

ENGINEERING--DICTIONARIES (620.03)
Jones, Franklin D. Engineering encyclopedia. il. 1954. 10.00. Industrial Pr.

ENGINEERING--HANDBOOKS, MANUALS, ETC. (620.2)
American Institute of Physics. American Institute of Physics handbook. ed.
  by Dwight E. Gray. il. 1957. 18.50. McGraw
Eshbach, Ovid W. Handbook of engineering fundamentals. 2nd ed. 1952. 13.50.
  Wiley
Perry, Robert H. Engineering manual. 1959. 9.50. McGraw

ENGINEERING--HISTORY (620.9)
Forbes, R. J. Man the maker: A history of engineering and technology. rev.
  ed. il. 1958. 5.00. Abelard
Poirier, Rene. Fifteen wonders of the world. tr. by Margaret Crosland. il.
  1961. 5.95. Random

ENGINEERING--PROBLEMS, EXERCISES, ETC. (620.1)
Dana, Forest C., and Laurence R. Hillyard. Engineering problems manual.
  5th ed. il. 1958. 5.50. McGraw
Gaskell, Robert E. Engineering mathematics. 1958. 7.75. Holt, Rinehart &
  Winston
Hutchinson, Charles A., and others. Engineering problems. 1956. 3.50. Harper

ENGINEERING--STUDY AND TEACHING (620.1)
Holstein, Edwin J., and Earl J. McGrath. Liberal education and engineering.
  1960. pap. 2.75. T. C.
Layton, Wilbur, ed. Selection and counseling of students in engineering. 1954.
  pap. 1.75. U. of Minn.

ENGINEERING AS A PROFESSION (620.069)
Constance, John. How to become a professional engineer. 1958. 6.00. McGraw
Hartung, W. M., and G. W. Brush, Jr. How to choose your technical institute.
  pap. 1.00. Bellman
McGuire, J. G., and H. W. Barlow. Introduction to the engineering profession.
  2nd ed. il. 1951. 2.75. Addison-Wesley
Pollack, Philip. Careers and opportunities in engineering. il. 1959. 3.75.
  Dutton

ENGINEERING MATHEMATICS (530.151)
Fogel, Charles M. Introduction to engineering computations. 1960. 6.50.
  Int. Textbook

ENGINEERS (926.2)
Steinman, David B., and Sara Ruth Watson. Bridges and their builders. 2nd
  ed. 1957. pap. 1.95. Dover

ENGINES (621. 4)

Church, A. H. Centrifugal pumps and blowers. 1944. 7. 00. Wiley

Duncan, John. Steam and other engines. 1950. 2. 50. St. Martins

ENGLAND (942)

Wright, Louis B. Middle-class culture in Elizabethan England. 1958. 7. 50.
Cornell

ENGLAND--DESCRIPTION AND TRAVEL (914. 2)

Fellows, Arnold. Wayfarer's companion: England's history in her buildings
and countryside. rev. ed. 1946. 3. 40. Oxford U. P.

Halsey, Margaret. With malice toward some. il. 1959. pap. 1. 45. S. and S.

Hawthorne, Nathaniel. English notebooks of Nathaniel Hawthorne. ed. by
Randall Stewart. 12. 50. Russell

Joad, C. E. M. , ed. English counties. il. 1959. 4. 95. Norton

Parker, Cornelia Stratton. English summer. 1931. 3. 50. Liveright

Trent, Christopher. Changing face of England. il. 1960. 4. 95. Norton

Vesey-Fitzgerald, Brian. English villages in pictures. il. 1960. 3. 95. Norton

Vesey-Fitzgerald, Brian, ed. Historic towns of England in pictures. il. 1960.
3. 95. Norton

ENGLAND--HISTORIC HOUSES, ETC. (942)

Dutton, Ralph, and Ivor Brown. Stately homes of England. il. 1961. 4. 50.
Hastings

ENGLAND--SOCIAL LIFE AND CUSTOMS (942)

Bennett, Henry Stanley. Life on the English manor. 1937. 5. 50; 1960. Cambridge U. P.

Burton, Elizabeth. Pageant of Elizabethan England. il. 1962. 4. 50. Scribner

Burton, Elizabeth. Pageant of Stuart England. il. 1962. 5. 95. Scribner

Byrne, M. St. Clare. Elizabethan life in town and country. il. 1961. 4. 00;
Barnes & Noble

Davis, William Stearns. Life in Elizabethan days. il. 1930. 4. 50. Harper

Hardy, Thomas. Wessex tales. 3. 50. St. Martins

Jusserand, Jean J. English wayfaring life in the Middle Ages. 4th ed. tr. by
Lucy Toulmin Smith. 1950. 4. 50. Barnes & Noble

Kronenberger, Louis. Kings and desperate men. 1959. pap. 1. 45. Vintage

Myers, A. R. England in the late Middle Ages. 1952. pap. 1. 25. Penguin

Nicoll, Allardyce. Elizabethans. 1957. 5. 00. Cambridge U. P.

Plumb, J. H. England in the eighteenth century. 1950. pap. 0. 95. Penguin

Salzman, L. F. English life in the Middle Ages. il. 1926. 3. 40. Oxford U. P.

Stephen, Leslie. English literature and society in the eighteenth century. 1947.
2. 00. Barnes & Noble

Thomson, David. England in the nineteenth century. 1950. pap. 0. 95. Penguin
0. 95. Penguin

ENGLISH BALLADS AND SONGS (784. 3)

Book of British ballads. 1. 95. Dutton

Child, Francis J., ed. English and Scottish popular ballads. 5 vols. bound in 3.
40. 00. Cooper (R)

Fellowes, E. H., ed. English madrigal verse: 1588-1632. 2nd ed., 1929. 4. 00.
Oxford U. P.

Friedman, Albert B., ed. Viking book of folk-ballads of the English-speaking
world. 1956. 4. 95; Viking

Leach, MacEdward. Ballad book. 1955. 10. 00. Harper

Popular ballads, English and Scottish. 5. 00. Houghton

Quiller-Couch, Arthur, ed. Oxford book of ballads. 1910. 5. 50. Oxford U. P.

Sargent, H. C., and G. L. Kittredge, eds. English and Scottish popular ballads.
8. 50. Houghton

Wells, Evelyn K. Ballad tree. 1950. 6. 00. Ronald

ENGLISH BALLADS AND SONGS--HISTORY AND CRITICISM (784. 3)

Gummere, F. B. Popular ballad. 3. 75. Smith, Peter

Wimberley, Lowry C. Folklore in the English and Scottish ballads. 1959.
5. 75. Ungar

ENGLISH CHANNEL (942. 2)

Williamson, James A. English channel: A history. il. 1959. 6.00. World Pub.

ENGLISH DRAMA (COLLECTIONS) (822. 08)

Barnet, Sylvan, and others, eds. Genius of the Irish theater. pap. 0. 75. New. Am. Lib.

Bentley, Gerald Eades, ed. Development of English drama: An anthology. 1950. 7.00. Appleton

Cohen, Helen L. , ed. One act plays by modern authors. rev. ed. 1934. 4.50. Harcourt

Morrell, Janet M. , ed. Four English comedies. 1959. pap. 1.25. Penguin

Sixteen famous British plays 2. 95. Modern Lib.

Tatlock, John S. P. , and Robert G. Martin, eds. Representative English plays. rev. ed. 7.00. Appleton

Thirty famous one-act plays 2. 95. Modern Lib.

Webb, Marie. One-act plays. il. 1940. 4.60. Macmillan

ENGLISH DRAMA (COLLECTIONS)--MEDIEVAL (822)

Adams, Joseph Q. , ed. Chief pre-Shakespearean dramas. 6. 75. Houghton

Everyman and medieval miracle plays. il. 1. 95. 1959. Dutton

Malcolmson, Anne B. Miracle plays. il. 1959. 3.00. Houghton

Pollard, Alfred W. English miracle plays, moralities and interludes: Specimens of the pre-Elizabethan drama. 8th ed. rev. ed. il. 1927. 2.90. Oxford U. P.

ENGLISH DRAMA (COLLECTIONS)--EARLY MODERN AND ELIZABETHAN (822. 9)

Baskervill, Charles Read and others. Elizabethan and Stuart plays. 1934. 12.50. Holt

Boas, Frederick S. , ed. Five pre-Shakespearean comedies: Early Tudor period. 2. 75. Oxford U. P.

Brooke, Charles T. , and Nathaniel B. Paradise. English drama, 1580-1642. 1933. 9.00. Heath

Heilman, Robert B. , ed. Anthology of English drama before Shakespeare. 1952. pap. 1.45. Rinehart

Mack, Maynard, and others, eds. Elizabethan drama. vol. 2. 2.95. Prentice-Hall

Minor Elizabethan drama: 2 vols. vol. 1. Pre-Shakespearian tragedies vol. 2. Pre-Shakespearian comedies. 1. 95 ea. Dutton

Neilson, William Allan, ed. Chief Elizabethan dramatists, except Shakespeare. 8.50. Houghton

Spencer, Hazelton. Elizabethan plays. 1945. 9.00. Heath

ENGLISH DRAMA (COLLECTIONS--RESTORATION (822)

MacMillan, Dougald, and Howard Mumford Jones, eds. Plays of the Restoration and eighteenth century. 1938. 9. 50. Holt Rinehart & Winston

Restoration plays. 1.95. Modern Lib.

Twelve famous plays of the Restoration and eighteenth century. 2. 95. Modern Lib.

ENGLISH DRAMA (COLLECTIONS)--18TH CENTURY (822)

Beggar's Opera, and other Eighteenth Century plays. (Everyman pap. 1818) 1.85. Dutton

Eighteenth century plays. 1. 95. Dutton

Nettleton, George H. , and Arthur E. Case, eds. British dramatists from Dryden to Sheridan. 1939. 8.50. Houghton

Twelve famous plays of the Restoration and eighteenth century. 2. 95. Modern Lib.

ENGLISH DRAMA (COLLECTIONS)--19TH CENTURY (822)

Nicoll, Allardyce. Late 19th century drama, 1850-1900. 2 vols. vol. 1, 5.50; vol. 2, 11.00. Cambridge U. P.

Rowell, George, ed. Nineteenth century plays. 1953. 2. 75. Oxford U. P.

ENGLISH DRAMA (COLLECTIONS) 20TH CENTURY (822)

Cerf, Bennett A. and Van H. Cartmell, eds. Twenty-four favorite one-act plays. 1958. 4. 95. Doubleday

Cordell, Richard A. , ed. Twentieth century plays - British, American Continental. 3rd ed. 1947. 3.50. Ronald

Warnock, Robert, ed. Representative modern plays, British. key ed. 1953.
2. 95. Scott
ENGLISH DRAMA--BIBLIOGRAPHY (822.016)
Ribner, I. English history play in the age of Shakespeare. 1957. 5.00. Princeton
ENGLISH DRAMA--HISTORY AND CRITICISM (822.09)
Barish, Jonas A. Ben Jonson and the language of prose comedy. 1960. 5.00.
  Harvard
Eliot, T. S. Poetry and drama. 1951. 1.50. Harvard
Granville-Barker, Harley. On dramatic method. 1960. 3.00. Smith, Peter
Hazlitt, William. Hazlitt on theatre. ed. by William Archer and Robert Lowe.
  3.00. 1957. Hill & Wang
Nicoll, Allardyce. British drama. 4th rev. ed. 1957. 5.50. Barnes & Noble
Nicoll, Allardyce. History of English drama. 1660-1900. 6 vols. vol. 1,
  Restoration drama, 8.50; vol. 2, Early 18th century drama, 9.50; vol. 3,
  Late 18th century drama, 9.50; vol. 4, Early 19th century drama, 12.50; vol.
  5, Late 19th century drama, 1959. 14.00; vol. 6, Alphabetical catalogue of
  the plays. 1959. 12.50. Cambridge U. P.
Sharpe, Robert B. Irony in the drama. 1959. 5.00. U. of N. C.
ENGLISH DRAMA--HISTORY AND CRITICISM--MEDIEVAL (822.4)
Prosser, Eleanor. Drama and religion in the English mystery plays. 1961. 5.00.
  Stanford
Rossiter, A. P. English drama from early times to the Elizabethans. 1959.
  4.50. Barnes & Noble
Williams, Arnold. Drama of Medieval England. 1961. 5.00. Mich. State
ENGLISH DRAMA--EARLY MODERN AND ELIZABETHAN--HISTORY AND
  CRITICISM (822)
Bentley, G. E. Jacobean and Caroline stage: vols. 1 and 2, Dramatic companies
  and players. 1941. 17.60; vols. 3-5, Plays and playwrights. 1956. 24.80.
  Oxford U. P.
Boas, F. S. Introduction to Stuart drama. 1946. 4.50. Oxford U. P.
Boas, F. S. Introduction to Tudor drama. 1933. 2.90. Oxford U. P.
Chambers, E. K. Elizabethan stage. il. 4 vols. 1923. 26.90. Oxford U. P.
Eliot, T. S. Essays on Elizabethan drama. 1956. pap. 0.95. Harcourt
Knights, L. C. Drama and society in the age of Jonson. 1957. 4.00. Barnes &
  Noble
Lea, Kathleen M. Italian popular comedy: A study in the commedia del arte,
  1560-1620, with special reference to the English stage. 2 vols. 15.00.
  Russell
Leech, Clifford. Shakespeare's tragedies and other studies in seventeenth
  century drama. 1950. 3.80. Oxford U. P.
Parrott, T. M., and R. H. Ball. Short view of Elizabethan drama. 3.50. Smith,
  Peter
Peter, John. Complaint and satire in early English literature. 1956. 7.20.
  Oxford U. P.
Ribner, I. English history play in the age of Shakespeare. 1957. 5.00.
  Princeton
Ribner, Irving. Jacobean tragedy: Quest for moral order. 1962. 4.50. Barnes
  & Noble
ENGLISH DRAMA--RESTORATION--HISTORY AND CRITICISM (822)
Krutch, Joseph Wood. Comedy and conscience after the Restoration. rev. ed.
  1949. 5.00. Columbia
ENGLISH DRAMA--18TH CENTURY--HISTORY AND CRITICISM (822)
Boas, Frederick Samuel. Introduction to eighteenth century drama: 1700-
  1780. 1953. 5.60. Oxford U. P.
Goldstein, Malcolm. Pope and the Augustan stage. 1958. 4.00. Stanford
Loftis, John Clyde. Comedy and society from Congreve to Fielding. 1959.
  4.00. Stanford

ENGLISH DRAMA--19TH CENTURY--HISTORY AND CRITICISM (822)

Evans, Bertrand. Gothic drama from Walpole to Shelley. 1947. 3.50. U. of Calif.

Sawyer, Newell W. Comedy of manners from Sheridan to Maugham. 1961. pap. 1.95. Barnes A. S.

ENGLISH DRAMA--20TH CENTURY--HISTORY AND CRITICISM (822. 9109)

Reynolds, Ernest. Modern English drama: A survey of the theatre from 1900. il. 1951. 3.50. U. of Okla.

Weales, Gerald. Religion in modern English drama. 1961. 7.50. U. of Pa.

Wickham, Glynne. Drama in a world of science. 1962. 3.25. U. of Toronto

ENGLISH ESSAYS (824)

Baudin, Maurice, and Karl G. Pfeiffer. Essays for study. 1960. 5.50. McGraw

Brown, James I. Explorations in college reading. 1959. pap. 2.75. Heat

Century of English essays: Anthology. 1.95. Dutton

Fiedler, Leslie. Art of the essay. 1958. 4.25. Crowell

Jones, E. D., ed. English critical essays, 16th-18th centuries. 2. '5. Oxfor' U. P.

Kazin, Alfred. Open form. 2.95. Harcourt

Kiefer, Christian, and Laurence Muir. Forum: A book of essays for college English. 2.40. Appleton

Mead, Douglass S., ed. Great English and American essays. rev. e . 195'. pap. 0. '5. Holt, Rinehart & Winston

Morgan, Stewart S., and others. Readings for thought and expression. 1955. 4.50. Macmillan

Stewart, John L., ed. Essay: A critical anthology. 1952. 6.35. Prentice-Hall

ENGLISH ESSAYS--HISTORY AND CRITICISM (824)

Humphreys, A. R. Addison and Steele. pap. 0.50. British Bk.

ENGLISH FICTION (COLLECTIONS) (823)

Connolly, Cyril, ed. Great English short novels. 1953. 6.00. Dial

Schorer, Mark, ed. Modern British fiction. 1961. 2.25. Oxford U. P. Oxford U. P.

ENGLISH FICTION (COLLECTIONS)--18TH CENTURY (823. 5)

18th century shorter novels. 1.95. Dutton

ENGLISH FICTION--BIBLIOGRAPHY (823. 016)

Anderson, James. British novels of the twentieth century. 1959. 0.75. Cambridge U. P.

ENGLISH FICTION--HISTORY AND CRITICISM (823)

Allen, Walter. English novel 1955. 4.75; (D9) Dutton

Baker, E. A. History of the English novel. 10 vols. 5.00 ea.

Cross, Wilbur L. Development of the English novel. 1900. 4.75. Macmillan

Forster, E. M. Aspects of the novel. 1947. 3.95. Harcourt

Lanier, Sidney. English novel and essays on literature. Ed. by Charles Gohdes, and Kemp Malone. 6.00. Johns Hopkins

McCullough, Bruce. Representative English novelists: Defoe to Conrad. 1946. 4.50. Harper

Shapiro, Charles, ed. Twelve original essays on great English novels. 1960. 5.50? Wayne

Stevenson, Lionel. English novel. 1960. 4.00. Houghton

Tillyard, E. M. W. Epic strain in the English novel. 1958. 3.40. Oxford U. P. Bks.) Oxford U. P.

Van Ghent, Dorothy. English novel: Form and function. 1953. 5.50. Rinehart

Wagenknecht, Edward. Cavalcade of the English novel. rev. ed. 1954. 9.45; Holt, Rinehart & Winston

Woolf, Virginia. Room of one's own. 1929. 3.75. Harcourt

Zabel, Morton Dauwen. Craft and character in modern fiction. 1957. 4.75. Viking

ENGLISH FICTION--HISTORY AND CRITICISM--19TH CENTURY (823. 8)

Cecil, David. Victorian novelists. 1958. 5.00. pap. 1.75. U. of Chicago Chicago

Rathbun, Robert C., and Martin Steinmann, Jr., eds. From Jane Austen to
   Joseph Conrad. 1958. 5.75. U. of Minn.
Stang, Richard. Theory of the novel in England, 1850-1870. 1959. 5.00.
   Columbia

ENGLISH FICTION--HISTORY AND CRITICISM--20TH CENTURY (823.91)
Aldridge, J. W. Critiques and essays on modern fiction, 1920-1951. 1952. 7.50.
   Ronald
Daiches, David. Novel and the modern world. rev. ed. 1960. 5.00. U. of
   Chicago
Karl, Frederick R. Contemporary English novel. 1962. 4.95. Farrar, Straus
O'Faolain, Sean. Vanishing hero. 1957. 3.75. Little
Schorer, Mark, ed. Modern British fiction, essays in criticism. 1962. 4.25.
   Smith, Peter

ENGLISH LANGUAGE (420)
Fowler, Henry Watson. Dictionary of modern English usage. 1937. 4.50.
   Oxford U. P.
Marckwardt, Albert H. Introduction to the English language. 1942. 4.50.
   Oxford U. P.
Opdycke, John B. Get it right! il. 1941. 3.75. Funk
Scott, Harry F., and others. Language and its growth. 1957. 6.75. Scott
Warfel, Harry R. Language: A science of human behavior. 3.95. Allen, Howard
Webster, Noah. Dissertations on the English language (1789) 1952. 7.50.
   Scholars' Facs.

ENGLISH LANGUAGE--ANTONYMS (424)
Allen, F. Sturges. Allen's synonyms and antonyms. rev. ed. 1938. ed. by T. H.
   Vail Motter. 4.95. Harper
Fernald, James C. Standard handbook of synonyms, antonyms and prepositions
   rev. ed. 1947. 3.95. Funk
Roget, Peter. New Roget's thesaurus of the English language in dictionary
   form. rev. ed. by Norman Lewis. 1961. 4.50. Putnam
Webster's synonyms and antonyms. Ottenheimer

ENGLISH LANGUAGE--BUSINESS ENGLISH (651.7)
Aurner, Robert R., and Paul S. Burtness. Effective English for business. 5th
   ed. 1962. 4.40. South-Western Pub.
Aurner, Robert R. Practical business English. 3rd ed. 1960. 3.20. South-
   Western Pub.
Parkhurst, Charles C. Business communication for better human relations.
   il. 1961. 8.25. Prentice-Hall
Parkhurst, Charles C. Practical problems in English for business. 3rd ed.
   1958. 1.92. Prentice-Hall
Stewart, M., and others. Business English and communication. 2nd ed. 1961.
   4.56. McGraw

ENGLISH LANGUAGE--COMPOSITION AND EXERCISES (428.2)
Adams, R. J., Jr., and others. Way to good English. bk.1: The complete
   sentence; bk. 2: The correct form; bk. 3: The precise word. Odyssey
Allen, Edward F. How to write and speak effective English. pap. 0.50. Fawcett
Bachelor, Joseph M., and Harold L. Haley. Practice of English fundamentals.
   Forms A and B. 1949. pap. 1.90 ea. Appleton
Bailey, James O. Creative exercises in college English. 3.00. Am. Bk. Co.
Bailey, J. O. Proper words in proper places. 3.75. Brown Book
Besosa, Margaret N., de. English composition for Spanish-speaking students.
   1945. 3.50. Appleton
Bushman, John C., and Ernst G. Mathews. Readings for college English. 2.00;
   4.50. Am. Bk. Co.
Flesch, Rudolf. Art of plain talk. 1946. 3.95. Harper
Flesch, Rudolf, and A. H. Lass. Way to write. 2nd ed. 1955. 4.96. McGraw
Foerster, Norman, and others. Writing and thinking. 5th ed. 3.75. exercises in
   Writing and thinking. by Phil S. Grant and Walter C. Foreman. pap. 1.75; pt.
   2. separate, Handbook of revision, 1.00. Houghton

Gehimann, John, ed. Challenge of ideas. rev. ed. 1961. 3.00. Odyssey
Glock, Marvin D. Improvement of college reading. 1954. pap. 3.75; 2nd ed. by
    Marvin D. Glock, and W. Pank. Houghton
Hodges, John C.. and Francis X. Connolly. Harbrace college handbook. 1962. 3.50.
Jones, Everett L. Approach to college reading. 1953; alternate ed. 1955;
    form 3 ed. 1959. 2.50 ea. Holt, Rinehart & Winston
Kammer, Michael P., and others. Adult writing. il. 1953. 2.40. Loyola
McCrimmon, James M. Writing with a purpose. 2nd ed. 5.25. Houghton
Norwood, J. E. Concerning words and phrasing. 4th ed. 1956. pap. 3.25.
    Prentice-Hall
Rorabacher, Louise E. Concise guide to composition. 1956. 3.00. Harper
Wykoff, George S., and Harry Shaw.. Harper handbook of college composition.
    3rd. ed. 1962. 4.50 Harper
ENGLISH LANGUAGE--COMPOUND WORDS (428.3)
Ball, Alice M. Compounding and hypenation of English words. 1951. 4.00.
    Funk
ENGLISH LANGUAGE--DIALECTS (408.7)
Herman, Lewis, and Marguerite.. American dialects. 1959. 6.50. Theatre
    Arts (R)
ENGLISH LANGUAGE--DICTION (420)
Opdycke, John B. Say what you mean. 1944. 3.75. Funk
ENGLISH LANGUAGE--DICTIONARIES (423)
American college dictionary. il. 5.00. Random
Bryant, Margaret M. Current American usage. 1962. 5.00. Funk (R)
Cousins, Norman, ed. March's thesaurus-dictionary. 1958. 9.75. Doubleday (R)
Craigie, William A. Dictionary of American English. 4 vols. 100.00. U. of
    Chicago
Evans, Bergen, and Cornelia. Dictionary of contemporary American usage.
    1957. 5.95. Random
Fowler, Henry Watson, and F. G., eds. Concise Oxford dictionary of current
    English. 4th ed. rev. by E. McIntosh. 1951. 5.50; with thumb index, 7.00;
    polished mor, 17.50; half calf, plain, blue or maroon, 17.50. Oxford U. P.
Funk and Wagnalls. New College standard dictionary. emphatype ed. il. 1950.
    5.50. Funk
Funk and Wagnalls. New standard dictionary of the English language. un-
    abridged. il. 1952. buckram, 40.00. Funk
Funk and Wagnalls. Standard dictionary of the English language, International
    edition. il. thumb-indexed. 34.50. 2 vols. Funk
Mathews, Mitford McLeod, ed. Dictionary of Americanisms on historical
    principles. 2 vols. il. 1951. 1 vol. ed. il. 1956. 12.50. U. of Chicago
Merriam Co., G. and C. Webster's new collegiate dictionary. 1960.
Merriam Co., G. and C. Webster's new international dictionary. 3rd ed. by
    William A. Neilson and others. il. 1961. 47.50. Merriam
Murray, J. A. H., and others, eds. Oxford English dictionary. 13 vols. 300.00.
    Oxford U. P.
Murray, J. A. H., and others, eds. Shorter Oxford English dictionary on
    historical principles. 3rd ed. rev. 2 vols. 1944. with addenda. 1955. 32.00;
    boxed, 33.50; 2 vol. ed. 37.50; boxed, 39.00. Oxford U. P.
Pelo, William Joseph, and others, eds. New secretary's desk book: A manual
    of correct usage. il. 1959. 5.50. Holt, Rinehart & Winston (R)
Webster's College dictionary. 1960. 5.75. Macmillan (R)
ENGLISH LANGUAGE--DICTIONARIES--SWEDISH (439.7)
Tornberg, Astrid, and others, eds. McKay's modern Swedish-English and
    English-Swedish dictionary. 1954. 4.00. McKay (R)
ENGLISH LANGUAGE--ETYMOLOGY (422)
Ernst, Margaret, and James Thurber. In a word. 3.95. Channel Pr.,
    Manhasset, N. Y.

Funk, Charles Earle. Thereby hangs a tale: Stories of curious word origins.
1950. 3.75. Harper

Garrison, Webb B. Why you say it. il. 1955. 3.95. Abingdon

Greenough, James B., and George L. Kittredge. Words and their ways in
English speech. 1962. pap. 1.95. Beacon

Hart, Archibald. Twelve ways to build a vocabulary. rev. ed. 1939. 2.95. Dutton

Partridge, Eric. Charm of words. 3.50. Macmillan

Weekley, Ernest. Romance of words. pap. 1.25. Dover

ENGLISH LANGUAGE--ETYMOLOGY--DICTIONARIES (422)

Partridge, Eric. Origins. a short etymological dictionary of modern English.
1959. 16.00. Macmillan

Shipley, Joseph T. Dictionary of word origins. 1956. pap. 2.25. Littlefield

Skeat, W. W., ed. Concise etymological dictionary of the English language.
1911. 4.00. Oxford U. P. (R)

Skinner, Henry A. Origin of medical terms. 2nd ed. il. 1961. 12.50. Williams
& Wilkins (R)

ENGLISH LANGUAGE--ETYMOLOGY--NAMES (422)

Ekwall, Eilert. Concise Oxford dictionary of English place-names. 4th ed.
1960. 8,80. Oxford U. P. (R)

ENGLISH LANGUAGE--FOREIGN WORDS AND PHRASES (422)

Jones, Hugh P., ed. Dictionary of foreign phrases and classical quotations.
6.00. Spencer (R)

ENGLISH LANGUAGE--GLOSSARIES, VOCABULARIES, ETC. (428)

Cass, Angelica W. Everyday English and basic word list for adults. il. 1960.
1.20. Noble

Funk, Wilfred. Way to vocabulary power and culture. 1946. 4.95. Funk

Gilmartin, John G. Building your vocabulary. 1950. 2.92. Prentice-Hall

Holt, Alfred H. Phrase and word origins, a study of familiar expressions.
3.35. Smith, Peter

Lewis, Norman, ed. Comprehensive word guide to the English language. 1958.
5.95, Doubleday

Rodale, Jerome I., ed. Word finder. thumb-indexed. 1952. 7.95. Rodale

ENGLISH LANGUAGE--GRAMMAR (425)

Bachelor, Joseph M., and others. Introductory English composition for college
students. 1939. pap. 3.50. Appleton

Bowyer, John W., and others. Better college English. 3.25. Appleton

Bryant, Margaret M. Modern English and its heritage. 2nd ed. 1962. 6.00.
Macmillan

Buckler, William E., and William C. McAvoy. American college handbook of ·
English fundamentals. 1960. 3.25. Am. Bk. Co.

Dean, Howard H., and Bryson. Effective communication. 1961. 5.25. Prentice-
Hall

Fowler, Henry Watson, and F. G. Fowler. King's English. 3rd ed. 1934. 3.75.
abridged for school use, Oxford U. P.

Guth, Hans P. Words and ideas. 1959. 4.75. Wadsworth

Hook, Julius N. Guide to good writing: Grammar, style, usage. 1962. 6.00.
Ronald

Kittredge, G. L., and F. E. Farley. Advanced English grammar. 1913. 4.20.
Ginn

Opdycke, John Baker. Harper's English grammar. 1941. 4.50. Harper

Partridge, Eric. Usage and abusage. 5th ed. 1957. 5.25. British Bk.

Perrin, Porter G., and George H. Smith. Handbook of current English. rev. ed.
1962. 4.25. Scott

Pooley, Robert C. Teaching English grammar. 1957. 3.25. Appleton

Roberts, Paul M. Understanding English. 1958. 4.50. Harper

Roberts, Paul M. Understanding Grammar. 1954. 6.25. Harper

Wykoff, George S., and Harry Shaw. Harper handbook of college composition.
3rd ed. 1962. 4.50. Harper *

ENGLISH LANGUAGE--HISTORY (420.9)

Baugh, Albert C. History of the English language. 2nd ed. il. 1957. 5.75.
Appleton

Bryant, Margaret M. Modern English and its heritage. 2nd ed. 1962. 6.00.
Macmillan

Jespersen, Otto. Growth and structure of the English language. 9th ed. 2.50.
Macmillan

Pei, Mario. Story of English. 1952. 6.00. Lippincott

Sutherland, James, ed. Oxford book of English talk. 1953. 5.75. Oxford U. P.

ENGLISH LANGUAGE--IDIOMS, CORRECTIONS, ERRORS (428)

Berry, Thomas E. Most common mistakes in English usage. 1961. 2.95.
Chilton

Colby, Frank. Practical handbook of better English. 1.50. Grosset

Evans, Bergen. Comfortable words. il. 1962. 5.95. Random

Fowler, Henry Watson. Dictionary of modern English usage. 1937. 4.50.
Oxford U. P.

ENGLISH LANGUAGE--LEXICOGRAPHY (423)

Hulbert, James Root. Dictionaries, British and American. 1955. 2.50.
(Essential Books) Oxford U. P.

ENGLISH LANGUAGE--PHONETICS (421.5)

Bates, Alma. Speed phonics. 1962. 20.00. Colonial Pr.

Dust, Laurel M. Teaching the fundamentals of reading and spelling phonetic-
ally. 2.50. Vantage

Gleason, Henry A., Jr. Introduction to descriptive linguistics. rev. ed. 1961.
7.00. Holt, Rinehart & Winston

ENGLISH LANGUAGE--PHONOLOGY (421.5)

Ross, Alan S. C. Etymology. 1958. 7.00. Oxford U. P.

ENGLISH LANGUAGE--PRONUNCIATION (421.5)

Bender, James F. NBC handbook of pronunciation. 2nd ed. 1962. 5.75; 3rd ed.
in prep. Crowell (R)

Eisenson, Jon. Improvement of voice and diction. il. 5.25. Macmillan

Jones, Daniel. English pronouncing dictionary, on phonetic principles. 11th
rev. ed. 5.95; Outline of English phonetics. 8th ed. 4.50. Dutton (R)

Kenyon, John Samuel, and Thomas Albert Knott. Pronouncing dictionary of
American English. 2nd ed. 1953. 3.75. Merriam

Wyld, Henry Cecil. History of modern colloquial English. 3rd ed. rev. 1953.
5.50. Barnes & Noble

ENGLISH LANGUAGE--PUNCTUATION (421.9)

Partridge, Eric. You have a point there. 1953. 3.50. British Bk. (R)

Smith, Kellogg, and Leighton Steele. Proper punctuation. 4.95. Doubleday

ENGLISH LANGUAGE--RHETORIC (808)

Altick, Richard D. Preface to critical reading. 4th ed. 1960. 3.75. Holt,
Rinehart & Winston

Barrett, Laurence. Writing for college. 4.50. Am. Bk. Co.

Bowen, Robert O. College style manual. 1.00. Colonial Pr.

Brooks, Cleanth, and Robert Penn Warren. Fundamentals of good writing.
5.75. Harcourt

Brooks, Cleanth, and Robert Penn Warren. Modern rhetoric. 2nd ed. 1958.
5.95. Harcourt

Chase, Mary Ellen, and Henry W. Sams, eds. Constructive theme writing 3rd
ed. 1957. 5.25. Holt

Dodge, Richard H. How to read and write in college. 1962. pap. 2.95. Harper

Flesch, Rudolf. Art of readable writing. 1949. 3.95. Harper

Flesch, Rudolf. How to make sense. 1954. 3.95. Harper

Flesch, Rudolf F. How to write, speak, and think more effectively. il. 1960.
4.95. Harper

Flesch, Rudolf. New way to better English. 1958. 3.00. Harper
Grebanier, Bernard D. N., and Seymour Reiter. College writing and reading.
   1959. 4.25. Holt, Rinehart & Winston
Greever, Garland, and others. Century collegiate handbook. 3rd ed. 1950.
   2.95. Appleton
Hegarty, Edward J. How to write a speech. 1951. 4.00. McGraw
Hutchinson, Lois D. Standard handbook for secretaries. 7th ed. 1956. 5.95;
   text ed. 4.50. McGraw
Kierzek, John M., and Walker Gibson. Macmillan handbook of English. 4th ed.
   3.50; workbk. 1.90. Macmillan
Kierzek, John M., and Walker Gibson. Macmillan handbook of English. 4th ed.
   1960. 3.50; workbk. 4th ed. pap. 1.90. practice of composition, form A, 3rd
   ed. o.p; form B, 3rd ed. 3.95. Macmillan
Kitzhaber, Albert R., and Don Lee. Handbook for basic composition. 1961.
   4.75. Prentice-Hall
McKenzie, Belle, and Helen F. Olson. Experiences in writing. 1962. 1.80.
   Macmillan
Marckwardt, A. H., and F. G. Cassidy. Scribner handbook of English. 3rd ed.
   3.35. Scribner
Morsberger, Robert E. How to improve your verbal skills. 1962. 4.95. Crowell
O'Connor, William Van, ed. Modern prose, form and style. 1959. 4.50.
   Crowell
Oggel, Elizabeth. Thoughts into themes. 1955. pap. 1.00. Holt, Rinehart &
   Winston
Pulsifer, Susan N. Creative writing through letters. il. 1961. 4.50. Chapman
Sachs, H. J., and others, eds. Readings for college writers. 1962. 5.00.
   Ronald
Smith, Reed. Learning to write in college. rev. ed. by William S. Hastings.
   1949. 5.25. Heath
Strunk, William, Jr., and E. B. White. Elements of style. rev. ed. 2.50. Mac-
   millan
Thomas, Joseph M., and others. Composition for college students. 5th ed. 5.50.
   Macmillan
Williams, George G. Creative writing. rev. ed. 1954. 4.50. Harper
Woolley, Edwin C., and others. College handbook of composition. 6th ed.
   1958. 3.85. Heath

ENGLISH LANGUAGE--RIME--DICTIONARIES (426.6)
Johnson, Burges, ed. New rhyming dictionary and poets' handbook. rev. ed.
   1957. 5.00. Harper
Walker, J. Rhyming dictionary. 1924. 4.95. Dutton
Wood, Clement, ed. Complete rhyming dictionary. 1936. 3.50. (Garden City)
   Doubleday
Wood, Clement, ed. Wood's unabridged rhyming dictionary. 1943. 6.00. World
   Pub.

ENGLISH LANGUAGE--SEMANTICS (422)
Barfield, O. History in English words. 3.75. Hillary
Hayakawa, S. I. Language in thought and action. 1949. 4.95. Harcourt

ENGLISH LANGUAGE--SLANG (427.09)
Berrey, Lester V., and Melvin Van Den Bark. American thesaurus of slang.
   2nd ed. 1953. 15.00. Crowell
Partridge, Eric. Slang today and yesterday. 4th ed. 1954. 8.00. Macmillan (R)

ENGLISH LANGUAGE--SLANG--DICTIONARIES (427.09)
Holt, Alfred H. Phrase and word origins, a study of familiar expressions.
   3.35. Smith, Peter
Partridge, Eric, ed. Dictionary of slang and unconventional English. 5th ed.
   2 vols. in 1. 1961. 16.00. Macmillan
Wentworth, Harold, and Stuart B. Flexner. Dictionary of American slang. 1960.
   7.50. Crowell

ENGLISH LANGUAGE--STUDY AND TEACHING (420.7)
Hook Julius N. Teaching of high school English. 2nd ed. 1959. 6.00. Ronald
Marsh, Philip M. How to teach English in high school and college. 3.00,
    Twayne
Warfel, Harry R. Who killed grammar? 1952. pap. 2.50. U. of Fla.
ENGLISH LANGUAGE--STYLE (808)
Bateson, Frederick W. English poetry and the English language. 1961. 5.00.
    Russell
Cobree, Bonamy. Modern prose style. 1934. 2.40. Oxford U. P.
Read, Herbert. English prose style. 1955. pap. 1.45. Beacon
ENGLISH LANGUAGE--SYNONYMS (424)
Allen, F. Sturges. Allen's synonyms and antonyms. rev. ed. 1958. ed. by T. H.
    Vail Motter. 4.95. Harper
Crabb, George. Crabb's English synonyms, 3.50. Grosset
Merriam Co., G. and C. Webster's dictionary of synonyms. 1951. 6.00. Merriam
Roget, Peter Mark. Roget's international thesaurus. 3rd ed. 1962. 5.95. Crowell
Soule, Richard. Dictionary of English synonyms. rev. ed. by Alfred D.
    Sheffield. 1959. 6.00. Little (R)
ENGLISH LANGUAGE--SYNTAX (421.5)
Curme, George O., and Hans Kurath. Grammar of the English language. 3 vols.
    vol. 1. History of the English language, sounds and spellings. in prep. vol. 2.
    Parts of speech and accidence. 1935. 6.00; vol. 3. Syntax. 1931. 7.00. Heath
Vallins, George H. Pattern of English. 1956. 3.50. Oxford U. P.
ENGLISH LANGUAGE--TERMS AND PHRASES (428.3)
Duffy, Charles, and Henry Pettit. Dictionary of literary terms. rev. ed.
    2.50, Brown Book
Fairchild, Henry Pratt. Dictionary of sociology. 1956. pap. 1.95. Littlefield
Funk, Charles Earle. Heavens to Betsy and other curious saying. il. 1955.
    3.50. Harper
Funk, Charles Earle. Hog on ice and other curious expressions. il. 1948.
    4.50. Harper
Kleiser, Grenville. Fifteen thousand useful phrases. 1917. 3.50. Funk (R)
Partridge, Eric. Dictionary of cliches. 4th ed. 1950. 2.50. Macmillan
Rodale, Jerome I. Phrase finder. 1954. 7.95. Rodale
Shipley, Joseph T. Dictionary of world literature. 1959. pap. 1.95. Littlefield
Thrall, William F., and others. Handbook to literature. rev. ed. 1960. 3.75;
    pap. 2.50. Odyssey (R)
ENGLISH LANGUAGE--VERSIFICATION (426.2)
Allen, Gay W. American prosody. 1935. 4.00. Pacific Bk. Supply
Johnson, Burges, ed. New rhyming dictionary and poets' handbook. rev. ed.
    1957. 5.00. Harper (R)
ENGLISH LANGUAGE--WORD FORMATION (425)
Bryant, Margaret M. Modern English and its heritage. 2nd ed. 1962. 6.00.
    Macmillan
ENGLISH LANGUAGE--WORDS--HISTORY (422)
Asimov, Isaac. Words in Genesis. il. 1962. 3.00. Houghton
Asimov, Isaac. Words of science and the history behind them. il. 1959. 5.00.
    Houghton
Bridges, Ronald, and Luther A. Weigle. Bible word book, concerning obsolete
    or archaic words in the King James version of the Bible. 1960. 5.00. Nelson
Funk, Wilfred. Word origins and their romantic stories. 1950. 4.95. Funk
Merriam Co., G. and C. Picturesque word origins. il. by Louis Szanto. 3.00.
    Merriam
Pei, Mario. Families of words. 1962. 6.00. Harper
ENGLISH LITERATURE (COLLECTIONS) (820)
Barnet, Sylvan, and others. Introduction to literature: Fiction, poetry and
    drama. 1961. pap. 3.95. Little
College requirements in English. 2.52. Houghton

Cowardin, Samuel P., Jr., and Paul Elmer More. Study of English literature. rev. ed. 1939. 4.95. Holt, Rinehart & Winston

Cross, Ethan A., and others, eds. Interpreting literature. rev. ed. 4.36; Macmillan

Davenport, William H., and others. Dominant types in British and American literature. 1949. 7.50. Harper

Grebanier, Bernard D. N. English literature. 2 vols. vol. 1. Through the 18th century; vol. 2. Through the 20th century. 3.50. ea; pap. 1.95. ea. Barron's

Herrington, Hunley W., ed. English masterpieces. rev. 2 vols. 1937. 3.95 ea. Norton

James, Eirian. Anthology of English prose, 1400-1900. 1956. 2.50. Cambridge U. P.

Lieder, Paul R., and others, eds. British poetry and prose. 3rd ed. vols. 1 and 2. 7.25 ea. Houghton

MacDonald, Dwight, ed. Parodies: An anthology from Chaucer to Beerbohm and after. 1960. 7.50. Random

Stewart, Randall, and Dorothy Bethurum, eds. Living masterpieces of English literature. 1954. 1 vols. 4 vols. 1954. vol. 1. Classics of the Christian tradition: The Bible, Milton, 2.50; vol. 2, Classics of the Enlightenment; Pope, Swift 2.50: vol. 3, English lyric poetry: Donne, Wordsworth, Keats, 2.50; vol. 4, Chaucer and Shakespeare: Dramatic vision, 2.50. Scott

Tobin, James E., and others. College book of English literature. 7.50. Am. Bk. Co.

Waite, Harlow O., and Benjamin P. Atkinson, eds. Literature for our time: An anthology for college students. 3rd ed. 1958. 7.50. Holt, Rinehart & Winston

ENGLISH LITERATURE (COLLECTIONS)--MIDDLE ENGLISH (1100-1500) (820)

Loomis, Roger S., and Rudolph Willard, eds. Medieval English verse and prose. 1948. 6.00. Appleton

ENGLISH LITERATURE (COLLECTIONS)--EARLY MODERN (TO 1700) (820)

Coffin, Robert P. Tristram, and Alexander M. Witherspoon, eds. Seventeenth-century prose and poetry. 1946. 7.95. Harcourt

Haydn, Hiram C., ed. Portable Elizabethan reader. 1946. 2.95. Viking

Hebel, J. William, and others. Tudor poetry and prose. 1953. 7.50. Appleton

Lamson, Roy, and Hallett Smith. Renaissance England. 1956. 8.95. Norton

Rollins, Hyder E., and Herschel Baker. Renaissance in England. 1954. 9.00. Heath

Shepard, Odell, and P. S. Wood. English prose and poetry, 1660-1800. 8.75. Houghton

White, Helen C., and others. Seventeenth-century verse and prose. vol. 1. 1600-1660. vol. 2. 1660-1700. 5.50 ea. Macmillan

ENGLISH LITERATURE (COLLECTIONS)--18TH CENTURY (820)

Bernbaum, E. Anthology of romanticism. 3rd ed. 1948. 7.50. Ronald

Bredvold, Louis I., and others. Eighteenth century poetry and prose. 2nd ed. 1956. 8.00. Ronald

Noyes, Russell, ed. English romantic poetry and prose. 1956. 8.50. Oxford U. P.

Shepard, Odell, and P. S. Wood. English prose and poetry, 1660-1800. 8.75. Houghton

Woods, George B. English poetry and prose of the romantic movement. rev. ed. 1950. 9.50. Scott

ENGLISH LITERATURE (COLLECTIONS) --19TH CENTURY (820)

Bernbaum, E. Anthology of romanticism. 3rd ed. 1948. 7.50. Ronald

Bowyer, John W., and John L. Brooks, eds. Victorian age; Prose, poetry and drama. 2nd ed. 1954. 6.75. Appleton

Dean, Leonard F., ed. College omnibus. 8th ed. 6.50. Harcourt

ENGLISH LITERATURE (COLLECTIONS)--20TH CENTURY (820)

Life. Great reading from Life. by the Editors of Life. 1960. 7.50. Harper

Stauffer, Ruth M. , and others. Adventures in modern literature. 3rd ed. 4.76;
  Harcourt

ENGLISH LITERATURE (SELECTIONS: EXTRACTS, ETC.) (820. 82)

Abrams, Meyer H. , and others, eds. Norton anthology of English literature. 2
  vol. 1962. 6. 95 ea; pap. 5. 45 ea. major authors ed. in 1 vol. 8. 95. Norton
Anderson, George K. , and others. England in literature. 1957. 4. 52. Scott
Ball, John, ed. From Beowulf to modern British writers. 1959. 8. 50. Odyssey
Baugh, Albert C. , and George W. McClelland. English literature: A period
  anthology. il. 1954. 2 vol. ed. 4. 50 ea; set, 9. 00; text ed. 1 vol. 7. 50. Appleton
Brooks, Cleanth, Jr. , and others. Approach to literature. 3rd ed. 5. 75. Appleton
Chase, Mary Ellen, and Henry W. Sams, eds. Constructive theme writing. 3rd
  ed. 1957. 5. 25. Holt
Clark Donald B. , and others, eds. English literature. il. 1960. 8. 50.
  Macmillan
Cook. Luella B. , and others. America through literature. 1948. 4. 60. Harcourt
Cunliffe, J. W. , and others, eds. Century readings in English literature. 5th
  ed. 1940. 6. 75. Appleton
De La Mare, Walter. Behold this dreamer. 1939. 5. 75. Knopf
Depew, Ollie. Freshman writing. 1948. 3. 50. Funk
Graham, Carey B. Freshman English program. 1960. 7. 50. Scott
Grebanier, Bernard, and others, eds. English literature and its backgrounds.
  rev. ed. 2 vols. 1949. vol. 1, From the Old English Period through the Age of
  Reason. vol. 2, From the forerunners of Romanticism to the present. 8. 95 ea;
  1 vol. abridged ed, 1959. 9. 95. Holt, Rinehart & Winston
Harrison, G. B. , ed. Major British writers. 2 vols. 1959. 6. 75 ea. Harcourt
Hughes, Richard E. , and P. Albert Duhamel. Rhetoric: Principles and usage.
  1962. 4. 95. Prentice-Hall
Knickerbocker, Kenneth L. Ideas for writing. 3rd ed. 1962. 5. 75. Holt, Rinehart
  & Winston
Lupton, Martha, ed. Speaker's desk book. 2. 98. Grosset
Robertson, James D. , ed. and comp. Handbook of preaching resources from
  English literature. 5. 00. Macmillan
Shafer, R. From Beowulf to Thomas Hardy. rev. ed. vol. 1 and 2. 6. 00 ea.
  Odyssey
Spencer, Hazelton, and others. British literature. vol. 1. From Beowulf to
  Sheridan. 1951. vol. 2. From Blake to the present day. 1952. 8. 00 ea. Heath
Thonssen, Lester, and W. L. Finkel. Ideas that matter. 1961. 2. 75. Ronald
Walcutt, Charles C. Anatomy of prose. 1962. 3. 75. Macmillan
Wise, Jacob H. , ed. , and others. College English. 3rd ed. il. 1960. 6. 50.
  Harcourt
Witherspoon, Alexander M. , ed. College survey of English literature. rev.
  ed. 8. 50. Harcourt

ENGLISH LITERATURE--ADDRESSES, ESSAYS, LECTURES (820. 4)

Carlyle, T. Essays. English and other critical essays. 1. 95. Dutton
Gleckner, Robert, and Gerald Enscoe. Romanticism: Points of view. 1962. pap.
  3. 50. Prentice-Hall
Highet, Gilbert. People, places, and books. 1953. 3. 50. Oxford U. P.
Hunt, Leigh. Literary criticism. ed. by Lawrence H. and Carolyn W.
  Houtchens. 1956. 8. 50. Columbia
Saturday Review. Saturday Review gallery. ed. by Jerome Beatty, Jr. , and
  others. 1959. 6. 00. S. and S.
Tate, Allen. Collected essays. 1959. 6. 00. Swallow, A.
Thompson, Francis. Real Robert Louis Stevenson and other critical essays.
  ed. by Terence L. Connolly. 1959. 10. 50, Univ. Pub.
Tillyard, E. M W. Myth and the English mind: From Piers Plowman to
  Edward Gibbon. pap. 0. 95. Collier
Walsh, William. Use of imagination. 1961. 5. 00. Barnes & Noble

ENGLISH LITERATURE--BIBLIOGRAPHY (820. 016)

Bush, Douglas. English literature in the earlier seventeenth century: 1600-
  1660. 1945. 7. 50. Oxford U. P.

Cambridge bibliography of English literature. 5 vols. vols. 1-4 37.50; vol. 5,
13.50; set 45.00. Cambridge U. P.
Chambers, Edmund K. English literature at the close of the Middle Ages.
1945. 7.00. Oxford U. P.
Daiches, David. Present age in British literature. 1958. 5.75. Indiana
De Sola Pinto, V. English Renaissance, 1510-1688. 1950. 4.50. Dover
Kennedy, Arthur G., and Donald B. Sands. Concise bibliography for students
of English. Systematically arranged. rev. ed. 1960. pap. 5.00. Stanford (R)
Watson, George. Concise Cambridge Bibliography of English literature 600-
1950. 3.75. Cambridge U. P.

ENGLISH LITERATURE--DICTIONARIES, INDEXES, ETC. (820.3)

Barnhart, Clarence L., and William D. Halsey, eds. New century handbook of
English literature. 1956. 12.00. (Appleton) Meredith
Harvey, Paul, ed. Oxford companion to English literature. 3rd ed. 1946. 10.00.
Oxford U. P.
Mulgan, John, ed. Concise Oxford dictionary of English literature. 1939. 4.50.
Oxford U. P.

ENGLISH LITERATURE--HISTORY AND CRITICISM (820.9)

Altick, Richard D. English common reader: A social history of the mass
reading public, 1800-1900. 1957. 6.00. U. of Chicago
Ball, John, ed. From Beowulf to modern British writers. 1959. 1.25. Cam-
bridge U. P.
Baugh, Albert C., and George W. McClelland. English literature: A period
anthology. il. 1954. 2 vol. ed. 4.50 ea; set, 9.00. Appleton
Baugh, Albert C., and others. Literary history of England. 1 vol. ed. 14.95.
Meredith (R)
Boas, Guy, and Cyril Aldred. New English course: Based on the study of
literature. 1935. 1.50. St. Martins
Boas, Ralph P., and Edwin Smith. Enjoyment of literature. 1934. 3.80.
Harcourt
Browne, R. M. Theories of convention in contemporary American criticism.
1956. 3.00. Catholic U. of Am. Pr.
Cambridge history of English literature. 15 vols. without bibliographies.
65.00. Cambridge U. P.
Chambers, Raymond W. Man's unconquerable mind: Studies in English authors.
6.00. Saifer
Craig, Hardin, ed. History of English literature. 4 vols. 0.95 ea. Collier
Daiches, David, ed. Barron's studies in English literature. For complete
list see Barron's catalog
Grierson, H. J. C. Background of English literature. 2nd ed. 1960. 4.50. Barnes
& Noble
Hazlitt, William. Lectures on the English comic writers. 1.95. Dutton
Holmes, Charles S., and others, eds. Major critics: The development of
English literary criticism. 1957. 3.00. Knopf
Johnson, Samuel. Critical opinions of Samuel Johnson. ed. by Joseph E.
Brown. 1960. 10.00. Russell
Leary, Lewis, ed. Contemporary literary scholarship. 1958. 5.00. Appleton
Legouis, E. H. Short history of English literature. il. tr. by V. F. Boyson,
and J. Coulson. 1934. 3.75. Oxford U. P.
Legouis, Emile, and Louis Cazamian. History of English literature. 1960.
4.50. Macmillan
Long, W. J. English literature. rev. ed. 1945. 6.50. Ginn
Macaulay, T. B. Essays. 2 vols. 1.95 ea. Dutton
McLeod, Alan L., ed. Commonwealth pen. 1961. 3.50. Cornell
Mair, George H. Modern English literature. 1944. 3rd ed. 1960. 1.70. Oxford
U. P.
Modder, Montagu F. Jew in the literature of England. pap. 1.65. Meridian

Moody, William V., and Robert M. Lovett. History of English literature. rev. 1956. 3.50. Scribner (R)

Moulton, Charles W. Library of literary criticism of English and American authors. 8 vols. 10.00 ea. Smith, Peter (R)

Mulgan, John, and D. M. Davin. Introduction to English literature. 1947. 1.20. Oxford U. P.

Neilson, William A., and A. H. Thorndike. History of English literature. rev. ed. il. 6.88. Macmillan

Osgood, Charles G. Voice of England. 2nd ed. 1952. 6.25. Harper

Rubinstein, A. T. Great tradition in English literature from Shakespeare to Shaw. 7.50. Russell

Saintsbury, George. Short history of English literature. 4.75. St. Martins

Sampson, George. Concise Cambridge history of English literature. 2nd ed. 1962. 4.95. Cambridge U. P.

Stallman, Robert W. Critiques and essays in criticism, 1920-1948. 1949. 7.50. Ronald

Thomson. J. A. K. Classical background of English literature. pap. 0.95. Collier

Tillyard, Eustace M. W. English epic and its background. 1954. 4.00. Oxford U. P.

Woolf. Virginia. Common reader. 1st and 2nd ser. 1st ser. pap. 1.15; 2nd common reader. pap. 1.15. Harcourt

ENGLISH LITERATURE--HISTORY AND CRITICISM--MIDDLE ENGLISH (1100-1500) (820.903)

Baugh, Albert C., and others. Middle ages (Literary history of England. vol.1) 3.25. Appleton (R)

Chambers, Edmund K. English literature at the close of the Middle Ages. 1945. 7.00. Oxford U. P.

Craig, Hardin. Literature of the English Renaissance, 1485-1660. pap. 0.95. Collier

Leach, MacEdward, ed. Studies in Medieval literature. 1961. 7.50. U. of Pa.

Robertson, D. W., Jr. Preface to Chaucer: Studies in medival perspective. 1962. 10.00. Princeton

Schlauch, M. Medieval English literature and its social foundations. 6.00. Hillary

Ward, Alfred C. Chaucer to Shakespeare. (Illustrated history of English literature. vol. 1) 10.00. McKay (R)

ENGLISH LITERATURE--HISTORY AND CRITICISM--EARLY MODERN (TO 1700) (820.903)

Baugh, Albert C., and others. Renaissance (Literary history of England. vol. 2) 3.50. Appleton (R)

Brooke, Tucker. Essays on Shakespeare and other Elizabethans. 1948. 3.25. Yale

Bullen, A. H. Elizabethans. 1962. 6.50. Russell

Bush, Douglas. English literature in the earlier seventeenth century: 1600-1660. 1945. 7.50. Oxford U. P.

Coleridge, Samuel Taylor. Coleridge on the seventeenth century. ed. by Roberta F. Brinkley. 1955. 12.50. Duke

Grierson, Herbert J. C. Cross currents in 17th century English literature. 1959. 3.75. Smith, Peter

Lewis, C. S. English literature in the sixteenth century excluding drama. 1954. 9.50. Oxford U. P.

Mason, Harold A. Humanism and poetry in the early Tudor period. 1960. 6.50. Barnes & Noble

Sherburn, George. Restoration and eighteenth century. (Literary history of England, vol. 3) 3.50. Appleton (R)

Tillyard, E. M. W. Elizabethan world picture. 1946. 2.25. Macmillan

Tillyard, E. M. W. English Renaissance: Fact or fiction. 1952. 3.00. Johns Hopkins

Ward, Alfred C. Ben Jonson to Samuel Johnson. (Illustrated history of English literature. vol. 2) 10. 00. McKay (R)
Ward, Alfred C. Chaucer to Shakespeare. (Illustrated history of English literature. vol. 1) 10. 00. McKay (R)
Wright, Louis B. Middle-class culture in Elizabethan England. 1958. 7. 50. Cornell

ENGLISH LITERATURE--HISTORY AND CRITICISM--18TH CENTURY (820. 9)

Baugh, Albert C. , and others. Restoration and eighteenth cnetury (Literary history of England. vol. 3) 3. 50. Appleton (R)
Bernbaum, Ernest. Guide through the Romantic Movement. 2nd ed. 1949. 5. 00. Ronald
Clifford. James L. Eighteenth-century English literature. 1959. pap. 2. 25. Oxford U. P.
McKillop, Alan D. English literature from Dryden to Burns. il. 1948. 3. 25. ' Appleton
Thackeray, W. M. English humorists, and Four Georges. 1. 95. Dutton
Wellek, Rene. Rise of English literary history. 1941. 3. 00. U. of N. C.
Willey, B. Eighteenth century background. 1941. 4. 50. Columbia

ENGLISH LITERATURE--HISTORY AND CRITICISM--19TH CENTURY (820. 9)

Battenhouse, Henry. English romantic writers. 3. 50, Bar~. 's
Baugh, Albert C. , and others. Nineteenth century and after (Literary history of England. vol. 4) 3. 50. Appleton (R)
Beach, Joseph Warren. English literature of the nineteenth and twentieth centuries, 1798 to the First World War. (AS13) pap. 0. 95. Collier
Brandes, Georg. Naturalism in 19th century English literature. 5. 00. Russell
Brinton, Crane. Political ideas of English romanticists. 1962. 6. 50. Russell
Campbell, Oscar J. , and others, eds. Poetry and criticism of the Romantic movement. 6. 50. Appleton
Chesterton, G. K. Victorian age in literature. 1946. 1. 70. Oxford U. P.
Gilfillan, George. Literary portraits. 1. 95. Dutton
Hazlitt, William. Spirit of the age, and English poets. 1. 95. Dutton
Tindall, William York. Forces in modern British literature, 1885-1946. 1956. pap. 1. 25. Vintage
Vine, Sherard. Hundred years of English literature. 3. 50. Macmillan
Ward, Alfred C. William Blake to Bernard Shaw. (Illustrated history of English literature. vol. 3) 10. 00. McKay
Willey, B. Nineteenth century studies. 1949. 4. 50. Columbia
Wright, Austin. Victorian literature, modern essays in criticism. 4. 25. Smith, Peter
Daiches, David. Present age in British literature. 1958. 5. 75. Indiana
Longaker, Mark, and Edwin C. Bolles. Contemporary English literature. il. 1953. 3. 50. Appleton
Tindall, William York. Forces in modern British literature, 1885-1946. 1956. pap. 1. 25. Vintage
Van Doren, Carl, and Mark Van Doren. American and British literature since 1890. 1939. 3. 00. Appleton
Vines, Sherard. Hundred years of English literature. 3. 50. Macmillan
Ward, A. C. Twentieth century literature, 1901-1950. 12th rev. ed. 1957. 3. 25. Barnes & Noble

ENGLISH LITERATURE--IRISH AUTHORS (820. 904)

Anthology of Irish literature. 1. 95. Modern Lib.
Russell, Diarmuid, ed. Portable Irish reader. 1946. 2. 95. Viking

ENGLISH LITERATURE--OUTLINES, SYLLABI, ETC. (820. 7)

Thrall, William F. , and others. Handbook to literature. rev. ed. 1960. 3. 75; Odyssey

ENGLISH LITERATURE--STUDY AND TEACHING (820. 7)

Altick, Richard D. , and Andrew Wright. Selective bibliography for the study of English and American literature. pap. 2. 50. Macmillan

Fowler, John H. Art of teaching English. 1.50. St. Martins
Pooley, Robert C. Perspectives on English. 1960. 4.00. Appleton
ENGLISH LITERATURE--TRANSLATIONS FROM FOREIGN LITERATURE (808.8)
Buck, Philo M., Jr. Anthology of world literature. 3rd ed. 7.25. Macmillan
Grebanier, Bernard, and others, eds. English literature and its backgrounds.
  rev. ed. 2 vols. 1949. vol. l, From the Old English Period through the Age of
  Reason. vol. 2, From the forerunners of Romanticism to the present. 8.95 ea;
  Holt, Rinehart & Winston
Pound, Ezra. Translations. 1953. 6.00. New Directions
Ross, James Bruce and Mary Martin McLaughlin, eds. Portable Medieval
  reader. 1946. 1.65. Viking
Ross, James Bruce, and Mary Martin McLaughlin, eds. Portable Renaissance
  reader. 1953. 2.95. Viking
Rutherford, Peggy ed. African voices: An anthology of native African
  writings. 1959. 3.95. Vanguard
Thompson, Stith, and John Gassner, eds. Our heritage of world literature.
  2 bks. rev. ed. 1942. in one vol. 10.95; bk. l, Literature in translation, 8.95.
  Holt, Rinehart & Winston
ENGLISH LITERATURE--TRANSLATIONS FROM LATIN (870)
Murphy, C. T., and others. Greek and Roman classics in translation. 1947.
  6.95. McKay
ENGLISH LITERATURE--TRANSLATIONS FROM ORIENTAL LITERATURE (890)
Anderson, George L., ed. Masterpieces of the Orient. 1961. 3.95. Norton
ENGLISH LITERATURE--TRANSLATIONS FROM PORTUGUESE (869)
Onis, Harriet de, ed. Golden land: An anthology of Latin American folklore.
  1948. 5.75. Knopf
ENGLISH POETRY (COLLECTIONS) (821.08)
Alexander, A. L., ed. Poems that touch the heart. rev. ed. 1956. 3.95.
  Doubleday
Anthology of famous English and American poetry. (G67) 2.95. Modern Lib.
Auden, W. H., ed. Oxford book of light verse. 1938. 5.00. Oxford U. P.
Auden, W. H., and Norman Holmes Pearson, eds. Poets of the Englsih
  language. 5 vols. vol. l. Langland to Spenser; vol. 2. Marlowe to Marvell;
  vol. 3. Milton to Goldsmith; vol. 4. Blake to Poe; vol. 5. Tennyson to Yeats.
  1950. 2.95 ea. Viking
Auslander, Joseph, and Frank E. Hill, eds. Winged horse anthology il. 1949. 4.95.
  Doubleday
Blair, Walter, and W. K. Chandler. Approaches to poetry. 2nd ed. 1953. 4.75.
  Appleton
Brooks, Cleanth, and Robert Penn Warren. Understanding poetry. 3rd ed. 1960.
  8.30. Holt, Rinehart & Winston
Ciardi, John. How does a poem mean? (Introduction to literature, pt. 3) 1960.
  4.00. Houghton
Coffin, Charles M., ed. Major poets: English and American. 1954. 5.25. Harcourt
Cole, William, ed. Fireside book of humorous poetry. il. 1959. 6.50. S. and S.
Daiches, David., and William Charvat. Poems in English: 1530-1940. 1950.
  5.50. Ronald
Daringer, Helen F., and Anne T. Eaton, eds. Poet's craft. 1935. 3.20.
  Harcourt
De La Mare, Walter. Come hither. il. 1957. 7.50. Knopf
Derleth, August. Dark of the moon. 1947. 3.50. Arkham
Eastman, Max. Enjoyment of poetry, and Anthology for the enjoyment of
  poetry. 7.50. Scribner
Felleman, Hazel, ed. Best loved poems of the American people. 1936. 2.95.
  Doubleday
Fifteen poets: Chaucer to Arnold. 1941 2.00. Oxford U. P.
Frankenberg, Lloyd, ed. Invitation to poetry. 1956. 6.75. pap. 0.95. Doubleday
Gannett, Lewis S., ed. Family book of verse. 1961. 4.95. Harper

George, David L., comp. Family book of best loved poems. 1952. 3.95. Doubleday

Harrington, Mildred P., and J. H. Thomas, eds. Our holidays in poetry. 1929. 3.00. Wilson (R)

Hodnett, Edward, ed. Poems to read aloud. 1957. 4.95. Norton

Holmes, John, ed. Little treasury of love poems. il. 1950. 5.00. Scribner

Holt, Lucius H. ed. Leading English poets from Chaucer to Browning. 1915. 6.50. Houghton

Lawson, J. G., ed. World's best loved poems. 1927. 2.75. Harper

Lowry, Howard F., and Willard Thorp, eds. Oxford anthology of English poetry. 2nd ed. 1956. 7.50. Oxford U. P.

Millett, Fred. Reading poetry. 1950. 3.00. Harper

Mudge, James. Poems with power to strengthen the soul. rev. ed. 3.75. Abingdon

Nicholson, D. H. S., and A. H. E. Lee, eds. Oxford book of English mystical verse. 1917. 5.00. Oxford U. P.

Palgrave, Francis T., ed. Golden treasury. (232) 1.95. Modern Lib.

Palgrave, Francis T., ed. Golden treasury of songs and lyrics, with additional poems. 5.00. Macmillan

Parker, Elinor, ed. 100 poems about people. il. 1955. 3.50. Crowell

Peacock, William, ed. English verse. 5 vols. 2.75 ea. Oxford U. P.

Quiller-Couch, Arthur, ed. Oxford book of English verse. 1939. 7.50. Oxford U. P.

Rosenthal, M. L., and A. J. M Smith. Exploring poetry. 1955. 5.50. Macmillan

Stevenson, Burton Egbert, ed. Home book of verse. 9th ed. 2 vols. 25.00. Holt (R)

Stevenson, Burton Egbert, ed. Home book of verse for young folks. rev. ed. 5.00. Holt

Untermeyer, Louis, ed. Book of living verse. 1949. 2.50. Harcourt

Untermeyer, Louis, ed. Golden treasury of poetry. il. 1959. 5.00. Golden Press

Untermeyer, Louis. Story poems: An anthology of narrative verse. pap. 0.50. Pocket Bks.

Untermeyer, Louis, ed. Treasury of great poems. rev. ed. 1955. 7.50. S. and S.

Van Doren, Mark. Introduction to poetry. 1951. pap. 3.75. Holt, Rinehart & Winston

Williams, Oscar, ed. Little treasury of British poetry. rev. ed. il. 1955. 5.00. Scribner

Williams, Oscar. ed. Little treasury of great poetry. rev. ed. il. 1955. 5.00. Scribner

Williams, Oscar, ed. Pocket book of modern verse. pap. 0.60. Washington Square

Williams, Oscar, ed. Silver treasury of light verse. 1957. pap. 0.75. New Am. Lib.

Young, William T., ed. Poetry of the age of Shakespeare. 1910. 1.75. Cambridge U. P.

ENGLISH POETRY (COLLECTIONS)--MIDDLE ENGLISH (1100-1500) (821.1)

Mack, Maynard, and others, eds. Age of Chaucer. (English masterpieces. vol. 1.) 2.75; 2nd ed. pap. 1.95. Prentice-Hall

Person, Henry A., ed. Cambridge middle English lyrics. 2nd ed. 1962. pap. 3.00. U. of Wash.

Robbins, R. H. Historical poems of the 14th and 15th centuries. 7.50. Columbia

ENGLISH POETRY (COLLECTIONS)--EARLY MODERN (to 1700) (821.4)

Auden, Wystan H. and Norman H. Pearson, eds. Langland to Spenser (Poets of the English language, vol. 1) 2.95. Viking

Auden, Wystan H., and Norman H. Pearson, eds. Marlowe to Marvell (Poets of the English language, vol. 2) 2.95. Viking

Gardner, Helen, ed. Metaphysical poets. 1961. 4.25. Oxford U. P.

Grierson, Herbert J. C., ed. Metaphysical lyrics and poems of the seventeenth century, Donne to Butler. 1959. pap. 1.75. Oxford U. P.

Grierson, Herbert J. C., and G. Bullough, eds. Oxford book of seventeenth century verse. 1934. 5.75. Oxford U. P.

Mack, Maynard, and others, eds. Milton (English masterpieces, vol.4) 2.75; Prentice-Hall

Mack, Maynard, and others, eds. Renaissance poetry. (English masterpieces, vol.3) 2nd ed. pap. 1.95. Prentice-Hall

Minor poets of the 17th century. 1.95. Dutton

Rollins, Hyder Edward, ed. Poetical rhapsody, 1602-1621. 2 vols. vol. 1. text 1931. o.p.; vol. 2. introduction, notes and index. 1932. 4.00. Harvard

ENGLISH POETRY (COLLECTIONS)--18TH CENTURY (821.6)

Auden, W. H., and N. H. Pearson, eds. Restoration and Augustan poets (Poets of the English Language, vol. 3) pap. 1.65. Viking

Bloom, Harold, ed. English romantic poetry. 4.50. Doubleday

Crane, Ronald S. Collection of English poems: 1660-1800. 1932. 8.00. Harper

Smith, David N., ed. Oxford book of eighteenth century verse. 1926. 5.75. Oxford U. P.

ENGLISH POETRY (COLLECTIONS)--19TH CENTURY (821.7)

Auden, Wystan H. and Norman H. Pearson, eds. Blake to Poe (Poets of the English language. vol. 4) 2.95. Viking

Auden, Wystan H. and Norman H. Pearson, eds. Romantic poets (Poets of the English language, vol. 4) pap. 1.65. Viking

Auden, Wystan H. and Norman H. Pearson, eds. Tennyson to Yeats (Poets of the English language, vol. 5) 2.95. Viking

Auden, Wystan H., and Norman H. Pearson, eds. Victorian and Edwardian poets (Poets of the English language, vol. 5) pap. 1.65. Viking

Buckley, Jerome H., and George B. Woods. Poetry of the Victorian period. 1955. 9.50. Scott

Carr, Arthur J., ed. Victorian poetry: Clough to Kipling. 1958. pap. 1.25. Rinehart

Clark, Thomas Curtis, ed. One thousand quotable poems. 1937. 5.00. Harper

Friar, Kimon, and John M. Brinnin, eds. Modern poetry: American and British. 4.00. Appleton

Mack, Maynard, and others, eds. Romantic and Victorian poetry (English masterpieces, vol. 6) 2.95, Prentice-Hall

Quiller-Couch, Arthur, ed. Oxford book of Victorian verse. 1913. 5.75. Oxford U. P.

Stephens, James, and others. English romantic poets. 8.00. Am Bk. Co.

Stephens, James, and others. Victorian and later English poets. 8.75. Am. Bk. Co.

Untermeyer, Louis, ed. Modern American poetry, and modern British poetry. rev. ed. 1962. 11.00; Harcourt

Untermeyer, Louis, ed. Modern British poetry. rev. ed. 1962. 8.25. Harcourt

Yeats, W. B., ed. Oxford book of modern verse, 1892-1935. 6.00. Oxford U. P.

ENGLISH POETRY (COLLECTIONS)--20TH CENTURY (821.91)

Cecil, David, and Allen Tate, eds. Modern verse in English, 1900-1950. 1959. 3.75. Macmillan

Drew, Elizabeth, and George Connor. Discovering modern poetry. 1961. pap. 3.25. Holt, Rinehart & Winston

Hall, Donald, and others, eds. New poets of England and America: Second selection. 1962. pap. 1.65. Meridian

Robinson, James K., and Walter B. Rideout, eds. College book of modern verse. 1958. 5.60. Harper

Sanders, Gerald de W., and John H. Nelson. Chief modern poets of England and America. 4th ed. 1962. 6.75. Macmillan

Stevenson, Burton Egbert, ed. Home book of modern verse. 2nd ed. rev. 10.00. Holt (R)

Untermeyer, Louis, ed. New modern American poetry and modern British poetry. 1950. 2.68. Harcourt

Williams, Oscar, ed. Little treasury of modern poetry. rev. ed. il. 1955. 5.00; Scribner

ENGLISH POETRY (SELECTIONS: EXTRACTS, ETC.) (821)

Aldington, Richard, ed. Viking book of poetry of the English-speaking world. rev. ed. 1958. 2 vols. in l. 7.95. Viking

Gayley, Charles M. Classic myths in English literature and in art. rev. ed. 1939. 6.75. Ginn

Sitwell, Edith, ed. Atlantic book of British and American poetry. 1958. 12.50. Little (R)

Ungar, Leonard, and William Van O'Connor. Poems for study. 1953. 5.50. Holt, Rinehart & Winston

ENGLISH POETRY--DICTIONARIES, INDEXES, ETC. (808.81)

Bernhardt, W. F., ed. Granger's index to poetry. 5th ed. 1962. 65.00; 4th ed. suppl., 1951-1955. ed. by R. J. Dixon. 1957. 20.00. Columbia

ENGLISH POETRY--HISTORY AND CRITICISM (821.09)

Blackmur, R. P. Language as gesture. 5.75. Harcourt

Brooks, Cleanth. Well wrought urn. 1956. pap. 1.35. Harcourt

Bush, Douglas. English poetry. 1952. 2.50. Oxford U. P.

Drew, Elizabeth. Discovering poetry. 1933. 3.95. Norton

Drew, Elizabeth. Poetry: A modern guide. 1959. 3.95. Norton

Eliot, T. S. Use of poetry and the use of criticism. 1955. 3.00. Barnes and Noble

Frankenberg, Lloyd, ed. Invitation to poetry. 1956. 6.75; Doubleday

Grierson, H. J. C., and J. C. Smith. Critical history of English poetry. 1946. 8.00. Oxford U. P.

Highet, Gilbert. Powers of poetry. 1960. 6.00. Oxford U. P.

Murray, Gilbert. Classical tradition in poetry. 1927. 3.00. Harvard

Reeves, James. Short history of English poetry, 1340-1940. 4.75. Dutton

Rosenthal, M. L., and A. J. M. Smith. Exploring poetry. 1955. 5.50. Macmillan

Tillyard, E. M. W. Poetry and its background. il. 1961. 2.50. Barnes & Noble

Untermeyer, Louis. Lives of the poets. 1959. 7.95. S. and S.

Van Doren, Mark. Introduction to poetry. 1951. pap. 3.75. Holt, Rinehart & Winston

ENGLISH POETRY--HISTORY AND CRITICISM--EARLY MODERN (TO 1700) (821.309)

Bennett, Joan. Four metaphysical poets. 2nd ed. 1953. 3.00. Cambridge U. P.

Bradbrook, M. C. Shakespeare and Elizabethan poetry. 1952. 3.40. Oxford U. P.

Johnson, Samuel. Lives of the English poets. 2 vols. 2.25 ea. Oxford U. P.

Johnson, Samuel. Lives of the poets. 2 vols. vol. 1. Cowley to Prior; vol. 2. Congreve to Gray. (Dolphin) pap. 1.45 ea. Doubleday

Lanier, Sidney. Shakespeare and his forerunners. ed. by Kemp Malone. 6.00. Johns Hopkins

Martz, Louis L. Poetry of meditation. il. 1954. 7.50. Yale

Willey, B. Seventeenth century background. 1942. 5.00. Columbia

Williamson, George. Donne tradition, study in English poetry from Donne to the death of Cowley. 1959. 3.50. Smith, Peter

ENGLISH POETRY--HISTORY AND CRITICISM--19TH CENTURY (821.709)

Abrams, M. H., ed. English romantic poets: Modern essays in criticism. 4.50. Smith, Peter

Beach, Joseph W. Concept of nature in nineteenth century English poetry. 1956. 7.50. Cooper

Bloom, Harold. Visionary company: English Romantic poetry. 4.50. Doubleday

Faverty, Frederic E., ed. Victorian poets: A guide to research. 1956. 5.50. Harvard

ENGLISH POETRY--HISTORY AND CRITICISM--20TH CENTURY (821.909)

Bullough, Geoffry, Trend of modern poetry. 3rd ed. rev. 2.50. Hillary

Deutsch, Babette. Poetry in our time. 1956. 6.00; 1961. Columbia
Leavis, F. R. New bearings in English poetry. 1960. 4.40. U. of Mich.
Schlauch, Margaret. Modern English and American poetry. 1959. 4.50.
  Hillary
ENGLISH POETRY--IRISH AUTHORS (821.904)
Colum, Padraic, ed. Anthology of Irish verse. rev. ed. 1948. 3.95. Liveright
MacDonagh, Donagh, and Lennox Robinson, eds. Oxford book of Irish verse:
  17th - 20th century. 1958. 5.75. Oxford U. P.
ENGLISH POETRY--TRANSLATIONS FROM FRENCH (841)
Flores, Angel, ed. Anthology of French poetry from Nerval to Valery in
  English translation. 1958. pap. 1.45. Doubleday
MacIntyre, Carlyle F. French symbolist poetry. bilingual, in English and
  French. 1958. pap. 1.50. U. of Calif.
ENGLISH PROSE LITERATURE (COLLECTIONS) (820.8)
Anthology of English prose. 1.95. Dutton
Brooks, Cleanth, and Robert Penn Warren. Modern rhetoric. 2nd ed. 1958.
  5.95. Harcourt
Quiller-Couch, Arthur, ed. Oxford book of English prose. 1925. 6.50. Oxford
  U. P.
Stone, Wilfred H., and Robert Hoopes. Form and thought in prose. 2nd ed.
  1960. 5.00. Ronald
ENGLISH PROSE LITERATURE (COLLECTIONS)--EARLY MODERN (TO 1700) (820)
Nugent, Elizabeth M. Thought and culture of the English Renaissance, 1481-
  1555. 1956. 6.50. Cambridge U. P.
Wilson, John Dover. Life in Shakespeare's England. 2nd ed. 1913. 2.00.
  Cambridge U. P.
ENGLISH PROSE LITERATURE (COLLECTIONS)--18TH CENTURY (820)
Bredvold, L. I., and others. Eighteenth century prose. 1932. 7.00. Ronald
Pettit, Henry, comp. Collection of English prose, 1660-1800. 1962. 8.00.
  Harper
ENGLISH PROSE LITERATURE (COLLECTIONS)--19TH CENTURY (820)
Craig, Hardin, and J. M. Thomas. English prose of the nineteenth century.
  6.00. Appleton
ENGLISH PROSE LITERATURE (COLLECTIONS)--20TH CENTURY (820)
Boas, Guy. Modern English prose. 3 ser. ser. 1 and 2, 1.00 ea; ser. 3, 1.25.
  St. Martins
Cerf, Bennett, ed. Reading for pleasure. 1957. 6.50. Harper
ENGLISH PROSE LITERATURE--HISTORY AND CRITICISM (820)
Chambers, R. W. On the continuity of English prose from Alfred to More and
  his school. 1932. 2.25. Oxford U. P.
Dobree, Bonamy. Modern prose style. 1934. 2.40. Oxford U. P.
Sutherland, James. On English prose. il. 1957. 3.50. U. of Toronto
Thomson, J. A. K. Classical influences on English prose. pap. 0.95. Collier
ENGLISH WIT AND HUMOR (820)
Cole, William, ed. Best humor from Punch. 3.50. World Pub.
Cole, William, ed. Fireside book of humorous poetry. il. 1959. 6.50. S. and S.
Parkinson, C. Northcote. Parkinson's law. il. 1957. 3.00. 1962. Houghton
Wells, Carolyn. Nonsense anthology. pap. 1.25. Dover
ENGRAVING (760)
Buckland-Wright, John. Etching and engraving. il. 1954. 7.50. (Studio) Viking
Heller, Jules. Printmaking today. il. 1958. 8.75. Holt, Rinehart & Winston
ENGRAVINGS (769)
Haas, Irvin. Treasury of great prints. il. 1961. 1.45. Barnes, A. S. (R)
Longstreet, Stephen, ed. Treasury of the world's great prints. 1961. 15.00.
  S. and S. (R)
Sachs, Paul J. Modern prints and drawings. il. 1954. 7.50. Knopf
ENLIGHTENMENT (190)
Berlin, Isaiah. Age of enlightenment. 1956. 3.00. Houghton
Brinton, Crane, ed. Portable Age of Reason reader. 1956. 2.95. Viking

Cassirer, Ernst. Philosophy of the Enlightenment. tr. by Fritz Koelin and
James Pettegrove. 1959. 3.50. Smith, Peter
Cobban, Alfred. In search of humanity. 1960. 4.50. Braziller
Nicolson, Harold G. Age of reason, the eighteenth century. 1961. 5.95.
Doubleday
Snyder, Louis L. Age of reason. 1955. pap. 1.25. Van Nostrand

ENTERTAINING (395.3)
Allen, Catharine. Fun for parties and programs. 1956. 4.35. Prentice-Hall
Anderson, Kenneth. Ideas for young people's parties. 1950. pap. 0.75.
Zondervan
Beeker, Mabel King. Banquets plus! 1958. 3.00. Broadman
Crocker, Betty. Betty Crocker's guide to easy entertaining. il. 1959. 1.00; lib.
bdg. 1.89 net. Golden Press
Crocker, Betty. Betty Crocker's party book. il. 1960. 1.00. Golden Press
Daly, Maureen. Perfect hostess. 1950. 3.00. Dodd
Dennison complete party guide. 1961. pap. 1.00. Pocket Bks.
Good Housekeeping. Good Housekeeping party book. by the Editors of Good
Housekeeping. ed. by Dorothy Marsh and Carol Brock. il. 1958. 4.95. Harper
Harbin, E. O. Gay parties for all occasions. il. 1950. 2.95. Abingdon
Hedgecock, Elizabeth. Successful hostess. 1949. 3.75. Burgess
Kaufman, S. Jay. How to arrange a public function. 1953. 2.50. McKay
Kirk, Jane. Group socials for every month. 1957. 2.95. Abingdon
Lee, Nata. Complete book of entertaining. il. 1961. 5.95. Hawthorn
McLean, Beth Bailey. Meal planning and table service. rev. ed. 1955. 4.40.
Bennett
Maguire, Clyde Merrill. Abingdon party and banquet book. 1956. 1.95. Abingdon
Maguire, Clyde M. Cokesbury dinner and banquet book. 1953. 1.95. Abingdon
Mulac, Margaret Elizabeth. Party fun, for holidays and special occasions. il.
1960. half cl. 4.95. Harper
Mulac, Margaret E., and Marian S. Holmes. Party game book. il. 1951. 4.50;
Harper
Plumb, Beatrice. Master banquet and party book. 1961. 3.95. Denison
Van Rensselaer, Alexander. Complete book of party games. il. 1952. 3.75.
Sheridan

ENTOMOLOGY (595.7)
Borror, Donald J., and Dwight M. DeLong. Introduction to the study of insects.
1954. 10.75. Holt, Rinehart & Winston
Campbell, Frank L., ed. Physiology of insect development. 1959. 4.00. U. of
Chicago
Comstock, John Henry. Introduction to entomology. 9th ed. rev. il. 1940.
7.50. Cornell
Frost, S. W. Insect life and insect natural history. 2nd ed. il. pap. 2.25. Dover
Graham, Samuel A. Forest entomology. 3rd ed. 1952. 7.75. McGraw
Haviland, Elizabeth E. Laboratory notebook for introductory entomology. il.
1959. spiral bdg. 2.25. Burgess
Kalmus, H. 101 simple experiments with insects. il. 2.95. Doubleday
Klots, Alexander B., and Elsie B. Living insects of the world. il. 1959. 9.95.
Doubleday (R)
Little, V. A. General and applied entomology. 1957. 7.00. Harper
Oldroyd, Harold. Collecting, preserving and studying insects. il. 1959. 6.00.
Macmillan
Pesson, P. World of insects. 1959. 15.00. McGraw

ENZYMES (574.193)
Burnet, F. Macfarlane. Enzyme, antigen and virus. 1957. 3.75. Cambridge U. P.
Ciba Foundations. Enzymes and drug action. 1962. 12.50. Little
Houssay, B. A., ed. Enzymes and metabolism. il. 1956. 9.75. Am Elsevier
Laidler, Keith J. Introduction to the chemistry of enzymes. il. 1954. 7.50.
McGraw

EPIC LITERATURE (808)
Dillon, Myles. Early Irish literature. 1948. 4.00. U. of Chicago
Joyce, P. W. Old Celtic romances. 1962. 4.50. Devin
Tillyard, Eustace M. W. Epic strain in the English novel. 1958. 3.40.
Oxford U. P.
EPIC POETRY (808.1)
Hutson, Arthur E., and Patricia McCoy. Epics of the western world. 1954.
6.00. Lippincott
EPIC POETRY--HISTORY AND CRITICISM (808.13)
Bowra, Cecil Maurice. From Virgil to Milton. 4.50. St. Martins
Bowra, Cecil Maurice. Heroic poetry. 1952. 8.00. St. Martins
Foerster, D. M. Fortunes of epic poetry: A study in English and American
criticism 1750-1950. 1962. 4.95. Catholic U. of Am. Pr.
Lawrence, William W. Beowulf and epic tradition. 5.75. Hafner
Lord, Albert B. Singer of tales. il. 1960. 6.75. Harvard
McNamee, Maurice B. Honor and the epic hero. 1960. 5.50. Holt, Rinehart &
Winston
Tillyard, Eustace M. W. English epic and its background. 1954. 4.00. Oxford U. P.
EPICURUS (921)
DeWitt, Norman W. Epicurus and his philosophy. 1954. 6.00. U. of Minn.
EPIDEMICS (614.94)
Zinsser, Hans. Rats, lice and history. 1935. 6.00. (Atlantic Monthly Press)
Little
EPILEPSY (616.853)
Lunt, Carroll, How to live with epilepsy. 4.00. Twayne
Penfield, Wilder, and Herbert Jasper. Epilepsy and the functional anatomy of
the human brain. il. 1954. 18.00. Little
EPITAPHS (929.5)
Croy, Homer. Last word: Epitaphs. 1.00. Wehman
Wallis, Charles L. Stories on stone: A book of American epitaphs. 1954. 6.50.
Oxford U. P.
EQUALITY (323.41)
Gardner, John W. Excellence: Can we be equal and excellent too? 1961. 3.95.
Harper
Myers, Henry Alonzo. Are men equal? pap. 1.45. Cornell
Sexton, Patricia C. Education and income: Inequalities of opportunity in our public
schools. il. 1961. 6.00. Viking
EQUALITY BEFORE THE LAW (323.42)
Harris, Robert. Quest for equality. 1960. 4.00. La. State
EQUATIONS (512.82)
Borofsky, Samuel. Elementary theory of equations. 5.75. Macmillan
Conkwright, N. B. Introduction to the theory of equations. 1941. 5.50. Ginn
Dickson, Leonard E. First course in the theory of equations. 1921. 3.95. Wiley
Dickson, Leonard Eugene. New first course in the theory of equations. 1939. 3.75.
Wiley
MacDuffee, C. C. Theory of equations. 1954. 3.95. Wiley
ERASMUS, DESIDERIUS, d. 1536 (922.24)
Bouyer, Louis. Erasmus and his times. 1960. 3.75. Newman
Huizinga, Johan. Erasmus of Rotterdam. il. 1952. 2.95. N. Y. Graphic
Luther, Martin. Bondage of the will. tr. by J. I. Packer, and O. R. Johnston.
4.00. Revell
Smith, Preserved. Erasmus: A study of his life, ideals and place in history. 7.50.
Ungar
Taylor, Henry O. Erasmus and Luther. 0.95. Collier
ERIE CANAL (977)
Chalmers, Harvey, II. Birth of the Erie Canal. il. 1960. bds. 3.50. Twayne
Miller, Nathan. Enterprise of a free people. 1962. 6.00. Cornell
Wyld, Lionel D. Low bridge! Folklore and the Erie Canal. il. 1962. 5.50. Syracuse

EROSION (631.455)
Ayres, Quincy C. Soil erosion and its control. 1936. 8.50. McGraw
Bennett, Hugh H. Elements of soil conservation. il. 1955. 5.00. McGraw
Bennett, Hugh Hammond. Soil conservation. il. 1939. 13.50. McGraw
ERRORS (519.6)
Maxwell, Edwin A. Fallacies in mathematics. il. 1959. 2.95. Cambridge U. P.
Tabori, Paul. Natural science of stupidity. 1959. 4.50. Chilton
Evans, Bergen. Natural history of nonsense. 1946. 4.50. Knopf
Beers, Y. Theory of error. il. 1957. 2.00. Addison-Wesley
Burnside, William. Theory of probability. il. 1960. pap. 1.00. Dover
Parratt, Lyman G. Probability and experimental errors in science. 1961. 6.50.
    Wiley
Topping, J. Errors of observation and their treatment. 1957. 1.50. Reinhold
ESCAPES (365.643)
Clark, Ronald. Great moments in escaping. il. 1958. 2.50. Roy Pub.
Williams, Eric. Book of famous escapes. 1954. 4.95. Norton
Williams, Eric. Wooden horse. il. 1958. 3.50. Abelard
ESCHATOLOGY (236)
Berdyaev, Nikolai. Destiny of man. 6.00. Hillary
Boettner, Loraine. Immortality. 1956. 2.50. Eerdmans
Budge, Wallis. Egyptian religion. 5.00. Wehman
Henry, Antonin M. Triumph of Christ. 1962. pap. 0.95. Fides
Pelikan, Jaroslav. Shape of death. 1961. 2.25. Abingdon
Pohle, Joseph. Eschatology. 3.25. Herder
ESKIMOS (998)
Birket-Smith, Kaj. Eskimos. C. Daryll Forde. 1959. 6.50. Humanities
Freuchen, Peter. Book of the Eskimos. il. 1961. 7.50. World Pub.
Lantis, Margaret. Eskimo childhood and interpersonal relationships: Nunivak
    biographies and genealogies. il. 1960. 4.75. U. of Wash.
Stefansson, Vilhjalmur. My life with the Eskimo. pap. 1.50. Collier
Weyer, Edward M. Eskimos: Their environment and folkways. il. 1962. 12.50.
    Shoe String
Carpenter, Edmund, and others. Eskimo. il. 1959. 4.95. U. of Toronto
Miles, Charles. Indian and Eskimo artifacts of North America. il. 1962. 25.00.
    Regnery
Carrighar, Sally. Moonlight at midday. 1958. 6.50. Knopf
Hughes, Charles C., and Jane M. Eskimo village in the modern world. il. 1960.
    6.75. Cornell
Jenness, Diamond. Dawn in Arctic Alaska. 1957. 4.75. U. of Minn.
Blanche, Guy. Search in the north. 1960. 4.50. St. Martins
Mowat, Farley. Desperate people. il. 1959. 4.50. Little
ESOPHAGUS (616.32)
Lerche, William. Esophagus and pharynx in action: A study of structure in relation
    to function. il. 1950. 6.50. Thomas, C. C.
Terracol, Jean, and Richard H. Sweet. Diseases of the esophagus. il. 1958. 20.00.
    Saunders
Vinson, Porter P. Diseases of the esophagus. 1947. lexide. 0.90. Thomas, C. C
ESSAYS (808.4)
Hamalian, Leo, and Edmond L. Volpe. Great essays by Nobel prize winners. 1960.
    pap. 1.95. Farrar, Straus
Lester, John A. Essays of yesterday and today. 1943. 2.28. Harcourt
Rudman, Harry W., and Irving Rosenthal. Contemporary reader: Essays for
    today and tomorrow. 1961.pap. 3.40. Ronald
Starr, Nathan C. Pursuit of learning. 4.75. Harcourt
Essay and general literature index. Sold on service basis. Wilson (R)
ESTHETICS (111.85, 801.9)
Aristotle Rhetoric and poetics: Rhetorica, De rhtorica ad Alexandreem, De poetica.
    by J. A. Smith, and W. D. Ross. 4.50. Oxford U. P.

Arnett, W. E. Santayana and the sense of beauty. 1960. 3.25. Smith, Peter

Ball, Albert H. R. Ruskin as literary critic. 1928. 1.25. Cambridge U. P.

Bate, W. J. From classic to romantic. 1961. pap. 1.35. Harper

Bate, Walter J. From Classic To Romantic. 3.35. Smith, Peter

Bell, Clive. Art. 1959. 1.25. Putnam

Berenson, Bernard. Aesthetics and history. 1954. 0.95. Doubleday

Blunt, Anthony. Artistic theory of Italy, 1450-1600. 1956. 4.50. Oxford U. P.

Boas, George. Primer for critics. 1937. 2.00. Johns Hopkins

Bosanquet, Bernard. History of aesthetic. 4.75. Macmillan

Bullough, Edward. Aesthetics. by E. M. Wilkinson. 1957. 4.50. Stanford

Butcher, Samuel H. Aristotle's theory of poetry and fine art. 1955. pap. 2.00. Dover

Carpenter, Rhys. Esthetic basis of Greek art. il. 1959. 3.50. Indiana

Carritt, E. F. Philosophies of beauty from Socrates to Robert Bridges. 1931. 4.50. Oxford U. P.

Church, Ralph W. Essay on critical appreciation. 3.50. Cornell

Croce, Bendetto. Aesthetic as science of expression and general linguistic. 4.25. Smith, Peter

Crocker, Lester G. Two Diderot studies: Ethics and esthetics. 1952. 2.50. Johns Hopkins

Dewey, John. Art as experience. 1959. 2.50. Putnam

Ducasse, Curt J. Art, the critics and you. 1955. 2.50. Bobbs

Dudley, Louise, and Austin Faricy. Humanities. 1960. 7.50. McGraw

Edman, Irwin. Arts and the man. 1939. pap. 1.85. Norton

Faulkner, Ray, and others. Art today: An introduction to the fine and functional arts. il. 1956. 10.10. Holt, Rinehart & Winston

Forsyth, Peter T. Christ on Parnassus. 1959. 4.00. Allenson

Guggenheimer, Richard. Creative vision. 1960. 3.50. Harper

Gump, Richard. Good taste costs no more. il. 1951. 5.00. Doubleday

Hamilton, G. R. Poetry and contemplation. 2.50. Cambridge U. P.

Heyl, Bernard Chapman. New bearings in esthetics and art criticism. 1943. 3.75. Yale

Itten, Johannes. Art of color. il. 1961. 30.00. Reinhold (R)

Jarrett, James L. Quest for beauty. 1957. 10.00. Prentice-Hall

Jenkins, I. Art and the human enterprise. 1958. 5.50. Harvard

Jordan, Elijah. Essays in criticism. 1952. 7.00. U. of Chicago

Kaminsky, Jack. Hegel on art. 1962. 6.00. Univ. Pub.

Kant, Immanuel. Observations on the feeling of the beautiful and sublime. tr. by John T. Goldthwait. pap. 1.50. U. of Calif.

Knox, Israel. Aesthetic theories of Kant, Hegel and Schopenhauer. 5.00. Humanities

Krutch, Joseph Wood. Experience and art. pap. 0.95. Collier

Langer, Susanne K. Problems of art. 1957. 3.50. Scribner

Langer, Susanne K. Reflections on art. il. 1958. 6.50. Johns Hopkins

Lynes, Russell. Tastemakers. il. 1954. 6.00. Harper

MacGregor, Geddes. Aesthetic experience in religion. 3.00. St. Martins

Maritain, Jacques. Art and scholasticism and the frontiers of poetry. tr. by Joseph W. Evans. 1962. 5.00. Scribner

Monk, Samuel H. Sublime: A study of critical theories in 18th century England. 1960. 4.40. U. of Mich.

Ortega y Gasset, Jose. Dehumanization of art and other writings on art and culture. 2.85. Smith, Peter

Ortega y Gasset, Jose. Meditations on Quixote. 1961. 4.50. Norton

Pepper, Stephen C. Work of art. 1955. 3.00. Indiana

Rader, Melvin. Modern book of esthetics. 1960. 6.75. Holt, Rinehart & Winston

Rawlins, F. I. G. Aesthetics and the Gestalt. 3.75. Humanities

Read, Herbert E. Forms of things unknown. il. 6.00. Horizon

Sachs, Hanns. Creative unconscious. 1951. 6.00. Sci-Art

Santayana, George. Interpretations of poetry and religion. 1958. 3.50. Smith, Peter

Santayana, George. Sense of beauty. 1955. 1.95. Modern Lib.
Stolnitz, Jerome. Aesthetics and philosophy of art criticism. il. 1960. 6.95.
Houghton
Vivas, Eliseo, and Murray Krieger. Problems of aesthetics. 1953. 6.95. Holt,
Rinehart & Winston
Weiss, Paul. Nine basic arts. il. 1961. 5.00. Southern Ill.
Weitz, Morris. Problems in aesthetics. 1959. 6.90. Macmillan
Wulf, Maurice de. System of Thomas Aquinas. 3.25. Smith, Peter
ESTHETICS--ANCIENT (801.9)
Aristotle. Art of poetry: A Greek view of poetry and drama. by W. H. Fyfe. 1940.
1.60. Oxford U. P.
Aristotle. On poetry and style. tr. by G. M. A. Grube. 1958. 3.00. Bobbs
Aristotle. On the art of fiction. tr. by L. J. Potts. 1953. 1.75. Cambridge U. P.
Aristotle. On the art of poetry. tr. by Ingram Bywater. 1920. pap. 1.00. Oxford
U. P.
Aristotle. Poetics. tr. by S. H. Butcher. 1961. 3.50. Hill & Wang
Burke, E. Philosophical enquiry into the origin of our ideas of the sublime and
beautiful. by J. T. Boulton. 1958. 5.00. Columbia
Cooper, Lane. Aristotle on the art of poetry. 1962. pap. 1.50. Cornell
Hogarth, William. Analysis of beauty. by Joseph Burke. 1955. 7.20. Oxford U. P.
Kant, Immanuel. Critique of judgement. tr. by. J. C. Meredith. 1952. 4.50.
Oxford U. P.
ETHICS (170)
Adler, Mortimer J. Dialectic of morals: Towards the foundation of political
philosophy. 1941. 3.50. Ungar
Aiken, Henry D. Reason and conduct. 1962. 6.75. Knopf
Albert, Ethel M., and others. Great traditions in ethics. 5.75. Am. Bk. Co.
Bentham, Jeremy. Introduction to the principles of morals and legislation. by
Laurence J. Lafleur. 1948. pap. 1.50. Hafner
Bentham, Jeremy, and John S. Mill. Utilitarians. 3.50. Smith, Peter
Bergson, Henri. Two sources of morality and religion. 1954. pap. 0.95. Doubleday
Bourke, Vernon J. Ethics: A textbook in moral philosophy. 1951. 5.75. Macmillan
Brennan, Bernard P. Ethics of William James. 1961. 4.00. Twayne
Bridges, Horace J. Humanity on trial. 1941. 3.00. Liveright
Carritt, E. F. Ethical and political thinking. 1947. 2.40. Oxford U. P.
Castell, Alburey. Elementary ethics. 1954. 6.50. Prentice-Hall
Copleston, F. C. Bergson on morality. 1955. 0.85. Oxford U. P.
DeBoer, Cecil. Ifs and oughts of ethics. 1936. 3.00. Eerdmans
Dewey, John, and James H. Tufts. Ethics. 1932. 6.00. Holt
Dewey, John. Theory of the moral life. 3.30. Holt, Rinehart & Winston
Dewey, Robert E., and others. Problems of ethics. 1961. 6.00. Macmillan
Fagothey, Austin. Right and reason: Ethics in theory and practice. 1959. 6.00.
Mosby
Fite, Warner. Examined life. 1957. 4.50. Indiana
Fite, Warner. Examined life, an adventure in moral philosophy. 1960. 3.75.
Smith, Peter
Flugel, John C. Man, morals, and society. 1957. 4.50. Int. Univs.
Fromm, Erich. Man for himself: An inquiry into the psychology of ethics. 3.75.
Rinehart
Garnett, A. C. Moral nature of man. 1952. 4.25. Ronald
Garvin, Lucius. Modern introduction to ethics. 6.00. Houghton
Gilson, Etienne H. Moral values and the moral life. tr. by Leo R. Ward. 1961.
7.00. Shoe String
Glenn, Paul J. Ethics. 1930. 3.25. Herder
Hampshire, Stuart. Thought and action. 1960. 4.50. Viking
Hegal, G. W. F. Philosophy of right. by T. M. Knox. 1942. 4.80. Oxford U. P.
Higgins, Thomas. Man as man. 1958. 4.50. Bruce
Hollingworth, H. L. Psychology and ethics. 1949. 5.00. Ronald

Hospers, John. Human conduct. 1962. 9.00. Harcourt
Hume, David. Enquiries concerning the human understanding. 1927. 2.90. Oxford
   U. P.
Hyde, William D. Five great philosophies of life. il. 1930. 4.50. Macmillan
James, William. Essays on faith and morals. pap. 1.55. Meridian
Jones, William T., and others. Approaches to ethics. 1962. 7.50. McGraw
Kant, Immanuel. Foundations of the metaphysics of morals and What is enlighten-
   ment? 1959. pap. 0.80. Bobbs
Kant, Immanuel. Moral law. by J. J. Paton. 4.00. Barnes & Noble
Lippmann, Walter. Preface to morals. 5.00. Macmillan
McAllister, Joseph B. Ethics. 1955. 4.00. Saunders
Maritain, Jacques. Person and the common good. 2.50. Scribner
Moore, Thomas V., Dom. Principles of ethics. by Dom Gregory Stevens. 1959.
   6.00. Lippincott
Mukerjee, Radhakamal. Dynamics of morals. 6.00. St. Martins
Nietzsche, Friedrich. Birth of tragedy, and Genealogy of morals. 1956. pap. 0.95.
   Doubleday
Otto, Max. Science and the moral life. pap. 0.50. New Am. Lib.
Pepper, Stephen C. Ethics. 1960. 4.00. Appleton
Ross, W. D. Foundations of ethics. 1939. 4.50. Oxford U. P.
Selsam, Howard. Socialism and ethics. 1943. 2.50. Int. Pubs.
Singer, Marcus George. Generalization in ethics. 1961. 6.00. Knopf
Spinoza, Benedict de. Ethics, etc. 1.95. Dutton
Spinoza, Benedict. Philosophy. 1.95. Modern Lib.
Stace, Walter T. Concept of morals. pap. 1.75. Macmillan
Titus, Harold H. Ethics for today. 6.00. Am. Bk. Co.
Toulmin, S. Reason in ethics. 1950. 4.50. 1960. Cambridge U. P.
Veatch, Henry B. Rational man: A modern interpretation of Aristotelian ethics.
   1962. 5.00. Indiana
Walsh, Vivian C. Scarcity and evil. 1961. 3.95. Prentice-Hall
Ward, Leo R. Ethics and the social sciences. 1959. 3.25. U. of Notre Dame
Waterman, Leroy. Religion faces the world crisis. 1943. 2.25. Wahr
Wilson, John. Reason and morals. 1961. 2.95. Cambridge U. P.
Wylie, Philip. Essay on morals. 1947. 3.50. Rinehart
ETHICS--DICTIONARIES (170.3)
Hastings, James. Encyclopedia of religion and ethics. 13 vols. 1951. 195.00.
   Scribner
ETHICS--HISTORY (170.9)
Albert, Ethel M., and others. Great traditions in ethics. 5.75. Am. Bk. Co.
Brinton, Crane. History of Western morals. 1959. 7.50. Harcourt
Eby, L. S. Quest for moral law. 1944. 3.75. Columbia
Hertzler, Joyce O. Social thought of the ancient civilizations. 1961. 7.50. Russell
Johnson, Oliver A. Ethics: A source book. 1958. 5.75. Holt, Rinehart & Winston
Riley, Woodbridge. Men and morals: The story of ethics. il. 6.50. Ungar
Rogers, Reginald A. P. Short history of ethics, Greek and modern. 1961. 3.00.
   St. Martins
ETHICS, CHINESE (170)
Confucius. Analects. by Arthur Waley. 1938. 3.50. Macmillan
Confucius. Analects; or, The conversations of Confucius with his disciples and
   certain others. tr. by W. E. Soothill. by D. S. Hosie. 1941. 2.25. Oxford U. P.
Confucius. Wisdom of Confucius. 1943. 1.95. Modern Lib.
ETHICS, GREEK (880)
Aristotle. Ethics: Ethica Nicomachea, Magna moralia, Ethica eudamia. by J. A.
   Smith, and W. D. Ross. 5.60. Oxford U. P.
Aristotle, Nicomachean ethics. tr. by W. David Ross. 1954. 2.25. Oxford U. P.
Gould, John. Development of Plato's ethics. 1955. 6.00. Cambridge U. P.
Pearson, Lionel. Popular ethics in ancient Greece. 1962. 5.50. Stanford
ETHICS, HINDU (170)
Krishnamurti, Jiddu. Commentaries on living. 1960. 11.50. Harper

ETHIOPIA (963)
Lipsky, George O., and others. Ethiopia. 1962. 8.75. Taplinger
Ullendorff, Edward. Ethiopians: An intorduction to country and people. 1960. 4 80.
  Oxford U. P.
Jones, A. H. M., and E. Monroe. History of Ethiopia. 1955. 2.90. Oxford U. P.
ETHNOLOGY (572)
Ashley, Montagu, M. F. Man in process. 1961. 4.50. World Pub.
Diamond, Stanley. Culture in history. 1960. 15.00. Columbia
Evans-Pritchard, E. E. Social anthropology. 1954. 3.50. Free Press
Firth, R. Man and culture. 6.00. Humanities
Keesing, Felix. Cultural anthropology: Science of custom. 1958. 6.00. Rinehart
Lowie, R. H. Culture and ethnology. 3.00. Smith, Peter
Lowie, Robert H. Selected papers in anthropology. by Cora Dubois. 1960. 10.00.
  U. of Calif.
Taylor, Griffith. Environment, race and migration. 1937. 4.50. U. of Toronto
Thompson, Laura. Toward a science of mankind. 1961. 5.95. McGraw
Murdock, George P. Ethnographic bibliography of North America. il. 1960. pap.
  6.75. Taplinger (R)
Spencer, Robert F., and E. Johnson. Atlas for anthropology. 1956. pap. 2.00.
  Brown, W. C. (R)
Radcliffe-Brown, A. R. Method in social anthropology. by M. R. Srinivas. 1958.
  3.75. U. of Chicago
Bascom, William R., and Melville J. Herskovits. Continuity and change in African
  cultures. 1958. 7.00. U. of Chicago
Gluckman, Max. Custom and conflict in Africa. 1956. 3.50. Free Press
Malinowski, Bronislaw. Dynamics of culture change. by Phyllis M. Kaberry. il.
  1945. 4.00. Yale
Ottenberg, Simon, and Phoebe. Cultures and societies of Africa. 1960. 10.00.
  Random
Seligman, C. G. Races of Africa. 1957. 1.70. Oxford U. P.
Ehrenfels, Omar R. Light continent. 6.95. Taplinger
Kenyatta, Jomo. Facing Mount Kenya. il. 1956. 6.00. British Bk.
ETHNOPSYCHOLOGY (136.48)
Boas, Franz. Mind of primitive man. 5.50. Macmillan
Cassirer, Ernst. Language and myth. 3.00. Smith, Peter
Davis, Roland C. Ability in social and racial classes. il. 1932. 1.75. Appleton
Kardiner, A. Individual and his society. 1939. 6.50. Columbia
Kardiner, A., and others. Psychological frontiers of society. 1945. 6.50.
  Columbia
Read, C. Man and his superstitions. 1925. 6.50. Cambridge U. P.
Riesman, David. Lonely crowd. 1950. 7.50. Yale
ETIQUETTE (395)
Cambell, Jean. Etiquette for all occasions. 1961. 1.00. Ottenheimer
Cole, Emma A. Modern bride book of etiquette and entertaining. 1961. 5.95.
  Barnes, A. S.
Eldridge, Elizabeth. Co-ediquette: Poise and popularity for every girl. 3.50.
  Dutton
Free, Anne R. Social usage. il. 1960. pap. 1.95. Appleton
Lee, Nata. Complete book of entertaining. il. 1961. 5.95. Hawthorn
Post, Emily. Etiquette. il. 1950. 5.95. Funk
Vanderbilt, Amy. Amy Vanderbilt's complete book of etiquette. il. 1958. 6.00.
  Doubleday
Vogue. Vogue's book of etiquette. by Millicent Fenwick. 1948. 6.50. S. and S.
ETRUSCANS (945.5)
Ciba Foundation. Medical biology and Etruscan origins. 1959. 9.50. Little
Hus, Alain. Etruscans. tr. by Jeanne U. Duell. il. 3.35. Smith, Peter
Vacano, Otto-Wilhelm von. Etruscans in the ancient world. tr. by Shelia Ann
  Ogilvie. 1960. 6.50. St. Martins

EUGENICS (613.94)

Dunn, L. C., and T. Dobzhansky. Heredity, race and society. 1952. pap. 0.50. New Am. Lib.

Hardin, Garrett. Nature and man's fate. il. 6.00. Holt, Rinehart & Winston

Rostand, Jean. Can man be modified? 1959. 3.00. Basic Books

Sinnott, Edmund W., and others. Principles of genetics. 1958. 7.50. McGraw

EURIPIDES, d. 406 B.C. (921.9)

Grube, G. M. A. Drama of Euripides. 1960. 7.50. Barnes & Noble

Murray, Gilbert. Euripides and his age. 1946. 1.70. Oxford U. P.

Norwood, Gilbert. Essays on Euripidean drama. 1954. 5.00. U. of Toronto

EUROPE--CIVILIZATION (901)

Barker, Ernest, and others. European inheritance. 3 vols. 1954. 19.20. Oxford U. P.

Bruun, Geoffrey. Nineteenth Century European civilization, 1815-1914. 1960. 3.50. Smith, Peter

Clark, George N. Seventeenth century. 1947. 4.50. Oxford U. P.

Dawson, Christopher. Understanding Europe. 0.85. Doubleday

Huxley, Michael. Root of Europe. 1953. 2.70. Oxford U. P.

Malraux, Andre. Temptation of the West. pap. 0.95. Vintage

Mosse, George L. Culture of western Europe. 6.50. Rand McNally

Ortega y Gasset, Jose. Revolt of the masses. 1932. 3.95. Norton

Randall, John H., Jr. Making of the modern mind. 1940. 6.00. Houghton

Wolf, John B. Emergence of European civilization. 1962. 7.50. Harper

Boak, A. E. R., and others. Growth of Western civilization. il. 2 vol. 3.75. ea. Appleton

Burns, Edward M. Western civilizations. il. 1958. 8.95. Norton

Childe, V. Gordon. Dawn of European civilization. 1958. 7.50. Knopf

Dawson, Christopher. Making of Europe. 1946. 4.50. Sheed

Ferguson, Wallace K., and Geoffrey Bruun. Survey of European civilization: Since 1500. 8.50. Houghton

Friedell, Egon. Cultural history of the modern age. 3 vols. 1954. 6.75 ea. Knopf

Mendenhall, Thomas C., and others. Problems in western civilization. 1956. 3.85. Holt, Rinehart & Winston

Moss, H. St. L. B. Birth of the Middle Ages, 395-814. il. 4.80. Oxford U. P.

Schapiro, Jacob S. Modern and contemporary European history. 7.50. Houghton

Stephenson, Carl. Mediaeval history: Europe from the second to the sixteenth century. by Bryce Lyon. 1962. 8.75. Harper

Tschan, Francis J., and others. Western civilization: Decline of Rome to 1660. 1942. 6.00. Lippincott

EUROPE--DESCRIPTION AND TRAVEL (914)

Abecassis, Guy. Tours and detours. 1960. 3.50. Random

Beadle, Muriel. These ruins are inhabited. 4.95. Doubleday

Halsey, Margaret. With malice toward some. il. 1959. pap. 1.45. S. and S.

Hoffman, George Walter, and others. Geography of Europe. 1961. 9.50. Ronald

Kimbrough, Emily. Forty plus and fancy free. il. 1954. 3.95. Harper

Morrison, Helen B. Golden age of travel. 5.00. Twayne

Shirer, William L. Midcentury journey. 1952. 3.50. Farrar, Straus

Thomas, Lowell, and Charles Hurd. Cavalcade of Europe. 1960. 4.95. Doubleday

Clemens, Samuel Langhorne. Innocents abroad. il. 4.00. Harper

Hilen, Andrew. Diary of Clara Crowinshield: A European tour with Longfellow, 1835-1836. il. 1956. 5.00. U. of Wash.

Melville, Herman. Journal of a visit to Europe and the Levant. by H. Horsford. 1954. 5.00. Princeton

EUROPE--ECONOMIC CONDITIONS (330.94)

Agrarian life of the Middle Ages. 6.00. Cambridge U. P.

Clough, Shepard B., and Charles W. Cole. Economic history of Europe. 1952. 8.50. Heath

Economic survey of Europe, in 1961. 1962. pap. 4.00? U. N.

Heaton, Herbert. Economic history of Europe. 1948. 7.25. Harper

Ogg, Frederic Austin, and Walter Rice Sharp. Economic development of modern Europe. 7.25. Macmillan

Pirenne, Henri. Economic and social history of Medieval Europe. 1956. pap. 1.25. Harcourt

Reynolds, Robert L. Europe emerges: Transition toward an industrial world-wide society, 600-1750. 1961. 7.50. U. of Wis.

Thompson, James W. Economic and social history of Europe in the later Middle Ages, 1300-1530. il. 8.50. Ungar

Thompson, James W. Economic and social history of the Middle Ages. 1959. 15.00. Ungar

Scitovsky, Tibor. Economic theory and western European integration. 1958. 3.50. Stanford

Spulber, N. Economics of communist eastern Europe. 1957. 12.50. Wiley

EUROPE--HISTORY (940.9)

Ausubel, Herman. Making of modern Europe. 2 vols. 5.00 ea. Holt, Rinehart & Winston

Boak, A. E. R., and others. Growth of Western civilization. il. 1 vol. 6.00; 2 vol. 3.75. ea. Appleton

Bruun, Geoffrey. Europe in evolution, 1415-1815. 6.75. Houghton

Ergang, Robert. Europe from the Renaissance to Waterloo. il. 1954. 8.25. Heath

Ferguson, Wallace K., and Geoffrey Bruun. Survey of European civilization. 7.25. Houghton

Ferguson, Wallace K., and Geoffrey Bruun. Survey of European civilization: Since 1500. 8.50. Houghton

Gottschalk, Louis, and Donald Lach. Europe and the modern world. 2 vols. 7.50 ea. Scott

Haskins, Charles H. Normans in European history. 1959. 4.50. Ungar

Hayes, Carlton J. H., and others. History of Europe il. 2 vols. 5.75 ea. Macmillan

Hayes, Carlton J. H., and Charles W. Cole. History of Europe. Since 1648. 5.75. Macmillan

Hayes, Carlton J. H. Modern Europe to 1870. il. 1953. 7.00. Macmillan

Higby, Chester Penn. Europe: 1492 to 1815. il. 1948. 6.00. Lippincott

Schapiro, Jacob S., and Richard B. Morris. Civilization in Europe. 1930. 5.88. Houghton

Schevill, Ferdinand. History of Europe: From the Reformation to the present day. 1951. 11.50. Harcourt

EUROPE--HISTORY--476-1492 (940.1)

Bloch, Marc L. B. Feudal society. 1961. 8.50. U. of Chicago

Cheyney, Edward P. Dawn of a new era: 1250-1453. il. 1936. 6.00. Harper

Davis, Henry W. C. Medieval Europe. 1960. 1.70. Oxford U. P.

Davis, R. H. C. History of medieval Europe from Constantine, to St. Louis. 1957. 5.25. McKay

Deanesly, Margaret. History of early Medieval Europe, 476-911. 1956. 7.50. Barnes & Noble

Duckett, Eleanor S. Gateway to the Middle Ages. 3 vols. 1961. 15.75. U. of Mich.

Ferguson, Wallace K., and Geoffrey Brunn. Ancient times to 1660. 7.25. Houghton

Froissart, Jean. Chronicles of England, France, Spain, and other places adjoining. 1961. pap. 2.15. Dutton

Lot, Ferdinand. End of the ancient world and the beginnings of the Middle ages. 4.75. Smith, Peter

O'Sullivan, Jeremiah, and J. F. Burns. Medieval Europe. il. 6.00. Appleton

Pirenne, Henri. History of Europe. 2 vols. 1958. pap. 0.95 ea. Doubleday

Pirenne, Henri. History of Europe: From the invasions to the 16th century. 1956. 7.50. U. Books

Pirenne, Henri. Mohammed and Charlemagne. 1955. 4.00. Barnes & Noble

Russell, P. E. English intervention in the time of Edward III and Richard II. 1955. 8.00. Oxford U. P.

Thompson, James Westfall, and Edgar N. Johnson. Introduction to medieval Europe. il. 1937. 8.90. Norton

Thorndike, Lynn. History of Medieval Europe. 1949. 7.50. Houghton

Waugh, W. T. History of Europe: 1378-1494. 1949. 7.00. Barnes & Noble

EUROPE--HISTORY--1492-1648 (940.2)

Clark, George. Early modern Europe, from about 1450 to about 1720. 1960. 3.50. Smith, Peter

Fischer-Galati, Stephen A. Ottoman imperialism and German Protestantism, 1521-1555. 1959. 4.00. Harvard

Grant, A. J. History of Europe: 1494-1610. 1951. 6.00. Barnes & Noble

Wedgewood, Cicely V. Thirty years war. il. 3.50. Smith, Peter

EUROPE--HISTORY--17TH CENTURY (940.2)

Friedrich, Carl J. Age of the baroque: 1610-1660. 1952. il. 6.00. Harper

Ogg, David. Europe in the seventeenth century. 5.25. Macmillan

Reddaway, W. F. History of Europe: 1610-1715. 1948. 6.00. Barnes & Noble

EUROPE--HISTORY--1648-1789 (940.2)

Beloff, Max. Age of absolutism, 1660-1815. 1954. 2.50. Hillary

Clark, George N. Early modern Europe, from about 1450 to about 1720. 1960. 3.50. Smith, Peter

Dorn, Walter L. Competition for empire, 1740-1763. 6.00. Harper

Gershoy, Leo. From despotism to revolution: 1763-1789. il. 1944. 6.00. Harper

Nussbaum, Frederick L. Triumph of science and reason: 1660-1685. il. 1953. 6.00. Harper

EUROPE--HISTORY--18TH CENTURY (940.2)

Reddaway, W. F. History of Europe: 1715-1814. 1951. 7.00. Barnes & Noble

Roberts, Penfield. Quest for security: 1715-1740. il. 1947. 6.00. Harper

EUROPE--HISTORY--1789-1815 (940.2)

Brinton, Crane. Decade of revolution: 1789-1799. il. 1935. 6.00. Harper

Bruun, Geoffrey. Europe and the French imperium: 1799-1814. il. 1938. 6.00. Harper

Bryant, Arthur. Age of elegance. England: 1812-1822. il. 1951. 5.00. Harper

Mackesy, Piers. War in the Mediterranean, 1803-1810. il. 1958. 3.00. Harvard

Markham, F. M. H. Napoleon and the awakening of Europe. 1954. 2.50. Macmillan

EUROPE--HISTORY--19TH CENTURY (940.2)

Groce, Benedetto. History of Europe in the 19th century. 1933. 4.00. Humanities

Hall, Walter Pehlps, And William Sterns Davis. Course of Europe since Waterloo. il. 1957. 6.75. Appleton

Littlefield, Henry W. History of Europe since 1815. 1959. pap. 1.75. Barnes & Noble

Morgan, M. C. Freedom and compulsion: A survey of European history between 1789 and 1939. 1956. 4.50. St. Martins

Namier, Lewis. 1848: The revolution of the intellectuals. 1946. 2.00. Oxford U. P.

Scott, J. F., and Alexander Baltzly. Readings in European history since 1814. 5.00. Appleton

Tocqueville, Alexis de. European correspondence with Gobineau. tr. by John Lukacs. 3.25. Smith, Peter

EUROPE--HISTORY--1815-1871 (940.2)

Artz, Frederick B. Reaction and revolution: 1815-1832. il. 6.00. Harper

Binkley, Robert C. Realism and nationalism: 1852-1871. 1935. 6.00. Harper

Slosson, Preston. Europe since 1815. 1954. 6.50. Scribner

Robertson, Priscilla. Revolutions of 1848. 1960. 2.25. Harper

Taylor, Alan J. P. Struggle for mastery in Europe: 1848-1918. 1954. 9.25. Oxford U. P.

EUROPE--HISTORY--1871-1918 (940.2)

Hayes, Carlton J. H. Generation of materialism: 1871-1900. il. 1941. 6.00.
Harper
Lipson, E. Europe in the 19th century, 1815-1914. 1961. 4.50. Macmillan
Taylor, Alan J. P. Struggle for mastery in Europe: 1848-1918. 1954. 9.25.
Oxford U. P.
EUROPE--HISTORY--20TH CENTURY (940.5)
Albrecht-Carrie, Rene. Diplomatic history of Europe since the Congress of
Vienna. 1958. 8.00. Harper
Albrecht-Carrie, Rene. Europe since 1815: From the Ancient Regime to the atomic
age. 1962. 8.00. Harper
Anderson, Eugene. Modern Europe in world perspective: 1914 to the present. 1958.
8.50. Holt, Rinehart & Winston
Black, Cyril E., and E. C. Helmreich. Twentieth century Europe. 1959. 10.75.
Knopf
Craig, Gordon A. Europe since 1815. 1961. 8.50. Holt, Rinehart & Winston
Ergang, Robert. Europe in our time: 1914 to the present. il. 1958. 8.50. Heath
Ergang, Robert. Europe since Waterloo. il. 1961. 8.50. Heath
Garrett, Mitchell B., and James L. Godfrey. Europe since 1815. il. 1947. 6.00.
Appleton
Gottschalk, Louis, and Donald Lach. Europe and the modern world since 1870.
1954. 6.50. Scott
Hayes, Carlton J. H. Contemporary Europe since 1870. il. 1953. 7.00. Macmillan
Hughes, H. Stuart. Contemporary Europe: A history. il. 1961. 10.60. Prentice-
Hall
Marriott, J. A. R. History of Europe: 1815-1939. 1952. 6.50. Barnes and Noble
Pakeman, S. A. Modern world, 1789-1957. 1960. 2.25. St. Martins
Schapiro, Jacob S. Modern and contemporary European history. 7.50. Houghton
Slosson, Preston. Europe since 1815. 1954. 6.50. Scribner
Thomson, David. Europe since Napoleon. 1962. 10.00. Knopf
EUROPE--HISTORY--1918-1945 (940.5)
Benns, F. Lee. Europe since 1914. il. 1954. 6.50. Appleton
Benns, F. Lee. European history since 1870. il. 1955. 7.00. Appleton
Chambers, Frank P. This age of conflict: The Western world, 1914 to the present.
il. 8.95. Harcourt
EUROPE--HISTORY--1945- (940.5)
Brinton, Crane. Temper of Western Europe. 1953. 2.50. Harvard
EUROPE--MAPS (914)
Ferriday, A. Map book of Europe. 1.00. St. Martins
Kingsbury, Robert G., and Norman J. G. Pounds. Atlas of European affairs. 1962.
3.50. Praeger (R)
EUROPE--POLITICS (940)
Camus, Albert. Resistance, rebellion and death. 1960. 4.00. Knopf
Dragnich, Alex N. Major European governments. 1961. 9.35. Dorsey
Europa year book, 1962. 2 vols. 25.00 ea. Int. Pub. Service
Fischer-Galati, Stephen A. Ottoman imperialism and German Protestantism,
1521-1555. 1959. 4.00. Harvard (R)
Hayes, Carlton J. H. Historical evolution of modern nationalism. 1931. 6.00.
Macmillan
Hill, David J. History of diplomacy in the international development of Europe.
3 vols. il. in prep. Russell
Munro, William B., and Morley Ayearst. Governments of Europe. 1954. 7.25.
Macmillan
Neumann, Robert G. European and comparative government. il. 1960. 8.75.
McGraw
Shotwell, James T. Governments of continental Europe. 7.25. Macmillan
Wolf, John B. Emergence of the great powers: 1685-1715. il. 1951. 6.00. Harper
Bemis, Samuel F. Diplomacy of the American Revolution. 1957. 3.75. Smith,
Peter

Palmer, Robert R. Age of the democratic revolution: A political history of Europe
  and America, 1760-1800. 1959. 7.50 Princeton
Butterfield, H. Napoleon's peace tactics. 1929. 5.00. Cambridge U. P.
Gulick, Edward V. Europe's classical balance of power. 5.50. Cornell
Nicolson, Harold. Congress of Vienna, a study in allied unity, 1812-1822. 3.50.
  Smith, Peter
Marx, Karl, and Friederich Engels. Russian menace to Europe. 1952. 4.50.
  Free Press
Seton-Watson, R. W. Britain in Europe. 1937. 7.50. Cambridge U. P.
Langer, William L. Diplomacy of imperialism. 1935. 9.75. Knopf
Langer, William L. European alliances and alignments. il. 1931. 7.50. Knopf
Medicott, W. N. Bismarck, Gladstone, and the concert of Europe. 1956. 5.60.
  Oxford U. P.
Sontag, Raymond J. European diplomatic history, 1871-1932. il. 1933. 5.50.
  Appleton
Gunther, John. Inside Europe. 1940. 6.95. Harper
Millis, Walter. Why Europe fights. il. 1940. 2.50. Morrow
Seton-Watson, R. W. Britain in Europe. 1937. 7.50. Cambridge U. P.
Beard, Charles A. Cross currents in Europe today. 2.50. Jones, Marshall
Benson, Oliver. Through the diplomatic looking-glass: Immediate origins of·
Carr, Edward H. International relations between the two world wars 1919-1939.
  2.25. St. Martins
Kulischer, E. M. Europe on the move. 1948. 5.00. Columbia
Royal Institute of International Affairs. Hitler's Europe. by Arnold J. and
  Veronica M. Toynbee. 1954. 11.20. Oxford U. P.
Royal Institute of International Affairs. Initial triumph of the Axis. by Arnold J.
  and Veronica M. Toynbee. 1958. 13.45. Oxford U. P.
Royal Institute of International Affairs. Realignment of Europe. by Arnold J.
  and Veronica M. Toynbee. 1955. 10.40. Oxford U. P.
Adenauer, Konrad. World indivisible, with liberty and justice for all. 1955. 2.75.
  Harper
Andrews, William G. European political institutions. 1962. 3.95. Van Nostrand
Beer, Samuel H., and others. Patterns of government: The major political
  systems of Europe. 1962. 6.75. Random
Gunther, John. Inside Europe today. 1962. 5.95. Harper
McClellan, Grant S. Two Germanies. il. 1959. 2.50. Wilson
Nutting, Anthony. Europe will not wait. 1960. 3.50. Praeger
Robertson, Arthur H. European institutions. 1959. 8.25. Praeger
Shirer, William L. Midcentury journey. 1952. 3.50. Farrar, Straus
White, Theodore H. Fire in the ashes: Europe in mid-century. 1953. 5.95. Sloane
EUROPE, EASTERN (940)
Borsody, Stephen. Tragedy of central Europe. pap. 0.95. Collier
Halecki, O. Borderlands of western civilization. 1952. 7.50. Ronald
Mutton, A. F. A. Central Europe. 1961. 8.75. Wiley
Barth, Karl, and Johannes Hamel. How to serve God in a Marxist land. 1959.
  2.50. Assn. Pr.
Byrnes, Robert F. Bibliography of American publications on East Central Europe,
  1945-57. pap. 2.50. Indiana
Byrnes, Robert F. East-central Europe under the Communists series. 1959. 10.00.
  per vol. Praeger
Kertesz, Stephen D. East Central Europe and the world. 1962. 6.50. U. of Notre
  Dame
Ripka, Hubert. Eastern Europe in the postwar world. 5.95. Praeger
Seton-Watson, Hugh. Eastern Europe between the wars. 5.00. Shoe String
Halasz, Nicholas. In the shadow of Russia. 1959. 5.00. Ronald
Kertesz, Stephen. Fate of East Central Europe: Hopes and failures of American
  foreign policy. 1956. 6.25. U. of Notre Dame
Seton-Watson, Hugh. East European revolution. il. 1961. 6.00. Praeger

EUROPEAN COAL AND STEEL COMMUNITY (334)
Diebold, W. H., Jr. Schuman plan. 6.50. Praeger
Lister, Louis. Europe's Coal and Steel Community. il. 1960. 8.00. Twentieth
Century
EUROPEAN COMMON MARKET (1955-) (382)
American Management Association. European common market. by Elizabeth
Marting. 1958. 6.00. Am. Management Assn.
Lippmann, Walter. Western unity and the common market. 1962. 2.75. Little
Meyer, Frederick F. European Free Trade Association. 1960. 4.50. Praeger
Stein, Eric, and Thomas L. Nicholson. American enterprise in the European
Common Market. 2 vols. 30.00. U. of Mich.
Churchill, Winston S. In the balance. 1952. 5.00. Houghton
Europa year book, 1961. 2 vols. 44.00. Int. Pub. Service
Robertson, Arthur H. European institutions. 1959. 8.25. Praeger
Schmitt, Hans A. Path to European union: From the Marshall Plan to the Common
Market. 1962. 6.00. La. State
Zurcher, Arnold J. Struggle to unite Europe, 1940-1958. 1958. 5.00. N. Y. U.
EUROPEAN WAR, 1914-1918 (940.444)
Baldwin, Hanson. World War I: An outline history. il. 1962. 4.00. Harper (R)
Cruttwell, C. R. M. F. History of the Great War, 1914-1918. il. 1936. 4.50.
Oxford U. P.
Falls, Cyril. Great war: 1914-1918. 5.95. Putnam
Taylor, Henry Osborn. Layman's view of history. 1935. 1.50. Harvard
Veblen, Thorstein. Essays in our changing order. by Leon Ardzrooni. 1934.
4.00. Viking
Mitchell, William. Memoirs of World War I: From first to last in our greatest
war. il. 1960. 4.95. Random
Reynolds, Quentin. They fought for the sky. 1957. 3.95. Rinehart
Whitehouse, Arch. Years of the sky kings. il. 1959. 4.95. Doubleday
Siney, Marion C. Allied blockade of Germany, 1914-1916. 1957. 6.50. U. of Mich.
Moorehead, Alan. Gallipoli. il. 1956. 5.50. Harper
Tuchman, Barbara W. Guns of August. il. 1962. 5.95. Macmillan
Albertini, Luigi. Origins of the War of 1914 by I. M. Massey. vol. 1, 1952. 8.80;
vol. 2, 1953. 10.40; vol. 3, 1957. 11.20. Oxford U. P.
Fay, Sidney B. Origins of the World War. il. 1938. 7.50. Macmillan
Feis, Herbert. Europe the World's banker. 1870-1914. 1930. 8.50. Kelley
Lee, Dwight E. Outbreak of the First World War: Who was responsible? 1958.
pap. 1.50. Heath
Tuchman, Barbara W. Zimmermann telegram. 1958. 3.95. Viking
Birnbaum, Karl E. Peace moves and U-boat warfare: A study of imperial Germany's
policy towards the United States, April 18, 1916 - January 9, 1917. 1958. 9.50.
Lounz
Mamatey, V. S. The United States and East Central Europe, 1914-1918: A study
in Wilsonian diplomacy and propaganda. 1957. 7.50. Princeton
Martin, Laurence W. Peace without victory. 1958. 4.50. Yale
Leuchtenburg, William E. Perils of prosperity: 1914-1932. 4.50. U. of Chicago
Ledrer, Ivo J. Versailles settlement: Was it foredoomed to failure? 1960. pap.
1.50. Heath
Cummings, E. E. Enormous room. 1934. 1.95. Modern Lib.
Bunyan, James, and Harold H. Fisher. Bolshevik Revolution, 1917-1918. 1934.
10.00. Stanford
Snyder, Louis L. Historic documents of World War I. 1958. pap. 1.25. Van
Nostrand (R)
Daniels, Josephus. Wilson era: Years of war and after, 1917-1923. (Autobiography
vol. 5) 1.30. U. of N. C.
Slosson, Preston W. Great crusade and after, 1914-1928. il. 1931. 6.75. Macmillan
Trask, David. U. S. In the Supreme War Council. 1961. 6.00. Wesleyan U. P.
EVENING AND CONTINUATION SCHOOLS (378.15)
McMahon, Ernest E. Emerging evening college. 1960. 4.50. T. C.

EVIDENCE (LAW) (343.1)

Maguire, John M. Evidence of guilt. 1959. 12.50. Little

Morgan, E. M. Some problems of proof under the Anglo-American system of litigation. 1956. 3.50. Columbia

Tracy, John E. Handbook of the law of evidence. 1952. 6.65. Prentice-Hall (R)

Wigmore, John H. Code of evidence. 1942. 10.00. Little

EVOLUTION (575)

American Academy of Arts and Sciences. Evolution and man's progress. 1.75. Am. Acad. of Arts & Sci.

Anfinson, C. B. Molecular basis of evolution. 1959. 7.00. Wiley

Ashley, Montagu, M. F. Direction of human development: Biological and sociel bases. 1955. 5.00. Harper

Ashley, Montagu, M. F. On being human. 1950. 2.50. Abelard

Asimov, Isaac. Wellsprings of life. 1960. 3.75. Abelard

Becker, J. A. Evolution and the Bible. 1946. 3.00. DeVorss

Bergson, Henri L. Creative evolution. il. 1944. 1.95. Modern Lib.

Berrill, N. J. Man's emerging mind. 1955. 4.00. Dodd

Cameron, T. W. M. Evolution, its science and doctrine. 1960. 5.00. U. of Toronto

Cannon, H. Graham. Evolution of living things. 1959. 3.50. Thomas, C. C

Cannon, H. Graham. Lamarck and modern genetics. 1960. 3.75. Thomas, C. C

Carrington, Richard. Story of our earth. il. 1956. 3.50. Harper

Clark, W. E. Le Gros. Antecedents of man: An introduction to the evolution of the primates. il. 6.00. Quadrangle

Darlington, Cyril D. Darwin's place in history. 1961. pap. 2.00. Macmillan

Darwin, Charles R. Evolution and natural selection. by Bert J. Loewenberg. il. 1959. 5.75. Beacon

Darwin, Charles. Origin of species: A variorum text. by Morse Peckham. 1958. 15.00. U. of Pa. (R)

Darwin, Charles. Origin of species by means of natural selection, or the preservation of favoured races in the struggle for life. 2.75. Oxford U. P.

Dewey, John. Influence of Darwin on philosophy and other essays. 3.75. Smith, Peter

Dobzhansky, Theodosius. Biological basis of human freedom. 1956. 2.95. Columbia

Dunn, Leslie Clarence. Heredity and evolution in human populations. il. 1959. 3.50. Harvard

Eiseley, Loren. Immense journey. 1957. 3.50. Random

Ellegard, Alvar. Darwin and the general reader. 1958. 7.75. Humanities

Ford, Edmund B. Mendelism and evolution. 1945. 2.25. Wiley

Goudge, Thomas A. Ascent of life, a philosophical study of evolution. 1961. 4.95. U. of Toronto

Herrick, C. Judson. Evolution of human nature. il. 1956. 7.50. U. of Tex.

Hofstadter, Richard. Social Darwinism in American thought. 1959. 4.00. Braziller

Hooton, Earnest Albert. Up from the ape. il. 8.50. Macmillan

Huxley, Julian. Evolution in action. il. 1953. 3.95. Harper

Huxley, Julian. Evolution: The modern synthesis. 1942. 7.50. Harper

Huxley, Julian S. Wonderful world of life. il. 1958. 2.95. Doubleday

Klotz, John. Genes, genesis and evolution. 1955. 6.00. Concordia

Krutch, Joseph W. Great chain of life. 1956. 4.50. Houghton

Lecomte du Nouy, Pierre. Human destiny. 1947. 5.00. McKay

Martin, Cecil P. Psychology, evolution and sex: A study of the mechanism of evolution based on a comprehensive view of biology. 1956. 4.75. Thomas, C. C

Millikan, R. A. Evolution in science and religion. 1927. 3.00. Yale

Moore, Ruth, Man, time, and fossils. il. 1961. 6.95. Knopf

Rimmer, Harry. Theory of evolution and facts of science. 1935. 2.50. Eerdmans

Simpson, G. G. Major features of evolution. 7.50. Columbia

Simpson, G. G. Meaning of evolution. 1949. 5.00. Yale

Sturtevant, Alfred H. Genetics and evolution. by E. B. Lewis. 1961. 7.50. Freeman

Tax, Sol. Evolution after Darwin. 3 vols. vol. 1, Evolution of life: Its origin, history and future. 10.00; vol. 2, Evolution of man: Mind, culture and society. 10.00; vol. 3, Issues in evolution; The University of Chicago Centennial discussions. by Sol Tax, and Charles Callender. 7.50. set 25.00. U. of Chicago

Teilhard de Chardin, Pierre. Phenomenon of man. 1959. 5.00. 1961. Harper

Hoagland, Hudson, and Ralph W. Burhoe. Evolution and man's progress. il. 1962. 4.50. Columbia

Howells, William. Ideas on human evolution: Selected essays, 1949-1957. in prep. Harvard

Huxley, Julian, and others. Evolution as a process. il. 1954. 6.00. Macmillan

Medawar, Peter B. Uniqueness of the individual. il. 1957. 4.00. Basic Books

Society for Experimental Biology. Evolution. 1953. 7.80. Academic Press

Eisley, Loren. Darwin's century: Evolution and the men who discovered it. 1958. 5.00. Doubleday

Hardin, Garrett. Nature and man's fate. il. 6.00. Holt, Rinehart & Winston

EXCAVATIONS (ARCHAEOLOGY) (571)

Albright, William Foxwell. Archaeology and the religion of Israel. 1941. 3.50. Johns Hopkins

Bacon, Edward. Digging for history. il. 1961. 10.00. Day

Coon, Carleton S. Seven caves: Archaeological explorations in the Middle East. il. 1957. 5.75. Knopf

Droop, J. P. Archaeological excavation. 1915. 2.00. Cambridge U. P.

Hibben, Frank C. Digging up America. il. 1960. 5.00. Hill & Wang

Robbins, Roland, and Evan Jones. Hidden America. il. 1959. 5.00. Knopf

Woolley, C. Leonard. History unearthed. il. 1958. 5.00. Praeger

EXCEPTIONAL CHILDREN (136.76)

Abraham, Willard. Guide for the study of exceptional children. il. 1955. 3.50. Sargent

Jenks, W. F. Forgotten ones: Our exceptional children. 1955. 2.25. Catholic U. of Am. Pr.

Kemp, Charles F. Church: The gifted and the retarded child. 1958. 3.50. Bethany

Louttit, C. M., and others. Clinical psychology of exceptional children. 1957. 7.00. Harper

Magary, James F., and John R. Eichorn. Exceptional child. 1960. 5.50. Holt, Rinehart & Winston

Strang, Ruth, and others. Mental health and guidance for exceptional children. 1956. pap. 1.25. Sargent

Trapp, Phillip E., and Philip Himelstein. Readings on the exceptional child. 7.00. Appleton

EXCEPTIONAL CHILDREN--EDUCATION (371.9)

Cruickshank, William M., and G. Orville Johnson. Education of exceptional children and youth. 1958. 10.00. Prentice-Hall

Kirk, Samuel A. Educating exceptional children. 6.00. Houghton

National Education Association, American Educational Research Association. Education of exceptional children. 1959. 2.00. N. E. A.

EXECUTIVE ABILITY (658.3)

Bellows, Roger M., and others. Executive skills: Their dynamics and development. 1962. 10.00. Prentice-Hall

Bender, James F. Technique of executive leadership. 1950. 4.95. McGraw

Black, J. M. How to grow in management. 1957. 4.95. Prentice-Hall

Cooper, Joseph D. Art of decision making. 4.95. Doubleday

Rowland, Virgil K. Managerial performance standards. 1960. 5.25. Am. Management Assn.

Schell, Erwin H. Technique of administration: Administration proficiency in business. 1951. 5.95. McGraw

Uris, Auren. Developing your executive skills. 1955. 4.50. McGraw

EXECUTIVE POWER (350)

Corwin, Edward S. President: Office and powers. 1957. 6.50. N. Y. U.

Cotter, Cornelius P. , and J. Malcolm Smith. Powers of the President during
national crises. 1959. 5. 00. Pub. Affairs
Horn, Stephen. Cabinet and Congress. 1960. 6. 00. Columbia
Koenig, Louis. Invisible presidency: The behind-the-scenes story of seven pres-
edential confidants from Hamilton to Sherman Adams. 1960. 6. 95. Holt; Rinehart
& Winston
Longaker, Richard P. Presidency and individual liberties. 1961. 4. 50. Cornell
May, Ernest R. Ultimate decision. 1960. 6. 00. Braziller
Patterson, C. Perry. Presidential government in the United States. 1947. 4. 00.
U. of N. C.
Tobin, Richard L. Decisions of destiny. 1961. 5. 00. World Pub.
Tugwell, Rexford G. Enlargement of the Presidency. 1960. 6. 95. Doubleday
EXECUTIVES (651. 34)
Bellows, Roger M. , and others. Executive skills: Their dynamics and development.
1962. 10. 00. Prentice-Hall
Black, James M. Assignment: Management. 1961. 5. 95. Prentice-Hall
Bursk, C. E. How to increase executive effectiveness. 1954. 3. 25. Harvard
Cantor, Nathaniel. Learning process for managers. 1958. 3. 50. Harper
Cerami, C. A. Successful leadership in business. 4. 95. Prentice-Hall
De Armond, Fred. Executive at work. 1958. 4. 95. Prentice-Hall
Ginzberg, Eli. What makes an executive? 1955. 4. 00. Columbia
Greenewalt, Crawford H. Uncommon man: The individual in the organization. 1959.
4. 00. McGraw
Harvard University. Graduate School of Busniess Administration. Research needs
in executive selection: A symposium. by Renato Tagiuri. 1961. pap. 2. 00. Harv.
Bus. School
Heal, Edith.Young executive's wife: You and your husband's job. il. 1958. 2. 95.
Dodd
Heyel, Carl. Organizing your job in management. il. 1960. 5. 25. Am. Management
Assn.
Kienzle, George, and Edward Dare. Climbing the executive ladder. 1950. 4. 95.
McGraw
Newcomer, M. Big business executive. 1955. 4. 00. Columbia
Selznick, Philip. Leadership in administration: A sociological interpretation. 1957.
4. 00. Harper
Shartle, Carroll L. Executive performance and leadership. 6. 95. Prentice-Hall
Warner, William L. , and Norman H. Martin. Industrial man. 1959. 6. 50. Harper
Warner, W. Lloyd, and James Abegglen. Occupational mobility in American
business and induatry, 1928-1952. 1955. 5. 50. U. of Minn.
EXISTENTIALISM (111 fil).
Allers, Rudolf, and Francis J. Bracland. Existentialism and psychiatry. 1960.
5. 50. Thomas, C. C.
Barrett, William. Irrational man. 1958. 5. 00. Doubleday
Blackham, H. J. Six existentialist thinkers. 3. 50. Macmillan
Breisach, Ernst. Introduction to modern existentialism. 1962. 4. 95. Grove
Collins, James. Existentialists: A critical study. 1959. pap. 1. 45. Regnery
Desan, W. Tragic finale: An essay on the philosophy of Jean-Paul Sartre. 1954.
4. 25. Harvard
Grene, Marjorie. Introduction to existentialism. 1948. 5. 00. U. of Chicago
Hanna, Thomas. Lyrical existentialists. 1962. 5. 00. Atheneum
Heidegger, Martin. Existence and being. pap. 1. 95. Regnery
Jaspers, Karl. Reason and existenz. 1955. 3. 50. Farrar, Straus
Kaufmann, Walter. Existentialism from Dostoevsky to Sartre. 1958. 3. 50.
Smith, Peter
Marcel, Gabriel. Philosophy of existentialism. 1961. pap. 1. 50. Citadel
Maritain, Jacques. Existence and the existent. 1957. pap. 0. 75. Doubleday
Michalson, Carl. Hinge of history: An existential approach to the Christian
faith. 1959. 3. 95. Scribner

Murdoch, Iris. Sartre: Romantic rationalist. 1953. pap. 1.25. Yale

Reinhardt, Kurt F. Existentialist revolt. 5.00. Ungar

Sartre, Jean-Paul. Literature and existentialism. 1962. pap. 1.75. Citadel

Sartre, Jean-Paul. Transcendence of the ego. 1957. 3.00. Farrar, Straus

Schaldenbrand, Mary A., Sister. Phenomenologies of freedom: An essay on the philosophies of Jean-Paul Sartre and Gabriel Marcel. 1960. 1.75. Catholic U. of Am. Pr.

Tillich, Paul. Courage to be. 1952. 3.75. 1959. Yale

Wild, John. Challenge of existentialism. 1955. 6.00. Indiana

EXPERIENCE (331.114)

Ayer, Alfred Jules. Language, truth, and logic. 1952. pap. 1.25. Dover

Dewey, John. Art as experience. 1959. 2.50. Putnam

Dewey, John. Experience and nature. 5.00. Open Ct.

Fiske, Donald W., and Salvatore R. Maddi. Functions of varied experience. 1961. 10.60. Dorsey

Hunt, Joseph M. Intelligence and experience. 1961. 8.00. Ronald

James, William. Works. Essays in radical empiricism, and Pluralistic universe. by Ralph B. Perry. 1943. 4.50. McKay

Mead, George H. Mind, self, and society: From the standpoint of a social behaviorist. by Charles W. Morris. 1934. 6.75. U. of Chicago

EXPLORERS (923.9)

Herrmann, Paul. Conquest by man. il. 1955. 7.50. Harper

Herrmann, Paul. Great age of discovery. il. 1958. 6.50. Harper

Stefansson, Vilhjalmur. Great adventures and explorations. 1947. 6.00. Dial

Wright, Helen, and Samuel Rapport. Great explorers. il. 1957. 6.50. Harper

EXPLOSIVES (662.2)

Dutton, William S. One thousand years of explosives. 1960. 2.95. Holt, Rinehart & Winston

Sax, Newton I. Dangerous properties of industrial materials. 1957. 22.50. Reinhold (R)

EXTRASENSORY PERCEPTION (133.8)

Hart, Hornell. Enigma of survival. il. 1960. 4.50. Thomas, C. C.

Rhine, J. B. Extra-sensory perception. 1962. pap. 1.95. Humphries

Rhine, Louisa E. Hidden channels of the mind. 1961. 5.00. Sloane

Schmeidler, Gertrude Raffel, and R. A. McConnell. ESP and personality patterns. 1958. 4.00. Yale

EXTREMITIES (ANATOMY) (611.97)

Bassett, David L. Lower extremity. 1962. 27.50. Williams & Wilkins

Cunningham, D. J. General introduction, upper limb, lower limb. by J. C. Brash. 1958. 6.50. Oxford U. P.

Hellinshead, W. Henry. Back and limbs. 23.50. Hoeber

Hollinshead, W. Henry. Functional anatomy of the limbs and back. il. 1960. 9.00. Saunders (R)

Quiring, Daniel P., and John H. Warfel. Extremities. il. 1960. 3.25. Lea & F

Goff, Charles W. Surgical treatment of unequal extremities. il. 1960. 11.00. Thomas, C. C.

Haymaker, Webb, and Barnes Woodhall. Peripheral nerve injuries. il. 1953. 7.00. Saunders

EYE (611.84)

Barber, Aeleta. Embryology of the human eye. 1955. 7.00. Mosby

Mann, Ida. Development of the human eye. 1950. 7.25. Grune

Corbett, Margaret D. Help yourself to better sight. 1949. 3.95. Prentice-Hall

EYE--DISEASES AND DEFECTS (617.701)

Gordon, Dan M. Clinical use of corticotropin and cortisone in eye disease: Including a preliminary report on hydrocortisone. il. 1954. 3.75. Thomas, C. C

Parkinson, Roy H. Eye, ear, nose, and throat manual for nurses. il. 1959. 3.85. Mosby

Perkins, Edward S., and Peter Hansell. Atlas of diseases of the eye. 1957. 13.50. Little

Scholz, Roy O. Sight: A handbook for laymen. il. 1960. 3.50. Doubleday
Walsh, Frank B. Clinical neuro-ophthalmology. il. 1957. 29.00. Williams &
  Wilkins
Woods, Alan C. Allergy and immunity of ophthalmology. 1933. 2.25. Johns
  Hopkins

F

FABLES (398.21)
Aesop. Aesop without morals. by Lloyd W. Daly. il. 1961. 2.95. Yoseloff
Aesop. Aesop's Fables, told by Valerius Babrius. by Denison B. Hull. 1960. 5.00.
  U. of Chicago
LaFontaine, Jean de. Fables of LaFontaine. tr. by Marianne Moore. 1954. 5.00.
  Viking
Vladislav, Jan. Persian fables. il. 4.95. Crown
FACTOR ANALYSIS (517.21)
Adcock, C. J. Factorial analysis for non⌐mathematicians. 1955. 3.50. Cambridge
  U. P.
British Association for the Advancement of Science. Factor table. 7.00. Cambridge
  U. P.
Fruchter, Benjamin A. Introduction to factor analysis. il. 1954. 6.00. Van Nos-
  trand
Henrysson, S. Applicability of factor analysis in the behavioral sciences. 4.50.
  Lounz
Solomon, Herbert. Mathematical thinking in the measurement of behavior. 1959.
  7.50. Free Press
Thurstone, Louis L. Multiple factor analysis: A development and expansion of
  the vectors of mind. il. 1947. 8.50. U. of Chicago
FACTORY MANAGEMENT (658.2)
American Management Association. New concepts in manufacturing management.
  il. 1961. pap. 4.50. Am. Management Assn.
Gardner, Burleigh B., and David G. Moore. Human relations in industry. 1955.
  9.35. Irwin
Gotterer, Malcolm H. Profitable small plant management. 1954. 5.50. Chilton
Heyel, Carl. Foreman's handbook. 1955. 8.50. McGraw
Plant, Engineering Editors. Plant engineering practice. 1958. 18.50. McGraw
Rice, William B. Control charts in factory management. 1947. 4.25. Wiley
Taylor, Frederick Winslow. Scientific management. 1947. 6.50. Harper
Zinck, W. Clements. Dynamic work simplification. il. 1962. 7.95. Reinhold
FAITH (234.2)
Bars, Henry. Faith, hope and charity. 1961. 3.50. Hawthorn
Buttrick, George A. Faith and education. 1952. 2.00. Abingdon
D'Arcy, Martin C. Nature of belief. 1959. 3.95. Herder
Ferre, Nels F. S. Faith and reason. 1946. 3.50. Harper
Fosdick, Harry Emerson. Meaning of faith. 1917. 3.50. Assn. Pr.
Guardini, Romano. Life of faith. 1961. 2.95. Newman
Hook, Sidney. Religious experience and truth. 1961. 5.00. N. Y. U.
Mouroux, Jean. I believe. tr. by Michael Turner. 1959. 2.75. Sheed
Newman, John Henry. Essay in aid of a grammar of assent. by C. F. Harrold
  3.50. McKay
Stringfellow, William. Private and public faith. 1962. 3.00. Eerdmans
Tillich, Paul. Dynamics of faith. 1957. 3.00. Harper
FAMILY (301.423)
Ackerman, Nathan W. Psychodynamics of family life. il. 1958. 6.75. Basic Books
Anshen, Ruth Nanda. Family. 1959. 6.50. Harper
Baber, Ray E. Marriage and the family. il. 1953. 7.95. McGraw
Becker, Howard, and Reuben Hill. Family, marriage, and parenthood. 1955.
  8.00. Heath

Bell, Norman W., and Ezra F. Vogel. Modern introduction to the family. 7.50. Free Press

Blood, Robert, and Donald Wolfe. Husbands and wives: The dynamics of married living. 5.00. Free Press

Bossard, James H. S. Parent and child: Studies in family behavior. 1953. 5.00. U. of Pa.

Bossard, James H. S. Ritual in family living. 1957. 4.00. U. of Pa.

Bossard, James H. S., and Eleanor S. Boll. Large family system. 1956. 6.00. U. of Pa.

Burgess, Ernest W., and Harvey J. Locke. Family: From institution to companionship. 7.50. Am. Bk. Co.

Byrd, Oliver E. Family life sourcebook. 1956. 7.50. Stanford

Cavan, Ruth S. Marriage and family in the modern world. 1960. pap. 3.75. Crowell

Community Service Society: Family in a democratic society. 1949. 3.75. Columbia

Duvall, Evelyn. Family development. il. by Paul Hazelrigg. 1957. 8.75. Lippincott

Duvall, Evelyn Millis. Family living. by D. S. Lewis. il. 1961. 4.12. Macmillan

Dyer, Dorothy T. Family today: A guide for leaders in family life education. 1950. 2.50. U. of Minn.

Eisenstein, Victor W. Neurotic interaction in marriage. 1956. 6.50. Basic Books

Fleck, Henrietta, and others. Exploring home and family living. 5.24. Prentice-Hall

Flugel, J. C. Psychoanalytic study of the family. 3.00. Hillary

Foote, Nelson N., and Leonard Cottrell, Jr. Identity and interpersonal competence: A new direction in family research. 1955. u. of Chicago

Gladston, Iago. Family in contemporary society. 1958. 3.00. Int. Univs.

Gilbreth, Lillian M. Living with our children. 1951. 4.00. Norton

Groves, Ernest R., and Gladys H. Contemporary American family. 1947. 6.00. Lippincott

Groves, Ernest R., and others. Family and its relationships. il. 1953. 4.84. Lippincott

Hess, Robert D., and Gerald Handel. Family worlds: A psychosocial approach to family life. il. 1959. 5.00. U. of Chicago

Kenkel, William F. Family in perspective. il. 1960. 6.00. Appleton

Kirkpatrick, Clifford. Family as process and institution. 1955. 7.00. Ronald

Landis, Judson T., and Mary G. Personal adjustment, marriage, and family living. 1960. 4.60. Prentice-Hall

Landis, Judson T., and Mary G. Readings in marriage and the family. 1952. 6.60. Prentice-Hall

Landis, Paul H. Your marriage and family living. il. 1954. 4.88. McGraw

Levy, John, and Ruth Munroe. Happy family. 1938. 4.00. Knopf

Martinson, Floyd M. Marriage and the American ideal. 1960. 5.50. Dodd

Mihanovich, Clement S., and others. Marriage and the family. 1952. 5.50. Bruce

Murdock, George Peter. Social structure. 1949. 5.00. Macmillan

Nickell, P., and J. M. Dorsey. Management in family living. 1959. 6.95. Wiley

Nimkoff, Meyer F. Marriage and the Family. 1947. 6.75. Houghton

Ogburn, W. F., and M. F. Nimkoff. Technology and the changing family. 1955. 5.00. Houghton

Parsons, Talcott, and Robert F. Bales. Family, socialization and interaction process. 1955. 6.75. Free Press

Queen, Stuart, and others. Family in various cultures. 1961. pap. 1.85. Lippincott

Scudder, C. W. Family in Christian perspective. 1962. 3.50. Broadman

Simpson, George. People in families: Sociology, psychoanalysis, and the American family. 1960. 7.95. Crowell

Sussman, Marvin. Sourcebook in marriage and the family. 1955. pap. 3.75. Houghton

Thomas, John L. American Catholic family. 9.25. Prentice-Hall

Truxal, Andrew G., and F. E. Merrill. Marriage and the family in American culture. 1953. 10.60. Prentice-Hall
Waller, Willard W., and Reuben Hill. Family. 1951. 6.60. Holt, Rinehart & Winston
Winch, Robert F., and Robert McGinnis. Selected studies in marriage and the family. il. 1953. 5.00. Holt
Zimmerman, Carle C., and Lucius F. Cervantes. Marriage and the family. 1956. 9.00. Regnery

FARRAGUT, DAVID GLASGOW, 1801-1870 (923.5)
Lewis, Charles L. David Glasgow Farragut. 2 vols. 1943. 8.00. U. S. Naval Inst.

FASCISM (335.437)
Bramstedt, E. K. Dictatorship and political police: The technique of control by fear. 1945. 2.40. Oxford U. P.
Cole, George D. H. Socialism and fascism. 1960. 8.00. St. Martins
Payne, Stanley G. Falange: History of Spanish Fascism. 1961. 6.00. Stanford

FASHION (646.01)
Ballard, Bettina. In my fashion. 1960. 4.50. McKay
Birmingham, Frederic A. Esquire fashion guide for all occasions. il. 1957. 3.95. Harper
Chambers, Helen G., and Verna Moulton. Clothing selection. il. 1961. 9.25. Lippincott
Danville, Bea. Dress well on 1 dollar a day. il. 1956. 3.65. Funk, Wilfred
Fashion Group. Your future in the fashion world. 1960. 2.95. Richards Rosen
McCardell, Claire. What shall I wear? 1956. 3.50. S. and S.
Sronkova, O. Fashions through the centuries: Renaissance, Baroque and Rococo. il. 1960. 7.95. Tudor

FATHER FLANAGAN'S BOYS' HOME, BOYS TOWN, NEB. (360)
Oursler, Fulton, and Will. Father Flanagan of Boys Town. il. 1949. 3.95. Double day

FATHERS (301.42)
Geissler, Eugene S. Father of the family. 2.95. Fides
Genne, William H. Husbands and pregnancy: Handbook for expectant fathers. 1956. 2.50. Assn. Pr.
Ostrovsky, Everett S. Father to the child. 1959. 3.75. Putnam
Reich, Hanns. Children and their fathers. 1962. 3.50. Hill & Wang
Wile, Ira S. Man takes a wife. 3.50. Emerson

FATIGUE (158.7)
Bullen, Adelaide K. New answers to the fatigue problem. 1956. 4.50. U. of Fla.
Clark, Marguerite. Why so tired. 1961. 3.95. Meredith
Laird, Donald A., and Eleanor C. Tired feelings and how to master them. il. 1960. 4.50. McGraw
Philpott, S. J. F. Fluctuations in human output. 1932. 3.00. Cambridge U. P.

FAULKNER, WILLIAM, 1897-1962 (813.52)
Beck, Warren. Man in motion: Faulkner's trilogy. 1961. pap. 1.75. U. of Wis.
Hoffman, Frederick J. William Faulkner. 3.50. Twayne
Hoffman, Frederick J., and Olga W. Vickery. William Faulkner: Three decades of criticism. 1960. 5.95. Mich. State
Howe, Irving. William Faulkner, a critical study. 1962. 1.45. Vintage
Meriwether, James B. Literary career of William Faulkner. il. 1961. 6.00. Princeton Univ. Lib.
Miner, Ward. World of William Faulkner. 1959. 3.50. Cooper
O'Connor, William Van. Tangled fire of William Faulkner. 1954. 4.00. U. of Minn.
Slatoff, Walter J. Quest for failure: A study of William Faulkner. 1960. 4.00. Cornell
Swiggart, Peter. Art of Faulkner's novels. 1962. 4.50. U. of Tex.
Vickery, Olga. Novels of William Faulkner. 1959. 5.00. La. State
Waggoner, Hyatt H. William Faulkner: From Jefferson to the world. 1959. 5.00. U. of Ky.

FAUST (398.22)
Butler, E. M. Fortunes of Faust. 1952. 6.50. Cambridge U. P.
FAUVISM (709.04)
Leymarie, Jean. Fauvism. il. 1959. 6.50. World Pub.
FEAR (157.3)
Cantril, Hadley, and others. Invasion from Mars. 1940. 3.50. Princeton
Coleman, Lester L. Freedom from fear. 1959. 4.95. Hawthorn
Freeman, Lucy. Fight against fears. 1951. 3.50. Crown
Freud, Sigmund. Problem of anxiety. 1936. 3.00. Norton
Kierkegaard, Soren. Concept of dread. tr. by Walter Lowrie. 1944. 4.00. Princeton
May, Rollo. Meaning of anxiety. 1950. 6.75. Ronald
Overstreet, Bonaro W. Understanding fear. 1951. 4.50. Harper
FEDERAL GOVERNMENT (351)
Bowie, Robert R., and Carl J. Friedrich. Studies in federalism. 1954. 18.00.
    Little
Dietze, Gottfried. Federalist: A classic on federalism and free government. 1960.
    6.50. Johns Hopkins
Hendry, James McLeod. Treaties and federal constitutions. 1955. 4.50. Pub.
    Affairs
Hicks, Ursula K., and others. Federalism and economic growth in underdeveloped
    countires. 1961. 4.00. Oxford U. P.
Livingston, W. S. Federalism and constitutional change. 1956. 7.20. Oxford
    U. P.
Mogi, Sobei. Problem of federalism. 2 vols. 11.00. Hillary
Roettinger, Ruth. Supreme Court and state police power. 1957. 4.50. Pub. Affairs
Vile, M. J. C. Structure of American federalism. il. 1961. 4.00. Oxford U. P.
Wheare, Kenneth C. Federal government. 1953. 4.00. Oxford U. P.
Wilcox, Thomas. States' rights vs. the Supreme Court. 1960. 3.00. Forum
FEDERAL RESERVE BANKS (332.11)
Prochnow, Herbert V. Federal Reserve System. il. 1960. 6.50. Harper
Vennard, Wickliffe B., Sr. Federal Reserve hoax. 1955. 2.00. Forum
FERMI, ENRICO, 1901- (925)
Fermi, Laura. Atoms in the family: My life with Enrico Fermi. il. 1954. 4.75.
    U. of Chicago
FERNS (587.31)
Wherry, Edgar T. Fern guide. il. 1961. 3.95. Doubleday (R)
Cobb, Boughton. Field guide to the ferns. il. 1956. 4.50. Houghton (R)
Parsons, Frances T. How to know the ferns. il. 3.25. Smith, Peter
FERTILITY (612.663)
Bogue, Donald J. Population of the United States. 1959. 17.50. Free Press
Eversley, David E. C. Social theories of fertility and the Malthusian debate.
    il. 1959. 5.60. Oxford U. P.
Farris, Edmond J. Human ovulation and fertility. 1956. 6.50. Lippincott
Lorimer, F., and others. Culture and human fertility. pap. 4.50. Int. Doc.
    Service-Columbia
Van de Velde, Theodoor H. Fertility and sterility in marriage. 7.50. Random
Westoff, Charles, and others. Family growth in metropolitan America. 1961.
    10.00. Princeton
Biochemical Society. Biochemistry of fertilization and the gametes. 2.25.
    Cambridge U. P.
Meeuse, Bastiaan J. D. Story of pollination. il. 1961. 7.50. Ronald
Rothschild, N. M. V. Fertilization. 1956. 3.95. Wiley
FESTIVALS (394.2)
Cooper, Gordon. Festivals of Europe. il. 1961. 3.75. British Bk. (R)
James, Edwin O. Seasonal feasts and festivals. 1961. 6.50. Barnes & Noble (R)
Spicer, Dorothy Gladys. Festivals of western Europe. 1958. 5.00. Wilson
FEUDALISM (321.3)
Bloch, Marc. Feudal society. tr. by L. A. Manyon. 1961. 8.50. U. of Chicago

Coulborn, R. Feudalism in history. 1956. 8.50. Princeton
Davis, William Stearns. Life on a medieval barony. 1928. 5.00. Harper
Ganshof, Francois L. Feudalism. tr. by Philip Grierson. il. 1961. pap. 1.65.
   Harper
Hoyt, Robert S. Feudal institution: Cause or consequence of decentralization?
   1961. pap. 0.75. Holt, Rinehart & Winston
Lyon, Bryce D. From fief to indenture: The transition from feudal to nonfeudal
   contract in western Europe. 1957. 8.00. Harvard
Stephenson, Carl. Mediaeval feudalism. il. 1956. pap. 1.25. Cornell
Barrow, G. W. S. Feudal Britain. 4.75. St. Martins
Painter, Sidney. Studies in the history of the English feudal barony. 1943. 3.00.
   Johns Hopkins
Powicke, Michael. Military obligation in Medieval England. 1962. 7.20. Oxford
   U. P.
Stenton, Frank M. First century of English feudalism. 1066-1166. 1961. 7.20.
   Oxford U. P.

FICTION (808.3)
Allott, Miriam. Novelists on the novel. 1959. 5.00. Columbia
Auchincloss, Louis. Reflections of a Jacobite. 1961. 4.00. Houghton
Bluestone, George. Novels into film. 1957. 5.00. Johns Hopkins (R)
Forster, E. M. Aspects of the novel. 1947. 3.95. Harcourt
Haines, H. E. What's in a novel. 5.00. Columbia
Miller, James E., Jr. Myth and method: Modern theories of fiction. 1960. pap.
   1.00. U. of Nebr.
Ortega, y Gasset, Jose. Dehumanization of art and other writings on art and
   culture. 2.85. Smith, Peter
Stang, Richard. Theory of the novel in England, 1850-1870. 1959. 5.00. Columbia
FICTION--BIBLIOGRAPHY (016.8)
Fiction catalog. 1960. with suppls. 12.00. Wilson
Kerr, Elizabeth. Bibliography of the sequence novel. 1950. 10.00. U. of Minn. (R)
FICTION--COLLECTIONS (808.83)
Bement, Douglas, and Ross M. Taylor. Fabric of fiction. il. 1943. 4.75. Harcourt
Costain, Thomas B., comp. Twelve short novels. 7.50. Doubleday
Neider, Charles. Short novels of the masters. 1948. 5.00. Rinehart
Wagenknecht, Edward. Six novels of the supernatural. 1944. 2.95. Viking
FICTION--HISTORY AND CRITICISM (809.3)
Booth, Wayne C. Rhetoric of fiction. 1961. 6.95. U. of Chicago
Brooks, Cleanth, Jr., and Robert Penn Warren. Scope of fiction. 1960. 2.75.
   Appleton
Brooks, Cleanth, Jr., and Robert Penn Warren. Understanding fiction. 5.00.
   Appleton'
Buckler, Willaim E. Novels in the making. 1961. pap. 1.75. Houghton
Dillistone, F. W. Novelist and the Passion story. 1961. 3.00. Sheed
Gardiner, Harold C. Norms for the novel. 1960. 2.95. Doubleday
Gardner, John, and Lennis Dunlap. Forms of fiction. 1961. 3.75. Random
Howells, William Dean. Criticism and fiction, and other essays. by Clara Marburg
   Kirk and Rudolf. 1959. 6.00. N. Y. U.
Howells, William D. European and American masters. pap. 0.95. Collier
Howells, W. D. Novel-writing and novel-reading, an impersonal explanation. by
   William M. Gibson. bd. with Henry James and the Bazar letters. by Leon Edel
   and Lyall H. Powers, in Howells and James, a double billing. 1958. 0.50.
   N. Y. P. L.
James, Henry. Art of the novel: 1934. 3.95. Scirbner
James, Henry. Future of the novel. by Leon Edel. 1956. pap. 1.25. Vintage
Kennedy, Margaret. Outlaws on Parnassus. 1960. 3.00. Viking
Kronenberger, Louis. Novelists on novelists. pap. 1.45. Doubleday
Krutch, Joseph W. Five masters, a study in the mutations of the novel. 1959.
   3.75. Smith, Peter

Lesser, S. Fiction and the unconscious. 1957. 3.00. Beacon
Lubbock, Percy. Craft of fiction. 1957. 3.95. Viking
McMahon, Helen. Criticism of fiction. 3.50. Twayne
Maugham, W. Somerset. Points of View: Five essays. 1959. 4.50. Doubleday
Maurois, Andre. Seven faces of love. pap. 0.95. Doubleday
O'Connor, Frank. Mirror in the roadway. 1956. 5.00. Knopf
Rideout, Walter B., and James K. Robinson. College book of modern fiction. 1961. 6.50. Harper
Scholes, Robert. Approaches to the novel. 1961. 3.25. Chandler Pub.
Udell, Mary Gonzaga. Philosophical approach to literature. 1962. 3.50. Pageant
Uzzell, Thomas. Technique of the novel. 1959. 4.00. Citadel
Wallace, Irving. Fabulous originals. 1955. 4.50. Knopf
Beach, Joseph Warren. Twentieth century novel: Studies in technique. 1932. 4.50. Appleton
Brewster, Dorothy, and John A. Burrell. Modern world of fiction. 1953. pap. 1.50. Littlefield
Humphrey, Robert. Stream of consciousness in the modern novel. 1954. pap. 1.25. U. of Calif.
Moseley, Edwin. Pseudonyms of Christ in the modern novel. 1962. 4.95. U. of Pittsburgh
Mueller, William R. Prophetic voice in modern fiction. 1959. 3.50. Assn. Pr.
FICTION--TECHNIQUE (808.3)
Aldridge, J. W. Critiques and essays on modern fiction, 1920-1951. 1952. 7.50. Ronald
Cowley, Malcolm. Writers at work: The Paris Review interviews. 1958. 5.00. 1959. Viking
Cross, Wilbur L. Development of the English novel. 1900. 4.75. Macmillan
Derleth, August. Writing fiction. 1946. 3.00. Writer
De Voto, Bernard. World of fiction. 1950. 3.50. Houghton
Fisher, Vardis. God or Caesar? The writing of fiction for beginners. 1959. 5.00. Swallow, A.
Fox, Edward S. How to write stories that sell. 3.95. Writer
Glasgow, Ellen. Certain measure: An interpretation of prose fiction. 1943. 3.95. Harcourt
Harris, William F. Basic formulas of fiction. 1960. 3.95. U. of Okla.
Hoffman, Arthur Sullivant. Writing of fiction. 1934. 4.50. Writer
McGraw, Eloise J. Techniques of fiction writing. 1959. 4.00. Writer
Mirrielees, Edith R. Story writing. 1947. 4.00. Writer
O'Connor, William V. Forms of modern fiction. 1959. pap. 1.75. Indiana
FIELD CROPS (633)
Fergus, E. N., and others. Field crops: Including Southern crops. il. 1958. 5.60. Lippincott
Rather, Howard C., and C. M. Harrison. Field crops. il. 1951. 8.25. McGraw
FIELDING, HENRY, 1707-1754 (823.5)
Johnson, Maurice O. Fielding's art of fiction. 1961. 5.00. U. of Pa.
Paulson, Ronald. Fielding: A collection of critical essays. 1962. 3.95. Prentice-Hall
FIELDS, ALGEBRAIC (512.815)
Artin, Emil. Goemetric algebra. il. 1957. 7.50. Wiley
Pollard, H. Theory of algebraic numbers. 1950. 4.00. Wiley
Weyl, H. Algebraic theory of numbers. 1954. 3.00. Princeton
FIGURE DRAWING (743.4)
Dobkin, Alexander. Principles of figure drawing. il. 1948. 7.50. World Pub.
Doust, L. A. Sketching people. 1.50. Warne
Loomis, Andrew. Figure drawing for all it's worth. il. 1943. 5.95. Viking
Zaidenberg, Arthur. Drawing the human figure in action. 1960. 3.95. Abelard
FILLMORE, MILLARD, PRES. U.S., 1800-1874 (923.173)
Rayback, Robert J. Millard Fillmore. 1959. 7.50. Stewart

FILMSTRIPS (371.335)
Diffor, John W., and Mary F. Horkheimer. Educators guide to free filmstrips.
    1961. 6.00. Educators Progress
Enoch Pratt Free Library. Catalog of 16 mm films and sound filmstrips. 1957.
    0.60. Enoch Pratt
Library of Congress. Films: Bibliography, 1951-1952. 6.00. Edwards (R)
FINANCE (332)
Curtis, Edward. Company organization of the finance function. 1962. 4.50. Am.
    Management Assn.
Groves, H. M. Trouble spots in taxation. 1948. 2.00. Princeton
Hansen, Alvin H. Fiscal policy and business cycles. 1941. 6.95. Norton
Jacobsson, Per. Some monetary problems international and national. by Erin
    E. Jucker-Fleetwood. 1958. 7.20. Oxford U. P.
Kelso, Louis O., and Mortimer J. Adler. New capitalists. il. 1961. 3.50. Random
Porter, Sylvia. How to get more for your money. 1961. 3.95. World Pub.
Scherman, Harry. Promises men live by. 1938. 3.75. Random
Walker, Ernest W., and William H. Baughn. Financial planning and policy. il.
    1961. 8.00. Harper
Williams, John Henry. Money, trade, and economic growth. 6.00. Macmillan
FINANCE--U.S. (332.973)
Fortune. Readings in finance. by J. Fred Weston. 1958. pap. 2.20. Holt, Rinehart
    & Winston
Hamilton, Alexander. Papers on public credit, commerce and finance. 1957. 3.50.
    Bobbs
Lundberg, Ferdinand. America's 60 families. pap. 1.95. Citadel
Upham, Cyril B., and Edwin Lamke. Closed and distressed banks. 1934. 2.50.
    Brookings
Bogart, Ernest L. Financial history of Ohio. 1912. 2.50. U. of Ill.
Miller, Edmund Thornton. Financial history of Texas. 1916. pap. 1.50. U. of Tex.
Studenski, Paul, and H. E. Krooss. Financial history of the United States. 1952.
    7.95. McGraw
FINANCE, PERSONAL (332)
Armbruster, Dorothy M. Pennies and millions. 1962. 4.50. Doubleday
Changing Times Staff. Kiplinger's family buying guide. 5.95. Prentice-Hall
Clarke, Joyce and Sally Dickson. Woman's guide to financial security. 1953.
    2.75. Barrows
Cohen, Jerome B., and Arthur W. Hanson. Personal finance: Principles and
    case problems. 1958. 10.00. Irwin
Donaldson, Elvin F., and J. K. Pfahl. Personal finance. 1961. 7.50. Ronald
Jordan, David F., and Edward F. Willett. Managing personal finances. 1951.
    7.95. Prentice-Hall
Lasser, Jacob K., and Sylvia F. Porter. Managing your money. 1962. 4.95.
    Holt, Rinehart & Winston
Morgan, James N. Consumer economics. 1955. 10.00. Prentice-Hall
Springer, John L. Make the most of your income. 1961. 4.95. Prentice-Hall
FINANCE, PUBLIC (336)
Musgrave, R. A. Theory of public finance. 1959. 12.50. McGraw
Allen, H. K., and R. G. Axt. State public finance and state institutions of
    higher education in the United States. 1952. 3.00. Columbia
Buchanan, James M. Public finances. 1960. 10.60. Irwin
Cauley, Troy J. Public finance and the general welfare. il. 1960. 5.95. Merrill,
    C. E.
Copeland, M. I. Trends in government financing. 1961. 5.00. Princeton
Kimmel, Lewis H. Federal budget and fiscal policy, 1789-1958. 1959. 5.00.
    Brookings
Shultz, William J., and Clement L. Harriss. American public finance. 1959.
    10.60. Prentice-Hall
Taylor, Philip E. Economics of public finance. 1961. 7.50. Macmillan

FINANCIAL STATEMENTS (657.3)
Rogers, Donald I. Financial facts of life: How to read a financial statement. 1959.
    2.95. Holt
FINLAND (947.1)
Shirer, William L. Challenge of Scandinavia. 1955. 6.50. Little
American Geographical Society. Finland and its geography. il. 1955. 9.00. Duell
Nagel guide book to Finland. 4.00. Taplinger
Jutikkala, Eino, and Kauko Pirinen. History of Finland. 1962. 7.75. Praeger
FIRE PREVENTION (614.841)
National Fire Protection Association. Fire protection handbook. il. 1962. 17.50.
    Nat. Fire Protection (R)
FIREARMS (683.4)
Allen, Walter G. B. Pistols, rifles and machine guns. 4.00. Borden
Chapel, Charles Edward. Gun care and repair: A manual of gunsmithing. il.
    1942. 7.50. Coward
Craige, John Huston. Practical book of American guns. il. 1950. 4.95. World
    Pub.
Gun Digest. Encyclopedia of modern firearms. by the Editors of Gun Digest. 1960.
    20.00. Gun Digest
Hatch, Alden. Remington arms in American history. il. 6.50. Rinehart
Peterson, Harold D. Treasury of the gun. il. 1962. 15.00. Golden Press
Smith, Walter H. B. Small arms of the world. il. 1960. 15.00. Stackpole (R)
Outdoor Life. Story of American hunting and firearms. by the Editors of Outdoor
    Life. il. 1959. 8.50. McGraw
FIRST AID IN ILLNESS AND INJURY (614.88)
American Red Cross. First aid textbook. il. 1957. 1.00. Doubleday (R)
Bolton, William. What to do until the doctor comes. 1960. 3.50. Reilly & Lee
Brennan, W. T., and D. J. Ludwig. Guide to problems and practices in first
    aid and civil defense. pap. 2.75. Brown, W. C.
Cole, Warren H., and Charles B. Puestow. First aid: Surgical and medical.
    il. 1960. 6.25. Appleton
Henderson, John. Complete book of first aid. il. 1956. 3.75. Duell
Leone, Nicholas C., and Elisabeth C. Phillips. Medical emergencies in pleasure
    boating. il. 2.95. Ziff-Davis
Smith, Martin A., and William E. Eliason. Family survival handbook. (X-201-
    BB). pap. 0.75. Belmont Bks.
Warwick, Francis James, and A. G. Tunstall. First aid to the injured and sick.
    il. by A. P. Gorham. 1952. 1.50. Williams & Wilkins
Wells, Helen. Cherry Ames' book of first aid and home nursing. il. 1959. 1.95.
    Grosset
Young, Carl B., Jr. First aid and resuscitation. il. 1954. 8.50. Thomas, C. C
FISHES (597)
Artedi, P. Ichthyologia. by C. Linnaues. 1960. 19.60. Hafner (R)
Curtis, Brian. Life story of the fish, his manners and morals. il. 3.50. Smith,
    Peter
Hardy, Alister C. Fish and fisheries. 1959. 7.50. Houghton
Herald, Earl Stannard. Living fishes of the world. il. 1961. 12.50. Doubleday (R)
LaMonte, Francesca. Marine game fishes of the world. il. 1952. 3.95. Doubleday'
Perlmutter, Alfred. Guide to marine fishes. il. 1961. 6.50. N. Y. U.
Trippensee, Reuben E. Furbearers, waterfowl and fish. 1953. 8.00. McGraw
FISHES--NORTH AMERICA (597.973)
Gabrielson, Ira N. Fisherman's encyclopedia. il. 1950. 17.50; with Hunter's
    encyclopedia, 30.00. Stackpole   s
LaMonte, Francesca. North American game fishes. il. 4.50. Doubleday
FISHING (799.1)
Bates, Joseph D., Jr. Spinning for fresh water game fish. il. 1957. 6.50. Little
Bennett, George W. Management of artificial lakes and ponds. 1962. 8.00. Reinhold
Clark, Eugenie. Lady with a spear. il. 1953. 4.50. Harper

Field and Stream. Sportsman's world. by the Editors of Field and Stream. il. 1959. 12.50? Holt

Major, Harlan. Basic fishing. il. 1947. 3.50. Funk

Walton, Izaak. Compleat angler. 1.95. Dutton

McCormick, Robert C. Angler's almanac. il. 1955. 3.95. Harper

Migdalski, E. C. Angler's guide to the fresh water game fishes of North America. il. 1962. 8.00. Ronald

FITZGERALD, FRANCIS SCOTT KEY, 1896-1940 (813.5)

Hoffman, Frederick J. Great Gatsby: A study. 1962. pap. 2.35. Scribner

Kazin, Alfred. F. Scott Fitzgerald: The man and his work. pap. 0.95. Collier

Mizener, Arthur. Far side of paradise: Biography of F. Scott Fitzgerald. 5.00. Houghton

Shain, Charles. F. Scott Fitzgerald. 1961. pap. 0.65. U. of Minn.

Stern, Milton. F. Scott Fitzgerald. il. Barnes & Noble. 2.50.

Turnbull, Andrew W. Scott Fitzgerald. il. 1962. 5.95. Scribner

FLAGS (929.9)

Evans, I. O. Observer's book of flags. il. 1959. 1.25. Warne

Flags of the United Nations. il. 1.00. U.N.

Kannik, Preben. Flag book. il. 1960. 3.95. Barrows

Quaife, Milo M., and others. History of the United States flag. il. 1961. 4.95. Harper

FLAUBERT, GUSTAVE, 1821-1880 (928)

Fairlie, Alison. Flaubert: Madama Bovary. 1962. 1.95. Barron's

Steegmuller, Francis. Flaubert, and Madame Bovary. pap. 1.25 Vintage

Tillett, Maragaret G. On reading Flaubert. 1961. 2.40. Oxford U. P.

FLEMING, SIR ALEXANDER, 1881-1955 (925)

Maurois, Andre. Life of Sir Alexander Fleming. tr. by Gerald Manley Hopkins. il. 1959. 5.95. Dutton

FLETCHER, JOHN, 1579-1625 (928)

Leech, Clifford. John Fletcher plays. 1962. 3.50. Harvard

Wilson, John Harold. Influence of Beaumont and Fletcher on Restoration drama. 1928. 2.50. Ohio State

FLIGHT TRAINING (629.13252)

Zweng, Charles A. Flight instructor. il. 1956. 5.00. Pan Am. Navigation Service (R)

FLOOD CONTROL (627.4)

Hoyt, W. G., and W. B. Langbein. Floods. 1955. 7.50. Princeton

Hydrologic networks and methods. 1960. 3.00. U. N.

FLORENCE (945.51)

Machiavelli, Noccolo. History of Florence and of the Affairs of Italy. 4.00. Smith, Peter

Hurlimann, Martin, and Harold Acton. Florence. il. 1961. 6.95. Viking

FLORICULTURE (635.9)

McFarland, J. Horace, and others. Garden bulbs in color. 1941. 3.95. Macmillan

FLORIDA (975.9)

Williams, John L. Territory of Florida. facsimile ed. il. 1962. 7.50. U. of Fla.

Florida: Guide to the southernmost state. 6.50. Oxford U. P. (R)

Kennedy, Stetson. Palmetto country. 1942. 4.00. Duell

Langworthy, Fred H. Thunder at Cape Canaveral. 2.50. Vintage

Barcia, Andres G. Chronological history of the continent of Florida. tr. by Anthony Kerrigan. 1951. 10.00. U. of Fla.

Thompson, Arthur W. Jacksonian democracy on the Florida frontier. pap. 2.00. U. of Fla.

FLOWER ARRANGEMENT (635.966)

Berrall, Julia S. Flowers and table settings. il. 1951. 6.95. Viking

Berrall, Julia S. History of flower arrangement. il. 1953. 6.50. Viking

Better Homes and Gardens. Flower arranging. by the Editors of Better Homes and Gardens. 1957. 2.95. Meredith

Brooks, Myra J., and others. Magic world of flower arranging. 1956. 10.00.
  Barrows
Bunbury, Alice. Floral art for pleasure. il. 1961. 5.00. Branford
Carren, S. Manual for floral decoration in home. 6.45. Judd (R)
Conway, J. Gregory. Conway's encyclopedia of flower arrangements. il. 1957.
  6.00. Knopf
Easterby, Estelle G. Home book of flower arrangements. il. 1960. 3.50. Chilton
Hirsch, Sylvia. Art of table setting and flower arrangement. il. 1962. 7.95.
  Crowell (R)
FLOWERS (635.9)
Colette. For a flower album. il. 1959. 4.50. McKay
Jaeger, Paul. Wonderful life of flowers. il. 1961. 15.00. Dutton
Taylor, Norman. Guide to garden flowers. il. 1958. 4.95. Houghton
FLOWERS--PICTORIAL WORKS (635.9)
Kiaer, Eigil. Complete guide to indoor plants. il. 1958. 3.50. Crown
Schwarzenbach, Hans. Flowers in color. il. 1960. 20.00. Viking (R)
FLUID DYNAMICS (532)
Binder, Raymond C. Advanced fluid dynamics and fluid machinery. 1951. 10.00.
  Prentice-Hall
Birkhoff, G. Hydrodynamics. 1961. 6.50. Princeton
Hall, N. A. Thermodynamics of fluid flow. 1951. 8.65. Prentice-Hall
Richardson, Edward G. Dynamics of real fluids. 1962. 12.50. St. Martins
FLUID MECHANICS (532)
Brenkert, Karl, Jr. Elementary theoretical fluid mechanics. 1960. 7.50. Wiley
Eskinazi, Salamon. Principles of fluid mechanics. il. 1962. 11.65. Allyn & Bacon
Long, Robert R. Mechanics of solids and fluids. il. 1961. 8.00. Prentice-Hall
Olson, Reuben M. Essentials of engineering fluid mechanics. il. 1961. 10.50.
  Int. Textbook
Shames, I. Mechanics of fluids. 1962. 8.95. McGraw
FLUORESCENT LIGHTING (621.3273)
Amick, Charles L. Fluorescent lighting manual. 1961. 12.50. McGraw
FLUORINE (546.731)
Largent, Edward J. Fluorosis: The health aspects of fluorine compounds. 3.50.
  Ohio State
Slesser, Charles, and S. R. Schram. Preparation, properties, and technology of
  fluorine and organic-fluoro compounds. 1951. 11.50. McGraw
FOLK ART (745)
Lipman, Jean. American primitive painting. il. 1942. 8.50. Oxford U. P. (R)
Little, Nina F. American folk art from the Abby Aldrich Rockefeller folk art
  collection. 1959. 3.95. Holt, Rinehart & Winston
FOLK DANCING (793.31)
Duggan, Anne S., and others. Folk dance library. 1948. 5 vols. Ronald
Fox, Grace I., and K. G. Merrill. Folk dancing. 1957. 4.50. Ronald
Kirkell, Miriam H., and Irma K. Schaffnit. Partners all--places all! Forty-
  four enjoyable square and folk dances for everyone. il. 1949. 3.95. Dutton
Kraus, Richard G. Folk dancing: A guide for schools, colleges, and recreation
  groups. il. 1962. 4.75. Macmillan (R)
McIntosh, David S. Singing games and dances. 1957. 3.00. Assn. Pr.
Lawson, Joan. European folk dance. 1953. 8.95. Pitman (R)
FOLK-LORE (398)
Dorson, Richard M. Folklore research around the world. 1961. pap. 5.00. Indiana
Freud, Sigmund, and D. E. Oppenheim. Dreams in folklore. 1958. 3.00. Int.
  Univs.
Leach, Maria, and Jerome Fried. Funk and Wagnalls' standard dictionary of
  folklore, mythology, and legend. 2 vols. 10.00 ea. Funk (R)
Loomis, C. Grant. White magic: An introduction to the folklore of Christian
  legend. 1948. 5.00. Mediaeval
Weiser, Francis X. Handbook of Christian feasts and customs. 1958. 4.95.
  Harcourt (R)

FOLK-LORE, AFRICAN (398)
Jablow, Alta. Yes and no: The intimate folklore of Africa. 1961. 3.95. Horizon
FOLK-LORE, AMERICAN (398)
Ballowe, Hewitt L. Creole folk tales. 1948. 3.00. Louisiana State U. P.
Boatright, Mody C., and others. Texas folk and folklore. 1954. 5.00. S. M. U.
Botkin, B. A. Folk-say: A regional miscellany. 2 vols. 6.00. U. of Okla. (R)
Botkin, B. A. Treasury of American folklore. il. 1944. 5.95. Crown (R)
Botkin, Benjamin A. Treasury of Mississippi River folklore. 1955. 5.00. Crown
    (R)
Botkin, B. A. Treasury of Southern folklore. 1949. 5.00. Crown (R)
Botkin, Benjamin A. Treasury of Western folklore. 1951. 5.00. Crown
Chase, Richard. American folk tales and songs. pap. 0.75. New Am. Lib.
Dobie, J. Frank. Tales of old-time Texas. 1955. 5.00. Little
Dorson, Richard M. American folklore. 1959. 4.50. U. of Chicago
Flanagan, John T., and Arthur Palmer Hudson. Folklore in American literature.
    1958. 5.75. Harper (R)
Life, Life treasury of American folklore. by the Editors of Life. il. 1961. 12.50.
    Golden Press (R)
FOLK-LORE, GREEK (398)
Carpenter, Rhys. Folk tale, fiction, and saga in the Homeric epics. 1946. pap.
    1.50. U. of Calif.
FOLK-LORE, IRISH (398)
Colum, Padraic. Treasury of Irish folklore. 1954. 5.00. Crown (R)
Yeats, William Butler. Irish fairy and folk tales. (44) 1.95. Modern Lib.
FOLK SONGS (784.4)
Boni, Margaret Bradford, and Norman Lloyd. Fireside book of folk songs. il.
    1947. 6.00. Simon & Schuster
Glazer, Tom. New treasury of folk songs. 1961. pap. 0.60. Bantam
Russell, Martha Stockton. Sing, swing, play: Fifty-eight folk songs. 1938. 2.50.
    Viking
Thomas, Edith Lovell. Whole world singing. 1950. 2.95. Friendship
Weavers. Weavers song book. 1960. 5.95. Harper
Greenway, John. American folksongs of protest. 4.00. Smith, Peter
Vaughan Williams, Ralph. National music. 1934. 4.25. Oxford U. P.
FOLK-SONGS, AMERICAN (784.4)
Lomax, Alan. Folk songs of North America. il. 1960. 7.50. Doubleday
Lomax, John and Alan. Best loved American folk songs. 5.95. Grosset
Robb, John D. Hispanic folk songs of New Mexico. pap. 2.00. U. of N. Mex.
Spaeth, Sigmund. Read 'em and weep. 1960. pap. 1.25. Arco
FOLK SONGS, ENGLISH (784.4)
Wood, Thomas. Oxford song book. vol. 2. music ed. 2.00. Oxford U. P. (R)
FOOD (641)
Anderson, Linnea, and John H. Browe. Nutrition and family health service. il.
    1960. pap. 5.00. Saunders
Callow, A. B. Food and health: An introduction to the science of nutrition. il.
    1946. 2.40. Oxford U. P.
Charley, H. Food study manual. 1961. 4.25. Ronald
Desrosier, Norman W. Attack on starvation. il. 1961. 6.75. Avi Pub.
Fitch, Natalie K., and Charlotte A. Francis. Foods and principles of cookery.
    1948. 9.65. Prentice-Hall
Gorrell, Faith Lanman, and others. Food and family living. il. 1947. 4.40.
    Lippincott
Gt. Brit., Ministry of Agriculture, Fisheries and Food. ABC of cookery. il. 1962.
    spiral bdg. 1.00. British Info. Services
Harris, Jessie W., and Elisabeth V. Lacey. Everyday foods. il. 1954. 6.75.
    Houghton
Hughes, Osee G. Introductory foods. il. 1962. 6.00. Macmillan
Hutchinson, Robert. Hutchinson's food and the principles of dietetics. il. by
    V. H. Mottram, and George Graham. 1956. 8.25. Williams & Wilkins

Jacobs, Morris B. Chemistry and technology of food and food products. il. 1951. vol. 1, 16.50; vols. 2 and 3, 20.00 ea; set, 49.50. Wiley

Justin, Margaret M., and others. Foods: An introductory college course. 6.50. Houghton

Kinder, Faye. Meal management. il. 1956. 6.50. Macmillan

McDermott, Irene, and others. Food for better living. il. 1960. 5.40. Lippincott

Macdonald, Grace. Food facts and diet planning. 2.00. St. Martins

Prentice, E. Parmalee. Hunger and history. il. 1951. 5.00. Caxton

Stanley, Louise, and Jessie A. Cline. Foods, their selection and preparation. 1950. 6.00. Ginn

Sweetman, M. D., and I. MacKellar. Food selection and preparation. 1954. 6.95. Wiley

White, Ruth B. You and your food. il. 1961. 7.00. Prentice-Hall

Wilmot, Jennie S., and Margaret Q. Batjer. Food for the family. il. 1960. 6.95. Lippincott

Wright, Carlton. Food buying: Marketing information for consumer. il. 1962. 6.75. Macmillan

FOOD--ANALYSIS (543.1)

Bradley, Alice V. Tables of food values. 1956. 5.50. Bennett (R)

Rose, Mary Swartz. Laboratory handbook for dietetics. by Cla Taylor and Grace MacLeod. 5.75. Macmillan

FOOD--BACTERIOLOGY (641)

Frazier, William C. Food microbiology. 1958. 9.95. McGraw

FOOD--DICTIONARIES (641.03)

Bender, A. E. Dictionary of nutrition and food technology. 1960. 5.80. Academic Press

Montagne, Prosper. Larousse gastronomique. by Charlotte Turgeon and Nina Froud. 20.00. Crown (R)

Simon, Andre. Guide to good food and wines. 6.00. Collins

Ward, Artemus. Encyclopedia of food. vol. 1. 12.50. Smith, Peter

FOOD--PRESERVATION (664.8)

Bate-Smith, E. C., and T. N. Morris. Food science. 1952. 9.50. Cambridge U.P.

Singleton, W. Ralph. Nuclear radiation in food and agriculture. il. 1958. 9.50. Van Nostrand

Carlton, Harry. Frozen food industry. 1941. 2.00. U. of Tenn.

General Foods Kitchens. Frozen foods cookbook. il. 1961. 1.95. Random

Meyer, Hazel. Complete book of home freezing. il. 1960. 5.95. Lippincott

Cassady, R., Jr. Competition and price making in food retailing. 1962. 8.00. Ronald

Kotschevar, Lindal H. Quantity food purchasing. 1961. 14.00. Wiley

Prindiville, Kathleen. Production and application of enzyme preparations in food manufacture. 6.50. Macmillan

Simpson, J. I. Frozen food cookbook. 7.95. Avi Pub. (R)

FOOD ADULTERATION AND INSPECTION (614.3)

Longgood, William. Poisons in your food. 1960. 3.95. S. and S.

FOOD SUPPLY (338.19)

Calder, Richie. Common sense about a starving world. 1962. 2.95. Macmillan

De Castro, Josue. Geography of hunger. 1952. 6.00. Little

De Kruif, Paul. Hunger fighters. il. 2.50. Harcourt

Ethyl Corporation. Food for America's future. 3.95. McGraw

Food and Agriculture Organization. So bold an aim: Ten years of international co-operation toward freedom from want. 1.50. Int. Doc. Service-Columbia

Oser, Jacob. Must men starve?: The Malthusian controversy. 1957. 4.50. Abelard

Pearson, Frank A., and Floyd A. Harper. World's hunger. 1945. 1.50. Cornell

Root, Waverley. Food of France. il. 1958. 10.00. Knopf

Yates, Paul Lamartine. Food, land, and manpower in Western Europe. il. 1960. 7.00. St. Martins

FOOT (611.718)
Hiss, John M. Functional foot disorders. 11.50. Regent (R)
Rossi, William A. Your feet and their care. 1955. 3.95. Emerson
FOOTBALL (796.332)
Allen, G. Complete book of winning football drills. 1959. 7.50. Prentice-Hall
Bryant, Paul W. Building a championship football team. 1960. 5.35. Prentice-Hall
Caldwell, Charles W. Modern football for the spectator. il. 1953. 3.95. Lippincott
Dodd, R. L. Bobby Dodd on football. 1954. 5.50. Prentice-Hall
Holgate, J. G. Fundamental football. 1958. 4.00. Ronald
Sports Illustrated. Sports Illustrated book of football. by the Editors of Sports Illustrated. il. 1960. 2.95. Lippincott (R)
Wilkinson, Charles Burnham. Oklahoma split T, football. 1952. 6.60. 4.95. Prentice-Hall
Classen, Harold. Ronald encyclopedia of football. 1961. 10.00. Ronald (R)
Danzig, Allison. History of American football: Its great teams, players and coaches. 12.50. Prentice-Hall
Riger, Robert. Pros: A documentary of professional football in America. 1960. 10.00. S. and S.
FORD, FORD MADOX, 1873-1939 (823)
Meizner, John A. Ford Madox Ford's novels: A critical study. 1962. 5.50. U. of Minn.
FORD, HENRY, 1863-1947 (923.3)
Bulingame, Roger. Henry Ford. 1955. 3.00. Knopf
Nevins, Allan, and Frank E. Hill. Ford: Expansion and challenge (1915-1933). il. 1957. 8.95. Scribner
Nevins, Allan, and Frank E. Hill. Ford: The times, the man, the company. il. 1954. 8.95. Scribner
Sorensen, Charles E. My forty years with Ford. pap. 0.95. Collier
FOREIGN EXCHANGE (332.45)
Diebold, William, Jr. Trade and payments in western Europe: A study of economic cooperation, 1947-1951. 1952. 5.00. Harper
Ohlin, Bertil. Interregional and international trade. il. 1933. 6.00. Harvard
Scammell, W. M. International monetary policy. 1962. 10.00. St. Martins
Muhammad, Seyid. Legal framework of world trade. 1958. 10.00. Praeger
FOREST ECOLOGY (634.94)
Richards, Paul W. Tropical rain forest. 1952. 13.50. Cambridge U. P.
FOREST FIRES (634.9618)
Davis, K. P. Forest fires: Control and use. 1959. 12.50. McGraw
Schiff, Ashley L. Fire and water. 1962. bds. 5.00. Harvard
FOREST RESERVES (634.925)
Carhart, Arthur H. National forests. il. 1959. 4.75. Knopf (R)
FORESTRY AS A PROFESSION (634.9069)
Hanaburgh, David H. Your future in forestry. 1961. 2.95. Richards Rosen
Shirley, Hardy Lomax. Forestry and its career opportunities. 1952. 7.50. McGraw
FORESTS AND FORESTRY (634.9)
Baker, Richard St. Barbe. Green glory: The story of the forests of the world. il. 3.50. Wyn
Duerr, William A. Fundamentals of forestry economics. 1960. 9.50. McGraw
Forbes, R. D., and A. B. Meyer. Forestry handbook. 1955. 15.00. Ronald (R)
Hawley, R. C., and D. M. Smith. Practice of silviculture. 1954. 7.50. Wiley
Hiley, W. E. Woodland management. 1954. 12.00. De Graff
Preston, John F. Developing farm woodlands. il. 1954. 5.50. McGraw
Stoddard, Charles H. Essentials of forestry practice. il. 1959. 5.50. Ronald
Westveld, R. H. and R. H. Peck. Forestry in farm management. 1951. 5.95. Wiley
Allen, Shirley W., and Grant W. Sharpe. Introduction to American forestry. il. 1961. 7.95. McGraw

Barrett, J. W. Regional silviculture of the United States. 1962. 12.00. Ronald (R)

Guthrie, John A., and George R. Armstrong. Western forest industry. 6.50.
Johns Hopkins

McCormick, Jack. Living forest. il. 1959. 3.95. Harper

FORMOSA (951.249)

Davidson, James W. Island of Formosa. 12.50. Paragon

Riggs, Fred W. Formosa under Chinese Nationalist rule. 1952. 3.50. Inst. of
Pac, Rel.

FORMS OF ADDRESS (651.74)

Measure, Howard. Styles of address: A manual of usage in writing and in speech.
1962. 4.50. St. Martins

Titles and forms of address: A guide to their correct use. 1959. 2.25. Macmillan
(R)

FORSTER, EDWARD MORGAN, 1879- (823)

Crews, Frederick C. E. M. Forester: The perils of humanism. 1962. 4.00.
Princeton

McConkey, James. Novels of E. M. Forster. 1957. 3.75. Cornell

FORUMS (DISCUSSION AND DEBATE) (374.24)

Beckhard, Richard. How to plan and conduct workshops and conferences. 1956.
1.00. Assn. Pr.

Cortright, Rupert L., and George I. Hinds. Creative discussion. 4.75. Macmillan

FOSTER, STEPHEN COLLINS, 1826-1864 (927)

Howard, John T. Stephen Foster, America's troubadour. 4.00. Smith, Peter

FOURIER SERIES (517.355)

Byerly, William E. Fourier's series. 1893. 8.00. Ginn

Churchill, Ruel V. Fourier series and boundary value problems. 1941. 5.50.
McGraw

Goldberg, R. R. Fourier transforms. 1961. 3.75. Cambridge U. P.

Lighthill, M. J. Introduction to Fourier analysis and generalised functions. 1958.
3.50. Cambridge U. P.

FOURTH DIMENSION (115.4)

Manning, Henry Parker. Fourth dimension simply explained. 3.35. Smith, Peter

Ouspensky, P. D. New model of the universe. 1934. 7.50. Knopf

FRA ANGELICO (GIOVANNI DA FIESOLE) 1387-1455 (927)

Angelico, Fra. Paintings of Fra Angelico. by John Pope-Hennessy. il. 1953.
15.00. N. Y. Graphic

Argan, Guilio C. Fra Angelico. il. 1955. 5.75. World Pub.

FRANCE (944)

Lachouque, Henry. Anatomy of glory: Napoleon and his guard. by Anne S. K.
Brown. il. 1962. 15.00. Brown U.

Palmer, Robert R. Twelve who ruled: The year of the terror in the French
Revolution. 1958. 6.95. Princeton

FRANCE--CIVILIZATION (944)

Curtius, Ernst R. Civilization of France. pap. 1.45. Vintage

Havens, George R. Age of ideas: From reaction to revolution in eighteenth-
century France. pap. 1.50. Collier

Padover, Saul K., and others. French institutions: Values and politics. 1954.
pap. 1.75. Stanford

Taine, H. A. Ancient regime. 6.00. Smith, Peter

Taine, H. A. Modern regime. 2 vols. 6.00 ea. Smith, Peter

Tannenbaum, Edward R. New France. il. 1961. 5.00. U. of Chicago

Evans, Joan. Life in medieval France. 7.50. N. Y. Graphic

Painter, Sidney. French chivalry: Chivalric ideas and practices in Medieval
France. 1940. 3.50. Johns Hopkins

Lokke, C. L. France and the colonial question. 1932. 3.75. Columbia

Priestley, Herbert Ingram. France overseas through the Old Regime: A study
of European expansion. il. 1939. 6.00. U. of Calif.

Bolton, Herbert E., and Thomas M. Marshall. Colonization of North America.
1492-1783. il. 7.50. Macmillan

FRANCE (914)

Belloc, Hilaire. Path to Rome. il. 1956. pap. 0.85. Doubleday

Bemelmans, Ludwig. Holiday in France. 1957. 5.00. Houghton

Boswell, James. Boswell on the grand tour: Italy, Corsica, and France, 1765-1766. by Frank Brady, and Frederick A. Pottle. 1955. 5.50. McGraw

Clark, Sydney. All the best in France. il. 1961. 4.95. Dodd

Stevenson, Robert Louis. Inland voyage, and Travels with a donkey. 1.95. Dutton

Baedeker, Karl. Baedeker's autoguide: France, including Corsica. 1961. 8.75. Macmillan (R)

Fodor, Eugene. France. 1960. il. 1960. 4.95. McKay

Holiday, Travel guide to France. by the Editors of Holiday. il. 1960. pap. 1.45. Random

Pan American World Airways. Complete reference guide to France. 1962. 1.95. S. and S. (R)

FRANCE--ECONOMIC CONDITIONS (944)

Cameron, Rondo E. France and the economic development of Europe, 1800-1914. 1961. 10.00. Princeton

Greenlaw, Ralph W. Economic origins of the French Revolution: Poverty or prosperity? 1958. pap. 1.50. Heath

FRANCE--FOREIGN RELATIONS (944)

Albrecht-Carrie, Rene. France and the two world wars. 1961. 7.00. Harper

Cameron, R. E. France and the economic development of Europe, 1800-1914. 1960. 10.00. Princeton

FRANCE--HISTORY (944)

Ascendancy of France. (New Cambridge modern history. vol. 5) 1961. 8.50. Cambridge U. P.

Brogan, D. W. French nation: From Napoleon to Petain, 1814-1940. 1958. 5.00. Harper

Guerard, Albert L. France: A modern history. il. 1959. 8.75. U. of Mich.

Guerard, Albert Leon. France, a short history. 1946. 3.95. Norton

Maurois, Andre. History of France. il. 1957. 7.50. Farrar, Straus

Romier, Lucien. History of France. 6.50. St. Martins

Duckett, Eleanor Shipley. Carolingian portraits: A study in the ninth century. il. 1962. 4.95. U. of Mich.

Kingdon, R. Geneva and the coming of the wars of religion in France. 1954. pap. 6.00. Lounz

Neale, John E. Age of Catherine de Medici. 1959. 3.50. Barnes & Noble

Ashley, Maurice. Louis XIV and the greatness of France. 2.50. Macmillan

Voltaire, Francois Marie Arouet de. Age of Louis XIV. 1.95. Dutton

FRANCE--HISTORY--REVOLUTION (944.04)

Brinton, Crane. Decade of revolution: 1789-1799. il. 1935. 6.00. Harper

Carlyle, Thomas. French Revolution. 2.95. Modern Lib.

Gershoy, Leo. French Revolution and Napoleon. il. 1933. 6.00. Appleton

Gottschalk, Louis R. Era of the French Revolution. 7.00. Houghton

Lefebvre, George. French Revolution: From its origins to 1793. tr. by E. M. Evanson. 1961. 6.00. Columbia

Taine, H. A. French Revolution. 3 vols. 6.00 ea. Smith, Peter

Thompson, J. M. French Revolution. 1955. 6.00. Oxford U. P.

Thompson, James M. Leaders of the French Revolution. 1962. 5.00. Barnes & Noble

Tocqueville, Alexis de. European correspondence with Gobineau. tr. by John Lukacs. 3.25. Smith, Peter

Belloc, Hilaire. French Revolution. il. 1911. 1.70. Oxford U. P.

Burke, Edmund. Reflections on the revolution in France. 1955. 3.75; (LLA 46) pap. 1.25. Bobbs

Halevy, Elie. Growth of philosophic radicalism. 6.50. Kelley

Paine, Thomas. Rights of man. 1935. 2.95. Dutton

Tocqueville, Alexis de. Old regime and the French Revolution. tr. by Stuart Gilbert. 3.00. Smith, Peter

Brown, Esther E. French Revolution and the American man of letters. 1951. pap. 2.50. U. of Missouri

Sears, Louis M. George Washington and the French Revolution. 1960. 6.50. Wayne

Pernoud, Georges, and Sabine Flaissier. French Revolution. il. 1960. 5.00. Putnam

FRANCE--HISTORY--SECOND REPUBLIC, 1848-1852 (944.07)
Marx, Karl. Class struggles in France 1848-50. 1934. 1.50. Int. Pubs.

Tocqueville, Alexis de. Recollections. by Jacob P. Mayer. tr. by A. T. de Mattos. 1949. 5.00. Columbia

FRANCE--POLITICS AND GOVERNMENT (944)
Godfrev, Edwin D. Government of France. 1961. 2.95. Crowell

Wallace-Hadrill, J. M., and J. McManners. France: Government and society. 5.00. Hillary

Major, J. Russell, Representative institutions in Renaissance France. 1421-1559. 1960. 4.00. U. of Wis.

Richelieu, Cardinal. Political testament of Cardinal Richelieu. tr. by Henry B. Hill. 1961. 3.75. U. of Wis.

Van Deusen, G. G. Sieyes: His life and his nationalism. 1932. 3.00. Columbia

Gooch, R. K. Parliamentary government in France. 1960. 4.75. Cornell

Joughin, Jean T. Paris commune in French politics, 1871-1880. 2 vols. 1956. 3.75 ea. Johns Hopkins

Duverger, Maurice. French political system. 1958. 4.00. U. of Chicago

Padover, Saul K., and others. French institutions: Values and politics. 1954. pap. 1.75. Stanford

Godfrey, Edwin D. Government of France. 1961. 2.95. Crowell

LaPonce, J. A. Government of France under the Fifth Republic. 1960. 6.50? U. of Calif.

Pickles, Dorothy. Fifth French Republic. 1960. 4.00. Praeger

FRANCE--SOCIAL LIFE AND CUSTOMS (944)
Herbert, Eugenia W. Artist and social reform: France and Belgium, 1885-1898. 1961. 5.00. Yale

Evans, Joan. Life in medieval France. 7.50. N. Y. Graphic

Holmes, Urban T., Jr. Daily living in the Twelfth Century" Based on the observations of Alexander Neckam in London and Paris. il. 1952. 3.85. U. of Wis.

Huizinga, Johan. Waning of the Middle Ages. 4.75. St. Martins

Lewis, Warren Hamilton. Splendid century: Life in the France of Louis XIV. il. 1954. 5.00. Sloane

FRANCESCO D'ASSISI, SAINT, 1182-1226 (922.22)
Bedoyere, Michael de la. Francis: A biography of the saint of Assisi. 1962. 6.00? Harper

Goudge, Elizabeth. My God and my all. 1959. 4.95. Coward

Jorgensen, J. St. Francis of Assisi. 1912. 4.50. McKay

Meyer, James. Social ideals of St. Francis. 2.75. Franciscan Herald

FRANKFURTER, FELIX, 1882- (923.4)
Mendelson, Wallace. Justices Black and Frankfurter. 1961. 4.00. U. of Chicago

Thomas, Helen S. Felix Frankfurter: Scholar on the bench. 1960. 6.50. Johns Hopkins

FRANKLIN, BENJAMIN, 1706-1790 (923.273)
Amacher, Richard E. Benjamin Franklin. 3.50. Twayne

Franklin, Benjamin. Autobiography. 1.40. Harper

Franklin, Benjamin. Autobiography and selected writings. 1.95. Modern Lib.

Schnapper, M. B. Benjamin Franklin: A pictorial biography. il. 1959. 4.50. Pub. Affairs

Van Doren, Carl. Benjamin Franklin: A biography. il. 1956. 7.50. Viking

FREE MATERIAL (371.335)
Diffor, John W., and Mary F. Horkheimer. Educators guide to free films. 1961. 9.00. Educators Progress (R)

Fowlkes, John G., and Paul T. Cody. Educators index of free materials. 1961. 24.00. Educators Progress

LeFevre, John R., and Donald Boydston. Annotated guide to free and inexpensive health instruction materials. 1959. pap. 2.50. Southern Ill. (R)

Pepe, Thomas J. Free and inexpensive educational aids. 1962. pap. 1.35. Dover

Saterstrom, Mary H., and John W. Renner. Educators guide to free science ' materials. 1961. 6.25. Educators Progress (R)

Wittich, Walter A., and Gertie H. Halsted. Educators guide to free tapes, scripts, and transcriptions. 1959. 5.75. Educators Progress (R)

FREE WILL AND DETERMINISM (159.1)

Bergson, Henri. Time and free will. tr. by F. L. Pogson. 1913. 3.75. Macmillan

Edwards, Jonathan. Freedom of the will. by P. Ramsey. 1957. 6.50. Yale

Erasmus, Desiderius, and Martin Luther. Discourse on free will. tr. by Ernst F. Winter. 1961. 3.75. Ungar

Hook, Sidney. Determinism and freedom: In the age of modern science. pap. 1.50. Collier

Luther, Martin. Bondage of the will. tr. by J. I. Packer, and O. R. Johnston. 4.00. Revell

Morris, Herbert. Freedom and responsibility. 1961. 11.50. Stanford

Pontifex, Mark. Freedom and providence. 1961. 3.50. Hawthorn

Sullivan, Robert P. Man's thirst for good. 1952. 3.00. Newman

FRENCH DRAMA (COLLECTIONS)(842.82)

Grant, Elliott. Chief French plays of the nineteenth century. 1934. 7.00. Harper

Grant, Elliott. Four French plays of the twentieth century. 1949. 4.00. Harper

Stanton, Stephen. Camille and other plays. 1960. 3.50. Smith, Peter

FRENCH DRAMA--HISTORY AND CRITICISM (842.09)

Bennetton, Norman A. Social significance of the duel in seventeenth century French drama. 1938. pap. 1.25. Johns Hopkins

Bishop, Thomas W. Pirandello and the French theater. 1960. 4.50. N. Y. U.

Chiari, Joseph. Contemporary French theatre. 1959. 6.50. Macmillan

Falk, Eugene H. Renunciation as a tragic focus: A study of five plays. 1954. 3.00. U. of Minn.

Frank, Grace. Medieval French drama. 1954. 6.10. Oxford U. P.

Cheon, Henri. Art of the theatre. tr. by Adele M. Fiske. 1961. 3.50. pap. 1.25. Hill & Wang

Guicharnaud, Jacques, and June Beckelman. Modern French theatre. 1961. 5.00. Yale

Lancaster, H. Carrington. French tragedy in the time of Louis XV and Voltaire 1715-1774. 2 vols. 1950. 5.00 ea. Johns Hopkins

Lancaster, Henry Carrington. Sunset: A history of Parisian drama in the last years of Louis XIV, 1701-1715. 1945. 5.00. Johns Hopkins

FRENCH FICTION--HISTORY AND CRITICISM (843.09)

Bree, Germaine, and Margaret Guiton. Age of fiction: The French novel from Gide to Camus. 1957. 5.00. Rutgers

Ferrier, Janet M. Forerunners of the French novel. 1955. 3.00. Barnes & Noble

Peyre, Henri. Contemporary French novel. 1955. 6.00. Oxford U. P.

Turnell, Martin. Art of French fiction. 1959. 6.00. New Directions

FRENCH LANGUAGE--DICTIONARIES--ENGLISH (443)

Cassell's new French dictionary. French-English and English-French. 7.50. Funk

Larousse. Modern French-English, English-French dictionary. 1960. 8.95. McGraw

Mansion, J. E. Concise French and English dictionary. 1949. 4.00. Heath

Mansion, J. E. Heath's standard French and English dictionary. 2 vols. vol. 1, French-English. bd. with 1955 suppl. 20.00; vol. 2, English-French bd. with 1955 suppl. 24.00; set, 40.00. Heath (R)

Van Nostrand. Van Nostrand's concise student dictionary: English-French, French-English. 1962. 5.95. Van Nostrand (R)
FRENCH LITERATURE (840)
Bree, Germaine. Twentieth century French literature: An anthology of prose and poetry. 1962. 7.00. Macmillan
Guthrie, Ramon, and George E. Diller. French literature and thought since the Revolution. il. 1942. 6.50. Harcourt
Grant, Elliott M., and others. French stories, plays and poetry. 1959. pap. 2.95. Oxford U. P.
Sirich, Edward H., and Francis B. Barton. Harper's French anthology. 1935. 4.50. Harper
Stewart, H. F., and Arthur A. Tilley. French romanticists. (in French) 1914. 4.00. Cambridge U. P.
FRENCH LITERATURE--DICTIONARIES, INDEXES, ETC. (840.03)
Braun, S. D. Dictionary of French literature. 1961. pap. 2.25. Littlefield (R)
Harvey, Paul, and Janet E. Heseltine. Oxford companion to French literature. 1959. 12.50. Oxford U. P.
FRENCH LITERATURE--HISTORY AND CRITICISM (840.09)
Cazamain, L. History of French literature. 1955. 8.25. Oxford U. P.
Evans, David O. Social romanticism in France, 1830-1848. 1951. 2.90. Oxford U.P.
Fowlie, Wallace. Guide to contemporary French literature: From Valery to Sartre. (M48) pap. 1.55. Meridian
Gide, Andre. Pretexts. 5.00. Meridian
Hatzfeld, H. A. Literature through art: New approach to French literature. il. 1952. 7.50. Oxford U. P.
James, Henry. Literary reviews and essays. by Albert Mordell. 10.00. Twayne
Mauriac, Claude. New literature. 1959. 4.00. Braziller
Moore, Will G. French classical literature. 1961. 2.90. Oxford U. P.
Tilley, Arthur A. Decline of the age of Louis XIV. 1929. 9.50. Cambridge U. P.
Tilley, Arthur. Literature of the French Renaissance. 2 vols. 1959. 17.50. Hafner
FRENCH POETRY (COLLECTIONS) (841.08)
Flowlie, Wallace. Mid-century French poets. 4.50. Twayne
Hackett, Cecil Arthur. Anthology of modern French poetry. 1952. 3.50. Macmillan (R)
Lucas, St. John, and P. M. Jones. Oxford book of French verse, thirteenth century in twentieth century. in French. 1957. 5.75. Oxford U. P.
Steele, Alan J. Three centuries of French verse, 1511-1819. 1956. 4.50. Aldine (R)
FRENCH POETRY--HISTORY AND CRITICISM (841.09)
Brereton, Geoffrey. Introduction to the French poets: Villon to the present day. 1957. 5.00. Oxford U. P.
Carter, Marion E. Role of the symbol in French Romantic poetry. 1946. 1.75. Catholic U. of Am. Pr.
Jones, Percy M. Background of modern French poetry. 1951. 4.50. Cambridge U. P.
Fowlie, Wallace. Mid-century French poets. 4.50. Twayne (R)
FRESH-WATER BIOLOGY (574.929)
Brown, E. S. Life in fresh water. 1955. 3.00. Oxford U. P.
Coker, Robert Ervin. Streams, lakes, ponds. 1954. 6.00. U. of N. C.
Edmondson, W. T., and others. Freshwater biology. il. 1959. 35.50. Wiley
Morgan, Ann. Field book of ponds and streams. il. 1930. 5.00. Putnam (R)
Reid, George K. Ecology of inland waters and estuaries. 1961. 7.50. Reinhold
Pennak, R. W. Fresh-water invertebrates of the United States. 1953. 15.00. Ronald (R)
Prescott, Gerald W. How to know the freshwater algae. by Harry E. Jacques. 1954. 2.75. Brown, W. C. (R)
FREUD, SIGMUND, 1856-1939 (926.1)
Brill, A. A. Freud's contribution to psychiatry. 1962. 1.45. Norton

Fine, Reuben. Freud: A critical re-evaluation. 1962. 6.95. McKay
Freud, Martin. Sigmund Freud: Man and father. il. 1958. 5.00. Vanguard
Freud and psychoanalysis. Jung, Carl G. by Herbert Read and others. 5.00.
   Pantheon
Fromm, Erich. Life without illusions. 1962. 3.95. S. and S.
Fromm, Erich. Sigmund Freud's mission. 1959. 3.00. Harper
H. D. Tribute to Freud. 1956. 2.50. Pantheon
Hall, Calvin S. Primer of Freudian psychology. 1954. 2.50. World Pub.
Hoffman, Frederick J. Freudianism and the literary mind. 1957. 5.00. La. State
   (R)
Hyman, Stanley E. Tangled bank: Darwin, Marx, Frazer and Freud as imaginative
   writers. 1962. 10.00. Atheneum
Jones, Ernest. Life and work of Sigmund Freud. abridged by Lionel Trilling and
   Steven Marcus. il. 1961. 7.50. Basic Books (R)
MacIntyre, Alasdair C. Unconscious. 2.50. Humanities
Marcuse, Herbert. Eros and civilization. 1956. 3.95. Beacon
Nelson, Benjamin. Freud and the 20th century. 1958. 3.50. Smith, Peter
Rieff, Philip. Freud: The mind of the moralist. 1959. 6.00. Viking
Wittels, Fritz. Freud and his time. 1931. 4.50. Liveright
Zilboorg, Gregory. Psychoanalysis and religion. by Margaret Stone Zilboorg. 1962.
   4.50. Farrar, Straus
FRIENDS, SOCIETY OF (289.6)
Spencer, Cornelia. American Quakers. 1960. 4.50. Pub. Affairs
Braithwaite, William C. Beginnings of Quakerism. 4.75. Cambridge U. P.
Braithwaite, William C. Second period of Quakerism. 1961. 5.50. Cambridge U. P.
Van Etten, Henry. George Fox and the Quakers. il. 1959. 1.35. Harper
FRONTIER AND PIONEER LIFE (973)
American Heritage. American Heritage book of the pioneer spirit. by the Editors
   of American Heritage. 1959. 12.95. S. and S.
Billington, Ray A. Westward Movement in the United States. (Anvil 37) 1959. pap.
   1.25. Van Nostrand
Clark, Thomas D. Frontier America: The story of the westward movement. il.
   1959. 10.00. Scribner
Curti, Merle E. Making of an American community. 1959. 8.50. Stanford
Hazard, Lucy L. Frontier in American literature. 5.00. Ungar
Tryon, Warren S. Mirror for Americans. 3 vols. 1952. 5.00 ea. U. of Chicago
Tunis, Edwin. Frontier living. il. 1961. 5.95. World Pub.
Turner, Frederick J. Significance of the frontier in American history. 2.95. Ungar
Wright, Louis B. Culture on the moving frontier. 1955. 3.50. Indiana
Wyman, Walker D., and Clifton B. Koreber. Frontier in perspective. 1957. 5.50.
   U. of Wis.
FRONTIER AND PIONEER LIFE--THE WEST (973)
Chapel, Charles E. Guns of the old West. il. 1961. 12.50. Coward
Dick, Everett. Sod house frontier, 1854-1890. 1954. 6.50. Johnsen
Grant, Clarence G. Vanishing wagon tracks. 1961. 2.50. Exposition
Muir, John. Story of my boyhood and youth. il. in prep. Houghton
Parkman, Francis. Oregon Trail. 1959. 2.95. Doubleday
Sandoz, Mari. Buffalo hunters. il. 1954. 4.95. Hastings
Sandoz, Mari. Cattlemen. 1958. 6.50. Hastings
Sandoz, Mari. Old Jules. 1955. 4.95. Hastings
Ward, Don, and J. C. Dykes. Cowboys and cattle country. il. 1961. 3.79. Harper
Wolle, Muriel S. Bonanza Trail: Ghost towns and mining camps of the West. il.
   1953. 10.00. Indiana
FROST, ROBERT, 1874- (811.52)
Cox, James M. Robert Frost: A collection of critical essays. 1962. 3.95. Prentice-
   Hall
Cox, Sidney. Swinger of birches: A portrait of Robert Frost. 1957. 3.75. N. Y. U.
Greenberg, Robert A., and James G. Hepburn. Robert Frost: An introduction.
   1961. 1.75. Holt, Rinehart & Winston

Isaacs, Elizabeth. Introduction to Robert Frost. 1962. 3.75. Swallow, A.
Lynen, John F. Pastoral art of Robert Frost. 1960. 5.00. Yale
Nitchie, George W. Human values in the poetry of Robert Frost. 1960. 5.00. Duke
Sergeant, Elizabeth S. Robert Frost: The trial by existence. il. 1960. 6.00. Holt,
  Rinehart & Winston
Thompson, Lawrance R. Fire and ice: The art and thought of Robert Frost. 1961.
  7.50. Russell
FRUSTRATION (157)
Toynbee, Philip, ed. Underdogs: Anguish and anxiety. 1962. 4.50. Horizon
Wilson, Pauline Park. College women who express futility: A study based on
  fifty selected life histories of women college graduates. 1950. 2.75. T. C.
Yates, A. Frustration and conflict. 5.00. Wiley
FUEL (662.6)
Brame, John S. S., and J. G. King. Fuel: Solid, liquid and gaseous. 1955.
  11.50. St. Martins
Popovich, Milosh, and C. Hering. Fuels and lubricants. il. 1959. 8.50. Wiley
Smith, M. L., and K. W. Stinson, Fuels and combustion. 1952. 8.50. McGraw
FUGUE (781.4)
Kitson, C. H. Studies in fugue. 1909. 3.00. Oxford U. P.
Oldroyd, George. Technique and spirit of fugue. 1948. 6.00. Oxford U. P.
FULBRIGHT, JAMES, 1905- (923.273)
Meyer, K. Fulbright of Arkansas: The public positions of a private thinker.
  1962. 5.50. McKay
FULL EMPLOYMENT POLICIES (331.11)
Bernstein, Peter. Price of prosperity. 4.50. Doubleday
Casselman, Paul H. Economics of employment and unemployment. 1955. 3.25.
  Pub. Affairs
Greenhut, Melvin L. Full employment, inflation, and common stock. 1961.
  3.25. Pub. Affairs
FUMIGATION (632.94)
Cotton, Richard T. Pests of stored grain and grain products. 1956. 4.00.
  Burgess
FUNCTIONAL ANALYSIS (517.5)
Ayre, Henry Glenn. Basic mathematical analysis. 1950. 6.75. McGraw
Taylor, Angus E. Introduction to functional analysis. 1958. 12.50. Wiley
FUNCTIONAL EQUATIONS (517)
Boole, George. Calculus of finite differences. 3.95. Chelsea
Boole, George. Treatise on the calculus of finite differences. 3.75. Smith,
  Peter
FUNCTIONS (517.3)
Bergman, Stefan, and M. Schiffer. Kernel functions and elliptic differential
  equations in mathematical physics. 1953. 8.00. Academic Press
Hall, Dick W., and L. Kattsoff. Unified algebra and trigonometry. 1962. 6.75.
  Wiley
Hillman, Abraham P., and G. L. Alexanderson. Functional trigonometry. il/
  1961. 7.95. Allyn & Bacon
Rainville, Earl D. Special functions. il. 1960. 11.75. Macmillan
Ritt, Joseph F. Theory of functions. 1947. bds. 5.00. Columbia
Rudin, W. Principles of mathematical analysis. 1953. 6.75. McGraw
Saks, Stanislaw. Theory of the integral. tr. by L. C. Young. 1937. 5.00. Hafner
FUND RAISING (361.73)
Fellows, Margaret M., and Stella A. Koenig. Tested methods of raising
  money: For churches, colleges, and health and welfare agencies. 1959.
  6.95. Harper
Pollard, John A. Fund-raising for higher education. 1958. 4.75. Harper
FUNERAL RITES AND CEREMONIES (393)
Habenstein, Robert W., and William M. Lamers. Funeral customs the world
  over. il. 1960. 12.00. Bulfin

FUNGI (589. 2)
Bessey, E. A. Morphology and taxonomy of fungi. 15. 00. Hafner (R)
Cochrane, Vincent W. Physiology of fungi. il. 1958. 10. 50. Wiley
Duddington, C. L. Microorganisms as allies. 1961. 5. 95. Macmillan
Gray, William D. Relation of fungi to human affairs. 1959. 8. 50. Holt, Rinehart
    & Winston
Ingold, Cecil T. Dispersal in fungi. il. 1953. 3. 40. Oxford U. P.
Kleijn, H. Mushrooms and other fungi. il. 10. 50. Doubleday
Lilly, Virgil G., and Horace L. Barnett. Physiology of the fungi. il. 1951.
    10. 50. McGraw
Pilat, Albert, and Otto Usak. Mushrooms and other fungi. 12. 95. Tudor
Boyce, John Shaw. Forest pathology. il. 1961. 12. 50. McGraw
Nickerson, W. J. Biology of pathogenic fungi. 1947. 5. 50. Ronald
FUNGICIDES (632. 952)
Horsfall, J. G. Principles of fungicidal action. 1956. 6. 50. Ronald
Martin, Hubert. Scientific principles of crop protection. 4th ed. 12. 50.
    St. Martins
Sharvelle, Eric G. Nature and uses of modern fungicides. 1961. 6. 00. Burgess
FUR (675. 3)
Ashbrook, Frank G. Furs, glamorous and practical. il. 1954. 2. 95. Van
    Nostrand
Russell, Carl P. Guns on the early frontier. 4. 50. Smith, Peter
FUR TRADE (970)
Cleland, Robert Glass. This reckless breed of men: The trappers and fur
    traders of the Southwest. il. 1950. 5. 75. Knopf
De Voto, Bernard. Across the wide Missouri. il. 1947. 10. 95. Houghton
Frost, Donald McK. Notes on General Ashley the Overland Trail and South
    Pass. 1960. 5. 00. Barre
Godsell, A. Arctic trader. 1946. 3. 75. St. Martins
Moloney, Francis X. Fur trade in New England, 1620-1676. 1931. 1. 25. Harvard
Nasatir, A. P. Before Lewis and Clark. 15. 00. Glenn
Ross, Alexander. Fur hunters of the far West. ed. by Kenneth A Spaulding. il.
    1956. 5. 00. U. of Okla.
FURNITURE (729. 9)
Aronson, Joseph. Book of furniture and decoration. rev. ed. 5. 00. Crown
Baker, Bill. Furniture you can build. il. 1955. 2. 50. Arco
Better Homes and Gardens. Decorating book. by the Editors of Better Homes
    and Gardens. 1956. 5. 95. Meredith
Bick, Alexander F. Contemporary furniture. 1954. 2. 75. Bruce
Boger, Louise A. Complete guide to furniture styles. il. 1958. 15. 00. Scribner
Dal Fabbro, M. Modern furniture. 1958. 6. 95. Reinhold
Davis, Frank. Picture history of furniture. il. 7. 00. Macmillan
Haines, Ray E. Circular saw. il. 1952. 3. 95. Van Nostrand
Hooper, Rodney. Modern furniture making and design. 5. 00. Bennett
Menke, H. A. Contemporary wood furniture. 3. 60. Taplinger
National Education Association, Home Economics Department. Furnishing
    homes for family living. 1962. 0. 50. N. E. A.
Weeks, Verne. Contemporary and traditional furniture. il. 1959. 3. 50.
    Bruce
FURNITURE--COLLECTORS AND COLLECTING (749)
Bird, Anthony. English furniture for the private collector. 6. 95. Hearthside
Hughes, Bernard and Therle. Small antique furniture. il. 1959. 6. 50. Macmillan
Ormsbee, Thomas. Field guide to early American furniture. il. 1951. 4. 95.
    Little
FURNITURE--DICTIONARIES (749)
Aronson, Joseph. Encyclopedia of furniture. il. 6. 95. Crown
FURNITURE--REPAIRING (684)
Hochman, Louis. How to refinish furniture. il. 1955. 2. 50. Arco

Karcher, Paul W., and George A. Soderberg. Restoring and maintaining
   finishes, spot finishing. il. 1958. 2.75. Bruce
FURNITURE--U.S. (749.211)
Comstock, Helen. American furniture: A complete guide to seventeenth,
   eighteenth and early nineteenth century styles. il. 1962. 17.50. Viking
Comstock, Helen. 100 most beautiful rooms in America. il. 1958. 12.50.
   Viking
Drepperd, Carl W. Primer of American antiques. il. 1944. 3.95. Doubleday
Nutting, Wallace. Furniture treasury. 3 vols. Macmillan
Ormsbee, Thomas. Field guide to early American furniture. il. 1951. 4.95.
   Little
FUSION (536.42)
McCrone, Walter C., Jr. Fusion methods in chemical microscopy. il. 1957.
   8.00. Wiley
FUTURE LIFE (237)
Budge, Wallis. Egyptian religion. il. 1959. 5.00. U. Books
Cumont, Franz. After-life in Roman paganism. 3.35. Smith, Peter
Harlow, S. Ralph. Life after death. 1961. 3.95. Doubleday
FUTURISM (ART) (759)
Taylor, Joshua C. Futurism. il. 1961. 6.50. Mus. of Mod. Art

                                      G

GABON (967.21)
Schweitzer, Albert. African notebook. il. 1958. 3.00. Indiana
GAGE, THOMAS, 1721-1787 (923.5)
Alden, John Richard. General Gage in America. 1948. 4.00. La. State
GAGES (621.9)
Donaldson, Cyril, and George H. LeCain. Tool design. il. 1957. 6.75. McGraw
GALAPAGOS ISLANDS (986.65)
Melville, Herman. Encantadas, or Enchanted Isle. il. 1940. 7.50. Wreden
GALATIA--POLITICS AND GOVERNMENT (939.32)
Sherk, Robert. Legates of Galatia from Augustus to Diocletian. 1951. 2.50.
   Johns Hopkins
GALE, ZONA, 1874-1938 (928)
Simonson, Harold P. Zona Gale. 1962. 3.50. Twayne
GALENUS (925)
Sarton, George A. Galen of Pergamon. 1954. 2.50. U. of Kans.
GALILIO (GALILEO GALILEI), 1564-1642. (925.2)
Brophy, James, and Henry Paolucci, eds. Achievement of Galileo. 1962. 5.00.
   Twayne
Cooper, Lane. Aristotle, Galileo, and the tower of Pisa. 1.50. Cornell
GALLATIN, ALBERT, 1761-1849 (923.2)
Adams, Henry. Life of Albert Gallatin. 7.50. Smith, Peter
GALOIS THEORY (512.21)
Dehn, Edgar. Algebraic equations. pap. 1.45. Dover
Mathews, George B. Algebraic equations. by W. E. H. Berwick, 1930. 3.00. Hafner
GAMBLING (795)
Cardano, Girolamo. Book on games of chance. tr. by Sydney H. Gould. 1961.
   1.50. Holt, Rinehart & Winston
Scarne, John. Scarne's complete guide to gambling. 1961. 10.00. S. and S.
GAME AND GAME-BIRDS (799.2)
Kesting, Ted, ed. Lowland game birds. 1962. 4.95. Nelson
Kesting, Ted, ed. Upland game birds. 1962. 4.95. Nelson
Ovington, Ray. Young sportsman's guide to game animals. 1962. 2.50. Nelson
Scott, Peter. Colored key to the wildfowl of the world. il. 1961. 3.50. Scribner
GAME AND GAME-BIRDS--NORTH AMERICA (799)
Edminster, Frank C. American game birds of field and forest. il. 1954. 12.50.
   Scribner

Leopold, Aldo S., and Frank F. Darling. Wildlife in Alaska. 1953. 3.00. Ronald

O'Connor, Jack, and George Goodwin. Big game animals of North America. il. 1961. 10.00. Dutton

Seton, Ernest Thompson. Lives of game animals. 8 vols. set, 60.00. Branford

GAMES (790)

American Association for Health, Physical Education, and Recreation. How we do it game book. rev. ed. 1959. 3.00. Am. Assn. for Health, Phys. Ed. & Rec.

Bancroft, Jessie H. Games. rev. ed. il. 8.85; Macmillan

Borst, E., and E. D. Mitchell. Social games for recreation. 1959. 5.50. Ronald

Brobeck, Florence R. Family book of home entertaining. il. 1960. 4.95. Doubleday

Depew, Arthur M. Cokesbury game book. 2.95. Abingdon

Depew, Arthur M. Cokesbury party book. rev. ed. 1959. 2.95. Abingdon

Eisenberg, Helen, and Larry. Omnibus of fun. 1956. 7.95. Assn. Pr.

Frankel, Lillian. 101 best games for teen-agers. il. 1951. 2.50. Sterling

Frankel, Lillian. 101 best party games for adults. il. 1953. 2.50. Sterling

Harbin, E. O. Fun encyclopedia. il. 4.95. Abingdon

Harbin, E. O. Games of many nations. 1954. 1.95. Abingdon

Hindman, Darwin A. Complete book of games and stunts. il. 1956. 5.95. Prentice-Hall

Kauffman, Carolyn, and Patricia Farrell. If you live with little children. il. 1957. 3.50. Putnam

Kohl, Marguerite, and Frederica Young. Games for grownups. 1951. 3.00. Hill & Wang

McDonald, John. Strategy in poker, business and war. il. 1950. 3.50. Norton

Macfarlan, Allan and Paulette. Fun with brand-new games. 1961. 3.50. Assn. Pr.

Mulac, Margaret E. Fun and games. il. 1956. 4.50. Harper

National Education Association, American Association for Health, Physical Education and Recreation. Group games for girls and women. 1957. 0.50. N.E.A.

Stevens, Kate. Games for parties. 1.25. Warne

Tunis, J. R. Sport for the fun of it. 1958. 4.00. Ronald

Young, William P., and Horace J. Gardner. Games and stunts for all occasions. rev. ed. by Lee Wyndham. il. 1957. 2.50. Lippincott

GAMES OF STRATEGY (MATHEMATICS) (793.74)

Dresher, Melvin. Games of strategy: Theory and applications. 1961. 9.00; Prentice-Hall

McKinsey, John C. C. Introduction to the theory of games. 1952. 12.00. McGraw

Rapoport, Anatol. Fights, games, and debates. il. 1960. 6.95. U. of Mich.

GAMMA RAYS (539.752)

Davidson, Harold O. Biological effects of whole-body gamma radiation on human beings. 1957. 4.50. Johns Hopkins

Goldstein, Herbert. Fundamental aspects of reactor shielding. 1958. 9.75. Addison-Wesley

GANDHI, MOHANDAS KARAMCHAND, 1869-1948 (923.254)

Andrews, C. F. Mahatma Gandhi's ideas, including selections from his writings. 3.50. Macmillan

Bondurant, J. V. Conquesto of violence: The Ghandian philosophy of conflict. 1958. 5.00. Princeton

Fishcer, Louis. Life of Mahatma Gandhi. il. 1950. 6.50. Harper

Gandhi, Mohandas K. Gandhi's autobiography. 1948. 5.00. Pub. Affairs

Muzumdar, Haridas. Ghandi versus the empire. 3.95. Wehman

Nanda, B. R. Mahatma Gandhi. 1958. 6.50. Beacon

Power, Paul F. Gandhi on world affairs. 1960. 3.25. Pub. Affairs'

Sheean, Vincent. Mahatma Gandhi. 1955. 3.00, Knopf
GARCIA LORCA, FEDERICO, 1899-1936 (928(
Campbell, Roy. Lorca: An appreciation of his poetry. 1959. 0.95. Yale
GARDEN CITIES (711)
Stein, C. S. Toward new towns for America. 1957. 6.95. Reinhold
GARDEN ORNAMENTS AND FURNITURE (717)
Aul, Henry B. How to build garden structures: Plans, drawings, il. 1950.
5.00. Sheridan
Hawkins, R. R., and C. H. Abbe. Garden pools, fountains, swimming pools,
sprinkling systems, recreation areas. 3.25. Van Nostrand
Walkden, G. B. Garden carpentry. il. 1961. 3.75. Transatlantic
GARDEN PESTS (632)
Everett, T. H., ed. Illustrated book of garden pests and diseases. il. 1962.
5.00. Hawthorn
Hough, Walter S., and A. Freeman Mason. Spraying, dusting and fumigating of
plants. rev. ed. il. 1951. 7.95. Macmillan
Lawfield, W. N., and J. Van Lonynenburg. Encyclopaedia of garden pests and
diseases. 1959. 10.50. Transatlantic
Westcott, Cynthia. Garden enemies. il. 1953. 3.75. Van Nostrand
GARDENING (635)
Better Homes and Gardens. New garden book. 1962. 4.95. Meredith
Bush-Brown, James, and Louise. America's garden book. il. 1958. 8.95.
Scribner
Gardner, Victor R. Basic horticulture. il. 1951. 7.75. Macmillan
Gunnison, Olive Mason. Practical gardening. 1955. 4.50. Doubleday
Hellyer, Arthur G. L. Practical gardening for amateurs. il. 5.00. Transatlantic
Hills, A. Gardens and grounds that take care of themselves. 1958. 3.95.
Prentice-Hall
Laurie, Alex, and Victor H. Ries. Floriculture. il. 1950. 9.50. McGraw
Morse, Harriet K. Gardening in the shade. rev. ed. il. 1962. 5.95. Scribner
Taylor, Norman. Permanent garden, Color in the garden, Herbs in the
garden, Fragrance in the garden, and Everblooming garden. 5.vols. 2.50 ea;
set, 9.95. Van Nostrand
GARDENING--DICTIONARIES (635.03)
Bailey, Liberty H., and Ethel Z. Bailey. Hortus second. 13.50. Macmillan (R)
Bailey, Liberty H. Standard cyclopedia of horticulture. 3 vols. il. set. 52.00.
Macmillan (R)
Hellyer, Arthur G. L. Popular encyclopedia of flowering plants. 4.00. Trans-
atlantic (R)
Taylor, Norman, ed. Encyclopedia of gardening. il. 1961. 15.00. Houghton (R)
GARDENS, MINIATURE (635.967)
Ashberry, Anne. Miniature gardens. 1953. 4.95. Van Nostrand
McDonald, Elvin. Miniature plants for home and greenhouse. il. 1962. 5.95.
Van Nostrand
GARIBALDI, GIUSEPPE, 1807-1882 (923.2)
DePolnay, Peter. Garibaldi. 1961. 4.00. Nelson
Parris, John. Lion of Caprera: Life of Garibaldi. 1961. 5.95. McKay
GARLAND, HAMLIN, 1860-1940 (928)
Holloway, Jean. Hamlin Garland. il.1959. 6.00. U. of Tex.
GARRICK, DAVID, 1717-1779 (927)
Burnim, Kalman A. David Garrick, director. 1961. 5.00. U. of Pittsburgh
England, Martha W. Garrick and Stratford. 1962. 2.50. N.Y.P.L.
Norman, Charles. Pundit and the player: Dr. Johnson and Mr. Garrick. il.
1951. 3.00. McKay
GARRISON, WILLIAM LLOYD, 1805-1879 (923.273)
Korngold, Ralph. Two friends of man. 5.00. Brown Book
Nye, Russel B. William Lloyd Garrison and the humanitarian reformers. 1955.
3.75. Little

GAS AND OIL ENGINES (621. 4)
Audels gas engine manual. 1960. 4.00. Audel
Crouse, William H. Automotive fuel, lubricating and cooling systems. 1959. 8.00. McGraw
Diesel, Eugen, and others. From engines to autos. tr. by Peter White. il. 1960. 6.00. Regnery
Gill, Paul W., and others. Internal combustion engines. 4th ed. il. 1959. 5.00. U. S. Naval Inst.
Lichty, Lester. Internal combustion engines. 1951. 8.96. McGraw
Purvis, Jud. All about small gas engines. il. 1960. 4.50. Goodheart
Rogowski, A. R. Elements of internal combustion engines. il. 1953. 6.95. McGraw

GAS FLOW (533)
Emmons, Howard W., ed. Fundamentals of gas dynamics. 1958. 20.00. Princeton
Patterson, G. N. Molecular flow of gases. 1956. 7.75. Wiley

GAS-TURBINES (621.433)
Jennings, B. H., and Willard L. Rodgers. Gas turbines: Analysis and practice. il. 1953. 9.75. McGraw
Shepherd, D. G. Introduction to the gas turbine. il. 1960. 7.75. van Nostrand
Vincent, Edward T. Theory and design of gas turbines and jet engines. 1950. 10.75. McGraw

GASES (533)
Bird, R. B., and others. Fundamental physics of gases. 1961. pap. 1.95. Princeton
Cowling, T. G. Molecules in motion. 1950. 2.50. Hillary
Planck, Max. Theory of heat radiation. 1960. 1.50. Dover
Rossini, F. D., ed. Thermodynamics and physics of matter. 1955. 20.00. Princeton (R)
Townes, Charles H., and A. L. Schawlow. Microwave spectroscopy. 13.50. McGraw

GASES, KINETIC THEORY OF (530.13)
Guggenheim, E. A. Elements of the kinetic theory of gases. 3.00. Pergamon
Jeans, James. Dynamical theory of gases. 4th ed. 1954. pap. 2.45. Dover
Jeans, James H. Introduction to the kinetic theory of gases. 1940. 5.50; 1959. Cambridge U. P.
Loeb, L. B. Kinetic theory of gases. 3rd ed. 5.00. Smith, Peter

GASES, RARE (546.75)
Cook, Gerhard A., ed. Argon, helium, and the rare gases. 2 pts. il. 1961. 17.50. ea. Wiley (R)

GASKELL, ELIZABETH CLEGHORN (STEVENSON) 1810-1865 (928)
Sanders, Gerald DeWitt. Elizabeth Gaskell. 1929. 3.50. Cornell

GASTRONOMY (641.9)
Allen, Ida Bailey. Gastronomique: A cookbook for gourmets. il. 1962. 5.95. Doubleday
Brillat-Savarin, Jean A. Physiology of taste. il. 3.50. Smith, Peter
Gourmet cookbook. 2 vols. il. 12.50 ea. Gourmet (R)
Simon, Andre. Guide to good food and wines. 6.00. Collins

GAUDI Y CORNET, ANTONIO. 1852-1926. (921)
Collins, George R. Antonio Gaudi. il. 1960. 4.95. Braziller
Hitchcock, Henry-Russell. Gaudi. il. 1958. pap. 1.95. Doubleday

GAUGUIN, PAUL, 1848-1903 (927)
Estienne, Charles. Gauguin. il. 1953. 5.75. (also available at same price with French or German text) World Pub.
Gauguin, Paul. Gauguin. il. collectors ed. 3.95. Abrams
Gauguin, Paul. Gauguin. ed. by Robert Goldwater. il. 1957. 15.00. Abrams
Gauguin, Paul. Gauguin drawings. ed. by John Rewald. 1957. 7.50. Yoseloff
Huyghe, Rene. Gauguin. il. 1959. 3.50. Crown

GAUL (944)

Chadwick, Norah K. Poetry and letters in early Christian Gaul. 8.50. Hillary

GAUL--HISTORY (944.01)

Brady, Sidney G. Caesar's Gallic campaigns. il. 1960. 3.25. Stackpole
Caesar. Gallic War. 2.00. McKay
Caesar. Gallic War. bks. 1, 2 and 3. il. 1.25. St. Martins
Caesar, Julius. War commentaries. 1.85. Dutton

GAULLE, CHARLES DE, 1890- (923.244)

Ashcroft, Edward. De Gaulle, biography. il. 6.25. Transatlantic
Clark, Stanley F. Man who is France. 1960. 3.50. Dodd
Funk, Arthur L. Charles de Gaulle: The crucial years. 1943-1944. il. 1960.
     5.00. U. of Okla.
Furniss, Edgar S., Jr. France, troubled ally. 1960. 5.75. Harper
Grunnell-Milne, Duncan W. Triumph of integrity. il. 1962. 5.00. Macmillan
Hatch, Alden. De Gaulle nobody knows. il. 1960. 5.00. Hawthorn

GAUSS, KARL FRIEDRICH, 1777-1855 (925)

Dunnington, G. Waldo. Carl Friedrich Gauss: Titan of science. il. 1955. 5.00.
     Hafner

GAY, JOHN, 1685-1732 (928)

Armens, S. M. John Gay: Social critic. 1954. 4.00. Columbia
Irving, William. John Gay, favorite of the wits. 1962. 7.50. Russell

GEARING (621.83)

Dudley, Darle W. Practical gear design. 1954. 9.50. McGraw
Jones, Franklin D. Gear design simplified. 3rd ed. 1961. 6.00. Industrial Pr.

GEDDES, NORMAN BEL, 1893-1958. (928)

Geddes, Norman Bel. Miracle in the evening. ed. by William Kelley.
     1960. half cl. 4.95. Doubleday

GEISHAS (790)

Scott, Adolphe C. Flower and willow world. il. 1960. 5.00. Orion Press

GELATIN (668.32)

Stainsby, G., ed. Recent advances in gelatin and glue research. 12.00.
     Pergamon

GEMS (736.2)

Baxter, William T. Jewelry, gem cutting and metalcraft. 3rd ed. 1950. 7.50.
     McGraw
Liddecoat, Richard T., Jr. Handbook of gemstone indentification. 7.50.
     Gemological Inst.
Sinkankas, John. Gemstones and minerals. il. 1961. 8.95. Van Nostrand
Whitlock, Herbert P. Story of the gems. il. 5.95. Emerson

GENEALOGY (929.1)

Conrad, R. L. Your family tree. 7.50. Humphries
Doane, Gilbert H. Searching for your ancestors. il. 1960. 3.95. U. of Minn.
Pine, Leslie G. American origins. 1960. 7.50. Doubleday
Sweet, James S. Geneaolgy and local history: An archival and bibliographical
     guide. 1959. 5.00. Genealogical
Williams, Ethel W. Know your ancestory: A guide to genealogical research.
     4.50. Tuttle

GENERAL SEMANTICS (422)

Black, Max. Language and philosophy: Studies in method. il. 1949. 3.50.
     Cornell
Hayakawa, S. I. Language, meaning and maturiety, selections from Etc. a
     review of general semantics. 1954. 5.00. Harper
Hayakawa, Samuel I., ed. Our language and our world; selections from Etc. a
     review of general semantics. 1953-1958. il. 1959. 5.00. Harper
Johnson, Wendell. Your most enchanted listener. 1956. 4.50. Harper
Korzybski, Alfred. Science and sanity. 4th ed. 1958. 11.00. Inst. of Gen.
     Semantics
Lee, Irving. J. Customs and crises in communication. 1954. 4.00. Harper

Lee, Irving J. Language habits in human affairs: An introduction to general semantics. 1941. 2.75. Harper

Walpole, Hugh R. Semantics. 1941. 4.00. Norton

GENETIC PSYCHOLOGY (136)

Berg, Jan Hendrick ven den. Changing nature of man. tr. by H. F. Croes. 1961. 4.50. Norton

Carmichael, Leonard. Making of modern mind. 1956. 2.75. Van Nostrand

Fuller, John L., and W. Robert Thompson. Behavior genetics. 1960. 8.95. Wiley

Lane, Howard, and Mary Beauchamp. Understanding human development. 1959. 9.00. Prentice-Hall

Murphy, Gardner. Human potentialities. 1958. 6.50. Basic Books

Pikunas, J., and E. J. Albrecht. Psychology of human development. 1961. 6.95. McGraw

Thorpe, L. P., and W. W. Cruze. Developmental psychology. 1956. 7.00. Ronald

Wolff, Peter H. Developmental psychologies of Jean Piaget and psychoanalysis 1960. 3.00. Int. Univs.

GENETICS (575.1)

Auerbach, Charlotte. Genetics in the atomic age. 1956. 1.40. Oxford U. P.

Auerbach, Charlotte. Science of genetics. il. 1961. 5.95. Harper

Braun, Werner. Bacterial genetics. il. 1953. 6.50. Saunders

Castle, William Ernest. Mammalian genetics. il. 1940. 3.00. Harvard

Dobzhansky, T. Evolution, genetics and man. 1955. 5.75. Wiley

Dobzhansky, Theodosius. Mankind evolving. il. 1962. 7.50. Yale

Dodson, Edward O. Genetics. il. 1956. 6.50. Saunders

Haldane, J. B. S. Biochemistry of genetics. 1954. 3.00. Macmillan

Hogben, Lancelot. Introduction to mathematical genetics. 1946. 9.50. Norton

Huxley, Julian. Heredity east and west. 1949. 3.00. Abelard

Huxley, Julian, ed. New systematics. il. 1940. 4.50. Oxford U. P.

Lasker, Gabriel W. Evolution of man. il. 1961. 3.50. Holt, Rinehart & Winston

Medawar, Peter B. Future of man. 1960. 3.50. Basic Books

Newman, Horatio H. Evolution, genetics, and eugenics. il. 1932. 10.00. U. of Chicago

Rife, David C. Heredity and human nature. 4.50. Vantage

Stern, Curt. Principles of human genetics. 1960. 9.50. Freeman

Wallace, Bruce, and T. Dobzhansky. Radiation, genes, and man. 1959. 5.80; Holt, Rinehart & Winston

GENETICS--DICTIONARIES (575.03)

Clapper, Russell B. Glossary of genetics and other biological terms. 1960. 3.95. Vantage (R)

Knight, R. L. Dictionary of genetics. 1948. 5.00. Ronald (R)

GENIUS (136.7)

Galton, Francis. Hereditary genius: An inquiry into its laws and consequences. 1.45. Meridian

Kenmare, Dallas. Nature of genius. il. 1960. 5.25. Transatlantic

Terman, Lewis M., and Melita H. Oden. Gifted child grows up. 7.50. Stanford

Terman, Lewis M., and others. Mental and physical traits of a thousand gifted children. 7.50. Stanford

Wolfe, Don M. Image of man in America. 1957. 5.00. S. M. U.

GENOCIDE (341.4)

Hilberg, Raul. Destruction of the European Jews. il. 1961. 9.95. Quadrangle

GEOCHEMISTRY (551.9)

Goldschmidt, Victor M. Geochemistry, ed. by Alex Muir. 1954. 12.00. Oxford U. P.

Keller, Walter D. Chemistry in introductory geology. 1.35. Lucas Bros.

GEODESY (526.1)

Bomford, Guy. Geodesy. 1952. 9.60. Oxford U. P.

GEODYNAMICS (551)

Shimer, John A. This sculptured earth: The landscape of America. il. 1959. bds. 7.50. Columbia

GEOGRAPHICAL DISTRIBUTION OF ANIMALS AND PLANTS (591.9)

Dansereau, P. Biogeography. 1957. 8.50. Ronald

Elton, Charles S. Ecology of invasions by animals and plants. 1958. 5.25. Wiley

GEOGRAPHY (910)

Botts, Adelbert K., and Berenice M. Casper. Physical environment and man. 1961. pap. 2.40. Edwards

Davis, William M. Geographical essays. ed. by D. W. Johnson. 1909. pap. 2.95. Dover

Jeffries, William W., ed. Geography and national power. 2.50. U. S. Naval Inst.

Larousse, Larousse encyclopedia of world geography: Europe. il. 1961. 17.50. Putnam (R)

Miller, E. Willard, and others. Global geography. 2nd ed. il. 1957. 6.50. Crowell

Stamp, Dudley. Applied geography. 0.95. Penguin

Wooldridge, S. W. Geographer as scientist. 8.75. Nelson

GEOGRAPHY--DICTIONARIES (910.3)

Cohen, Benjamin A., ed. Worldmark encyclopedia of the nations. 1960. 30.00. Harper (R)

Collocott, T. C., and J. O. Thorne, eds. Macmillan world gazetteer and geographical dictionary. rev. ed. 6.95. Macmillan

Merriam Co., G. and C. Webster's geographical dictionary. rev. ed. il. 1960. 8.50. Merriam (R)

Seltzer, L. E., ed. Columbia Lippincott gazeteer of the world. 1962. 65.00. Columbia (R)

Stamp, L. Dudley, Glossary of geographical terms. 1961. 10.00. Wiley (R)

Freeman, T. W. Hundred years of geography. 6.95. Aldine

GEOGRAPHY--PICTORIAL WORKS (912)

Debenham, Frank. Global atlas: A new view of the world from space. il. 1958. 5.95. Golden Press

Life, and Rand McNally. Life pictorial atlas of world. by the Editors of Life and Rand McNally. il. 1961. 30.00. Rand McNally (R)

Rotkin, Charles E. Europe: An aerial close-up. 1962. 17.50. Lippincott

GEOGRAPHY--STUDY AND TEACHING (910.07)

Kohn, Clyde F. United States and the world today. il. 1957. 3.50. Rand McNally

National Education Association, National Council for the Social Studies. New viewpoints in geography, yearbook. 1959. 5.00. N. E. A.

National Education Association, World Confederation of Organizations of the Teaching Profession. Audio-visual aids for international understanding. 1961. 2.50. N. E. A.

Thralls, Zoe A. Teaching of geography. il. 1958. 3.75. Appleton

GEOGRAPHY, ANCIENT (911.3)

Hobley, L. F. Early explorers. 2.50. Roy Pub.

Sambursky, S. Physical world of late antiquity. 1962. 5.75. Basic Books

Thomson, J. O. Everyman's classical atlas. 1961. 5.00. Dutton (R)

GEOGRAPHY, ECONOMIC (330.9)

Brunhes, Jean. Human geography. 5.75. Rand McNally

Dicken, Samuel N. Economic geography. 1955. il. 8.50. Heath

Highsmith, Richard M., and others. Case studies in world geography. 1961. pap. 3.95. Prentice-Hall

Pounds, Norman J. G., and Edward L. Cooper. World geography. 1961. 4.80. South-Western Pub.

Renner, George T., and others. World economic geography. il. 1951. 8.25. Crowell

Zimmermann, Erich W. World resources and industries. 1951. 9.50. Harper
East, Gordon. Historical geography of Europe. il. 1950. 6.50. Dutton
East, William Gordon, and O. H. K. Spate. Changing map of Asia. 1959.
    6.95. Dutton
Penrose, Boies. Travel and discovery in the Renaissance, 1420-1620. il. 1952.
    6.00. Harvard
Rand McNally book of nations. 4.95. Rand McNally
Trent, Christopher. Changing face of England. il. 1960. 4.95. Norton
GEOGRAPHY, HISTORICAL--MAPS (912)
Muir, Ramsey, Muir's historical atlas: Ancient medieval and modern by George
    Goodall, and R. F. Treharne. 1956. 8.50. Barnes & Noble (R)
Muir, Ramsay. New school atlas of universal history. by R. F. Treharne, and
    Harold Fullard. 1961. bds. 3.00. Barnes & Noble
Shepherd, William R. Historical atlas. 1956. 15.00. Barnes & Noble (R)
GEOLOGICAL RESEARCH (550)
Bascom, Willard. Hole in the bottom of the sea. il. 4.95. Doubleday
GEOLOGY (550)
Cloos, Hans. Conversation with the earth. il. 1953. 5.75. Knopf
Croneis, Carey, and William C. Krumbein. Down to earth: An introduction to
    geology. il. 1936. 7.50. U. of Chicago
Darwin, Charles Robert. Voyage of the Beagle. 1.95; 1961. Dutton
Emmons, William H., and others. Geology. 8.50. McGraw
Gillispie, Charles Coulston. Genesis and geology: A study in the relations of
    scientific thought, natural theology, and social opinion in Great Britain,
    1790-1850. 1951. 4.50. Harvard
Gilluly, James and others. Principles of geology. 1959. 7.50. Freeman
Hood, Peter. How the earth is made. 1954. 3.00. Oxford U. P.
Longwell, Chester R., and R. F. Flint. Introduction to physical geology. 1962.
    7.95. Wiley
Reinfeld, Fred. Treasures of the earth. il. 1954. 3.95. Sterling
Richards, H. G. Record of the rocks. 1953. 6.50. Ronald
Seward, Albert Charles. Plant life through the ages. 1959. 12.50. Hafner
Velikovsky, Immanuel. Earth in upheaval. 1955. 3.95. Doubleday
Challinor, John. Dictionary of geology. 1962. 5.00. Oxford U. P.
Fenton, Carroll Lane, and Mildred A. Giants of geology. il. 1952. 4.50;
    Doubleday
Moore, Ruth. Earth we live on. 1956. 6.00. Knopf
GEOLOGY--ANTARCTIC REGIONS (550)
Scott, Robert F. Voyage of the Discovery. il. 1951. 4.25. Transatlantic
GEOLOGY--NORTH AMERICA (550)
Clark, Thomas H., and Colin W. Stearn. Geological evolution of North America.
    il. 1960. 7.50. Ronald
Hough, Jack L. Geology of the Great Lakes. il. 1958. 8.50. U. of Ill.
Hussey, R. C. Historical geology. 1947. 6.75. McGraw
King, P. B. Tectonics of Middle North America. 1951. 3.75. Princeton
Muir, John. Studies in the Sierra. il. 3.75. Sierra
Shimer, John A. This sculptured earth: The landscape of America. il. 1959.
    bds. 7.50. Columbia
Shuler, E. W. Rocks and rivers of America. 1945. 5.00. Ronald
GEOLOGY, STRATIGRAPHIC (551.7)
Brinkmann, Roland. Geologic evolution of Europe. tr. by John E. Sanders. il.
    1960. 8.50. Hafner
Coleman, A. P. Last million years. 1941. 3.75. U. of Toronto
Kummel, Bernhard. History of the earth: An introduction to historical geology.
    il. 1961. 8.75. Freeman
Stokes, William L. Essentials of earth history. 1960. 8.95. Prentice-Hall
GEOLOGY, STRUCTURAL (550)
Lobeck, A. K. Geomorphology. il. 1939. 11.50. McGraw

Longwell, C. R., and others. Physical geology. 1948. 6.95. Wiley

Shrock, Robert R. Sequence in layered rocks. il. 1948. 11.00. McGraw

GEOMETRICAL DRAWING (744)

Pearson, G. Geometrical drawing. 1957. 2.20. Oxford U. P.

Wolchonok, Louis. Art of three dimensional design. il. 1959. 8.50. Harper

GEOMETRY (513)

Abbott, P. Teach yourself geometry. 2.00. Dover

Brumfiel, Charles F., and others. Geometry. il. 1960. 5.08. Addison-Wesley

Coxeter, Harold S. M. Introduction to geometry. 1961. 8.75. Wiley

Harrison, J., and G. A. Baxandall. Practical geometry and graphics for advanced students. 1949. 3.00. St. Martins

Henderson, Kenneth B., and others. Modern geometry: Its structure and function. 1962. 5.36. McGraw

Meserve, B. E. Fundamental concepts of geometry. 1955. 7.75. Addison-Wesley

Euclid. Elements of Euclid. 1.95. Dutton

GEOMETRY--PROBLEMS, FAMOUS (513.9)

Ball, W. W. Rouse. Mathematical recreations and essays. il. 1960. 3.95; Macmillan

GEOMETRY, ANALYTIC (516)

Adams, Lovincy J., and Paul A. White. Analytic geometry and calculus. 1961. 9.75. Oxford U. P.

Boyer, Carl B. History of analytic geometry. il. 1956. 6.00. Scripta Mathematica

Brady, Wray G., and Maynard J. Mansfield. Analytic geometry. il. 1962. 5.00. Little

Eisenhart, Luther P. Coordinate geometry. 1960. pap. 1.65. Dover

Juszli, Frank L. Analytic geometry and calculus. il. 1960. 6.95. Prentice-Hall

Love, Clyde E., and Earl D. Rainville. Analytic geometry. 1955. 4.75. Macmillan

GEOMETRY, DESCRIPTIVE (515)

Bennett, Joseph A. Descriptive geometry. 1961. 4.25. Colonial Press

French, T. E., and C. J. Vierck, Graphic science: Engineering drawing descriptive geometry, graphical solutions. 1958. 8.95. McGraw

Grant, H. E. Practical descriptive geometry. 1952. 5.50. McGraw

Hood, George J., and Albert S. Palmerlee. Geometry of engineering drawing. 1958. 5.95; McGraw

Miller, Henry W. Descriptive geometry. 1941. 4.00. Wiley

Turner, W. W., and others. Basic engineering drawing. 1950. 6.00. Ronald

Vierck, Charles J., and R. I. Hang. Graphic science problems. 1958. 5.75. McGraw

Watts, Earle F., and John T. Rule. Descriptive geometry. 1946. 9.00. 5.25. Prentice-Hall

Whitehead, Alfred N. Axioms of descriptive geometry. 1907. 3.00. Hafner

GEOMETRY, DIFFERENTIAL (516.7)

Eisenhart, L. P. Introduction to differential geometry. 1947. 6.00. Princeton

Hilbert, David, and Stephen Cohn-Vossen. Geometry and the imagination. 1952. 6.00. Chelsea

Struik, Dirk J. Differential geometry. il. 1961. 9.75. Addison-Wesley

Willmore, T. J. Introduction to differential geometry. il. 1959. 7.75. Oxford U. P.

GEOMETRY, NON-EUCLIDEAN (513.8)

Artin, Emil. Geometric algebra. il. 1957. 7.50. Wiley

Bolyai. Science of absolute space. tr. by G. B. Halsted. bd. with Bonola, Robert. Non-Euclidean geometry: and Lobachevski, Nicholaus. Theory of parallels. 1954. pap. 1.95. Dover

Wolfe, Harold E. Introduction to non-Euclidean geometry. 1945. 5.50. Holt, Rinehart & Winston

GEOMETRY, PLANE (513)

Adams, Lovincy J. Plane geometry for colleges. 1958. 3.75. Holt

Hemmerling, Edwin M. College plane geometry. il. 1957. 4.95. Wiley

Leary, Arthur F., and Carl N. Shuster. Plane geometry. 1955. 4.20. Scribner

Schnell, Leroy H., and Mildred Crawford. Plane geometry. 1953. 4.40. McGraw

Seymour F. Eugene, and Paul J. Smith. Plane geometry. 1948. 3.80. Macmillan

Stone, William C. Plane geometry for college students. 1958. 6.60. Allyn & Bacon

GEOMETRY, PROJECTIVE (513.3)

Busemann, Herbert, and P. J. Kelly. Projective geometry and projective metrics. 1953. 8.00. Academic Press

Hopkins, E. J., and J. S. Hails. Introduction to plane projective geometry. 1953. 4.80. Oxford U. P.

Maxwell, Edwin A. Methods of plane geometry. 1946. 3.75. Cambridge U. P.

O'Hara, C. W., and D. R. Ward. Introduction to projective geometry. 1937. 4.00. Oxford U. P.

Seidenberg, Abraham. Lectures in projective geometry. il. 1962. 6.50. Van Nostrand

Struik, Dirk J. Analytic and projective geometry. il. 1953. 9.75. Addison-Wesley

Whitehead, A. N. Axioms of projective geometry. 1906. 3.00. Hafner

GEOMETRY, SOLID (513.3)

Hails, J. S., and E. J. Hopkins. Solid Geometry. 1957. 2.20. Oxford U. P.

Leighton, Henry L. C. Solid geometry. il. 1944. 3.40. Van Nostrand

National Education Association, National Council of Teachers of Mathematics. Vectors in three dimensional geometry. 1961. 1.20. N. E. A.

Simpson, James L. Solid geometry. 1960. 2.75. Harper

GEOPHYSICS (551)

Bates, D. R., Earth and its atomosphere. il. 1957. 6.75. Basic Books

Eve, A. S., and D. A. Keys. Applied geophysics. 1954. 9.50. Cambridge U. P.

Fraser, Ronald. Once round the sun. il. 1958. 3.95. Macmillan

Gutenberg, Beno. Physics of the earth's interior. 1959. 8.50. Academic Press

Howell, Benjamin Franklin. Introduction to geophysics. 1959. 9.95. McGraw

Lobeck, Armin K. Things maps don't tell us: Adventure into map interpretation. il. 1956. 5.95. Macmillan

Lyttleton, Raymond A. Modern universe. il. 1957. 3.50. Harper

Scientific American. Planet earth. by the Editors of Scientific American. 1957. 1.45. S. and S.

Shuler, E. W. Rocks and rivers of America. 1945. 5.00. Ronald

Spilhaus, Athelstan. Satellite of the sun. il. 1958. 3.50. Viking

GEOPOLITICS (321.04)

Carlson, Fred A. Geography and world politics. 1958. 11.95. Prentice-Hall

McGovern, William M. Strategic intelligence and the shape of tomorrow. 1961. 4.00. Regnery

Mattern, J. Geopolitik: National self-sufficiency and empire. 1942. 2.25. Johns Hopkins

Pearcy, G. Etzel, and others. World political geography. 1957. 7.50. Crowell

GEORGE, SAINT d. 303 (922.22)

Barclay, Alexander. Life of St. George. by William Nelson. 1955. 4.50. Oxford U. P.

GEORGE III, KING OF GREAT BRITAIN, 1737-1820 (923.142)

Long, J. C. George III: The story of a complex man. il. 1961. 6.00. Little

Pares, Richard. King George III and the politicians. 1953. 4.00. Oxford U. P.

GEORGE IV, KING OF GREAT BRITAIN, 1762-1830 (923.142)

Aspinall, A. George IV, King of England. Letters, 1812-1830. 3 vols. 1938. 22.50. Cambridge U. P.

GEORGE V, KING OF GREAT BRITAIN, 1865-1936 (923.142)

Fulford, Roger. Hanover to Windsor. il. 1960. 5.00. Macmillan

GEORGE VI, KING OF GREAT BRITAIN, 1895-1952 (923.142)

Wheeler-Bennett, John. King George VI, his life and reign. 1958. 10.00. St. Martins

GEORGE, HENRY, 1839-1897 (923.3)
Barker, Charles A. Henry George. 1955. 10.00. Oxford U. P.
Geiger, George R. Philosophy of Henry George. 1933. 3.00. Schalkenbach
GEORGE, STEFAN ANTON, 1868-1933 (831)
Viereck, Peter. Dream and responsibility: Tension between poetry and society.
　　1953. 2.00. U. Pr. of Wash., D. C.
GEORGIA--HISTORY (975.9)
Coulter, Ellis Merton. Georgia: A short history. 1960. 6.00. U. of N. C.
Tailfer, Patrick. True and historical narrative of the colony of Georgia. by
　　Clarence L. Ver Steeg. 5.00. U. of Ga.
GEORGIA--SOCIAL LIFE AND CUSTOMS (975.8)
Kemble, Frances A. Journal of a residence on a Georgian plantation in 1838-1839.
　　by John A. Scott. il. 1961. 5.75. Knopf
GERIATRICS (618.97)
Cowdry, E. V. Care of the geriatric patient. 1958. 8.00. Mosby
DeRopp, Robert S. Man against aging. 1960. 5.00. St. Martins
Newton, Kathleen. Geriatric nursing. 1960. 6.75. Mosby
Stieglitz, Edward J. Geriatric medicine. 1954. 16.50. Lippincott
GERMAN DRAMA (COLLECTIONS) (832.08)
Campbell, T. Moody. German plays of the nineteenth century. in German. 1930.
　　5.50. Appleton
Steinhauer, Harry. Das deutsche Drama. vols. 1 and 2. 1938. 3.80 ea. Norton
GERMAN DRAMA--HISTORY AND CRITICISM (832)
Feise, Ernst. Fifty years of German drama. 1941. 3.75. Johns Hopkins
Garten, H. F. Modern German drama. 1959. 6.00. Oxford U. P.
GERMAN DRAMA--TRANSLATIONS INTO ENGLISH (832)
Bentley, Eric. Five German plays. 3.50. Smith, Peter
GERMAN FICTION (833)
Bennett, E. K. History of the German Novelle. by H. M. Waidson. 1961. 5.50.
　　Cambridge U. P.
Boeschenstein, H. German novel, 1939-1944. 1949. 4.00. U. of Toronto
Pascal, Roy. German novel. 1956. 4.50. U. of Toronto
Waidson, Herbert M. Modern German novel. 1959. 4.25. Oxford U. P.
Pick, Robert. German stories and tales. 1954. 4.50. Knopf
Collinson, W. E. German language today: Its patterns and historical background.
　　1953. 2.50. Hillary
Priebsch, Robert and W. E. Collinson. German language. 1959. 7.00. Macmillan
Browning, Robert M. German poetry: A critical anthology. in German. 1962.
　　6.00. Appleton
GERMAN LANGUAGE--DICTIONARIES--ENGLISH (433.2)
Brockhaus. German-English, English-German dictionary. by Heraucourt and
　　Motekat. 1961. 9.95. McGraw (R)
Cassell's German dictionary. German-English and English-German. 7.50. Funk
Eggeling, H. F. Dictionary of modern German prose usage. 1961. 4.80. Oxford
　　U. P. (R)
Muret, E., and D. Sanders. Encyclopedic dictionary, German and English. 2
　　vols. 25.00. Ungar (R)
GERMAN LITERATURE (830)
Feise, Ernst, and Harry Steinhauer. German literature since Goethe. 2 vols. 8.00.
　　Houghton
Rose, Ernst. History of German literature. 1960. 6.50. N. Y. U.
GERMAN LITERATURE--HISTORY AND CRITICISM (830.903)
Bithell, Jethro. Modern German literature, 1880-1950. 1959. 10.00. Hillary
Blackall, Eric A. Emergence of German as a literary language. 1959. 10.00.
　　Cambridge U. P.
Bostock, J. K. Handbook on old High German literature. 1955. 4.80. Oxford U. P.
Bruford, W. H. Literary interpretation in Germany. 1952. 0.75. Cambridge U. P.
Era of Goethe: Essays presented to James Boyd. 8.50. Humanities

Lohan, Robert. Golden age of German literature. 3.75. Ungar
Mann, Thomas. Last essays. by Richard Winston and others. 1959. 4.50. Knopf
Rose, Ernst. History of German literature. 1960. 6.50. N. Y. U.
Wells, G. A. Herder and after. 1959. 8.50. Humanities

GERMAN POETRY (COLLECTIONS) (831.08)

Browning, Robert M. German poetry: A critical anthology. in German. 1962. 6.00.
   Appleton
Fiedler, H. G. Oxford book of German verse. 12th to 20th century. in German.
   1927. 5.00. Oxford U. P.
Kaufmann, Walter. Twenty German poets. 1962. 5.00. Random
Middleton, Christopher, and Michael Hamburger. Modern German poetry: 1910-
   1960. bilingual, German and English. 1962. 6.50. Grove
Rose, William. Book of modern German lyric verse, 1890-1955. 1960. 3.40.
   Oxford U. P.

GERMAN POETRY--HISTORY AND CRITICISM (831)

Robertson, John G. A. History of German literature. 1962. 8.75. British Bk.

GERMAN POETRY--TRANSLATIONS INTO ENGLISH (831)

Flores, Angel. Anthology of German poetry from Holderlin to Rilke. 1960.
   English tr. with German originals. 3.50. Smith, Peter
Middleton, Christopher, and Michael Hamburger. Modern German poetry: 1910-
   1960. bilingual, German and English. 1962. 6.50. Grove

GERMAN REUNIFICATION QUESTION (1949-) (943.087)

Freund, Gerald. Germany between two worlds. 1961. 5.75. Harcourt
Gt. Brit, Foreign Office. Selected documents on Germany and the question of
   Berlin, 1944-1961. 1961. British Info. Services
McInnis, Edgar, and others. Shaping of postwar Germany. il. 1960. 4.95.
   Praeger
Speier, Hans. Divided Berlin. 1961. 4.95. Praeger

GERMANY (943)

Bithell, J. Germany: Companion to German studies. 1955. 8.50. Pitman
Viereck, Peter. Metapolitics: The roots of the Nazi mind. 1961. Putnam
Logan, Rayford. African mandates in world politics. 3.00. Pub. Affairs
Lewis, Cleona. Nazi Europe and world trade. 1941. 2.00. Brookings
Carsten, F. L. Princes and parliaments in Germany, from the 15th to the 18th
   century. 1959. 8.00. Oxford U. P.

GERMANY--DESCRIPTION AND TRAVEL (914.3)

Boswell, James. Boswell on the grand tour: Germany and Switzerland, 1764. il.
   by Frank Brady and Frederick A. Pottle. 1953. 5.00. McGraw

GERMANY--ECONOMIC CONDITIONS (943.05)

Bonnell, Allen Thomas. German control over international economic relations,
   1930-1940. 1940. U. of Ill.
Bruford, W. H. Germany in the 18th century. 1952. 5.50. Cambridge U. P.
Poole, Kenyon E. German financial politics, 1932-1939. 1939. 5.00. Harvard

GERMANY--ECONOMIC CONDITIONS--1945- (943.087)

Slusser, R. Soviet economic policy in postwar Germany. 2.25. Praeger

GERMANY--HISTORY (943)

Barraclough, G. Origins of modern Germany. 5.00. Macmillan
Dill, Marshall. Germany: A modern history. 1961. 8.75. U. of Mich.
Flenley, Ralph. Modern German history. il. 1959. 7.00. Dutton
Hertz, Frederick. Development of the German public mind: Social history of
   German political sentiments, aspirations and ideas. 2 vols. 1957. vol. 1.
   Middle Ages; Reformation. 7.50; vol. 2. Age of Enlightenment. 9.00.
   Macmillan
Holborn, Hajo. History of modern Germany. il. 1959. 8.75. Knopf
Pollock, James K., and Homer L. Thomas. Germany in power and eclipse. il.
   1952. 12.50. Van Nostrand
Reinhardt, Kurt F. Germany: 2000 years. 2 vols. 1961. 9.50. Ungar (R)
Snyder, Louis L. Basic history of modern Germany. 1957. 1.25. Van Nostrand

Snyder, Louis, L. Documents of German history. 1958. 10.00. Rutgers
Tacitus. Agricola. bd.with Germania. 1.75. Cambridge U. P.
GERMANY--HISTORY--TO 1517 (943)
Kantorowicz, Ernst. Frederick the Second. il. 1957. 8.50. Ungar
Thompson, James W. Feudal Germany. 2 vols. 12.50. Ungar
GERMANY--HISTORY--1517-1648 (943.03)
Brandi, K. Emperor Charles V. 8.00. Humanities
Wedgewood, Cicely V. Thirty years war. il. 3.50. Smith, Peter
GERMANY--HISTORY--1871-1918 (943.07)
Nichols, J. Alden. Germany after Bismarck. il. 1958. 7.50. Harvard
GERMANY--HISTORY--20TH CENTURY (943.087)
Dehio, Ludwig. Germany and world politics in the twentieth century. 1959. 4.00.
    Knopf
Passant, Ernest J. Short history of Germany, 1815-1945. 1959. 3.95. Cambridge
    U. P.
Pinson, Koppel S. Modern Germany. 1954. 7.50. Macmillan
GERMANY--HISTORY--1918-1933 (943.085)
Waite, R. G. L. Vanguard of Nazism: The free corps movement in postwar
    Germany 1918-1923. 1952. 6.00. Harvard
GERMANY--HISTORY 1933-1945 (943.086)
Jarman, T. L. Rise and fall of Nazi Germany. il. 1956. 4.95. N. Y. U.
Shirer, William L. Rise and fall of the Third Reich. 1960. 10.00. S. and S.
GERMANY--HISTORY--ALLIED OCCUPATION, 1945 (943.087)
Davidson, Eugene. Death and life of Germany. 1959. 5.75. Knopf
Ebsworth, Raymond, Restoring democracy in Germany. 1960. 6.00. Praeger
McInnis, Edgar, and others. Shaping of postwar Germany. il. 1960. 4.95.
    Praeger
Zink, Harold. United States in Germany, 1944-1955. il. 1957. 7.50. Van Nostrand
GERMANY--INDUSTRY (943)
Klein, Burton H. Germany's economic preparations for war. 1959. 5.00. Harvard
Muhlen, Norbert. Incredible Krupps. il. 1959. 5.00. Holt
GERMANY--INTELLECTUAL LIFE (943)
Kohn, Hans. Mind of Germany. il. 1960. 5.95. Scribner
GERMANY--POLITICS AND GOVERNMENT (943)
Carter, Gwendolen M., and John H. Herz. Major foreign powers: The govern-
    ments of Great Britain, France, Germany and the Soviet Union. il. 8.95.
    Harcourt
Pollock, James K., and Homer L. Thomas. Germany in power and eclipse. il.
    1952. 12.50. Van Nostrand
Hamerow, T. S. Restoration, revolution, reaction: Economics and politics in
    Germany, 1815-1871. 1958. 6.00. Princeton
Mosse, Werner E. European powers and the German question, 1848-71. 9.50.
    Cambridge U. P.
Gatzke, Hans W. Germany's drive to the West. 1950. 5.00. Johns Hopkins
Schorske, C. E. German social democracy, 1905-1917: The development of the
    great schism. 1955. 5.50. Harvard
Finer, Herman. Major governments of modern Europe. il. 1960. 8.25. Harper
Hitler, Adolf. Mein kampf. tr. by Ralph Manheim. 1943. 6.00. 1962. Houghton
Bennett, Edward W. Germany and the diplomacy of the financial crisis, 1931.
    6.00. Harvard
Buck, Pearl S. and Erna von Pustau. How it happens. 1947. 3.00. Day
Wheeler-Bennett, John W. Nemesis of power. 12.50. St. Martins
Crankshaw, Edward. Gestapo: Instrument of tyranny. 1956. 3.75. Viking
Gallin, Mary A. German resistance to Hitler. 1962. 4.95. Catholic U. of Am. Pr.
Heydecker, Joe J., and Leeb, Johannes. Nuremberg trial. 1962. 6.00. World
    Pub.
Morgenthau, Hans J. Germany and the future of Europe. 1951. 3.50. U. of
    Chicago

GERMANY--SOCIAL CONDITIONS (943)
Engels, Friedrich. Peasant War in Germany. 1926. 2.50. Int. Pubs.
GERMANY (DEMOCRATIC REPUBLIC, 1949-) (943)
Prittie, Terence. Germany divided: The legacy of the Nazi era. 1960. 6.00.
    Little
Robertson, Edwin H. Bible in East Germany. 1961. 1.25. Assn. Pr.
GERMANY (FEDERAL REPUBLIC 1949-) (943)
Alexander, Edgar. Adenauer and the New Germany. 1957. 5.25. Farrar, Straus
Conant, James Bryant. Germany and freedom. 1958. 3.00. Harvard
Schlamm, William S. Germany and the East-West crisis. 1959. 3.95. McKay
GERMANY (FEDERAL REPUBLIC, 1949-) --FOREIGN RELATIONS (943)
Freund, Gerald. Germany between two worlds. 1961. 5.75. Harcourt
Neal. Fred W. War and peace and Germany. 1962. 3.95. Norton
GERMANY (FEDERAL REPUBLIC, 1949-)--POLITICS AND GOVERNMENT (943)
Heidenheimer, Arnold J. Governments of Germany. 1961. 2.95. Crowell
Kitzinger, Uwe W. German electoral politics. il. 1960. 7.20. Oxford U. P.
Speier, Hans. German rearmament and atomic war. 1957. 5.00. Harper
GERONIMO, APACHE CHIEF, 1829-1909 (979)
Betzinez, Jason, and W. S. Nye. I fought with Geronimo. il. 1959. 4.95. Stack-
    pole
GERSHWIN, GEORGE, 1898-1937 (927)
Ewen, David. Journey to greatness. il. 1956. 5.00. Holt
Goldberg, Isaac. George Gershwin: A study in American music. il. 1958. 5.50.
    Ungar
GESTALT PSYCHOLOGY (150.1924)
Ellis, W. D. Source book of Gestalt psychology. 5.50. Humanities
Hamlyn, D. W. Psychology of perception. 2.50. Humanities
Kohler, Wolfgang. Gestalt psychology. 3.95. Liveright, or Tudor
Lewin, Kurt. Dynamic theory of personality. 1945. 6.95. McGraw
Line, W. Visual perception in children. 3.00. Cambridge U. P.
GESTURE (419)
Lawson, Joan. Mime. 1958. 8.50. Pitman
GETTYSBURG, BATTLE OF, 1863 (973.7349)
Downey, Fairfax. Guns at Gettysburg. il. 1958. 5.00. McKay
Haskell, Frank Aretas. Battle of Gettysburg. by Bruce Catton. 1958. 4.00.
    Houghton
Stackpole, Edward J., and W. S. Nye. Battle of Gettysburg. il. 1960. Stackpole
GETTYSBURG CAMPAIGN, 1863 (973.7349)
Dowdey, Clifford. Death of a nation. 1958. 5.00. Knopf
Stackpole, Edward J. They met at Gettysburg. il. 4.95. Stackpole
GHANA (966.7)
Boateng, E. A. Geography of Ghana. 4.00. Cambridge U. P.
Ward, W. E. F. History of Ghana. il. 1959. 5.75. Macmillan
GHOST STORIES (398.4)
Cerf, Bennett. Famous ghost stories. 1.95. Modern Lib.
Davenport, Basil. Tales to be told in the dark. 1953. 3.50. Dodd
Great tales of terror and the supernatural. 2.95. Modern Lib.
Van Thal, Herbert. Great ghost stories. il. 1960. 3.50. Hill & Wang
GHOSTS (398.4)
Jones, Louis. C. Things that go bump in the night. il. 1959. 3.75. Hill & Wang
Lethbridge, T. C. Ghost and ghoul. il. 3.75. Doubleday
GIBBON, EDWARD, 1737-1794 (923.2)
Bond, Harold L. Literary art of Edward Gibbon. 1960. 4.00. Oxford U. P.
Fuglum, Per. Edward Gibbon: His view of life and conception of history. 3.75.
    Humanities
Gibbon, Edward. Autobiography. 2.75. Oxford U. P.
GIBRALTAR (946.89)
Andrews, Allen. Proud fortress: The fighting story of Gibraltar. il. 1959.
    3.75. Dutton

GIBRAN, KAHIL, 1883-1931 (928)
Young, Barbara. This man from Lebanon. il. 1945. 4.00. Knopf
GIDE, ANDRE PAUL GUILLAUME, 1869-1951 (928.42)
Bree, Germaine. Andre Gide. 1962. 6.00. Rutgers
Cocking, J. M., and others. Three studies in modern French literature: Proust,
    Gide, Mauriac. 1960. 1.75. Yale
Mann, Klaus. Andre Gide. 1944. 3.00. Farrar, Straus
March, Harold. Gide and the Hound of heaven. 1952. 5.00. U. of Pa.
O'Brien, Justin. Portrait of Andre Gide: Critical biography. il. 1953. 6.00. Knopf
GIDEON, JUDGE OF ISRAEL--DRAMA (812)
Chayevsky, Paddy. Gideon. 1962. 3.95. Random
GIFTED CHILDREN (371.95)
Abraham, Willard. Common sense about gifted children. 1958. 5.00. Harper
American Association for Gifted Children. Gifted child. by Paul Witty. 1953.
    5.25. Heath
Flanagan, John C., and others. Talents of American youth. no. 1. 4.00. Houghton
Lightfoot, Georgia. Personality characteristics of bright and dull children. 1951.
    2.35. T. C.
Narramore, Clyde M. Is your child gifted? 1961. Zondervan
Strang, Ruth M. Helping your gifted child. 1960. 4.50. Dutton
Terman, Lewis M., and Melita H. Oden. Gifted group at mid-life. 4.50. Stan-
    ford
Terman, Lewis M., and others. Promise of youth. 8.50. Stanford
GIFTED CHILDREN--EDUCATION (371.95)
DeHaan, Robert F., and Robert J. Havighurst. Educating gifted children. 1961.
    5.00. U. of Chicago
Everett, Samuel. Programs for the gifted. 1961. 5.50. Harper
Fliegler, Louis A. Curriculum planning for the gifted. 1961. 9.35. Prentice-Hall
Freehill, Maurice F. Gifted children. il. 1961. 5.75. Macmillan
French, Joseph L. Educating the gifted. 1959. 8.00. Holt, Rinehart & Winston
Havighurst, Robert J. Education for the gifted in school and college. 1958.
    NSSE, 57th yrbk. pt. 2. 4.50. U. of Chicago
Havighurst, Robert J., and others. Survey of the education of gifted children.
    1955. U. of Chicago
Hildreth, Gertrude H., and Florence N. Brumbaugh. Educating gifted children.
    1952. 4.00. Harper
National Education Association, Academically Talented Student Project. Research
    on the academically talented student. 1961. 1.00. N. E. A.
National Education Association, Academically Talented Student Project, and
    National Education Association, American Business Education Association.
    Business and economic education for the academically talented student. 1961.
    1.00. N. E. A.
Sumption, Merle R., and Evelyn M. Luecking. Education of the gifted. 1960.
    6.50. Ronald
GILBERT, SIR WILLIAM SCHWENICK, 1836-1911 (927)
Moore, Frank Ledlie. Crowell's handbook of Gilbert and Sullivan. il. 1962.
    4.95. Crowell
Pearson, Hesketh. Gilbert. il. 1958. 4.50. Harper
GILBERT ISLANDS (996.81)
Grimble, Arthur. Return to the islands: Life and legend in the Gilberts. il.
    1957. 4.50. Morrow
GILBRETH, FRANK BUNKER, 1868-1924 (817)
Gilbreth, Frank B., Jr., and Ernestine G. Carey. Cheaper by the dozen. il.
    1949. 3.95. Crowell
Gilbreth, Frank B., Jr., and Ernestine G. Carey. Belles on their toes. il.
    1950. 3.95. Crowell
GILDAS, 6thCENTURY (922.3)
Singer, Charles. From magic to science. 1960. 4.00. Smith, Peter

GILDS (929.8)
Bromley, John. Armorial bearings of the guilds of London. il. 1961. 20.00.
 Warne
GIORGIONE, GIORGIO BARBARELLI, KNOWN AS, 1477-1511 (927)
Giorgione. All the paintings of Giorgione. by Luigi Coletti. il. 1962. 3.95.
 Hawthorn
Venturi, L. Four steps toward modern art. 1956. 3.00. Columbia
GIOTTO DI BONDONE, 1266?-1337 (927)
Battisti, Eugenio. Giotto. il. 1960. 5.75. World Pub.
GIRAUDOUX, JEAN, 1882-1944 (928)
Inskip, Donald. Jean Giraudoux: The making of a dramatist. 1958. 3.40. Oxford
 U. P.
LeSage, Laurent. Jean Giraudoux, his life and works. 1959. 5.00. Penn. State
GIRLS (136.775)
Miller, Frances S., and H. H. Laitem. Personal problems of the high school
 girl. 1945. 4.95. Wiley
Roosevelt, Eleanor, and Helen Ferris. Your teens and mine. 2.95. Doubleday
GIRONDISTS (944.04)
Sydenham, M. J. Girondins. 1961. 5.60. Oxford U. P.
GLACIERS (551.312)
Dyson, James. World of ice. 1962. 6.95. Knopf
Flint, R. F. Glacial geology and the Pleistocene epoch. 1947. 9.00. Wiley
GLADSTONE, WILLIAM EWART, 1809-1898 (923.242)
Magnus, Philip. Gladstone. il. 1954. 7.95. Dutton
GLANDS (611.4)
American Medical Association. Glandular physiology and therapy. il. 1954.
 10.00. Lippincott (R)
GLASGOW, ELLEN ANDERSON GHOLSON, 1874-1945 (928)
Glasgow, Ellen. Woman within. il. 1954. 5.00. Harcourt
McDowell, Frederick. Ellen Glasgow and the ironic art of fiction. 1960. 4.50.
 U. of Wis.
Rouse, Blair. Ellen Glasgow. 1962. 3.50. Twayne
GLASS (666.12)
Jones, Gwyn O. Glass. 1956. 2.25. Wiley
Phillips, Charles Glass: The miracle maker. 1948. 8.50. Pitman
GLASS MANUFACTURE (666.12)
McKearin, Helen, and George S. American glass. il. 1948. 12.95. Crown
Revi, Albert C. Nineteenth century glass, its origins and development. 1959.
 8.50. Nelson
GLASS PAINTING AND STAINING (748)
Arnold, H. Stained glass of the Middle Ages in England and France. 10.00.
 Hillary
Young, Mary E. Singing windows. il. 1962. 3.75. Abingdon
GLASSWARE--U.S. (748.2)
Lee, Ruth Webb. Antique fakes and reproductions. 7.50. Lee Pub.
Lee, Ruth Webb. Handbook of early American pressed glass patterns. il. 3.00.
 Lee Pub.
GLAUCOMA (617.74)
Sugar, H. Saul. Glaucomas. 15.00. Hoeber
Weinstein, Paul. Glaucoma - Pathology and therapy. tr. by Julius Goedes. il.
 1953. 5.50. Mosby
GLIDERS (AERONAUTICS) (629.133)
Underwood, John. World aircraft illustrated. il. 1961. 8.50. Arco (R)
Kukuski, John. Theory and technique of soaring. 1952. 6.00. Pitman
Piggott, Derek. Gliding. il. 1959. 5.95. Macmillan
GLOBES (371.335)
Harris, Ruby M. Handbook of map and globe usage. il. 1959. 2.24. Rand McNally
GNOSTICISM (273.1)
Grant, Robert M. Gnosticism and early Christianity. 4.50. Columbia

<u>GOD</u> (231)

Brunner, H. Emil. Christian doctrine of God. 1950. 6.00. Westminster

Collins, James. God in modern philosophy. 1959. 6.50. Regnery

Ferre, Nels F. S. Christian understanding of God. 1951. 4.00. Harper

Guthrie, Harvey. God and history in the Old Testament. 1960. 4.25. Seabury

Phillips, J. B. Your God is too small. 2.50. Macmillan

Pohle, Joseph. God, His knowability. 4.00. Herder

Sheen, Fulton J. God and intelligence in modern philosophy. 1958. Doubleday

Voss, Carl H. Universal God. 1962. 3.75. Smith, Peter

<u>GOD--HISTORY OF DOCTRINES</u> (231)

Empson, William. Milton's God. 1961. 5.00. New Directions

Grabowski, Stanislaus J. All-present God: A study in St. Augustine. 1954. 4.50. Herder

Jevons, F. B. Idea of God in early religions. 1910. 1.75. Cambridge U. P.

<u>GOD--PROOF</u> (231)

Bryar, William. St. Thomas and the existence of God: Three interpretations. 1951. 5.00. Regnery

Gilson, E. God and philosophy. 1941. 3.00. 1959. Yale

Monsma, John Clover. Evidence of God. 1958. 3.75. Putnam

<u>GOD (GREEK RELIGION)</u> (182)

Jaeger, Werner. Theology of the early Greek philosophers. 1947. 4.50. Oxford U. P.

<u>GOD (THEORY OF KNOWLEDGE)</u> (231)

Buber, Martin. I and thou. 1958. 1.75. Scribner

Gilson, Etienne. Christian philosophy of Saint Augustine. 1960. 7.50. Random

Maritain, Jacques. Approaches to God. 1954. 3.00. Harper

Smith, Gerard. Natural theology: Metaphysics 2. 5.00. Macmillan

<u>GODS IN ART</u> (704.947)

Scully, Vincent J. Earth, the temple and the gods: Greek sacred architecture. il. 1962. 15.00. Yale

Thapar, Daya R. Icons in bronze. il. 1961. 9.25. Taplinger

Wechsler, Herman. Gods and goddesses in art and legend. 1961. Washington Square

<u>GOETHE, JOHANN WOLFGANG VON, 1749-1832</u> (832.62)

Atkins, Stuart. Goethe's Faust: A literary analysis. il. 1958. 6.00. Harvard

Butler, E. M. Byron and Goethe. 5.50. Humanities

Cassirer, Ernst. Rousseau, Kant. Goethe: two essays. 1945. 3.00. Shoe String

Fairley, Barker. Goethe's Faust. 1953. 2.00. Oxford U. P.

Goethe, Johann Wolfgang von. Goethe's autobiography. 1949. 5.00. Pub. Affairs

Leppmann, Wolfgang. German image of Goethe. 1961. 6.10. Oxford U. P.

Lewes, George H. Life and works of Goethe. il. 7.50. Ungar

Magnus, Rudolf. Goethe as a scientist. tr. by Heinz Norden. 1953. 3.50. Abelard

Needler, George H. Goethe and Scott. 1950. 3.15. Oxford U. P.

Peacock, Ronald. Goethe's major plays, an essay. 1959. 3.95. Hill & Wang

Schweitzer, Albert. Goethe: Five studies. 1961. Beacon

Vietor, Karl. Goethe the poet. 1949. 5.00. Harvard

Vietor, Karl. Goethe the thinker. 1950. 4.00. Harvard

Wilkinson, E. M., and L. A. Willoughby. Goethe: Poet and thinker. 1962. 6.00. Barnes & Noble

<u>GOLD COAST</u> (966.7)

Apter, D. E. Gold Coast in transition. 1955. 6.00. Princeton

<u>GOLDSMITH, OLIVER, 1728-1774</u> (928.42)

Goldsmith, Oliver, and others. Essays on Goldsmith by Scott, Macauley and Thackeray, and selections from his writings. 1918. 1.55. Oxford U. P.

Lucas, F. L. Search for good sense. il. 1959. 6.00. Macmillan

Percy, Thomas. Memoir of Goldsmith. by K. C. Balderston. 1926. 1.50. Cambridge U. P.

Wardle, Ralph M. Oliver Goldsmith. 5.00. U. of Kans.

GOLDWATER, BARRY MORRIS, 1909- (923.273)
Bell, Jack. Mr. Conservative: Barry Goldwater. 4.50. Doubleday
GOLF (796.352)
American Association for Health, Physical Education and Recreation, Division
    for Girls' and Women's sports. Official bowling, fencing and golf guide.
    1961. 1.00. Am. Assn. for Health, Phys. Ed. & Rec.
Berg, P., and M. Cox. Golf illustrated. 1950. 2.95. Ronald
Golf Magazine. Pro pointers and stroke savers. by Charles Price. il. 1960. 4.95.
    Harper
Hogan, Ben. Ben Hogan's five lessons of the modern fundamentals of golf. il.
    1957. 5.00. Barnes, A. S.
Snead, Sam. How to play golf. il. 1946. 2.50 Doubleday
Suggs, Louise. Golf for women. il. 1960. 3.95. Doubleday
GOLIARDS (809)
Waddell, Helen. Wandering scholars. 1949. 3.50. Barnes & Noble
Whicher, George F. Goliard poets. (Latin originals, translations and commentary)
    1949. 7.50. New Directions
GOMPERS, SAMUEL, 1850-1924 (923.373)
Gompers, Samuel. Seventy years of life and labor: An autobiography. by Philip
    Taft, and John A. Sessions. 1957. 5.00. Dutton
GOOD AND EVIL (232.963)
Augustine, Saint. Problem of free choice. 1955. 3.25. Newman
Buber, Martin. Good and evil. 3.25. Smith, Peter
Camus, Albert. Rebel. 1954. 4.00. Knopf
Camus, Albert. Resistance, rebellion and death. 1960. 4.00. Knopf
Ferre, Nels. F. S. Evil and Christian faith. 1947. 3.00. Harper
Lewis, C. S. Great divorce. 1946. 2.50. Macmillan
Lewis, C. S. Problem of pain. 1944. 3.95. Macmillan
Rice, Philip Blair. On the knowledge of good and evil. 1955. 4.50. Random
GORDON, CHARLES GEORGE, 1833-1885 (923.5)
Elton, Lord. Gordon of Khartoum: General Charles George Gordon. 1955. 6.75.
    Knopf
Strachey, Lytton. Eminent Victorians. 1.95. Modern Lib.
GORGAS, WILLIAM CRAWFORD, 1854-1920 (925)
Gibson, John M. Physician to the world: the life of General William C. Gorgas.
    il. 1950. 6.00. Duke
GORKI, MAXIM, 1868-1936 (928)
Hare, Richard. Maxim Gorky, romantic realist and conservative revolutionary.
    1962. 3.40. Oxford U. P.
GOTHS (936.36)
Jordanes, Bp. of Ravenna. Gothic history of Jordanes. by Charles C. Mierow.
    1962. 5.00. Barnes & Noble
GOUACHE PAINTING (751.42)
Dehn, Adolf. Water color, gouache, and casein painting. il. 1955. 5.95. Viking
GOULD, JAY, 1836-1892 (923.373)
Grodinsky, Julius. Jay Gould: His business career. 2 vols. 1957. 10.00. U. of
    Pa.
GOUT (616.399)
Weiss, Thomas E., and Albert Segaloff. Gouty arthritis and gout. il. 1959. 7.50.
    Thomas C. C.
GOVERNMENT OWNERSHIP (380.16)
Abraham, Henry J. Government as entrepreneur and social servant. 1956. 1.00.
    Pub. Affairs
Alfred, Helen. Public ownership in the U. S. A. 1961. 2.00. Peace Pub.
Kelf-Cohen, Reuben. Nationalisation in Britain. 1958. 5.50. St. Martins
Weiner, Herbert E. British labor and public ownership. 1960. 3.25. Pub. Affairs
GOVERNMENT PUBLICITY (350)
Cater, Douglass. Fourth branch of government. 1959. 3.50. Houghton

Rourke, Francis E. Secrecy and publicity: Dilemmas of democracy. 5.00.
  Johns Hopkins
GOVERNMENT SPENDING POLICY (350)
Egle, W. P. Economic stabilization. 1952. 4.00. Princeton
Maxwell, James A. Federal grants and the business cycle. 1952. 2.00. Princeton
GOVERNORS--U.S. (353.9)
Brooks, Glenn. When governors convene. 4.50. Johns Hopkins
Hesseltine, William B. Lincoln and the war governors. 1948. 5.75. Knopf
Ransone, Coleman B. Jr. Office of governor in the U. S. 1956. 6.00. U. of Ala.
GOYA Y LUCIENTES, FRANCISCO JOSE DE, 1746-1828 (927)
Gassier, Pierre. Goya. il. 1955. 5.75. World Pub.
Goya, Francisco de. Goya. by Jean Adhemer. il. 4.50. Boston Bk.
Malraux, Andre. Saturn: An essay on Goya. il. 1957. 10.00. N. Y Graphic
GRACE (THEOLOGY) (234.1)
Guardini, Romano. Freedom, grace, and destiny. 1961. 4.00. Pantheon
Pascal, Blaise. Pensees. 1951. 1.95. Dutton
Tournier, Paul. Guilt and grace. 1962. 3.75. Harper
GRACE AT MEALS (249)
Nyce, William, and Herbert Bunyea. Grace before meals. 1911. 1.50. Winston
GRADING AND MARKING (STUDENTS) (371.26)
Ahmann, J. Stanley, and Marvin D. Glock. Evaluating pupil growth. il. 1959.
  9.95. Allyn & Bacon
Brueckner, Leo J. Educational diagnosis. NSSE, 34th yrbk. 1935. 4.50. 3.00.
  U. of Chicago
Tiegs, E. W. Tests and measurements in the improvement of learning. 1939.
  5.50. Houghton
GRAF SPEE (BATTLESHIP) (940.545)
Pope, Dudley. Graf Spee: The life and death of a raider. il. 1957. 4.95. Lippin-
  cott
GRAF ZEPPELIN (AIR-SHIP) (629.13)
Eckener, Hugo. My zeppelins. il. 1958. 3.95. Aero
GRAHAM, WILLIAM FRANKLIN, 1918- (922)
McLoughlin, William G. Billy Graham, revivalist in a secular age. 1960. 4.50.
  Ronald
GRAHAME, KENNETH, 1859-1932 (928)
Green, Peter. Kenneth Grahame: A biography. 1959. 6.00. World Pub.
GRAIL (398.2)
Locke, Frederick W. Quest for the Holy Grail. 1960. 3.50. Stanford
Waite, Arthur E. Holy Grail. 1961. 10.00. U. Books
Weston, Jessie L. From ritual to romance. 3.00. Smith, Peter
GRAMMAR, COMPARATIVE AND GENERAL (415)
Chandler, Richard E., and Alden R. Heffler. Handbook of comparative grammar
  for students of foreign language. 1.75. Am. Bk. Co.
Pei, Mario. World's chief languages. 1949. 7.50. Devin
GRAMONT, ANTOINE, DUC DE, 1604-1678 (923.2)
Lewis, W. H. Assault on Olympus. 1958. 4.00. Harcourt
GRAND CANYON (979.132)
Krutch, Joseph Wood. Grand Canyon: Today and all its yeaterdays. il. 1958.
  5.00. Sloane
Powell, John W. Exploration of the Colorado River and its canyons. il. 1895.
  Dover
GRANT, ULYSSES SIMPSON. PRES. U.S., 1822-1885 (923.173)
Cadwallader, Sylvanus. Three years with Grant. by Benjamin P. Thomas. 1955.
  5.00. Knopf
Catton, Bruce. U. S. Grant and the American military tradition. 1954. 3.75.
  Little
Fuller, John Frederick C. Generalship of Ulysses S. Grant. il. 1958. 7.50.
  Indiana

Fuller, J. F. C. Grant and Lee: A study in personality and generalship. il. 1957.
5.00. Indiana
Hesseltine, William B. Ulysses S. Grant: Politician. il. 7.00. Ungar
Lewis, Lloyd. Captain Sam Grant. 1950. 6.50; with letters, 7.50. Little
Miers, Earl Schenck. Web of victory: Grant at Vicksburg. il. 1955. 5.75. Knopf
Williams, Harry T. McClellan, Sherman and Grant. 1962. 3.50. Rutgers
GRANVILLE-BARKER, HARLEY GRANVILLE, 1877-1946 (927)
Purdom, C. B. Harley Granville-Barker: Man of the theatre, dramatist and
scholar, il. 1956. 6.00. Harvard
GRAPHIC ARTS (655)
Arnold, Edmund C. Ink on paper: Handbook of the graphic arts. il. 7.00. Harper
Brunner, Felix. Handbook of graphic reproduction processes. il. 1962. 25.00.
Hastings
Karch, R. Randolph. Graphic arts procedures. il. 1957. 4.75. Am. Tech. Soc.
Kauffmann, Desire. Graphic arts crafts. il. 1948. 3.95. Van Nostrand
Zaidenberg, Arthur. New encyclopedia of drawing, painting, and the graphic arts.
5.95. Barnes, A. S.
GRAPHIC METHODS (311)
Giachino, J. W., and Henry J. Beukema. Engineering-technical drafting and
graphics. il. 1961. 9.75. Am. Tech. Soc.
Lipka, J. Graphical and mechanical computation. 1918. 6.50. Wiley
Williams, J. Harold. Graphic methods in education. 1924. 4.75. Houghton
GRAPHOLOGY (137.7)
Bunker, M. N. Handwriting analysis: The art and science of reading character
by grapho-analysis. 6.95. Nelson-Hall
Mendel, Alfred O. Personality in handwriting. 5.00. Ungar
Singer, Eric. Personality in handwriting. 1956. 2.50. Assoc. Booksellers
GRASSES (584.9)
Archer, Sellers, and Clarence Bunch. American grass book: Manual of pasture
and range grasses. il. 1953. 4.95. U. of Okla.
Moore, Alam. Grasses. il. 1960. 5.00. Macmillan
Pohl, R. W. How to know the grasses. by Harry E. Jaques. 1954. 2.75. Brown,
W. C.
GRAVES, ROBERT RANKE, 1895- (928)
Cohen, J. M. Robert Graves. 3.25. Smith, Peter
GRAVITATION (521.12)
Eddington, Arthur S. Space, time and gravitation. 1960. 5.50. Cambridge U. P.
Gamow, George. Gravity: Classic and modern views. il. 1962. Doubleday
Weber, Joseph. General relativity and gravitational waves. 1961. 4.50. Wiley
GRAY, ASA, 1810-1888 (925)
Depree, A. Hunter. Asa Gray. il. 1959. 7.50. Harvard
GRAY, THOMAS, 1716-1771 (928)
Ketton-Cremer, Robert W. Thomas Gray. 1955. 5.50. Cambridge U. P.
Reed, Amy. Background of Gray's Elegy: A study in the taste for melancholy
poetry, 1700-1751. 6.00. Russell
GRAZING (636.0842)
Calef, Westley. Private grazing and public lands. 1960. 9.50. U. of Chicago
Foss, Philip O. Politics and grass. il. 1960. 4.50. U. of Wash.
GREAT AWAKENING (325.3)
Maxson, Charles H. Great awakening in the Middle Colonies. 3.25. Smith, Peter
GREAT BARRIER REEF, AUSTRALIA (943.6)
Clarke, Arthur C. Coast of coral. il. 1956. 5.00. Harper
GREAT BRITAIN (942)
Barker, Ernest. Character of England. 1947. 7.20. Oxford U. P.
GT. BRIT.--ANTIQUITIES (942)
Collingwood, R. G. Roman Britain. il. 1932. 2.40. Oxford U. P.
Durant, G. M. Journey into Roman Britain. il. 1957. 4.50. Norton
Hawkes, Jacquetta. History in earth and stone: Prehistoric and Roman monu-
ments in England and Wales. il. 1952. 3.75. Harvard

Leeds, E. T. Early Anglo-Saxon art and archaeology. il. 1936. 4.50. Oxford
U. P.
Piggott, Stuart. British prehistory. 1949. 1.70. Oxford U. P.
GT. BRIT. --ARMY (942)
Churchill, Winston L. S. My early life: A roving commission. il. 1930. 3.95:
1.65. Scribner
Davies, Godfrey. Wellington and his army. il. 1954. 3.00. Huntington Lib.
GT. BRIT.--BIOGRAPHY (920.042)
Aubrey, John. Aubrey's brief lives. by Oliver Lawson Dick. 1957. 5.95. U. of
Mich.
Bennett, H. S. Six medieval men and women. 1955. 3.25. Cambridge U. P.
Briggs, Asa. Victorian people. 1955. 2.00. U. of Chicago
British historical portraits. 4.50. Cambridge U. P.
Fuller, Thomas. Worthies of England. by John Freeman. 1952. 10.00. Barnes &
Noble
Rosenbaum, Robert A. Earnest Victorians. il. 1961. 7.50. Hawthorn
Smith, George. Dictionary of national biography. by Leslie Stephen, and others.
1953. 22 vols. 208.00. 2 pts. 1900. 9.60, pt. 2, 1901-1950, 6.75. Oxford U. P.
(R)
Stern, Gertrude B. And did he stop and speak to you? 1958. 3.75. Regnery
Who was who. 1897-1915. 11.00. 1916-1928, 11.00; 1929-1950, 11.00; 1941-1950,
15.00; 1951-1960, 17.50. Macmillan (R)
Who's who. 1962. 24.00. St. Martins
GT. BRIT.--CHURCH HISTORY (274.42)
Cantor, N. F. Church, kingship, and lay investiture in England, 1089-1135. 1958.
6.00. Princeton
Moorman, J. R. H. History of the church in England. 1954. 7.50. Morehouse
Bede, The Venerable. Ecclesiastical history of the English nation. 1935. 1.95.
Dutton
Bede. Historical works. 2 vols. 3.50 ea. Harvard
Coulton, George G. Ten medieval studies. 1959. 3.75. Smith, Peter
Pantin, W. A. English church in the fourteenth century. 6.50. U. of Notre
Dame
Smith, L. B. Tudor prelates and politics. 1953. 5.00. Princeton
Cragg, G. R. Puritanism in the period of the great persecution, 1660-1688.
1957. 5.50. Cambridge U. P.
Westfall, Richard S. Science and religion in seventeenth-century England. 1958.
4.50. Yale
GT. BRIT.--CIVILIZATION (942)
Barker, Ernest. Britain and the British people. 1955. 2.00. Oxford U. P.
Barker, Ernest. Character of England. 1947. 7.20. Oxford U. P.
Brinton, Crane. United States and Britain. il. 1948. 4.25. Harvard
Dodd, Arthur H. Life in Elizabethan England. il. 1962. 3.50. Putnam
Ferguson, Arthur B. Indian summer of English chivalry. 1960. 3.00. Duke
Halevy, Elie. History of the English people in the nineteenth century. 6 vols.
35.00. Barnes & Noble
Harrison, Frederick. Medieval man and his notions. il. 1947. 3.00. Hillary
Houghton, Walter. Victorian frame of mind, 1830-1870. 1957. 6.50. Yale
Laver, James. Between the wars. 1961. 6.95. Houghton
Middleton, Drew. These are the British. 1957. 4.50. Knopf
Petrie, Charles. Victorians. 1961. 6.75. McKay
GT. BRIT--COLONIES (325.3)
Eden, Anthony. Days for decision. 1950. 3.00. Houghton
Beer, G. L. Old colonial system. 2 vols. 5.00 ea. Smith, Peter
Beer, George L. Origins of British colonial system. 6.00. Smith, Peter
Dickerson, Olive M. American colonial government, 1696-1765. 1961. 8.50.
Russell
Hall, Michael G. Edward Randolph and the American colonies, 1676-1703. in
prep. U. of N. C.

Jennings, Ivor. British Commonwealth of Nations. 2.50. Hillary
MacMillan, W. M. Road to self-rule. 1960. 7.50. Praeger
Van der Post, Laurens. Venture to the interior. il. 1951. 3.50. Morrow
Hall, Walter P., and others. History of England and the Empire - Common-
    wealth. il. 1962. 9.00. Ginn
McGuire, Paul. Experiment in world order. 1948. 4.00. Morrow
Snape, R. H. Britain and the empire, 1867-1945. 1952. 2.00. Cambridge U. P.
Walker, E. A. British empire: Its structure and spirit, 1497-1953. 1956. 5.00.
    Harvard
Williamson, James A. British Empire and Commonwealth. il. 3.00. St. Martins
Williamson, J. A. Ocean in English history. 1941. 4.00. Oxford U. P.
Williamson, James A. Short history of British expansion. 2 vols. il. vol. 1.
    Old colonial empire. 1945. 5.00; vol. 2. Modern empire and commonwealth.
    1951. 5.00. St. Martins
GT. BRIT.--COLONIES--AFRICA (942)
Batten, T. R. Problems of African development. 1960. 2.40. Oxford U. P.
Cohen, Andrew B. British policy in changing Africa. 1959. 5.00. Northwestern
    U.
De Kiewiet, C. W. History of South Africa, social and economic. 1941. 4.50.
    Oxford U. P.
GT. BRIT.--COLONIES--AMERICA (942)
Adams, Randolph G. Political ideas of the American Revolution. 1958. 3.75.
    Barnes & Noble
Andrews, Charles M. Colonial background of the American Revolution. 1931.
    5.00. Yale
Beer, G. L. Commercial policy of England toward the American colonies. 4.00.
    Smith, Peter
Bolton, Herbert E., and Thomas M. Marshall. Colonization of North America.
    1492-1783. il. 7.50. Macmillan
Burke, Edmund. American speeches and letters. 1.95. Dutton
Miller, John C. Origins of the American Revolution. il. 1959. 7.50. Stanford
Osgood, H. L. American colonies in the 17th century. 3 vols. 7.50 ea. Smith,
    Peter
Osgood, H. L. American colonies in the 18th century. 4 vols. 7.50 ea. Smith,
    Peter
Van Tyne, C. H. Causes of the War of Independence. 5.00. Smith, Peter
Wright, Louis B. Colonial search for a southern Eden. 1953. U. of Ala.
GT. BRIT.--COMMERCE (942)
Saul, S. B. Studies in British overseas trade, 1870-1914. 1959. 6.00. Lounz
Tawney, R. H. Business and politics under James I. 1958. 7.50. Cambridge U. P.
Power, Eileen, and M. M. Postan. Studies in English trade in the 15th century.
    7.50. Humanities
Williamson, James A. Short history of British expansion. 2 vols. il. vol. 1
    Old colonial empire. 1945..5.00. vol. 2. Modern empire and commonwealth.
    1951. 5.00. St. Martins
GT. BRIT.--COMMERCIAL POLICY (942)
Fay, C. R. Corn laws. 1933. 5.00. Cambridge U. P.
Schuyler, Robert L. Fall of the old colonial system: A study in British free trade,
    1770-1870. 1945. 4.75. Oxford U. P.
GT. BRIT.--CONSTITUTIONAL HISTORY (942.9)
Chrimes, Stanley B. English constitutional history. 1953. 1.70. Oxford U. P.
Jolliffe, J. E. A. Constitutional history of medieval England: From the English
    settlement to 1485. 1947. 8.75. Van Nostrand
Keir, Davil L. Constitutional history of modern Britain since 1485. 1960. 6.50.
    Van Nostrand
Maitland, Frederic W. Constitutional history of England. 1908. 4.50. Cambridge
    U. P.
Maitland, Frederic W. Writings of Frederic William Maitland, historian. by
    Robert Schuyler. 3.50. Smith, Peter

GT. BRIT.--CONSTITUTIONAL LAW (942)
Adams, George B., and H. M. Stephens. Select documents of English constitutional history. 1901. 6.75. Macmillan
Bagehot, Walter. English constitution. 1933. 2.75. Oxford U. P.
Elton, G. R. Tudor constitution: Documents and commentary. 1960. 10.00. Cambridge U. P.
Jennings, Ivor. British Constitution. 1961. 3.95. Cambridge U. P.
GT. BRIT.--COURT AND COURTIERS (942)
Corbitt, Frederick. My twenty years in Buckingham Palace. 1956. 3.95. McKay
Turner, E. S. Court of St. James's 1960. 5.00. St. Martins
GT. BRIT.--DESCRIPTION AND TRAVEL (914.42)
Dobie, J. Frank. Texan in England. 1945. 4.50. Little
Tocqueville, Alexis de. Journeys to England and Ireland. by J. P. Mayer. tr. by George Lawrence, and K. P. Mayer. 1958. 4.50. Yale
Fisher, Graham. Historic Britain. il. 1958. 4.95. Norton
Ogrizek, Dore. Great Britain. il. 1949. 7.95. McGraw
GT. BRIT.-- ECONOMIC CONDITIONS (942)
Ashton, Thomas S. Economic fluctuations in England, 1700-1800. 1959. 4.00. Oxford U. P.
Ashton, T. S. Industrial revolution 1760-1830. 1948. 1.70. Oxford U. P.
Carus-Wilson, E. M. Essays on economic history. 1954. 10.00. St. Martins
Clapham, John H. Concise economic history of Britain. vol. 1. 1949. 5.50. Cambridge U. P.
Clark, G. N. Wealth of England from 1496 to 1760. 1946. 1.70. Oxford U. P.
Cole, G. D. H., and Raymond Postgate. British common people, 1746-1946. 1961. Barnes & Noble
Hicks, John R. Essays in world economics. 1959. 5.00. Oxford U. P.
Knights, Lionel C. Drama and society in the age of Jonson. 1957. 4.00. Barnes & Noble
Mantoux, Paul. Industrial revolution in the eighteenth century. tr. by Marjorie Vernon. 1961. 7.75. Macmillan
Power, E. E. Wool trade in English medieval history. 1941. 2.90. Oxford U. P.
Pressnell, L. S. Studies in the Industrial Revolution. 1960. 6.75. Oxford U. P.
Rostow, W. W. British economy of the nineteenth century. 1948. 4.00. Oxford U. P.
Toynbee, Arnold. Industrial Revolution. 1959. 3.25. Smith, Peter
GT. BRIT.--FOREIGN RELATIONS (942)
Arnold, Matthew. England and the Italian question. by Merle M. Beuington. 1953. 2.75. Duke
Attlee, Clement, and Francis Williams. Twilight of empire. 1962. 5.00. Barnes, A. S.
Bishop, Donald G. Administration of British foreign relations. il. 7.00. Syracuse
Campbell-Johnson, Alan. Eden: The making of a statesman. il. 1955. 5.00. Washburn
Churchill, Winston S. In the balance. 1952. 5.00. Houghton
Connell, John. Office: British foreign policy and its makers, 1919-1951. 5.75. St. Martins
Halifax, E. F. L. Speeches on foreign policy. by H. H. E. Craster. 1940. 2.40. Oxford U. P.
Rowse, A. L. Expansion of Elizabethan England. 1955. 5.75. St. Martins
Seton-Watson, R. W. Britain in Europe. 1937. 7.50. Cambridge U. P.
Strang, William. Britain in world affairs: The fluctuation in power and influence from Henry VIII to Elizabeth II. 6.95. Praeger
Woodhouse, Christopher M. British foreign policy since the Second World War. 1962. 6.50. Praeger
Woodward, E. L. British foreign policy during the Second World War. 1962. 7.50. British Info. Services

GT. BRIT.--FOREIGN RELATIONS--U.S. (942)

Adams, Ephraim. Great Britain and the American Civil War. 2 vols. bd. as 1. 7.50. Russell

Allen, Harry C. Great Britain and the United States: History of Anglo-American relations, 1783-1952. 1955. 10.00. St. Martins

Brinton, Crane. United States and Britain. il. 1948. 4.25. Harvard

Mallalieu, William C. British reconstruction and American policy, 1945-1955. 1956. 5.00. Scarecrow

Perkins, Bradford. Prologue to war: England and the United States, 1805-1812. 1961. 7.95. U. of Calif.

GT. BRIT.--HISTORY (942)

Ashley, Maurice. Great Britain to 1688: A modern history. il. 1961. 7.50. U. of Mich.

Churchill, Winston S. History of the English-speaking peoples. 4 vols. 20.00 Dodd

Green, John R. Short history of the English people. 2 vols. 1.95 ea. Dutton

Hall, Walter P., and others. History of England and the Empire - Commonwealth. il. 1962. 9.00. Ginn

Jerrold, Douglas. England: Past, present, and future. 1951. 4.00. Norton

McElwee, William. Story of England. 5.95. Roy Pub.

Maurois, Andre. History of England. il. 1958. 6.50. Farrar, Straus

Rowse, A. L. Spirit of English history. il. 1945. 2.75. Oxford U. P.

Smellie, K. G. Great Britain since 1688. il. 1962. 7.50. U. of Mich.

Trevelyan, G. M. History of England. 3 vols. vol. 1, From the earliest times to the Reformation; vol. 2, Tudors and the Stuart era; vol. 3, From Utrecht to modern times. Doubleday

Trevelyan, G. M. Illustrated English social history. 4 vols. il. 1949-1952. vol. 1, Chaucer's England and the early Tudors; vol. 2, Age of Shakespeare and the Stuart period; vol. 3, Eighteenth century; vol. 4, Nineteenth century; 7.50 ea. McKay

Trevelyan G. M. Illustrated history of England. 1956. 14.50. McKay

Macaulay, T. B. Essays. 2 vols. 1.95 ea. Dutton

Maitland, Frederic W. Selected historical essays. by H. M. Cam. 1957. 5.00. Cambridge U. P.

Newman, Bertram. English historians: Selected passages. 1957. 2.90. Oxford U. P.

Pollard, Albert F. Factors in modern history. 1960. 4.40. Beacon

Quennell, Peter, and Alan Hodge. Past we share: An illustrated history of the British and American peoples. 1960. 12.50. Putnam

GT. BRIT.--HISTORY--TO 1485 (942)

Cam, Helen M. England before Elizabeth. 1950. 2.50. Hillary

Churchill, Winston S. Birth of Britain to 1485. 6.00. Dodd

Costain, Thomas B. Conquerors. il. 1949. 4.50. Doubleday

Duckett, Eleanor S. France and Britain. 1938. 4.40. 1961. U. of Mich.

Trevelyan, G. M. From the earliest times to the Reformation. Doubleday

GT. BRIT.--HISTORY TO 449 (942)

Burn, Andrew Robert. Agricola and Roman Britain. 1954. 2.50. Macmillan

Monmouth, Geoffrey of. History of the kings of Britain. Dutton

Moore, Ralph W. Romans in Britain. 1954. 3.50. St. Martins

GT. BRIT.--HISTORY--ANGLO-SAXON PERIOD, 449-1066 (942)

Biair, Peter Hunter. Introduction to Anglo-Saxon England. 1959. 6.50. Cambridge U. P.

Collingwood, R. G., and J. N. L. Myres. Roman Britain and the English settlements. il. 1937. 5.60. Oxford U. P.

Stenton, Frank M. Anglo-Saxon England. 1947. 5.60. Oxford U. P.

Anglo-Saxon Chronicle. 1934. 1.95. Dutton

Plummer, Charles. Anglo-Saxon chronicle. 2 vols. 1892, 1899. 8.00. Oxford U. P.

Robertson, Agnes J. Anglo Saxon charters. 1939. 11.50. Cambridge U. P.

GT. BRIT.--HISTORY--MEDIEVAL PERIOD, 1066-1485 (942)

Costain, Thomas B. Last Plantagenets. il. 1962. 5.75. Doubleday

Costain, Thomas B. Magnificent century. il. 1951. 4.50. Doubleday

Coulton, George G. Medieval panorama. il. 1955. Meridian

Davis, Henry W. C. England under the Normans and Angevins. 7.00. Barnes
& Noble

Froissart, Jean. Chronicles of England, France, Spain, and other places
adjoining. 1961. Dutton

Green, Vivian H. H. Later Plantagenets: A survey of English history between
1307 and 1485. 1955. 4.00. St. Martins

Haskins, Charles H. Normans in European history. 1959. 4.50. Ungar

Hunt, Percival. Fifteenth century England. 1962. 4.50. U. of Pittsburgh

Kelly, Amy. Eleanor of Aquitaine, and the four kings. 1957. Vintage

Morris, W. A., and others. English government at work, 1327-1336. 3 vols.
vol. 1, o.p; vol. 2, Fiscal.administration (with J. R. Strayer); vol. 3, Local
administration and justice (with W. H. Dunham). 5.00 ea. Mediaeval

Painter, Sidney. Reign of King John. 1949. 6.00. Johns Hopkins

Poole, A. L. From Domesday Book to Magna Carta, 1087-1216. 1955. 5.60.
Oxford U. P.

Poole, Austin L. Medieval England. 2 vols. il. 1958. 19.00. Oxford U. P.

Powicke, Frederick M. King Henry III and the Lord Edward: The community
of the realm in the thirteenth century. 2 vols. il. 1947. set 11.20. Oxford U. P.

Powicke, Frederick M. Medieval England, 1066-1485. 1931. 1.70. Oxford U. P.

Vickers, Kenneth H. England in the later Middle Ages. 1950. 7.00. Barnes &
Noble

GT. BRIT.--HISTORY--TUDORS--1485-1603 (942)

Churchill, Winston S. New world, 1485 to 1688. 6.00. Dodd

Einstein, Lewis. Tudor ideals. in prep. Russell

Elton, Geoffrey R. England under the Tudors. 1955. 6.00. Barnes & Noble

Feiling, Keith. England under the Tudors and Stuarts, 1485-1688. 1.70. Oxford
U. P.

Pollard, Albert F. Factors in modern history. 1960. 4.40. Beacon

Read, Conyers. Tudors. il. 1936. 4.00. Holt

Sitwell, Edith. Fanfare for Elizabeth. il. 1962. Macmillan

Sitwell, Edith. Queens and the hive. il. 1962. 7.50. Little

Trevelyan, G. M. Age of Shakespeare and the Stuart period. 7.50. McKay

Trevelyan, G. M. Chaucer's England and the early Tudors. 7.50. McKay

Williamson, J. A. Tudor age. 1953. 6.50. McKay

GT. BRIT.--HISTORY--ELIZABETH, 1558-1603 (942.055)

Black, J. B. Reign of Elizabeth, 1558-1603. 1959. 6.10. Oxford U. P.

Cheyney, E. P. History of England from the defeat of the Armada to the death
of Elizabeth. 2 vols. 13.00. Smith, Peter

Neale, John Ernest. Essays in Elizabethan history. 1959. 3.50. St. Martins

Rowse, A. L. Elizabethans and America. il. 1959. 5.00. Harper

Rowse, Alfred L. England of Elizabeth. il. 1950. 10.50. Macmillan

Stafford, Helen G. James VI of Scotland and the throne of England. 3.75. Appleton

Williamson, James A. Age of Drake. il. 1961. 5.75. Macmillan

GT. BRIT.--HISTORY--STUARTS--1603-1714 (942)

Churchill, Winston S. New world, 1485 to 1688. 6.00. Dodd

Clark, George N. Later Stuarts, 1660-1714. 1955. 5.60. Oxford U. P.

Davies, Godfrey. Early Stuarts, 1603-1660. il. 1959. 6.10. Oxford U. P.

Davies, Godfrey. Essays on the later Stuarts. il. 1958. 4.00. Huntington Lib.

Evelyn, John. Diary of John Evelyn. (Oxford stand. authors) by E. S. de Beer.
1959. 7.00. Oxford U. P.

Hill, Christopher. Century of revolution: 1603-1714. 1961. 6.25. Nelson

Notestein, Wallace. English people on the eve of colonization: 1603-1630. 1954.
5.00. 1962. Harper

Trevelyan, G. M. Age of Shakespeare and the Stuart period. 7.50. McKay
Trevelyan, George M. England under the Stuarts. 6.00. Barnes & Noble
Wedgwood, C. V. King's peace. il. 1955. 6.95. Macmillan
Wedgwood, C. V. Poetry and politics under the Stuarts. 1960. 4.75. Cambridge
    U. P.
Wedgewood, Cicely V. Truth and opinion. 1960. 4.50. Macmillan
Pepys, Samuel. Diary. 2 vols. 1946. 15.00. Random
Pepys, Samuel. Diary of Samuel Pepys. by O. F. Morshead. il. 1960. 4.50.
    Smith, Peter
GT. BRIT.--HISTORY--PURITAN REVOLUTION, 1642-1660 (942)
Cromwell, Oliver. Writings and speeches. by Wilbur Cortez Abbot. 4 vols. vol.
    1, 1937. 5.00; vol. 2, 1939. 5.00; vols. 3 and 4, o.p. Harvard
Firth, Charles H. Oliver Cromwell and the rule of the Puritans in England. 2.75.
    Oxford U. P.
Hobbes, Thomas. Behemoth: The history of the causes of the Civil War in
    England. 1840. 14.50. Franklin, B.
Wedgwood, C. V. King's war. 6.00. Macmillan
GT. BRIT.--HISTORY--RESTORATION, 1660-1688 (942)
Macaulay, T. B. History of England. 4 vols. 1.95 ea. Dutton
Ogg, David. England in the reign of Charles II. 2 vols. 1955. 14.40. Oxford U. P.
Ogg, David. England in the reigns of James II and William III. 1955. 8.80. Oxford
    U. P.
Trevelyan, G. M. English Revolution, 1688-1689. 1938. 1.70. Oxford U. P.
GT. BRIT.--HISTORY--18TH CENTURY (942)
Briggs, Asa. Age of improvement. 1959. 7.25. McKay
Churchill, Winston S. Age of revolution, 1688-1815. 6.00. Dodd
Green, Vivian H. H. Hanoverians, 1714-1815. 1948. 4.25. St. Martins
Trevelyan, G. M. Eighteenth century. 7.50. McKay
Turberville, Arthur Stanley. Johnson's England: An account of the life and manners
    of his age. 2 vols. il. 1953. 12.00. Oxford U. P.
Watson, John S. Reign of George, III, 1760-1815. 1960. 5.60. Oxford U. P.
George III, King of Great Britain. Later correspondence. 2 vols. by A. Aspinall.
    vol. 1, 1783-1793. vol. 2, in prep. Cambridge U. P.
Trevelyan, G. M. Select documents for Queen Anne's reign. 1929. 3.50.
    Cambridge U. P.
GT. BRIT.--HISTORY--1714-1837 (942)
Gipson, Lawrence H. British Empire before the American Revolution. 10 vols.
    vol. 1, British Isles and the American colonies. 1958; vol. 2, Southern planta-
    tions. 1960; vol. 3, Northern plantations. 1960; vol. 4, - 5, Zones of interna-
    tional friction; vols. 6-8, Great war for the Empire; vol. 9, Triumphant Empire.
    1956; vol. 10, Triumphant Empire. 1961. 8.50. ea. Knopf
Plumb, J. H. First four Georges. il. 5.00. Macmillan
Robertson, Charles G. England under the Hanoverians. 6.00. Barnes & Noble
Williams, Basil. Whig supremacy, 1714-1760. by C. H. Stuart. 6.75. Oxford U. P.
Nelson, Horatio. Letters from Lord Nelson. comp. by Geoffrey Rawson. 1961.
    1.95. Dutton
GT. BRIT.--HISTORY--19TH CENTURY (942)
Briggs, Asa. Age of improvement. 1959. 7.25. McKay
Marriott, John A. R. England since Waterloo. 6.00. Barnes & Noble
Trevelyan, G. M. British history in the nineteenth century and after: 1782-
    1919. 1937. 7.00. McKay
Trevelyan, G. M. Nineteenth century. 7.50. McKay
Woodward, Ernest L. Age of reform, 1815-1870. 1962. 6.75. Oxford U. P.
GT. BRIT.--HISTORY--VICTORIA, 1837-1901 (942)
Ensor, R. C. K. England, 1870-1914. 1936. 5.60. Oxford U. P.
Marriott, John A. R. Modern England, 1885-1945. 6.00. Barnes & Noble
Parrott, Thomas Marc, and Robert Bernard Martin. Companion to Victorian
    literature. 1955. 3.00. Scribner

Young, G. M.   Early Victorian England, 1830-1865.   2 vols.   1934.   11.20.   Oxford
U. P.

GT. BRIT.--HISTORY--20TH CENTURY (942)

Butler, James.   History of England, 1815-1939.   1960.   1.70.   Oxford U. P.

Ensor, R. C. K.   England, 1870-1914.   1936.   5.60.   Oxford U. P.

Havighurst, Alfred F.   Twentieth-century Britain, 1962.   7.90?   Harper

GT. BRIT.--HISTORY, COMIC, SATIRICAL, ETC. (942)

Sellar, Walter C., and Robert J. Yeatman.   1066. and all that.   il.   2.95.   Dutton

GT. BRIT.--HISTORY, MILITARY (942)

Fortescue, John W.   Wellington.   1960.   5.00.   Barnes & Noble

Powicke, Michael.   Military obligation in Medieval England.   1962.   7.20.   Oxford
U. P.

Wellington, Duke of.   Wellington at War 1749-1815: A selection of his wartime
letters.   by Antony Brett-James.   1961.   10.00.   St. Martins

GT. BRIT.--HISTORY, NAVAL (942)

Marcus, Geoffrey J.   Naval history of England.   il.   1962.   12.50.   Little

Mattingly, Garrett.   Armada.   il.   1959.   6.00.   1962.   Houghton

GT. BRIT.--INTELLECTUAL LIFE (942)

Craig, Hardin.   Enchanted glass: The Elizabethan mind in literature.   1952.   4.00.
Oxford U. P.

Dobson, Austin.   Eighteenth century vignettes.   2.75.   Oxford U. P.

Harrison, George B.   Elizabethan journals.   1955.   8.50.   U. of Mich.

Harrison, G. B.   Second Jacobean journal: Being a record of those things most
talked of during the years 1607-10.   1958.   5.50.   U. of Mich.

Hazlitt, William.   Spirit of the age, and English poets.   1.95.   Dutton

Hazlitt, William.   Spirit of the age: or, Contemporary portraits.   1904.   1.85.
Oxford U. P.

Somervell, D. C.   English thought in the 19th century.   1947.   2.75.   McKay
Longmans

Wright, Louis B.   Middle-class culture in Elizabethan England.   1958.   7.50.   Cornell

GT. BRIT.--KINGS AND RULERS (942)

Berton, Pierre.   Royal family.   1954.   4.50.   Knopf

Farjeon, Eleanor and Herbert.   Kings and queens.   il.   1955.   3.75.   Lippincott

Harvey, John H.   Plantagenets.   il.   1959.   5.00.   Macmillan

Marie Louise, Princess.   My memories of six reigns.   il.   1957.   5.50.   Dutton

Michie, Allan A.   God save the queen.   il.   1953.   5.00.   Sloane

Trease, Geoffrey.   Seven kings of England.   1955.   3.00.   Vanguard

Trease, Geoffrey.   Seven queens of England.   1953.   3.00.   Vanguard

GT. BRIT.--PARLIAMENT (942)

Boardman, Harry.   Glory of parliament.   by Francis Boyd.   1960.   3.95.   Taplinger

Jennings, Ivor.   Parliament.   1957.   10.50.   Cambridge U. P.

Young, Roland.   British Parliament.   1962.   6.50.   Northwestern U.

Campion, Gilbert, Lord.   Introduction to the procedure in the House of Commons.
5.00.   St. Martins

Judd, G. P.   Members of Parliament, 1734-1832.   1955.   6.00.   Yale

Williams, Orlo, C.   Clerical organization of the House of Commons, 1661-1850.
1954.   5.60.   Oxford U. P.

GT. BRIT.--POLITICS AND GOVERNMENT (942)

Brinton, Crane.   United States and Britain.   il.   1948.   4.25.   Harvard

British historical speeches and orations.   1.95.   Dutton

Dodd, A. H.   Growth of responsible government, from James I to Victoria.   4.50.
Hillary

Gooch, R. K.   Government of England.   1937.   4.50.   Van Nostrand

Jennings, Ivor.   Cabinet government.   1959.   9.50.   Cambridge U. P.

Jennings, Ivor.   Parliament.   1957.   10.50.   Cambridge U. P.

Marcham, Frederick G.   Constitutional history of modern England: 1485-1960.
1960.   7.50.   Harper

Marriott, John A. R.   English political institutions: An introductory study.   2.90.
Oxford U. P.

Ogg, Frederic A.   English government and politics. 6.30. Macmillan
Rowse, Alfred L.   End of an epoch. 3.00. St. Martins
GT. BRIT.--POLITICS AND GOVERNMENT--1485-1603 (942)
Neale, John E.   Elizabeth I and her parliaments. 2 vols. vol. 1. 1559-1581; vol.
   2. 1584-1601. 6.50. ea. St. Martins
Read, Conyers.   Social and political forces in the English Reformation. 1953.
   2.75. Van Nostrand
Rowse, A. L.   Expansion of Elizabethan England. 1955. 5.75. St. Martins
GT. BRIT.--POLITICS AND GOVERNMENT--1603-1714 (942)
Gooch, G. P.   English democratic ideas in the 17th century. 1955. 3.50. Cambridge
   U. P.
GT. BRIT.--POLITICS AND GOVERNMENT--18TH CENTURY (942)
Burke, Edmund.   Selected writings. 1.95. Modern Lib.
Fox, Charles James.   Speeches during the French Revolutionary War Period.
   1.95. Dutton
Paine, Thomas.   Rights of man. bd. with Edmund Blake's Reflections on the
   Revolution in France. Doubleday
Paine, Thomas.   Rights of man. 1935. 2.95. Dutton
Ritcheson, Charles R.   British politics and the American revolution. il. 1954.
   4.00. U. of Okla.
GT. BRIT.--POLITICS AND GOVERNMENT--19TH CENTURY (942)
McEowell, R. B.   British conservatism, 1832-1914. 1959. 4.50. Hillary
Pelling, Henry.   American and the British left: From Bright to Bevan. 1957. 3.50.
   N. Y. U.
Williams, William E.   Rise of Gladstone. 1932. 2.50. Cambridge U. P.
Woodward, Ernest L.   Age of reform, 1815-1870. 1962. 6.75. Oxford U. P.
GT. BRIT.--POLITICS AND GOVERNMENT--20TH CENTURY (942)
Brome, Vincent.   Aneurin Bevan. 1953. 3.00. Wellington
Kennedy, John F.   Why England slept. 1961. 3.50. Funk
Morrison, Herbert.   Government and Parliament. 1959. 4.80. Oxford U. P.
Pelling, Henry.   America and the British left: From Bright to Bevan. 1957. 3.50.
   N. Y. U.
Rowse, Alfred L.   Appeasement. il. 1961. 3.00. Norton
Spearman, Diana.   Democracy in England. 7.50. Macmillan
GT. BRIT.--POLITICS AND GOVERNMENT--1945- (942)
Churchill, Winston S.   In the balance. 1952. 5.00. Houghton
Churchill, Winston S.   Sinews of peace. 1949. 3.50. Houghton
Eden, Anthony.   Days for decision. 1950. 3.00. Houghton
Eden, Anthony.   Full circle. il. 1960. 6.95. Houghton
Theobald, Robert.   Britain in the sixties. 1961. 2.50. Wilson
GT. BRIT.--SOCIAL CONDITIONS (942)
Carlyle, Thomas.   Past and present. 2.25. Oxford U. P.
Carr-Saunders, Alexander M., and others.   Survey of social conditions in England
   and Wales as illustrated by statistics. il. 1958. 4.00. Oxford U. P.
Cole, G. D. H., and Raymond Postgate.   British common people, 1746-1946. 1961.
   Barnes & Noble
Cole, G. D. H.   Post-war condition of Britain. 6.75. Praeger
Einstein, Lewis.   Tudor ideals. 4.50. Russell
Hill, Christopher.   Puritanism and revolution. Studies in interpretation of the
   English revolution of the 17th century. 8.50. Humanities
Johnson, L. G.   Social evolution of industrial Britain. 4.50. Lounz
Knights, Lionel C.   Drama and society in the age of Jonson. 1957. 4.00. Barnes
   & Noble
GT. BRIT.--SOCIAL LIFE AND CUSTOMS (942)
Campbell, Mildred L.   English yeoman under Elizabeth and the early Stuarts. 1942.
   8.50. Barnes & Noble
Coulton, G. G.   Social life in Britain. 1957. 7.50. Cambridge U. P.
Defoe, Daniel.   Best of Defoe's review. by W. L. Payne. 1951. 4.00.
   Columbia

Morton, Henry V. In search of England. il. 5.00. Dodd
Rickert, Edith, and others. Chaucer's world. 1948. 6.75. Columbia
GREAT LAKES--HISTORY (977.9)
Hatcher, Harlan. Great Lakes. il. 1944. 3.50. Oxford U. P.
Havighurst, Walter. Long ships passing. il. 1942. 5.00. Macmillan
GREAT PLAINS (978)
Custer, George A. My life on the plains. 4.00. Smith, Peter
Webb, Walter P. Great Plains. 1931. 8.00. Ginn
Wedel, Waldo R. Prehistoric man on the Great Plains. il. 1961. 5.95. U. of
    Okla.

GREECE--ANTIQUITIES (938)
Petrie, Alexander. Introduction to Greek history, antiquities and literature. 1932.
    1.10. Oxford U. P.
Quennell, Marjorie, and C. H. B. Everyday things in ancient Greece. il. 1954.
    3.50. Putnam
Ridgeway, William. Early age of Greece. 2 vols. 12.50 ea. Cambridge U. P.
Payne, Robert. Splendor of Greece. il. 1960. 5.95. Harper
GREECE--BIOGRAPHY (921.9)
Plutarch. Everybody's Plutarch. by Raymond T. Bond. il. 1962. 4.50. Dodd
Plutarch. Lives. 2.95. Modern Lib.
Plutarch. Parallel lives. 11 vols. 3.50 ea. Harvard
GREECE--HISTORY (938)
Barr, Stringfellow. Will of Zeus: A history of Greece from the origins of
    Hellenic culture to the death of Alexander. 1961. 10.00. Lippincott
Botsford, George W., and Charles A. Robinson. Hellenic history. il. 7.75.
    Macmillan
Bury, John B. History of Greece. 4.75. St. Martins
Hammond, Nicholas G. L. History of Greece to 322 B.C. il. 1959. 8.00. Oxford
    U. P.
Herodotus. Works. 2 vols. tr. by J. E. Powell. 1949. 4.80. Oxford U. P.
Herodotus. History. tr. by George Rawlinson. 2.98. Tudor
Herodotus. Persian wars. 1.95. Modern Lib.
Polybius. Histories. 2 vols. tr. by Evelyn S. Shuckburgh. 1962. 10.00. Indiana
Robinson, Cyril E. History of Greece. il. 1957. 4.00. Barnes and Noble
Rostovtzeff, Mikhail I. Social and economic history of the Hellenistic world.
    3 vols. il. 1941. 33.60. Oxford U. P.
Thucydides. Complete writings. 1934. 1.95. Modern Lib.
Thucydides. History of the Peloponnesian War. 1936. 2.95. Dutton
Thucydides. Peloponnesian war: The Thomas Hobbes translation. 2 vols. by
    David Grene. 1959. set, 6.95. U. of Mich.
Toynbee, Arnold J. Greek historical thought. 1954. 0.60. New Am. Lib.
GREECE--HISTORY--HISTORIOGRAPHY (938.9)
Bury, John Bagnell. Ancient Greek historians. 1957. Dover
GREECE--HISTORY--SOURCES (938)
Hill, G. F., and others. Sources for Greek history between the Persian and
    Peloponnesian wars. 1951. 4.80. Oxford U. P.
GREECE--INTELLECTUAL LIFE (949.5)
Cooper, Lane. Greek genius and its influence. 1917. 3.00. Cornell
Snell, Bruno. Discovery of the mind: The Greek origins of European thought.
    1953. 5.50. Harvard
GREECE--POLITICS AND GOVERNMENT (938)
Agard, Walter R. What democracy meant to the Greeks. 1960. U. of Wis.
Fowler, William Warde. City state of the Greeks and Romans. 2.75. St. Martins
Fustel de Coulanges, Numa Denis. Ancient city. 1959. 3.00. Smith, Peter
GREECE--RELIGION (292)
Cornford, F. M. From religion to philosophy. 1958. 3.25. Smith, Peter
Guthrie, William K. C. Religion and mythology of the Greeks. 1.25. Cambridge
    U. P.

Hus, Alain. Greek and Roman religion. 1962. 3.50. Hawthorn
Kerenyi, C. Religion of the Greeks and Romans. il. 10.00. Dutton
Nilsson, M. P. Greek folk religion. il. 3.25. Smith, Peter
Nilsson, M. P. History of Greek religion. tr. by F. J. Fielden. 1949. 4.50.
  Oxford U. P.
Otto, Walter F. Homeric gods. tr. by Moses Hadas. il. 1954. 5.00. Pantheon
Snell, Bruno. Discovery of the mind: The Greek origins of European thought.
  1953. 5.50. Harvard
GREECE--SOCIAL LIFE AND CUSTOMS (938)
Mireaux, Emile. Daily life in the time of Homer. 1959. 5.00. Macmillan
Robinson, Cyril E. Everyday life in ancient Greece. il. 1933. 1.20. Oxford U. P.
Van Hook, La Rue. Greek life and thought. 1923. 4.00. Columbia
GREECE, MODERN (949.5)
Larrabee, Stephen A. Hellas observed: The American experience of Greece.
  il. 1957. 6.00. N. Y. U.
GREECE, MODERN--DESCRIPTION AND TRAVEL (914.95)
Kimbrough, Emily. Water, water everywhere. il. 1956. 4.50. Harper
Miller, Helen H. Greek horizons. il. 1961. 6.95. Scribner
GREECE, MODERN--DESCRIPTION AND TRAVEL--GUIDEBOOKS (914.95)
Fodor, Eugene. Greece. il. 4.50. McKay
GREECE, MODERN--HISTORY (949.5)
Gonatas, Stylianos. Greece in the Twentieth century. 7.50. Speller
GREECE, MODERN--SOCIAL CONDITIONS (949.5)
Sanders, Irwin T. Rainbow in the rock. il. 1962. 7.50. Harvard
GREEK DRAMA--HISTORY AND CRITICISM (882.9)
Cooper, Lane. Aristotelian theory of comedy, with an adaptation of the Poetics
  and a translation of the Tractatus Coislinianus. 1922. 3.00. Cornell
Driver, Tom Faw. Sense of history of Greek and Shakespearean drama. 1960.
  5.00. Columbia
Flickinger, Ray C. Greek theater and its drama. 1946. 6.50. U. of Chicago
Hyman, Stanley E. Poetry and criticism: Four revolutions in literary taste.
  1961. 4.00. Atheneum
Kitto, Humphrey D. F. Form and meaning in drama. 1957. 6.00. Barnes &
  Noble
Kitto, Humphrey D. F. Greek tragedy: A literary study. 1961. 6.00. Barnes &
  Noble
Lattimore, Richmond. Poetry of Greek tragedy. 1958. 3.50. Johns Hopkins
Nietzsche, Friedrich. Birth of tragedy, and Genealogy of morals. 1956.
  Doubleday
Norwood, Gilbert. Greek comedy. 5.00. Humphries
Norwood, Gilbert. Greek tragedy. il. 4.95. 1960. Hill & Wang
GREEK DRAMA--TRANSLATIONS INTO ENGLISH (880)
Arnott, Peter D., tr. Three Greek plays for the theatre. 1961. 5.00. Indiana
Fitts, Dudley. Greek plays in modern translation. 1947. 6.00. Dial
Grene, David, and Richmond Lattimore. Complete Greek tragedies. 4 vols.
  1959. boxed, 20.00. U. of Chicago
Hamilton, Edith. Three Greek plays: The Trojan women of Euripides and the
  Prometheus and Agamemnon of Aeschylus. 1937. 3.95. 1958. Norton
Lind, L. R. Ten Greek plays in contemporary translations. 1958. 4.50. Houghton
Oates, Whitney J., and Eugene O'Neill, Jr. Complete Greek drama. 2 vols.
  10.00. Random
GREEK LITERATURE (COLLECTIONS) (880)
Chase, Alston H., and Henry Phillips, Jr. New Greek reader. 1954. Harvard
GREEK LITERATURE--HISTORY AND CRITICISM (880)
Baldry, H. C. Greek literature for the modern reader. 1959. 3.95. Cambridge
  U. P.
Bowra, Cecil M. Ancient Greek literature. 1933. 1.70. 1960. Oxford U. P.
Hadas, Moses. History of Greek literature. 1950. 4.25. Columbia

Hamilton, Edith. Greek way. 1930. 4.50. Norton
Jaeger, Werner. Paideia: Ideals of Greek culture. 1944. 7.50 ea. tr. by Gilbert
  Highet. Oxford U. P.
Jebb, Richard C. Essays and addresses. 1907. 5.50. Cambridge U. P.
Livingstone, R. W. Greek genius and its meaning to us. 1915. 2.40. Oxford U. P.
Murray, Gilbert. Greek studies. 1946. 3.40. Oxford U. P.
Rose, Herbert J. Handbook of Greek literature. 7.95. 1.85. Dutton (R)
Trenkner, Sophie. Greek novella in the Classical Period. 1958. 5.50. Cambridge
  U. P.
Webster, T. B. L. Art and literature in fourth century Athens. 1956. 4.00.
  Oxford U. P.
Webster, T. B. L. Greek art and literature, 700-530 B.C. il. 5.95. Praeger
GREEK LITERATURE--TRANSLATIONS INTO ENGLISH (880)
Auden, W. H. Portable Greek reader. 1948. 2.95. Viking
Howe, George, and others. Greek literature in translation. 1948. 8.00. Harper
Oates, Whitney J., and C. T. Murphy. Greek literature in translation. 1944.
  6.95. McKay
Toynbee, Arnold J. Greek historical thought. 1954. New Am. Lib.
GREEK ORATIONS (885)
Genner, E. E. Selections from the Attic orators. 1928. 1.70. Oxford U. P.
Maidment, K. J., and J. O. Burtt, trs. Minor Attic orators. 2 vols. 3.50 ea.
  Harvard
Jebb, Richard C. Attic orators from Antiphon to Isaeos. 2 vols. 1962. 15.00.
  Russell
GREEK POETRY (COLLECTIONS) (881)
Edmonds, J. M. tr. Greek bucolic poets: Theocritus, Bion, and Moschus.
  Works. 3.50. Harvard
Gow, Andrew S. F. Bucolici Graece. 1952. 2.40. Oxford U. P.
Paton, W. R., tr. Greek anthology. 5 vols. 3.50 ea. Harvard
GREEK POETRY--HISTORY AND CRITICISM (881)
Bowra, Cecil Maurice. Early Greek elegists. 1960. 4.00? Barnes & Noble
Snell, Bruno. Poetry and society: The role of poetry in ancient Greece. 1961.
  3.75. Indiana
GREEK POETRY--TRANSLATIONS INTO ENGLISH (881)
Edmonds, J. M., tr. Lyra Graeca. 3 vols. 3.50 ea. Harvard
Fitts, Dudley. Greek anthology. 1956. 3.00. New Directions
Hadas, Moses. Greek poets. 1.95. Modern Lib.
Higham, T. F., and C. M. Bowra. Oxford book of Greek verse in translation.
  1938. 5.75. Oxford U. P.
Lattimore, Richmond. Greek lyrics. 1960. 4.00. U. of Chicago
Lucas, F. L. Greek poetry for everyman. 1956. Beacon
GREELEY, HORACE, 1811-1871 (923.7)
Granberg, W. J. Spread the truth: The life of Horace Greeley. 1959. 3.00.
  Dutton
Van Glyndon G. Horace Greeley: Nineteenth century crusader. 1953. 5.00. U. of
  Pa.
GREENE, GRAHAM, 1904- (823)
Kunkel, Frank. Labyrinthine ways of Graham Greene. 1960. 3.50. Sheed
GREENE, NATHANAEL, 1742-1786 (923.5)
Thayer, Theodore. Nathanael Greene, strategist of the American Revolution.
  6.96. Twayne
GREENHOUSES (635)
Dulles, Marion. Greenhouse gardening around the year. il. 3.75. Macmillan
Northen, Henry T., and Rebecca T. Complete book of greenhouse gardening.
  1956. 6.50. Ronald
Sunset. Garden and patio building book. by the Editors of Sunset. il. 1960. 6.95.
  Lane
GREENLAND (998.2)

Freuchen, Dagmar. Peter Freuchen's adventures in the arctic. 1960. 4.95. Messner

Kent, Rockwell. Greenland journal. 1962. 7.50; limited ed. 25.00. Obolensky

Wager, Walter. Camp Century: City under the ice. il. 1962. 3.95. Chilton

GRENFELL, SIR WILFRED THOMASON, 1865-1940 (925)

Kerr, Lennox J. Wildred Grenfell: His life and work. il. 1959. 4.00. Dodd

GRENVILLE, SIR RICHARD, 1600-1658 (942)

Rowse, A. L. Sir Richard Grenville's place in English history. 1957. 0.70. Oxford U. P.

GRIEG, EDVARD HAGERUP, 1843-1907 (927)

Abraham, Gerald, and others. Grieg: A symposium. il. 1950. 3.00. U. of Okla.

GRIFFITH, ARTHUR, 1872-1922 (923.2)

Colum, Padraic. Ourselves alone! 1959. 6.00. Crown

GROESBECK, ALEXANDER JOSEPH, 1873-1953 (923.473)

Woodford, Frank B. Alex J. Groesbeck: Portrait of a public man. il. 1962. 6.50. Wayne

GROPIUS, WALTER, 1883- (926)

Fitch, James M. Walter Gropius. il. 1960. 4.95. Braziller

GROUP COUNSELING (371.422)

Bennett, M. E. Guidance in groups. 1955. 6.50. McGraw

Glanz, Edward C. Groups in guidance. il. 1962. 8.65. Allyn & Bacon

GROUP PSYCHOTHERAPY (616.891)

Bach, G. R. Intensive group psychotherapy. 1954. 7.00. Ronald

Beukenkamp, Cornelius, Jr. Fortunate strangers: an experience in group psychotherapy. 1959. Grove

Chapman, Myfanwy. Self-inventory: Group therapy for those who stutter. 1959. 2.75. Burgess

Driver, Helen I., and others. Counseling and learning through small-group discussion. il. 7.00. Monona

Ginott, Haim G. Group psychotherapy with children. 1961. 5.95. McGraw

Powdermaker, Florence B., and Jerome D. Frank. Group psychotherapy: Studies in methodology of research and therapy. 1953. 6.50. Harvard

Roman, Melvin. Reaching delinquents through reading. il. 1958. 4.50. Thomas, C. C

Slavson, Samuel R. Fields of group psychotherapy. 1956. 6.00. Int. Univs.

Wolf, Alexander, and Emanuel K. Schwartz. Psychoanalysis in groups. 1962. 8.00. Grune

GROUPS, THEORY OF (512.86)

Carmichael, Robert D. Introduction to the theory of groups of finite order. 1956. 3.95. Dover

Hall, Marshall. Theory of groups. 1959. 8.75. Macmillan

Zassenhaus, H. Theory of groups. 6.00. Chelsea

GROWTH (612.6)

Bernard, Harold. Human development in western culture. il. 1962. 9.95. Allyn & Bacon

Bonner, J. T. Evolution of development. 1958. 3.50. Cambridge U. P.

Boyd, Edith. Growth of the surface area of the human body. 1935. 5.00. U. of Minn.

Crow, Lester D., and Alice. Human development and learning. 6.25. Am. Bk. Co.

Gesell, Arnold, and Catherine S. Amatruda. Developmental diagnosis. il. 1949. 8.50. Hoeber

Gordon, Ira J. Human development: From birth through adolescence. 1962. 5.75. Harper

Gordon, Myron. Pigment cell growth: Proceedings of the third conference on the biology of normal and atypical pigment cell growth. 1953. 10.00. Academic Press

Hardy, Martha C., and Carolyn Hoefer. Healthy growth: A Study of the influence of health education on growth and development of school children. il. 1936. 6.00. U. of Chicago

Horrocks, John E., and others. Case study tests in human growth and development. 1960. 24.00. Merrill, C. E.

Jones, Harold E. Motor performance and growth: A developmental study of static dynamometric strength. il. 1949. 3.00. U. of Calif.

National Education Association, American Educational Research Association. Growth, development, and learning: 1958; 1961. 2.00 ea. N. E. A.

Rudnick, D. Aspects of synthesis and order in growth. 1955. 6.00. Princeton

Rudnick, D. Rhythmic and synthetic processes in growth. 1957. 7.50. Princeton

Scammon, Richard E., and Leroy A. Calkins. Development and growth of the external dimensions of the human body in the fetal period. il. 1929. 6.00. U. of Minn.

Society for the study of Development and Growth. Cell, organism and milieu. 1959. 8.00. Ronald

Tanner, James M. Growth at adolescence. il. 1961. 9.00. Davis

Watson, Ernest H., and George H. Lowrey. Growth and development of children. 1952. 7.75. Year Bk.

GROWTH (PLANTS) (631. 547)

Audus, Leslie J. Plant growth substances. 1960. 10.00. Wiley

Kozlowski, Theodore T. Tree growth. 1962. 12.00. Ronald

Russell, E. J. Soil conditions and plant growth. 1961. 10.75. Wiley

Yocum, Lawson E. Plant growth. 1945. 4.00. Ronald

GRUNDTVIG, NICOLAI FREDERIK SEVERIN, 1783-1872 (928)

Koch, Hal. Grundtvig. 1952. 3.50. Antioch

GUADALCANAL, BATTLE OF (940.5426)

Griffith, Samuel B. Battle of Guadalcanal. il. 1962. 3.95. Lippincott

GUATEMALA (972.81)

Kelsey, Vera, and Lilly de Jongh Osborne. Four keys to Guatemala. il. 1961. 4.50. Funk

Whetten, Nathan L. Guatemala: The land and the people. 1961. 7.50. Yale

GUATEMALA--DESCRIPTION AND TRAVEL (972.81)

Huxley, Aldous. Beyond the Mexique Bay. 1934. Vintage

Morton, Friedrich. In the land of the Quetzal feather. il. 1960. 4.50. Devin

Rittlinger, Herbert. Last of the Maya. 1962. 4.95. Taplinger

GUATEMALA--HISTORY (972.81)

Rosenthal, Mario. Guatemala. 1962. 4.50. Twayne

GUERRILLA WARFARE (355.425)

Bohannan, Charles T. R., and others. Anti-guerrilla warfare: Lessons from the Philippines. 1962. 5.00. Praeger

Greene, T. N. Guerrilla - And how to fight him. il. 1962. 5.00. Praeger

Guevara, Che. Guerrilla warfare. tr. by H. C. Peterson. 3.95. Praeger

Mao, Tse-tung. Mao Tse-tung on guerilla warfare. tr. by Samuel B. Griffith. 4.50. Praeger

Jones, V. C. Gray ghosts and rebel raiders. 1956. 4.50. Holt

GUIANA (966.5)

Waterton, Charles. Wanderings in South America. 1925. 1.95. Dutton

GUIDED MISSILES (623.451)

Baar, James, and William E. Howard. Spacecraft and missiles of the world, 1962. il. 1962. 5.95. Harcourt

Bergaust, Erik. Reaching for the stars. il. 1960. 4.95. Doubleday

Bonney, E. A., and others. Aerodynamics, propulsion, structures and design practice. il. 1956. 13.50. Van Nostrand

Burgess, Eric. Guided weapons. il. 1957. 5.95. Macmillan

Dornberger, Walter. V-2. il. 1954. 5.00. Viking

Dow, Richard B. Fundamentals of advanced missiles. il. 1958. 11.75. Wiley

Frank, Robert G. and William F. Zimmerman. Materials for rockets and missiles. il. 1959. 4.95. Macmillan

Hobbs, Marvin. Fundamentals of rockets, missiles, and spacecraft. il. 1962. 8.95. Rider

Humphries, John. Rockets and guided missiles. il. 1956. 6.95. Macmillan
Hunter, Mel. Missilemen. il. 1960. 4.95. Doubleday
Mallan, Thrust into space: The story of America's growth in missile power. 1962.
    4.95. Prentice-Hall
Merrill, Grayson, and others. Operations research, armament, launching. 1956.
    14.75. Van Nostrand
Newell, Homer E., Jr. Guide to rockets, missiles, and satellites. il. 1961. 3.25.
    McGraw
Parson, N. A., Jr. Guided missiles in war and peace. il. 1956. 3.50. Harvard
Van Nostrand. Van Nostrand's dictionary of guided missiles and space flight.
    il. 1959. 1950. Van Nostrand
GUILT (131.34)
Bergler, Edmund. Battle of the conscience. 1948. 3.75. Assoc. Booksellers
Reik, Theodor. Myth and guilt. 1957. 5.75. Braziller
Sherrill, Lewis J. Guilt and redemption. 1957. 3.50. John Knox
GUINEA (REGION) (966.5)
Davidson, Basil. Black mother: The years of the African slave trade. il. 1961.
    6.50. Little
Panikkar, Kavalam M. Revolution in Africa. il. 1961. 6.50. Taplinger
GULF STATES (976)
Hartog, Jan de. Waters of the new world. il. 1961. 5.95. Atheneum
GULF STREAM (551.471)
Chapin, Henry, and F. G. Walton Smith. Ocean river. il. 1952. 3.95. Scribner
Stommel, Henry. Gulf stream. 1958. 6.00. U. of Calif.
GULLS (598.33)
Bent, Arthur Cleveland. Life histories of North American gulls and terns. 1947.
    5.00. Dodd
GUMS AND RESINS (634.986)
Kappelmeier, C. P. A. Chemical analysis of resin-based coating materials. il.
    1959. 21.00. Wiley (R)
Smith, Fred and Rex Montgomery. Chemistry of plant gums and mucilages. 1959.
    18.00. Reinhold (R)
GUMS AND RESINS, SYNTHETIC (668.4)
Martens, Charles R. Alkyd resins. 1961. 5.95. Reinhold
Smith, Mayo W. Vinyl resins. 1958. 5.75. Reinhold
Thompson, Mortimer S. Gum plastics. il. 1958. 4.50. Reinhold
GUNNERY (623.5)
Wrigley, Walter, and John Hovorka. Fire control principles. 1959. 10.00. McGraw
GUNPOWDER (662.3)
Partington, James R. History of Greek fire and gunpowder. 1960. 13.50. Barnes
    & Noble
GUNSMITHING (683.4)
Gardner, Robert E. Five centuries of gunsmiths, etc. 10.00. Long's College Bk.
Kauffman, Henry J. Early American gunsmiths, 1650-1850. il. 1952. 5.00.
    Stackpole
GUNTHER, JOHN, 1929-1947 (928)
Gunther, John. Death be not proud: A memoir. 1949. 3.95. Harper
GUSTAV I VASA, KING OF SWEDEN, 1496-1560--DRAMA (839.72)
Strindberg, August. Last of the knights, The regent, Earl Birger of Bjalbo. tr.
    by Walter Johnson. 1957. 4.50. U. of Wash.
Strindberg, August. Vasa trilogy: Master Olof, Gustav Vasa, Erik XIV. by
    Walter Johnson. 1959. 6.00. U. of Wash.
GUSTAV III, KING OF SWEDEN, 1746-1792--DRAMA (839.72)
Strindberg, August. Queen Christina, Charles XII, Gustav III. tr. by Walter
    Johnson. 1955. 4.50. U. of Wash.
GUSTAV V, KING OF SWEDEN, 1858-1950 (923.1)
Ander, O. Fritiof. Building of modern Sweden: The reign of Gustav V, 1907-
    1950. 1958. 3.75. Augustana College Lib.
GYMNASTICS (796.4)
Cotteral, Bonnie, and Donnie. Teaching of stunts and tumbling. 1936. 4.50. Ronald

Duggan, Anne S., and others. Conditioning exercises for girls and women. 1945. 4.00. Ronald

Loken, Newton C. and Robert J. Willoughby. Complete book of gymnastics. 1959. 9.25. Prentice-Hall

Ruff, W. K. Gymnastics, beginners to competitors. 1959. Brown, W. C.

Sparger, Celia. Anatomy and ballet. il. 1961. 3.25. Macmillan

V-Five Association of America. Gymnastics and tumbling. il. 1959. 4.50. U. S. Naval Inst.

GYMNASTICS, MEDICAL (615.824)

Gardiner, M. Dena. Principles of exercise therapy. il. 1957. 4.00. Macmillan

Rathbone, Josephing Langworthy. Corrective physical education. il. 1959. 5.00. Saunders

GYNECOLOGY (618)

Brady, Leo and others. Essentials of gynecology. il. 1949. 3.50. Macmillan

Fluhmann, C. Frederic. Medical treatment in obstetrics and gynecology. il. 1951. 3.00. Williams & Wilkins

Graber, Edward A. Gynecologic and endocrinology. 1961. 7.50. Lippincott

Parker, Elizabeth. Seven ages of woman. by Evelyn Breck. 1960. 6.50. Johns Hopkins

Taylor, E. Stewart. Essentials of gynecology. il. 1962. 12.00. Lea & F

GYROSCOPE (531.34)

O'Hara, Walter J. Mariner's gyro-navigation manual. il. 1951. 4.00. Cornell

Scarborough, James B. Gyroscope, theory and applications. il. 1958. 7.00. Wiley

Gray, Andrew. Treatise on gyrostatics and rotational motion. il. 1959. Dover

Savet, Paul H. Gyroscopes. 1961. 12.75. McGraw

Siff, Elliott J.. ..:d Claude L. Emmerich. Engineering approach to gyroscopic instruments. ?.50. Speller

H

HABIT (158.43)

Dewey, John. Human nature and conduct. 1930. 1.95. Modern Lib.

Dunlap, Knight. Habits: Their making and unmaking. 1949. 4.00. Liveright

HABSBURG, HOUSE OF (943.6)

Jaszi, Oscar. Dissolution of the Habsburg monarchy. 2.25. U. of Chicago

Wedgewood, Cicely V. Thirty years war. il. 3.50. Smith, Peter

HADRAMAUT, ARABIA (953.2)

Phillips, Wendell. Qataban and Sheba. il. 1955. 5.00. Harcourt

Stark, Freya. Southern gates of Arabia. il. 1945. 3.25. Transatlantic

Stark, Freya. Winter in Arabia. il. 2.75. Transatlantic

HADRIAN, EMPEROR OF ROME, 76-138 (923.1)

Perowne, Stewart. Hadrian. il. 1962. 5.00. Norton

HAGEDORN FAMILY (928)

Hagedorn, Hermann. Hyphenated family: An American saga. 1960. 5.00. Macmillan

HAGGARD, SIR HENRY RIDER, 1856-1925 (928)

Cohen, Morton N. Rider Haggard. 1961. 6.00. Walker

HAGIOGRAPHY (922)

Delehaye, Hoppolyte. Legends of the saints. tr. by Donald Attwater. 1962. 5.95. Fordham

HAGUE--INTERNATIONAL COURT OF JUSTICE (341.63)

Lauterpacht, Hersch. Development of international law by the international court. 12.50. Praeger

HAIKU (895.6)

Stewart, Harold. Net of fireflies: Japanese Haiku and Haiku painting. 1960. 4.50. Tuttle

Yasuda, Ken. Japanese haiku: Essential nature, history and possibilities in English. 5.00. Tuttle

HAIL (551.559)
Flora, Snowden D. Hailstorms of the United States. il. 1956. 3.50. U. of Okla.
HAIR (611.78)
King, John W. Give your hair a chance. 2.50. Regent
Lubowe, Irwin I. New hope for your hair. 1960. 4.50. Dutton
HAIRDRESSING (646)
Cordwell, Miriam, and Marion Rudoy. Hair design and fashion. il. 7.50.
  Crown
Hillier, Norman G. Life and beauty of your hair. 3.00. Devin
HAITI (972.94)
Leyburn, J. G. Haitian people. 1941. 5.00. Yale
HAITI--DESCRIPTION AND TRAVEL (917.294)
Bossu, Jean B. Travels in the interior of North America, 1751-1762. tr. by
  Seymour Feiler. il. 1962. 4.50. U. of Okla.
Cave, Hugh B. Haiti: Highroad to adventure. 1952. 5.00. Holt
Morison, Samuel E. Route of Columbus along the north coast of Haiti, and
  the site of Navidad. 1940. 1.00. Am. Philos. Soc.
HAITI--SOCIAL LIFE AND CUSTOMS (972.94)
Wilson, Edmund. Red, black, blond and olive. 1956. 6.75. Oxford U. P.
HALE, EDWARD EVERETT, 1822-1809 (928)
Holloway, Jean. Edward Everett Hale. il. 1956. 4.95. U. of Tex.
HALIFAX, EDWARD FREDERICK LINDLEY WOOD, 1ST EARL OF, 1881 (923.242)
Halifax, Lord. Fullness of days. 1957. 6.00. Dodd
HALL-MARKS (739.21)
Chaffers, William. Handbook of hallmarks on gold and silver plate. by Cyril
  Bunt. 3.95. Borden
Kovel, Ralph M., and Terry H. Directory of American silver, pewter, and
  silver plate. il. 1960. 5.95. Crown
HALLECK, HENRY WAGER, 1815-1872 (923.573)
Ambrose, Stephen E. Halleck: Lincoln's chief of staff. il. 1962. 5.00. La. State
HALLOWEEN (394)
Linton, Ralph and Adelin. Halloween through twenty centuries. il. 1950. 2.50.
  Abelard
HALLUCINATIONS AND ILLUSIONS (133.2)
Mackay, Charles. Extraordinary popular delusions and the madness of crowds.
  7.00. Farrar, Straus
West, Louis J. Hallucinations. il. 1962. 9.75. Grune
HAMILTON, ALEXANDER, 1757-1804 (923.273)
Hacker, Louis M. Alexander Hamilton in the American tradition. 1957. 4.75.
  McGraw
Miller, John C. Alexander Hamilton. il. 1959. 8.50. Harper
Mitchell, Broadus. Alexander Hamilton. 2 vols. vol. 1, Youth to maturity,
  1755-1788. il. 1957. 10.00; vol. 2, National adventure, 1788-1804. 12.50;
  boxed set. 20.00. Macmillan
Mitchell, B. Heritage from Hamilton. 1957. 4.75. Columbia
Morris, Richard B. Alexander Hamilton and the founding of the nations. 1957.
  7.50. Dial
Syrett, Harold C., and others. Interview in Weehawken. il. 1960. 3.75.
  Wesleyan U. P.
HAMMARSKJOLD, DAG HJALMAR AGNE CARL, 1905-1961 (923.2)
Lash, Joseph P. Dag Hammarskjold, custodian of the brushfire peace. 1961.
  4.50. Doubleday
Soderberg, Sten. Hammarskjold: A pictorial biography. il. 1962. 5.95. Viking
HAND (611.717)
Byrne, John J. Hand: Its anatomy and diseases. 1959. 10.50. Thomas, C. C
Mendlowitz, M. Digital circulation. il. 1954. 7.00. Grune
HAND BALL (796.31)
Phillips, B. E. Handball. 1957. 2.95. Ronald

HAND IN ART (743.4)
Loomis, Andrew. Drawing the head and hands. il. 1956. 5.95. Viking
HAND WEAVING (746.1)
Blumenau, Lili. Art and craft of hand-weaving. il. 1955. 2.95. Crown
Coates, Helen. Weaving for amateurs. il. 1946. 5.00. Viking
Overman, Ruth, and Lula E. Smith. Contemporary handweaving. il. 1955. 4.95.
    Iowa State
Zielinski, Stanislaw A. Encyclopaedia of handweaving. il. 1959. 8.50. Funk
HANDEL, GEORG FRIEDRICH, 1685-1759 (780.81)
Abraham, Gerald. Handel: A symposium. 1954. 7.50. Oxford U. P.
Deutsch, Otto Erich. Handel: A documentary biography. il. 1955. 15.00. Norton
    (R)
Larsen, Jens Peter. Handel's Messiah. 1957. 8.50. Norton
Weinstock, Herbert. Handel. il. 1959. 7.50. Knopf
Young, Percy M. Handel. 1949. 3.50. Farrar, Straus
HANDICAPPED (790.196)
Pintner, Rudolph, and others. Psychology of the physically handicapped. il. 1941.
    3.50. Appleton
HANDICAPPED CHILDREN (371.91)
Katz, Alfred H. Parents of the handicapped. 1961. 6.00. Thomas, C. C.
Orton, Samuel T. Reading writing and speech problems in children. 1961. 4.95.
    Norton
Riessman, Frank. Culturally deprived child. 1962. 3.95. Harper
White House Conference on Child Health and Protection. Organization for the
    care of handicapped children: National, state, and local. 2.75. Appleton
HANDICRAFT (745)
Biddle, Dorothy, and Dorathea Blom. Christmas idea book. 1953. 3.95. Barrows
Gottshall, Franklin H. Craftwork in metal, wood, leather, plastics. 1954. 4.00.
    Bruce
Haines, Ray Edward. Home crafts handbook. il. 1960. 8.95. Van Nostrand
Jenkins, Louisa, and Barbara Mills. Art of making mosaics. 1957. 5.95. Van
    Nostrand
Lewis, G. Handbook of crafts. 6.95. Branford
Newkirk, Louis V., and Lavada Zutter. Your craft book. il. 1946. 6.75. Van
    Nostrand
Seibel, Kathryn H. Arts and crafts for flower arrangers. il. 1961. 5.95. Van
    Nostrand
Turner, G. Alan. Creative crafts for everyone. il. 1959. 6.50. Viking
Zechlin, Ruth. Complete book of handcrafts. 6.50. Branford
HANGING (343.23)
Koestler, Arthur. Reflections on hanging. 4.95. Macmillan
HANNIBAL, 247-183 B.C. (930)
De Beer, Gavin. Alps and elephants: Hannibal's march. il. 1959. 2.75. Dutton
Lamb, Harold. Hannibal: One man against Rome. 1958. 4.50. Doubleday
HAPPINESS (171.4)
De La Vega, Francis J. Social progress and happiness in the philosophy of St.
    Thomas Aquinas and contemporary American sociology. 1949. 1.75. Catholic
    U. of Am. Pr.
Jones, Howard Mumford. Pursuit of happiness. 1953. 3.50. Harvard
MacIver, R. M. Pursuit of happiness. 1955. 3.00. S. and S.
Maltz, Maxwell. Five minutes to happiness. 1962. 2.50. Obolensky
Russell, Bertrand. Conquest of happiness. 1930. 3.50. Liveright
Sheldon, William H. Psychology and the Promethean will. 4.50. Harper
Shoemaker, Samuel M. How you can find happiness. 1947. 2.95. Dutton
Wilton, Mabel. Road to happiness. 1950. 1.00. DeVorss
HARDY, THOMAS, 1840-1928 (823)
Bailey, J. O. Thomas Hardy and the cosmic mind: A new reading of The dynasts.
    1956. 5.00. U. of N. C.

Beach, Joseph W. Technique of Thomas Hardy. 1961. 6.50. Russell
Blunden, Edmund. Thomas Hardy. 2.00. St. Martins
Day Lewis, C. Lyrical poetry of Thomas Hardy. 1953. 0.85. Oxford U. P.
Firor, Ruth A. Folkways in Thomas Hardy. 4.50. Smith, Peter
Hardy, Florence E. Life of Thomas Hardy, 1840-1928. 7.00. St. Martins
Rutland, William. Thomas Hardy: A study of his writings and their background. 1962. 7.50. Russell
Weber, Carl J. Hardy of Wessex, his life and literary career. 1962. 7.50. Shoe String
HARMONIC ANALYSIS (517.35)
Byerly, William E. Fourier's series. 1893. 8.00. Ginn
Cunningham, W. J. Introduction to nonlinear analysis. 1958. 10.50. McGraw
HARMONY (781.3)

Bairstow, Edward C. Counterpoint and harmony. 1945. 4.25. St. Martins
Kitson, C. H. Elementary harmony. 1920. 3.40. Oxford U. P.
Ottman, Robert W. Advanced harmony. 1961. 9.00. Prentice-Hall
Ottman, Robert W. Elementary harmony. 1961. 8.35. Prentice-Hall
Persichetti, Vincent. Twentieth-century harmony. il. 1961. 5.45. Norton
Robinson, Raymond C. Progressive harmony. 4.50. Humphries
Schoenberg, Arnold. Structural functions of harmony. il. 1954. 5.50. Norton
HARNESS RACING (798.46)
Wolverton, Clair Cutler. Fifty years with harness horses. il. 5.00. Stackpole
HARPER'S FERRY, W. VA. (973.7336)
Furnas, J. C. Road to Harper's Ferry. 1959. 6.00. Sloane
Keller, Allan. Thunder at Harper's ferry. 1958. 4.95. Prentice-Hall
HARRIS, JOEL CHANDLER, 1848-1908 (928)
Brookes, Stella Brewer. Joel Chandler Harris: Folklorist. 4.00. U. of Ga.
HARRISON, BENJAMIN, PRES. U.S., 1833-1901 (923.173)
Sievers, Harry J. Benjamin Harrison: Hoosier statesman. 2 vols. il. 1959. 6.00 ea. Univ. Pub.
HART, MOSS, 1904- (927)
Hart, Moss. Act one. 1959. 5.00. Random
HARUN AL-RASHID, CALIPH, 763 ca. (809)
Buckler, F. W. Harunu'l Rashid and Charles the Great. 1931. 3.00. Mediaeval
HARVARD UNIVERSITY (378)
MacLeish, Archibald. Next Harvard. 1941. 1.00. Harvard
HARVEY, WILLIAM, 1578-1657 (925)
Keynes, Geoffrey. Portraiture of William Harvey. il. 1949. 6.50. Bentley
HATE (157.3)
Saul, Leon J. Hostile mind: The sources and consequences of rage and hate. 1956. 3.50. Random House
HAUPTMANN, BRUNO RICHARD, 1899-1936 (923.41)
Waller, George. Kidnap. 1961. 6.95. Dial
HAUPTMANN, GERHART JOHANN ROBERT, 1862-1946 (832)
Sinden, Margaret E. Gerhart Hauptmann, the prose plays. 1957. 5.00. U. of Toronto
HAWAIIAN ISLANDS (996.9)
Adams, Ben. Hawaii: The Aloha state. il. 1959. 3.95. Hill & Wang
Pratt, Julius. Expansionists of 1898: The acquisition of Hawaii and the Spanish Islands. 5.00. Smith, Peter
HAWAIIAN ISLANDS--DESCRIPTION AND TRAVEL (919.69)
Clark, Sydney. All the best in Hawaii. il. 1960. 4.95. Dodd
Clemens, Samuel Langhorne. Roughing it. il. 1875. 3.95. Harper
Helbig, Ray. Hawaii, all in natural color. 1959. 0.75. Hawaiian Service
Krauss, Robert. Here's Hawaii. 1960. 4.50. Coward
HAWAIIAN ISLANDS--HISTORY (996.9)
Kuykendall, Ralph S., and A. Grove Day. Hawaii: A history from Polynesian king to American State. il. 1961. 5.95. Prentice-Hall

Weaver, Samuel P. Hawaii, U.S.A. 1959. 4.00. Pageant
HAWAIIAN ISLANDS--POLITICS AND GOVERNMENT (996.9)
Chickering, William H. Within the sound of these waves. 1956. 5.00. Harcourt
HAWAIIAN ISLANDS--SOCIAL CONDITIONS (996.9)
Lind, Andrew W. Hawaii's people. 2.75. U. of Hawaii
HAWAIIAN ISLANDS--SOCIAL LIFE AND CUSTOMS (996.9)
Von Tempski, Armine. Born in paradise. 1940. 4.50. Duell
HAWKINS, SIR JOHN, 1532-1595 (942.052)
Unwin, Rayner. Defeat of John Hawkins. 1960. 6.00. Macmillan
HAWKINS, SIR JOHN, 1719-1789 (942.073)
Scholes, P. A. Life and activities of Sir John Hawkins. il. 1953. 5.60. Oxford
   U. P.
HAWTHORNE, NATHANIEL, 1804-1864 (813)
Arvin, Newton. Hawthorne. 1960. 7.50. Russell
Fogle, Richard Harter. Hawthorne's fiction: The light and the dark. 1952. 3.75.
   U. of Okla.
Gross, Seymour L. Scarlet Letter handbook. 1960. 1.95. Wadsworth
Hoeltje, Hubert H. Inward sky, the mind and heart of Nathaniel Hawthorne. 1962.
   10.00. Duke
James, Henry. Hawthorne. 0.95. Doubleday
Levin, Harry. Power of blackness. 1958. 4.00. Knopf
Male, Roy R. Hawthorne's tragic vision. 3.75. U. of Tex.
Matthiessen, F. O. American renaissance: Art and expression in the age of
   Emerson and Whitman. il. 1941. 10.00. Oxford U. P.
Stewart, Randall. Nathaniel Hawthorne: A biography. 1948. 5.00. Yale
Van Doren, Mark. Nathaniel Hawthorne: A critical biography. 1957. 1.25.
   Viking
Wagenknecht, Edward C. Nathaniel Hawthorne. 1961. 5.50. Oxford U. P.
Waggoner, Hyatt H. Hawthorne: A critical study. 1955. 4.75. Harvard
HAWTHORNE, SOPHIA AMELIA (PEABODY) 1811-1871 (921)
Tharp, Louise Hall. Peabody sisters of Salem. il. 1950. 5.75. Little
HAY-FEVER (616.202)
Swartz, Harry. Your hay fever and what to do about it. 3.00. Ungar
HAYDN, JOSEPH, 1732-1809 (927)
Burke, Cornelius G. Collector's Haydn. 1959. 3.50. Lippincott
Geiringer, Karl. Haydn, a creative life in music. il. 1946. 6.50. Norton
Hughes, Rosemary. Haydn. il. 1950. 3.50. Farrar, Straus
HAYS, JOHN COFFEE, 1817-1883 (923.4)
Henderson, Harry M. Colonel Jack Hays, Texas Ranger. 1954. 2.50. Naylor
HAZLITT, WILLIAM, 1778-1830 (928)
Baker, Herschel C. William Hazlitt. il. 1962. 10.00. Harvard
HEAD (611.91)
Cunningham, D. J. Head and neck, brain. by J. C. Brash. 1958. 6.50. Oxford U.P.
Edgeworth, F. H. Cranial muscles of vertebrates. 1935. 28.50. Cambridge U. P.
   (R)
Truex, R. C., and C. E. Kellner. Detailed atlas of the head and neck. 1948. 19.75.
   Oxford U. P. (R)
HEADACHE (696.072)
Friedman, Arnold P., and H. Houston Merritt. Headache: Diagnosis and treat-
   ment. il. 1959. 8.00. Davis
Wolf, Stewart, and Harold G. Wolff. Headaches: Their nature and treatment. 1953.
   3.00. Little
HEALTH AND HYGIENE (613.12)
Anderson, Carl L., and Clair V. Langton. Health principles and practice. il.
   1961. 5.75. Mosby
Bauer, William W. Your health today. 1955. 5.50. Harper
Cureton, Thomas. Physical fitness and dynamic health. 1962. 5.00. Dial
Diehl, Harold S. Elements of healthful living. 1955. 5.95. McGraw

Etheredge, Maude Lee. Health facts for college students. il. 1958. 4.75.
Saunders
Guild, Warren R. How to keep fit and enjoy it. il. 1962. 3.95. Harper
Hickman, C. P. Health for college students. 1958. 9.35. Prentice-Hall
Laird, Donald A., and Eleanor C. Be active and feel better. 3.95. McGraw
HEALTH EDUCATION (371.76)
Gladston, Iago. Family: A focal point in health education. 1961. 3.00. Int. Univs.
Latchaw, Marjorie, and Camille Brown. Evaluation process in health education,
physical education and recreation. 1962. 7.65. Prentice-Hall
Mann, Hannah. Use of psychodrama in health education. 1960. 2.75. Carlton
National Education Association, American Association for Health, Physical
Education and Recreation. Research methods in health, physical education,
and recreation. 1959. 6.00. N. E. A.
Rodale, J. I. Skits and conversations toward better health. 4.95. Rodale
Turner, Clair E., and others. School health and health education. il. 1961. 5.00.
Mosby
Williams, Jesse F., and others. Administration of health education and physical
education. il. 1958. 4.75. Saunders
HEALTH SURVEYS (614)
American Public Health Association. Guide to a community health study. 1961.
2.50. Am. Public Health
Paul, Benjamin D. Health culture, and community. 1955. 5.00. Russell Sage
HEARING (612.85)
Barbara, Dominick A. Psychological and psychiatric aspects of speech and
hearing. 1960. 19.50. Thomas, C. C.
Broadbent, D. E. Perception and communication. 8.50. Pergamon
Canfield, Norton. Hearing, a handbook for laymen. 1959. 3.50. Doubleday (R)
Fletcher, Harvey. Speech and hearing in communication. il. 1953. 11.50. Van
Nostrand (R)
Palmer, Charles E. Speech and hearing problems. il. 1961. 5.50. Thomas, C. C
Stevens, S. `S., and Hallowell Davis. Hearing: Its psychology and physiology. 1938.
8.95. Wiley
Wever, E. G. Theory of hearing. 1949. 8.75. Wiley
HEARN, LAFCADIO, 1850-1904 (920.5)
Stevenson, Elizabeth. Lafcadio Hearn. il. 1961. 6.95. Macmillan
HEARST, WILLIAM RANDOLPH, 1863-1951 (920.5)
Swanberg, W. A. Citizen Hearst. il. 1961. 7.50. Scribner
HEART (612.17)
Keele, K. D. Leonardo da Vinci on movement of the heart and blood. il. 1952.
15.00. Lippincott
Spitzer, Alexander. Spitzer's architecture of normal and malformed hearts: A
phylogenetic theory of their development. by Maurice Lev, and Aloysius
Vass. il. 1951. 5.75. Thomas, C. C
HEART--DISEASES (616.12)
D'Alonzo, C. A. Heart disease, blood pressure and strokes. il. 1960. 3.50.
Gulf
Fishbein, Morris. Heart care. 1960. 2.95. Doubleday
Friedberg, Charles K. Diseases of the heart. il. 1956. 18.00. Saunders
Gofman, John W. and others. Dietary prevention and treatment of heart disease.
il. 1958. 3.95. Putnam
Gubner, Richard. Your heart is in your hands. 1962. 3.95. Bobbs
Marvin, H. M. Your heart. il. 1960. 4.50. Doubleday
Mozes, Eugene B. Living beyond your heart attack. il. 1959. 3.50. Prentice-
Hall
Needles, Robert J., and Edith M. Stoney. Primer for coronary patients. il.
1958. 3.75. Meredith
Waldo, Myra. Cooking for your heart and health. il. 1961. 3.95. Putnam
Wood, Paul. Diseases of the heart and circulation. il. 1956. 17.50. Lippincott

HEAT (536.4)
Roberts, John K. Heat and thermodynamics. il. 1960. 7.25. Wiley
Sears, Francis W. Mechanics, heat, and sound. il. 1950. 9.75. Addison-Wesley
Semat, Henry, and Robert Katz. Mechanics, heat, wave motion, and sound. 1958.
    5.00. Holt, Rinehart & Winston
Tyler, Frank. Heat, light and sound. 1951. 3.00. St. Martins
HEAT--TRANSMISSION (536.2)
Gebhart, B. Heat transfer. 1961. 10.75. McGraw
Geiringer, Paul L. Handbook of heat transfer media. 1962. 12.50. Reinhold (R)
HEAT ENGINEERING (620)
Bransom, Stanley H. Applied thermodynamics. il. 1961. 6.00. Van Nostrand
Fischer, L. J. Combustion engineers handbook. il. 7.50. Transatlantic
HEAT-ENGINES (621.4)
Faires, Virgil Moring. Thermodynamics of heat power. il. 8.25. Macmillan
Morse, Frederick T. Elements of applied energy. il. 1947. 6.75. Van Nostrand
Solbert, H. L., and others. Elementary heat power. 1952. 6.75. Wiley
HEATING (697)
Carrier, Willis K., and others. Modern air conditioning, heating and ventilating.
    1959. 12.00. Pitman
Jennings, B. H. Heating and air conditioning. 9.25. Int. Textbook
Porges, John. Handbook of heating, ventilating and air conditioning. 1959. 7.50.
    Transatlantic
HEAVEN (237.4)
Bonnell, John S. Heaven and hell. 1956. 1.00. Abingdon
Hugel, F. von. Essays and addresses on the philosophy of religion. 2 vols. 5.50.
    Dutton
HEGEL, GEORG WILHELM FRIEDRICH, 1770-1831 (921.3)
Hook, Sidney. From Hegel to Marx. 1950. 6.00. Humanities
Kaminsky, Jack. Hegel on art. 1962. 6.00. Univ. Pub.
Marcuse, Herbert. Reason and revolution: Hegel and the rise of social theory.
    1955. 6.00. Humanities
HEINE, HEINRICH, 1797-1856 (833.6)
Eairley, Barker. Heinrich Heine: An interpretation. 1954. 2.90. Oxford U. P.
Prawer, S. S. Heine: The tragic satirist. 1961. 6.50. Cambridge U. P.
HELICOPTERS (629.13335)
Fay, John. Helicopter and how it flies. 1954. 2.95. Pitman
Nikolsky, A. A. Helicopter analysis. 1951. 11.50. Wiley
Shapiro, J. S. Principles of helicopter engineering. 1955. 13.00. McGraw
Underwood, John. World aircraft illustrated. il. 1961. 8.50. Arco
HELLENISM (913.38)
Eddy, Samuel K. King is dead: Studies in the Near-Eastern resistance to
    Hellenism, 334-31 B.C. il. 1961. 8.50. U. of Nebr.
Hadas, Moses. Hellenistic culture fusion and difussion. 1959. 6.00. Columbia
Jaeger, Werner W. Early Christianity and Greek paideia. 1961. 3.25. Harvard
Livingstone, Richard W. Greek ideals and modern life. 1935. 2.00. Oxford U. P.
Murray, Gilbert. Hellenism and the modern world. 1954. 1.50. Beacon
Tarn, William W., and G. T. Griffith. Hellenistic civilization. 1952. 5.75.
    St. Martins
Toynbee, Arnold J. Greek civilization and character. 1954. pap. 0.50. New Am.
    Lib.
Toynbee, Arnold J. Hellenism. il. 1959. 4.50. Oxford U. P.
Trevelyan, H. Goethe and the Greeks. 1941. 5.50. Cambridge U. P.
HEMINGWAY, ERNEST, 1898-1961 (813.5)
Baker, Carlos. Hemingway. 1956. 5.00. Princeton
Baker, Carlos. Hemingway and his critics. 1961. 4.95. Hill & Wang
Fenton, Charles A. Apprenticeship of Ernest Hemingway. 1958. pap. 1.45. Viking
Hemingway, Leicester. My brother, Ernest Hemingway. il. 1962. 4.95. World
    Pub.

Killinger, John. Hemingway and the dead gods. 1960. 4.00. U. of Ky.
Lania, Leo. Hemingway: A pictorial biography. il. 1961. 5.95. Viking
McCaffery, John. Ernest Hemingway: The man and his work. 3.50. World Pub.
Sanderson, Dtewart. Ernest Hemingway. 1961. 3.00. Smith, Peter
Sanford, Marcelline H. At the Hemingways: A family portrait. il. 1962. 4.95.
    Little
Weeks, Robert P. Hemingway: A collection'of critical essays. 1962. 3.95.
    Prentice-Hall
Young, Philip. Ernest Hemingway. 1952. 3.65. Holt, Rinehart & Winston
HEMOPHILIA (616.15)
Brinkhous, Kenneth M. Hemophilia and hemophilioid diseases. 1957. 7.50. U.
    of N. C.
Dameshek, William. Symposium: What is hemophilia? il. 1954. pap. 1.75. Grune
HENDERSON, ALEXANDER, 1583-1646 (922.5)
Loane, Marcus. Makers of religious freedom in the 17th century. 1960. 4.00.
    Eerdmans
HENRIQUE, O NAVEGADOR, INFANTE OF PORTUGAL, 1394-1460 (923.9469)
Bradford, Ernle D. S. Wind from the north: The life of Henry the Navigator. il.
    1960. 5.00. Harcourt
HENRY II, KING OF ENGLAND, 1133-1189 (923.142)
Duggan, Alfred. Devil's brood. il. 1957. 5.00. Coward
HENRY III, KING OF ENGLAND, 1207-1272 (923.142)
Costain, Thomas B. Magnificent century. il. 1951. 4.50. Doubleday
HENRY VIII, KING OF ENGLANL 1491-1547 (923.142)
Hackett, Francis. Henry VIII. 1945. 3.95. Liveright
Smith, H. Maynard. Henry VIII and the Reformation. 1962. 7.50. Russell
HENRY, ALEXANDER, d. 1814 (923.973)
O'Meara, Walter. Savage country. il. 1960. 5.00. Houghton
HENRY, JOSEPH, 1797-1878 (925)
Jahns, Patricia. Matthew Fontaine Maury and Joseph Henry: Scientists of the
    Civil War. 1961. 5.95. Hastings
Riedman, Sarah R. Traiblazer of American science: The life of Joseph Henry.
    il. 1961. 3.50. Rand McNally
HENRY, PATRICK, 1736-1799 (923.273)
Mayo, Bernard. Myths and men. 1959. 2.50. U. of Ga.
Meade, Robert Douthat. Patrick Henry: Patroit in the making. il. 1957. 7.50.
    Lippincott
Tyler, Moses C. Patrick Henry. 1962. pap. 2.25. Cornell
HERALDRY (929.6)
Fox-Davies, A. C. Complete guide to heraldry. 10.50. Nelson (R)
Lynch-Robinson, Christopher, and Adrian. Intelligible heraldry. il. 1949. 6.75.
    Van Nostrand
Moncreiffe, Iain, and Don Pottinger. Simple heraldry. il. 1953. 3.50. Nelson
Rogers, H. C. B. Pageant of heraldry. il. 1956. 7.50. Pitman
Scott-Giles, C. W. Romance of heraldry. il. 5.00. Dutton
Wagner, A. R. Heralds and heraldry in the Middle Ages. 1956. 5.60. Oxford U. P.
HERBERT, GEORGE, 1593-1633 (821.3)
Bennett, Joan. Four metaphysical poets. 1953. 3.00. Cambridge U. P.
Chute, Marchette. Two gentle men: The lives of George Herbert and Robert
    Herrick. 1959. 5.00. Dutton
Walton, Kzaak. Lives of John Donne, Sir Henry Wotton, Richard Hooker, George
    Herbert, and Robert Sanderson. 2.75. Oxford U. P.
HERBS (635.7)
Clarkson, Rosetta E. Herbs, their culture and uses. il. 1942. 4.75. Macmillan
HEREDITY (575.1)
Ashley, Montagu, M. F. Human heredity. il. 1959. 5.00. World Pub.
Ciba Foundation. Biochemistry of human genetics. 1959. 9.50. Little
Darlington, Cyril D. Evolution of genetic systems. 1958. 5.50. Basic Books

Darwin, Charles. Origin of species and Descent of man. 2.95. Modern Lib.
Fuller, John L., and W. Robert Thompson. Behavior genetics. 1960. 8.95.
    Wiley
Goldschmidt, R. B. Understanding heredity. 1952. 4.95. Wiley
Grobman, Arnold. Our atomic heritage. il. 1951. 2.95. U. of Fla.
Harris, H. Human biochemical genetics. 1959. 7.00. Cambridge U. P.
Li, Ching-chun. Human genetics. 1961. 8.50. McGraw
Lysenko, T. D. Heredity and its variability. 1946. pap. 1.00. Columbia
Penrose, Lionel S. Outline of human genetics. il. 1959. 2.75. Wiley
Penrose, L. S. Recent advances in human genetics. 1961. 8.00. Little
Schenifeld, Amram. Human heredity handbook. il. 1956. 3.95. Lippincott
Schenifeld, Amram. New you and heredity. 1950. 7.50. Lippincott
Shull, A. Franklin. Heredity. il. 1948. 6.95. McGraw
HERESIES AND HERETICS (273)
Christiani, Leon. Heresies and heretics. tr. by Roderick Bright. 1959. 3.50.
    Hawthorn
Cozens, M. L. Handbook of heresies. 1959. pap. 0.75. Sheed
Kaufman, Walter. History of heresy. 5.00. Putnam
Nigg, Walter. Heretics. 1962. 6.95. Knopf
Prestige, G. L. Fathers and heretics. 1950. 3.75. (S.P.C.K.) Seabury
HERMITS (922)
Leclercq, Jean, Dom. Alone with God. 1961. 3.95. Farrar, Straus
Waddell, Helen. Desert fathers. 1954. 3.50. Barnes & Noble
HERODOTUS (928.38)
De Selincourt, Aubrey. World of Herodotus. il. 1962. 6.50. Little
How, Walter W., and Joseph Wells. Commentary on Herodotus. 2 vols. 1928.
    2.90 ea. Oxford U. P.
HEROES (398.22)
Bentley, Eric. Century of hero-worship. 3.75. Smith, Peter
Carlyle, Thomas. On heroes, hero-worship and the herioc in history. 2.25.
    Oxford U. P.
Carlyle, T. Sartor resartus, and Heroes and hero-worship. 1.95. Dutton
Fishwick, Marshall. American heroes: Myth and reality. 1954. 3.75. Pub. Affairs
Hook, Sidney. Hero in history. 1950. 3.50. Humanities
Lehman, B. H. Carlyle's theory of the hero. 1928. 3.50. Duke
Rank, Otto. Myth of the birth of the hero: A psychological interpretation of
    mythology. 1952. 3.00. Basic Books
HIAWATHA (398.22)
Henry, Thomas R. Wilderness Messiah: The story of Hiawatha and the Iroquios.
    1955. 4.00. Sloane
Schoolcraft, Henry R. Indian legends. by Mentor L. Williams. 1956. 7.50. Mich.
    State
HIGH-FIDELITY SOUND SYSTEMS (621.3818)
Boyce, William F. Hi-fi stereo handbook. il. 1961. pap. 3.95. Bobbs
Canby, Edward. High fidelity and the music lover. il. 1958. 4.95. Harper
Crowhurst, N. H. High fideltiy and sound engineering. 1960. 10.00. Pitman
Fowler, Charles. High fidelity: A practical guide. 1956. 4.95. McGraw
Hahn, Steven. Hi-fi handbook: A guide to monaural and sterophonic reproduction. il
    1962. 4.95. Crowell
Wellman, William R. High fidelity home music systems. il. 1962. 6.50. Van
    Nostrand
HIGH SCHOOLS (373)
Alberty, Harold B., and Elsie J. Reorganizing the high-school curriculum. il.
    1962. 6.50. Macmillan
Austin, D. B., and others. American high school administration. 1961. 7.00.
    Holt, Rinehart & Winston
Conant, James B. American high school today. il. 1959. 2.95. McGraw
Conant, James Bryant. Child, the parent, and the state. 1959. 3.50. Harvard

Crow, Lester D., and others. Education in the secondary school. 5.90. Am. Bk.
Co.
Douglass, Harl R. High school curriculum. 1956. 6.50. Ronald
Edmonson, James B., and others. Administration of the modern secondary school.
il. 6.00. Macmillan
Flanagan, John C., and others. Design for a study of American youth. 1962.
5.00. Houghton
Franzen, Carl Gustav F. Improvement sheets for the teaching of high school
subjects. 1951. pap. 3.00. Brown, W. C.
Wales, John N. Schools of democracy. 1962. 3.95. Mich. State
HILL, JAMES JEROME, 1838-1916 (923.873)
Holbrook, Steward H. James J. Hill. 1955. 3.00. Knopf
HILLHOUSE, JAMES THEODORE 1890-1956 (823.912)
Rathburn, Robert C., and Martin Steinmann, Jr. From Jane Austen to Joseph
Conrad. 1958. 5.75. U. of Minn.
HIMALAYA MOUNTAINS (915.42)
Douglas, William O. Beyond the high Himalayas. il. 1952. 5.00. Doubleday
HINDUISM (294.5)
Lemaitre, Solange. Hinduism. tr. by John Francis Brown. 1959. 3.50. Hawthorn
Nikhilananda, Swami. Hinduism: Its meaning for the liberation of the Spirit.
1958. 4.00. Harper
Radhakrishnan, Sarvepalli. Eastern religions and Western thought. 1940. 4.00.
Oxford U. P.
Radhakrishnan, Sarvepalli. Hindu view of life. 1927. 2.00. Macmillan
Renou, Louis. Hinduism. 1961. 4.00. Braziller
Schweitzer, Albert. Indian thought and its development. 1962. 3.60. Smith, Peter
Soper, Edmund D. Inevitable choice: Vedanta philosophy or Christian gospel.
1957. 2.50. Abingdon
Weber, Max. Religion of India. 1958. 6.50. Free Press
Ghoshal, U. N. History of Indian political ideas, the ancient period and the
period of transition to the Middle Ages. 1959. 7.95. Oxford U. P.
HIPPOCRATES (610.6942)
Edelstein, Ludwig. Hippocratic oath. 1954. 2.00. Johns Hopkins
HIROSHIMA (940.544)
Hachiya, Michihiko. Hiroshima diary. 1955. 3.50. U. of N. C.
Knebel, Fletcher, and Charles W. Bailey, II. No high ground. 1960. 4.00. Harper
HISS, ALGER, 1904- (923.573)
Andrews, B. Tragedy of history: A journalist's confidential role in the Hiss-
Chambers Case. by Peter Andrews. 1962. 4.95. McKay
Cook, Fred J. Unfinished story of Alger Hiss. 1958. 3.50. Morrow
Cooke, Alistair. Generation on trial: USA v. Alger Hiss. 1950. 4.50. Knopf
HISTOCHEMISTRY (574.192)
Ciba Foundation Study Group, 5. Regulation of inorganic ion content of the cell.
1960. 2.50. Little
Davenport, Harold A. Histological and histochemical technics. il. 1960. 7.00.
Saunders
HISTOLOGY (574.82)
Arey, Leslie B. Human histology. 1957. 6.50. Saunders
Garven, H. S. D. Student's histology. 1957. 11.00. Williams & Wilkins
Werner, Henry J. Synopsis of histology. 1961. 4.25. McGraw
HISTORIOGRAPHY (907.2)
Barzun, Jacques, and Henry F. Graff. Modern researcher. 1957. 6.50. Harcourt
Bellot, H. Hale. American history and American historians: Review of recent
contributions to the interpretation of the history of the United States. 1952.
4.00. U. of Okla.
Bryant, Arthur. Art of writing history. 1946. 1.00. Oxford U. P.
Butterfield, Herbert. Man on his past. 1954. 5.00. Cambridge U. P.
Cohen, Morris R. Meaning of human history. 1947. 5.00. Open Ct.

Collingwood, R. G. Idea of history. by T. M. Know. 1946. 4, 80. Oxford U. P.
Croce, Benedetto. History as the story of liberty. 3.00. Humanities
Croce, Benedetto. History: Its theory and practice. 6.00. Russell
Ferguson, Wallace K. Renaissance in historical thought. 1948. 7.75. Houghton
Gooch, G. P. History and historians in the 19th century. 1959. pap. 2.75. Beacon
Gottschalk, Louis. Understanding history: A primer of historical method. 1950.
    3.50. Knopf
Halperin, Samuel William. Some twentieth-century historians. 1961. 5.95. U.
    of Chicago
Hexter, Jack H. Reappraisals in history. 1962. 6.00. Northwestern U.
Jaspers, Karl. Origin and goal of history. tr. by Michael Bullock. 1953. 5.00.
    Yale
Jernegan, Marcus W. Essays in American historiography. by Willian T. Hutchinson.
    1958. 7.50. Russell
Levin, David. History as romantic art: Bancroft, Prescott, Motley, and Parkaman.
    1959. 5.50. Stanford
Nevins, Allan. Gateway to history. pap. 1.45. Doubleday
Schevill, Ferdinand. Six historians. 1957. 5.00. U. of Chicago
Shera, Jesse H. Historians, books and libraries. 1953. 3.50. Western Reserve
Shotwell, J. T. History of history. vol. 1. 1939. 4.25. Columbia
Teggart, F. J. Theory and processes of history. 3.50. Smith, Peter
Wedgwood, C. V. Literature and the historian. 1956. 1.00. Oxford U. P.
Hockett, Homer C. Critical method in historical research and writing. 1955. 5.75.
    Macmillan
HISTORICAL FICTION (813.09)
Dickinson, A. T., Jr. American historical fiction. 1958. 7.50. Scarecrow
Duggan, Alfred. Historical fiction. 1957. 0.75. Cambridge U. P.
Leisy, Ernest E. American historical novel. 1952. 3.75. U. of Okla. (R)
Lively, Robert A. Fiction fights the Civil War: An unfinished chapter in the
    literary history of the American people. 1957. 5.00. U. of N. C. (R)
Ribner, I. English history play in the age of Shakespeare. 1957. 5.00. Princeton
HISTORY (901)
American Historical Association. Guide to historical literature. by George F.
    Howe and others. 1961. 16.50. Macmillan (R)
Becker, C. L. Everyman his own historian. 3.75. Appleton
Krey, August C. History and the social web: A collection of essays. 1955. 4.00.
    U. of Minn.
Hale, Richard W. Guide to photocopied historical materials in the United States
    and Canada. 1961. 5 00. Cornell (R)
Mozley, John R. Divine aspect of history. 2 vols. 1916. 13.50. Cambridge U. P.
Toynbee, Arnold. Civilization on trial, and The world and the West. pap. 1.55.
    Meridian
Trevor-Roper, H. R. Men and events. 1958. 4.50. Harper
Widgery, A. G. Interpretations of history, from Confucius to Toynbee. 5.50.
    Humanities
HISTORY--DICTIONARIES (903)
Arnold-Baker, C., and Anthony Dent. Dictionary of dates. 1954. 4.25. Dutton
Cohen, Benjamin A. Worldmark encyclopedia of the nations. 1960. 30.00. Harper
Elliott, Florence and Summerskill, Michael. Dictionary of politics. 3.50. Smith,
    Peter
HISTORY--METHODOLOGY (907.2)
Quigley, Carroll. Evolution of civilizations. il. 1961. 5.95. Macmillan
Rickard, John A., and Albert Hyma. Ancient, medieval and modern history. 1957.
    pap. 1.75. Barnes & Noble
Teggart, F. J. Theory and processes of history. 3.50. Smith, Peter
HISTORY--PHILOSOPHY (901)
Albright, William Foxwell. From the Stone Age to Christianity. 1957. pap. 1.45.
    Doubleday

Arendt, Hannah. Between past and future: Six exercises in political thought. 1961.
    5. 00. Viking
Aron, Raymond. Introduction to the philosophy of history. 1961. 7. 50. Beacon
Becker, Carl L. Heavenly city of the eighteenth century philosophers. 1932. 3. 50.
    Yale
Becker, Carl L. Heavenly city revisited. by Raymond O. Rockwood. 1958. 4. 50.
    Cornell
Berlin, Isaiah. Historical inevitability. 1954. 2. 50. Oxford U. P.
Burke, Kenneth. Attitudes toward history. 1959. 6. 75. Hermes
Bury, J. B. Idea of progress. 1960. 3. 75. Smith, Peter
Caponigri A. Robert. History and liberty: The historical writings of Benedetto
    Croce. 4. 00. Hillary
Carr, Edward H. What is history? 1962. 3. 50. Knopf
Cohen, Morris R. Meaning of human history. 1947. 5. 00. Open Ct.
D'Arcy, Martin C. Meaning and matter of history. 1959. 5. 50. Farrar, Straus
Dawson, Christopher. Dynamics of world history. by John J. Mulloy. 1956. 6. 00.
    Sheed
Dawson, Christopher H. Movement of world revolution. 1959. 3. 00. Sheed
Dentan, R. C. Idea of history in ancient Near East. 1955. 5. 00. Yale
Dray, William. Laws and explanation in history. 1957. 3. 40. Oxford U. P.
Forbes, D. Liberal Anglican idea of history. 1952. 5. 00. Cambridge U. P.
Gardiner, Patrick. Theories of history. 1958. 8. 50. Free Press
Geyl, Pieter. Use and abuse of history. 1955. 3. 00. Yale
Hegel, Georg. W. F. Philosophy of history. 3. 85. Smith, Peter
Highet, Gilbert. Migration of ideas. 1954. 2. 50. Oxford U. P.
Jelenski, K. A. History and hope: Tradition, idealogy, and change in modern
    society. 1962. 5. 50. Praeger
McIntyre, John. Christian doctrine of history. 1958. 2. 50. Eerdmans
Maritain, Jacques. On the philosophy of history. 1957. 3. 50. Scribner
Nehru, Jawaharlal. Nehru on world history. by Saul K. Padover. 1962. 2. 45.
    Indiana
Niebuhr, Reinhold. Beyond tragedy. 1937. 3. 95. Scribner
Niebuhr, Reinhold. Faith and history. 1949. 3. 95. Scribner
Ortega y Gasset, Jose. History as a system. 1941. 4. 50. Norton
Randall, John H. Nature and historical experience. 1958. 5. 50. Columbia
Seligman, Edwin. Economic interpretation of history. 1924. 3. 00. Columbia
Sorokin, P. A. Crisis of our age: The social and cultural outlook. il. 5. 00.
    Dutton
Sorokin, Pitirim A. Social and cultural dynamics. 4 vols. 1962. 11. 00 ea.
    Bedminster
Strayer, J. R. Interpretation of history. 3. 50. Smith, Peter
Toynbee, Arnold J. Study of history. 12 vols. 85. 00. Oxford U. P.
Walsh, W. H. Introduction to philosophy of history. 2. 50. Hillary
Walsh, Warren B. Perspectives and patterns: Discourses on history. 1962. 4. 50.
    Syracuse
Wedgewood, Cicely V. Truth and opinion. 1960. 4. 50. Macmillan
Whitehead, Alfred N. Adventures of ideas. 1933. 5. 00. Macmillan
Wilson, Edmund. To the Finland station, a study in the writing and acting of
    history. 1959. 3. 25. Smith, Peter

HISTORY--SOURCES (901. 6)
Setton, Kenneth M., and Henry Winkler. Great problems in European civilization.
    1954. 7. 00. Prentice-Hall

HISTORY--YEARBOOKS (905. 8)
Annual register of world events. 1961. 25. 00. St. Martins (R)
Current history review of 1959. il. 4. 95. Rand McNally
Facts on file yearbooks. 30. 00 ea. Facts on file
Funk and Wagnalls. Book of the year, events of 1961. il. 3. 00. Funk
Macadam, Ivison. World Events: Annual register. 3 vols. 10. 00. Penguin

New international 1962 year book, events of 1961. 10.00. Funk (R)

HISTORY, ANCIENT (930)

Breasted, James H. Ancient times. 1944. 6.80. Ginn

Easton, Stewart. Heritage of the ancient world: From the earliest times to the fall of Rome. 1960. 3.95. Holt, Rinehart & Winston

Finegan, Jack. Light from the ancient past. 1959. 10.00. Princeton

Godolphin, Francis R. B. Greek historians. 2 vols. 1942. 15.00. Random

Hall, H. R. Ancient history of the Near East. 8.50. Macmillan

Hayes, Carlton J. H., and P. T. Moon. Ancient and medieval history. il. 1929. 6.52; workbook by J. O. Foster and Edgar B. Wesley. 2.20. Macmillan

Herodotus. Works. 2 vols. tr. by J. E. Powell. 1949. 4.80. Oxford U. P.

Herototus. Persian wars. 1.95. Modern Lib.

Mattingly, H. Outlines of ancient history. 1914. 4.50. Cambridge U. P.

McDermott, William C., and Wallace E. Caldwell. Readings in the history of the ancient world. 1952. pap. 3.50. Holt, Rinehart & Winston

Muller, Herbert J. Freedom in the ancient world. il. 1961. 7.50. Harper

Pirenne, Jacques. From the beginnings to Islam. 8.95. Dutton

Polybuis. Histories. 6 vols. 1922-27. 6.50. ea. Harvard

Polybius. Histories. 2 vols. 1962. 10.00. Indianna

Robinson, Charles Alexander, Jr. Ancient history: From prehistoric times to the death of Justinian. il. 1951. 6.95. Macmillan

Robinson, Charles A., Jr. Selections from Greek and Roman historians. 1957. pap. 1.25. Holt, Rinehart & Winston

Sanford, Eva M. Mediterranean world in ancient times. 1951. 7.50. Ronald

Scramuzza, Vincent M., and Paul MacKendrick. Ancient world. il. 1958. 8.95. Holt, Rinehart & Winston

Smith, Charles E., and Paul G. Moorhead. Short history of the ancient world. 1939. 5.75. Appleton

Swain, Joseph Ward. Ancient world. 2 vols. il. 1950. 6.75 ea. Harper

Swain, Joseph Ward, and William H. Armstrong. Peoples of the ancient world. 1959. 6.75. Harper

Trever, Albert A. History of ancient civilization. 2 vols. il. 7.95 ea. Harcourt

Van Sickle, C. E. Political and cultural history of the ancient world. 2 vols. 1947-8. 7.25. ea. Houghton

HISTORY, MODERN (909)

Acton, John E. Lectures on modern history. 3.75. St. Martins

Bloom, Solomon F. Europe and America. 11.75. Harcourt

Brace, Richard M. Making of the modern world: From the Renaissance to the present. 1961. 8.95. Holt, Rinehart & Winston

Bromley, J. S., and E. H. Kossmann. Britain and the Netherlands. 1961. 5.00. Humanities

Bruce, Maurice. Shaping of the modern world. 1958. 10.00. Random

Bruun, Geoffrey. World in the twentieth century. 1957. 8.00. Heath

Chambers, Frank P. This age of conflict: The Western world, 1914 to the present. il. 8.95. Harcourt

Fuller, J. F. C. From the Seven Days battle, 1862, to the battle of Leyte Gulf, 1944. 6.00. Funk

Fuller, J. F. C. From the earliest times to the battle of Lepanto (Military history of the Western world. vol. 1) 6.00. Funk

Fuller, J. F. C. From the defeat of the Spanish Armada, 1588, to the battle of Waterloo, 1815. 6.00. Funk

Gooch, George P. History of our time: 1885-1914. 1946. 1.70. Oxford U. P.

Hasluck, E. L. Foreign affairs, 1919-1937. 1938. 3.00. Cambridge U. P.

Hayes, Carlton J. H., and P. T. Moon. Modern history. il. 1941. 6.88. Macmillan

Howe, Quincy. World history of our times. 2 vols. 7.50 ea. S. and S.

Kohn, Hans. Reflections on modern history. 7.50. Van Nostrand

Langer, William L. Diplomacy of imperialism. 1935. 9.75. Knopf

Langsam, Walter Consuelo. World since 1919. il. 1954. 6.75. Macmillan

Lukacs, John. History of the cold war. il. 3.95. Doubleday
Palmer, Robert R., and Joel Colton. History of the modern world. il. 1956. 10.00. Knopf
Schmitt, Bernadotte E. Fashion and future of history. 5.50. Western Reserve (R)
Snow, Edgar. Journey to the beginning. 1958. 5.00. Random
Snyder, Louis L. World in the twentieth century. (Anvil 4) 1955. pap. 1.25. Van Nostrand
Snyder, Louis L. Fifty major documents of the nineteenth century. 1955. pap. 1.25. Van Nostrand
Stearns, Raymond Phineas. Pageant of Europe: Sources and selections from the Renaissance to the present day. 11.00. Harcourt
Stoessinger, John G. Might of nations. 1962. 8.95. Random
Taylor, Alan J. P. Rumours of war. 3.00. Humanities
Wallace, Lillian Parker and William C. Askew. Power, public opinion, and diplomacy: Essays in honor of Eber Malcolm Carroll by his former students. 1959. 8.75. Duke

HITLER, ADOLF, 1889-1945 (923.143)
Bullock, Alan. Hitler: A study in tyranny. il. 1960. 8.50. Harper
Hanfstaengl, Ernst. Unheard witness. il. 1957. 4.95. Lippincott
Jenks, William A. Vienna and the young Hitler. 1960. 5.00. Columbia
Snyder, Louis L. Hitler and Nazism. il. 1961. 2.95. Watts
Trevor-Roper, H. R. Last days of Hitler. pap. 0.95. Collier

HITTITES (939)
Ceram, C. W. Secret of the Hittites. il. 1956. 5.75. Knopf
Gurney, O. R. Hittites. 1961. pap. 1.45. Penguin

HOBBES, THOMAS, 1588-1679 (921.2)
Bowle, John. Hobbes and his critics. 1952. 1.70. Oxford U. P.
Collingwood, R. G. New leviathan; or, Man, society, civilization and barbariam. 1942. 6.10. Oxford U. P.
James, D. G. Life of reason: Hobbes, Locke, and Bolingbroke. 4.50. Hillary
Stephen, Leslie. Hobbes. 1961. 4.40. U. of Mich.
Warrender, Howard. Political philosophy of Hobbes: His theory of obligation. 1957. 7.20. Oxford U. P.

HOBBIES (790.2)
Ickis, Marguerite. Handicrafts and hobbies for recreation and retirement. il. 1960. 4.00. Dodd
Mulac, Margaret E. Hobbies. 1959. 4.50. Harper
Zarchy, Harry. Here's your hobby. il. 1950. 3.25. Knopf

HOCKEY (796.962)
Jeremiah, E. Ice hockey. 1958. 4.00. Ronald
Percival, Lloyd. Hockey handbook. il. 1961. 4.50. Barnes, A. S.

HOGARTH, WILLIAM, 1697-1764 (927)
Hazlitt, William. Lectures on English comic writers. 1951. 2.25. Oxford U. P.
Moore, Robert E. Hogarth's literary relationships. 1948. 3.75. U. of Minn.

HOLBEIN, HANS THE YOUNGER, 1497-1543 (927.5)
Holbein, Hans. Holbein. by K. T. Parker. il. 2.95. N. Y. Graphic
Holbein, Hans. Paintings of Hans Holbein. by Paul Ganz. il. 1956. 10.00. N. Y. Graphic

HOLIDAYS (394.26)
Clark, Thomas Curtis, and Robert Earle Clark. Poems for the great days. 3.00. Abingdon
Dobler, Lavinia. Customs and holidays around the world. il. 4.50. Fleet
Douglas, George W. American book of days. by Helen Douglas Compton. 1948. 6.00. Wilson (R)
Harrington, Mildred P., and J. H. Thomas. Our holidays in poetry. 1929. 3.00. Wilson
Hazeltine, Mary E. Anniversaries and holidays. 1944. 6.00. A. L. A. (R)
Ickis, Marguerite. Book of patriotic holidays. il. 1962. 3.75. Dodd

Krythe, Maymie R. All about American holidays. 1961. 4.50. Harper
Schauffler, Robert Haven. Days we celebrate. 4 vols. 3.50 ea. Dodd
Schauffler, Robert Haven, and A. P. Sanford. Plays for our American holidays.
  4 vols. 3.50 ea. Dodd
Van Buren, Maud. Quotations of special occasions. 1938. 3.00. Wilson
Weiser, Francis X. Holyday book. 1956. 3.00. Harcourt
HOLMES, OLIVER WENDELL (923.473)
Biddle, Francis. Justice Holmes, natural law, and the Supreme Court. 1961.
  2.50. Macmillan
Bowen, Catherine Drinker. Yankee from Olympus: Justice Holmes and his family.
  1944. 5.00. Little
Frankfurter, Felix. Mr. Justice Holmes and the Supreme Court. il. 1961. 3.00.
  Harvard
Konefsky, Samuel J. Legacy of Holmes and Brandeis: Study in the influence of
  ideas. 6.00. Macmillan
Richardson, Dorsey. Constitutional doctrines of Justice Oliver Wendell Holmes.
  1924. 1.50. Johns Hopkins
Small, Miriam. Oliver Wendell Holmes. 1962. 3.50. Twayne
HOLY ALLIANCE (940.28)
Bertier de Sauvigny, Guillaume de. France and the European alliance. 1816-1821.
  1958. 2.75. U. of Notre Dame
HOLY ROMAN EMPIRE (943)
Brandi, K. Emperor Charles V. 8.00. Humanities
Bryce, James. Holy Roman Empire. 1956. 5.50. St. Martins
Kantorowicz, Ernst. Frederick the Second. il. 1957. 3.50. Ungar
HOME (301.42)
Chapman, Denis. Home and social status. 6.00. Humanities
Lane, Bess B. Enriching family life. 1957. 3.25. Pub. Affairs
Silver, Fern, and Mildred Graves Ryan. Foundations for living. il. 1943. 3.00.
  Appleton
HOME ECONOMICS (640)
Cuppy, Will. How to be a hermit: or, a bachelor keeps house. 1929. 3.00. Live-
  right
Earle, Alice M. Home life in colonial days. il. 1913. 5.50. Macmillan
Gilbreth, Lillian E. M., and others. Management in the home. il. 1959. 5.00.
  Dodd
Gillies, Mary Davis. How to keep house. il. 1961. 4.50. Harper
Good Housekeeping. Good Housekeeping's guide to successful homemaking. 1961.
  5.95. Harper
Gross, Irma H., and Elizabeth W. Crandall. Management for modern families.
  il. 1954. 5.50. Appleton
Kinder, Faye. Meal management. il. 1956. 6.50. Macmillan
Lewis, Dora S., and others. Housing and home management. il. 1961. 4.60.
  Macmillan
Manly, Harold P. Householders' cyclopedia, home repair. 4.00. Drake, F. J.
Peet, Louise J., and Lenore S. Thye. Household equipment. 1961. 7.75. Wiley
Spock, Benjamin, and others. Every woman's standard guide to home and child
  care. il. 1959. 10.00. Hawthorn
Wallace, Inez, and Bernice McCullar. Building your home life. il. 1960. 5.28.
  Lippincott
HOME ECONOMICS AS A PROFESSION (640.069)
Hall, Olive A. Home economics: Careers and homemaking. il. 1958. 4.75. Wiley
Phillips, Velma. Home economics careers for you. 1962. 4.50. Harper
Tate, M. T. Home economics as a profession. 1961. 5.50. McGraw
HOME NURSING (649.8)
American Red Cross. Home nursing textbook. il. 1951. 1.00. Doubleday
Gidseg, Lucille, and Dorothy Sara. Home nurse's handbook. il. 1951. 3.00. Funk
Long, Alma. Home health and nursing. il. 2.00. Appleton

HOMER (883)

Bassett, Samuel Eliot. Poetry of Homer. 1938. 6.00. U. of Calif.

Bespaloff, Rachel. On the Iliad. 1947. 2.50. Pantheon

Bowra, C. M. Tradition and design in the Iliad. 1930. 4.50. Oxford U. P.

Carpenter, Rhys. Folk tale, fiction, and saga in the Homeric epics. 1946. pap. 1.50. U. of Calif.

Knight, D. Pope and the heroic tradition. 1951. 3.00. Yale

Lord, G. DeF. Homeric Renaissance: The Odyssey of George Chapman. 1956. 3.00. Yale

Lorimer, Hilda L. Homer and the monuments. 13.50. St. Martins

McKay, L. A. Wrath of Homer. 1948. 3.50. U. of Toronto

Murray, Gilbert. Rise of the Greek epic. pap. 1.75. Oxford U. P.

Page, Denys. History and the Homeric Iliad. il. 1959. 8.00. U. of Calif.

Page, D. L. Homeric odyssey. 1955. 4.00. Oxford U. P.

Wade-Gery, H. T. Poet of the Iliad. 1952. 4.50. Cambridge U. P.

Whitman, Cedric. Homer and the herioc tradition. 1958. 6.75. Harvard

HOMER, WINSLOW, 1836-1910 (927)

Gardner, Albert Ten E. Winslow Homer, American artist. il. 1962. 25.00. Potter, C. N.

Gould, Jean. Winslow Homer: A portrait. il. 1962. 4.00. Dodd

HONDURAS (972.83)

Stokes, William S. Honduras: An area study in government. il. 1950. 6.00. U. of Wis.

HONGKONG (951.25)

Endacott, G. B. History of Hong Kong. 1958. 4,80. Oxford U. P.

Clark, Sydney. All the best in Japan. il. 1960. 4.95. Dodd

HOOVER, HERBERT CLARK, PRES. U. S. 1874- (923.173)

Bane, Suda Lorena, and Ralph Haswell Lutz. Organization of American relief in Europe, 1918-1919. 10.00. Stanford

Comfort, Mildred H. Herbert Hoover, humanitarian. 1960. 3.00. Denison

Hinshaw, David. Herbert Hoover: American Quaker. il. 1950. 5.00. Farrar, Straus

HOPKINS, GERALD MANLEY, 1844-1889 (821.8)

Kenyon Critics. Gerard Manley Hopkins. 2.00. New Directions

Ritz, Jean-Georges. Robert Bridges and Gerard Manley Hopkins, 1863-1889: A literary friendship. 1960. 3.40. Oxford U. P.

HOPKINS, MARK, 1802-1887 (923.773)

Rudolph, F. Mark Hopkins and the log. 1956. 4.75. Yale

HORACE (QUINTUS HORATIUS FLACCUS) (871)

Commager, Steele. Odes of Horace: A critical study. 1962. 8.50. Yale

D'Alton, J. F. Horace and his age. 1962. 7.50. Russell

HORMONES (574.194)

Beach, Frank. Hormones and behavior. 6.95. Cooper

Hall, Peter F. Functions of the endocrine glands. il. 1959. 5.75. Saunders

Wigglesworth, Vincent B. Control of growth and form. il. 1959. 3.00. Cornell

HORMONES (PLANTS) (581.194)

Audus, Leslie J. Plant growth substances. 1960. 10.00. Wiley

Tukey, Harold B. Plant regulators in agriculture. 1954. 6.95. Wiley

HORSES (636.1)

Alexander, David. Romance and history of the horse. 4.50. Cooper

Berg, William A. Mysterious horses of western North America. 1960. 3.50. Pageant

Benoist-Gironiere, Yves. Conquest of the horse. il. 1957. 7.50. Funk

Churchill, Peter. Riding for everybody. 1962. 4.00. Pitman

Disston, Harry. Know about horses. il. 1961. 6.95. Devin

Homeland, Paul. Art of horsemanship. il. 1962. 5.95. Barnes, A. S.

Kays, Donald Jackson. Horse: judging, breeding, feeding, management, selling. 1953. 6.95. Holt, Rinehart & Winston

Littauer, Vladimir S. Horseman's progress. il. 1962. 7.50. Van Nostrand

Reese, Herbert H. Horses of today. 7.50. Borden

Roe, Frank G. Indian and the horse. il. 1955. 5.95. U. of Okla.

Self, Margaret Cabell. Horseman's encyclopedia. il. 1946. 6.95. Barnes, A. S.

Simpson, George G. Horses: The story of the horse family in the modern world and through sixty million years of history. 1951. 8.50. Oxford U. P.

Steinkraus, William. Riding and jumping. 1961. 3.95. Doubleday

Widmer, Jack. Practical guide for horse owners. il. 1957. 4.50. Scribner

Wyman, Walker D. Wild horse of the West. il. 1945. 4.00. Caxton

HORTICULTURE (635)

Christopher, E. P. Introductory horticulture. 1958. 7.95. McGraw

Denison, Ervin L. Principles of horticulture. il. 1958. 7.25. Macmillan

Edmond, J. B., and others. Fundamentals of horitculture. il. 1957. 7.95. McGraw

Hay, Roy. Modern gardener. 1959. 15.00. Transatlantic

Shoemaker, James Sheldon. General horticulture. il. 1956. 7.95. Lippincott

Shoemaker, James S., and Benjamin J. E. Teskey. Practical horticulture. 1955. 4.20. Wiley

HOSPITALS (362.11)

American Council on Education, Commission on University Education, University education for administration in hospitals. 1954. 3.00. A. C. E.

Barnes, Elizabeth. People in hospital. il. 1962. 3.00. St. Martins

Cunningham, R. Hospitals, doctors, and dollars. 1961. 6.95. McGraw

Field, Mina. Patients are people. 1958. 6.00. Columbia

Richards, Ralph T. Of medicine, hospitals, and doctors. 1953. 4.50. U. of Utah.

Rosenfield, Isadore. Hospitals. 1951. 18.50. Reinhold

HOTEL MANAGEMENT (647.94)

Lattin, Gerald W. Modern hotel management. 1958. 4.00. Freeman

Lundberg, D. E. Personnel management in hotels and restaurants. 1955. 6.00. Brown, W. C.

HOUDINI, HARRY, 1874-1926 (927.938)

Gibson, Walter B., and Morris N. Young. Houdini's fabulous magic. il. 1961. 4.50. Chilton

Gresham, William L. Houdini: The man who walked through walls. il. 1959. 4.50. Holt, Rinehart & Winston

HOUSING (331.833)

Callender, John H., and others. Methods of reducing the cost of public housing. il. 3.50. Pratt Inst.

Fisher, Robert Moore. Twenty years of Public housing: The economic aspects of the federal program. 1959. 6.50. Harper

Gropius, Walter. New architecture and Bauhaus. 3.50. Branford

Hemdahl, Reuel. Urban renewal. 1959. 8.00. Scarecrow

Keats, John C. Crack in the picture window. il. 1957. 3.25. Houghton

McDonnell, Timothy L. Wagner Housing Act. 1957. 4.00. Loyola

Meyerson, Martin, and Edward Banfield. Politics, planning and the public interest. 1955. 5.00. Free Press

Meyerson, Martin, and others. Housing, people, and cities. il. 1962. 9.75. McGraw

Mumford, Lewis. From the ground up. 1956. pap. 1.25. Harcourt

Tyler, Poyntz. City and suburban housing. 1957. 2.00. Wilson

Wilner, Daniel M., and others. Housing environment and family life: A long-itudinal study of the effects of housing on morbidity and mental health. 1962. 7.50. Johns Hopkins

HOUSMAN, ALFRED EDWARD, 1859-1936 (821.8)

Gow, A. S. F. A. E. Housman: A sketch. 1936. 3.00. Cambridge U. P.

Marlow, Norman. A. E. Housman: Scholar and poet. 1957. 3.50. U. of Minn.

Robinson, Oliver. Angry dust: The poetry of A. E. Housman. 2.50. Humphries

HOUSTON, SAMUEL, 1793-1863 (923.273)

Houston, Sam. Autobiography. il. by Donald Doy, and Harry Herbert Ullom. 1954. 5.00. U. of Okla.

Wisehart, M. K. Sam Houston: American giant. il. 1962. 10.00. McKay
HOWE, JULIA (WARD) 1819-1910 (811.4)
Tharp, Louise Hall. Three saints and a sinner. 1956. 5.75. Little
HOWELLS, WILLIAM DEAN, 1837-1920 (813.4)
Bennett, George N. William Dean Howells, the development of a novelist. il. 1959. 4.00. U. of Okla.
Brooks, Van Wyck. Howells: His life and world. il. 1959. 5.00. Dutton
Eble, Kenneth E. Howells: A century of criticism. 1962. 4.50. S. M. U.
Kirk, R., and C. William Dean Howells. 3.50. Twayne
HUDSON RIVER AND VALLEY (917.473)
Carmer, Carl. Hudson. il. 1939. 6.00. Holt, Rinehart & Winston
HUDSON'S BAY COMPANY (971.011)
Galbraith, John S. Hudson's Bay Company as an imperial factor. 1957. 6.75. U. of Calif.
Godsell, A. Arctic trader. 1946. 3.75. St. Martins
Johnson, Robert C. John McLoughlin: Father of Oregon. il. 3.75. Binfords
Radisson, Peter Esprit. Voyages of Peter Esprit Radisson (1652-1684) 7.50. Smith, Peter
Rich, Edwin Ernest. Hudson's Bay Company, 1670-1870. 3 vols. 1960. 35.00. Macmillan
Wilson, Clifford. Adventures from the Bay: The story of Hudson's Bay Company. 1962. 2.95. St. Martins
HUGO, VICTOR MARIE, COMTE, 1802-1885 (928.43)
Grant, Elliott Mansfield. Career of Victor Hugo. 1945. 3.50. Harvard
Maurois, Andre. Olympio: The life of Victor Hugo. il. 1956. 6.50. Harper
HUGUENOTS IN FRANCE (272.4)
Bien, David D. Calas affair; persecution, toleration, and heresy in eighteenth-century Toulouse. 1960. 4.00. Princeton
Scoville, Warren. Persecution of Huguenots and French economic development. 1680-1720. 1960. 6.50. U. of Calif.
HULL HOUSE, CHICAGO (361.43)
Addams, Jane. Twenty years at Hull-House. il. 1923. 6.00. Macmillan
Judson, Clara I. City neighbor: Story of Jane Addams. il. 1951. 2.95. Scribner
HUMAN BEHAVIOR (150)
Bernard, Harold. Human development in western culture. il. 1962. 9.95. Allyn & Bacon
Brown, Judson S. Motivation of behavior. il. 1961. 7.50. McGraw
Cole, Lawrence E. Human behavior. 7.50. Harcourt
Coleman, James C. Personality dynamics and effective behavior. 1960. 6.00. Scott
Holland, James, and B. F. Skinner. Analysis of behavior. 1961. 5.95. McGraw
Lane, Howard, and Mary Beauchamp. Understanding human development. 1959. 9.00. Prentice-Hall
Miller, George A., and others. Plans and the structure of behavior. il. 1960. 6.00. Holt, Rinehart & Winston
Parnell, Richard W. Behavior and physique. il. 1958. 7.00. Williams & Wilkins
Roe, A., and G. Simpson. Behavior and evolution. il. 1958. 10.00. Yale
Russell, Claire, and W. M. S. Human behaviour. 1961. 6.50. Little
HUMAN ECOLOGY (301.3)
Dice, Lee R. Man's nature and nature's man: The ecology of human communities. 1955. 5.00. U. of Mich.
Hawley, Amos H. Human ecology. 1950. 7.50. Ronald
Theodorson, George A. Studies in human ecology. 1961. 8.50. Harper
Wagner, Philip. Human use of the earth. 6.00. Free Press
HUMAN FIGURE IN ART (704.942)
Macnab, Iain. Figure drawing. il. 1959. 4.50. Viking
Perard, Victor. Anatomy and drawing. 1955. 4.95. Pitman
Rubins, David K. Human figure. An anatomy for artists. il. 1953. 4.50. Viking

Zaidenberg, Arthur. Anyone can draw. il. 1947. 4.45. Doubleday

HUMANISM (144)
Fulton, John F. Humanism in an age of science. 1950. pap. 0.75. Abelard
Gilmore, Myron P. World of humanism: 1453-1517. il. 1952. 6.00. Harper
Hough, Lynn Harold. Great humanists. 1952. 3.50. Abingdon
Hulme, T. E. Speculations: Essays on humanism and the philosophy of art.
    4.00. Humanities
Huxley, Julian. Humanist frame. 1962. 6.50. Harper
Huxley, Julian. New bottles for new wine. il. 1958. 5.00. Harper
Jones, Howard Mumford. American humanism. 1957. 3.50. Harper
Kristeller, Paul O. Renaissance thought, the classic, scholastic and humanistic
    strains. 3.50. Smith, Peter
Muller, Herbert J. Science and criticism. 1956. 3.00. Braziller
Norlin, George. Quest of American life. 1945. 2.50. U. of Colo.
Perry, Ralph Barton. Humanity of man. 1956. 3.75. Braziller
Reiser, Oliver. Integration of human knowledge. 1958. 8.00. Sargent
Sarton, George. History of science and the new humanism. 4.00. Smith, Peter
Seznec, Jean. Survival of the pagan gods. il. 1953. 6.50. Pantheon
Spinka, Matthew. Christian thought from Erasmus to Berdyaev. 1962. 6.60.
    Prentice-Hall
Taylor, Henry O. Thought and expression in the sixteenth century. 2 vols. 1959.
    9.00. Ungar

HUMANITIES (373.24)
Cassirer, Ernst. Logic of the humanities. tr. by Clarence S. Howe. 1961. 4.50.
    Yale
Davidson, Robert F., and others. Humanities in contemporary life. il. 1960. 6.95.
    Holt, Rinehart & Winston
Jones, Howard M. One great society. 1959. 4.50. Harcourt
Leisy, Ernest. Integration of the humanities and the social sciences: A symposium.
    1948. 2.00. S. M. U.

HUMBOLDT RIVER, NEV. (917.9354)
Morgan, Dale L. Humboldt: Highroad of the West. il. 1943. 4.50. Rinehart

HUME, DAVID, 1711-1776 (921.2)
Flew, Antony G. N. Hume's philosophy of belief. 1961. 6.00. Humanities
Hendel, Charles W. Studies in the philosophy of David Hume. 1962. 5.00. Bobbs
Morris, C. R. Locke, Berkeley, Hume. 1931. 2.40. Oxford U. P.
Mossner, Ernest Campbell. Life of David Hume. il. 1954. 7.50. U. of Tex.
Smith, Norman Kemp. Philosophy of David Hume. 7.00. St. Martins

HUMMING-BIRDS (598.899)
Greenewalt, Crowford H. Hummingbirds. il. 25.00. Doubleday

HUMORISTS (809.7)
Thackeray, W. M. English humorists, and Four Georges. 1.95. Dutton

HUMUS (631.8)
Hopkins, Donald P. Chemicals, Humus, and the soil. 1948. 8.50. Tudor
Kononova, M. M. Soil organic matter. 1962. 15.00. Pergamon

HUNDRED YEARS' WAR, 1339-1453 (944.025)
Burne, Alfred H. Agincourt War. 1956. 5.60. Oxford U. P.
Froissart, Jean. Chronicles of England, France, Spain, and other places adjoining.
    1961. 2.15. Dutton
Hewitt, Herbert J. Black Prince's expedition of 1355-1357. 1958. 6.50. Barnes &
    Noble
Perroy, Edouard. Hundred Years War. 1960. 6.50. Indiana

HUNGARY (943.91)
Bain, Leslie B. Reluctant satellites. 1960. 3.95. Macmillan
Horthy, Nicholas. Admiral Horthy memoirs. 6.00. Speller
Kecskemeti, Paul. Unexpected revolution. 1961. 4.75. Stanford
Kertesz, Stephen D. Diplomacy in a whirlpool: Hungary between Nazi Germany
    and Soviet Russia. 1953. 4.75. U. of Notre Dame

Macartney, C. A. Hungary: A short history. il. 4.50. Aldine
May, Arthur James. Hapsburg monarchy, 1667-1914. 1951. 6.00. Harvard
Meray, Tibor. Thirteen days that shook the Kremlin. 1959. 5.00. Praeger
Michener, James A. Bridge at Andau. 1957. 3.50. Random
Schramm, Wilbur L. One day in the world's press. il. 1959. pap. 6.95. Stanford
Sinor, Dennis. History of Hungary. 1960. 5.00. Praeger
Survey, Hungary today. by the Editors of Survey. 1962. 3.85. Praeger
Washington Post, Anatomy of revolution: A condensation of the United Nations
   report of the Hungarian uprising of 1956. by the editors of Washington Post.
   1957. pap. 1.00. Pub. Affairs
HUNTING (799.2)
Burden, W. Douglas. Look to the wilderness. il. 1960. 6.50. Little
Crowe, Philip K. Sport is where you find it. il. 1953. 7.50. Van Nostrand
Hirsch, Peter I. Last man in paradise. il. 1961. 4.50. Doubleday
Outdoor Life. Story of American hunting and firearms. il. 1959. 8.59. McGraw
Peattie, Donald Culross. Sportsman's country. il. 1952. 3.00. Houghton
Roosevelt, Theodore. Theodore Roosevelt's America. by Farida Wiley. il. 1955.
   5.75. Devin
Vale, Robert B. How to hunt American game. 1952. 4.00. Stackpole
HURRICANES (551.552)
Douglas, Marjory Stoneman. Hurricane. il. 1958. 5.95. Rinehart
Dunn, Gordon E., and Banner I. Miller. Atlantic hurricanes. 1960. 10.00. La.
   State
HUXLEY, ALDOUS LEONARD, 1894- (925)
Atkins, John. Aldous Huxley. 5.00. Roy Pub.
Ghose, Sisirkumar. Aldous Huxley. 1962. 6.95. Taplinger
HYDRAULIC ENGINEERING (627)
Carhart, Arthur H. Water - or your life. 1959. 4.95. Lippincott
Langbein, Walter B., and W. G. Hoyt. Water facts for the nation's future. 1959.
   5.00. Ronald
Linsley, R. K., and J. Franzini. Elements of hydraulic engineering. 1955. 11.00.
   McGraw
Maass, A. A. Muddy waters: The Army engineers and the nation's rivers. il.
   1951. 4.75. Harvard
Schwab, G. O., and others. Elementary soil and water engineering. 1957. 6.25.
   Wiley
HYDRAULICS (532)
Binder, Raymond C. Fluid mechanics. 1962. 11.65. Prentice-Hall
Daugherty, Robert L., and A. C. Ingersoll. Fluid mechanics: With engineering
   applications. 1954. 8.50. McGraw
Davis, Calvin V. Handbook of applied hydraulics. il. 1952. 20.00. McGraw
King, Horace W., and Ernest F. Brater. Handbook of hydraulics. 1954. 12.50.
   McGraw (R)
Lea, Frederick C. Hydraulics. 1938. 6.50. St. Martins
HYDROCARBONS (547)
Ferris, S. W. Handbook of hydrocarbons. 1955. 8.50. Academic Press (R)
Maxwell, J. B. Data book on hydrocarbons. il. 1950. 7.75. Van Nostrand
HYDROGEN BOMB (623.45119)
Shepley, James, and Clay Blair, Jr. Hydrogen bomb: The men, the menace, the
   mechanism. 1954. 3.50. McKay
HYDROLOGY (551.49)
Galilei, Galileo. Discourse on bodies in water. tr. by Thomas Salusbury. il.
   1961. 5.00. U. of Ill.
Helfman, Elizabeth. Water for the world. 1960. 3.75. McKay
Johns, R. V., and others. Hydrostatics, statics, and dynamics. 1.50. St. Martins
Linsley, Ray K., Jr., and others. Applied hydrology. il. 1949. 11.50. McGraw
Starling, Sydney G. Mechanical properties of matter. 1951. 2.25. St. Martins
Tyler, Frank. Mechanics and hydrostatics. 1954. 2.00. St. Martins

HYMNS (783. 9)
Benson, Louis F. English hymn. 1962. 6.50. John Knox
Foote, Henry W. Three centuries of American hymnody. 1961. 8.50. Shoe String
Geer, E. H. Hymnal for colleges and schools. 1956. 6.50. Yale
Smith, H. Augustine. New hymnal for American youth. 1.75. Revell
HYPERSPACE (513. 82)
Sommerville, Duncan M. Y. Introduction to the geometry of N. dimensions. pap.
   1.50. Dover
Veblen, O., and J. H. C. Whitehead. Foundations of differential geometry. 1932.
   3.00. Cambridge U. P.
HYPNOTISM (134)
Ambrose, Gordon, and George Newbold. Handbook of medical hypnosis. 5.75.
   Williams & Wilkins
Bennett. Hypnotic power, hypnotism its use and development. 2.75. Borden
Bramwell, J. Milne. Hypnotism, its history, practice and theory. 6.50. Julian
Dorcus, R. M. Hypnosis and its therapeutic applications. 1956. 8.00. McGraw
Estabrooks, George H. Hypnotism. 1943. 3.95. Dutton
Kline, Milton. Freud and hypnosis. 4.00. Julian
Kuhn, Lesley, and Salvatore Russo. Modern hypnosis. 5.00. Borden
Moll, Albert. Study of hypnosis. 6.00. Julian
Orton, Louis J. Hypnotism made practical. 1.00. DeVorss
Schilder, Paul. Nature of hypnosis. 1956. 4.00. Int. Univs.
Schneck, Jerome M. Hypnosis in modern medicine. 1959. 8.75. Thomas, C. C.
HYSTERIA (616. 852)
Breuer, Josef, and Sigmund Freud. Studies on hysteria. tr.by James Strachey,
   and others. 1957. 5.50. Basic Books
Murray, Robert K. Red scare: A study in national hysteria. il. 1955. 4.75.
   U. of Minn.
Szasz, Thomas S. Myth of mental illness. 1961. 6.95. Harper

I

IBN SAUD, KING OF SAUDI ARABIA, 1880-1953 (923.153)
Glubb, John B. War in the desert. il. 1961. 5.50. Norton
IBSEN, HENRIK, 1828-1906 (839.73)
Downs, Brian W. Study of the six plays of Ibsen. 1950. 4.00. Cambridge U. P.
Tennant, Peter F. D. Ibsen's dramatique technique. il. 4.00. Saifer
ICELAND (949.1)
Fietz, Helga, and others. Iceland. 1960. 7.95. Hill & Wang
Nuechterlein, Donald E. Iceland, reluctant ally. 1961. 4.50. Cornell
O'Dell, A. C. Scandinavian world. 1957. 10.00. Longmans
Snorri Sturluson. Heimskringla. 1948. 1.95. Dutton
Sutton, George M. Iceland summer. il. 1961. 5.95. U. of Okla.
ICELANDIC AND OLD NORSE LITERATURE (839.6)
Einarsson, Stefan. History of Icelandic literature. 1957. 5.50. Johns Hopkins
Jones, Gwyn. Eirik the Red and other Icelandic sagas. 2.75. Oxford U. P.
Kershaw, N. Stories and ballads. 1921. 3.50. Cambridge U. P.
Turville-Petre, Gabriel. Origins of Icelandic literature. 1953. 5.60. Oxford U. P.
IDAHO (979. 6)
Idaho: Guide in word and picture. 6.50. Oxford U. P.
IDEALISM (141)
Berkeley, George. Treatise concerning the principles of human knowledge. 2.00.
   Open Ct.
Butler, J. Donald. Four philosophies and their practice in education and religion.
   1957. 6.50. Harper
Ewing, A. C. Idealism; a critical survey. 7.00. Humanities
Marx, Karl, and Friedrich Engels. German idealogy. 4.00. Int. Pubs.
Radhakrishnan, Sarvepalli. Idealist view of life. 1932. 4.75. Macmillan

IDEOLOGY (141)
Aiken, Henry D. Age of ideology. 1957. 3.00. Houghton
Whitehead, Alfred N. Adventures of ideas. 1933. 5.00. Macmillan
ILLINOIS (977.3)
Monaghan, Jay. This is Illinois: A pictorial history. il. 1949. 5.00. U. of Chicago
Pease, Theodore C. Story of Illinois. il. 1949. 6.00. U. of Chicago
Writers' Project. Illinois. 6.00. Hastings
ILLITERACY (379.2)
Ginzberg, E. and Bray, D. W. Uneducated. 1953. 4.50. Columbia
Laubach, Frank C. Thirty years with the silent billion. il. 1959. 3.95. Revell
Laubach, Frank C., and Robert S. Toward world literacy. il. 1960. 4.75. Syracuse
Roberts, Helen M. Champion of the silent billion. 3.50. Macalester
UNESCO. Basic facts and figures. 1961. pap. 3.00. Int. Doc. Service-Columbia
ILLUMINATION OF BOOKS AND MANUSCRIPTS (096)
Book of Kells. il. 1952. 8.50. Viking
Gray, Basil. Persian painting. il. 1961. 22.50. World Pub.
Gray, Basil. Persian painting from miniatures of the 13th-16th centuries. il. 1945. 6.00. Oxford U. P.
Herbert, John Alexander. Illuminated manuscripts. il. 1958. 16.50. Franklin, B.
Porcher, Jean. Rohan book of hours. 1959. 4.95. Yoseloff
Weitzmann, Kurt. Ancient book illumination. il. 1959. 9.00. Harvard
Bland, David. History of book illustration. il. 1958. 15.00. World Pub.
IMAGINATION (155)
Chiari, Joseph. Realism and imagination. 1961. 6.00. Macmillan
Copland, Aaron. Music and imagination. 1952. 2.75. Harvard
Furlong, E. J. Imagination. 1961. 3.25. Macmillan
Henry, W. E. Analysis of fantasy. 1956. 6.95. Wiley
James, Davis G. Scepticism and poetry. 1960. 5.00. Barnes & Noble
Lowes, John L. Road to Xanadu. 6.00. Houghton
McKellar, Peter. Imagination and thinking. 1957. 5.00. Basic Books
Osborn, Alex F. Your creative power. 1948. 4.50. Scribner
Sartre, Jean Paul. Imagination: A psychological critique. tr. by Forrest Williams. 1962. 3.95. U. of Mich.
Walsh, William. Use of imagniation. 1961. 5.00. Barnes & Noble
IMAGIST POETRY (808.1)
Coffman, Stanley K., Jr. Imagism: A chapter for the history of modern poetry. 1951. 3.00. U. of Okla.
Hughes, Glenn. Imagism and the imagists. 6.00. Humanities
IMMORTALITY (129.6)
Ashley Montagu, M. F. Immortality. 1955. 2.50. Grove
Augustine, Saint. Concerning the teacher, bd. with On the immortality of the soul. tr. by George G. Leckie. pap. 0.95. Appleton
Clark, Walter Eugene. Indian conceptions of immortality. 1934. 1.00. Harvard
Ducasse, C. J. Critical examination of the belief in a life after death. 1960. 8.75. Thomas, C. C.
Rank, Otto. Psychology and the soul. 1961. pap. 1.65. Barnes, A. S.
Unamuno, Miguel de. Tragic sense of life. 3.75. Smith, Peter
IMMUNITY (612.1182)
Boyd, William C. Fundamentals of immunology. il. 1956. 12.00. Wiley
Burnet, Frank M. Integrity of the body. il. 1962. 4.75. Harvard
Kabat, E. A. Blood group substances: Their chemistry and immunochemistry. 1956. 8.00. Academic Press
Talmage, David W., and John R. Cann. Chemistry of immunity in health and disease. 1961. 5.75. Thomas, C. C.
IMPERIAL FEDERATION (942)
Grigg, Edward. British Commonwealth. 1944. 2.75. Liveright
Jennings, Ivor. British Commonwealth of Nations. 2.50. Hillary

Mansergh, Nicholas, and others. Commonwealth perspectives. 1958. 4.50. Duke
Walker, E. A. British empire: Its structure and spirit, 1497-1953. 1956. 6.00.
  Harvard
IMPERIAL TRANS-ANTARCTIC EXPEDITION, 1914-1917 (999)
Lansing, Alfred. Endurance: Shackleton's incredible voyage. 1959. 5.95. McGraw
Shackleton, Ernest H. South! il. 1962. 4.50. Macmillan
IMPERIALISM (321.03)
Arendt, Hannah. Origins of totalitarianism. 1958. pap. 2.25. Meridian
Deutsch, Harold C. Genesis of Napoleonic imperialism. 1938. 4.50. Harvard
Langer, William L. Diplomacy of imperialism. 1935. 9.75. Knopf
Moon, Parker T. Imperialism and world politics. 6.50. Macmillan
Nearing, Scott. Tragedy of empire. 1945. 2.00. Soc. Sci. Inst.
Niebuhr, Reinhold. Structure of nations and empires. 1959. 5.00. Scribner
Robinson, Ronald, and others. Africa and the Victorians. il. 1961. 9.00. St.
  Martins
Schuman, Frederick L. International politics. il. 1958. 7.75. McGraw
Schumpeter, Joseph A. Imperialism and social classes. by Paul M. Sweezy. 1919.
  4.00. Kelley
Snyder, Louis L. Imperialism reader. 1962. 8.50. Van Nostrand
Strachey, John. End of empire. 1960. 5.00. Random
Sturzo, Don Luigi. Nationalism and internationalism. 3.50. Roy Pub.
Van Alstyne, Richard W. Rising American empire. 1960. 6.00. Oxford U. P.
IMPOSTORS AND IMPOSTURE (133.7)
Mackay, Charles. Extraordinary popular delusions and the madness of crowds.
  7.00. Farrar, Straus
IMPRESSIONISM (ART) (759.05)
Cogniat, Raymond. Century of the impressionists. 12.50. Crown
Hanson, Lawrence, and Elisabeth. Impressionism: Golden decade. 1961. 5.00.
  Holt, Rinehart & Winston
Impressionists and their world. il. 1956. 5.50. Pitman
Rewald, John. History of Impressionism. il. 1961. 20.00. Mus. of Mod. Art,
  or Doubleday
Serullaz, Maurice. Impressionist painters. 1960. 10.00. Universe
Taylor, Basil. Impressionists and their world. 1957. 6.75. Pitman
INCARNATION (232.1)
Ferrier, Francis. What is incarnation. 1962. 3.50. Hawthorn
Orr, James. Christian view of God and the world. 5.00. Eerdmans
INCAS (985.01)
Baudin, Louis. Daily life in Peru under the last Incas. il. 1962. 4.00. Macmillan
Baudin, Louis. Socialist empire: The Incas of Peru. 1961. 8.00. Van Nostrand
Bingham, Hiram. Lost city of the Incas. il. 1948. 6.00. Duell
Gieza de Leon, Pedro de. Incas of Pedro de Cieza de Leon. by Victor Wolfgang
  von Hagen. il. 1959. 5.95. U. of Okla.
Garcilaso de la Vega. Incas, the royal commentaries of Garcilaso the Inca.
  by Alain Gheerbrant. il. 1961. 12.50. Orion
Prescott, William H. Conquest of Peru. pap. 1.45. Doubleday
Von Hagen, Victor W. Ancient sun kingdoms of the Americas. il. 1960. 12.50.
  World Pub.
INCOME (339)
Coons, Alvin E. Income of nations and persons. il. 1959. 6.75. Rand McNallt
Dahlberg, A. O. How U.S. output is measured. 1956. pap. 1.00. Columbia
Dahlberg, A. O. National income visualized. 1956. 5.00. Columbia
Greenhut, Melvin L. Full employment, inflation, and common stock. 1961. 3.25.
  Pub. Affairs
Hanks, J. Whitney, and Roland Stucki. Money, banking, and national income.
  1956. 6.00. Knopf
Hanna, Frank. State income differentials, 1919-1954. 1959. 7.50. Duke
Kurihara, Kenneth K. National income and economic growth. il. 1961. 4.25.
  Rand McNally

Kuznets, Simon. Income and wealth in the United States: Trends and structures. 1952. 5.75. Quadrangle

Marschak, Jacob. Income, employment, and the price level. 1.00. Kelley

Miller, Herman P. Income of the American people. 1955. 6.95. Wiley

Millikan, M. F. Income stabilization for a developing democracry. 1953. 5.00. Yale

Morgan T. Income and employment. 1952. 8.35. Prentice-Hall

Pigou, Arthur C. Veil of money. 1949. 2.50. St. Martins

Stone, Richard, and Giovanna. National income and expenditure. 1962. 3.95. Quadrangle

Weintraub, S. Approach to the theory of income distribution. 1958. 6.50. Chilton

INCOME TAX--U.S. (336.24)

Dickerson, W. E., and Leo D. Stone. Federal income tax fundamentals. 1961. 7.95. Wadsworth

Harris, Ronald M. Taxes: Curse or blessing? 1961. 2.00. Carlton

Holzman, Robert S. Federal income taxation. 1960. 8.00. Ronald

Lasser, J. K. Handbook of successful tax procedures. 1956. 4.95. S. and S. (R)

Lasser, J. K. Standard handbook of business tax techniques. 1957. 4.95. McGraw

Lasser, Jacob K. Your income tax. 1961. 1963. 1.95. S. and S.

Malloy, Gerald Q. Income tax story. 1960. 2.50. Carlton

Norwood, Fred W., and S. W. Chisholm. Federal income taxes. il. 1962. 9.25. Prentice-Hall

INCUNABULA (093)

Buhler, Curt F. Fifteenth-century book: The scribes, the printers, the decorators. 1960. 5.00. U. of Pa.

Stillwell, Margaret B. Incunabula and Americana, 1450-1800. 15.00. Cooper

INDENTURED SERVANTS (331.54)

Jernegan, Marcus W. Laboring and dependent classes in Colonial America, 1607-1783. 3.75. Ungar

Smith, Abbott Emerson. Colonists in Bondage: White servitude and convict labor in America, 1607-1776. 1947. 5.00. U. of N. C.

INDEXING (029.5)

Carey, G. V. Making an index. 1951. 0.75. Cambridge U. P.

Collison, Robert L. Indexes and indexing. 1959. 4.50. De Graff

Kahn, G. and Yerian. Progressive filing. 1955. 3.16. McGraw

Weeks, B. M. How to file and index. 1951. 4.50. Ronald

INDIA (954)

Alexandrowicz, C. H. Constitutional developments in India. 1957. 3.15. Oxford U. P.

Bailey, Frederick G. Tribe, caste, and nation. il. 1960. 6.50. Humanities

Ballhatchet, Kenneth. Social policy and social change in western India, 1817-1830. 1957. 7.20. Oxford U. P.

Basham, A. L. Wonder that was India. il. 1955. 9.00. Macmillan

Bowles, Chester. Ambassador's report. il. 1954. 5.50. Harper

Dean, Vera M. New patterns of democracy in India. il. 1959. 4.75. Harvard

Douglas, William O. Strange lands and friendly people. 1951. 6.00. Harper

Edwardes, Michael. History of India. il. 1961. 7.50. Farrar, Straus

Faillozat. India: The country and its traditions. 1962. 15.00. Prentice-Hall

Gandhi, Mohandas K. Non-violent resistance. 1961. 4.50. Schocken

Garratt, G. T. Legacy of India. il. 1937. 7.00. Oxford U. P.

Griffiths, Percival. Modern India. 1962. 6.50. Praeger

Hallock, Constance M. This is India, Pakistan, and Ceylon. 1954. pap. 0.60. Friendship

Harrison, Selig S. India: The most dangerous decades. il. 1960. 6.50. Princeton

Majumdar, D. N. Races and cultures of India. 1961. 9.50. Taplinger

Mehta, G. L. Understanding India. 1962. 5.50. Taplinger

Moraes, Frank. India today. 1960. 4.00. Macmillan

Moreland, W. H., and A. C. Chatterjee. Short history of India. 1957. 6.50. McKay

Murphy, Gardner. In the minds of men. 1953. 4.50. Basic books

Nehru, Jawaharlal. Independence and after. 1950. 4.50. Day

Nevins, Allan. New India. 1962. pap. 2.50. Macmillan

Panikkar, K. M. Hindu society at cross-roads. 1961. 3.00. Taplinger

Rama Rau, Santha. Home to India. 1945. 3.50; lib. bdg. 3.19. Harper

Rama Rau, Santha. This is India. il. 1954. 3.50; lib. ed. 3.19. Harper

Rawlingson, Hugh G. India. il. 1952. 10.00. Praeger

Riencourt, Amaury de. Soul of India. 1960. 6.95. Harper

Sengupta, Padmini. Everyday life in ancient India. il. 1950. 1.90. Oxford U. P.

Smith, Vincent A. Oxford history of India. 3 pts. by Percival Spear. il. 1958.
   6.75. Oxford U. P.

Smith, Vincent A. Early history of India. by S. M. Edwardes. 1957. 7.20. Oxford
   U. P.

Spear, Percival. India, Pakistan, and the West. 1950. 1.70. Oxford U. P.

Spear, Percival. India: A modern history. il. 1961. 10.00. U. of Mich.

Strachey, John. End of empire. 1960. 5.00. Random

Ward, Barbara, India and the West. 1961. 4.95. Norton

Wheeler, Mortimer. Indus civilization. 4.50. Cambridge U. P.

Woodruff, Philip. Men who ruled India: 2 vols. 5.00 ea. St. Martins

Woytinsky, W. S. India: The awakening giant. 1957. 3.75. Harper

Zimmer, Heinrich. Myths and symbols in Indian art and civilization. il. by Joseph
   Campbell. 1946. 4.50. Pantheon

INDIANA (977.2)

Indiana: Guide to the hoosier state. 6.50. Oxford U. P.

INDIANS (970.1)

American Heritage book of Indians. by the Editors of American Heritage. 1961.
   15.00. S. and S. (R)

Appleton, Leroy H. Indian art of the Americas. 15.00. Boston Bk.

Bowden, A. O., and others. Day before yesterday in America. il. 1946. 3.60.
   Macmillan

Catlin, George. Episodes from Life among the Indians, and Last rambles. by
   Marvin C. Ross. il. 1959. 12.50. U. of Okla.

Collier, John. Indians of the Americas. il. 1947. 6.50. Norton

Embree, Edwin R. Indians of the Americas. il. 1939. 4.50. Houghton

Fairchild, Hoxie N. Noble savage. 1961. 8.50. Russell

Hagan, William T. American Indians. il. 1961. 4.50. U. of Chicago

Hibben, Frank C. Digging up America. il. 1960. 5.00. Hill & Wang

Keiser, Albert. Indian in American literature. 1933. 4.00. Oxford U. P.

Lothrop, Samuel K., and others. Pre-Columbian art. il. 1959. 30.00. boxed.
   N. Y. Graphic

Pozas Arciniegas, Ricardo. Juan the Chamula: An ethnological re-creation of
   the life of a Mexican Indian. tr. by Lysander Kemp. il. 1962. 3.50. U. of Calif.

Radin, Paul. Story of the American Indian. 1944. 4.50. Liveright

Ray, George Whitfield. American Indian: Who is he? 1951. 3.00. Forum

Simpson, Lesley Byrd. Encomienda in New Spain: The beginnings of Spanish
   Mexico. il. 1950. 3.75. U. of Calif.

Wissler, Clark. American Indian. 5.50. Smith, Peter

Wolf, Eric. Sons of the shaking earth. 1959. 5.00. U. of Chicago

INDIANS OF NORTH AMERICA (970.1)

Benedict, Ruth. Patterns of culture. 3.75. Houghton

Colton, Ray C. Civil War in the western territories. il. 1959. 5.00. U. of Okla.

Covarrubias, Miguel. Eagle, the jaguar, and the serpent. il. 1954. 15.00. Knopf

Davis, Robert Tyler. Native arts of the Pacific Northwest. 1949. 10.00. Stanford

De Voto, Bernard. Course of empire. 1952. 6.50. Houghton

Dockstader, Frederick J. Indian art in America. il. 1961. 25.00. N. Y. Graphic

Douglas, Frederic H., and Rene d' Harnoncourt. Indian art of the United States.
   il. 1958. 5.00. Doubleday

Driver, Harold E. Indians of North America. 1961. 10.95. U. of Chicago

Griffin, James B. Archeology of the eastern United States. il. 1952. 11.50. U. of Chicago

James, Edwin. Narrative of the captivity and adventures of John Tanner during thirty years residence among the Chippewa, Ottawa and Objibwa tribes. by Noel Loomis. 8.75. Ross & Haines

Kroeber, Theodora. Ishi in two worlds: A biography of the last wild Indian in North America. 1961. 5.95. U. of Calif.

Kroeber, A. L. Cultural and natural areas of native North America. il. 1954. 5.00. U. of Calif.

La Farge, Oliver. Pictorial history of the American Indian. il. 1956. 7.50. Crown

McReynolds, Edwin C. Seminoles. il. 1957. 5.75. U. of Okla.

Marriott, Alice L. First comers: Indians of America's dawn. il. 1960. 4.50. lib. bdg. 3.79. net. McKay

Martin, Paul, and others. Indians before Columbus: Twenty thousand years of North American history revealed by archeology. il. 1947. 8.50. U. of Chicago

Mead, Margaret, and Ruth Bunzel. Golden age of American anthropology. 10.00. Braziller

Roe, Frank G. Indian and the horse. il. 1955. 5.95. U. of Okla.

Underhill, Ruth. Red man's America. il. 1953. 7.50. U. of Chicago

Wedel, Waldo R. Prehistoric man on the Great Plains. il. 1961. 5.95. U. of Okla.

Wissler, Clark. Indians of the United States: Four centuries of their history and culture. il. 1940. 4.50. Doubleday

INDIANS OF NORTH AMERICA--SOCIAL LIFE AND CUSTOMS (970.1)

Edmonson, Munro S. Status terminology and the social structure of the North American Indians. 1958. 3.00. U. of Wash.

Macfarlan, Allan A. Book of American Indian games. 1958. 3.95. Assn. Pr.

Sandoz, Mari. These were the Sioux. il. 1961. 3.50. Hastings

INDIANS OF SOUTH AMERICA (980.1)

Disselhoff, Hans-Dietrich, and Sigvald Linne. Art of ancient America. il. 1961. 5.95. Crown

Freyre, Gilberto. Masters and the slaves. 1956. 8.50. Knopf

Huxley, Francis. Affable savages: An anthropologist among the Urubu Indians of Brazil. il. 1957. 4.75. Viking

Leicht, Hermann. Pre-Inca art and culture. il. 1959. 6.95. Orion

Stein, William W. Hualcan: Life in the Highlands of Peru. 1961. 6.00. Cornell

Steward, Julian H., and Louis C. Faron. Native peoples of South America. 1959. 8.95. McGraw

INDIC LITERATURE (891.1)

Lin, Yu-t'ang. Wisdom of India. 5.00. Random

Wisdom of China and India. 2.95. Modern Lib.

INDIVIDUALISM (330.153)

Bettelheim, Bruno. Informed heart: Autonomy in a mass age. 1960. 5.00. Free Press

Cooley, Charles H. Social organization, and Human nature and the social order. 2 vols. in 1. 1955. 7.50. Free Press

Dewey, John. Individualism old and new. 1962. pap. 1.25. Putnam

Heimann, Eduard. Reason and faith in modern society. 1961. 6.50. Wesleyan U. P.

Joad, Cyril E. M. Introduction to modern political theory. 1924. 1.20. Oxford U. P.

Knight, Everett W. Objective society. 1959. 3.75. Braziller

Morley, Felix. Essays on individuality. 1958. 5.00. U. of Pa.

Russell, Bertrand. Authority and the individual. 1960. pap. 1.25. Beacon

Spencer, Herbert. Man versus the state. by Albert Jay Nock. 1940. 3.50. Caxton

INDIVIDUALITY (137)

Combs, Arthur W., and Donald Snygg. Individual behavior. 1959. 6.00. Harper

Frohock, Wilbur M. Strangers to this ground: Cultural diversity in contemporary American writing. 1961. 4.50. S. M. U.

Gardner, John W. Excellence: Can we be equal and excellent too? 1961. 3.95. Harper

Huxley, J. S. Individual in the animal kingdom. 1912. 1.75. Cambridge, U. P.
Jung, C. G. Psychological types. 1959. 7.50. Pantheon
Marcel, Gabriel. Man against mass society. 1962. 1.95. Regnery
Strauss, Anselm. Mirrors and masks: The search for identity. 1959. 4.00. Free
   Press
Whyte, William H., Jr. Organization man. 1956. 5.00. S. and S.
INDOCHINA, FRENCH (959.7)
Hammer, Ellen J. Struggle for Indochina. 1954. 6.00. Stanford
INDONESIA (991)
Boeke, J. H. Evolution of the Netherlands Indies economy. 1946. 3.00. Inst. of
   Pac. Rel.
Bro, Margueritte Harmon. Indonesia: Land of challenge. 1954. 4.00. Harper
Callard, Keith B., and others. Major governments of Asia. by George McTurnan
   Kahin. il. 1958. 7.25. Cornell
Fischer, Louis. Story of Indonesia: Old land, new nation. il. 1959. 5.00. Harper
Lewis, R. Indonesia: Troubled paradise. il. 1962. 5.95. McKay
Mintz, Jeanne. Indonesia: A profile. il. 1961. 4.25. Van Nostrand'
Sundstrom, Harold W. Garuda: Introducing Indonesia. il. 1962. 3.00. Exposition
Vlekke, Bernard H. M. Nusantara: A history of Indonesia. 10.00. Quadrangle
Wertheim, William F. Indonesian society in transition. 6.50. Inst. of Pac. Rel.
INDUSTRIAL ACCIDENTS (331.823)
Gordon, Albert C. Y. Code: The cause and prevention of industrial accidents.
   3.25. Pagoda
INDUSTRIAL ARTS (600)
Bedell, Earl L., and Ernest G. Gardner. Household mechanics. il. 1945. 6.25.
   Van Nostrand
Steinmetz, Rollin C., and Charles S. Rice. Vanishing crafts and their craftsmen.
   il. 1959. 4.75. Rutgers
Van Doren, Harold. Industrial design. 1954. 9.00. McGraw
Forbes, R. J. Man the maker: A history of engineering and technology. 1958.
   5.00. Abelard
Mumford, Lewis. Technics and civilization. 1934. 6.00. Harcourt
Wolf, Abraham. History of science, technology, and philosophy in the 16th and
   17th centuries. 2 vols. il. 1959. 1.95 ea. 2 vols. il. 1961. 2.50 ea. Harper
INDUSTRIAL MANAGEMENT (658)
Anderson, R. C. Management practices. 1960. 7.00. McGraw
Balderston, C. Canby, and others. Management of an enterprise. 1949. 7.95.
   Prentice-Hall
Bethel, Lawrence L., and others. Essentials of industrial management. il. 1959.
   6.95. McGraw
Blake, Robert R., and J. S. Mouton. Group dynamics: Key to decision making.
   il. 1961. 3.50. Gulf
Braun, Carl F. Management and leadership. 1954. 3.25. Braun
Cerami, Charles A. How to solve management problems. 1957. 5.95. Prentice-
   Hall
Drucker, Peter F. Practice of management. 1954. 5.50. Harper
Gabriel, H. W. Techniques of creative thinking for management. 1961. 4.95.
   Prentice-Hall
Gilmer, Beverly Von H. Industrial psychology. 1961. 7.50; tests, 1.00. McGraw
Gray, J. Seton. Common sense in business: A digest of management procedures.
   1956. 4.75. McGraw
Haire, Mason. Psychology in management. 1956. 5.95. McGraw
Jones, Manley H. Executive decision making. il. 1962. 10.00. Irwin
Kelley, Pearce C., and Kenneth Lawyer. How to organize and operate a small
   business. 1961. 10.60. Prentice-Hall
Lasser, Jacob K. Business management handbook. 1960. 12.50. McGraw
Lewis, Ralph F. Management uses of accounting. il. 1961. 3.95. Harper
Lincoln, James F. Incentive management. 1.00. Lincoln Electric
Lincoln, James F. New approach to industrial economics. 1961. 3.50. Devin

Maier, Norman R. F., and John J. Hayes. Creative management. il. 1962. 5.95. Wiley

Owens, Richard N. Introduction to business policy. 1954. 9.25. Irwin

Scott, William G. Human relations in management. 1962. 10.00. Irwin

Slichter, Sumner H., and others. Impact of collective bargaining on management. 1960. 8.75. Brookings

Villers, Raymond. Dynamic management in industry. il. 1960. 10.65. Prentice-Hall

Warner, William L., and Norman H. Martin. Industrial man. 1959. 6.50. Harper

Weimer, Arthur M. Business administration. 1962. 9.35. Irwin

INDUSTRIAL ORGANIZATION (658)

Allen, L. A. Management and organization. 1958. 7.00. McGraw

Brady, Robert A. Organization, automation, and society: The scientific revolution in industry. 1961. 8.00. U. of Calif.

Dimock, Marshall E. Administrative vitality: The conflict with bureaucracy. 1959. 5.75. Harper

King, W. L. Industry and humanity. 1947. 6.00. St. Martins

Udy, Stanley H., Jr. Organization of work. 1959. 3.95. Taplinger

INDUSTRIAL RELATIONS (331.1)

Aly, Bower. Labor and management. 1959. 4.50. Noble

Bloom, Gordon F., and Herbert R. Northrup. Economics of labor relations. 1961. 10.65. Irwin

Chamberlain, Neil W. Sourcebook on labor. il. 1958. 12.00. McGraw

Galenson, Walter, and Seymour M. Lipset. Labor and trade unionism: An interdisciplinary reader. il. 6.95. Wiley

Labor Relations Reporter, editorial staff. Primer of labor relations. 1.00. Bur. of Nat. Affairs

Mann, Floyd C., and L. Richard Hoffman. Automation and the worker. il. 1960. 4.50. Holt, Rinehart & Winston

Myers, James, and Harry W. Laidler. What do you know about labor? 1956. 4.75. Day

Reynolds, Lloyd C. Labor economics and labor relations. 1959. 8.50. Prentice-Hall

Shultz, George P., and George D. Baldwin. Automation: A new dimension to old problems. 1955. pap. 1.00. Pub. Affairs

Spates, Thomas G. Human values where people work. 1960. 4.50. Harper

Whyte, William F. Man and organization. 1959. 4.50. Irwin

Whyte, William F. Money and motivation. 1955. 4.50. Harper

INDUSTRIAL SOCIOLOGY (331.8)

Davis, Keith. Human relations at work. 1962. 7.95. McGraw

Nosow, Sigmund, and William H. Form. Man, work, and society. 1962, 8.50. Basic Books

Sofer, Cyril. Organization from within. 1962. 6.50. Quadrangle

Whyte, William F. Men at work. 1961. 10.60. Irwin

INDUSTRY (338)

Drucker, Peter F. New society. 1950. 5.95. Harper

Fanning, Leonard. Fathers of industries. il. 1962. 4.75. Lippincott

Fenn, Dan H. Business responsibility in action. il. 1960. 4.75. McGraw

Frankel, S. H. Economic impact on underdeveloped societies. 1953. 3.25. Harvard

Hoselitz, Bert F. Progress of underdeveloped areas. 1952. 5.50. U. of Chicago

Moore, Wilbert E. Industrial relations and the social order. 1951. 6.75. Macmillan

Tawney, Richard H. Acquisitive society. 1946. 3.00. Harcourt

Trade and industry in the Middle Ages. (Cambridge economic history of Europe. vol. 2) Cambridge U. P.

Unwin, George. Industrial organization in the 16th and 17th centuries. 6.00. Kelley

Veblen, Thorstein. Engineers and the price system. 1921. 2.75. Viking

Warner, W. Lloyd. Corporation in the emergent American society. 1962. 3.00.
   Harper
Wilensky, Harold L., and Charles N. Lebeaux. Industrial society and social
   welfare. 1958. 5.00. Russell Sage
INDUSTRY AND STATE (338.9)
Anshen, Melvin, and Francis D. Wormuth. Private enterprise and public policy.
   1954. 7.50. Macmillan
Dimock, Marshall E. Business and government. il. 1961. 6.75. Holt, Rinehart &
   Winston
Fainsod, Merle, and others. Government and the American economy. 1959. 7.35.
   Norton
Goyder, George. Future of private enterprise: A study in responsibility. 2.50.
   Macmillan
Handlin, Oscar, and Mary F. Commonwealth: A study of the role of government
   in the American economy: Massachusetts, 1774-1861. 1952. 3.50. Harvard
Koontz, H. D., and R. Gable. Public control of economic enterprise. 1956. 7.75.
   McGraw
Laski, Harold J. Grammar of politics. 1957. 6.00. Humanities
Lyon, L. S., and others. Government and economic life. 2 vols. vol. 1, 1939,
   3.50; vol. 2, 1940, 4.00. Brookings
MacIver, Robert M. Democracy and the economic challenge. 1952. 3.00. Knopf
Mund, Vernon A. Government and business. 1960. 7.00. Harper
Prothro, James W. Dollar decade. 1954. 4.75. La. State
Rostow, Eugene V. Planning for freedom. 1960. 6.00. Yale
INFINITE (517.21)
Lieber, Lillian R. Infinity. il. 1953. 5.00. Rinehart
Peter, Rozsa. Playing with infinity: Mathematics for everyman. il. 1962. 4.95.
   S. and S.
INFLATION (FINANCE) (332.414)
Bach, George L. Inflation: A study in economics, ethics, and politics. 1958. 2.50.
   Brown U.
Brown, Arthur J. Great inflation, 1939-1951. 1955. 5.60. Oxford U. P.
Burns, Arthur F. Prosperity without inflation. 1958. 3.00. Fordham
Conference on Economic Progress. Inflation, cause and cure. il. 1959. 0.50.
   Conf. on Econ. Progress
Hart, Albert G. Defense without inflation. 1951. 2.00. Twentieth Century
Hazlitt, Henry. What you should know about inflation. 1960. 3.50. Van Nostrand
Palyi, Melchior. Inflation primer. 1961. 4.00. Regnery
Thorp, Willard L., and Richard E. Quandt. New inflation. 1959. bds. 5.00.
   McGraw
Weintraub, Sidney. Classical Keynesianism, monetary theory and the price level.
   1961. 4.00. Chilton
Wilson, Thomas. Inflation. il. 1961. 5.50. Harvard
INFLUENZA (614.518)
Hoehling, Adolph A. Great epidemic. il. 1961. bds. 3.95. Little
INFORMATION THEORY (006)
Broadbent, Donald E. Perception and communication. 1958. 8.50. Pergamon
Hancock, J. Introduction to the principles of communication theory. 9.50.
   McGraw
Reza, Fazlollah M. Introduction to information theory. il. 1961. 13.50. McGraw
INQUISITION (272.2)
Coulton, George Gordon. Inquisition and liberty. 1959. 4.00. Smith, Peter
Lea, Henry C. Inquisition of the Middle Ages. abridged ed. by Margaret Nicholson.
   1961. 10.00. Macmillan
INSANITY (132.1)
Beers, Clifford W. Mind that found itself. 1948. 3.95. Doubleday
Lindman, Frank T., and Donald M. McIntyre, Jr. Mentally disabled and the
   law. 1961. 7.50. U. of Chicago

Roche, Philip Q. Criminal mind. 1958. 5.00. Farrar, Straus
Zilboorg, G., and J. K. Hall. One hundred years of American psychiatry.
   1944. 10.00. Columbia
INSECTS (595.7)
Barker, Will. Familiar insects of America. il. 1960. 5.95; lib. bdg: 5.11.
   Harper
Brues, Charles T. Insects and human welfare. il. 1947. 3.00. Harvard
Brues, Charles Thomas. Insect dietary: An account of the food habits of insects.
   il. 1946. 5.00. Harvard
Campbell, Frank L. Physiology of insect development. 1959. 4.00. U. of Chicago
Chandler, Asa C., and C. P. Read. Introduction to parasitology. 1961. 9.75.
   Wiley
Cheesman, Evelyn. Insects, their secret world. il. 3.75. Smith, Peter
DuPorte, Ernest M. Manual of insect morphology. 1959. 5.50. Reinhold
Edney, E. B. Water relations of terrestrial arthropods. 1957. 3.00. Cambridge
   U. P.
Fabre, Jean Henri. Insect world of J. Henri Fabre. by Edwin Way Teale. 1949.
   3.75. Dodd
Fenton, C. H. Field crop insects. il. 1952. 7.75. Macmillan
Fernald, H. T., and Harold H. Shepard. Applied entomology. 1955. 8.50. McGraw
Gunther, F. A., and L. R. Jeppson. Modern insecticides and world food pro-
   duction. 1960. 8.50. Wiley
Jaques, Harry E. How to know the insects. 1947. 2.75. Brown, W. C.
Herms, William B., and Maurice T. James. Medical entomology. il. 1961. 12.50.
   Macmillan
Lutz, Frank E. Field book of insects. il. 1935. 3.95. Putnam
Metcalf, C. L., and others. Destructive and useful insects. 1963. 15.00. McGraw
Michener, Charles D., and Mary H. American social insects. il. 1951. 7.95.
   Van Nostrand
Pesson, Paul. World of insects. 1959. 15.00. McGraw
Pfadt, Robert E., ed. Fundamentals of applied entomology. il. 1962. 9.50.
   Macmillan
Pringle, J. W. S. Insect flight. 1957. 3.00. Cambridge U. P.
Richards, O. W. Social insects. il. 3.50. Smith, Peter
Snodgrass, R. E. Anatomy of the honey bee. il. 1956. 6.00. Cornell
Symes, Cecil B., and others. Insect control in public health. 1962. 11.00. Am.
   Elsevier
Teale, Edwin Way. Grassroot jungles. il. 6.00. Dodd
Teale, Edwin W. Strange lives of familiar insects. il. 1962. 4.00. Dodd
Wigglesworth, V. B. Insect physiology. 1956. 2.25. Wiley
Wigglesworth, V. B. Principles of insect physiology. il. 12.50. Dutton
INSTINCT.(158.424)
Birney, Robert C., and Richard C. Teevan. Instinct. 1961. pap. 1.45. Van Nostrand
Fletcher, Ronald. Instinct in man. 1957. 7.50. Int. Univs.
Tinbergen, Nikolaas. Study of instinct. 1951. 5.60. Oxford U. P.
INSTRUMENTAL MUSIC (785)
Barlow, Harold, and Sam Morgenstern. Dictionary of musical themes. 1949. 5.00.
   Crown (R)
Davison, Archibald Thompson, and Willi Apel. Historical anthology of music.
   2 vols. vol. 1, Oriental, medieval, and Renaissance music. 1949. vol. 2,
   Baroque, rococo, and pre-classical music. 1950. 11.50 ea. Harvard
Geiringer, K. Music of the Bach family: An anthology. 1955. 9.00. Harvard
Parrish, Carl. Treasury of early music. 1958. 6.50. Norton
Parrish, Carl, and John F. Ohl. Masterpieces of music before 1750. il. 1951.
   4.95. Norton
INSTRUMENTATION AND ORCHESTRATION (781.63)
Adkins, Hector E. Treatise on military band. 10.00. Boosey
Kennan, Kent. Technique of orchestration. 1952. 7.00. Prentice-Hall

Piston, Walter. Orchestration. il. 1955. 6.95. Norton
INSURANCE (368)
Ackerman, S. B. Insurance. 1951. 7.50. Ronald
Athearn, James L. Risk and insurance. il. 1962. 6.95. Appleton
Brainard, Calvin H. Automobile insurance. 1961. 11.00. Irwin
Dickerson, O. D., Jr. Health insurance. 1959. 6.95. Irwin
Elliott, Curtis M. Property and casualty insurance. 6.00. McGraw
Goldmann, Franz. Voluntary medical care insurance in the United States. 1948.
    3.25. Columbia
Gregg, Davis W. Life and health insurance handbook. 1959. 14.50. Irwin (R)
Huebner, Solomon S., and Kenneth Black, Jr. Property insurance. 1957. 5.75.
    Appleton
Kulp, C. A. Casualty insurance. 1956. 8.00. Ronald
Lincoln, Walter O., and others. Fire insurance, inspection and underwriting.
    il. 1953. 15.00. Chilton
Mayerson, Allen L. Introduction to insurance. 1962. 6.95. Macmillan
McCahan, David. Accident and sickness insurance. 1954. 5.00. Irwin
Mehr, Robert I., and Emerson Cammack. Principles of insurance. 1961. 10.60.
    Irwin
Pickrell, Jesse F. Group health insurance. 1961. 5.75. Irwin
Rodda, William H. Fire and property insurance. 1956. 10.00. Prentice-Hall
Schoeck, Helmut. Financing medical care. 1962. 5.50. Caxton
Somers, Herman M., and Anne R. Doctors, patients, and health insurance. 1961.
    7.50. Brookings
Spiegelman, Mortimer. Ensuring medical care for the aged. 1960. 6.25. Irwin
Weeks, H. Ashley. Family spending patterns and health care. 1961. 3.50. Harvard
INSURANCE, LIFE (368.3)
Hathaway, Barbara H. Your life insurance. il. 5.95. Doubleday
Huebner, Solomon S., and Kenneth Black, Jr. Life insurance. il. 1958. 6.50.
    Appleton
McGill, Dan M. Life insurance. 1959. 10.60. Irwin
Maclean, Joseph B. Life insurance. 1962. 7.95. McGraw
Magee, John H. Life insurance. 1958. 10.60. Irwin
West, Carl J. Understanding life insurance. 2.75. Long's College Bk.
INSURANCE, SOCIAL (368.4)
Burns, Eveline M. American social security system. 6.50. Houghton
Clarke, Charles E. Social insurance in Britain. 1950. 2.75. Cambridge U. P.
De Schweinitz, Karl. England's road to social security. 1961. pap. 1.65.
    Barnes, A. S.
Haber, William, and Wilbur J. Cohen. Social Security: Programs, problems,
    and policies. 1960. 8.75. Irwin
Larson, Arthur. Know your social security. 1959. 3.95. Harper
INTEGRALS (517.3)
Kestelman, Hyman. Modern theories of integration. pap. 2.00. Dover
McShane, Edward J. Integration. 1961. 6.00. Princeton
Peirce, B. O., and R. M. Foster. Short table of integrals. 4.50. Ginn
Smithies, F. Integral equations. 1958. 4.50. Cambridge U. P.
Zaanen, A. C. Introduction to the theory of integration. 1958. 8.75. Wiley
INTELLECT (151)
Getzels, J. W., and P. W. Jackson. Creativity and intelligence. 1962. 5.95.
    Wiley
Hunt, Joseph M. Intelligence and experience. 1961. 8.00. Ronald
Jenkins, James J., and Donald G. Paterson. Studies in individual differences.
    8.50. Appleton
Peaget, J. Psychology of intelligence. 3.75. Humanities
Scher, Jordan. Theories of the mind. 1962. 12.50. Free Press
Wechsler, David. Measurement and appraisal of adult intelligence. il. 1958.
    5.00. Williams & Wilkins

INTELLECTUAL LIFE (001)

Alexander, Franz G. Western mind in transition. 1950. 5.00. Random
Barlow, S. L. M. Astonished muse. 1961. 5.00. Day
Brombert, Victor H. Intellectual hero. 1961. 5.00. Lippincott
Curti, Merle. American paradox. 1956. 2.75. Rutgers
Fisher, Margaret. Leadership and intelligence. 1953. 3.74. T. C
Johnson, Edgar N. Introduction to the history of western tradition. 2 vols. il.
    1959. 8.25 ea; study guides by Orville H. Zabel. 1.00 ea. Ginn
Kerr, Walter. Decline of pleasure. 1962. 5.00. S. and S.
Molnar, Thomas. Decline of the intellectual. 3.75. Smith, Peter
Nelson, James. Wisdom for our time. il. 1961. 4.50. Norton
Odegaard, Charles E., and others. Man and learning in modern society. il. 1959.
    5.00. U. of Wash.
Sertillanges, Antonin G. Intellectual life. 1956. 3.00. Newman
Suhr, Elmer G. Ancient mind and its heritage. vol. 1, Exploring the Primitive,
    Egyptian and Mesopotamian cultures. 1959. 3.50; vol. 2, Exploring the
    Hebrew, Hindu, Greek and Chinese cultures. 1950. 5.00. Exposition
Wiener, Philip P., and Aaron Noland. Ideas in cultural perspective. 1962. 9.00.
    Rutgers

INTELLIGENCE SERVICE (355.343)

Ransom, Harry Howe. Central intelligence and national security. 1958. 4.75.
    Harvard

INTERCULTURAL COMMUNICATION (384)

Bunker, Robert, and John Adair. First look at strangers. il. 1959. 5.00. Rutgers

INTERCULTURAL EDUCATION (370.196)

Heaton, Margaret and Helen B. Lewis. Reading ladders for human relations.
    1955. 1.75. A. C. E. (R)
Simerville, Clara L. Home visits abroad. il. 1961. pap. 2.00. Oregon State
Taba, Hilda, and others. Intergroup education in public schools. 1952. 4.00.
    A. C. E.
Taba, Hilda. Leadership training in intergroup education. 1953. 2.50. A. C. E.
Taba, Hilda, and others. Literature for human understanding. 1948. 1.00. A. C. E.
Taba, Hilda. School culture: Studies in participation and leadership. 1955. 1.50.
    A. C. E.
Tipton, James H. Community in crisis: The elimination of segregation from a
    public school system. 1953. 3.75. T. C.

INTEREST AND USURY (332.8)

Breban, James M. Breban's interest tables. 6.50. McKay
Conrad, Joseph W. Introduction to the theory of interest. 1959. 7.50. U. of Calif.
Divine, Thomas F. Interest, an historical and analytical study in economics and
    ethics. 7.00. Marquette
Fisher, Irving. Mathematical investigations in the theory of value and prices.
    1892, and Appreciation and interest. 1896. 6.00. Kelley
Glover, James W. Compound interest and insurance tables and 7 place logarithms
    of numbers from 1 to 100,000. 1948. 6.00. Wahr
Hart, William LeRoy. Mathematics of investment. 1958. 7.50. Heath
Keynes, John Maynard. General theory of employment, interest, and money.
    1936. 6.00. Harcourt
Timlin, Mabel F. Keynesian economics. 1948. 4.25. U. of Toronto
Wilson, Thomas. Discourse on usury. by R. H. Tawney. 1925. 8.50. Kelley

INTERIOR DECORATION (747)

Alexander, Mary J. Decorating begins with you. il. 1958. 4.50. Doubleday
Austin, Ruth E., and Jeanette O. Parvis. Furnishing your home. 1961. 4.75.
    Houghton
Ball Victoria K. Art of interior design. il. 8.50. Macmillan
Better Homes and Gardens. Decorating book. by the Editors of Better Homes and
    Gardens. 1956. 5.95. Meredith
Birren, Faber. New horizons in color. 1955. 10.00. Reinhold

Carney, Clive. Impact of design. 1960. 12.50. Hastings
Derieux, Mary, and Isabelle Stevenson. Complete book of interior decorating. il. 1954. 7.95. Hawthorn
Goldstein, Harriet, and Vetta. Art in everyday life. 1954. 7.50. Macmillan
Hatje, Gerd, and Ursula. Design for modern living: A practical guide to home furnishing and interior decoration. il. 1962. 15.00. Abrams
House and Garden. Revised House and Garden guide to interior decoration. by the Editors of House and Garden. il. 1960. 12.95. S. and S.
Rutt, Anna. Home furnishing. 1961. 7.75. Wiley
Strange, T. A. English furniture, decoration, woodwork and allied arts. il. 1950. 15.00. Museum Bks.
Vanderwalker, Fred Norman. Drakes's cyclopedia of painting and decorating. 1945. 3.50. Drake, F. J. (R)
Wheeler, Esther, and Anabel Lasker. Complete book of flowers and plants for interior decoration. 7.95. Hearthside
INTERNATIONAL AGENCIES (341.11)
Yearbook of international organizations. 16.00. Int. Pub. Service (R)
INTERNATIONAL COOPERATION (341.)
Alder, Vera S. Humanity comes of age. 2.50. Wehman
Andrade, J. Freire d'. Freedom chooses slavery. il. 1959. 3.50. Coward
Asher, Robert E., and others. United Nations and promotion of the general welfare. 1957. 8.75. Brookings
Balassa, Bela A. Theory of economic integration. 1961. 7.35. Irwin
Carr, Edward H. Nationalism and after. 1.25. St. Martins
Chisholm, Brock. Can people learn to learn? 1958. 4.00. Harper
Elliott, William Y., and others. Political economy of American foreign policy. 1960. 7.30. Holt, Rinehart & Winston
Ellsworth, Paul T. International economy: Its structure and operation. 7.25. Macmillan
Gaitskell, H. Challenge of coexistence. 1957. 2.50. Harvard
Hanock, William K. Four studies of war and peace in this century. 1961. 3.75. Cambridge U. P.
Hendry, J. Treaties and federal constitutions. 1955. 4.50. Pub. Affairs
Islam, R. International Economic Cooperation and the United Nations. 1958. 3.00. Lounz
Islam, R. International cooperation and the United Nations. 1958. 3.00. Lounz
Krause, Walter. International economy. 6.50. Houghton
Levi, Werner. Fundamentals of world organizations. 1950. 3.00. U. of Minn.
Liska, George. Nations in alliance: The limits of interdependence. 1962. 6.00. Johns Hopkins
McClure, Wallace. World legal order. 1960. 7.50. U. of N. C.
Myrdal, Gunnar. Beyond the welfare state. 1960. 4.50. Yale
Ridgeway, George L. Merchants of peace. 1959. 4.50. Little
Theobald, Robert. Challenge of abundance. 1961. 4.50. Potter, C. N.
Thorp, Willard L. Trade, aid, or what? 1954. 4.50. Johns Hopkins
INTERNATIONAL EDUCATION (370.196)
Bidwell, Percy W. Undergraduate education in foreign affairs. 1962. 5.00. Columbia
Guerard, Albert Leon. Education of a humanist. 1949. 5.00. Harvard
Houle, Cyril O., and Charles A. Nelson. University, the citizen, and world affairs. 1956. 3.00. A. C. E.
Martin, Clyde I. Venture in international understanding. 1958. pap. 2.00. U. of Tex.
Washburne, Carleton. World's good. 1953. 4.50. Day
INTERNATIONAL GEOPHYSICAL YEAR 1957-1958 (530)
Chapman, Sydney. IGY: Year of discovery. 1959. 4.95. U. of Mich.
Clarke, Arthur C. Making of a moon. 3.50. Wehman
Fraser, Ronald. Once round the sun. il. 1958. 3.95. Macmillan

Ronne, Finn. Antarctic command. 1961. 5.00. Bobbs
Sullivan, Walter. Assault on the unknown: The International Geophysical Year.
  il. 1961. 7.95. McGraw
Wilson, J. Tuzo. IGY: The year of the new moons. il. 1961. 5.95. Knopf
INTERNATIONAL LAW (341)
Brierly, James L. Law of nations: An introduction to the international law of
  peace. 1955. 3.50. Oxford U. P.
Carlston, Kenneth S. Law and organization in world society. 1962. 6.50. U. of
  Ill.
Corbett, Percy E. Law in diplomacy. 1959. 6.00. Princeton
Dickinson, Edwin DeWitt. Equality of states in international law. 1920. 4.00.
  Harvard
Fenwick, Charles G. International law. 6.50. Appleton
Gould, Wesley L. Introduction to international law. 1957. 8.00. Harper
Grotius, Hugo. Prolegomena to the law of war and peace. tr. by F. W. Kelsey.
  1957. pap. 0.60. Bobbs
Hsu, Immanuel C. Y. China's entrance into the family of nations: The diplomatic
  phase, 1858-1880. 1960. 5.50. Harvard
Jenks, C. Wilfred. Common law of mankind. 1958. 12.50. Praeger
Jessep, Philip C. Modern law of nations. 1948. 5.00. Macmillan
Jessep, Philip D. Use of international law. 1959. 5.50. U. of Mich.
Kaplan, Morton A., and N. deB. Katzenbach. Political foundations of international
  law. 1961. 6.95. Wiley
Kelsen, Hans. General theory of law and state. 1961. 10.00. Russell
Kelsen, Hans. Principles of international law. 1952. 5.75. Rinehart
Nassbaum, Arthur. Concise history of the law of nations. 6.50. Macmillan
Orfield, Lester B., and Edward D. Re. Cases and materials on international
  law. 1955. 12.00. Bobbs
Stone, Julius. Quest for survival: The role of law and foreign policy. 1961.
  2.75. Harvard
Wright, Quincy. Contemporary international law. 1961. pap. 0.95. Random
Wright, Quincy. International law and the U. N. 1962. 4.25. Taplinger
INTERNATIONAL ORGANIZATION (341)
Anthony, P. J. America, the hope of the ages. 1959. 4.75. Christopher
Borgese, Giuseppe A. Foundations of the World Republic. 1953. 6.50. U. of
  Chicago
Brinton, Crane. From many one: The process of political integration and the
  problem of world government. 1948. 2.25. Harvard
Cheever, Daniel S., and H. Field Haviland, Jr. Organizing for peace: International
  organizing in world affairs. 1954. 12.00. Houghton
Claude, Inis L., Jr. Swords into plowshares. 1959. 9.00. Random
Deutsch, Karl W. Political community at the international level. 1954. pap. 0.95.
  Random
Eagleton, Clyde. Forces that shape our future. 1945. 3.25. N. Y. U.
Goodman, Elliot R. Soviet design for a world state. 1960. 6.75. Columbia
Goodspeed, Stephen S. Nature and function of international organization. il. 1959.
  7.50. Oxford U. P.
Hill, Norman. International organization. 1952. 6.00. Harper
Hutchins, Robert M. St. Thomas and the world state. 1949. 2.50. Marquette
Levi, Werner. Fundamentals of world organization. 1950. 3.00. U. of Minn.
Mangone, Gerard J. Short history of international organizations. 1954. 6.50.
  McGraw
Streit, Clarence K. Freedom's frontier: Atlantic union now. 1961. 4.50. Harper
INTERNATIONAL RELATIONS (172.4)
Atkinson, James D. Edge of war. 1960. 6.00. Regnery
Beloff, Max. Foreign policy and the democratic process. 1955. 3.00. Johns
  Hopkins
Bloomfield, Lincoln P. Evolution or revolution: The United Nations and the
  problem of peaceful territorial change. 1957. 4.50. Harvard

Boulding, Kenneth E. Conflict and defense. il. 1962. 7.00. Harper
Bozeman, A. Politics and culture in international history. 1960. 10.00. Princeton
Browne, Robert S. Race relations in international affairs. 1961. 1.00. Pub. Affairs
Buchanan, William, and Hadley Cantril. How nations see each other. 1953. 5.00. U. of Ill.
Buck, Philip W., and Martin Travis, Jr. Control of foreign relations in modern nations. 1957. 7.25. Norton
Carnegie Endowment for International Peace. Perspectives on peace, 1910-1960. 1960. 3.00. Praeger
Carr, Edward H. Twenty Years' Crisis. 1919-1939: An introduction to the study of international relations. 1946. 4.00. St. Martins
Corbett, Percy E. Law in diplomacy. 1959. 6.00. Princeton
Dickinson, Edwin D. Law and peace. 1951. 3.25. U. of Pa.
Duchacek, Ivo D., and Kenneth W. Thompson. Conflict and cooperation among nations. 1960. 6.50. Holt, Rinehart & Winston
Fitzsimons, Matthew A., and Stephen D. Kertesz. Diplomacy in a changing world. 1959. 7.50. U. of Notre Dame
Fox, William T. R. Theoretical aspects of international relations. 1959. 3.25. U. of Notre Dame
Graham, Malbone W. American diplomacy in the international community. 1948. 3.25. Johns Hopkins
Haas, Ernst B., and A. S. Whiting. Dynamics of international relations. 1956. 7.25. McGraw
Hartmann, Frederick H. Relations of nations. il. 1962. 7.00. Macmillan
Hocking, William Emest. Strength of men and nations. 1959. 3.50. Harper
Hoffmann, Stanley. Contemporary theory in international relations. il. 1960. 6.00. Prentice-Hall
International Union of Social Studies. Code of international ethics. by John Eppstein. 1953. 4.00. Newman
Kalijarvi, Thorsten V., and others. Modern world politics. il. 1953. 8.00. Crowell
Kaplan, M. A. System and process in international politics. 1957. 6.50. Wiley
Lerche, Charles O., Jr., and Margaret E. Readings in international politics, concepts and issues. 1958. pap. 2.95. Oxford U. P.
London, Kurt. How foreign policy is made. il. 1950. 5.00. Van Nostrand
Macridis, Roy C. Foreign policy in world politics. 1962. 4.95. Prentice-Hall
Madariaga, Salvador de. Blowing up of the Parthenon. 1960. 2.95. Praeger
Morgenthau, Hans J. Politics among nations. 1960. 10.00. Knopf
Organski, A. F. K. World politics. 1958. 6.50. Knopf
Palmer, Norman D., and Howard C. Perkins. International relations. 1954. 7.95. Houghton
Perkins, Dexter. America's quest for peace. 1961. 3.00. Indiana
Range, Willard. Jawaharlal Nehru's world view: A theory of international relations. 1961. 3.50. U. of Ga.
Schleicher, Charles P. Introduction to international relations. 1954. 11.35. Prentice-Hall
Schuman, Frederick L. International politics. il. 1958. 7.75. McGraw
Seton-Watson, Hugh. Neither war nor peace. 1960. 7.50. Praeger
Snyder, Louis L. Fifty major documents of the twentieth century. 1955. pap. 1.25. Van Nostrand
Thompson, Kenneth W. Christian ethics and the dilemmas of foreign policy. 1959. 3.50. Duke

INTERNATIONALISM (321.041)
Davis, Jerome. Citizens of one world. 1961. 3.95. Citadel
Hammond, Mason. City-state and world state: In Greek and Roman political theory until Augustus. 1951. 4.00. Harvard
Niebuhr, Reinhold. Structure of nations and empires. 1959. 5.00. Scribner

INTERPERSONAL RELATIONS (301)
Berrien, F. K., and Wendell H. Bash. Human relations: Comments and cases. 1957. 6.00. Harper

Gardner, Eric F., and George G. Thompson. Social relations and morals in small groups. il. 6.00. Appleton

Heider, Fritz. Psychology of interpersonal relations. 1958. 6.25. Wiley

Hodnett, Edward. Art of working with people. 1959. 3.95. Harper

Kaplan, Louis. Mental health and human relations in education. il. 1959. 5.50. Harper

Moore, Robert E. Human side of successful communication. 1961. 4.95. Prentice-Hall

Thibaut, John W., and Harold H. Kelley. Social psychology of groups. il. 1959. 6.00. Wiley

Wilner, Daniel M., and others. Human relations in interracial housing. 1955. 4.00. U. of Minn.

INTERSTATE COMMERCE (381)
Corwin, Edward S. Commerce power versus states rights. 1959. 4.00. Smith, Peter

Leach, Richard H., and Redding S. Sugg. Administration of interstate compacts. 1959. 4.50. La. State

INTERVIEWING (658.311)
Balinsky, Benjamin, and Ruth Burger. Executive interview. 1959. 4.00. Harper

Bellows, Roger M., and M. Frances Estep. Employment psychology: The interview. 1954. 5.00. Holt, Rinehart & Winston

Bingham, Walter V., and Bruce V. Moore. How to interview. 1959. 4.50. Harper

Fear, R. A. Evaluation interview. 1958. 6.00. McGraw

Hyman, Herbert H., and others. Interviewing in social research. il. 1954. 8.00. U. of Chicago

Kahn, R. L., and C. F. Cannell. Dynamics of interviewing. 1957. 6.75. Wiley

Langdon, Grace and Irving W. Stout. Teacher-parent interviews. 1954. 7.35. Prentice-Hall

Maier, Norman R. F. Appraisal interview. il. 1958. 5.50. Wiley

Weinland, J. D., and M. V. Gross. Personnel interviewing. 1952. 6.50. Ronald

INTESTINES (611.34)
Hodges, Fred J. Gastrointestinal tract: A handbook of Roentgen diagnosis. 1944. 7.00. Year Bk.

Spencer, Richard P. Intestinal tract. il. 1960. 12.75. Thomas, C. C.

Welch, Claude E. Intestinal obstruction. 1958. 10.50. Year Bk.

INVENTIONS (608.7)
Berle, Alf K., and L. Sprague de Camp. Inventions, patents and their management. 1959. 12.50. Van Nostrand

De Camp, L. Sprague. Heroic age of American invention. il. 1961. 4.50. Doubleday

Fuller, Edmund. Tinkers and genius. 1955. 4.50. Hastings

Woodling, George V. Inventions and their protection. 1955. 10.00. Boardman, Clark

Becker, Carl L. Progress and power. 1949. 3.00. Knopf

Burlingame, Roger. Machines that built America. 1953. 3.50. Harcourt

Mumford, Lewis. Technics and civilization. 1934. 6.00. Harcourt

Usher, Abbott P. History of mechanical inventions. il. 1954. 9.75. Harvard

INVENTORIES (658.787)
Abramovitz, M. Inventories and business cycles. 1950. 6.00. Princeton

Fetter, Robert B., and Winston C. Dalleck. Decision models for inventory management. 1961. 5.75. Irwin

Starr, Martin K., and David W. Miller. Inventory control: Theory and practice. il. 1962. 10.00. Prentice-Hall

INVENTORS (926)
Darrow, Floyd L. Masters of science and invention. il. 1923. 5.75. Harcourt

Leithauser, Joachim G. Inventors's progress. il. 1959. 4.50. World Pub.

INVERTEBRATES (592)
Borradaile, L. A., and F. A. Potts. Invertebrata. 1961. 9.50. Cambridge U. P.
Buchsbaum, Ralph. Animals without backbones: An introduction to the invertebrates.
   il. 1948. 9.00. U. of Chicago
Buchsbaum, Ralph M., and others. Lower animals: Living invertebrates of the
   world. il. 1960. 12.50. Doubleday
Bullough, William S. Practical invertebrate anatomy. 7.50. St. Martins
Carter, G. S. General zoology of the invertebrates. 1961. 6.50. Macmillan
Carthy, J. D. Introduction to the behaviour of invertebrates. il. 1959. 8.00.
   Macmillan
Easton, William H. Invertebrate paleontology. il. 1960. 11.00. Harper
Hegner, Robert W. Invertebrate zoology. 1933. 6.00. Macmillan
Hyman, Libbie Henrietta. Invertebrates. 1959. 15.00. McGraw
Light, Sol F., and others. Intertidal invertebrates of the Central California
   Coast. il. 1957. 6.50. U. of Calif.
Moore, Raymond C., and others. Invertebrate fossils. 1952. 13.50. McGraw
Pennak, R. W. Fresh-water invertebrates of the United States. 1953. 15.00.
   Ronald
Pratt, H. S. Manual of the common invertebrate animals. 1935. 12.50. McGraw
Ricketts, Edward F., and Jack Calvin. Between Pacific tides. 1962. 8.75.
   Stanford
Savory, Theodore H. Instinctive living. il. 1959. 3.00. Pergamon
Scheer, Bradley T. Recent advances in invertebrate physiology. 1957. 5.50.
   U. of Ore.
Shrock, Robert R., and William H. Twenhofel. Principles of invertebrate
   paleontology. 1953. 13.50. McGraw
Woods, Henry. Invertebrate palaeontology. 1946. 4.25. Cambridge U. P.
INVESTMENT BANKING (332.66)
Clark, Fred G., and Richard S. Rimanoczy. Where the money comes from. il.
   1961. 4.95. Van Nostrand
INVESTMENTS (332.6)
Babson, Roger W. Business barometers for profits, security, income. 1961.
   5.00. Harper
Badger, Ralph E., and Harry Guthmann, Investment principles and practices.
   1961. 11.95. Prentice-Hall
Bullock, Hugh. Story of investment companies. il. 1959. 5.95. Columbia
Fisher, Philip A. Common stocks and uncommon profits. 1960. 3.95. Harper
Greenhut, Melvin L. Full employment, inflation, and common stock. 1961. 3.25.
   Pub. Affairs
Howard, and Coit. Kiplinger guide to investing for the years ahead. 1962. 4.95.
   Prentice-Hall
Jordan, David F., and Herbert E. Dougall. Investments. 1960. 10.60. Prentice-
   Hall
Loftus, John A. Investment management. 1941. 2.50. Johns Hopkins
Richardson, George B. Information and investment: A study in the working of
   the competitive economy. il. 1960. 3.40. Oxford U. P.
Sauvain, Harry C. Investment management. 1959. 10.60. Prentice-Hall
INVESTMENTS, FOREIGN (332.6)
Feis, Herbert. Diplomacy of the dollar. 1950. 2.25. Johns Hopkins
IONIZATION (541.372)
Albert, A., and E. P. Serjeant. Ionization constants of acids and bases. in prep.
   Wiley
Francis, Gordon. Ionization phenomena in gases. il. 1960. 10.50. Academic Press
IONS (541.372)
Alexander, E. R. Principles of ionic organic reactions. 1950. 6.50. Wiley
Whipple, Omer K. Chemical properties and identification of ions. 1961. 3.95.
   Wadsworth
IOWA (977.7)
Writers' Project. Iowa. 1938. 6.50. Hastings

IRAN (955)
Arrian. History of Alexander. Indica. 2 vols. 3.50 ea. Harvard
Banani, Amin. Modernization of Iran, 1921-1941. 1961. 5.00. Stanford
Coon, C. S. Cave explorations in Iran: 1949. 1951. 1.50. U. Museum
Frye, Richard N.. Heritage of Persia. il. 1962. 7.50. World Pub.
Persian empire and the West. (Cambridge ancient history. vol. 4) 13.50. Cambridge U. P.
Sykes, Percy. History of Persia. 2 vols. 16.00. St. Martins
Upton, Joseph M. History of modern Iran. 1960. pap. 4.00. Harvard
Wilber, Donald. Iran: Past and present. 1958. 5.00. Princeton
Xenophon. Anabasis (Selections) by W. Welch, and C. G. Duffield. 1.50. St. Martins
Xenophon. Anabasis. 5 bks. bks. 1 and 2 by A. S. Walpole; bks. 3 and 5 by
    G. H. Nall; bk. 4 by E. D. Stone. bk. 1, 1.50; bks. 2 and 4, 1.25 ea; bk. 3,
    1.75; bk. 5, 1.10. St. Martins
IRAQ (956.7)
Glubb, John B. War in the desert. il. 1961. 5.50. Norton
Khadduri, Majid. Independent Iraq, 1932-1958. 1960. 7.20. Oxford U. P.
Dickson, Mora. Baghdad and beyond. 4.95. Rand McNally
IRELAND (941.5)
Beckett, James C. Short history of Ireland. 1952. 2.50. Hillary
Bennett, Richard L. Black and Tans. il. 1960. 4.50. Houghton
Berardis, Vincenzo. Italy and Ireland in the Middle Ages. il. 1950. 3.00. Dufour
Falls, Cyril. Elizabeth's Irish wars. 1959. 5.00. Hillary
Muirhead, Russell. Blue guide to Ireland. 4.95. Rand McNally
O'Faolain, Sean. Irish: A character study. 1949. 2.75. Devin
Piehler, H. A. Ireland for everyman. il. 1961. 2.95. Norton
Schrier, Arnold. Ireland and the American emigration, 1850-1900. il. 1958.
    4.50. U. of Minn.
Scowen, Kenneth. Ireland in color. il. 1960. 3.00. Viking
IRISH LITERATURE (891.62)
Anthology of Irish literature. 1.95. Modern Lib.
Flanagan, Thomas J. Irish novelists, 1800-1950. 1959. 6.75. Columbia
Howarth, Herbert. Irish writers. 1959. 4.50. Hill & Wang
Russell, Diarmuid. Portable Irish reader. 1946. 2.95. Viking
IRISH POETRY (COLLECTIONS) (891.62)
Colum, Padraic. Anthology of Irish verse. 1948. 3.95. Liveright
Taylor, Geoffrey. Irish poets of the nineteenth century. 1951. 2.50. Harvard
IRON (669.1)
Charles, James A., and others. Oxygen in iron and steel making. il. 1956. 7.00.
    Wiley
Dearden, John. Iron and steel today. il. 1956, 2.40. Oxford U. P.
IRON INDUSTRY AND TRADE (670)
Havighurst, Walter. Vein of iron: the Pickands, Mather story. 1958. 4.00.
    World Pub.
Wertime, Theodore A. Coming of the age of steel. il. 1962. 6.95. U. of Chicago
Ashton, Thomas S. Iron and steel in the Industrial Revolution. 1951. 5.00.
    Barnes & Noble
IRONY (808.8)
Sedgewick, G. G. Of irony expecially in drama. il. 1934. 3.95. U. of Toronto
Sharpe, Robert B. Irony in the drama. 1959. 5.00. U. of N. C.
IRRIGATION (631.7)
Addison, Herbert. Land, water and food. 1955. 3.40. Oxford U. P.
Israelsen, O. W. Irrigation principles and practices. 1950. 8.25. Wiley
IRVING, WASHINGTON, 1783-1859 (928)
Leary, Lewis. Washington Irving. 3.95. U. of Minn.
Lydenberg, Harry Miller. Irving's Knickerbocker and some of its sources. 1953.
    0.60. N. Y. P. L.

ISLANDS (990)
Brooks, Lillie. Islands of the world. 2.00. Brooks
Huxley, Anthony. Standard encyclopedia of the world's oceans and islands. 1962. 10.95. Putnam (R)
Oliver, Douglas Llewellyn. Pacific islands. il. 1951. 6.00. Harvard
Tressol, James. Strange patterns in the South Seas. il. 1961. 3.50. Doubleday'
Wood, Gordon L., and Patricia R. McBride. Pacific basin: A human and economic geography. il. 1955. 2.05. Oxford U. P.
ISOTOPES (541.38)
Aston, Francis W. Mass-spectra and isotopes. 1942. 6.50. St. Martins
Grobman, Arnold. Our atomic heritage. il. 1951. 2.95. U. of Fla.
Putnam, J. L. Isotopes. 1961. pap. 1.95. Penguin
Sacks, Jacob. Atom at work. 1956. 5.50. Ronald
ISRAEL (956.94)
Badi, Joseph. Religion in Israel today. 1959. 3.50. Twayne
Bernstein, M. H. Politics of Israel. 1957. 6.00. Princeton
Crossman, Richard H. S. Nation reborn. 3.50. Atheneum
Elath, Eliahu. Israel and her neighbors. 1957. 2.75. World Pub.
Heller, Abraham Mayer. Israel's odyssey. 1959. 4.00. Farrar, Straus
Holiday. Travel guide to Israel. 1.45. Random
Izis. Israel. il. 1960. 8.50. Orion
Kraines, Oscar. Government and politics in Israel. 1962. 3.50. Houghton
Sachar, Howard M. Aliyah, the peoples of Israel. il. 1961. 7.50. World Pub.
ISTANBUL (949.61)
Downey, Glanville. Constantinople in the age of Justinian. 1960. 2.75. U. of Okla.
ITALIAN DRAMA (852)
Bentley, Eric. Six Italian plays. 3.25. Smith, Peter
Goldberg, Isaac, tr. Plays of the Italian theatre. 3.00. Humphries
ITALIAN LANGUAGE (450)
Berlitz Schools of Languages. Berlitz basic Italian dictionary. 1957. 2.00. Grosset
Cassell's Italian dictionary. Italian-English, English-Italian. 1959. plain 7.50; thumb-indexed 8.50. Funk (R)
ITALIAN LITERATURE (850)
Sanctis, Francesco de. History of Italian literature. 2 vols. 1960. 12.50. Basic Books
Vittorini, Domenico. High points in the history of Italian literature. 1958. 4.75. McKay
Weinberg, Bernard. History of literary criticism in the Italian Renaissance. 2 vols. 1961. 20.00. U. of Chicago
Whitfield, John H. Short history of Italian literature. 3.00. Smith, Peter
Wilkins, Ernest Hatch. History of Italian literature. 1954. 8.00. Harvard
Arrowsmith, William. Image of Italy. il. 1961. 4.00. U. of Tex.
ITALIANS IN THE U.S. (325.73)
Pisani, Lawrence Frank. Italian in America. 1957. 3.50. Exposition
Whyte, William Foote. Street-corner society: The social structure of an Italian slum. il. 1955. 6.00. U. of Chicago
ITALO-ETHIOPIAN WAR, 1935-1936 (963)
Schaefer, Ludwig F. Ethiopian crisis: Touchstone of appeasement. 1961. pap. 1.50. Heath
ITALY--ANTIQUITIES (945)
Randall-MacIver, David. Italy before the Romans. il. 1928. 1.60. Oxford U. P.
Whatmough, Joshua. Foundations of Roman Italy. 6.00. Humanities
ITALY--DESCRIPTION AND TRAVEL (914.5)
Berenson, Bernard. Passionate sightseer. il. 1960. 10.00. S. and S.
Coates, Robert M. Beyond the Alps. il. 4.00. Sloane
Highet, Gilbert. Poets in a landscape. il. 1957. 6.50. Knopf
Lawrence, D. H. Twilight in Italy. pap. 1.35. Viking

ITALY--ECONOMIC CONDITIONS (945)
Luzzatto, Gino. Economic history of Italy from the fall of the Roman Empire to
the beginning of the 16th century. tr. by Philip Jones. 1961. 5.00. Barnes &
Noble
ITALY--FOREIGN RELATIONS (945)
Kogan, Norman. Italy and the allies. 1956. 4.25. Harvard
ITALY--HISTORY (945)
Albrecht-Carrie, Rene.. Italy from Napoleon to Mussolini. 1950. 5.00. Columbia
Bowsky, William M. Henry VII in Italy: The conflict of empire and city-state,
1310-1313. il. 1960. 5.25. U. of Nebr.
Heriot, A. French in Italy, 1796-1799. 6.00. Humanities
Jamison, E. M., and others. Italy: Mediaeval and modern. il. 1917. 2.90. Oxford
U. P.
Mack Smith, Denis. Italy: A modern history. 1959. 7.50. U. of Mich.
Trevelyan, J. P. Short history of the Italian people. 1956. 8.50. Pitman
ITALY--HISTORY--SOURCES (945)
Mussolini, Benito. Fall of Mussolini. 1948. 3.00. Farrar, Straus
ITALY--POLITICS AND GOVERNMENT (945)
Baron, Hans. Crisis of the early Italian Renaissance. 1955. 10.00. Princeton
Dante Alighieri. On world government. tr. by Schenider. 1957. pap. 0.65.
Bobbs
Einaudi, Mario, and Francois Goguel. Christian democracy in Italy and France;
1952. 4.00. U. of Notre Dame
Hughes, Henry Stuart. United States and Italy. il. 1953. 4.50. Harvard
Kogan, Norman. Government of Italy. 1962. 2.95. Crowell
Mazzini, Guiseppe. Duties of man and other essays. 1.95. Dutton
Noether, E. P. Seeds of Italian nationalism, 1700-1815. 1951. 3.00. Columbia
Schneider, H. W. Fascist government of Italy. 1936. 3.00. Van Nostrand
ITALY--RELATIONS WITH FOREIGN COUNTRIES (945)
Hale, John R. England and the Italian Renaissance. 4.50. Humanities
Rossi, Joseph. Image of America in Mazzini's writings. 1954. 3.50. U. of Wis.
Sells, A. Lytton. Italian influence in English poetry: From Chaucer to Southwell.
il. 1955. 6.75. Indiana
ITALY--SOCIAL CONDITIONS (945)
Banfield, Edward C. Moral basis of a backward society. 4.00. Free Press
Neufeld, Maurice F. Italy: School for awakening countries. 9.00. N. Y. State
School of Ind. & Labor Rel.
ITALY--SOCIAL LIFE AND CUSTOMS (914.5)
Baldrige, Letita. Roman candle. 1956. 3.75. Houghton
Deane, Shirley. Rocks and olives: Portrait of an Italian village. il. 1955. 3.25.
Transatlantic
IVAN IV, CZAR OF RUSSIA, 1530-1584 (923.1)
Eisenstein, S. M. Ivan the Terrible. 1962. 7.00? S. and S.
Koslow, Jules. Ivan the Terrible. il. 1962. 5.95. Hill & Wang
IVORIES (736.6)
Ray, Dorothy. Artists of the tundra and the sea. il. 1961. 5.75. U. of Wash.

J

JACKSON, ANDREW, PRES. U.S., 1767-1845 (923.173)
Ahl, Frances N. Andrew Jackson and the Constitution. 1939. 2.00. Christopher
James, Marquis. Andrew Jackson: Border captain. 1959. 1.65. Grosset
James, Marquis. Andrew Jackson: Portrait of.a president. pap. 1.95. Grosset
Schlesinger, Arthur M., Jr. Age of Jackson. 1945. 6.50. Little
Van Deusen, Glyndon G. Jacksonian era, 1828-1848. il. 1959. 5.00. Harper
Ward, John W. Andrew Jackson: Symbol for an age. 1955. 5.00. Oxford U. P.
JACKSON, THOMAS JONATHAN (STONEWALL JACKSON), 1824-1863 (923.5)
Chambers, Lenoir. Stonewall Jackson. 2 vols. il. 1959. boxed, 20.00. Morrow
Davis. Burke. They called him Stonewall. il. 1954. 6.95. Holt, Rinehart &
Winston

Henderson, G. F. R.   Stonewall Jackson and the American Civil War. 1936, 8.95.
   McKay
Tate, Allen.   Stonewall Jackson. 1957. pap. 1.65. U. of Mich.
Vandiver, Frank E.   Mighty Stonewall. il. 1957. 6.50. McGraw
JACOBINS (944)
Brinton, Crane.   Jacobins, an essay in the new history. 1962. 7.50. Russell
JACOBITES (942)
Jones, G. H.   Main stream of Jacobitism. 1954. 4.50. Harvard
JADE (736)
Nott, Stanley C.   Chinese jade throughout the ages: A review of its characteris-
   tics, decoration, folklore and symbolism. il. 1962. 15.00. Tuttle
JAMAICA (972.92)
Carley, Mary Manning.   Jamaica. 1962. 6.00. Praeger
JAMES I, KING OF GREAT BRITAIN, 1566-1625 (942.061)
Stafford, Helen G.   James VI of Scotland and the throne of England. 3.75. Appleton
Willson, David.   King James VI and I. 1956. 6.00. Holt
JAMES, HENRY, 1843-1916.   (928)
Anderson, Quentin.   American Henry James. 1956. 6.50. Rutgers
Andreas, Osborn.   Henry James and the expanding horizon. 1948. 3.50. U. of
   Wash.
Bayley, John.   Characters of love. 1961. 6.00. Basic Books
Beach, Joseph Warren.   Method of Henry James. rev. ed. 6.00. Saifer
Bowden, Edwin T.   Themes of Henry James. 1956. 4.00. Yale
Cargill, Oscar.   Novels of Henry James. 1961. 7.95. Macmillan
Dupee, F. W.   Henry James. 1951. 4.75. Sloane
Edel, Leon.   Henry James. 3 vols. il. vol. 1. Untried years: 1843-1870. 1953.
   8.00; vol. 2. Conquest of London. 1962. vol. 3. Middle years. 1962. 8.50 ea;
   vols. 2 and 3, 16.00; 3 vols. 24.00. Lippincott
James, Henry.   Autobiography. by F. W. Dupee. 8.50. Criterion
LeClair, Robert C.   Young Henry James. 6.50. Twayne
McCarthy, Harold T.   Henry James: The creative process. 5.00. Yoseloff
Matthiessen, F. O.   James family. 1947. 7.50. Knopf
Poirier, William R.   Comic sense of Henry James. 1960. 6.50. Oxford U. P.
Ward, Joseph A.   Imagination of disaster: Evil in the fiction of Henry James.
   1961. 3.00. U. of Neb.
JAMES, JESSE WOODSON, 1847-1882 (923.4173)
Breihan, Carl W.   Complete and authentic life of Jesse James. 4.50. Fell
JAMES, WILLIAM, 1842-1910 (921.1)
Compton, Charles H.   William James: Philosopher and man. 1957. 4.50. Scare-
   crow
Moore, Edward C.   American pragmatism. 1961. 6.00. Columbia
Perry, Ralph Barton.   Thought and character of William James. 1948. 6.00.
   Harvard
Perry, Ralph B.   Thought and character of William James. 2 vols. il. set, 15.00.
   Little
Santayana, George.   Character and opinion in the United States. 1956. 0.95.
   Doubleday
JAMESTOWN, VA. (975.5425)
Miers, Earl S.   Blood of freedom. il. 1958. 3.50. Colonial Williamsburg. Order
   from Holt, Rinehart & Winston
JAN VERMEER VAN DELFT, 1632-1675 (927)
Vermeer, Jan.   Jan Vermeer Van Delft. by Ary Bob de Vries. il. 7.50. Boston
   Bk.
JAPAN (952)
Dening, Esler.   Japan. il. 1960. 6.50. Praeger
JAPAN--CHURCH HISTORY (275.2)
Boxer, C. R.   Christian century in Japan (1549-1650) il. 1951. 10.00. U. of Calif.

JAPAN--CIVILIZATION (952)
Benedict, Ruth. Chrysanthemum and the sword. 4.50. Houghton
Bennett, John W., and others. In search of identity: The Japanese overseas
 scholar in America and Japan. il. 1958. 7.50. U. of Minn.
Hearn, Lafcadio. Japan, and interpretation. 1955. bds. 3.75. Tuttle
Keene, Donald. Living Japan. il. 1959. 7.95. Doubleday
Sansom, G. B. Japan: A short cultural history. il. 1962. text ed. 5.75. Appleton
Sansom, G. B. Western world and Japan. il. 1950. 8.50. Knopf
Silberman, Bernard S. Japanese character and culture: Selected readings. il.
 1962. 7.50. U. of Ariz.
JAPAN--DESCRIPTION AND TRAVEL (915)
Harris, Townsend. Complete journal of Townsend Harris. by Marlo E. Cosenza.
 1958. 7.50. Tuttle
Tourist Industry Division of the Ministry of Transportation. Japan: Official guide.
 6.50. Tuttle
JAPAN--DICTIONARIES AND ENCYCLOPEDIAS (803)
Bush, Lewis. Japanalia. 5.50. Tuttle (R)
JAPAN--ECONOMIC CONDITIONS (952.033)
Allen, G. C. Japan's economic recovery. 1958. 5.75. Oxford U. P.
Lockwood, W. Economic development of Japan. 1954. 10.00. Princeton
JAPAN--FOREIGN RELATIONS (952.327)
Borton, Hugh, and others. Japan between East and West. 1957. 4.75. Harper
Lensen, G. A. Russian push toward Japan: Russo-Japanese relations, 1697-
 1875. 1959. 10.00. Princeton
Mendel, Douglas H., Jr. Japanese people and foreign policy. il. 6.50. U. of
 Calif.
Shigemitsu, Mamoru. Japan and her destiny. by F. S. G. Piggott. 1958. 7.50.
 Dutton
JAPAN--FOREIGN RELATIONS--U.S. (952)
Feis, H. Road to Pearl Harbor. 1950. 6.00. Princeton
Hunsberger, Warren S. Japanese-American economic relations. 1961. 6.00?
 Harper
Reischauer, Edwin O. United States and Japan. 1957. 5.50. Harvard
JAPAN--HISTORY (952)
Hall, John W. Japanese history: Guide to Japanese reference and research
 materials. 1954. pap. 5.00. U. of Mich.
Latourette, Kenneth Scott. History of Japan. il. 1957. 6.00. Macmillan
Shinoda, Minoru. Founding of the Kamakura shogunate, 1180-1185. 1960. 7.50.
 Columbia
Storry, Richard. History of modern Japan. 3.25. Smith, Peter
JAPAN--POLITICS AND GOVERNMENT (952)
Burks, Ardath W. Government of Japan. 1961. 2.95. Crowell
Callard, Keith B., and others. Major governments of Asia. by George McTurnan
 Kahin. il. 1958. 7.25. Cornell
Cary, James. Japan today: Reluctant ally. 1962. 4.95. Praeger
Kodama, Yoshio. I was defeated. 2.75. Tuttle
Norman, E. Herbert. Japan's emergence as a modern state. 1940. 6.00. Inst.
 of Pac. Rel.
JAPAN--POLITICS AND GOVERNMENT--1945- (952)
Ike, Nobutaka. Japanese politics: An introductory survey. il. 1957. 4.00. Knopf
Morris, Ivan I. Nationalism and the Right Wing in Japan: A study of post-war
 trends. 1960. 8.00. Oxford U. P.
JAPAN--RELATIONS (GENERAL) WITH FOREIGN COUNTRIES (952.327)
Lancaster, Clay. Japanese influence in America. 1962. 10.00? Twayne
JAPAN--RELIGION (294.32)
Bunce, William K. Religion in Japan. bds. 3.00. Tuttle
JAPAN--SOCIAL CONDITIONS (952.30145)
Cornell, John B., and Robert J. Smith. Two Japanese villages. 1956. pap. 6.00.
 U. of Mich.

Mishima, Sumie Seo. Broader way: A woman's life in the new Japan, 1953. 3.75. Day

JAPAN--SOCIAL LIFE AND CUSTOMS (952)

Bosworth, Allan R. Lovely world of Richi-san. il. 1960. 4.50. Harper
Statler, Oliver. Japanese inn. il. 1961. 6.50. Random
Vining, Elizabeth G. Return to Japan. 1960. 5.95. Lippincott
Vining, Elizabeth Gray. Windows for the crown prince. il. 1952. 6.00. Lippincott

JAPANESE DRAMA--HISTORY AND CRITICISM (792. 0952)

Bowers, Faubion. Japanese theatre. il. 1952. 6.00. Nelson

JAPANESE IN THE U.S. (361)

Eaton, Allen H. Beauty behind barbed wire: The arts of the Japanese in our war relocation centers. il. 1952. 6.00. Harper
Japanese American evacuation and resettlement. 2 vols. il. vol. 1. Thomas, Dorothy S., and Richard Nishimoto. Spoliage. 1946. 3.75; vol. 2. Thomas, Dorothy S., and others. Salvage. 1952. 7.50. U. of Calif.
Murphy, Thomas D. Ambassadors in arms. 5.00. U. of Hawaii
Shapiro, H. L. Migration and environment: A study of the physical characteristics of the Japanese immigrants to Hawaii and the effects of environment on their descendants. il. 1939. 7.50. Oxford U. P.

JAPANESE LITERATURE--HISTORY AND CRITICISM (895.6)

Hibbett, Howard. Floating world in Japanese fiction. il. 1959. 6.50. Oxford U. P.
Keene, Donald. Japanese literature. 1955. pap. 1.45. Grove

JAPANESE POETRY--TRANSLATIONS INTO ENGLISH (895. 61082)

Henderson, Harold Gould. Introduction to haiku, an anthology of poems and poets from Basho to Shiki. il. 1958. 4.50. Doubleday
Kono, Ichiro, and Rikutaro Fukuda. Anthology of modern Japanese poetry. 2.00. Tuttle
Rexroth, Kenneth. 100 poems from the Japanese. 1955. 3.50. New Directions
Waley, Arthur. Japanese poetry, Uta. pap. 2.00. Tuttle

JAZZ MUSIC (785.42)

Balliett, Whitney. Sound of surprises, 46 pieces on jazz. 1959. 3.75. Dutton
Blesh, Rudi. Shining trumpets: A history of jazz. il. 1958. 7.50. Knopf
Charters, Samuel B. Country blues. il. 4.95. Holt, Rinehart & Winston
Ewen, David. Panorama of American popular music. 1957. 4.95. Prentice-Hall
Feather, Leonard. Encyclopedia of jazz. il. 15.00. Horizon
Panassie, Hugues. Real jazz. rev. ed. 1.95. Barnes, A. S.
Spaeth, Sigmund. History of popular music. 1948. 5.00. Random
Ulanov, Barry. History of jazz in America. 1952. 5.00. Viking
Waters, Ethel. His eye is on the sparrow. by Charles Samuels. 1951. 3.95. Doubleday

JEANNE D'ARC, SAINT, 1412-1431 (923.544)

Michelet, Jules. Joan of Arc. tr. by Albert Guerard. 1957. 3.75. U. of Mich.

JEANNERET-GRIS, CHARLES EDOUARD (724.9)

Blake, Peter. Master builders. il. 1960. 8.00. Knopf
Choay, Francoise. Le Corbusier. il. 1960. 4.95. Braziller

JEANS, SIR JAMES HOPWOOD, 1877-1946 (501)

Stebbing, Susan. Philosophy and physicists. 1959. pap. 1.65. Dover

JEFFERS, ROBINSON, 1887- (811.5)

Carpenter, Frederick I. Robinson Jeffers. 1962. 3.50. Twayne

JEFFERSON, THOMAS, PRES. U. S., 1743-1826 (923.173)

Becker, Carl L. Declaration of Independence: A study in the history of political ideas. 1942. 4.00. Knopf
Boorstin, Daniel J. Lost world of Thomas Jefferson. 4.00. Smith, Peter
Frary, I. T. Thomas Jefferson: Architect and builder. il. 6.00. Garrett
Jefferson, Thomas. Autobiography of Thomas Jefferson. 1959. 2.50. Putnam
Kimball, Marie. Thomas Jefferson's cook book. 1938. 2.50. Garrett
Malone, Dumas. Jefferson and the ordeal of liberty. il. 1962. 7.50. Little
Malone, Dumas. Jefferson and the rights of man. il. 1951. 7.50. Little
Malone, Dumas. Jefferson the Virginian. il. 1948. 7.50. Little

Malone, Dumas. Thomas Jefferson as a political leader. 7.50. U. of Calif.
Peterson, Merrill D. Jefferson image in the American mind. 1960. 8.50.
   Oxford U. P.
Schachner, Nathan. Thomas Jefferson: A biography. 1957. 3.95. Yoseloff
JENGHIS KHAN, 1162-1227 (923.1)
Lamb, Harold. Genghis Khan. 1952. 3.95. Doubleday
Prawdin, Michael. Mongol empire. 8.00. Macmillan
JENNER, EDWARD, 1749-1823 (925)
Dolan, Edward F., Jr. Jenner and the miracle of vaccine. 1960. 3.50. Dodd
JENSEN, POVL BANG, 1909- (923)
Copp, DeWitt, and Marshall Peck. Betrayal at the UN: The story of Paul
   Bang-Jensen. 1961. 4.75. Devin
JEREMIAH, THE PROPHET (224.2)
Blank, Sheldon H. Jeremiah: Man and prophet. 1961. 6.50. Univ. Pub.
Hyatt, J. Philip. Jeremiah: Prophet of courage and hope. 1958. 2.00. Abingdon
JERICHO (913)
Kenyon, Kathleen. Digging up Jericho. il. 1957. 6.00. Praeger
JERUSALEM--HISTORY (956.94)
Joseph, Dov. Faithful city. 1960. 5.95. 10.00. S. and S.
JESUITS (271.5)
Harney, Martin. Jesuits in history. 1962. 5.00. Loyola
LaFarge, John, and Margaret Bourke-White. Report on American Jesuits. 1956.
   4.75. Farrar, Straus
JESUS CHRIST (232)
Hunter, Archibald M. Work and words of Jesus. 1951. 3.00. Westminster
Konroff, Manuel. Jesus through the centuries. 6.00. Sloane
Schweitzer, Albert. The psychiatric study of Jesus. 3.00. Smith, Peter
JESUS CHRIST--BIOGRAPHY (232.9)
Bauman, Edward W. Life and teaching of Jesus. 1960. 3.95. Westminster
Beck, Dwight M. Through the Gospels of Jesus. 1954. 5.00. Harper
Braden, Charles S. Jesus compared: A comparative study of Jesus and the
   other great founders of religion. 1957. 6.50. Prentice-Hall
Daniel-Rops, Henry J. Jesus and his times. tr. by Ruby Millar. 1954. Catholic
   ed. 5.00. Dutton
Deane, Anthony C. World Christ knew. 1953. 3.00. Mich. State
Edersheim, Alfred. Life and times of Jesus the Messiah. 2 vols. 1953. 8.50.
   Eerdmans
Edersheim, Alfred. Life and times of Jesus the Messiah. 2 vols. 1957. 12.50.
   McKay
Erskine, John. Human life of Jesus. 1945. 3.50. Morrow
Farrar, Frederic W. Life of Christ. il. 1874. 5.00. Shank
Fernandez, Andres. Life of Christ. 1958. 12.50. Newman
Ferris, Theodore Parker. Story of Jesus. 1953. 3.00. Oxford U. P.
Fosdick, Harry Emerson. Man from Nazareth. 1949. 4.00. Harper
Goodspeed, Edgar J. Life of Jesus. 1950. 4.00. Harper
Goudge, Elizabeth. God so loved the world. 1951. 4.50. Coward
Lamsa, George M. My neighbor Jesus. 2.50. Holman
Laubach, Frank C. Greatest life. 1956. 2.50. Revell
Ludwig, Emil. Son of man: The story of Jesus. 3.95. Liveright
Mauriac, Francois. Life of Jesus. 1951. 3.00. McKay
Oursler, Fulton. Greatest story ever told. il. 1949. 3.50; Catholic ed. 3.50.
   Doubleday
Prat, Ferdinand. Jesus Christ. 2 vols. 1950. 13.50. Bruce
Ricciotti, Giuseppe. Life of Christ. 1947. 8.25. popular ed. 1952. 4.50. Bruce
Schweitzer, Albert. Mystery of the Kingdom of God. tr. by Walter Lowrie.
   American ed. 3.95. Macmillan
Sheed, F. J. To know Christ Jesus. in prep. Sheed
Sheen, Fulton J. Life of Christ. 1958. 7.95. McGraw

Shepard, John W. Christ of the Gospels. rev. ed. 1946. 6.00. Eerdmans

JESUS CHRIST--BIOGRAPHY --APOCRYPHAL AND LEGENDARY LITERATURE (229.9)

Gaer, Joseph. Lore of the New Testament. 1952. 6.00. Little

Goodspeed, E. Modern Apocrypha. 1956. 2.75. Beacon

JESUS CHRIST--BIOGRAPHY--HISTORY AND CRITICISM (232.9)

Schweitzer, Albert. Quest of the historical Jesus. tr. by Montgomery. 5.95. Macmillan

JESUS CHRIST--CHARACTER (232.9)

Barton, Bruce. Man and Book nobody knows. 1960. 5.00. Bobbs

Hamilton, Edith. Witness to the truth: Christ and his interpreters. 1957. 3.95. Norton

JESUS CHRIST--ETHICS (232.9)

Knox, John. Ethic of Jesus in the teaching of the church. 1961. bds. 2.00. Abingdon

Manson, Thomas W. Ethics and the Gospel. 1960. 2.75. Scribner

JESUS CHRIST--HISTORICITY (260)

Coneybeare, Frederic C. Origins of Christianity. 1958. 6.00. U. Books

Kepler, Thomas S. Contemporary thinking about Jesus: An anthology. 5.00. Abingdon

Robinson, James M. New quest of the historical Jesus. 1959. pap. 2.25. Allenson

Schweitzer, Albert. Quest of the historical Jesus. tr. by Montgomery. 5.95. Macmillan

JESUS CHRIST--PARABLES (226.8)

Allen, Charles L. When the heart is hungry. 1955. 2.50. Revell

Dodd, Charles H. Parables of the kingdom. rev. ed. 1961. 3.50. Scribner

Filas, Francis L. Parables of Jesus. 1959. 3.75. Macmillan

Hunter, Archibald M. Interpreting the parables. 1961. 2.50. Westminster

Jeremias, Joachim. Parables of Jesus. 1955. 3.50. Scribner

JESUS CHRIST--RESURRECTION (232.5)

Barnhouse, Donald G. Cross through the open tomb. 1961. 3.00. Eerdmans

Durrwell, F. X. Resurrection of Christ. 1960. 6.00. Sheed

Niebuhr, Richard. Resurrection and historical reason. 1957. 3.95. Scribner

JESUS CHRIST-- TEACHINGS (232.954)

Ballou, Robert O. This he believed: The religion of Jesus of Nazareth as revealed in readings from the Old and New Testaments and other sources. 1959. 3.00. Viking

Laymon, Charles M. Life and teachings of Jesus. 1962. 4.50. Abingdon

JESUS CHRIST--WORDS (229.951)

Hinds, Arthur. Complete sayings of Jesus. 1955. 2.00. Winston

Poling, D. Jesus says to you. 1961. 2.95. McGraw

JET PLANES--FUELS (629.13434)

Paushkin, Y. M. Chemical composition and properties of fuels for jet propulsion. 1962. 15.00. Pergamon

JET PROPULSION (629.134353)

Liston, Joseph. Power plants for aircraft. 1953. 10.50. McGraw

Roberson, Edwin C. True book about jet engines and gas turbines. il. 1962. 3.00. Soccer Assoc.

JEWELRY (739.27)

Baerwald, Marcus, and Tom Mahoney. Story of jewelry. il. 1958. 6.50. Abelard

Clegg, Helen, and Mary Larom. Jewelry making for fun and profit. 1951. 3.95. McKay

Curran, Mona. Treasury of jewels and gems. il. 1962. 3.95. Emerson

Von Neumann, Robert. Design and creation of jewelry. il. 1961. 7.50. Chilton

JEWETT, SARAH ORNE, 1849-1909 (928)

Buchan, A. M. Our dear Sarah. 1953. pap. 1.50. Washington U.

Cary, Richard. Sarah Orne Jewett. 1962. 3.50. Twayne

JEWISH LAW (348. 96)
Rabinowitz, Jacob J. Jewish law: Its influence in the development of legal
institutions. 1956. 7. 50. Bloch
Smith, John M. P. Origin and history of Hebrew Law. 1931. 4. 50. U. of Chicago
JEWISH LITERATURE (892. 4)
Greenberg, Sidney. Modern treasury of Jewish thoughts. 1960. 5. 95. Yoseloff
Schwarz, Leo W. Golden treasury of Jewish literature. il. 1937. 5. 95. Rinehart
JEWS (956. 93)
Buber, Martin. Israel and the world. 3. 75. Schocken
Konroff, Manuel. Contemporaries of Marco Polo. 3. 95. Tudor
Ribalow, Harold U. Mid-century: An anthology of Jewish life and culture in our
times. 6. 00. Yoseloff
Shapiro, Harry L. Jewish people: A biological study. (UNESCO) pap. 0. 70. Int.
Doc. Service-Columbia
JEWS--BIOGRAPHY (956. 93)
Noveck, Simon. Great Jewish personalities in ancient and medieval times. 4. 95.
Taplinger
Noveck, Simon. Great Jewish personalities in modern times. 4. 95. Taplinger
JEWS--CIVILIZATION (956. 93)
Bevan, Edwyn, and C. J. Singer. Legacy of Israel. il. 1927. 6. 00. Oxford U. P.
Blau, Joseph L. , and others. Essays on Jewish life and thought. 1959. 7. 50.
Columbia
Steinberg, Milton. Making of the modern Jew. 3. 00. Behrman
JEWS--HISTORY (956. 93)
Bailey, Albert E. , and Charles F. Kent. History of the Hebrew commonwealth.
1945. 3. 50. Scribner
Baron, S. W. Social and religious history of the Jews. 8 vols. and index. vols.
1 and 2, 1952. 6. 75 ea; vols. 3, 4, 5, 1957, 6. 00 ea; vol. 6, 1958, 7. 50; vol.
7, 1958. 5. 50; vol. 8, 1958, 7. 00; index, 1960. 6. 00. Columbia
Browne, Lewis. Stranger than fiction: Short history of the Jews from earliest
times to the present day. il. 3. 95. Macmillan
Finkelstein, Louis. Jews: Their history, culture, and religion. 2 vols. 1960.
27. 50. Harper
Goodman, Paul. History of the Jews. by Israel Cohen. 1951. 3. 95. 1959. Dutton
Grayzel, Solomon. History of the Jews. 4. 50. Jewish Pub. Soc.
Josephus, Flavius. Complete works. 1960. 6. 95. Kregel
Josephus, Flavius. Life and works of Flavius Josephus. tr. by William Whiston.
7. 50. Winston
Noth, Martin. History of Israel. 1960. 7. 50. Harper
Ricciotti, Giuseppe. History of Israel. 2 vols. 1955. 16. 00. Bruce
Robinson, T. H. , and W. O. E. Oesterley. History of Israel. 2 vols. 1932. 4. 50
ea. Oxford U. P.
JIU-JITSU (796. 8)
Blanchard, Robert G. Mechanics of judo. il. 1961. 3. 75. Tuttle
Harrington, Anthony P. Science of judo. il. 1962. 3. 95. Emerson
Lowell, F. P. Way to better judo. 2. 50. Wehman
Smith, Robert W. Complete guide to judo. il. 3. 95. Tuttle
JOB ANALYSIS (658. 5)
Currie, R. M. Work study. 1960. 5. 50. Pitman
Jaques, Elliott. Measurement of responsibility: A study of work, payment and
individual capacity. 1956. 3. 00. Harvard
Otis, Jay L. , and Richard H. Leukart. Job evaluation. 1954. 10. 00. Prentice-Hall
Shartle, Carroll L. Occupational information: Its development and application.
10. 00. Prentice-Hall
JOB SATISFACTION (658. 3)
Herzberg, Frederick, and others. Motivation to work. 1959. 4. 50. Wiley
Zalenznik, Abraham, and others. Motivation, productivity, and satisfaction of
workers. 1958. 6. 00. Harv. Bus. School

JOHN, KING OF ENGLAND, 1167-1216 (923.142)
Appleby, John T. John, King of England. 1959. 5.00. Knopf
Painter, Sidney. Reign of King John. 1949. 6.00. Johns Hopkins
Warren, Wilfred L. King John. il. 1961. 6.50. Norton
JOHN XXIII, POPE, 1881- (922.21)
Aradi, Zsolt. Pope John XXIII. il. 1959. 4.95. Farrar, Straus
Bolton, Glorney. Living Peter: A biographical study of Pope John 23rd. 6.35.
    Transatlantic
McGurn, Barrett. Reporter looks at the Vatican. 1962. 5.00. Coward
JOHN, AUGUSTUS (927)
John, Augustus. Drawings of Augustus John. by David Cecil. il. 1957. 30.00.
    N. Y. Graphic
JOHNSON, ANDREW, PRES. U. S., 1808-1875 (973.81)
Beale, Howard K. Critical year: A study of Andrew Johnson and Reconstruction.
    il. 1958. 5.00. Ungar
Bowers, Claude G. Tragic era: The revolution after Lincoln. il. 1929. 6.00.
    Houghton
Lomask, Milton. Andrew Johnson: President on trial. 196 . 6.00. Farrar, Straus
McKitrick, Eric L. Andrew Johnson and Reconstruction. 1960. 8.50. U. of
    Chicago
JOHNSON, SAMUEL 1696-1772 (922)
Johnson, Samuel. Works. 4 vols. by Herbert and Carol Schneider. 1929. 25.00.
    Columbia
JOHNSON, SAMUEL, 1709-1784 (928)
Bailey, John. Dr. Johnson and his circle. 1945. 1.70. Oxford U. P.
Bate, W. J. Achievement of Samuel Johnson. 1955. 5.00. Oxford U. P.
Boswell, James. Life of Johnson. bd. with Journal of a tour to the Hebrides,
    and Samuel Johnson's Diary of a journey into North Wales. by G. B. Hill,
    and L. F. Powell. vols. 1-4, 20.80; vols. 5-6, 17.60. Oxford U. P.
Boswell, James. Life of Johnson. 1953. 6.00. Oxford U. P.
Clifford, James L. Young Sam Johnson. 1955. 5.95. McGraw
Davis, Bertram. H. Johnson before Boswell. 1957. 5.00. Yale
Hawkins, John. Life of Samuel Johnson. il. 1961. 5.95. Macmillan
McLaren, Moray. Highland jaunt: A study of James Boswell and Samuel Johnson
    upon their Highland and Hebridean tour of 1733. il. 1955. 4.00. Sloane
Pearson, Hesketh. Johnson and Boswell. il. 1958. 5.50. Harper
Sledd, James H., and Gwin J. Kolb. Dr. Johnson's dictionary. il. 1955. 1.50.
    U. of Chicago
Voitle, Robert B., Jr. Samuel Johnson the moralist. 1961. 4.25. Harvard
JOINTS--DISEASES (616.72)
Hollander, Joseph L. Arthritis and allied conditions. il. 1960. 20.00. Lea & F
Roaf, Robert, and others. Surgical treatment of bone and joint tuberculosis.
    il. 1960. 7.00. Williams & Wilkins
JOINTS--RADIOGRAPHY (616.72)
Brailsford, James F. Radiology of bones and joints. 1953. 19.00. Williams &
    Wilkins
JOLIET, LOUIS, 1645-1700 (923.9)
Eifert, Virginia S. Louis Jolliet, explorer of rivers. 1961. 4.00. Dodd
JONES, JOHN PAUL, 1747-1792 (923.5)
Morison, Samuel Eliot. John Paul Jones: A sailor's biography. il. 1959. 6.50.
    Little
JONES, ROBERT EDMOND, 1887-1954 (927)
Pendleton, Ralph. Theatre of Robert Edmond Jones. il. 1958. 12.50. Wesleyan
    U. P.
JONSON, BEN, 1573-1637 (928)
Chute, Marchette, Ben Jonson of Westminster. 1953. 5.95. Dutton
Partridge, E. B. Broken compass: A study of the major comedies of Ben Jonson.
    1958. 4.25. Columbia

JORDAN (956. 95)
Hussein, King of Jordan. Uneasy lies the head. 1962. 4. 95. Random
Patai, R. Kingdom of Jordan. 1958. 5. 00. Princeton
JOSEPH, NEZ PERCE CHIEF, 1840-1904 (923. 1)
Davis, Russell G. , and B. Ashabranner. Chief Joseph: War chief of the Nez
   Perce. 1962. 3. 25. McGraw
JOURNALISM (070)
Barnhart, Thomas F. Weekly newspaper writing and editing. 1949. 6. 00. Holt,
   Rinehart & Winston
Bastian, George C. , and others. Editing the day's news. il. 6. 00. Macmillan
Bery, Thomas E. Journalism today. il. 1958. 6. 50. Chilton
Byerly, Kenneth R. Community journalism 1961. 6. 50. Chilton
Campbell, L. R. , and R. E. Wolseley. Newsmen at work. 5. 25. Houghton
Coblentz, Edmond D. Newsmen speak: Journalists on their craft. 1954. 3. 50.
   U. of Calif.
English, Earl E. , and Clarence W. Hach. Scholastic journalism. il. 1962. 3. 95.
   Iowa State
Harral, Stewart. Profitable public relations for newspapers. 1957. 4. 75. Edwards
Hinkle, Olin E. , and John Henry. How to write columns. il. 1952. 5. 00. Iowa
   State
Hohenberg, John. Professional journalist. il. 1960. 8. 30. Holt, Rinehart & Winston
MacDougall, Curtis D. Interpretative reporting. il. 1957. 6. 00. Macmillan
Neal, Robert M. News gathering and news writing. 1949. 9. 00. Prentice-Hall
Patterson, Helen M. Writing and selling feature articles. 1956. 7. 75. Prentice-
   Hall
Pepper, William M. Dictionary of newspaper and printing terms (English-Spanish
   Spanish-English) 1959. 10. 00. Columbia
Rucker, Frank W. , and H. L. Williams. Newspaper organization and manage-
   ment. 1955. 7. 50. Iowa State
Seldes, Gilbert. Seven lively arts. 1957. 4. 95. Sagamore
Waldrop A. Gayle. Editor and editorial writer. 1955. 5. 50. Holt, Rinehart &
   Winston
Wolseley, Roland E. , and Laurence R. Campbell. Exploring journalism. 1957.
   7. 95. Prentice-Hall
Wolseley, Roland, and Laurence Campbell. How to report and write the news.
   1961. 10. 60. Prentice-Hall
JOURNALISM--HANDBOOKS, MANUALS, ETC. (070. 02)
Garst, Robert E. , and T. M. Bernstein. Headlines and deadlines. 1961. 5. 00.
   Columbia
National Education Association, World Confederation of Organizations of the
   Teaching Profession. Handbook for editors of educational journals. 1961.
   0. 75. N. E. A.
Ross, Donald K. Newspaper correspondent's manual. 1959. pap. 0. 75. Marquette
JOURNALISM--U. S. (071)
Kobre, Sidney. Development of the colonial newspaper. 4. 50. Smith, Peter
Mott, Frank Luther. American journalism. 1962. 8. 00. Macmillan
JOURNALISM, COMMERCIAL (070. 486)
Baird, Russell N. , and Arthur T. Turnbull. Industrial and business journalism
   1961. 7. 50. Chilton
JOURNALISM, TECHNICAL (070. 486)
McGuire, Delbert. Technical and Industrial journalism; writing for the specialized
   press. 1956. 5. 00. Stackpole.
JOURNALISM AS A PROFESSION (070. 486)
Ryan, Bernard, Jr. , and Leonard E. So you want to go into journalism. 1962.
   3. 50? Harper
Schaleben, Arville. Your future in journalism. 1961. 2. 95. Richards Rosen
JOURNALISTS (070. 69)
Coblentz, Edmond D. Newsmen speak: Journalists on their craft. 1954. 3. 50.
   U. of Calif.

Davenport, Walter, and James C. Derieux. Ladies, gentlemen, and editors.
   1960. 4.95. Doubleday
Drewry, John E. Post biographies of famous journalists. 3.50. U. of Ga.
JOURNALISTS--CORRESPONDENCE, REMINISCENCES, ETC. (920.5)
Corum, Bill. Off and running. by Arthur Mann. il. 1959. 4.95. Holt, Rinehart
   & Winston
Daniels, Josephus. Tar Heel editor. (Autobiography, vol. 3) 1.95. U. of N. C.
De Toledano, Ralph. Lament for a generation. 1960. 3.95. Farrar, Straus
Diehl, Joe. West of Broadway. il. 1960. 3.75. Taplinger
Fowler, Gene. Skyline. 1961. 5.00. Viking
Heatter, Gabriel. There's good news tonight. 1960. 3.95. Doubleday
Ingersoll, Ralph M. Point of departure: An adventure in autobiography. 1961.
   4.50. Harcourt
North, Joseph. No men are strangers. 1957. 4.50. Int. Pubs.
St. John, Robert. This was my world. 1953. 3.95. Doubleday
Sevareid, Eric. Not so wild a dream. 1946. 5.00. Knopf
Smith, H. Allen. To hell in a handbasket. 4.95. Doubleday
Ybarra, T. R. Young man of Caracas. 1941. 4.00. Washburn
JOYCE, JAMES, 1882-1941 (823.912)
Atherton, James S. Books at the wake: A study of literary allusions in James
   Joyce's Finnegans wake. 1959. 5.00. Viking
Budgen, Frank. James Joyce and the making of Ulysses. il. 1960. 4.95. Indiana
Campbell, Joseph, and Henry Morton Robinson. Skeleton key to Finnegans
   wake. 4.75. Harcourt
Colum, Mary, and Padraic. Our friend James Joyce. 3.00. Smith, Peter
Gilbert, Stuart. James Joyce's Ulysses. 1955. pap. 1.45. Vintage
Goldberg, S. L. Classical temper: A study of James Joyce's Ulysses. 1961.
   6.00. Barnes & Noble
Hutchins, P. James Joyce's world. 6.00. Hillary
Jones, William Powell. James Joyce and the common reader. 1955. 3.00. U.
   of Okla.
Kain, Richard M. Fabulous voyager. James Joyce's Ulysses. il. 1947. 5.00.
   U. of Chicago
Levin, Harry. James Joyce: A critical introduction. 1960. pap. 1.45. New
   Directions
Magalaner, Marvin, and Richard M. Kain. Joyce: The man, the work, the
   reputation. 1956. 5.00. N. Y. U.
Schutte, William M. Joyce and Shakespeare. 1957. 4.00. Yale
Smidt, Kristian. James Joyce and the cultic use of fiction. 4.00. Humanities
Tindall, William Y. Joyce country. il. 1960. 5.95. Penn State
Tindall, William Y. Reader's guide to James Joyce. 1959. 5.00. Farrar, Straus
Ussher, Arland. Three great Irishmen: Shaw, Yeats, Joyce. il. 1953. 3.00.
   Devin
JOYCE, WILLIAM, 1906-1946 (923)
West, Rebecca. Meaning of treason. 4.25. St. Martins
JUAN, DON (923)
Toman, Josef. Don Juan. 1958. 4.95. Knopf
JUAN DE FUCA (STRAIT) (971.134)
McCurdy, James G. By Juan de Fuca's strait. il. 4.00. Binfords
JUAREZ, BENITO PABLO, PRES. MEXICO, 1806-1872 (923)
Roeder, Ralph. Juarez and his Mexico, a biographical history. 2 vols. il. 1947.
   boxed, 10.00. Viking
JUDAISM--HISTORY (296)
Agus, Jacob. Meaning of Jewish history. 1962. 7.50. Abelard
Albright, William Foxwell. Archaeology and the religion of Israel. 2nd ptg.
   1941. 3.50. Johns Hopkins
Guignebert, Charles. Jewish world in the time of Jesus. 1959. 6.00. U. Books
McCown, Chester C. Man, morals and history. il. 1958. 5.00. Harper

Meek, Theophile James. Hebrew origins. 1960. 3.50. Smith, Peter

Schwarz, Leo W. Great ages and ideas of the Jewish people. 1956. 5.00. Random House

JUDGES (347.9)

Peltason, Jack W. Fifty-eight lonely men. 1961. 4.95. Harcourt

JUDGES--CORRESPONDENCE, REMINISCENCES, ETC. (923.4)

Frankfurter, Felix. Felix Frankfurter reminisces. by Harlan B. Phillips. 5.00. Reynal

Holmes, Oliver Wendell Jr., and Harold J. Laski. Holmes-Laski letters: The correspondence of Mr. Justice Holmes and Harold J. Laski, 1916-1935. 2 vols. il. by Mark De Wolfe Howe. 1953. 12.50; 1 vol. ed. 1957. 7.50. Harvard

Medina, Harold R. Anatomy of freedom. 1959. 3.50. Holt, Rinehart & Winston

JUDGMENT (153)

Kant, Immanuel. Critique of judgement. tr. by J. C. Meredith. 1952. 4.50. Oxford U. P.

Piaget, Jean. Judgment and reasoning in the child. 1947. 5.00. Humanities

JUDICIAL ERROR (347.9)

Borchard, Edwin M. Convicting the innocent. 1961. 9.00. Shoe String

JUDICIAL OPINIONS (347.9)

Bickel, Alexander M. Unpublished opinions of Mr. Justice Brandeis: The Supreme Court at work. 1957. 6.00. Harvard

Douglas, William O. Douglas of the Supreme Court: A selection of his opinions. by Vern Countryman. 1959. 5.95. Doubleday

Warren, Earl. Public papers of Chief Justice Earl Warren. by Henry M. Christman. 1959. 5.00. S. and S.

JUDICIAL PROCESS (347.9)

Auerbach, Carl A., and others. Legal Process: An introduction to decision-making. by judicial legislative, executive, and administrative agencies. 1961. 10.00. Chandler Pub.

Cardozo, Benjamin N. Nature of the judicial process. 1921. 3.00. Yale

JUDICIAL REVIEW (347.9)

Black, Charles L., Jr. People and the court. 1960. 5.00. Macmillan

Commager, Henry Steele. Majority rule and minority rights. 2.50. Smith, Peter

Corwin, Edward S. Court over constitution: A study of judicial review as an instrument of popular government. 3.50. Smith, Peter

Haines, Charles G. American doctrine of judicial supremacy. 1959. 10.00. Russell

Powell, T. R. Vagaries and varieties in constitutional interpretation. 1956. 4.00. Columbia

JULIAN THE APOSTATE, EMPEROR OF ROME, 331-363 (923.1)

Ricciotti, Guiseppe. Julian the apostate. 1960. 4.75. Bruce

JUNG, CARL GUSTAV, 1875-1961 (926)

Dry, A. M. Psychology of Jung: A critical interpretation. 1961. 6.00. Wiley

Hostie, Raymond. Religion and the psychology of Jung. 1957. 3.50. Sheed

Martin, P. W. Experiment in depth: A study of Jung, Eliot and Toynbee. 5.00. Humanities

JUNIOR COLLEGES (378)

Clark, Burton R. Open door college. il. 1960. 5.50. McGraw

Gleazer, Edmund J., Jr. American junior colleges, 1960. 1960. 9.00. A. C. E.

Hillway, Tyrus. American two-year college. 1958. 4.00. Harper

Johnson, B. L. General education in action. 1952. 4.00. A. C. E.

Johnson, B. Lamar. Public junior college. 1956. 4.50. U. of Chicago

Medsker, Leland L. Junior college: Progress and prospect. il. 1960. 6.50. McGraw

Wattenbarger, James L. State plan for public junior colleges. il. 1953. pap. 1.50. U. of Fla.

JUNIOR COLLEGES--DIRECTORIES (378)

Eskow, Seymour. Guide to two-year colleges. 4.95. Barron's

Gleazer, Edmund J., Jr. American junior colleges, 1960. 1960. 9.00. A. C. E.
Sargent, Porter. Junior colleges, specialized schools and colleges. 1959. 5.00.
   Sargent
JUNIOR COLLEGES--LIBRARIES (027.7)
Trinkner, Charles L., ed. Baisc Books for Junior College Libraries: 20,000
   Vital Titles. 1963, Colonial Press.
Trinkner, Charles L., ed. Library Services for Junior Colleges. in prep.
JUPITER (PLANET) (523.45)
Peek, Bertrand M. Planet Jupiter. il. 1958. 8.95. Macmillan
JURISPRUDENCE (340)
Allen, Carleton K. Law in the making. 1958. 8.00. Oxford U. P.
Davitt, Thomas, E. Elements of law. 1960. 9.00. Little
Henson, Ray D., ed. Landmarks of law. 1960. 8.50. Harper
Reuschlein, Harold G. Jurisprudence: Its American prophets. 1951. 6.50. Bobbs
JURY (343)
Keeney, Barnaby Conrad. Judgment by peers. 1949. 2.50. Harvard
Vanderbilt, Arthur T. Judges and jurors: Their functions, qualifications and
   selection. 1956. 3.00. Boston U.
JUSTICE (323.42)
Cardozo, B. N. Paradoxes of legal science. 1928. 2.50. Columbia
Parker, M. D. H. Slave of life: Shakespeare and the idea of justice. 4.00. Hillary
Pound, Roscoe. Justice according to law. 1951. 3.75. Yale
Tillich, Paul. Love, power and justice. 1960. 3.00. Smith, Peter
Vecchio, Giorgia del. Justice: An historical and philosophical essay. by A. H.
   Campbell. tr. by Lady Guthrie. 1952. 6.00. Aldine
JUSTICE, ADMINISTRATION OF (347.9)
Calamandrei, Piero. Procedure and democracy. 1956. 4.00. N. Y. U.
Dienstein, William. Are you guilty?: An introduction to the administration of
   criminal justice in the United States. 1953. 4.50. Thomas, C. C.
Frank, Jerome. Courts on trial. 1949. 6.00. Princeton
Hazard, John N. Settling disputes in Soviet society. il. 1960. 6.00. Columbia
Mayers, Lewis. American legal system. 1955. 8.50. Harper
Tannenbaum, F. Crime and the community. 1938. 4.50. Columbia
Vanderbilt, A. T. Challenge of law reform. 1955. 3.50. Princeton
JUSTINIANUS I, EMPEROR OF THE EAST, 483-565 (923.1)
Lamb, Harold. Constantinople: Birth of an empire. il. 1957. 5.75. Knopf
JUTLAND, BATTLE OF, 1916 (948.9)
Macintyre, Donald. Jutland. 1958. 5.00. Norton
JUVENILE COURTS (364)
Glueck, Sheldon, ed. Problem of delinquency. il. 1959. 10.50. Houghton
Rosenheim, Margaret K. Justice for the child: The juvenile courts in transition.
   1962. 6.95. Free Press
JUVENILE DELINQUENCY (364)
Bandura, Albert, and Richard H. Walters. Adolescent aggression. il. 1959. 7.50.
   Ronald
Barron, Milton L. Juvenile in delinquent society. 1954. 5.25. Knopf
Bloch, Herbert A., and Frank T. Flynn. Delinquency: The juvenile offender in
   America today. 1956. 7.95. Random
Cavan, Ruth S. Juvenile delinquency. il. 9.00. Lippincott
Eaton, Joseph W., and Kenneth Polk. Measuring delinquency. 1961. 7.00. U. of
   Pittsburgh
Fyvel, T. R. Troublemakers: Rebellious youth in an affluent society. 1962. 4.95.
   Schocken
Glueck, Sheldon, and Eleanor. Delinquents in the making. 1952. 3.95. Harper
Glueck, Sheldon, and Eleanor. Family environment and delinquency. 6.50.
   Houghton
Gran, John M. Why children become delinquent. 1960. 3.95. Taplinger
Hathaway, Starke R., and Elio D. Monachesi. Atlas of juvenile MMPI profiles.
   1961. 8.00. U. of Minn.

Herbert, W. L., and F. V. Jarvis. Dealing with delinquents. 1961. 3.00. Emerson
Jones, Howard. Reluctant rebels. 1960. 5.00. Assn. Pr.
Kvaraceus, William C. Juvenile delinquency and the school. 3.50. Harcourt
Levy, A. J. V. Other people's children. 1956. 4.50. Ronald
McCann, Richard V. Delinquency: Sickness or sin? 1957. 3.50. Harper
Martin, John M. Juvenile vandalism. il. 1961. 6.50. Thomas, C. C.
Neumeyer, Martin H. Juvenile delinquency in modern society. il. 1961. 6.50.
    Van Nostrand
Nye, F. Ivan. Family relationships and delinquent behavior. il. 1958. 4.95. Wiley
Redl, Fritz, and David Wineman. Aggressive child: Children who hate, and
    Controls from within. 1957. 2 vols. bd. in 1. 7.50. Free Press
Robison, Sophia M. Juvenile delinquency. il. 1960. 6.75. Holt, Rinehart & Winston'
Salisbury, Harrison E. Shook-up generation. 1958. 4.50. Harper
Scudder, Kenyon J., and Denneth S. Beam. Twenty billion dollar challenge: A
    national program for delinquency prevention. 1961. 4.50. Putnam
Shulman, Harry M. Juvenile delinquency in American society. 1961. 8.00. Harper
Stearn, Jess. Wasted years. 1959. 3.95. Doubleday
Steiner, Lee R. Understanding juvenile delinquency. 1960. 3.95. Chilton
Strang, Ruth. Juvenile delinquency and the schools. NSSE, 47th yearbook, pt. 1.
    1948. 4.50. U. of Chicago
Tappan, Paul W. Juvenile delinquency. il. 1949. 6.75. McGraw
Tyler, Gus. Organized crime in America. 1962. 7.50. U. of Mich.

K

KAFKA, FRANZ, 1883-1924 (928)
Brod, Max. Franz Kafka. 1960. 4.50. Schocken
Flores, Angel, and Homer Swander. Franz Kafka today. 1958. 5.00. U. of Wis.
Frynta, Emanuel. Kafka and Prague. il. 5.95. Tudor
Gray, R. D. Kafka's Castle. 1956. 2.75. Cambridge U. P.
KANSAS--HISTORY (978.1)
Monaghan, Jay. Civil War on the Western Border, 1854-1865. 1955. 6.00. Little
Rich, Everett. Heritage of Kansas: Selected commentaries on past times. 5.00.
    U. of Kans.
Zornow, William F. Kansas: A history of the Jayhawk State. il. 1957. 4.95.
    U. of Okla.
KANT, IMMANUEL, 1724-1804 (921.3)
Beck, Lewis W. Commentary of Kant's Critique of practical reason. 1960. 6.00.
    U. of Chicago
Cassirer, H. W. Kant's first Critique. 1962. 6.50. Barnes & Noble
Heidegger, Martin. Kant and the problem of metaphysics. tr. by James S.
    Churchill. 1962. 7.50. Indiana
Martin, Gottfried. Kant's metaphysics and theory of science. 1955. 5.00.
    Barnes & Noble
Milmed, Bella K. Kant and current philosophical issues. 1961. 5.00. N. Y. U.
Weldon, Thomas D. Kant's Critique of pure reason. 1958. 6.10. Oxford U. P.
KARATE (746.8)
Harrison, E. J. Manual of karate. 3.95. Wehman
Oyama, Masutatsu. What is Karate? il. 1958. 7.00. Tuttle
KARL V, EMPEROR OF GERMANY, 1500-1558 (923.1)
Tyler, Royall. Emperor Charles the Fifth. 1956. 7.50. Oxford U. P.
KATANGA (960)
Hempstone, Smith. Rebels, mercenaries, and dividends: The Katanga story:
    il. 1962. 4.95. Praeger
KAUTZKY, THEODORE, 1896- (927)
Kinghan, Charles R. Ted Kautzky: Master of pencil and watercolor. 1959. 5.95.
    Reinhold
KEARNEY, STEPHEN WATTS, 1794-1848 (923.5)
Clarke, Dwight L. Stephen Watts Kearny, soldier of the West. il. 1961. 5.95.
    U. of Okla.

KEATS, JOHN, 1796-1821 (821.78)
Bate, Walter J. Stylistic development of Keats. 6.00. Humanities
Colvin, Sidney. Keats. 1957. 1.75. St. Martins
Fogle, R. H. Imagery of Keats and Shelley. 1949. 6.00. Shoe String
Gittings, R. John Keats: The living years, 21 September 1818 to 21 September 1819.
     il. 1954. 3.50. Harvard
Gittings, Robert. Mask of Keats: A study of problems. 1956. 3.25. Harvard
Houghton, Lord. Life and letters of John Keats. 1.95. Dutton
Muir, K. John Keats: A reassessment. 6.00. Lounz
Murray, John M. Keats. 1955. 4.00. Farrar, Straus
Murry, John M. Keats and Shakespeare: A study of Keats' poetic life from 1816-
     1820. 1924. 3.40. Oxford U. P.
Perkins, David. Quest for permanence: The symbolism of Wordsworth, Shelley,
     and Keats. 1959. 5.50. Harvard
Rollins, Hyder Edward. More letters and poems of the Keats circle. 1955. 3.00.
     Harvard
Slote, Bernice. Keats and the dramatic principle. 1958. 4.50. U. of Nebr.
Wasserman, Earl R. Finer tone: Keats' major poems. 1953. 4.00. Johns Hopkins
KELLER, HELEN ADAMS, 1880- (928)
Brooks, Van Wyck. Helen Keller. 1955. 3.00. Dutton
Keller, Helen. Story of my life. il. 1954. 3.95. Doubleday
KELLEY, FLORENCE, 1859-1932 (923.6)
Goldmark, Josephine. Impatient crusader: Florence Kelley's life story. 1953.
     3.50. U. of Ill.
KELLOGG, FRANK BILLINGS, 1856-1937 (923.2)
Bemis, Samuel F., and Robert H. Ferrell. American secretaries of state and
     their diplomacy, 1925-1961. vol. 1. Frank B. Kellogg, and Henry L. Stimson,
     1925-1933. in prep. Cooper
Ellis, L. Ethan. Frank B. Kellogg and American foreign relations, 1915-1929.
     1961. 7.50. Rutgers
KENNEDY, JACQUELINE LEE (BOUVIER), 1929- (920.7)
Rhea, Mini. I was Jacqueline Kennedy's dressmaker. il. 1961. 5.50. Fleet
Thayer, Mary Van R. Jacqueline Bouvier Kennedy. 1961. 4.95. Doubleday
KENNEDY, JOHN FITZGERALD, PRES. U. S., 1917- (923.1)
Burns, James MacGregor. John Kennedy: A political profile. il. 1959. 4.95.
     Harcourt
Dinneen, Joseph F. Kennedy family. 1960. 3.95. Little
Donovan, Robert J. PT109: John F. Kennedy in World War II. il. 1961. bds.
     4.95. McGraw
Lowe, Jacques. Portrait: The emergence of John F. Kennedy. il. 1961. 8.95.
     McGraw
Manchester, William. Portrait of a president: John F. Kennedy in profile.
     1962. 4.75. Little
KENNEDY-NIXON DEBATES, 1960 (329)
Kraus, Sidney. Great debates. il. 1962. 7.95. Indiana
KENSINGTON RUNE STONE (571)
Wahlgren, Erik. Kensington Stone: A mystery solved. 1958. 5.00. U. of Wis.
KENTUCKY--DESCRIPTION AND TRAVEL (917.69)
Writers' Project. Kentucky. 1954. 6.50. Hastings
KENTUCKY--HISTORY (976.9)
Abernethy, Thomas P. Three Virginia frontiers. 3.00. Smith, Peter
Townsend, William H. Lincoln and the Bluegrass: Slavery and Civil War in
     Kentucky. 1955. 6.50. U. of Ky.
KENYA COLONY AND PROTECTORATE (967.62)
Dinesen, Isak. Out of Africa. 1952. 1.95. Modern Lib.
Huxley, Elspeth. New earth. 1960. 6.00. Morrow
KEPLER, JOHANNES, 1571-1630 (925)
Caspar, Max. Kepler. 1959. 7.50. Abelard

KERN, JEROME, 1885-1945 (927)
Ewen, David. World of Jerome Kern. il. 1960. 3.95. Holt, Rinehart & Winston
KERSTEN, FELIX, 1898-1960 (925)
Kessel, Joseph. Man with the miraculous hands. tr. by Helen Weaver and
Leo Raditsa. 1961. 3.95. Farrar, Straus
KETTERING, CHARLES FRANKLIN, 1876-1958 (926)
Boyd, T. A. Professional Amateur: The biography of Charles Franklin Kettering
il. 1957. 4.50. Dutton
KEYES, FRANCES PARKINSON (WHEELER), 1885- (928)
Keyes, Frances Parkinson. Roses in December. 1960. 4.95. Doubleday
KEYNES, JOHN MAYNARD, 1883-1946 (923.3)
Hazlitt, Henry. Critics of Keynesian economics. 1960. 7.00. Van Nostrand
McCracken, Harlan L. Keynesian economics in the stream of economic thought.
il. 1961. 5.00. La.
Weintraub, Sidney. Classical Keynesianism, monetary theory and the price
level. 1961. 4.00. Chilton
Wright, David McCord. Keynesian system. 1962. 3.00. Fordham
KHRUSHCHEV, NIKITA SERGEEVICH, 1894- (923.1)
Hastie, Roy M. Man from nowhere: The life and times of Nikita Khrushchev.
1961. 4.00. Coward
Paloczi-Horvath, George. Khrushchev, the making of a dictator. 1960. 5.50.
Little
Pistrak, Lazar. Grand tactician: Khrushchev's rise to power. 6.00. Praeger
Werth, Alexander. Russia under Khrushchev. 1962. 5.00. Hill & Wang
KIDNEYS (611.61)
Smith, Homer W. From fish to philosopher. 1953. 4.75. Little
KIDNEYS--DISEASES (616.61)
McManus, Joseph F. A. Medical diseases of kidney. il. 1950. 6.00. Lea & F
KIERKEGAARD, SOREN AABYE, 1813-1855 (921.8)
Collins, James. Mind of Kierkegaard. 1953. 5.00. Regnery
Gates, John A. Life and thought of Kierkegaard for everyman. 1960. 3.75.
Westminster
Heinecken, Martin J. Moment before God. 1956. 5.95. Muhlenberg
Lowrie, Walter. Kierkegaard. 2 vols. 7.75. Smith, Peter
KILMER, ALFRED JOYCE, 1886-1918 (928)
Smaridge, Norah. Pen and bayonet. 1962. 2.95. Hawthorn
KINDERGARTEN (372.2)
Berson, Minnie P. Kindergarten, your child's big step. il. 1959. 3.50. Dutton
Foster, Josephine C., and Neith E. Headley. Education in the kindergarten.
by Neith E. Headley. il. 1959. 6.50. Am. Bk. Co.
Heffernan, Helen, and Vivian Todd. Kindergarten Teacher. il. 1960. 6.75. Heath
Lambert, Hazel M. Teaching the kindergarten child. il. 1958. 8.50. Harcourt
Peterson, Helen Thomas. Kindergarten: The key to child growth. 1958. 4.50.
Exposition
KINEMATICS (531.1)
Baldin, Aleksandr M., and others. Kinematics of nuclear reactions. il. 1961.
6.50. Pergamon
Kepler, H. B. Basic graphical kinematics. 1960. 6.00. McGraw
KING CLARENCE, 1842-1901 (926)
Wilkins, Thurman. Clarence King. il. 1958. 7.50. Macmillan
KING, WILLIAM LYON MACKENZIE, 1874-1950 (923.2)
Hardy, Henry R. Mackenzie King of Canada. il. 1949. 3.50. Oxford U. P.
KING PHILIP'S WAR, 1675-1676 (973.2)
Lincoln, C. H. Narratives of the Indian wars, 1675-1699. 1913. 5.75. Barnes &
Noble
KING RANCH, TEXAS (976.4)
Lea, Tom. King ranch. il. 2 vols. 1957. 20.00. Little
KINGDOM OF GOD (261)
Augustine, Saint. City of God. 2.95. Modern Lib.

Barrow, Reginald H. Introduction to St. Augustine's City of God. 6.00. Humanities

Niebuhr, H. Richard. Kingdom of God in America. 4.00. Shoe String

Schwietzer, Albert. Mystery of the Kingdom of God. tr. by Walter Lowrie. American ed. 3.95. Macmillan

KINGDOM OF GOD--BIBLICAL TEACHING (261)

Dodd, C. H. Parables of the kingdom. 1961. 3.50. Scribner

KINGS AND RULERS (920)

Nicolson, Harold. Kings, courts, and monarchy. 1962. 12.50? S. and S.

KINGS AND RULERS (IN RELIGION, FOLK-LORE, ETC.) (291.13)

Frankfort, Henri. Kingship and the gods. A study of ancient Near Eastern religion as the integration of society and nature. il. 1948. 9.00. U. of Chicago

Hooke, Samuel H. Myth, ritual, and kingship. 1958. 6.10. Oxford U. P.

KINGSLEY, CHARLES, 1819-1875 (922)

Martin, Robert B. Dust of combat: A life of Charles Kingsley. 1960. 5.95. Norton

KINO, EUSBIUS FRANCISCO, 1644-1711 (922)

Bolton, Herbert E. Rim of Christendom. 1960. 10.00. Russell

KINSHIP (301.442)

Edmonson, Munro S. Status terminology and the social structure of North American Indians. 1958. 3.00. U. of Wash.

Leach, Edmund R. Rethinking anthropology. il. 1961. bds. 4.25. Humanities

Radcliffe-Brown, Alfred R., and Daryll Forde. African systems of kinship and marriage. 1950. 6.40. Oxford U. P.

Yap, A. Q. Study of a kinship system: Its structural principles. 1961. 1.50. Catholic U. of Am. Pr.

KIPLING, RUDYARD, 1865-1936 (928)

Livingston, Flora Virginia. Supplement to Bibliography of the works of Rudyard Kipling. 1938. 10.00; special ed. 25.00. Harvard (R)

Sutcliff, Rosemary. Rudyard Kipling. 1961. 2.50. Walck

Tompkins, J. M. S. Art of Rudyard Kipling. 5.00. Humanities

KITCHENER, HORATIO HERBERT, 1ST EARL, 1850-1916 (923.5)

Magnus, Philip. Kitchener: Portrait of an imperialist. il. 1959. 6.50. Dutton

KITCHENS (643)

Ehrenkranz, Florence, and Lydia Inman. Equipment in the home. il. 1958. 6.00. Harper

KITTREDGE, GEORGE LYMAN, 1860-1941 (923.7)

Hyder, Clyde K. George Lyman Kittredge: Teacher and scholar. 1962. 4.50. U. of Kans.

KLEE, PAUL, 1879-1940 (927)

Klee, Felix. Paul Klee. tr. by Richard Winston. il. 1962. 7.50. Braziller

Spiller, Jurg. Klee. 1962. pap. 0.75. Barnes & Noble

KLEIST, HEINRICH VON, 1777-1811 (928)

Silz, Walter. Heinrich von Kleist. 1962. 6.00. U. of Pa.

KLONDIKE GOLD FIELDS (979.803)

Berton, Pierre. Klondike fever: The life and death of the last great stampede. 1958. 5.75. Knopf

KNEE (617.472)

Smillie, I. S. Injuries of the knee joint. il. 1962. 17.00. Williams & Wilkins

KNITTING (646)

Abbey, Barbara. 101 ways to improve your knitting. il. 1962. 2.00. Viking

Duncan, Ida Riley. Complete book of progressive knitting. 1961. 3.95. Tudor

Duncan, Ida R. Knit to fit. il. 1962. 4.95. Liveright

Mathieson, Elizabeth L. Complete book of knitting. il. 4.95. World Pub.

KNOSSOS (CRETE) (939.18)

Vaughan, Agnes Carr. House of the double axe. il. 1959. 5.95. Doubleday

KNOTS AND SPLICES (677.7)

Gibson, Walter. Fell's official guide to knots and how to tie them. 1961. 2.95. Fell

KNOWLEDGE, THEORY OF (121)
Ayer, Alfred J. Problem of knowledge. 1956. 4.50. St. Martins
Berkeley, George. Treatise concerning the principles of human knowledge.
    2.00. Open Ct.
Blanshard, Brand. Nature of thought. 2 vols. set. 9.00. Macmillan
Boas, George. Inquiring mind: An introduction to epistemology. 1958. 6.00.
    Open Ct.
Cassirer, Ernst. Essay on man. 1944. 5.00. Yale
Cassirer, Ernst. Problem of knowledge. tr. by William H. Woglom, and
    Charles W. Hendel. 1950. 6.00. Yale
Childe, V. G. Society and knowledge. 1956. 3.00. Harper
Coffey, P. Epistemology. 2 vols. 4.95. ea. Smith, Peter
D'Arcy, Martin C. Nature of belief. 1959. 3.95. Herder
Dewey, John, and Arthur F. Bentley. Knowing and the known. 1960. pap. 1.95.
    Beacon
Eddington, Arthur. Philosophy of physical science. 1958. pap. 1.75. U. of Mich.
Gibson, James. Locke's theory of knowledge. 1917. 5.00. Cambridge U. P.
Gulley, Norman. Plato's theory of knowledge. 1962. 4.50. Barnes & Noble
Hall, Everett W. Our knowledge of fact and value. 1961. 5.00. U. of N. C.
Hill, T. E. Contemporary theories of knowledge. 1961. 8.00. Ronald
Hume, David. Enquiries concerning the human understanding. by L. A. Selby-
    Bigge. 1927. 2.90. Oxford U. P.
Kant, Immanuel. Critique of pure reason. 1.95. Modern Lib.
Locke, John. Essay concerning human understanding. 2 vols. by Alexander
    Campbell Fraser. 8.50. Smith, Peter
Macmurray, John. Interpreting the universe. 2.50. Hillary
Mannheim, Karl. Essays on the sociology of knowledge. by Paul Kecskemeti.
    1952. 5.60. Oxford U. P.
Maritain, Jacques. Degrees of knowledge. 1959. 7.50. Scribner
Mill, John Stuart. John Stuart Mill's philosophy of scientific method. by Ernest
    Nagel. 1950. Hafner
Pap, Arthur. Semantics and necessary truth. 1958. 6.75. Yale
Parkinson, George H. R. Spinoza's theory of knowledge. 1954. 3.40. Oxford
Polanyi, Michael. Personal knowledge: Towards a post-critical philosophy.
    1958. 6.75. U. of Chicago
Polanyi, Michael. Study of man. 1.75. 1959. U. of Chicago
Russell, Bertrand. Analysis of mind. 1921. 3.50. Macmillan
Russell, Bertrand. Human knowledge, its scope and limits. 1948. 6.95. S. and S.
Spier, J. M. Introduction to Christian philosophy. tr. by David H. Freeman.
    1954. 3.75. Presbyterian & Reformed
Sturt, H. Principles of understanding. 1915. 3.00. Cambridge U. P.
Taylor, Stanley. Conceptions of institutions. 4.00. Twayne
Thomas Aquinas, Saint. On the teacher, On the mind. 1959. pap. 0.95. Regnery
Weigel, Gustav, and Arthur Madden. Knowledge: Its value and limits. 1961. 3.95.
    Prentice-Hall
Whitehead, A. N. Concept of nature. 1919. 3.50. Cambridge U. P.
Whitehead, A. N. Principles of natural knowledge. 4.00. Cambridge U. P.
KNOWLEDGE, THEORY OF (RELIGION) (201)
Greene, Theodore Meyer. Moral, aesthetic, and religious insight. 1958. 2.75.
    Rutgers
Harkness, Georgia. Foundations of Christian knowledge. 1955. 2.75. Abingdon
Randall, John H., Jr. Role of knowledge in Western religion. 1958. 3.50. Beacon
KNOX, HENRY, 1750-1806 (923.5)
Callahan, North. Henry Knox: General Washington's general. 1958. 6.50. Rinehart
KNOX, JOHN, 1505-1572 (923.2)
McEwen, James. S. Faith of John Knox. 1961. 2.50. John Knox
MacGregor, Geddes. Thundering Scot: A portrait of John Knox. 1957. 3.95.
    Westminster

KNOX, RONALD ARBUTHNOTT, 1888-1957 (922)
Waugh, Evelyn. Msgr. Ronald Knox. 1960. 5.00. Little
KOESTLER, ARTHUR, 1905- (928)
Koestler, Arthur. Arrow in the blue. il. 1952. 5.00. Macmillan
KON-TIKI (990)
Heyerdahl, Thor. Kon-Tiki. 1950. 5.95. Rand McNally
KORAN (297)
Ali, Abdullah Yusuf. Koran. Holy Qur-an. Arabic text, translation and commen-
    tary. 2 vols. 1946. 12.50. Hafner (R)
KOREA (951. 9)
Chung, Kyung Cho. Korea tomorrow: Land of the morning calm. il. 1956. 5.95.
    Macmillan
Korea, its land, people and culture of all ages. il. 1960. 25.00. Vanous
KOREA--HISTORY (951. 9)
Hulbert, Homer B. History of Korea. by C. N. Weems. 2 vols. 15.00. Hillary
KOREA--POLITICS AND GOVERNMENT (951. 9)
King, O. H. P. Tail of the paper tiger. 1961. 6.00. Caxton
KOREAN WAR, 1950-1953 (951. 9042)
Geer, Andrew. New breed: The story of the U. S. Marines in Korea. il. 1952.
    5.50. Harper
Higgins, Trumbull. Korea and the fall of MacArthur. il. 1960. 5.00. Oxford U. P.
Leckie, Robert. Conflict: The history of the Korean War. 1962. 6.95. Putnam
Marshall, S. L. A. Pork Chop Hill: The American fighting man in action--
    Korea, Spring, 1953. 1956. 5.00. Morrow
Spanier, John W. Truman-MacArthur controversy and the Korean War. 1959.
    6.50. Harvard
Whiting, Allen. China crosses the Yalu. 1960. 7.50. Macmillan
Whitney, Courtney. MacArthur: His rendezvous with history. 1956. 7.50. Knopf
KOREAN WAR, 1950-1953--ARMISTICES (951. 9042)
Vatcher, William H., Jr. Panmunjom. 4.75. Praeger
KRISTINA, QUEEN OF SWEDEN, 1626-1689 (923.1)
Lewis, Paul. Queen of caprice: A biography of Kristina of Sweden. 1962. 4.95.
    Holt, Rinehart & Winston
KRUPP FAMILY (920)
Muhlen, Norbert. Incredible Krupps. il. 1959. 5.00. Holt
KU KLUX KLAN (973. 8)
Rice, Arnold S. Ku Klux Klan in politics. 1961. 3.25. Pub. Affairs
KUNIYOSHI, YASUO, 1893- (927)
Goodrich, Lloyd, and others. Yasuo Kuniyoshi. il. 15.00. Tuttle
KURDS (956. 67)
Edmonds, C. J. Kurds, Turks and Arabs. 1957. 6.75. Oxford U. P.

L

LABOR AND LABORING CLASSES (331)
Baerwald, Friedrich. Fundamentals of labor economics. 1952. 4.75. Fordham
Dankert, Clyde E. Introduction to labor. 1954. 9.25. Prentice-Hall
Friedmann, Georges. Industrial society. 1955. 6.00. Free Press
Galenson, Walter. Labor and economic development. 1959. 6.75. Wiley
Galenson, Walter. Labor in developing economies. 1962. 6.00. U. of Calif.
Gould, E. R. L. Social condition of labor. 1893. 1.00. Johns Hopkins
Gross, Edward. Work and society. il. 1958. 6.75. Crowell
Hicks, J. R. Theory of wages. 1958. 4.00. Smith, Peter
Kwant, R. C. Philosophy of labor. 5.25. Duquesne
Perlman, Selig. Theory of the labor movement. 3.50. Kelley
Reynolds, Lloyd G. Labor economics and labor relations. 1959. 8.50. Prentice-
    Hall
Tannenbaum, Frank. Philosophy of labor. 3.00. 1951. Knopf

Unwin, George.   Industrial organization in the 16th and 17th centuries. 6. 00.
    Kelley
LABOR AND LABORING CLASSES--MEDICAL CARE (614. 2)
Brecher, Ruth, and Edward.   How to get the most out of medical and hospital
    benefit plans. 1961. 3. 95. Prentice-Hall
McGrath, Bethel J.   Nursing in commerce and industry. il. 1946. 3. 00. Harvard
Stern, Bernhard J.   Medicine in industry. 1946. 1. 50. Harvard
LABOR AND LABORING CLASSES--FINLAND (331)
Knoellinger, Carl E.   Labor in Finland. 1961. 6. 00. Harvard
LABOR AND LABORING CLASSES--FRANCE (331)
Godfrey, E. Drexel, Jr.   Fate of the French non-communist left. 1955. pap. 0. 95.
    Random
LABOR AND LABORING CLASSES--GT. BRIT. (331)
Furniss, Edgar S.   Position of the laborer in a system of nationalism. 6. 00.
    Kelley
Toynbee, Arnold.   Industrial revolution. 1959. 3. 25. Smith, Peter
Zweig, Ferdynand.   Workers in an affluent society. 1962. 4. 50. Free Press
LABOR AND LABORING CLASSES--GT. BRIT.--HISTORY (331)
Cole, G. D. H.   Short history of the British working-class movement. 1948. 6. 75.
    Macmillan
LABOR AND LABORING CLASSES--LATIN AMERICA (331)
Jaffe, A. J.   People, jobs, and economic development. 1959. 6. 00. Free Press
LABOR AND LABORING CLASSES--RUSSIA (331)
Bergson, Abram.   Soviet economic growth: Conditions and perspectives. 1953.
    6. 00. Row
LABOR AND LABORING CLASSES--U. S. (331)
Butler, Arthur D.   Labor economics and institutions. il. 1961. 6. 50. Macmillan
Chamberlain, Neil W.   Labor. 1958. 7. 95. McGraw
Cole, Gordon H., and others.   Labor's story. 1961. 5. 50. Community Pubs.
Commons, John R., and others.   History of labour in the United States. 4 vols.
    vols. 1 and 2. 1951; vol. 3. Working conditions. by Don D. Lescohier; Labor
    legislation. by Elizabeth Brandis, 1935; vol. 4. Labor movements. by Selig
    Perlman and Philip Taft. 7. 25 ea; set, 27. 00. Macmillan
Daugherty, C. R., and J. B. Parrish.   Labor problems of American society.
    8. 00. Houghton
Derber, Milton, and Edwin Young.   Labor and the New Deal. 1958. 6. 00. U. of
    Wis.
Douglas, Paul H.   Theory of wages. 8. 50. Kelley
Dulles, Foster Rhea.   Labor in America. 1960. 7. 50. Crowell
Fine, Nathan.   Labor and farmer parties in the United States, 1828-1928. 8. 00.
    Russell
Gompers, Samuel.   Seventy years of life and labor: An autobiography. by Philip
    Taft, and John A. Sessions. 1957. 5. 00. Dutton
McMaster, John B.   Acquisition of political, social, and industrial rights of man
    in America. 1961. 3. 00. Ungar
Miller, Glenn W.   Problems of labor. 7. 00. Macmillan
Myers, James, and Harry W. Laidler.   What do you know about labor? 1956. 4. 75.
    Day
Rayback, Joseph G.   History of American labor. 1959. 6. 95. Macmillan
Tripp, Louis R.   Labor problems and processes. il. 1961. 6. 00. Harper
Ware, Norman.   Industrial worker (1840-1860) 1958. 4. 50. Smith, Peter
Ware, Norman.   Labor movement in the United States, 1860-1895. 1959. 5. 50.
    Smith, Peter
LABOR AND LABORING CLASSES--U. S.--HISTORY (331)
Adamic, Louis.   Cynamite, the story of class violence. in America. il. 1959.
    6. 00. Smith, Peter
Dulles, Foster R.   Labor in America: A history 1960. 7. 50. Crowell

LABOR CONTRACT (331)
Collective Bargaining Negotations and Contracts o editorial staff. Basic patterns
in union contracts. 1.25. Bur. of Nat. Affairs
LABOR COURTS (331.16)
Braun, Kurt. Labor disputes and their settlement. 1955. 6.00. Johns Hopkins
LABOR DISCIPLINE (331.116)
Phelps, Orme W. Discipline and discharge in unionized firms. 1959. 5.00. U.
Of Calif.
LABOR ECONOMICS (331)
Phelps Brown, E. H. Economics of labor. 1962. 6.00? Yale
Shister, Joseph. Readings in labor economics and industrial relations. 1956.
6.95. Lippincott
Yoder, Dale, and Herbert G. Heneman, Jr. Labor economics of industrial
relations. 1959. 7.95. South-Western Pub.
LABOR LAWS AND LEGISLATION--U.S. (331)
Cook, Franklin H. Principles of business and the federal law. 1951. 7.00.
Macmillan
Daugherty, C. R., and J. B. Parrish. Labor problems of American society.
8.00. Houghton
Gregory, Charles O. Labor and the law. 1958. 6.90. Norton
Millis, Harry A., and Emily C. Brown. From the Wagner Act to Taft-Hartley
1950. 9.50. U. of Chicago
Petro, S. Labor policy of the free society. 1957. 5.00. Ronald
Young, Dallas M. Understanding labor problems. 1959. 8.50. McGraw
LABOR LAWS AND LEGISLATION--U.S.--CASES (331)
Wollett, Donald, and others. Labor relations and the law. 1960. 12.50. 1962
suppl. in prep. Little
LABOR MOBILITY (331.127)
Jaffe, Abram J., and R. O. Carleton. Occupational mobility in the United States,
1930-1960. 1954. 2.75. Columbia
Rogoff, Natalie. Recent trends in occupational mobility. 1962. 4.00. Free Press
LABOR PARTY (GT. BRIT.) (329.9)
Pelling, Henry M. Short history of the Labour Party. 1961. 4.75. St. Martins
Weiner, Herbert E. British labor and public ownership. 1960. 3.25. Pub. Affairs
LABOR SUPPLY (331)
Bancroft, Gertrude. American labor force. 1958. 7.50. Wiley
National Manpower Council. Improving the work skills of the nation. 1955. 3.50.
Columbia
National Manpower Council. Womanpower. 1957. 5.00. Columbia
Salant, Walter S., and Beatrice N. Vaccara. Import liberalization and employ-
ment. 1961. 6.75. Brookings
Thomas, Brinley. Economics of international migration. 1958. 9.00. St. Martins
LABORATORIES (607.2)
Ansley, A. J. Introduction to laboratory technique. 1950. 3.25. St. Martins
Hiscocks, E. S. Laboratory administration. 1957. 8.00. St. Martins
LABORATORY ANIMALS (619)
Farris, Edmond J. Care and breeding of laboratory animals. 1950. 14.00. Wiley
Lane-Petter, William. Provision of laboratory animals for research. il. 1961.
4.00. Am. Elsevier
LACE AND LACE MAKING (746.2)
Kinmond, Jean. Anchor book of lace crafts. il. 1961. 9.95. Branford
Maidment, Margaret. Manual of handmade Bobbin lacework. 6.95. Branford
LACROSSE (796.34)
American Association for Health, Physical Education and Recreation, Division
for Girls' and Women's Sports. Field hockey and lacrosse rules and guide.
1.00. Am. Assn. for Health, Phys. Ed. & Rec.
Boyd, Margaret. Lacrosse. il. 1959. 5.00. Barnes, A. S.
LA FAYETTE, MARIE ADRIENNE FRANCOISE (DE NOAILLES) d. 1807 (928)
Maurois, Andre. Ardrienne: The life of the Marquise de La Fayette. 7.95.
McGraw

Wright, Constance. Madame de Lafayette. il. 1959. 5.00. Holt, Rinehart & Winston

LAFAYETTE, MARIE JOSEPH PAUL YVES ROCH GILBERT DU MOTIER, MARQUIS DE, 1757-1834 (923.2)

Gottschalk, Louis. Lafayette and the Close of the American Revolution. 1942. 7.50. U. of Chicago

Gottschalk, Louis. Lafayette between the American and the French Revolution. (1783-1789) 1950. 7.50. U. of Chicago

Wright, Constance. Chance for glory. il. 1957. 3.95. Holt

LAFITTE, JEAN, 1782-1854 (923.41)

De Grummond, Jane L. Baratarians and the Battle of New Orleans. il. 1961. 4.50. La. State

Saxon, Lyle. Lafitte the pirate. il. 10.00. Crager

LA FOLLETTE, ROBERT MARION, 1855-1925 (923.2)

La Follette, Belle C., and Fola. Robert M. La Follette, 1855-1925. 2 vols. il. 1953. 8.95. Macmillan

Maxwell, Robert S. La Follette and the rise of the Progressives in Wisconsin. il. 1956. 4.50. Wis. State Hist. Soc.

LA FONTAINE, JEAN DE, 1621-1695 (928)

Guiton, Margaret. La Fontiane: Poet and counter-poet. 1960. 5.00. Rutgers

Mourgues, Odette de. La Fontaine: Fables. 1962. 1.95. Barron's

LAGARDE, PAUL ANTON DE, 1827-1891 (928)

Stern, Fritz R. Politics of cultural despair: A study in the rise of the Germanic ideology. 1961. 8.00. U. of Calif.

LAGERLOF, SELMA OTTILIANA LOUISA, 1858-1940 (928)

Vrieze, F. S. de. Fact and fiction in the autobiographical works of Selma Lagerlof. 1958. 5.50. Hillary'

LAGUARDIA, FIORELLO HENRY, 1882-1947 (923.2)

LaGuardia, Fiorello H. Making of an insurgent. 1961. 3.25. Smith, Peter

Mann, Arthur. La Guardia: A fighter against his time, 1882-1933. il. 1959. 6.50. Lippincott

Rodman, Bella. Fiorello LaGuardia. il. 1962. 3.95. Hill & Wang

LAISSEZ-FAIRE (330.153)

Belknap, Joel R. Story of free enterprise. 1962. 3.50. Devin

Fine, Sidney. Laissez faire and the general-welfare state. 1956. 7.50. U. of Mich.

LAKE CHAMPLAIN (973.525)

Bird, Harrison. Navies in the mountains: The Battles on the waters of Lake Champlain and Lake George, 1609-1814. 1962. 6.50. Oxford U. P.

LAMAISM (755.943)

Nebesky-Wojkowitz, R. de. Oracles and demons of Tibet: The cult and iconography of Tibetan protective deities. 15.00. Humanities

LAMB, LADY CAROLINE (PONSONBY) 1785-1828 (928)

Cecil, David, Lord. Melbourne. 1954. pap. 2.75. Bobbs

LAMB, GEORGE R. (928)

Lamb, George. Roman road. 2.25. Sheed

LAMBARENE, GABON (276.721)

Schweitzer, Albert. On the edge of the primeval forest, and More from the primeval forest. il. 5.00. Macmillan

LAMINATED PLASTICS (674.835)

Bick, Alexander F. Plastics: Projects and procedures with polyesters. 1962. 4.75. Bruce

Duffin, Daniel J., and Charles Nerzig. Laminated plastics, including high-pressure and low-pressure types and reinforced plastics. il. 1958. 5.75. Reinhold

LAMPS (621.32)

Allphin, Willard. Primer of lamps and lighting. il. 1959. 10.00. Chilton

LAND (333)

Clawson, Marion, and Charles H. Stoddard. Land for the future. il. 1960. 8.50. Johns Hopkins

Davies, Pearl J. Real estate in American history. 1958. 5.00. Pub. Affairs

Johnson, Hugh A., and Harold T. Jorgenson. Land resources of Alaska. il. 1962. 15.00. Univ. Pub.

Land Economics Institute. Modern land policy. il. 1960. 8.50. U. of Ill.

LAND--TAXATION (336.22)

Sakolski, A. M. Land tenure and land taxation in America. 1957. 3.00. Schalkenbach

Wald, Haskell P. Taxation of agricultural land in underdeveloped economies. 1959. 4.50. Harvard

LAND--U.S. (333)

Bartholomew, Harland, and Jack Wood. Land uses in American cities. il. 1955. 6.50. Harvard

Gates, Paul Wallace. Fifty million acres: Conflicts over Kansas Land Policy. 1854-1890. il. 1954. 4.50. Cornell

Land Economics Institute. Modern land policy. il. 1960. 8.50. U. of Ill.

LAND SETTLEMENT (325.3)

Treadgold, D. W. The great Siberian migration. 1957. 5.00. Princeton

LAND TENURE--ASIA (333.315)

Hoffman, Daniel P. India's social miracle. 3.95. Naturegraph

Smith, Thomas C. Agrarian origins of modern Japan. 5.00. Stanford

LAND TENURE--GT. BRIT. (333.314)

John, Eric. Land tenure in early England. 6.00. Humanities

Simpson, Alfred W. B. Introduction to the history of the Land Law. 1961. 4.00. Oxford U. P.

LAND TENURE--LATIN AMERICA (333.318)

Senior, Clarence O. Land reform and democracy. 1958. 6.75. U. of Fla.

LAND TENURE--NEAR EAST (333.315)

Warriner, Doreen. Land reform and development in the Middle East. 2.90. Oxford U. P.

LAND TENURE--U.S. (333.317)

Abernethy, Thomas P. Western lands and the American Revolution. il. 1959. 7.50. Russell

Harris, Marshall. Origin of the land tenure system in the United States. il. 1953. 5.00. Iowa State

Hibbard, B. H. History of the public land policies. 6.00. Smith, Peter

Sakolski, A. M. Land tenure and land taxation in America. 1957. 3.00. Schalkenbach

LANDOR, WALTER SAVAGE, 1775-1864 (928)

Super, R. H. Walter Savage Landor: A biography. il. 1954. 7.50. N. Y. U.

LANDSCAPE DRAWING (741.7)

Black, Arthur. Landscape sketching. il. 1950. 5.75. McGraw

Doust, L. A. Sketching the countryside. 1.50. Warne

LANDSCAPE GARDENING (710)

Bushey, Donald J. Guide to home landscaping. 1956. 4.95. McGraw

Lees, Carlton B. Budget landscaping. il. 1960. 3.95. Holt, Rinehart & Winston

Ortloff, Henry S. and Henry B. Raymore. Book of landscape design. 1959. 3.95. Barrows

Simonds, J. O. Landscape architecture. 1961. 12.75. McGraw

LANDSCAPE PAINTING (758)

Carlson, John F. Guide to landscape painting. il. 1958. 6.00. Sterling

Gasser, Henry M. Techniques of painting the waterfront. il. 1959. 12.50. Reinhold

Kautzky, Theodore. Painting trees and landscapes in watercolor. 1952. 9.95. Reinhold

Muncaster, Claude. Landscape and marine painting. 1958. 10.95. Pitman

LANDSCAPE PROTECTION (712)

Hubbard, Alice H. This land of ours. 1960. 4.95. Macmillan

LANGLAND, WILLIAM (928)
Fowler, David C. Piers the plowman. 1961. 5.75. U. of Wash.
Salter, Elizabeth. Piers Plowman: An introduction. 1962. 3.75. Harvard
LANGTRY, LILLIE, 1852-1929 (927)
Sichel. Jersey Lily: Story of the fabulous Mrs. Langtry. 1958. 4.95. Prentice-
    Hall
LANGUAGE, UNIVERSAL (408.91)
Pei, Mario. One language for the world. 5.00. Devin
LANGUAGE AND LANGUAGES (400)
Auvray, Paul, and others. Sacred languages. tr. by J. Tester. 1960. 3.50.
    Hawthorn
Black, Max. Critical thinking. 1952. 7.25. Prentice-Hall
Bloomfield, Leonard. Language. 1933. 6.75. Holt
Bodmer, Frederick. Loom of language. il. by Lancelot Hogben. 1944. 8.95.
    Norton
Brown, Roger. Words and things. 6.75. Free Press
Carnap, Rudolf. Logical syntax of language. 1937. 6.00. Humanities
Cassirer, E. Language and myth. 3.00. Smith, Peter
Chase, Stuart. Power of words. 1954. 3.95. Harcourt
Chase, Stuart. Tyranny of words. 1938. 4.50. 1959. Harcourt
Francis, W. Nelson. Structure of American English. 1958. 7.00. Ronald
Gardiner, Alan. Theory of speech and language. 1951. 3.40. Oxford U. P.
Gellner, Ernest. Words and things. il. 1960. 5.00. Beacon
Hayakawa, Samuel I. Our language and our world, selections from Etc. a
    review of general semantics, 1953-1958. il. 1959. 5.00. Harper
Hook, J. N., and E. G. Mathews. Modern American grammar and usage. 1956.
    5.50. Ronald
Hughes, John P. Science of language. 1961. 6.95. Random
Huppe, Bernard F., and Jack Kaminsky. Logic and language. 1956. 2.25. Knopf
Jespersen, Otto. Language, its nature, development and origin. 1934. 5.75.
    Macmillan
Laird, Charlton. Miracle of language. 1953. 4.00. World Pub.
Meader, Clarence L., and John H. Muyskens. Handbook of biolinguistics. 2 pts.
    pt. 1, Structures and processes of expression. il. 1962. 10.00; pt. 2, General
    semantics. 1959. 7.50. Weller
Ogden, Charles K., and Ivor A. Richards. Meaning of meaning. 1959. 5.95.
    Harcourt
Pederson, Holger. Discovery of language. tr. by John W. Spargo. il. 1962. 6.50.
    Indiana
Pei, Mario. All about language. il. 1954. 2.95. Lippincott
Pei, Mario. One language for the world. 5.00. Devin
Pei, Mario. Talking your way around the world. 1961. 3.95. Harper
Potter, Simeon. Modern linguistics. 1957. 3.25. Oxford U. P.
Tylor, Edward B. Primitive culture. 2 vols. vol. 1, Origins of culture; vol. 2,
    Religion in primitive culture. 4.00 ea. Smith, Peter
Urban, Wilbur Marshall. Language and reality: The philosophy of language and
    the principles of symbolism. 6.50. Macmillan
Vendryes, Joseph. Language: A linguistic introduction to history. 1925. 7.00.
    Barnes & Noble
Wheelwright, Philip. Burning Fountain: A study in the language of symbolism.
    il. 1954. 6.75. Indiana
LANGUAGE AND LANGUAGES--ADDRESSES, ESSAYS, LECTURES (404)
Diamond, Stanley. Culture in history. 1960. 15.00. Columbia
LANGUAGE AND LANGUAGES--ETYMOLOGY (412)
Hatcher, Anna Granville. Modern English word formation and neo-Latin. 1951.
    4.25. Johns Hopkins
Ross, Alan S. C. Etymology. 1958. 7.00. Oxford U. P.
LANGUAGE AND LANGUAGES--STUDY AND TEACHING (407)
Brooks, Nelson. Language and language learning. 1960. 3.75. Harcourt

Carroll, John Bissell. Study of language: A survey of linguistics and related disciplines in America. 1953. 4.75. Harvard

Cornelius, Edwin T., Jr. How to learn a foreign language. il. 1955. 2.95. Crowell

LANGUAGES, MODERN--STUDY AND TEACHING (372.65)

Fotitch, Tatiana Z. Teaching foreign languages in the modern world. 1961. 3.95. Catholic U. of Am. Pr.

Holton, James S., and others. Sound language teaching. il. 1961. 5.50. Univ. Pub.

Huebener, Theodore. Audio-visual techniniques in teaching foreign languages. il. 1960. 3.25. N. Y. U.

Huebener, Theodore. How to teach foreign languages effectively. 1959. 3.00. N. Y. U.

Huebener, Theodore. Why Johnny should learn foreign languages. 1961. 4.00. Chilton

Jespersen, Otto. How to teach a foreign language. 2.25. Macmillan

Meras, Edmond A. Language teacher's guide. 1962. 4.75. Harper

LANTERN SLIDES (778.2)

Rothschild, Norman, and George Wright. Mounting, projecting and storing slides 1960. 1.95. Hastings

LAO-TZU (299.514)

Welch, Holmes. Parting of the way: Lao Tzu and the Taoist movement. 1961. 5.00. U. Books

LAOS (959.4)

Dooley, Thomas A. Dr. Tom Dooley's three great books: Deliver us from Evil, Edge of tomorrow, and The night they burned the mountain. il. bds. 5.00. Farrar, Straus

LeBar, Frank. Laos. il. 1960. 6.50. Taplinger

LAPLACE TRANSFORMATION (517.352)

Day, William D. Introduction to Laplace transforms for radio and electronics engineers. 1960. 5.50. Wiley

LAPPS (947.17)

Collinder, Bjorn. Lapps. 1949. 3.75. Princeton

LA ROCHEFOUCAULD, FRANCOIS, DUC DE, 1613-1680 (928)

Zeller, M. F., Sister. New aspects of style in the maxims of La Rochefoucauld. 1954. 3.00. Catholic U. of Am. Pr.

LA SALLE, ROBERT CAVELIER, SIEUR DE, 1643-1687 (923.9)

Parkman, Francis. Discovery of the great west: La Salle. by William R. Taylor. 1956. pap. 1.65. Holt, Rinehart & Winston

LASCAUX CAVE, FRANCE (944)

Bataille, Georges. Lascaux: Prehistoric painting. il. 1955. in English, French, or German. 17.50. World Pub.

LASKER, ALBERT DAVIS, 1876-1952 (923)

Gunther, John. Taken at the flood. il. 1960. 5.00. Harper

LASKI, HAROLD JOSEPH, 1893-1950 (923.2)

Deane, H. A. Political ideas of Harold J. Laski. 1955. 6.75. Columbia

LAST WORDS (808.88)

Conrad, Barnaby, comp. Famous last words. 1961. bds. 3.95. Doubleday (R)

LATHES (621.942)

Haines, Ray E. Wood-turning lathe. il. 1952. 3.95. Van Nostrand

LATIMER, HUGH, BP. OF WORCESTER, 1485-1555 (922)

Chester, Allan G. Hugh Latimer: Apostle to the English. 1954. 6.00. U. of Pa.

LATIN AMERICA (980)

Beals, Carleton. Worlds in revolution. 1962. 5.00. Abelard

James, Preston, E. Latin America. 1959. 8.00. Odyssey

McEoin, Gary. Latin America: The eleventh hour. 4.50. Kenedy

Tannenbaum, Frank. Ten keys to Latin America. 1962. 4.95. Knopf

LATIN AMERICA--ANTIQUITIES (980)

Lothrop, Samuel K. , and others. Pre-Columbian art. il. 1959. boxed 30. 00.
N. Y. Graphic
LATIN AMERICA--BIBLIOGRAPHY (016. 980)
Humphreys, Robert A. Latin American history, a guide to the literature in
English. 1958. 4. 00. Oxford U. P. (R)
LATIN AMERICA--BIOGRAPHY (980)
Alexander, Robert J. Prophets of the revolution. 1962. 4. 95. Macmillan
Szulc, Tad. Twilight of the tyrants. il. 1959. 4. 50. Holt
LATIN AMERICA--CIVILIZATION (980)
Bailey, Helen and Abraham Nasatir. Latin America, the development of its
civilization. 1960. 7. 95. Prentice-Hall
Crawford, William R. Century of Latin-American thought. 1961. 6. 00. Harvard
Foster, George M. Culture and conquest: America's Spanish heritage. il. 1960.
6. 00. Quadrangle
Keen, Benjamin. Readings in Latin-American civilization. 1955. 3. 95. Houghton
Picon-Salas, Mariano. Cultural history of Spanish America: From conquest to
independence. tr. by Irving A. Leonard. 1962. 5. 00. U. of Calif.
Schurz, William L. This new world: The civilization of Latin America. il. 1954.
6. 00. Dutton
Stokes, William S. Latin American politics. 1959. 6. 50. Crowell
Williams, Mary W. , and others. People and politics of Latin America: A history.
1955. 7. 50. Ginn
LATIN AMERICA--DESCRIPTION AND TRAVEL (980)
Butland, G. J. Latin America. 1960. 5. 00. Wiley
Carlson, Fred A. Geography of Latin America. 1951. 8. 75. Prentice-Hall
LATIN AMERICA--ECONOMIC CONDITIONS (980)
Benham, Frederic C. , and H. A. Holley. Short introduction to the economy of
Latin America. 1960. 2. 90. Oxford U. P.
International Economic Association Conference. Economic development for Latin
America. by Howard Ellis. and Henry C. Wallich. 1961. 10. 00. St. Martins
Stark, H. Social and economic frontiers in Latin America. 1961. 7. 25. Brown,
W. C.
LATIN AMERICA--FOREIGN RELATIONS (980)
Madariaga, Salvador de. Latin America between the eagle and the bear. 4. 50.
Praeger
LATIN AMERICA--FOREIGN RELATIONS--U. S. (980)
Bemis, Samuel Flagg, Latin American policy of the United States: An historical
interpretation. il. 6. 50. Harcourt
LATIN AMERICA--HISTORY (980. 01)
Bannon, John F. , and Peter M. Dunne. Latin America. 1958. 7. 50. Bruce
Chapman, Charles E. Colonial Hispanic America. 1933. 6. 50. Macmillan
Dozer, Donald M. Latin America: An interpretative history. 1962. in prep.
text ed. 7. 95. McGraw
Herring, Hubert. History of Latin America. 1961. 10. 75. Knopf
Rippy, J. Fred. Latin America: A modern history. 1958. 10. 00. U. of Mich.
Thomas, Alfred Barnaby. Latin America. il. 6. 75. Macmillan
LATIN AMERICA--HISTORY --TO 1600 (980)
Graham, R. B. Cunninghame. Horses of the conquest. il. by Robert H. Denhardt.
1949. 5. 00. U. of Okla.
LATIN AMERICA--HISTORY-- TO 1830 (980)
Whitaker, Arthur P. United States and the independence of Latin America. 1800-1830.
1962. 10. 00. Russell
LATIN AMERICA--POLITICS (980)
Adams, Richard N. , and others. Social change in Latin America today. 1960. 5. 00.
Harper
Benton, William. Voice of Latin America. 1961. 3. 95. Harper
Berle, Adolf A. , Jr. Latin America: Diplomacy and reality. 1962. 2. 95? Harper
Christensen, Asher N. Evolution of Latin American government: Book of readings.
1951. 6. 75. Holt

American Assembly. United States and Latin America. by Herbert L. Matthews. 1960. 2.00. Am. Assembly
Bernstein, Harry. Making an inter-American mind. 1961. 5.50. U. of Fla.
Dozer, Donald M. Are we good neighbors? Three decades of inter-American relations, 1930-1960. 8.00. U. of Fla.
Matthews, Herbert L. Cuban story. 1961. 4.50. Braziller
Perkins, Dexter. United States and Latin America. 1961. 3.00. La. State
Plaza, Galo. Problems of democracy in Latin America. 1955. 2.50. U. of N. C.
Radler, D. H. El gringo: The Yankee image in Latin America. 1962. 3.95. Chilton
Tomlinson, Edward. Look southward, Uncle. 1959. 6.00. Devin

LATIN AMERICA--SOCIAL CONDITIONS (980)

Davis, H. E. Government and politics in Latin America. 1958. 7.50. Ronald
Gunther, John. Inside Latin America. 1941. 6.00. Harper
Johnson, John J. Political change in Latin America. 1958. 5.00. Stanford
Lieuwen, Edwin. Arms and politics in Latin America. 1960. 5.00. Praeger
Mecham, John L. United States and inter-American security, 1889-1960. il. 1961. 7.50. U. of Tex.
Palmer, Thomas W., Jr. Search for a Latin American policy. 1957. 4.50. U. of Fla.
Pierson, William W., and Federico G. Gil. Governments of Latin America. il. 1957. 7.75. McGraw
Pike, Fredrick B. Freedom and reform in Latin America. 1959. 6.00. U. of Notre Dame
Porter, Charles O., and Robert J. Alexander. Struggle for democracy in Latin America. 1961. 4.50. Macmillan
Stark, H. Social and economic frontiers in Latin America. 1961. 7.25. Brown, W. C.
Stokes, William S. Latin American politics. 1959. 6.50. Crowell
Wood, Bryce M. Making of the good neighbor policy. 1961. 7.50. Columbia

LATIN AMERICA--RELATIONS (GENERAL) WITH THE U. S. (980)

LATIN-AMERICAN LITERATURE (COLLECTIONS) (870)

Arciniegas, German. Green continent: A comprehensive view of Latin America by its leading writers. 1944. 5.00. Knopf
Hespelt, E. H., and others. Anthology of Spanish American literature. in Spanish. 2 vols. 1946. vol. 1, Cortes to Ricardo Palma; vol. 2, Gutierres Najera to Neruda. 3.75 ea. complete in 1 vol. 6.00. Appleton

LATIN-AMERICAN LITERATURE--HISTORY AND CRITICISM (870)

Torres-Rioseco, Arturo. Epic of Latin American literature. 1959. 3.50. Smith, Peter
Torres-Rioseco, Arturo. New World literature: Tradition and revolt in Latin America. 1949. 3.75. U. of Calif.

LATIN DRAMA--HISTORY AND CRITICISM (870)

Beare, William. Roman stage. rev. ed. 7.50. Hillary
Duckworth, G. E. Nature of Roman comedy. 1952. 7.50. Princeton
Harsh, Philip W. Handbook of classical drama. 1944. 7.50. Stanford

LATIN DRAMA--TRANSLATIONS INTO ENGLISH (870)

Duckworth, George E. Complete Roman drama. 2 vols. boxed. 15.00. Random

LATIN DRAMA, MEDIEVAL AND MODERN (870)

Young, Karl. Drama of the Medieval church. 2 vols. il. 1933. 20.20. Oxford U. P.

LATIN FICTION--HISTORY AND CRITICISM (870)

Haight, E. H. Essays on ancient fiction. 1936. 2.50. McKay
Haight, E. H. More essays on Greek romances. 1945. 2.50. McKay

LATIN LANGUAGE--DICTIONARIES--ENGLISH (470.019)

Cassell's new Latin dictionary. Latin-English and English-Latin, 7.50; thumb-indexed, 8.50. Funk
Latin-English and English-Latin classic dictionary. 5.95; indexed, 6.95. Follett
(R)

Lewis, C. T., and Charles Short. Latin dictionary: Founded on Andrews' edition of Freund's Latin dictionary. 12. 80. Oxford U. P.

White's Latin-English and English-Latin dictionary. indexed, 7. 50. Follett (R)

LATIN LANGUAGE--GRAMMAR (470)

Allen, Joseph Henry, and Greenough. New Latin grammar. 1931. 5. 80. Ginn

DeWitt, Norman, and others. College Latin. 1954. 5. 00. Scott

Gildersleeve, Basil L., and G. Lodge. Latin grammar. 3rd ed. 3. 75. St. Martins

Lewis, Carolyn D. Medical Latin. 2. 50. Jones, Marshall (R)

LATIN LANGUAGE--GRAMMAR, COMPARATIVE (470)

Buck, Carl D. Comparative grammar of Greek and Latin. 1933. 8. 00. U. of Chicago

LATIN LANGUAGE--HISTORY (470)

Elcock, W. D. Romance languages. il. 1960. 8. 50. Macmillan

LATIN LANGUAGE--PRONUNCIATION (470)

Westaway, F. W. Latin quantity and accent. 1930. 2. 25. Cambridge U. P.

LATIN LANGUAGE--WORD FORMATION (470)

Johnson, Edwin Lee. Latin words of common English. 1931. 4. 00. Heath

LATIN LANGUAGE, MEDIEVAL AND MODERN--DICTIONARIES (470. 019)

Deferrari, Roy J. Latin-English dictionary of St. Thomas Aquinas. 1960. 10. 00. Daughters of St. Paul (R)

LATIN LANGUAGE, MEDIEVAL AND MODERN--GLOSSARIES, VOCABULARIES, ETC. (470)

Cooper, Lane. Concordance of the Latin. Greek and Italian poems of John Milton. 1923. 4. 00. Cornell

Jones, Putnam F. Concordance to the Historia ecclesiastica of Bede. 1929. 10. 00. Mediaeval

LATIN LANGUAGE, MEDIEVAL AND MODERN--GRAMMAR (470)

Grandgent, Charles H. Introduction to vulgar Latin. 1961. 3. 75. Hafner

LATIN LANGUAGE, POSTCLASSICAL--GLOSSARIES, VOCABULARIES, ETC. (470)

Souter, Alexander. Glossary of later Latin to 600 A. D. 1949. 10. 10. Oxford U. P. (R)

LATIN LITERATURE (SELECTIONS, EXTRACTS, ETC.) (870)

Kennedy, Eberhard C. Roman poetry and prose. 1957. 1. 50. Cambridge U. P.

Wright, Frederick A. Book of Latin prose and Latin verse from Cato and Plautus to Bacon and Milton. 2. 00. St. Martins

LATIN LITERATURE--HISTORY AND CRITICISM (870)

D'Alton, J. F. Roman literary theory and criticism. 1962. 10. 00. Russell

Duff, John W. Literary history of Rome. 2 vols. by A. M. Duff. vol. 1, From the origins to the close of the Golden Age. 1960. 8. 75; vol. 2, Silver Age: From Tiberius to Hadrian. 1960. 10. 00. Barnes & Noble

Duff, J. W. Writers of Rome. il. 1923. 1. 20. Oxford U. P.

Hadas, M. History of Latin literature. 1952. 5. 50. Columbia

Hamilton, Edith. Roman way. 1932. 4. 50. Norton

Kennedy, Eberhard C., and George W. White. Roman history, life, and literature. 2. 50. St. Martins

Lockwood, Dean F. Survey of classical Roman literature. 2 vols. 3. 00 ea. U. of Chicago

Lofstedt, Einar. Roman literary portraits. 1958. 4. 00. Oxford U. P.

Mackail, John W. Latin literature. pap. 1. 50. Collier

Reinhold, Meyer. Classics, Greek and Roman: A guide to the humanities. 3. 50. Barron's (R)

LATIN LITERATURE--TRANSLATIONS INTO ENGLISH (870)

Davenport, Basil. Portable Roman reader. 1961. 2. 95. Viking

Guinagh, Kevin, and A. P. Dorjahn. Latin literature in translation. 1952. 6. 00. McKay

Howe, George, and others. Roman literature in translation. 1959. 8. 00. Harper

LATIN LITERATURE, MEDIEVAL AND MODERN--HISTORY AND CRITICISM (870)
Curtius, Ernst Robert. European literature and the Latin middle ages. 1953.
    5.50. Pantheon
Haskins, Charles Homer. Studies in medieval culture. 1958. 4.50. Ungar
LATIN POETRY (COLLECTIONS) (871)
Duff, J. Wight, tr. Minor Latin poets. 3.50. Harvard
Garrod, Heathcote W. Oxford book of Latin verse from the earliest fragments
    to the end of the 5th century. A. D. 1912. in Latin. 5.00. Oxford U. P.
LATIN POETRY--HISTORY AND CRITICISM (871)
Highet, Gilbert. Poets in a landscape. il. 1957. 6.50. Knopf
LATIN POETRY--TRANSLATIONS INTO ENGLISH (871)
Godolphin, F. R. B. Latin poets. 1.95. Modern Lib.
LATIN POETRY, MEDIEVAL AND MODERN--HISTORY AND CRITICISM (871)
Raby, Frederick J. E. History of Christian Latin poetry from the beginnings
    to the close of the Middle Ages. 1953. 6.10. Oxford U. P.
Raby, Frederick J. E. History of secular Latin poetry in the Middle Ages.
    2 vols. 1957. 14.40. Oxford U. P.
Waddell, Helen. Poetry in the Dark Ages. 1958. boards, 1.50. Barnes & Noble
Waddell, Helen. Wandering scholars. 1949. 3.50. Barnes & Noble
LATIN POETRY, MEDIEVAL AND MODERN--TRANSLATIONS INTO ENGLISH
    (871)
Waddell, Helen. Medieval Latin lyrics. 1948. 3.50. Barnes & Noble
LATOURETTE, KENNETH SCOTT, 1884- (922)
Harr, Wilber C. Frontiers of the Christian world mission since 1938. 1962.
    5.00. Harper
LATROBE, BENJAMIN HENRY, 1764-1820 (926)
Hamiln, Talbot. Benjamin Henry Latrobe. 1955. 15.00. Oxford U. P.
LATTIMORE, OWEN, 1900- (928)
Flynn, John T. Lattimore story. 1953. 1.75. Devin
LAUBACH, FRANK CHARLES, 1884- (923.7)
Medary, Marjorie. Each one, teach one: Frank C. Laubach. 1954. 3.75. McKay
LAUD, WILLIAM, ABP. OF CANTERBURY, 1573-1645 (922)
Trevor-Roper, H. R. Archbishop Laud, 1573-1645. 1962. 6.50. Shoe String
LAUE, MAX THEODOR FELIX VON (925)
Frisch, Otto R., and others. Trends in atomic physics. il. 1959. 7.50. Wiley
LAUGHTER (157)
Bergler, Edmund. Laughter and the sense of humor. 1956. 6.50. Grune
Bergson, Henri. Laughter bd. with George Meredith's Essay on comedy. 3.00.
    Smith, Peter
Grotjahn, Martin. Beyond laughter. il. 1957. 6.50. McGraw
Kimmons, C. W. Springs of laughter: Changing theories of laughter from century
    to century. 3.00. Saifer
Swabey, Marie C. Comic laughter. 1961. 5.00. Yale
LAVOISIER, ANTOINE LAURENT, 1743-1794 (925)
Duveen, Denis I., and Herbert S. Klickstein. Bibliography of the works of
    Antoine Laurent Lavoisier, 1743-1794. il. 1954. 40.00. Bentley
French, S. J. Torch and crucible: Life and death of Antoine Lavoisier. 1941.
    4.50. Princeton
Guerlac, Henry. Lavoisier: The crucial year. il. 1961. 4.50. Cornell
McKie, Douglas. Antoine Lavoisier: Scientist, economist, social reformer. il.
    1952. 6.00. Abelard
LAW (340)
Becker, Olga. Master research guide. 1951. 12.50. Bobbs
Frank, Jerome. Law and the modern mind. 1962. pap. 1.65. Putnam
London, Ephraim. World of law. 2 vols. 1960. 17.50. S. and S.
LAW--ADDRESSES, ESSAYS, LECTURES (328.373)
Hand, Learned. Spirit of liberty: Papers and addresses of Learned Hand. by
    Irving Dilliard. 1960. 4.00. Knopf

Henson, Ray D. Landmarks of law. 1960. 8.50. Harper
Holmes, Oliver Wendell. Mind and faith of Justice Holmes. by Max Lerner.
    1954. 2.95. Modern Lib.
Hurst, James W. Law and social process in United States history. 1960. 6.00.
    U. of Mich.
Miller, Perry. Legal mind in America. pap. 1.45. Doubleday
Pound, Roscoe. Formative era of American law. 3.00. Smith, Peter
Radcliffe, Cyril J. Law and its compass. 1960. 4.50. Northwestern U.
LAW--HISTORY AND CRITICISM (340)
Edmunds, Palmer D. Law and civilization. 1959. 6.00. Pub. Affairs
Friedmann, Wolfgang. Law in a changing society. 1959. 8.50. U. of Calif.
Wormser, Rene. Story of law. 1962. 7.50. S. and S.
LAW--PHILOSOPHY (340)
Bentham, Jeremy, and John S. Mill. Utilitarians. 3.50. Smith, Peter
Boorstin, Daniel J. Mysterious science of the law. 4.00. Smith, Peter
Cairns, Huntington. Legal philosophy from Plato to Hegel. 1950. 7.50. Johns
    Hopkins
Cardozo, B. N. Growth of the law. 1924. 3.75. Yale
Friedrich, Carl J. Philosophy of the law in historical perspective. 1958. 5.75.
    U. of Chicago
Hegel, G. W. F. Philosophy of right. by T. M. Knox. 1942. 4.80. Oxford U. P.
Henson, Ray D. Landmarks of law. 1960. 8.50. Harper
Montesquieu, Charles de. Spirit of the laws, (Hafner library of classics no. 9)
    2 vols. in 1. tr. by Thomas Nugent. 1949. pap. 2.95. Hafner
Morris, Clarence. Great legal philosophers. 1958. 10.00. U. of Pa.
Pound, Roscoe. Introduction to the philosophy of law. 1954. 4.00. Yale
LAW--PSYCHOLOGY (347.9)
Dienstein, William. Are you guilty?: An introduction to the administration of
    criminal justice in the United States. 1953. 4.50. Thomas, C. C
Frank, Jerome. Courts on trial. 1949. 6.00. Princeton
LAW--EGYPT (340)
Taubenschlag, Raphael. Law of Greco-Roman Egypt in the light of the Papyri.
    1944. 7.50. Franklin, B.
LAW--GT. BRIT. (346)
Geldart, William M. Elements of English law. by William Holdsworth, and H.
    G. Hanbury. 1959. 1.70. Oxford U. P.
LAW--GT. BRIT.--HISTORY AND CRITICISM (346)
Lovell, Colin R. English constitutional and legal history. 1962. 8.00. Oxford U. P.
Lyon, Bryce. Constitutional and legal history of medieval England. 1960. 7.50.
    Harper
Plucknett, Theodore F. T. Concise history of the common law. 1956. 12.50.
    Little
Winfield, Percy H. Chief sources of English legal history. 1935. 12.50. Franklin,
    B.
LAW--U. S. (345)
Davenport, William H. Voices in court. 1959. 6.95. Macmillan
Frankfurter, Felix. Law and politics. 1962. pap. 1.75. Putnam
Jackson, Percival E. Wisdom of the Supreme Court. 1962. 8.95. U. of Okla. (R)
Lavine, Abraham L. Manual on commercial law. 1958. 13.00. Prentice-Hall
Warren, Charles. Supreme Court in United States history. 2 vols. 1960. boxed
    15.00. Little
LAW--U.S.--HISTORY AND CRITICISM (345)
Hurst, James Willard. Growth of American law: The law makers. 1950. 8.00.
    Little
Pound, Roscoe. Formative era of American law. 3.00. Smith, Peter
LAW--U.S.--POPULAR WORKS (340)
Bernard, Will. Law for the family. 1962. 3.95? Scribner
Ross, Martin J. Handbook of everyday law. 1959. 4.95. Harper

Yeager, Philip B., and John R. Stark. Your inalienable rights. 1960. 5.00.
  Pub. Affairs
LAW, PRIMITIVE (340)
Diamond, A. S. Evolution of law and order. 5.00. Humanities
Malinowski, B. Crime and custom in savage society. 4.00. Humanities
LAW AND ETHICS (174)
Cahn, Edmond N. Moral decision: Right and wrong in the light of American law.
  5.00. Indiana
LAW AND POLITICS (340)
Kirchheimer, O. Political justice. 1961. 8.50. Princeton
LAW ENFORCEMENT (364.44)
Germann, A. C., and others. Introduction to law enforcement. 1962. 7.50.
  Thomas, C. C.
Mather, F. C. Public order in the age of the Chartists. 1959. 6.50. Barnes &
  Noble
LAW IN LITERATURE (809.93)
London, Ephraim. World of law. 2 vols. 1960. 17.50. S. and S.
LAW REFORM (340)
Friedmann, Wolfgang. Law in a changing society. 1959. 8.50. U. of Calif.
LAW REPORTS, DIGESTS, ETC. (340)
Williams, Jerre S. Supreme Court speaks. 1956. 5.95. U. of Tex.
LAWRENCE, DAVID HERBERT, 1885-1930 (823.91)
Freeman, Mary D. H. Lawrence: A basic study of his ideas. 1955. 5.00. U. of
  Fla.
Hoffman, Frederick J., and others. Achievement of D. H. Lawrence. 1953.
  4.00. U. of Okla.
Leavis, F. R. D. H. Lawrence, Novelist. 1956. 5.00. Knopf
Moore, Harry T. Intelligent heart. 1955. 6.50. Farrar, Straus
Murry, John M. Love, freedom and society. 3.75. Hillary'
Nehis, Edward, H. D. H. Lawrence: A composite biography. 3 vols. 1957-59.
  7.50 ea; set, 20.00. U. of Wis.
Vivas, Eliseo. D. H. Lawrence, the failure and the triumph of art. 1960. 4.75.
  Northwestern U.
LAWRENCE, THOMAS EDWARD, 1888-1935 (925)
Nutting, Anthony. Lawrence of Arabia. il. 1962. 5.00. Potter, C. N.
LAWYERS (340)
Blaustein, Albert P., and others. American lawyer. 1954. 5.50. U. of Chicago
Nourse, William B., and Alan E. So you want to be a lawyer. 1959. 3.50. Harper
LAWYERS--CORRESPONDENCE, REMINISCENCES, ETC. (340)
Darrow, Clarence. Story of my life. 1957. pap. 1.95. Grosset
Frankfurter, Felix. Felix Frankfurter reminisces. by Harlan B. Phillips. 5.00.
  Reynal
Mortlock, Bill. Lawyer, heal thyself! 1959. 3.95. Macmillan
LEADERSHIP (301.15)
American Academy of Arts and Sciences. Excellence and leadership in democracy.
  1961. 1.75. Am. Acad. of Arts & Sci.
Bass, Bernard M. Leadership, psychology, and organizational behavior. 1960.
  6.50. Harper
Biddle, William W. Cultivation of community leaders. 1953. 3.00. Harper
Cartwright, Dorwin, and Alvin Zander. Group dynamics: Research and theory.
  1960. 7.25. Harper
Dupuy, Richard E., and Trevor N. Brave men and great captains. 1959. 5.95.
  Harper
Fisher, Margaret. Leadership and intelligence. 1953. 3.75. T. C.
Fletcher, Cyril S. Education for public responsibility. 1961. bds. 4.50. Norton
Fletcher, Cyril S. Education: The challenge ahead. 1962. bds. 4.50. Norton
Gaulle, Charles de. Edge of the sword. tr. by Gerard Hopkins. 1960. 3.50.
  Criterion

Graubard, Stephen R., and Gerard Holton. Excellence and leadership in a
  democracy. 1962. 4.50. Columbia
Hegarty, Edward J. How to run a meeting. 1947. 4.00. McGraw
Hunter, Floyd. Community power structure. 1953. 5.00. U. of N. C.
Hunter, Floyd. Top leadership, U. S. A. il. 1959. 6.00. U. of N. C.
Jennings, Eugene E. Anatomy of leadership. 1960. 5.00. Harper
Roberts, Dorothy M. Leadership of teenage groups. 1950. 3.50. Assn. Press
Selznich, Philip. Leadership in administration: A sociological interpretation.
  1957. 4.00. Harper
Sheppard, John B. President's guide to club and organization management and
  meetings. 1961. 12.50. Hawthorn
Tannenbaum, R., and others. Leadership and organization: A behavioral
  science approach. 1961. 7.50. McGraw
Uris, Auren. How to be a successful leader. 1953. 4.95. McGraw
Urwick, L. F. Leadership in the twentieth century. 1957. 2.75. Pitman
White, Ralph K., and Ronald O. Lippitt. Autocracy and democracy. 1960. 6.00.
  Harper
Wilson, Woodrow. Leaders of men. by T. H. Vail Motter. 1952. 2.00. Princeton
LEAGUE OF NATIONS (341.12)
Carr, Edward H. International relations between the two world wars 1919-1939.
  2.25. St. Martins
Daniels, Josephus. Wilson era: Years of war and after, 1917-1923. (Autobiography
  vol. 5) 1.30. U. of N. C.
Walters, F. P. History of the League of Nations. 1 vol. 6.00. Oxford U. P. (R)
LEAGUE OF NATIONS--BIBLIOGRAPHY (341.12)
Aufricht, H. Guide to League of Nations publication. 1951. 12.50. Columbia (R)
LEARNING, PSYCHOLOGY OF (154.4)
Brueckner, Leo J., and Guy L. Bond. Diagnosis and treatment of learning diffi-
  culties. il. 1955. 6.00. Appleton
Crow, Lester D., and Alice. Human development and learning. 6.25. Am. Bk.
  Co.
Deese, James E. Psychology of learning. il. 1958. 6.95. McGraw
Guzie, Tad. Analogy of learning. 1960. 5.00? Sheed
Hilgard, Ernest R., and Donald G. Marquis. Conditioning and learning. by
  Gregory A. Kimble. il. 6.75. Appleton
Hilgard, Ernest R. Theories of learning. il. 1948. 6.00. Appleton
Johnson, George O., and Kathryn A. Blake. Learning performance of retarded
  and normal children. il. 1960. 5.00. Syracuse
Kingsley, Howard. Nature and conditions of learning. by Ralph Garry. 1957.
  10.00. Prentice-Hall
Koffka, Kurt. Growth of the mind. 6.00. Humanities
Meredith, Patrick. Learning, remembering, and knowing. 1961. 3.50. Assn. Pr.
Mowrer, Orval H. Learning theory and behavior. 1960. 7.50. Wiley
Mowrer, Orval H. Learning theory and personality dynamics. 1950. 12.00. Ronald
Murphy, Gardner. Freeing intelligence through teaching. 1961. 2.95. Harper
Pintner, Rudolf, and others. Educational psychology. (College outline ser.).
  1956. pap. 1.50. Barnes & Noble
Russell, W. Ritchie. Brain, memory, learning: A neurologist's view. 1959.
  5.00. Oxford U. P.
Sharpe, Joseph F. Retention of meaningful material. 1952. 1.50. Catholic U. of
  Am. Pr.
LEARNING AND SCHOLARSHIP (001)
Barzun, Jacques. House of intellect. 1959. 5.00. 1.75. Harper
Emerson, Ralph Waldo. American scholar. il. 1955. limited ed. 10.00. Cornell
Jones, Howard M. One great society. 1959. 4.50. Harcourt
Knapp, Robert H., and Joseph J. Grennbaum. Younger American scholar: His
  collegiate origins. 1953. 3.00; Published in cooperation with the Wesleyan
  University Press. U. of Chicago

Laistner, M. L. W. Thought and letters in Western Europe. 1957. 5.00. Cornell

Sandys, John E. History of classical scholarship. 3 vols. 1958. 25.00. Hafner

LEAVES (581)

Marx, David S. American book of the woods. 1940. 2.50. Botanic

LEBANON (956.92)

Hitti, Philip Khuri. Lebanon in history. 1957. 9.00. St. Martins

Qubain, Fahim. Crisis in Lebanon. 5.00. Middle East Inst.

LECOMTE DU NOUY, PIERRE, 1883-1947 (923)

Lecomte du Nouy, Mary B. H. Road to human destiny: The life of Pierre Lecomte du Nouy. 1955. 5.00. McKay

LEDERER, JOHN (923.9)

Lederer, John. Discoveries of John Lederer in Virginia and Caroline, 1672. by
William P. Cumming. 1958. 5.00. U. of Va.

LEE, ANN, 1736-1784 (922.88)

Joy, Arthur F. Queen of the Shakers. 3.95. Denison

LEE, ROBERT EDWARD, 1807-1870 (923.5)

Davis, Burke. Gray fox: Robert E. Lee and the Civil War. il. 1956. 6.75.
Rinehart

Freeman, Douglas Southall. Lee of Virginia. il. 1958. 4.50. Scribner

Miers, Earl Schenck. Robert E. Lee. 1956. 3.00. Knopf

LEECHES (583.28)

Mann, Kenneth H. Leeches (Hirudinea) their structure, physiology, ecology and
embryology. il. 1962. 7.50. Pergamon

LEEUWENHOEK, ANTHONY VAN, 1632-1723 (925)

Dobell, Clifford. Antony Van Leeuwenhoek and his "Little Animals" 10.00. Russell

Schierbeek, A. Measuring the invisible world: The life and works of Antoni van
Leeuwenhoek. 1959. 5.00. Abelard

LEGAL ETHICS (174)

Drinker, H. S. Legal ethics. 1953. 4.00. Columbia

LEGAL RESEARCH (340)

Price, Miles O., and Harry Bitner. Effective legal research. 1953. 7.50.
Little

LEGAL SECRETARIES (651.3741)

Leslie, Louis A., and Kenneth Coffin. Handbook for the legal secretary. 1958.
7.50. McGraw

Miller, Besse M. Legal secretary's handbook. 1953. 7.50. Prentice-Hall (R)

Prentice-Hall Editorial Staff. Legal secretary's encyclopedia dictionary. 1962.
7.50. Prentice-Hall

LE GALLIENNE, EVA, 1899- (927)

Le Gallienne, Eva. With a quiet heart. 1953. 4.50. Viking

LEGENDS (398.2)

Hazeltine, Alice I. Hero tales from many lands. il. 1961. 5.95. Abingdon

White, Anne T. Golden treasury of myths and legends. il. 1959. 5.00; lib. bdg.
4.99 net. Golden Press

LEGENDS--HISTORY AND CRITICISM (398.2)

Rudwin, Maximilian J. Devil in legend and literature. 1931. 5.00. Open Ct.

LEGENDS, AMERICAN (398.2)

Dobie, J. Frank. Apache gold and Yaqui silver. il. 1939. 6.50. Little

Dobie, J. Frank. Coronado's children. 1.95. Grosset

Rutledge, Archibald. From the hills to the sea. 1958. 4.50. Bobbs

LEGENDS, MEXICAN (398)

Dobie, J. Frank. Tongues of the Monte. 1947. 6.00. Little

LEGISLATION--U.S. (345)

Auerbach, Carl A., and others. Legal process: An introduction to decision-
making by judicial, legislative, executive, and administrative agencies. 1961.
10.00. Chandler Pub.

Galloway, George B. Legislative process in Congress. 1953. 6.50. Crowell

Walker, Harvey. Legislative process. 1948. 6.00. Ronald

LEGISLATIVE BODIES (328.3)
Bentham, Jeremy. Bentham's handbook of political fallacies. by Harold A.
Larrabee. 1952. 4.75. Johns Hopkins
Johnson, Alvin W. Unicameral legislature. 1938. 2.00. U. of Minn.
Morris-Jones, W. H. Parliament in India. 1956. 8.50. U. of Pa.
Wahike, John C., and Heinz Eulau. Legislative behavior. 1959. 7.50. Free Press
LEGISLATIVE POWER (353.02)
Galloway, George B. Legislative process in Congress. 1953. 6.50. Crowell
Horn, Stephen. Cabinet and Congress. 1960. 6.00. Columbia
LEIBNIZ, GOTTFRIED WILHELM, FREIHERR VON, 1646-1716 (921.3)
Russell, Bertrand. Critical exposition of the philosophy of Leibnitz. 4.50.
Humanities
LEICESTER, ROBERT DUDLEY, EARL OF, 1532 (?)-1588 (923.2)
Rosenberg, Eleanor. Leicester, patron of letters. 1955. 6.00. Columbia
LEIF ERIKSSON
Goodwin, William B. Truth about Leif Ericsson and the Greenland voyages. il.
6.00. Forum
LEISURE (331.84)
American Association for Health, Physical Education and Recreation. Leisure
and the schools, yearbook. 1961. 3.75. Am. Assn. for Health, Phys. Ed. &
Rec.
Anderson, Nels. Work and leisure. 1962. 5.00. Free Press
Denney, Reuel. Astonished muse. 1957. 4.50. U. of Chicago
Kaplan, M. Leisure in America: A social inquiry. 1960. 7.50. Wiley
Larrabee, Eric, and Rolf Meyersohn. Mass leisure. 1958. 6.00. Free Press
Neumeyer, Martin H., and E. S. Leisure and recreation. 1958. 6.00. Ronald
Pieper, Josef. Leisure, the basis of culture. 1952. 3.00. Pantheon
Ranganathan, S. R. Education for leisure. 1961. 4.75. Taplinger
LEISURE CLASS (323.3)
Veblen, Thorstein. Theory of the leisure class. 1934. 1.95. Modern Lib.
LEMAITRE, FREDERICK, 1800-1876 (925)
Baldick, Robert. Life and times of Frederick Lemaitre. 1959. 5.00. Oxford U. P.
LENIN, VLADIMIR ILICH, 1870-1924 (923.1)
Page, Stanley W. Lenin and world revolution. 1959. 5.00. N. Y. U.
Treadgold, Donald W. Lenin and his rivals. 1955. 6.00. Praeger
Wolfe, Bertram D. Three who made a revolution. 1960. 7.50. Dial
LENINGRAD (947.45)
Goure, Leon. Siege of Leningrad. il. 1962. 6.95. Stanford
LENNOX, MRS. CHARLOTTE (RAMSAY) 1720-1804 (928)
Maynadier, Gustavus H. First American novelist? il. 1940. 1.25. Harvard
LENT (264)
Fairweather, Eugene R. Meaning and message of Lent. 1962. bds. 3.00. Harper
Hole, Christina. Easter and its customs. 11. 1961. bds. 2.50. Barrows
Wallis, Charles L. Lenten-Easter sourcebook. 1961. 2.95. Abingdon
LENT--PRAYER-BOOKS AND DEVOTIONS (242.34)
Bayne, Stephen F., Jr. In the sight of the Lord. 1958. 2.50. Harper
LEO XIII, POPE, 1810-1903 (922.21)
Burton, K. Leo XIII: The first modern pope. 1962. 3.95. McKay
Gargan, Edward T. Leo XIII and the modern world. 1961. 4.50. Sheed
Kiefer, William J., Brother. Leo XIII. il. 1961. 3.95. Bruce
LEONARDO DA VINCI, 1452-1519 (927)
Clark, Kenneth. Leonardo da Vinci. 1952. 7.50. Cambridge U. P.
Goldscheider, Ludwig. Leonardo da Vinci: Life and work. 1959. il. 9.50. N. Y.
Graphic
Hart, Ivor B. World of Leonardo da Vinci: Man of science, engineer and dreamer
of flight. il. 1962. 7.95. Viking
Leonardo. All the paintings of Leonardo. by Constantino Baroni. il. 1961. 3.95.
Hawthorn

LEOPARDS (599. 7442)
Corbett, Jim. Man-eaters of India. 1957. 5.00. Oxford U. P.
LEOPOLD II, EMPEROR OF GERMANY, 1747-1792 (923.1)
Wangermann, Ernest. From Joseph II to the Jacobin trials. 1959. 4.00. Oxford
  U. P.
LEPROSY (616. 998)
Burgess, Perry. Who walk alone. il. 1940. 4.25. Holt
Cochrane, R. G. Leprosy in theory and practice. il. 1958. 15.00. Williams &
  Wilkins
Farrow, John. Damien the leper. 3.25. Sheed
Martin, Betty. Miracle at Carville. by Evelyn Wells. 1950. 3.95. Doubleday
LERNER, MAX, 1902- (928)
Hook, Sidney. Reason, social myths and democracy. 4.00. Humanities
LESLIE, MIRIAM FLORENCE (FOLLINE) SQUIER, d. 1914 (928)
Stern, Madeleine B. Purple passage: Life of Mrs. Frank Leslie. il. 1953. 3.75.
  U. of Okla.
LESSING, GOTTHOLD EPHRAIM, 1729-1781 (928)
Garland, H. A. Lessing, founder of modern German literature. 1962. 5.00.
  Saifer
LE TOURNEAU, ROBERT GILMOUR, 1888- (926)
LeTourneau, Robert G. Mover of men and mountains. il. 1960. 3.95. Prentice-
Hall
LETTER-WRITING (808.6)
Belson, David, and Ruth. How to write social letters for all occasions. 1961.
  3.95. Citadel
Butterfield, William H. Effective personal letters. 1951. 5.95. Prentice-Hall
Opdycke, John B. Take a letter please! il. 1944. 3.00. Funk
Sheff, Alexander L. , and Edna Ingalls. How to write letters for all occasions.
  by Mary S. Allen. 2.50. Doubleday
Taintor, Sarah A. , and Kate M. Monro. Handbook of social correspondence.
  7th ed. 5.50. Macmillan
Watson, Lillian E. Standard book of letter writing and correct social forms.
  1958. 5.95. Prentice-Hall
LETTERING (745.6)
Ballinger, R. A. Lettering art in modern use. 1952. 15.00. Reinhold
Benson, John H. , and Arthur Graham Carey. Elements of lettering. 1950. 7.75.
  McGraw
Bergling, John M. Art alphabets and lettering. 1948. 5.00. Bergling
Biegeleisen, J. I. ABC of lettering. 1958. spiral bd. 7.50. Harper
Buckley, Robert D. Basic guide to lettering. il. 1951. 5.00. Chilton
Durer, Albrecht. On the just shaping of letters: From the applied geometry of
  Albrecht Durer. tr. by R. T. Nichol. in prep. Dover
Holub, Rand. Lettering simplified. 3.75. Watson
Hornung, Clarence P. Lettering from A to Z. 1954. 3.95. Tudor
Hunt, W. Ben, and Ed. C. 101 alphabets. 1954. 3.75. Bruce
Laker, Russell. Anatomy of lettering. il. 1960. 6.50. Viking
Wade, Cecil. Modern lettering and layout. 1950. 5.75. Pitman
LETTERS--COLLECTIONS (808.86)
Schuster, M. Lincoln. Treasury of the world's great letters. il. 1940. 5.95.
  S. and S.
LEUCOCYTES (612.112)
Ciba Foundation Study Groups. Biological activity of the leucocyte. 1961. 2.50.
  Little
LEUKEMIA (616.15)
Hayhoe, F. G. J. Leukaemia. 1960. 17.50. Little
LEUTZE, EMANUEL GOTTLIEB, 1816-1868 (927)
Hutton, Ann H. Portrait of patriotism. il. 1959. 2.75. Chilton
LEVANT (956)
Joy, Charles R. Young people of the Eastern Mediterranean. 1959. 3.50. Duell

LEVANT--ANTIQUITIES (956)
Deuel, Leo. Treasures of time. il. 1961. 6.00. World Pub.
LEVANT--DESCRIPTION AND TRAVEL (956)
Bamm, Peter. Early sites of Christianity. 1957. 4.50. Pantheon
Brittain, Mary Z. Arab lands. il. 1947. 2.50. Holiday
Clemens, Samuel Langhorne. Traveling with the Innocents Abroad: Mark Twain's
     original reports from Europe and the Holy Land. by Daniel Morley McKeithan.
     1958. 5.00. U. of Okla.
Cressey, George B. Crossroads: Land and life in southwest Asia. il. 1960.
     12.00. Lippincott
Curzon, Robert, Jr. Visits to monasteries in the Levant. il. 4.00. Cornell
Kinglake, Alexander W. Eothen. 1.95. Dutton
Morton, Henry V. In the steps of St. Paul. il. 1936. 6.00. Dodd
LEVANT--DESCRIPTION AND TRAVEL--VIEWS (956)
Pernoud, Regine. In the steps of the crusaders. 1960. 8.50. Hastings
LEVANT--RELIGION (956)
Albright, William Foxwell. Archaeology and the religion of Israel. 2nd ptg. 1941.
     3.50. Johns Hopkins
LEVELLERS (942)
Frank, J. Levellers--A history of the writings of three seventeenth-century
     social democrats: John Lilburne, Richard Overton, and William Walwyn. 1955.
     5.00. Harvard
LEWIS, CECIL DAY, 1904- (928)
Day Lewis, C. Buried day. il. 1960. 3.95. Harper
LEWIS, CLIVE STAPLES, 1898- (928)
Moorman, Charles. Arthurian triptych: Mythic materials in Charles Williams,
     C. S. Lewis, and T. S. Eliot. (Perspectives in criticism, No. 5) 1960. 3.50.
     U. of Calif.
LEWIS, MERIWEATHER, 1774-1809 (923.9)
Bakeless, John E. Lewis and Clark, partners in discovery. il. 1962. pap. 1.95.
     Apollo
LEWIS, SINCLAIR, 1885-1951 (928)
Grebstein, Sheldon. Sinclair Lewis. 3.50. Twayne
Lewis, Grace Hegger. With love from Gracie. 1956. 5.75. Harcourt
Schorer, Mark. Sinclair Lewis: A collection of critical essays. 1962. 3.95.
     Prentice-Hall
Schorer, Mark. Sinclair Lewis: An American life. 1961. 10.00. McGraw
LEWIS, WYNDHAM, 1886-1957 (927)
Kenner, Hugh. Wyndham Lewis. 1954. 2.50. New Directions
LEWIS AND CLARK EXPEDITION (917.8)
Burroughs, Raymond D. Natural history of the Lewis and Clark Expedition.
     1961. 7.50. Mich. State
De Voto, Bernard. Journals of Lewis and Clark. 1953. 6.50. Houghton
Lewis, Meriwether. Lewis and Clark expedition. 3 vols. il. 1961. 12.50.
     Lippincott
LEXINGTON (U.S. AIRCRAFT CARRIER, FIRST OF THE NAME) (940.53)
Johnston, Stanley. Queen of the flat-tops: The U.S.S. Lexington and the Coral
     Sea Battle. 5.00. Dutton
LI PO, 705-762 (895)
Waley, Arthur. Poetry and career of Li Po: 701-762 A.D. 1950. 3.00. Macmillan
LIBEL AND SLANDER (070.13)
Spring, Samuel. Risks and rights in publishing, television, radio, motion
     pictures and the theatre. rev. 1956. 10.00. Norton
LIBERALISM (301.15)
Bratton, Fred G. Legacy of the liberal spirit. 3.75. Smith, Peter
Bullock, Alan, and Maurice Shock. Liberal tradition: From Fox to Keynes. 1957.
     4.50. N. Y. U.
De Ruggiero, Guido. History of European liberalism. 4.50. Smith, Peter

Ekirch, Arthur A., Jr. Decline of American liberalism. 1955. 7.50. McKay

Hartz, Louis. Liberal tradition in America. 1955. 4.75. Harcourt

Laski, Harold J. Rise of European liberalism. 3.00. Humanities

Lippmann, Walter. Good society. 1943. 5.00. Little

Panikkar, K. M. In defense of liberalism. 1962. 4.50? Taplinger

Perkins, Dexter. American way. 1959. pap. 1.45. Cornell

Ruggiero, Guido de. History of European liberalism. tr. by R. G. Collingwood. 4.50. Smith, Peter

Schapiro, J. Salwyn. Liberalism. 1953. pap. 1.25. Van Nostrand

Schlesinger, Arthur, Jr. Vital center. 3.50. 1962. pap. 1.55. Houghton

Taylor, Overton H. Classical liberalism, Marxism, and the twentieth century. 1960. 3.50. Harvard

Watkins, Frederick Mundell. Political tradition of the West: A study in the development of modern liberalism. 1948. 5.50. Harvard

Wittmer, Felix. Conquest of the American mind. 1956. 5.00. Forum

LIBERTY (323.4)

Acton, John E. Essays on freedom and power. 1955. pap. 1.55. Meridian

Adler, Mortimer J. Idea of freedom. 1958. 2 vols. 7.50 ea. Doubleday

Barth, Alan. Price of liberty. 1961. 4.50. Viking

Chafee, Zechariah, Jr. Blessings of liberty. 1956. 5.00. Lippincott

Commager, Henry Steele. Freedom, loyalty, dissent. 1954. 3.75. Oxford U. P.

Davenport, Russell W. Dignity of man. 1955. 5.00. Harper

Dirksen, Cletus F. Catholic social principles. 1961. 4.00. Herder

Fromm, Erich. Escape from freedom. 3.75. 1941. Rinehart

Fromm, Erich. Sane society. 1955. 5.00. Rinehart

Handlin, Oscar, and Mary F. Dimensions of liberty. 1961. 3.75. Harvard

Hayek, Friedrich A. von. Constitution of liberty. 1960. buck. 7.50. U. of Chicago

Hook, Sidney. Political power and personal freedom. 1959. 7.50. Criterion

Locke, John. On politics and education. 1947. 1.75. Van Nostrand

Locke, John. Two treatises of government. by Peter Laslett. 1960. 9.50. Cambridge U. P.

Maritain, Jacques. Rights of man. 1.50. Hillary

Meyer, Frank. Defense of freedom. 1962. 4.00. Regnery

Mill, John S. On liberty: Representative government; The subjection of women. 2.25. Oxford U. P.

Muller, Herbert J. Freedom in the ancient world. il. 1961. 7.50. Harper

Oppenheim, Felix E. Dimensions of freedom. 1961. 6.50. St. Martins

Pegis, Anton C. Christian philosophy and intellectual freedom. 1960. 2.75. Bruce

Rossiter, Clinton. Seedtime of the republic. 1953. 7.50. Harcourt

Stein, Maurice R., and others. Identity and anxiety: Survival of the person in mass society. 7.50. Free Press

Trueblood, Elton. Declaration of freedom. 1955. 1.50. Harper

Trueblood, Elton. Life we prize. 1951. 3.00. Harper

Ward, Barbara. Faith and freedom. 1954. 5.50. Norton

LIBERTY OF CONSCIENCE (262.8)

D'Arcy, Eric. Conscience and its right to freedom. 1962. bds. 3.50. Sheed

LIBERTY OF SPEECH (323.4)

Chafee, Zechariah, Jr. Free speech in the United States. 1941. 8.00. Harvard

Drinker, Henry S. Some observations on the Four Freedoms of the First Amendment. 1957. 3.00. Boston U.

Hudon, Edward G. Freedom of speech and press. 1962. 6.00. Pub. Affairs

Jones, Howard Mumford. Primer of intellectual freedom. 1949. 3.00. Harvard

Levy, Leonard W. Legacy of suppression. 1960. 6.50. Harvard

Meiklejohn, Alexander. Political freedom. 1960. 3.50. Harper

Rogge, O. John. First and the fifth, with some excursions into others. 1960. 8.50. Nelson

LIBRARIANS (023)
Downs, Robert B. Status of American college and university librarians. A. C. R. L.
   monograph no. 22. 1958. pap. 3. 50. A. L. A.
Marshall, John D. , comp. American library history reader. 1961. 9. 00. Shoe
   String
LIBRARIES (020)
Downs, Robert B. American library resources. 7. 00; suppl. 1950-1961. A. L. A.
Leigh, Robert Devore. Public library in the United States. 1950. 4. 75. Columbia
Union list of serials in libraries of the United States and Canada. 2nd suppl. 1944-
   1949. 1954. rates on request. Wilson
Wright, Wyllis E. , and Phyllis Steckler. Bowker annual of library and book
   trade information. rev. annually. 6. 95. net postpaid. Bowker
LIBRARIES-- CENSORSHIP (025. 21)
American Library Association. Freedom of book selection. 1954. pap. 3. 50.
   A. L. A.
Fiske, Marjorie. Book selection and censorship; a study of school and public
   libraries in California. 1959. 3. 75. U. of Calif.
LIBRARIES--DIRECTORIES (027. 073)
Steiner-Prag, Eleanor F. American library directory. 1962. 25. 00. net postpaid.
   Bowker (R)
Wright, Wyllis E. , and Phyllis Steckler. Book world almanac. 1961. 6. 95. net
   postpaid. Bowker
LIBRARIES--HISTORY (027)
Daniel, Hawthorne. Public libraries for everyone. 3. 95. Doubleday
Hessel, Alfred. History of libraries. tr. by Rueben Peiss. 1955. 3. 50. Scarecrow
Johnson, E. D. Communication: A concise introduction to the history of the
   alphabet, printing, books and libraries. 1960. 5. 00. Scarecrow
Morison, Samuel E. Intellectual life in colonial New England. 1956. 4. 95. N. Y. U.
LIBRARIES--REFERENCE DEPT. (027)
Hutchins, Margaret. Introduction to reference work. 1944. 3. 50. A. L. A.
Shores, Louis. Basic reference sources. 1954. 6. 25. A. L. A.
LIBRARIES--SPECIAL COLLECTIONS (027)
Ash, Lee. Subject collections: A guide to special book collections in libraries.
   1961. 17. 00 net postpaid. Bowker (R)
LIBRARIES, UNIVERSITY AND COLLEGE (027. 7)
Farber, Evan Ira. Classified list of periodicals for college library. 1957. 5. 00.
   Faxon (R)
Knapp, Patricia. College teaching and the college library. 3. 00. A. L. A.
Lyle, Guy R. , and others. Administration of the college library. 1961. 7. 00.
   Wilson
Wilson, Louis R. , and M. F. Tauber. University library. 1956. 9. 00. Columbia
LIBRARIES, JUNIOR COLLEGE (027. 7)
Trinkner, Charles L. , ed. Basic Books for Junior College Libraries: 20, 000
   Vital Titles. 1963. Colonial Press
Trinkner, Charles L. , ed. Library Services for Junior Colleges. in prep.
LIBRARIES AND PICTURES (027)
Ireland, Norma O. Picture file in school, college and public libraries. 1952.
   4. 50. Faxon
LIBRARIES AND READERS (028)
Aldrich, E. V. Using books and libraries. 1960. pap. 2. 25. Prentice-Hall
Alexander, Carter, and Arvid J. Burke. How to locate educational information
   and data. 1958. 6. 25. T. C.
Collison, Robert L. Library assistance to readers. 1956. 2. 75. De Graff
Russell, Harold, and others. Use of books and libraries. il. 1958. 1. 75. U. of
   Minn.
LIBRARY ADMINISTRATION (025)
Metcalf, Keyes D. Studies in library administrative problems. 1961. 5. 00.
   Rutgers

Shaffer, Kenneth R. Book collection: Policy case studies in public academic libraries. 1961. 4.75. Shoe String
Shaffer, Kenneth R. Twenty-five short cases in library personnel administration. 1959. 3.50. Shoe String
Stebbins, Kathleen B. Personnel administration in libraries. 1958. 6.00. Scarecrow
LIBRARY SCIENCE (020)
Asheim, Lester. Persistent issues in American librarianship. 1961. 3.75. U. of Chicago
Asheim, Lester, and others. Humanities and the library: Problems of the interpretation, evaluation and use of library materials. 1957. 5.00. A.L.A.
Bonn, George S. Training laymen in use of the library. bd. with Margaret S. Bryant's Bibliographies, abstracts and indexes. 1960. 5.00. Rutgers
Esdaile, Arundell, and Roy Stokes. Student's manual of bibliography. il. 1955. 5.00. Barnes & Noble
Marshall, John D. Of, for and by librarians. 1960. 7.00. Shoe String
Marshall, John D., and others. Books, libraries, librarians. 1955. 6.00. Shoe String
Ranganathan, S. R. Library manual. 1962. 6.75. Taplinger
Tauber, M. F. Technical services in libraries. 1954. 7.50. Columbia
LIBRARY SCIENCE--BIBLIOGRAPHY (020)
Library literature. 8. vols., 1936-1960. Sold on service basis. Wilson (R)
LIBRARY SCIENCE--DICTIONARIES, VOCABULARIES, ETC. (020)
American Library Association. Glossary of library terms. 1943. 3.50. A.L.A.
Landau, Thomas. Encyclopaedia of librarianship. 1958. 10.00. Hafner (R)
LIBRETTISTS (782)
Ewen, David. Complete book of the American musical theatre. il. 1959. 7.50; with Book of European light opera, in slip case. 13.95. Holt, Rinehart & Winston
LICHENS (589.1)
Alexopoulos, C. J. Introductory mycology. 1952. 8.50. Wiley
Howard, Grace E. Lichens of the State of Washington. 1951. pap. 3.00. U. of Wash.
Wiley, Farida A. Mosses and lichens. 1962. 10.00. Devin
LIFE (111)
Bergson, Henri L. Creative evolution. il. 1944. 1.95. Modern Lib.
Frank, Waldo. Rediscovery of man. 1958. 6.95. Braziller
Hocking, William Ernest. Meaning of immortality in human experience. 1957. 3.50. Harper
Koren, Henry J. Introduction to the philosophy of animate nature. 1955. 4.00. Herder
Lindbergh, Anne Morrow. Gift from the sea. 1955. 2.95. Pantheon
Mayer, Charles L. Sensation: The origin of life. tr. by Harold A. Larrabee. 1961. 3.50. Antioch
Mumford, Lewis. Conduct of life. 1951. 6.75. 1960. Harcourt
Sandbeck, H. C. Nature and destiny. 1959. 6.00. Humanities
Schweitzer, Albert. Animal world of Albert Schweitzer. by Charles R. Joy. il. 1962. 3.75. Smith, Peter
Steiner, Rudolf. Philosophy of spiritual activity and truth and science. 5.75. Steiner
Tolstoy, Leo. On life, and Essays on religion. tr. by Aylmer Maude. 2.75. Oxford U. P.
Wuellner, Bernard. Christian philosophy of life. 1957. 4.25. Bruce
LIFE--ORIGIN (575)
Florkin, Marcel. Aspects of the origin of life. 1960. 5.00. Pergamon
Rutten, M. G. Geological aspects of the origin of life on earth. 1962. 4.50. Am. Elsevier
LIFE (BIOLOGY) (574)

Agar, W. E. Contribution to the theory of the living organism. 1952. 5.50.
  Cambridge U. P.
Asimov, Isaac. Wellsprings of life. 1960. 3.75. Abelard
Berrill, N. J. You and the universe. 1958. 3.50. Dodd
Butler, John A. V. Inside the living cell. il. 1959. 3.50. Basic Books
Darlington, C. D. Facts of life. il. 1953. 8.00. Macmillan
Ludwig, Arnold M. Mystery of life. 1961. 5.75. Thomas, C. C.
MacIver, Robert M. Life: Its dimensions and its bounds. 1960. 3.50. Harper
Scientific American. Physics and chemistry of life. by the Editors of Scientific
  American. 1956. 1.45. S. and S.
Waddington, C. H. Nature of life. 1962. 4.00. Antheneum
LIFE ON OTHER PLANETS (523.43)
Gatland, Kenneth W., and Derek D. Dempster. Inhabited universe. il. 1958.
  3.95. McKay
Norman, Ernest. Truth about Mars. 1.50. DeVorss
Rubowsky, John. Is anybody out there? 1962. 3.95. Walker
LIFE-SAVING (614.81)
American Red Cross. Life saving and water safety. 1956. pap. 0.75. Doubleday
Silvia, Charles E. Lifesaving and water safety instruction. 1958. 4.50; 12 for
  45.00. Assn. Pr.
LIGATURE (SURGERY) (617.9178)
Bragg, William. Universe of light. 4.00. Smith, Peter
Ditchburn, R. W. Light. il. 1952. 9.00. Wiley
Dogigli, Johanns. Magic of rays. by Charles Fullman. il. 1960. 5.75. Knopf
Lyon, Kenneth W., and Donald W. Scott. Light. 1960. 3.50. St. Martins
Reinfeld, Fred. Rays: visible and invisible. il. 1958. 3.95. Sterling
LIGHTING (628.9)
Allphin, Willard. Primer of lamps and lighting. il. 1959. 10.00. Chilton
LIGHTNING (551.56)
Viemeister, Peter E. Lightning book. il. 1961. 4.50. Doubleday
LIMERICKS (808.17)
Cerf, Bennett A. Out on a limerick. 1960. half cl. 2.95. Harper
Untermeyer, Louis. Lots of limericks. il. 1961. bds. 2.75. Doubleday
LIMNOLOGY (551.48)
Coker, Robert Ervin. Streams, lakes, ponds. 1954. 6.00. U. of N. C.
Welch, Paul S. Limnology. il. 1952. 11.00. McGraw
LINCOLN, ABRAHAM, PRES., U.S. 1809-1865 (923.173)
Barton, William E. Lincoln at Gettysburg. il. 4.00. Smith, Peter
Barzun, Jacques. Lincoln the literary genius. 1960. limited ed. 5.00; leather,
  autographed ed. 12.50. Schori
Basler, Roy P., and others. Enduring Lincoln. by Norman A. Graebner. 1959.
  3.00. U. of Ill.
Bruce, Robert V. Lincoln and the tools of war. 1956. 6.00. Bobbs
Canby, Courtlandt. Lincoln and the Civil War. 1960. 5.00. Braziller
Current, Richard N. Lincoln nobody knows. 1958. 5.50. McGraw
Donald, David. Lincoln reconsidered. 1956. 3.50. Knopf
Fehrenbacher, Don E. Prelude to greatness: Lincoln in the 1850's. 1962. 4.75.
  Stanford
Hayes, Melvin L. Mr. Lincoln runs for president. 1960. 5.00. Citadel
Hendrick, B. J. Lincoln's war cabinet. 3.50. Smith, Peter
Herndon, William H., and Jesse W. Weik. Life of Lincoln. 1.95. World Pub.
Lincoln, Abraham. Lincoln encyclopedia. by Archer H. Shaw. 4.95. Macmillan
Nevins, Allan. Emergence of Lincoln. 2 vols. vol. 1, Douglas, Buchanan, and
  party chaos, 1857-1859; vol. 2, Prologue to civil war, 1859-1861. il. 1950. 7.50
  ea. Scribner
Nevins, Allan, and Irving Stone. Lincoln: A contemporary portrait. 1962. 4.50.
  Doubleday
Newman, Ralph G. Lincoln for the ages. 1960. 5.95. Doubleday

Sandburg, Carl. Abraham Lincoln: The prairie years and the war years. The complete life of Abraham Lincoln. 6 vols. il. boxed. 60.00. Harcourt

Thomas, Benjamin P. Abraham Lincoln. il. 1952. 6.50. Knopf

Tilley, John Shipley. Lincoln takes command. 1958. 5.00. U. of N. C.

Williams, Kenneth P. Lincoln finds a general. 5 vols. vol. 1 and 2. Military study of the Civil War, Fort Sumter to Gettysburg, 1949. 7.50 ea; vol. 3. Grant's first year in the West, 1952; vol. 4. Iuka to Vicksburg. 1956; vol. 5. Prelude to Chattanooga. 1959. 8.50 ea. Macmillan

Williams, T. Harry. Lincoln and his generals. il. 1952. 5.75. Knopf

LINCOLN, ABRAHAM, PRES. U.S. --ASSASSINATION (923.173)

Bishop, James A. Day Lincoln was shot. il. 1955. 4.95. Harper

Roscoe, T. Web of conspiracy. 10.00. Prentice-Hall

Stern, Philip Van Doren. Assassination of President Lincoln and the trial of the conspirators. il. 1954. 7.50. Funk

LINCOLN, ABRAHAM, PRES. U.S. --DRAMA (812)

Drinkwater, John. Abraham Lincoln. 2.04. Houghton

Sherwood, Robert E. Abe Lincoln in Illinois. 1939. 3.50. Scribner

LINCOLN, ABRAHAM, PRES. U.S. --MUSEUMS, RELICS, ETC. (973)

Redway, Maurine W., and Dorothy K. Bracken. Marks of Lincoln on our land. 1957. 3.75. Hastings

LINCOLN, JOHN CROMWELL, 1866-1959 (928)

Moley, Raymond. American century of John C. Lincoln. il. 1962. 4.95. Duell

LINCOLN, MARY (TODD) 1818-1882 (920.7)

Randall, Ruth Painter. Mary Lincoln: Biography of a marriage. il. 1953. 6.75. Little

Sandburg, Carl. Mary Lincoln: Wife and widow. il. 4.50. Harcourt

LINCOLN-DOUGLAS DEBATES, 1858 (973.7)

Jaffe, Harry V. Crisis of the house divided. 1959. 6.50. Doubleday

LINDBERGH, CHARLES AUGUSTUS, 1902- (926)

Lindbergh, Charles A. We. 1956. 1.95. Grosset

LINDSAY, NICHOLAS VACHEL, 1879-1931 (928)

Ruggles, Eleanor. West-going heart: A life of Vachel Lindsay. il. 1959. 6.50. Norton

LINE (ART) (700)

Ernst, J. Drawing the line: Fine and commercial art. 1962. 10.00. Reinhold

LINEAR PROGRAMMING (519.92)

Boulding, Kenneth E., and W. Allen Spivey. Linear programming and the theory of the firm. il. 1960. 6.00. Macmillan

Greenwald, D. U. Linear programming. 1957. 3.00. Ronald

LINKS AND LINK-MOTION (621.8)

Hall, Allen S. Kinematics and linkage design. 1961. 8.50. Prentice-Hall

LINOLEUM BLOCK-PRINTING (760)

Biggs, John R. Woodcuts. il. 1959. 5.95. Sterling

Erikson, Janet. Block printing on textiles. il. 1961. 10.00. Watson

LIONS (599.7442)

Adamson, Joy. Born free: A lioness of two worlds. il. 1960. 4.95. Pantheon

Taylor, John. Maneaters and marauders. il. 1959. 3.95. Barnes, A. S.

LIPCHITZ, JACQUES, 1891- (927)

Hammacher, A. M. Jacques Lipchitz: His sculpture. il. 1961. 15.00. Abrams

LIPIDS (612.397)

Hanahan, Donald J. Lipide chemistry. il. 1960. 10.00. Wiley

King, H. K. Chemistry of lipids in health and disease. il. 1960. 3.75. Thomas, C. C

LIPPMANN, WALTER, 1889- (928)

Childs, Marquis W., and James Reston. Walter Lippmann and his times. 1959. 3.95. Harcourt

Forcey, Charles. Crossroads of liberalism. 1961. 7.00. Oxford U. P.

LIPSIUS, JUSTUS, 1547-1606 (922)
Saunders, Jason Lewis. Justus Lipsius: The philosophy of Renaissance Stoicism.
4.50. 1955. Bobbs
LIQUID PROPELLANT ROCKETS (662.666)
Goddard, Robert H. Rocket development. by Esther C. Goddard, and G. E.
Pendray. il. 1961. 3.95. Prentice-Hall
LIQUIDS (532)
American Society of Mechanical Engineers. Thermodynamic and transport
properties of gases, liquids, and solids. 1959. 12.50. McGraw
Hirschfelder, J. O., and others. Molecular theory of gases and liquids. 1954.
22.50. Wiley
Reid, R. C., and T. K. Sherwood. Properties of gases and liquids. 1958. 11.00.
McGraw
LIQUIDS, KINETIC THEORY OF (532)
Frenkel, J. Kinetic theory of liquids. 1955. 3.95. Dover
LIQUOR PROBLEM (178)
McCarthy, Raymond G. Drinking and intoxication. 1959. 7.50. Free Press
McCarthy, Raymond G. Drinking and intoxication: Selected readings in social
attitudes and controls. 1959. 7.50. Rutgers Center of Alcohol Studies
Roueche, Berton. Neutral spirit. 1960. 3.75. Little
Straus, Robert, and Selden D. Bacon. Drinking in college. 1953. 4.00. Pacific
Bk. Supply
LISTER, JOSEPH LISTER, BARON, 1827-1912 (925)
Guthrie, Douglas. Lord Lister. 1949. 3.50. Williams & Wilkins
LISTERIOSIS (616)
Seeliger, Heinz P. R. Listeriosis. il. 1961. 14.25. Hafner
LISZT, FRANZ, 1811-1886 (927)
Beckett, Walter. Liszt. il. 1956. 3.50. Farrar, Straus
Friedheim, Arthur. Life and Liszt. by Theodore L. Bullock. il. 1961. 6.00.
Taplinger
LITCHFIELD, EDWARD HAROLD, 1914- (923.7)
Litchfield, Edward H., and others. New dimensions of learning in a free society.
1958. 4.50. U. of Pittsburgh
LITERARY RESEARCH (029)
Altick, Richard D. Scholar adventurers. 5.00. Macmillan
Foerster, Norman. Literary scholarship: Its aims and methods. 1941. 3.50.
U. of N. C.
Sanders, Chauncey. Introduction to research in English literary history. il. 1952.
6.50. Macmillan
LITERATURE (800)
Bacon, W. A., and R. S. Breen. Literature as experience. 1959. 5.95. McGraw
Boas, Ralph P., and Edwin Smith. Enjoyment of literature. 1934. 3.80. Harcourt
Grebanier, Bernard D. N., and Seymour Reiter. Introduction to imaginative
literature. 1960. 7.50. Crowell
LITERATURE--ADDRESSES, ESSAYS, LECTURES (808.06)
Boaz, Martha T., comp. Quest for truth. 1961. 3.50. Scarecrow
Burnshaw, Stanley. Varieties of literary experience. 1962. 7.50. N. Y. U.
Cooper, Lane. Evolution and repentance: Mixed essays and addresses on Aristotle,
Plato, and Dante, with papers on Matthew Arnold and Wordsworth. 1935. 2.25.
Cornell
Davies, Robertson. Voice from the attic. 1960. 4.75. Knopf
Dryden, John. Essays of John Dryden. 2 vols. by W. P. Ker. 1961. 15.00. Russell
Eliot, T. S. On poetry and poets. 1957. 4.50. Farrar, Straus
Eliot, T. S. Sacred wood. 1950. 2.50. Barnes & Noble
Eliot, T. S. Selected essays. 1950. 5.75. Harcourt
Elledge, Scott. Eighteenth century critical essays. 2 vols. 1961. 12.50 set.
Cornell
Fadiman, Clifton. Party of one: The selected writings of Clifton Fadiman. 1955.
5.00. World Pub.

Farrell, James T. League of frightened Philistines. 1945. 3.00. Vanguard
Fergusson, Francis. Human image in dramatic literature. 3.00. Smith, Peter
Highet, Gilbert. Clerk of Oxenford: Essays on literature and life. 1954. 4.00. Oxford U. P.
Highet, Gilbert. Talents and geniuses: The pleasures of appreciation. 1957. 5.00. Oxford U. P.
Horn, Frances. Literary masterpieces of the Western world. 1953. 3.50. Johns Hopkins
Huxley, Aldous. On art and artists. 1960. 4.50. Harper
Joyce, James. Critical writings of James Joyce. by Ellsworth Mason and Richard Ellmann. 1959. 5.00. Viking
Lawrence, David Herbert. Selected literary criticism. by Anthony Beal. 1956. 5.00. Viking
Lovejoy, Arhtur O. Essays in the history of ideas. 1952. 5.50. Johns Hopkins
Maugham, W. Somerset. Points of View: Five essays. 1959. 4.50. Doubleday
Pound, Ezra. Literary essays. by T. S. Eliot. 1953. 6.00. New Directions
Quiller-Couch, Arthur. Cambridge lectures. 1940. 1.95. Dutton
Quiller-Couch, A. T. Poet as citizen. 1934. 2.75. Cambridge U. P.
Sartre, Jean-Paul. Literary and philosophical essays. pap. 0.95. Collier
Schopenhauer, Arthur. Art of literature. 1960. 4.40. U. of Mich.
Stallknecht, Newton P., and Horst Frenz. Comparative literature: Method and perspective. 1961. 7.00. Southern Ill.
Tate, Allen. Man of letters in the modern world. 1958. 3.25. Smith, Peter
Van Doren, Mark. Happy critic and other essays. 1961. 3.50. Hill & Wang
Williams, William Carlos. Selected Essays. 1954. 4.50. Random
Wilson, Edmund. Wound and the bow: Seven studies in literature. 1947. 5.50. Oxford U. P.
Yeats, William Butler. Essays and introductions. 1961. 6.50. Macmillan
LITERATURE--BIBLIOGRAPHY (800.01b)
Lueders, Edward. College and adult reading list of books in literature and the fine arts. 1962. pap. 0.90. Washington Square (R)
Orton, Robert M. Catalog of reprints in series. 15.00; suppl. in prep. Scarecrow (R)
Weber, J. Sherwood, and others. From Homer to Joyce: A study guide to thirty-six great books. 1959. pap. 2.50. Holt, Rinehart & Winston
LITERATURE--BIO-BIBLIOGRAPHY (800.016)
Hornstein, Lillian H., and others. Reader's companion to world literature. 1956. 5.00. Holt, Rinehart & Winston (R)
Magill, Frank N. Cyclopedia of world authors. 1958. 8.95. Harper (R)
Steinberg, Sigfrid H. Cassell's encyclopedia of world literature. 2 vols. 1953. boxed, 25.00. Funk (R)
LITERATURE--COLLECTIONS (808)
Baldwin R. C., and J. A. S. McPeek. Introduction to philosophy through literature. 1950. 7.00. Ronald
Beardsley, Monroe, and others. Theme and form: An introduction to literature. 1962. 6.95. study aids, pap. 1.50. Prentice-Hall
Buck, Philo M., Jr. Anthology of world literature. 7.75. Macmillan
Cairns, Huntington. Limits of art. 1948. 8.50. Pantheon
Eliot, Charles W. Collier's Harvard classics. 51 vols. indexed. 349.00. Collier-Macmillan
Everett, Edwin M., and others. Masterworks of world literature. 2 vols. vol. 1. From Homer to Cervantes; vol. 2. From Shakespeare to Mann. 1955. 7.00 ea. Holt, Rinehart & Winston (R)
Fadiman, Clifton. Reading I've liked. 1958. pap. 2.25. S. and S.
Great books of the western world. 398.00 and up. Encycl. Britannica
Houston, Percy H., and R. M. Smith. Types of world literature. 1930. 5.00. Odyssey
Kennedy, Eberhard C. Roman poetry and prose. 1957. 1.50. Cambridge U. P.

Kronenberger, Louis. Pleasure of their company. 1946. 5.75. Knopf
Kronenberger, Louis. Portable reader's companion. 1945. 2.95. Viking
Locke, Louis G., and others. Literature of western civilization. 2 vols. 1952.
6.75 ea. Ronald
Mack, Maynard, and others. World masterpieces. 2 vols. 1956. 6.50 ea. in one
vol. 1962. 8.95. Norton (R)
Magill, Frank N. Masterpieces of world literature in digest form. 3 series.
1952, 1956, 1960. 8.50 ea. Harper (R)
Rapport, Samuel, and Kathryn. Light for the road. 1961. 4.95. Harper
Runes, Dagobert D. Treasury of world literature. 1961. pap. 3.45. Littlefield
Shrodes, Caroline, and others. Psychology through literature: An anthology.
1943. 5.50. Oxford U. P.
Thompson, Stith, and John Gassner. Our heritage of world literature. 2 bks. 1942.
in one vol. 10.95; bk. 1, Literature in translation, 8.95. Holt, Rinehart & Winston
Untermeyer, Louis. Treasury of ribaldry. 1956. 4.95. Doubleday
Woods, Ralph L. Second treasury of the familiar. 1955. 8.75; boxed with Treasury
of the familiar. 15.00. Macmillan
Woods, Ralph L. Treasury of friendship. 1957. 6.95. McKay

LITERATURE--DICTIONARIES (803)
Beckson, Karl, and Arthur Ganz. Reader's guide to literary terms: A dictionary.
1960. 4.95. Farrar, Straus
Benet, William Rose. Reader's encyclopedia. 1955. 7.95. Crowell (R)
Brewer's dictionary of phrase and fable. 1953. 5.95. Harper (R)
Deutsch, Babette. Poetry handbook: A dictionary of terms. 1962. 3.95. Funk (R)
Keller, Helen R. Reader's digest of books. 7.50. Macmillan (R)
Magill, Frank N. Cyclopedia of literary characters. 1962. 8.95? Harper
Shipley, Joseph T. Dictionary of world literature. 1959. pap. 1.95. Littlefield
Steinberg, Sigfrid H. Cassell's encyclopedia of world literature. 2 vols. 1953.
boxed. 25.00. Funk (R)

LITERATURE--ESTHETICS (801)
McGinn, Donald J., and George Howerton. Literature as a fine art. il. 1959.
bds. 6.50. Harper

LITERATURE--HISTORY AND CRITICISM (809)
Adams, Robert M. Strains of discord. 1958. 3.75. Cornell
Allen, Gay W., and Harry H. Clark. Literary criticism: Pope to Croce. 1962.
6.50. Wayne
Auerbach, Erich. Mimesis. 1957. pap. 1.45. Doubleday
Barzun, Jacques. Energies of art. 1956. 5.50. Harper
Beach, Joseph. Obsessive images. 1960. 6.75. U. of Minn.
Cairns, Huntington. Limits of art. 1948. 8.50. Pantheon
Cather, Willa. Willa Cather on writing. 1949. 3.50. Knopf
Cowley, Malcolm, and Bernard Smith. Books that changed our minds. 3.50.
Russell
Crane, Ronald S., and others. Critics and criticism: Ancient and modern. 1952.
10.00. U. of Chicago
Danziger, Marlies K., and Wendell Johnson. Introduction to literary criticism.
1961. pap. 2.75. Heath
Downs, Robert B. Books that changed the world. 1956. 2.25. A. L. A.
Drinkwater, John. Outline of literature. il. 1955. 10.50. Transatlantic
Farrell, James T. Note on literary criticism. 1936. 3.00. Vanguard
Goodman, Paul. Structure of literature. 1954. 5.00. U. of Chicago
Hauser, Arnold. Social history of art. 2 vols. il. 1951. boxed, 17.50. Knopf
Hibbard, Addison, and H. Frenz. Writers of the western world. 1954. 8.75.
Houghton
Holliday, Carl. Dawn of literature. 1961. 5.00. Ungar
Howe, Irving. Modern literary criticism. 1959. 6.50. Beacon (R)
Johnson, Samuel. Critical opinions of Samuel Johnson. by Joseph E. Brown. 1960.
10.00. Russell

Jones, Howard Mumford. Theory of American literature. 1948. 2.75. Cornell

Levin, A. Legacy of Philarete Chasles, 1957. 7.50. U. of N. C.

Levin, Harry. Contexts of criticism. 1957. 5.00. Harvard

Macy, John. Story of the world's literature. 1961. 4.50. Liveright or Tudor

Meyerhoff, Hans. Time in literature. 3.50. Smith, Peter

Murry, J. Middleton. Selected criticism, 1916-1957. by Richard Rees. 1960. 7.00. Oxford U. P.

Saintsbury, George. History of criticism and literary taste in Europe. 3 vols. 17.50. Humanities

Sewall, Richard B. Vision of tragedy. 1959. 4.00. Yale

Seward, Barbara. Symbolic rose. 1960. 5.00. Columbia

Smith, James Harry, and E. W. Parks. Great critics. 1951. 7.25. Norton

Wimsatt, William K., Jr. and Cleanth Brooks. Literary criticism. il. 1957. 9.75. Knopf

LITERATURE--PHILOSOPHY (801)

Burke, Kenneth. Philosophy of literary form. abridged. 1959. 3.25. Smith, Peter

Craig, Hardin. Enchanted glass: The Elizabethan mind in literature. 1952. 4.00. Oxford U. P.

Heller, Erich. Disinherited mind. 1957. 3.75. Farrar, Straus

Krutch, Joseph Wood. Experience and art. pap. 0.95. Collier

Lucas, F. L. Literature and psychology. 1957. pap. 1.95. U. of Mich.

Matthiessen, F. O. American renaissance: Art and expression in the age of Emerson and Whitman. il. 1941. 10.00. Oxford U. P.

Routh, Harold V. God, man, and epic poetry. 2 vols. 1927. vol. 1. Classical; vol. 2. Medieval. 5.50 ea. Cambridge U. P.

Wellek, Rene and Austin Warren. Theory of literature. 1956. pap. 1.65. Harcourt

LITERATURE--PSYCHOLOGY (800)

De Voto, Bernard. World of fiction. 1950. 3.50. Houghton

Hoffman, Frederick J. Freudianism and the literary mind. 1959. pap. 2.45. Grove

Humphrey, Robert. Stream of consciousness in the modern novel. 1954. pap. 1.25. U. of Calif.

Poggioli, Renato. Phoenix and the spider. 1957. 5.00. Harvard

Shumaker, Charles W. Literature and the irrational. 1960. 7.00. Prentice-Hall

LITERATURE--STUDY AND TEACHING (807)

Steinmetz, Lee. Analyzing literary works: A guide for college students. 1962. pap. 2.25. Harper

Taylor, J. F. A. and others. Introduction to literature and the fine arts. il. 1950. pap. 6.00. Mich. State

LITERATURE--YEARBOOKS (805)

Pine, L. G. Author's & writer's who's who. 1960. 7.00. Hafner

LITERATURE, COMPARATIVE (808.06)

Baldensperger, Fernand, And Werner P. Friederich. Bibliography of comparative literature. 15.00. Russell

Eoff, Sherman H. Modern Spanish novel. 1961. 6.00. N. Y. U.

Friederich, Werner P., and O. H. Malone. Outline of comparative literature from Dante Alighieri to Eugene O'Neill. 1955. 6.50. U. of N. C.

Frye, Prosser H. Romance and tragedy: A study of classic and romantic elements in the great tragedies of European literature. 1961. pap. 1.25. U. of Nebr.

Neff, Emery. Revolution in European poetry, 1660-1900. 1940. 3.50. Columbia

Stallknecht, Newton P., and Horst Frenz. Comparative literature: Method and perspective. 1961. 7.00. Southern Ill.

Stoll, Elmer E. Shakespeare and other masters. 8.50. Russell

Tillyard, Eustace M. W. English epic and its background. 1954. 4.00. Oxford U. P.

LITERATURE, COMPARATIVE--THEMES, MOTIVES (808.06)

Lewis, Clive S. Allegory of love: A study in medieval tradition. 1936. 4.00. Oxford U. P.

Longi, Olga. Terre et les morts dans l'oeuvre de Chateaubriand. 1934. pap. 1.25. Johns Hopkins

Loomis, Roger Sherman. Arthurian literature in the Middle Ages. 1959. 10.10.
   Oxford U. P.
Reid, Margaret J. C. Arthurian legend. 1961. bds. 5.00. Barnes & Noble
Rougemont, Denis de. Love in the western world. 1956. 4.50. Pantheon
Rudwin, Maximillian J. Devil in legend and literature. 1931. 5.00. Open Ct.
Young, Arthur M. Legend builders of the west. 1958. 4.00. U. of Pittsburgh
Zabara, Joseph B. M. Book of delight. by Moses Hadas. 1924. 3.00. Columbia
LITERATURE, COMPARATIVE--AMERICAN AND ENGLISH (800)
Eidson, John Olin. Tennyson in America. 1943. 3.00. U. of Ga.
Raiziss, Sona. Metaphysical passion: Seven modern American poets and the
   17th-century tradition. 1952. 5.00. U. of Pa.
Raleigh, John H. Matthew Arnold and American culture. 1962. 4.00. Smith, Peter
LITERATURE, COMPARATIVE--AMERICAN AND GERMAN (800)
Pochmann, Henry. German culture in America. 1956. 7.50. U. of Wis.
Shelley, Philip, and others. Anglo-German and American-German crosscurrents.
   2 vols. vol. 1, 1957. 7.00; vol. 2, in prep. U. of N. C.
LITERATURE, COMPARATIVE--AMERICAN AND JAPANESE (800)
Miner, E. Japanese tradition in British and American literature. 1958. 3.75.
   Princeton
LITERATURE, COMPARATIVE--CLASSICAL AND MODERN (800)
Highet, Gilbert. Classical tradition: Greek and Roman influences on western
   literature. 1949. 10.00. Oxford U. P.
LITERATURE, COMPARATIVE--ENGLISH AND CLASSICAL (800)
Alden, Raymond M. Rise of formal satire in England under classical influence.
   1962. 7.00. Shoe String
Driver, Tom Faw. Sense of history in Greek and Shakespearean drama. 1960.
   5.00. Columbia
Herrick, Marvin T. Poetics of Aristotle in England. 1930. pap. 1.75. Cornell
Jepsen, Laura. Ethical aspects of tragedy. 1953. 3.75. U. of Fla.
Murray, Gilbert. Classical tradition in poetry. 1927. 3.00. Harvard
Thomson, James A. K. Classical background of English literature. 1948. 3.50.
   Macmillan
Thomson, James A. Shakespeare and the classics. 4.00. Barnes & Noble
LITERATURE, COMPARATIVE--ENGLISH AND FRENCH (800)
De Mourgues, Odette. Metaphysical baroque and precieux poetry. 1954. 4.00.
   Oxford U. P.
Rickard, Peter. Britain in medieval French literature. 1957. 6.50. Cambridge
   U. P.
Wheatley, Katherine E. Racine and English classicism. 1956. 6.00. U. of Tex.
LITERATURE, COMPARATIVE--ENGLISH AND ITALIAN (800)
Praz, Mario. Flaming heart. 1958. 3.50. Smith, Peter
Prince, Frank T. Italian element in Milton's verse. 1954. 2.40. Oxford U. P.
Sells, A. Lytton. Italian influence in English poetry: From Chaucer to Southwell.
   il. 1955. 6.75. Indiana
LITERATURE, COMPARATIVE--ENGLISH AND RUSSIAN (800)
Brewster, D. East-west passage. 4.50. Humanities
LITERATURE, COMPARATIVE--FRENCH AND SPANISH (800)
Crooks, Esther J. Influence of Cervantes in France in the seventeenth century.
   1931. pap. 2.00. Johns Hopkins
LITERATURE, MEDIEVAL (809)
Chew, Samuel C. Pilgrimage of life. il. 1962. 15.00? Yale
Hauser, Arnold. Social history of art. 4 vols. vol. 1, Prehistoric to Middle Ages;
   vol. 2, Renaissance to Baroque; vol. 3, Rococo to Romanticism; vol. 4,
   Naturalism to the Film Age. pap. 1.45 ea. Vintage
LITERATURE, MEDIEVAL--BIBLIOGRAPHY (808)
Hopper, Vincent F., and Bernard D. N. Grebanier. Bibliography of essential
   European literature. 1952. 2.95. Barron's
LITERATURE, MEDIEVAL--HISTORY AND CRITICISM (809)
Baldwin, C. S. Medieval rhetoric and poetic to 1400. 1959. 4.50. Smith, Peter

Duckett, Eleanor S. Gateway to the Middle Ages. 3 vols. 1938. vol. 1. Italy.
   4.40. 1961. vol. 2. France and Britain. 4.40. 1961. vol. 3. Monasticism. 4.40.
   1961. U. of Mich.
Jackson, William T. H. Literature of the Middle Ages. 1960. 6.00. Columbia
Laistner, M. L. W. Thought and letters in Western Europe. 1957. 5.00. Cornell
Loomis, Laura H. Mediaeval romance in England. 1959. 12.50. Franklin, B.
Saintsbury, George. History of criticism and literary taste in Europe. 3 vols.
   17.50. Humanities
Taylor, Henry Osborn. Classical heritage of the Middle Ages. 4.50. Ungar
LITERATURE, MODERN (808)
Amory, Cleveland, and Frederic Bradlee. Vanity fair: A cavalcade of the 1920's
   and 1930's. il. 1960. 10.00. Viking
Fuller, Edmund. Books with men behind them. 1962. 3.95. Random
Hoffman, Frederick J. Perspectives on modern literature. 1962. pap. 2.25.
   Harper
Hugo, Howard E. Romantic reader. 1957. 4.95. 1962. 2.95. Viking
LITERATURE, MODERN--ADDRESSES, ESSAYS, LECTURES (804)
Fiedler, Leslie A. No! In thunder. 1960. 5.00. Beacon
Kazin, Alfred. Contemporaries. 1962. 7.50. Little
Moore, Marianne. Predilections. 1955. 3.50. Viking
Trilling, Lionel. Opposing self. 1959. pap. 1.25. Viking
Wilson, Edmund. Classics and commercials. 1950. 5.00. Farrar, Straus
Wilson, Edmund. Literary chronicle: 1920-1952. 3.50. Smith, Peter
Wilson, Edmund. Shores of light. 1952. 6.50. Farrar, Straus
LITERATURE, MODERN--DICTIONARIES, INDEXES, ETC. (808)
Smith, Horatio. Columbia dictionary of modern European literature. 1947. 10.00.
   Columbia
LITERATURE, MODERN--HISTORY AND CRITICISM (809)
Baird, James. Ishmael. 1956. 5.50. Johns Hopkins
Lowenthal, L. Literature and the image of man. 1957. 4.95. Beacon
Priestley, John B. Literature and Western man. 1960. 6.95. Harper
Sypher, Wylie. Rococo to cubism in art and literature. il. 1960. 7.00. Random
Turnell, Martin. Modern literature and Christian faith. 1961. 2.50. Newman
Warren, Austin. Rage for order. 1959. 4.40. U. of Mich.
Wellek, Rene. History of modern criticism. 2 vols. 1955. vol. 1. Later 18th-
   century. 5.50; vol. 2. Romantic age. 6.50. Yale
West, Rebecca. Court and the castle. 1957. 4.50. Yale
LITERATURE, MODERN--HISTORY AND CRITICISM--15TH AND 16TH CENTURIES
   (808)
Clements, Robert J. Peregrine Muse. 1959. pap. 2.50. U. of N. C.
LITERATURE, MODERN--HISTORY AND CRITICISM--19TH CENTURY (808)
Praz, Mario. Romantic agony. 1951. 5.60. Oxford U. P.
Wilson, Edmund. Axel's castle. 1931. 4.50. Scribner
Wilson, Edmund. Triple thinkers. 1948. 6.50. Oxford U. P.
LITERATURE, MODERN--HISTORY AND CRITICISM--20TH CENTURY (808)
Glicksberg, Charles I. Literature and religion. 1960. 4.50. S. M. U.
Heiney, Donald W. Contemporary literature. 1954. 3.50. Barron's
Mauriac, Claude. New literature. 1959. 4.00. Braziller
Rosenfeld, Isaac. Age of enormity: Life and writing in the forties and fifties. by
   Theodore Solotaroff. 1962. 5.00. World Pub.
Scott, Nathan A., Jr. Modern literature and the religious frontier. 1958. 2.50.
   Harper
Sypher, Wylie. Loss of the self in modern literature and art. 1962. 4.00. Random
LITERATURE, MODERN--15TH AND 16TH CENTURIES (808)
Blanchard, H. H. Prose and poetry of the continental Renaissance in translation.
   1955. 6.75. McKay'
LITERATURE, MODERN--20TH CENTURY (808)
Engle, Paul. Midland. 1961. 6.50. Random

New Directions in prose and poetry. vol. 10, 1948, 4.50; vol. 11, 1949, 4.50;
   vol. 12, 1950, 5.00; vol. 13, 1951, 5.00; vol. 14, 1952, o.p; vol. 15, 1955,
   3.50; vol. 16, 1957, 2.50; vol. 17, 1961. pap. 1.95. New Directions
LITERATURE AND HISTORY (808)
Neff, Emery. Poetry of history. 1961. pap. 1.80. Columbia
LITERATURE AND MORALS (809)
Jepsen, Laura. Ethical aspects of tragedy. 1953. 3.75. U. of Fla.
McKean, Keith F. Moral measure of literature. 1960. 3.00. Swallow, A.
Maritain, Jacques. Responsibility of the artist. 1960. 2.95. Scribner
LITERATURE AND SCIENCE (808)
Bush, Douglas. Science and English poetry: A historical sketch, 1590-1950. 1950.
   4.50. Oxford U. P.
Nicolson, M. Science and the imagination. 1.75. Cornell
Sewell, Elizabeth. Orphic voice: Poetry and natural history. 1960. 7.50. Yale
Zirkle, Conway. Evolution, Marxian biology, and the social scene. 1959. 7.50.
   U. of Pa.
LITHOGRAPHS (763)
Daumier, Honore V. Lithographs: Law and justice. by J. Cain. 5.95. Tudor
Mann, Felix H. One hundred and fifty years of artist's lithographs, 1803-1953.
   il. 15.00. Boston Bk.
LITHUANIA--HISTORY (947.5)
Senn, A. E. Emergence of modern Lithuania. 6.00. Columbia
Kuhlman, Charles. Legend into history: The Custer mystery. 1951. 5.00.
   Stackpole
LITURGIES, EARLY CHRISTIAN (264)
Srawley, J. H. Early history of the Liturgy. 3.50. Cambridge U. P.
LIVER--DISEASES (616.362)
Kleckner, Martin S., Jr. Cirrhosis of the liver. il. 1960. 24.50. Thomas, C. C
LIVING FOSSILS (591)
Burton, Maurice. Living fossils. 1954. 5.00. Vanguard
Ley, Willy. Exotic zoology. il. 1959. 4.95. Viking
LIVINGSTONE, DAVID, 1813-1873 (923.9)
Anstruther, Ian. Dr. Livingstone, I presume? il. 1957. 5.00. Dutton
Northcott, Cecil. Livingstone in Africa. 1957. 1.25. Assn. Pr.
LIVY (LIVIUS, TITUS) (923.7)
Walsh, P. G. Livy: His historical aims and methods. 1961. 8.00. Cambridge U. P.
LIZARDS (598.1)
Savage, Jay. Illustrated key to lizards, snakes and turtles of the West. 1959. pap.
   1.00. Naturegraph
Smith, Hobart M. Handbook of lizards. il. 6.00. Cornell (R)
LLOYD GEORGE, DAVID LLOYD GEORGE, 1st EARL, 1863-1945 (923.1)
Lloyd George, Richard. My father, Lloyd George. 4.00. Crown
LOBBYING (328)
Blaisdell, D. C. American democracy under pressure. 1957. 5.50. Ronald
Key, V. O., Jr. Politics, parties, and pressure groups. il. 1958. 6.50.
   Crowell
Truman, David B. Governmental process: Political interests and public opinion.
   1951. 5.50. Knopf
Turner, Henry A. Politics in the United States: Readings in political parties and
   pressure groups. 1955. pap. 3.95. McGraw
LOCAL ANESTHESIA (615.7)
Bonica, John J. Clinical application of diagnostic and therapeutic nerve blocks.
   il. 1959. 8.75. Thomas, C. C
LOCAL GOVERNMENT (352)
Adrian, Charles R. State and local governments. 1960. 7.50. McGraw
Anderson, William, and others. Government in the fifty states. il. 1960. 6.50.
   Holt, Rinehart & Winston
Burns, James M., and Jack W. Peltason. Government by the people. 1960.
   national ed. 7.95; national, state, and local ed. 8.25. Prentice-Hall

Johnson, Claudius O. American state and local government. 1961. pap. 3.50.
Crowell
Lancaster, Lane W. Government in rural America. il. 1952. 5.50. Van Nostrand
Macdonald, Austin F. State and local government in the United States. il. 1955.
6.50. Crowell
Maddox, Russell W., and Robert F. Fuquay. State and local governments. il.
1962. 7.75. Van Nostrand
Ogg, Frederic A., and P. Orman Ray. Essentials of American Government. il.
1959. 6.50. Appleton
Ogg, Frederic A., and P. Orman Ray. Introduction to American government.
by William H. Young. il. 8.00. Appleton
LOCKE, JOHN, 1632-1704 (921.2)
Cranston, Maurice. Locke. 1961. pap. 0.50. British Bk.
Gough, John W. John Locke's political philosophy. 1950. 3.40. Oxford U. P.
Kendall, Willmoore. John Locke and the doctrine of majority rule. 1960. pap.
2.50. U. of Ill.
Yolton, J. W. John Locke and the way of ideas. 1956. 4.80. Oxford U. P.
LOCOMOTIVES (621.13)
Carter, Ernest F. Unusual locomotives. 1960. 4.50. Macmillan
Ransome-Wallis, P. Concise encyclopedia of world railway locomotives. il. 1959.
15.00. Hawthorn (R)
LOCOMOTIVES--PICTORIAL WORKS (621.13)
Kinert, Reed. Early American steam locomotives. il. 1962. 15.00. Superior
Pub. Co. (R)
LOCUSTS (632.7)
Albrecht, F. O. Anatomy of the migratory locust. 1953. 4.80. Oxford U. P.
Helfer, J. R. How to know the grasshoppers, cockroaches and their allies. by
H. E. Jacques. in prep. Brown, W. C.
LODGE, HENRY CABOT, 1850-1924 (923.2)
Garraty, John A. Henry Cabot Lodge: A biography. il. 1953. 7.50. Knopf
LOG CABINS (728)
Angier, Bradford. Living off the country: How to stay alive in the woods. il. 5.00.
Stackpole
LOGAN, JAMES, 1674-1751 (923.2)
Tolles, Frederick B. James Logan and the culture of provincial America. 1957.
3.75. Little
LOGARITHMS (510.8)
Allen, Edward S. Six-place tables. 1947. 4.00. McGraw (R)
Bruhns, Karl C. New manual of logarithms. 1941. 4.50. Van Nostrand (R)
Bruhns, Karl C. Seven figure logarithmic and trigonometric tables. 1960. 4.50.
Landau
Clark, John J. Slide rule and logarithmic tables. 1957. 3.00. Drake, F. J.
Glover, James W. Tables of applied mathematics. 1951. 10.00. Wahr (R)
Hart, William L. Plane and spherical trigonoemtry and with applications. 1944.
with tables. 4.75. Heath
Rubey, Harry, and others. Engineering surveys: Elementary. 1958. il. 6.25.
Macmillan
Smoley, C. K. Logarithmic-trigonometric tables. by E. R., and N. G. Smoley.
1962. fabricoid. 2.00. Smoley
LOGIC (160)
Adams, Elie M. Fundamentals of general logic. 1954. 4.00. McKay
Aristotle. Prior and posterior analytics. by W. D. Ross. 1949. 8.00. Oxford U.P.
Bachhuber, Andrew H. Introduction to logic. il. 1957. 3.75. Appleton
Bacon, Francis. Advancement of learning. by W. A. Wright. 2.00. Oxford U.P.
Beardsley, Monroe C. Thinking straight: Principles of reasoning for readers and
writers. 1950. 3.50. Prentice-Hall
Bittle, Celestine N. Science of correct thinking. 1935. 3.25. Bruce
Black, Max. Critical thinking. 1952. 7.25. Prentice-Hall
Blyth, J. W. Modern introduction to logic. 5.50. Houghton

Bochenski, I. M. Ancient formal logic. 3.75. Humanities
Chase, Stuart. Guides to straight thinking, with thirteen common fallacies. 1956.
3.50. Harper (R)
Cohen, Morris R., and Ernest Nagel. Introduction to logic and scientific method.
1934. 5.50. Harcourt
Cohen, Morris. Preface to logic. pap. 1.35. Meridian
Copi, Irving M. Introduction to logic. 1961. 5.50. Macmillan
Dewey, John. Logic: Theory of inquiry. 1938. 6.50. Holt
Eaton, Ralph M. General logic: An introductory survey. 1961. pap. 3.50. Scribner
Flesch, Rudolf. Art of clear thinking. 1951. 3.50. Harper
Hegel, Georg Wilhelm Friedrich. Logic of Hegel. 1892. 4.00. Oxford U. P.
Hegel, Georg W. F. Science of logic. tr. by W. H. Johnston and L. G. Struthers
2 vols. 1929. 10.50. Macmillan
Hepp, Maylon H. Thinking things through. 1956. 6.25. Scribner
Inhelder, Barbel, and Jean Piaget. Growth of logical thinking from childhood to
adolescence. 1958. 7.50. Basic Books
Jevons, Stanley. Principles of science. pap. 2.98. Dover
Joseph, H. W. B. Introduction to logic. 1916. 4.00. Oxford U. P.
Kantor, Jacob R. Psychology and logic. 2 vols. 12.00. Principia Press, Inc.
Leonard, Henry S. Principles of right reason: An introduction to applied logic.
1957. 5.50. Holt
Mill, John Stuart. John Stuart Mill's philosophy of scientific method. (Hafner
library of classics no. 12) by Ernest Nagel. 1950. pap. 1.95. Hafner
Northrop, Filmer S. C. Logic of the sciences and the humanities. pap. 1.55.
Meridian
Oesterle, John A. Logic: The art of defining and reasoning. 1953. 4.75. Prentice-
Hall
Palmieri, L. E. Language and clear thinking. 1960. 3.50. Johnsen
Ruby, Lionel. Logic: An introduction. 1960. 6.00. Lippincott
Searles, Herbert L. Logic and scientific methods. 1956. 4.50. Ronald
Simmons, Edward. Scientific art of logic. 1961. 4.80. Bruce
Stebbing, L. Susan. Modern introduction to logic. 5.50. Humanities
Toohey, John J. Elementary handbook of logic. 2.25. Appleton (R)
LOGIC--ADDRESSES, ESSAYS, LECTURES (160)
Dewey, John. Essays in experimental logic. 3.75. Smith, Peter
LOGIC--HISTORY (160)
Bochenski, I. M. History of formal logic. 1959. 20.00. Notre Dame
Kneale, William C., and Martha. Development of logic. il. 1962.12.00. Oxford
U. P.
LOGIC--STUDY AND TEACHING (160)
Cohen, Morris R., and Ernest Nagel. Introduction to logic and scientific method.
1934. 5.50. Harcourt
LOGIC, SYMBOLIC AND MATHEMATICAL (160)
Beth, E. W. Formal methods. il. 1962. 9.75. Gordon and Breach
Black, Max. Nature of mathematics. 1950. 5.00. Humanities
Boole, George. Investigation of the laws of thought. 4.00. Smith, Peter
Boole, George. Laws of thought. 4.00. Smith, Peter
Carnap, Rudolf. Introduction to semantics and formalization of logic. 1959. 7.00.
Harvard
Church, A. Introduction to mathematical logic. 1956. 7.50. Princeton
Cooley, John C. Primer of formal logic. 1943. 5.25. Macmillan
De Morgan, Augustus. Formal logic. by A. E. Taylor. 6.00. Open Ct.
Exner, Robert M., and Myron S. Rosskopf. Logic in elementary mathematics.
1959. 6.75. McGraw
Fitch, Frederick Benton. Symbolic logic. 1952. 5.75. Ronald
Halberstadt, William H. Introduction to modern logic. 1960. 5.00. Harper
Halmos, Paul R. Algebraic logic. 1962. 3.75. Chelsea
Lieber, Hugh G., and Lillian R. Mitts, wits and logic. il. 1960. 3.95. Norton

Reichenbach, Hans. Elements of symbolic logic. 1947. 7.50. Macmillan
Reichenbach, Hans. Theory of probability. 1949. 12.50. U. of Calif.
Russell, Bertrand. Logic and knowledge: Essays 1901-1950. by Robert Charles Marsh. 4.50. Macmillan
Stabler, E. R. Introduction to mathematical thought. il. 1953. 7.75. Addison-Wesley
Whitehead, Alfred North, and B. Russell. Principia mathematica. 3 vols. 1925-1927. 45.00; vol. 1, 1962. pap. 1.95. Cambridge U. P. (R)

LOGICAL POSITIVISM (146.4)
Bergmann, Gustav. Meaning and existence. 1960. 6.50. U. of Wis.

LONDON, JACK, 1876-1916 (928)
Calder-Marshall, Arhtur. Lone wolf. 1962. 3.50. Meredith
Stone, Irving. Jack London, sailor on horseback. 1947. 3.95. Doubleday

LONDON--ANTIQUITIES (942)
Home, G. Roman London. 4.50. Humanities

LONDON--DESCRIPTION (942)
Bartel, Roland. Johnson's London. 1956. pap. 1.40. Heath
Morton, H. V. In search of London. il. 1951. 6.00. Dodd

LONDON--FIRE, 1666 (942)
Bartel, Roland. London in plague and fire, 1665-1666. 1957. pap. 1.40. Heath
Leasor, James. Plague and the fire. 1961. 5.95. McGraw

LONDON--HISTORY (942.12)
Collier, Richard. City that would not die, the bombing of London, May 10-11, 1941. il. 1959. 4.50. Dutton
Stuart, Dorothy Margaret. London through the ages. il. 1958. 3.75. Dutton

LONDON--SOCIAL CONDITIONS (942)
Willmott, Peter, and Michael Young. Family and class in a London suburb. il. 1960. 4.50. Humanities

LONDON--SOCIAL LIFE AND CUSTOMS (942)
Byrd, William. William Byrd of Virginia: The London diary, 1717-1721, and other writings. by Louis B. Wright and Marion Tinling. 1958. 10.00. Oxford U. P.
Holmes, Urban T., Jr. Daily living in the Twelfth Century: Based on the observations of Alexander Neckam in London and Paris. il. 1952. 3.85. U. of Wis.
Korg, Jacob. London in Dickens' day. il. 1960. pap. 2.50. Prentice-Hall
Morton, H. V. Morton's London. il. 1950. 2.75. British Bk.

LONDON--THEATERS (792)
Adams, Joseph Q. Shakespearean playhouses, a history of English theatres from the beginning to the Reformation. il. 1959. 6.50. Smith, Peter
Nagler, Alois M. Shakespeare's stage. il. 1958. 2.00. Yale
Prouty, Charles T. Studies in the Elizabethan theater. il. 1961. 4.75. Shoe String

LONG, CRAWFORD WILLIAMSON, 1815-1878 (926)
Boland, Frank K. First anesthetic: The story of Crawford W. Long. 3.00. U. of Ga.

LONG, HUEY PIERCE, 1893-1935 (923.2)
Opotowsky, Stan. Longs of Louisiana. 1960. 4.50. Dutton
Sindler, Allan P. Huey Long's Louisiana. 1956. 5.50. Johns Hopkins

LONGEVITY (612.68)
Dublin, Louis I., and others. Length of life. 1949. 10.00. Ronald
Pearl, Raymond, and Ruth De Witt. Ancestry of the long-lived. 1934. 3.00. Johns Hopkins

LONGFELLOW, HENRY WADSWORTH, 1807-1882 (928)
Wagenknecht, E. Mrs. Longfellow: Selected letters and journals of Fanny Appleton Longfellow. 1956. 5.00. McKay

LORD'S PRAYER (226)
Barth, Karl. Prayer. tr. by Sara F. Terrien. 1952. 1.50. Westminster
Buttrick, George A. So we believe, so we pray. 2.75. Abingdon
Green, Boyan. Being and believing. 1956. 2.95. Scribner

LORD'S PRAYER--MEDITATIONS (226)

Underhill, Evelyn. Fruits of the spirit, Light of Christ, and Abba: Meditations
based on the Lord's prayer. 1956. 3.50. McKay
LORD'S PRAYER--SERMONS (226)
Chappell, Clovis G. Sermons on the Lord's Prayer. 1934. 2.00. Abingdon
LORD'S SUPPER (265)
Lehmann, Helmut T. Meaning and practice of the Lord's Supper. 1961. 3.50.
Muhlenberg
Luthi, Walter, and Eduard Thurneysen. Preaching, confession, the Lord's supper.
1960. 2.50. John Knox
LOS ANGELES (979.494)
Nadeau, Remi. Los Angeles from mission to modern city. 1960. 5.95. McKay
Longmans
Writers' Project. Los Angeles. il. 1951. Hastings
LOUD-SPEAKERS (651.262)
Walker, A. J. Public address and sound distribution handbook. 5.50. Transatlantic
(R)
LOUDUN, FRANCE--URSULINE CONVENT (944)
Huxley, Aldous. Devils of Loudun. 1952. 5.00. Harper
LOUIS XIV, KING OF FRANCE, 1638-1715 (923.1)
Tilley, Arthur A. Decline of the age of Louis XIV. 1929. 9.50. Cambridge U. P.
LOUISIANA (976.3)
Writers' Project. Louisiana. 1947. 6.50. Hastings
LOUISIANA--DESCRIPTION AND TRAVEL (976.3)
Saxon, Lyle. Old Louisiana. il. 10.00. Crager
LOUISIANA--HISTORY (976.3)
Davis, E. A. Louisiana: A narrative history. il. 1961. 8.00. Claitors
Roosevelt, Theodore. Winning of the West. 1962. abridged ed. pap. 1.25. Putnam
LOUISIANA--POLITICS AND GOVERNMENT (976.3)
Williams, T. Harry. Romance and realism in Southern politics. 2.50. U. of Ga.
LOUISIANA--POPULATION (976.3)
Hitt, Homer L., and T. Lynn Smith. People of Louisiana. 1952. 5.00. La. State
LOUISIANA PURCHASE (973.46)
Brackenridge, Henry M. Views of Louisiana, and Journal of a voyage up the
Missouri River, in 1811. 1962. 7.00. Quadrangle
Chase, John. Louisiana purchase. il. 1960. 1.75. Hauser
LOURDES, NOTRE-DAME DE (232.9317)
Deery, Joseph. Our Lady of Lourdes. 1958. 4.50. Newman
LOVE (157)
Andreas Capellanus. Art of courtly love. by Frederick W. Locke. 1.75; complete
ed. tr. by John J. Parry. 5.00. Ungar
Fromm, Erich. Art of loving. 1956. 3.00. Harper
Gould, Thomas. Platonic love. 1962. 5.50. Free Press
Lewis, C. S. Four loves. 1960. 3.75. Harcourt
Magoun, F. Alexander. Love and marriage. 1956. 5.95. Harper
Menninger, Karl A., and Jeanetta L. Love against hate. 1959. 4.75. Harcourt
Raynolds, Robert. Choice to love. 1959. 3.75. Harper
Reik, Theodor. Of love and lust. 1957. 7.50. Farrar, Straus (R)
Strain, Frances B. Love at the threshold. il. 1952. 3.75. Meredith
Tillich, Paul. Love, power and justice. 1960. 3.00. Smith, Peter
Wood, Leland F. How love grows in marriage. 3.50. Channel Pr., Manhasset,
N. Y.
LOVE (THEOLOGY) (291.12)
Brunner, H. Emil. Faith, hope and love. 1956. 2.00. Westminster
Lewis, C. S. Four loves. 1960. 3.75. Harcourt
Niebuhr, Reinhold. Interpretation of Christian ethics. pap. 1.25. Meridian
Nygren, Anders. A grape and Eros. tr. by P. S. Watson. 1953. 7.00. Westminster
Thomas, Aquinas, Saint. On charity. tr. by Lottie H. Kendzierski. 1960. pap.
3.00. Marquette

Webb, Lance. Discovering love. 1959. 3.00. Abingdon

LOVE IN LITERATURE (808)

Dickey, Franklin M. Not wisely but too well: Shakespeare's Love tragedies. 1957. 5.00. Huntington Lib.

Slaughter, Eugene E. Virtue according to love in Chaucer. 5.00. Twayne

Vyvyan, John. Shakespeare and Platonic beauty. 1961. 4.50. Barnes & Noble

Vyvyan, John. Shakespeare and the rose of love. 1960. 4.00. Barnes & Noble

LOVE-LETTERS (808.6)

Fostini, John. Love letters of famous people. 1958. 3.00. Speller

LOVE POETRY--HISTORY AND CRITICISM (808.81)

Salomon, Louis B. Devil take her: A study of the rebellious lover in English poetry. 1961. pap. 1.95. Barnes, A. S.

LOW, JULIETTE (GORDON), 1860-1927 (923.6)

Shultz, Gladys Denny, and Daisy Gordon Lawrence. Lady from Savannah: The life of Juliette Low. 6.00. Lippincott

LOW TEMPERATURE RESEARCH (551.5)

White, Guy K. Experimental techniques in low-temperature physics. 1959. 7.70. Oxford U. P.

LOW TEMPERATURES (551.5)

Dillinger, Joseph R. Low temperature physics and chemistry. 1958. 6.00. U. of Wis.

Jackson, Leonard C. Low temperature physics. 1962. 3.50. Wiley

Mendelssohn, K. Cryophysics. 1960. 4.50. Wiley

LOWELL, JAMES RUSSELL, 1819-1891 (928)

Howard, Leon. Victorian knight-errant: A study of the early literary career of James Russell Lowell. 1952. 5.00. U. of Calif.

LOWELL FAMILY (PERCIVAL LOWELL, 1571-1664) (920)

Greenslet, Ferris. Lowells and their seven worlds. 1946. 5.00. Houghton

LOYALTY (172)

Schaar, John H. Loyalty in America. 1957. 3.50. U. of Calif.

Shyte, William H., Jr. Organization man. 1956. 5.00. S. and S.

LOYALTY OATHS (172)

Hyman, Harold M. To try men's souls: Loyalty oaths in America. il. 1959. 7.50. U. of Calif.

LUBRICATION AND LUBRICANTS (621.89)

Bouman, C. A. Properites of lubricating oil and engine deposits. 3.50. St. Martins

LUCE, CLARE (BOOTHE) 1908- (923.2)

Hatch, Alden. Ambassador extraordinary. 1956. 3.75. Holt

LUKE, SAINT (922.22)

Ramsay, William M. Luke the physician. 4.50. Baker Bk.

LUMBER (674)

Brown, Nelson C., and J. S. Bethel. Lumber. 1958. 7.50. Wiley

LUMBER TRADE (674)

Horn, Stanley F. This fascinating lumber business. 1951. 4.50. Bobbs

Zaremba, Joseph. Economics of the American lumber industry. 6.75. Speller

LUMBERING (674)

Andrews, Ralph W. This was logging. il. 10.00. Superior Pub. Co.

Wacherman, Albert E. Harvesting timber crops. 1949. 8.50. McGraw

LUMINESCENCE (548.9)

Harvey, E. Newton. History of luminescence from the earliest times until 1900. 1957. 6.00. Am. Philos. Soc.

LUNGS (612.2)

Hayek, Heinrich von. Human lung. tr. by Vernon E. Krahl. il. 1960. 13.50. Hafner

LUNGS--DISEASES (616.24)

Adams, Wright R., and Veith I. Pulmonary circulation. il. 1958. 4.50. Grune

Altschule, Mark David. Physiology in diseases of the heart and lungs. 1954. 8.50. Harvard

Drinker, Cecil K. Clinical physiology of the lungs. il. 1955. 5.50. Thomas, C. C
LUTHER, MARTIN, 1483-1546 (922.4)
Bainton, Roland H. Here I stand. il. 1951. 5.50. 1959. Abingdon
Boehmer, Heinrich. Road to reformation. 1946. 4.50. Muhlenberg
Bornkamm, Heinrich. Luther's world of thought. 1958. 3.00. Concordia
Erikson, Erik H. Young man Luther. 1958. 5.00. Norton
Fife, R. H. Revolt of Martin Luther. 1957. 12.50. Columbia
Mackinnon, J. Luther and the Reformation. 4 vols. 1962. 35.00. Russell
LUTHERAN CHURCH IN THE U. S. (284.1)
Wentz, Abdel Ross. Basic history of Lutheranism in America. 1955. 6.00.
    Muhlenberg
LUXEMBURG (949.3)
Clark, Sydney. All the best in Belgium and Luxembourg. il. 1956. 4.95. Dodd
LYCEUMS (791)
Bode, Carl. American lyceum. 1956. 6.00. Oxford U. P.
LYMPHATICS (611.0185)
Lumb, George. Tumors of lymphoid tissue. il. 1954. 8.00. Williams & Wilkins
Yoffey, J. M., and F. C. Courtice. Lymphatics, lymph and lymphoid tissue.
    il. 1956. 10.00. Harvard
LYMPHOMA (611.0185)
Bluefarb, Samuel M. Cutaneous manifestations of the malignant lymphomas. il.
    1959. 15.50. Thomas, C. C
LYNCHING (364.134)
Caughey, John W. Their majesties, the mob. 1960. 5.00. U. of Chicago
LYNX (639.11)
Young, Stanley P. Bobcat of North America. il. 7.50. Stackpole

M

MACAO--DESCRIPTION (910)
Clark, Sydney. All the best in Japan. il. 1960. 4.95. Dodd
MacARTHUR, DOUGLAS, 1880-
Gunther, John. Riddle of MacArthur. 1951. 3.95. Harper
MACAULAY, THOMAS BABINGTON MACAULAY, 1ST BARON, 1800-1859 (921)
Beatty, Richmond Croom. Lord Macaulay: Victorian liberal.1938. 5.00. U. of
    Okla.
Trevelyan, George O. Life and letters of Lord Macaulay. 2 vols. 1961. 3.40.
    Oxford U. P.
MACCABEES (229.7)
Farmer, W. R. Maccabees, zealots, and Josephus: An inquiry into Jewish
    nationalism in the Greco-Roman period. 1956. 4.50. Columbia
McCARTHY, GLENN HERBERT, 1907- (923.3)
Davis, Wallace. Corduroy Road, story of Glenn McCarthy. il. 7.50. Jones, Anson
McCARTHY, JOSEPH RAYMOND, 1909-1957 (923.273)
Rovere, Richard. Senator Joe McCarthy. 1959. 3.95. Harcourt
MacDONALD, GEORGE, 1824-1905 (923.7)
Wolff, Robert L. Golden key. 1961. 6.00. Yale
MacDONALD, SIR JOHN ALEXANDER, 1815-1891 (923.272)
Creighton, Donald Grant. John A. MacDonald. il. 1953. 7.50. Houghton
MACEDONIA (949.56)
Macedon, 401-301 B. C. (Cambridge ancient history. vol. 6) 13.50. Cambridge U. P.
Macurdy, Grace Harriet. Hellenistic queens: A study of woman-power in Macedonia,
    Seleucid Syria, and Ptolemaic Egypt. il. 1932. 4.00. Johns Hopkins
McGILLIVRAY, ALEXANDER, 1740 (ca.)--1793 (923.273)
Caughey, John W. McGillivray of the Creeks. il. 1938. 5.95. U. of Okla.
MACHIAVELLI, NICCOLO, 1469-1527 (923.245)
Butterfield, Herbert. Statecraft of Machiavelli. 2.25. Macmillan
Hale, John R. Machiavelli and Renaissance Italy. il. 1961. 2.50. Macmillan

Ridolfi, Roberto. Life of Niccolo Machiavelli. tr. by Cecil Grayson. 1962. 6.00.
U. of Chicago
Strauss, Leo. Thoughts on Machiavelli. 6.00. Free Press
MACHINE ACCOUNTING (657)
Johnson, Eldred. Accounting systems in modern business. 1959. 7.75; solutions
manual, 1.00. McGraw
Jones, Cardner M. Electronics in business. 1958. 3.50. Bur. of Bus. & Econ.
Res., Mich. State U.
MACHINE-SHOP PRACTICE (621.75)
Ashcroft, C. C., and J. A. G. Easton. General shop work. il. 4.20. Macmillan
Boston, O. W. Metal processing. 1951. 9.50. Wiley
Brooks, Phillip. Machine shop manual. 3.85. Lucas Bros. (R)
Graham, Frank D. Machinists and toolmakers handbook. 6.00. Audel
Wagener, A. M., and H. R. Arthur. Machine shop: Theory and practice. 1950.
4.20; workbook. pap. 2.80. Van Nostrand
Wakemen, Truamn J., and Vernon Lee McCoy. Farm shop. 1960. 5.96. Macmillan
MACHINE-TOOLS (621.9)
American Society of Tool and Manufacturing Engineers. Tool engineers' handbook.
by Frank W. Wilson. 1959. 23.50. McGraw
Electronic Industries Association. Numerical control systems for machine tools.
1957. 5.00. Reinhold
Hine, Charles R. Machine tools for engineers. 1959. 8.50. McGraw
MACHINE-TOOLS--DESIGN (621.9)
Jeffries, William R. Tool design. 1955. 4.25. Prentice-Hall
MACHINE-TOOLS--DICTIONARIES (621.9)
Thompson, Torger G., and Ross A. Peterson. Illustrated jig-tooling dictionary.
1947. 3.50. Macmillan (R)
MACHINERY (621)
Crossley, F. R. E. Dynamics in machines. 1954. 7.50. Ronald
McKay, Robert F. Theory of machines. 5.00. St. Martins
Oberg, Erik, and Franklin D. Jones. Machinery's handbook. il. 13.00. Industrial
Pr. (R)
MACHINERY--DRAWING (744.422)
Audels mechanical drawing guide. 2.50. Audel
Pearson, George. Engineering drawing. il. 1960. 2.20. Oxford U. P.
Turner, W. W., and others. Basic engineering drawing. 1950. 6.00. Ronald
MACHINERY--HISTORY (338.45)
Mumford, Lewis. Technics and civilization. 1934. 6.00. Harcourt
Usher, Abbott P. History of mechanical inventions. il. 1954. 9.75. Harvard
MACHINERY, KINEMATICS OF (621.81)
Billings, J. H. Applied kinematics. 1953. 6.00. Van Nostrand
Doughtie, V. L., and Walter H. James. Elements of mechanism. 1954. 6.50.
Wiley
Maxwell, Robert L. Kinematics and dynamics of machinery. 1960. 9.75. Prentice-
Hall
MACKENZIE, SIR ALEXANDER, 1763-1820 (923.9)
Sheppe, Walter. First man west. il. 1962. 7.50. U. of Calif.
McKINLEY, WILLIAM, PRES. U.S., 1843-1901 (923.173)
Leech, Margaret Kernochan. In the days of McKinley. il. 1959. 7.50. Harper
MACKINTOSH, CHARLES RENNIE, 1868-1928 (927)
Howarth, Thomas. Charles Rennie Mackintosh and the modern movement. il.
1953. 10.00. Wittenborn
MACKLIN, CHARLES, 1697-1797 (927)
Appleton, William W. Charles Macklin: An actor's life. il. 1960. 5.00. Harvard
MacMILLAN, DONALD BAXTER, 1874- (923.9)
Allen, Everett S. Arctic odyssey, the life of Rear Admiral Donald B. MacMillan.
il. 5.00. Dodd
MACROMOLECULES (539)
Albertsson, P. A. Partition of cell particles and macromolecules. il. 1961. 7.00.
Wiley

Melville, Harry W.   Big molecules. il. 1958. 4.50. Macmillan
Tanford, Charles.   Physical chemistry of macromolecules. 1961. 16.00. Wiley
MACY, ANNE (SULLIVAN) 1866-1936 (923.7)
Gibson, William.   Miracle worker. 1957. 3.95. Knopf
Hickock, Lorena A.   Touch of magic. il. 1961. 3.50. Dodd
Keller, Helen.   Teacher: Anne Sullivan Macy. 1955. 3.95. Doubleday¹
MADAGASCAR (969.1)
Attenborough, David.   Bridge to the past: Animals and people of Madagascar.
   il. 1962. 3.95? Harper
MADISON, JAMES, PRES. U.S., 1751-1836 (923.173)
Brant, Irving.   James Madison. 5 vols. vol. 1. Virginia revolutionist; vol. 2.
   Nationalist; vol. 3. Father of the Constitution; vol. 4. Secretary of State; vol.
   5. President. 1956; vol. 6. Commander-in-Chief. 1961. 7.50 ea. Bobbs
MADRIGAL (784.1)
Einstein, Alfred.   Italian Madrigal. 3 vols. 1949. 30.00. Princeton
Fellowes, Edmund H.   English madrigal composers. 1948. 5.60. Oxford U. P.
MAETERLINCK, MAURICE, 1862-1949 (928)
Halls, W. D.   Maurice Maeterlinck. il. 1960. 6.10. Oxford U. P.
MAFIA (364.14)
Allen, Edward J.   Merchants of menace: The Mafia. 11.50. Thomas, C. C
MAGELLAN, FERDINAND (FERNAO MAGALHAES) d. 1521 (923.9)
Nowell, Charles E.   Magellan's voyage around the world. il. 1962. 5.00? North-
   western U.
Parr, Charles McKew.   So noble a captain: The life and times of Ferdinand Magellan.
   il. 1953. 6.00; Spanish ed. 3.00. Crowell
MAGIC (398.3)
Bouisson, Maurice.   Magic: Its history and principal rites. tr. by G. Almayrac. il.
   5.00. Dutton
DeClaremont, L.   Ancient book of magic. 2.00. Wehman
Frazer, James G.   Golden bough: Study in magic and religion. 13 vols. 1955. 65.00.
   St. Martins (R)
Frazer, James G.   New Golden bough. abridged ed. by Theodor H. Gaster. 1959.
   8.50. Criterion (R)
Read, C.   Man and his superstitions. 1925. 6.50. Cambridge U. P.
Webster, Hutton.   Magic: A sociological study. 8.50. Stanford
MAGIC--HISTORY (398.3)
Levi, Eliphas.   History of magic. 6.00. Borden
Thorndike, L.   History of magic and experimental science. 8 vols. 1923-1956. vol.
   1-6, 8.50 ea; vols. 7-8, 10.00 ea. Columbia (R)
MAGINOT LINE (623.194)
Rowe, Vivian.   Great wall of France: The triumph of the Maginot Line. il. 1959.
   4.50. Putnam
MAGNA CARTA (942.033)
McKechnie, William S.   Magna Carta: A commentary of the Great Charter of
   King John, with historical introduction. 1914. 15.00. Franklin, B.
Thompson, Faith.   Magna Carta: Its role in the making of the English Constitution,
   1300-1629. il. 1948. 6.50. U. of Minn.
MAGNESIUM (620.187)
Roberts, C. Sheldon.   Magnesium and its alloys. il. 1960. 9.00. Wiley
MAGNETIC MATERIALS (538)
Osborn, J. A.   Magnetism and magnetic materials: Proceedings. 1962. 12.50.
   Plenum
Polydoroff, W. J.   High frequency magnetic materials. 1960. 9.00. Wiley
MAGNETIC MEMORY (CALCULATING MACHINES) (510.7832)
Meyerhoff, A. J.   Digital applications of magnetic devices. 1960. 14.00. Wiley
MAGNETIC RECORDERS AND RECORDING (681.8)
Guy, Percival J.   How to get the best out of your tape recorder. 2.50. Wehman
Haynes, N. M.   Elements of magnetic tape recording. 1957. 7.95. Prentice-Hall

Mark, David. How to select and use your tape recorder. il. pap. 2.95. Rider

MAGNETISM (538)

Abraham, Max. Classical theory of electricity and magnetism. by Richard Becker. il. 1951. 5.95. Hafner

Attwood, S. S. Electric and magnetic fields. 1949. 6.75. Wiley

Bates, Leslie F. Modern magnetism. 1961. 7.50. Cambridge U. P

Duckworth, Henry E. Electricity and magnetism. 1960. 8.00. Holt, Rinehart & Winston

Jeans, James H. Mathematical theory of electricity and magnetism. 9.50. Cambridge U. P.

Loeb, Leonard B. Fundâmentals of electricity and magnetism. 1947. Dover

Scott, William T. Physics of electricity and magnetism. il. 1959. 8.95. Wiley

Sears, Francis W. Electricity and magnetism.il. 1951. 9.75. Addison-Wesley

Swoope, C. W. Lessons in practical electricity. by Erich Hausmann. il. 1948. 5.40. Van Nostrand

MAGNETISM, TERRESTRIAL (538)

Heiskanen, Weikko, and F. A. Vening Meinesz. The earth and its gravity field. 1958. 13.50. McGraw

MAGNETOCHEMISTRY (538)

Selwood, Pierce W. Magnetochemistry. il. 1956. 13.50. Wiley

MAGNETS (538)

Parker, Rollin J., and R. J. Studders. Permanent magnets and their applications. 1962. 16.00. Wiley

MAHABHARATA, BHAGAVADGITA (891.1)

Edgerton, Franklin. Bhagavad-Gita. 2 vols. 1944. 5.00. Harvard

MAHAN, ALFRED THAYER, 1840-1914 (923.7)

Livezey, William E. Mahan on sea power. il. 1954. 4.50. U. of Okla.

MAHLER, GUSTAV, 1860-1911 (927)

Walter, Bruno. Gustav Mahler. 1958. 3.50. Knopf

MAILLIARD, ANNE ELIZA (WARD) 1824-1895 (920.7)

Tharp, Louise Hall. Three saints and a sinner. 1956. 5.75. Little

MAINE--DESCRIPTION AND TRAVEL (974.1)

Clifford, Harold. Maine and her people. il. 1961. 3.95. Wheelwright

Thoreau, Henry David. Maine woods. il. 1950. 5.50. Norton

MAINE--HISTORY (974.1)

Smith, Marion J. History of Maine from wilderness to statehood. il. 1961. 5.00. Wheelwright

MAINE--SOCIAL LIFE AND CUSTOMS (974.1)

Chase, Mary Ellen. Goodly heritage. il. by Maitland de Gogorza. 3.50. Holt,

MAITLAND, FREDERIC WILLIAM, 1850-1906 (923.4)

Cameron, James R. Frederick William Maitland and the history of English Law. il. 1961. 4.00. U. of Okla.

MAKE-UP, THEATRICAL (792.027)

Bamford, T. W. Practical make-up for the stage. 1953. 4.95. Pitman

Corson, Richard. Stage makeup. il. 9.50. Meredith

Downs, Harold, Theatre and stage. 2 vols. 1951. 25.00. Pitman

Kehoe, Vincent J. R. Technique of film and television make-up. 1957. 9.00. Hastings

MALARIAL FEVER (616.9)

Macdonald, George. Epidemiology and control of malaria. 1957. 8.25. Oxford U. P.

MALAY ARCHIPELAGO (959.5)

Cole, Fay Cooper. Peoples of Malaysia. il. 1945. 6.25. Van Nostrand

Robequain, C. Malaya, Indonesia, Borneo and the Philippines. 1958. 7.50. Wiley

Wallace, Alfred R. Malay Archipelago. 4.00. Smith, Peter

MALAY PENINSULA (959.5)

Winstedt, Richard. Malaya and its history. 2.50. Hillary

MALAYA (959.5)

Ginsburg, Norton, and Chester F. Roberts, Jr. Malaya. il. 1958. 6.75. U. of Wash.

Gullick, J. M. Indigenous political systems of western Malaya. 5.00. Humanities
International Bank for Reconstruction and Development. Economic development of
   Malaya. 1955. 7.50. Johns Hopkins
Kennedy, J. History of Malaya. 1962. 6.75. St. Martins
MALLORY, STEPHEN RUSSELL, 1813-1873 (923.7)
Durkin, Joseph T. Stephen R. Mallory: Confederate navy chief. 1954. 6.00. U.
   of N. C.
MALORY, SIR THOMAS, 15th CENTURY (928)
Simko, Jan. Word-order in the Winchester manuscript and in William Caxton's
   edition of Thomas Malory's Morte D'Arthur (1485) 3.50. Daub
Vinaver, Eugene. Malory. il. 1929. 3.00. Oxford U. P.
MALPRACTICE (614.26)
Regan, Louis J. Doctor, patient and the law. by C. Joseph Stetler and Alan R.
   Moritz. 1962. 15.00? Mosby
Roady, Thomas G., Jr., and William R. Andersen. Professional negligence.
   1960. 10.00. Vanderbilt
MALRAUX, ANDRE, 1895- (928)
Flanner, Janet. Men and monuments. il. 1957. 5.00. Harper
MALTA (945.85)
Evans, John D. Malta. il. 1959. 6.95. Praeger
Bradford, Ernle D. S. Great siege. il. 1962. 6.50. Harcourt
MALTHUS, THOMAS ROBERT, 1766-1834 (301.32)
McCleary, George F. Malthusian population theory. 3.50. Humanities
Marx, Karl, and Friedrich Engels. Marx and Engels on Malthus. by Ronald L.
   Meek. 1954. 2.25. Int. Pubs.
MAMMALS (599)
Baker, Mary, and William Bridges. Wild animals of the world. il. 1957. 4.50.
   Doubleday
Booth, Ernest S. How to know the mammals. by Harry E. Jaques. 1950. 3.25.
   Brown, W. C.
Burton, Maurice. Systematic dictionary of mammals of the world. il. 1962. 7.50.
   Crowell
Huxley, Julian, and W. Suschitzky. Kingdom of the beasts. il. 12.50. Vanguard
Palmer, E. Laurence. Palmer's fieldbook of mammals. il. 1957. 3.95. Dutton (R)
Sanderson, Ivan. Living mammals of the world. il. 1955. 9.95. Doubleday'
Scott, William B. History of land mammals in the Western Hemisphere. il. 1937.
   14.50. Hafner (R)
Young, J. Z. Life of mammals. 1957. 14.40. Oxford U. P.
MAMMALS--NORTH AMERICA (599.970)
Anthony, H. E. Field book of North American mammals. il. 1928. 3.95. Putnam
   (R)
Barker, Will. Familiar animals of America. il. 1956. 5.95; lib. bdg. 5.11. Harper
Burt, W. H., and R. P Grossenheider. Field guide to the mammals. il. 1952.
   4.50. Houghton (R)
Cahalane, Victor H. Mammals of North America. il. 7.95. Macmillan
Hall, E. R., and K. R. Kelson. Mammals of North America. 2 vols. 1959. 35.00.
   Ronald (R)
Hamilton, William John. American mammals. 1939. 7.95. McGraw
O'Connor, Jack, and George Goodwin. Big game animals of North America. il. 1961.
   10.00. Dutton
Palmer, Ralph S. Mammal guide: Mammals of North American, north of Mexico.
   il. 1954. 4.95. Doubleday (R)
Sanderson, Ivan T. How to know the American mammals. il. 1951. 3.95. Little
MAMMALS, FOSSIL (569)
Scott, William B. History of land mammals in the Western Hemisphere. il. 1937.
   14.50. Hafner
MAN (573)
Baker, Herschel C. Image of man. 1961. 3.85. Smith, Peter

Berdyaev, Nikolai. Destiny of man. 6.00. Hillary
Brennan, Robert E. Image of his Maker. 1948. 3.25. study aids, 1.25. Bruce
Brinton, Crane. Fate of man. 7.50. Braziller
Burr, H. S. Nature of man and the meaning of existence. 1962. 5.50. Thomas, C. C
Carrel, Alexis. Man, the unknown. 1939. 4.50. Harper
Davenport, Russell W. Dignity of man. 1955. 5.00. Harper
Dobzhansky, Theodosius. Biological basis of human freedom. 1956. 2.95. Columbia
Frank, Waldo. Rediscovery of man. 1958. 6.95. Braziller
Hensill, John S. Biology of man. 1954. 16.95. McGraw
Kahn, Fritz. Man in structure and function. 2 vols. il. 1943. 13.75. Knopf
Klubertanz, George P. Philosophy of human nature. 1953. 4.25. Appleton
Life. Epic of Man by the Editors of Life. 1961. 15.50. Prentice-Hall (R)
Linton, Ralph. Science of man in the world crisis. 1945. 4.75. Columbia
McKinley, G. M. Evolution: The ages and tomorrow. 1956. 4.50. Ronald
Maritain, Jacques. Person and the common good. 2.50. Scribner
Mead, Margaret. Male and female. 1949. 5.00. Morrow
Medawar, Peter B. Future of man. 1960. 3.00. Basic Books
Needham, James G. About ourselves. 1948. 4.50. Ronald
Percival, H. W. Democracy is self-government. 1952. 3.00. Word Foundation
Radhakrishnan, S., and P. T. Raju. Concept of man. 1960. 5.50. Johnsen
Wolfe, Don M. Image of man in America. 1957. 5.00. S. M. U.
Young, Clarence W., and others. Introduction to biological science. 1956. 6.50.
    Harper
MAN--CONSTITUTION (573)
Parnell, Richard W. Behaviour and Physique. il. 1958. 7.00. Williams & Wilkins
MAN--INFLUENCE OF ENVIRONMENT (573.4)
Burns, Neal M. Unusual environments and human behavior. by Randall M.
    Chambers, and Edwin Hendler. 1962. 10.00. Free Press
Rogers, Edward S. Human ecology and health. 1960. 7.75. Macmillan
Taylor, Griffith. Environment and nation: Geographical factors in the cultural
    and political history of Europe. il. 1936. 4.50. U. of Toronto
Taylor, Griffith. Environment, race and migration. 1937. 4.50. U. of Toronto
Vogt, William. Road to survival. il. 4.50. Sloane
MAN--ORIGIN (573.2)
Andrew, Roy Chapman. Meet your ancestors: A biography of primitive man. il.
    1945. 4.50. Viking
Ardrey, Robert. African genesis. il. 1961. 6.95. Atheneum
Bates, Marston. Man in nature. 1961. 3.75. Prentice-Hall
Clark, W. E. Le Gros. Fossil evidence for human evolution. il. 1955. 6.00.
    U. of Chicago
Corte, Nicholas. Origins of man. tr. by Eric Earnshaw Smith. 1959. 3.50.
    Hawthorn
Howells, William White. Mankind in the making. il. 1959. 4.95. Doubleday
Huxley, Thomas H. Man's place in nature. il. 1959. 4.40. U. of Mich.
Leakey, Louis S. B. Adam's ancestors, the evolution of man and his culture. 3.50.
    Smith, Peter
Read, C. Origin of man. 1925. 3.50. Cambridge U. P.
MAN (THEOLOGY) (233)
Belkin, Samuel. In His image. 1961. 6.50. Abelard
Brandon, S. G. F. Man and his destiny in the great religions. 1962. 7.50. U. of
    Toronto
Brunner, H. Emil. Man in revolt. 1947. 7.50. Westminster
Come, Arnold B. Human spirit and Holy Spirit. 1959. 4.00. Westminster
Fuller, Edmund. Man in modern fiction. 1958. 3.50. Random
Hamilton, William. Christian man. 1956. 1.00. Westminster
Messenger, Ernest C. Theology and evolution. 1952. 4.50. Newman
Niebuhr, Reinhold. Nature and destiny of man. 1 vol. 5.95. Scribner
Stamm, Frederick. I believe in man. 1959. 1.50. Abingdon

Thomas, Aquinas, Saint. Treatise on man. tr. by James F. Anderson. 1962.
Prentice-Hall
MAN, PREHISTORIC (571)
Augusta, Josef. Prehistoric man. il. 1961. 9.95. Tudor
Boule, Marcellin, and Henri V. Vallois. Fossil men. il. 1957. 9.50. Holt,
Rinehart & Winston
Childe, V. Gordon. Dawn of European civilization. 1958. 7.50. Knopf
Clark, John G. D. World prehistory: An outline. il. 1961. 6.00. Cambridge U.P.
Hawkes, Jacquetta. Man on earth. il. 1955. 3.75. Random
Howells, William. Back of history: The story of our own origins. il. 1954. 5.00.
Doubleday
Kuhn, Herbert. On the track of prehistoric man. il. 1955. 3.95. Random
Mellersh, H. E. L. Story of early man. il. 1959. 4.50. Viking
MAN, PREHISTORIC--AMERICA (571)
Bowden, A. O., and others. Day before yesterday in America. il. 1946. 3.60.
Macmillan
Brennan, Louis A. No stone unturned. 1959. 5.00. Random
Hibben, Frank C. Lost Americans. il. 3.25. Smith, Peter
MAN, PREHISTORIC--EUROPE (571)
Bibby, Geoffrey. Testimony of the spade. 1956. 6.75. Knopf
Burkitt, M. C. Old stone age: A study of Palaeolithic times. il. 1956. 3.75.
N. Y. U.
Burkitt, M. C. Our early ancestors. 1926. 4.50. Cambridge U. P.
MAN, PRIMITIVE (571)
Boas, Franz. Mind of primitive man. 5.50. Macmillan
Hoebel, Edward Adamson. Man in the primitive world. 1958. 9.95. McGraw
Murdock, George Peter. Our primitive contemporaries. il. 1934. 6.25. Macmillan
Radin, Paul. Primitive man as philosopher. 3.75. Smith, Peter
MANAGEMENT (658)
Albers, Henry H. Organized executive action. il. 1961. 7.50. Wiley
American Management Association. Shaping a new concept of administrative
management. 1961. 3.00. Am. Management Assn.
Barnard, Chester Irving. Organization and management. 1948. 4.50. Harvard
Cantor, Nathaniel. Learning process for managers. 1958. 3.50. Harper
Collier, Abram T. Management, men, and values. 1962. 5.00? Harper
Dale, John D. Managerial accounting in the small company. il. 1961. 5.00.
Reinhold
Dauten, Paul M., Jr. Current issues and emerging concepts in management.
Houghton
Folsom, Marion B. Executive decision making. 1962. 4.95. McGraw
Glover, John G. Fundamentals of professional management. il. 1958. 6.50.
Simmons-Boardman
Hastings, Paul G. Fundamentals of business enterprise. il. 1961. 6.95. Van
Nostrand
Lepawsky, Albert. Administration: The art and science of organization and
management. 1949. 6.00. Knopf
Marvin, Philip R. Administrative management. 1954. 5.00. Research Pr.
Newman, William H. Administrative action: The techniques of organization and
management. 1951. 10.60. cases. 1.50. Prentice-Hall
Preston, Lee E. Managing the independent business. il. 1962. 9.00. Prentice-
Hall
Richards, Max D., and William A. Nielander. Readings in management. 1958.
7.50. South-Western Pub.
Tead, Ordway. Art of administration. 1951. 5.00. McGraw
Umbach, Clayton A., Jr. How to prepare for management responsibilities. il.
1962. 5.50. Gulf
MANCHA, LA. SPAIN (946.4)
Croft-Cooke, Rupert. Through Spain with Don Quixote. il. 1960. 5.00. Knopf

MANDATES (325.3)
Joseph, Bernard. British rule in Palestine. 1948. 3.75. Pub. Affairs
Longrigg, Stephen H. Syria and Lebanon under French mandate. il. 1958. 6.75.
    Oxford U. P.
Upthegrove, Campbell L. Empire by mandate. 1954. 3.50. Twayne
MANET, EDOUARD, 1832-1883 (928.4)
Hamilton, G. H. Manet and his critics. 1954. 7.50. Yale
Venturi, L. Four steps toward modern art. il. 1956. 3.00. Columbia
MANIC-DEPRESSIVĖ PSYCHOSES (616.895)
Bellak, Leopold. Manic-depressive psychosis. 1952. 10.25. Grune
MANITOBA--HISTORY (971.272)
Morton, W. L. Manitoba, a history. il. 1957. 6.50. U. of Toronto
MANN, HORACE, 1796-1859 (923.7)
Tharp, Louise Hall. Until victory: Horace Mann and Mary Peabody. il. 1953.
    5.75. Little
MANN, MARY TYLER (PEABODY) 1806-1887 (923.7)
Tharp, Louise Hall. Peabody sisters of Salem. il. 1950. 5.75. Little
MANN, THOMAS, 1875-1955 (928.3)
Brenna, Joseph. Thomas Mann's world. 1962. 6.50. Russell
Mann, Thomas. Sketch of my life. 1960. 3.00. Knopf
MANNERS AND CUSTOMS (390)
Gordon, Cyrus H. Lands of the cross and crescent. 1952. 3.75. Ventnor
Harper, Howard V. Days and customs of all faiths. 4.95. Fleet (R)
Sumner, William G. Folkways. 1940. 10.00. Ginn (R)
Verrill, A. Hyatt. Strange customs, manners and beliefs. il. 1946. 4.00. Farrar,
    Straus
MANNING, HENRY EDWARD, CARDINAL, 1808-1892 (922.2)
Strachey, Lytton. Eminent Victorians. 1.95. Modern Lib.
MANORS (940.1)
Bennett, Henry Stanley. Life on the English manor. 1937. 5.50. 1960. Cambridge
    U. P.
Vinogradoff, Paul. Growth of the manor. 6.00. Franklin, B.
MANPOWER (355)
Ginzberg, Eli. Human resources: The wealth of a nation. 1958. 5.00. S. and S.
Lebergott, S. Manpower in economic growth: The American record since 1800.
    in prep. McGraw
MANSFIELD, KATHERINE, 1888-1923 (928.1)
Alpers, Antony. Katherine Mansfield: Biography. il. 1953. 5.75. Knopf
Berkman, Sylvia L. Katherine Mansfield: A critical study. 1951. 3.75. Yale
MANUAL TRAINING (331.86)
Bennet, Charles A. History of manual and industrial education. 2 vols. vol. 1.
    (to 1870) 1926. 6.00. vol. 2. (1870-1917) 1937. 6.50. Bennett
Groneman, Chris H., and John L. Feirer. General shop. il. 1956. 4.96. McGraw
MANUFACTURES (670)
Andrews, Philip W. S. Manufacturing business. 1955. 3.00. St. Martins
Ansley, A. C. Manufacturing methods and processes. 1957. 12.50. Chilton
Campbell, J. B. Principles of manufacturing materials and processes. 1961.
    9.75. McGraw
Clark, Victor S. History of manufactures in the United States. 3 vols. in prep.
    Dover
De Garmo, E. Paul. Materials and processes in manufacturing. il. 1962. 9.95.
    Macmillan
Miller, Willard E. Geography of manufacturing. il. 1962. 12.65. Prentice-Hall
MANUFACTURES--COSTS (670)
Gillespie, Cecil. Accounting procedure for standard costs. 1952. 8.00. Prentice-
    Hall
Nourse, Edwin G., and Horace B. Drury. Industrial price policies and economic
    progress. 1938. 2.50. Brookings

MANUSCRIPTS (091)
Dupont-Sommer, A. Dead Sea scrolls. il. 2.25. Macmillan
Hamer, Philip M. Guide to archives and manuscripts in the United States. 1961.
15.00. Yale (R)
MAO TSE-TUNG, 1893- (923.151)
MacGregor-Hastie, Roy. Red barbarians: The life and times of Mao Tse-tung.
il. 1962. 3.95. Chilton
Payne, Robert. Portriat of a revolutionary: Mao Tse-Tung. il. 1962. 5.00.
Abelard
Schwartz, Benjamin Isadore. Chinese communism and the rise of Mao. 1951. 5.00.
Harvard
MAPS (912)
Anderzhon, Mamie. Steps in map reading. 1.40. Rand McNally
Birch, T. W. Map and photo reading. il. 1956. 3.50; answer bk. 0.65. St. Martins
Dake, Charles L., and John Stafford Brown. Interpretation of topographic and
geologic maps. 1925. 8.50. McGraw (R)
Debenham, Frank. Global atlas: A new view of the world from space. il. 1958.
5.95. Golden Press (R)
Giachino, J. W., and Henry J. Beukema. Engineering-technical drafting and
graphics. il. 1961. 9.75. Am. Tech. Soc.
Harris, Ruby M. Handbook of map and globe usage. il. 1959. 2.24. Rand McNally
(R)
MARGARET, PRINCESS OF GREAT BRITAIN, 1930- (923.142)
Barrymaine, Norman. The Peter Townsend story. il. 1958. 3.95. Dutton
Crawford, Marion. Little princesses. il. 1950. 4.95. Harcourt
Hope, Alice. Princess Margaret: The story of a royal romance. 1961. 3.95. Bobbs
MARIE ANTOINETTE, CONSORT OF LOUIS XVI, KING OF FRANCE, 1755-1793
(923.144)
Castelot, Andre. Queen of France. il. 1957. 5.50. Harper
MARINE BIOLOGY (591.92)
Barnes, Harold. Oceanography and marine biology. il. 1959. 7.95. Macmillan
Carson, Rachel. Under the sea wind. 1952. 5.00. Oxford U. P.
Cousteau, Jacques-Yves, and Frederic Dumas. Silent world. il. 1953. 5.50.
lib. bdg. 4.79. Harper
Hardy, Alister C. Open sea. 2 vols. vol. 1, World of plankton. 1957. 7.50. Houghton
Robert, Paul A. Wonders of the sea: Life of the ocean. il. 1945. 4.00. Oxford U. P.
MARINE ENGINEERING (623.87)
Barr. MacGibbons marine engineering knowledge. 16.00. Simmons-Boardman
King, Reno C. Practical marine engineering. 1948. 8.90. Prentice-Hall
Witty, M. B., and others. Dictionary of marine engineering abbreviations. lib.
bdg. 20.00. Seti (R)
MARINE ENGINEERING--HANDBOOKS, MANUALS, ETC. (623.87)
Byrnes, Robert F. Practical book for machinists and engineers. 2.00. Christopher
MARINE ENGINES (623.87)
Miller, Conrad. Small boat engines, inboard and outboard. il. 6.00. Sheridan
MARINE FAUNA (591.92)
LaMonte, Francesca. Marine game fishes of the world. il. 1952. 3.95. Doubleday
MacGinitie, George E., and N. Natural history of marine animals. 1949. 9.95.
McGraw
Miner, Roy Waldo. Field book of seashore life. il. 1950. 7.00. Putnam (R)
Nicol, J. A. C. Biology of marine animals. il. 1960. 14.00. Wiley
Verrill, A. Hyatt. Strange creatures of the sea. 1955. 4.00. Farrar, Straus
MARINE FAUNA--BERMUDA ISLANDS (591.923)
Beebe, William. Half mile down. il. 1951. 7.95. Duell
MARINE PAINTING (758.2)
Cobb, David. Drawing and painting seascape. 1954. 10.00. Pitman
Kent, Norman. Seascapes and landscapes in watercolor. 7.50. Watson
MARINE RESOURCES (581.92)
Walford, Lionel Albert. Living resources of the sea. 1958. 6.00. Ronald

MARION, FRANCIS, 1732-1795 (923. 5)
Bass, Robert. Swamp fox. 1959. 4.50. Holt
MARITIME LAW (347.75)
Colombos, Constantine J. International law of the sea. 1959. 13.00. McKay
Reiff, Henry. United States and the treaty law of the sea. 1958. 8.00. U. of
    Minn.
MARITIME LAW--U.S. (347.75)
Turpin, Edward A., and William A. McEwen. Merchant Marine officers' handbook.
    il. 1950. 7.50. Cornell Maritime (R)
MARK, SAINT (922)
Williams, Albert, N. John Mark, first Gospel writer. (Heroes of God) 1956.
    2.00. Assn. Pr.
MARKET SURVEYS (658.83)
Brown, Lyndon O., and others. Advertising media. 1957. 7.50. Ronald
MARKETING (658.8)
American Management Association. Aspects of modern marketing. 1958. 3.00.
    Am. Management Assn.
Bartels, Robert. Development of marketing thought. 1962. 7.35. Irwin
Beckman, Theodore N., and W. R. Davidson. Marketing. 1962. 8.00. Ronald
Boyd, Harper W., Jr., and Richard M. Clewett. Contemporary American
    marketing. 1962. 7.95. Irwin
Brown, Milton P., and others. Problems in marketing. 1961. 8.95; key, 2.50.
    McGraw
Canfield, Bertrand R. Sales administration: Principles and problems. 10.60.
    Prentice-Hall
Converse, Paul D., and others. Elements of marketing. 1958. 8.75. Prentice-
    Hall
Crisp, Richard D. Sales planning and control. il. 1961. 8.50. McGraw
Hansen, Harry L. Marketing. 1961. 12.65. Irwin
Marketing handbook. 1948. 12.00. Ronald (R)
Nystrom, P. H. Marketing handbook. 1948. 12.00. Ronald (R)
Phillips, Charles F., and Delbert J. Duncan. Marketing: Principles and methods.
    1960. 10.60. Irwin
Shultz, William J. American marketing. 1961. 7.95. Wadsworth
Small, Richard L. Salesmanship. 1952. 4.50. Macmillan
Thompson Company, J. Walter. Population and its distribution: The United States
    market. 1961. 24.00. McGraw
Tousley, Rayburn D., and others. Principles of marketing. il. 1962. 8.00.
    Macmillan
Vaile, R. S., and others. Marketing in the American economy. 1952. 7.50.
    Ronald
Wales, Hugh. Changing perspectives in marketing. 1951. 4.00. U. of Ill.
MARKETING--COLLECTIONS (658.8)
McNair, Malcolm P., and Harry L. Hansen. Readings in marketing. 1956. 6.95.
    McGraw
MARKETING (HOME ECONOMICS) (641)
Wright, Carlton. Food buying: Marketing information for consumer. il. 1962.
    6.75. Macmillan
MARKETING RESEARCH (658.83)
Holmes, Parker. Marketing research, principles and readings. 1960. 7.50.
    South-Western Pub.
MARLOWE, CHRISTOPHER, 1564-1593 (822.32)
Boas, F. S. Christopher Marlowe: A biographical and critical study. il. 1940.
    4.50. Oxford U. P.
Kocher, Paul. Christopher Marlowe: A study of his thought, learning and character.
    1961. 7.50. Russell
Wilson, F. P. Marlowe and the early Shakespeare. 1953. 2.40. Oxford U. P.
MARQUAND, JOHN PHILLIPS, 1893- (928.7)
Gross, John. John P. Marquand. 1962. 3.50. Twayne

MARRIAGE (301.42)
Adams, Clifford R. Preparing for marriage: A guide to marital and sexual
   adjustment. 1951. 3.50. Dutton
Adams, Theodore F. Making your marriage succeed. 1953. 2.50. Harper
Baruch, Dorothy W., and Hyman Miller. Sex in marriage: New understanding
   1962. 4.95? Harper, or Hoeber
Bee, Lawrence S. Marriage and family relations. 1959. 6.00. Harper
Bernard, Jessie, and others. Dating, mating and marriage. 1958. 4.75. Allen,
   Howard
Boone, William Cooke. What God hath joined together. 1942. pap. 1.25. Boardman
Bossard, J. H. S., and E. S. Boil. Why marriages go wrong. 1958. 4.00.
   Ronald
Bowman, Henry A. Christian interpretation of marriage. 1959. 2.50. Westminster
Bowman, Henry A. Marriage for moderns. il. 1960. 9.50. McGraw
Briffault, Robert and Bronislaw Malinowski. Marriage past and present. 1956.
   2.50. Sargent
Brink, Frederick W. This man and this woman. 1948. 2.00. Assn. Pr.
Butterfield, Oliver M. Planning for marriage. il. 1956. 5.25. Van Nostrand
Camp, Wesley D. Marriage and family in France since the Revolution. 7.50.
   Twayne
Cavan, Ruth S. American marriage. il. 1960. 6.95. Crowell
Cavanagh, John Richard. Fundamental marriage counseling. 1957. 8.00. Bruce
Cuber, John Frank. Marriage counseling practice. 2.60. Appleton
Duvall, Evelyn M., and Reuben Hill. Being married. 1960. 5.50. Heath
Duvall, Evelyn M., and Reuben Hill. When you marry. 1962. 4.95. Assn. Pr.
Duvall, Sylvanus M. Before you marry. 1959. 3.50. Assn. Pr.
Ellis, Havelock. Sex and marriage. 1952. 3.00. Random
Fishbein, Morris, and Ernest W. Burgess. Successful marriage. il. 1955. 6.00.
   Doubleday
Foster, Robert Gelb. Marriage and family relationships. il. 5.50. Macmillan
Freeman, Lucy, and Harold Greenwald. Emotional maturity in love and marriage.
   1961. 4.95. Harper
Himes, Norman E., and Donald L. Taylor. Your marriage. il. 1955. 5.45.
   Holt, Rinehart & Winston
Jacobson, Paul. American marriage and divorce. 1959. 12.00? Rinehart
Landis, Judson T., and Mary G. Building a successful marriage. 1958. 10.60.
   Prentice-Hall
Landis, Paul H. Making the most of marriage. il. 6.75. Appleton
Lantz, H. R., and E. C. Snyder. Marriage. 1962. 6.50. Wiley
Mace, David Robert. Success in marriage. 1958. 2.95. Abingdon
Mace, David R. Whom God hath joined. 1953. 2.00. Westminster
Morgan, William H., and Mildred I. Thinking together about marriage and family.
   1955. 3.50. Assn. Pr.
Peterson, James A. Toward a successful marriage. il. 1960. 3.95. Scribner
Popenoe, Paul, and Dorothy C. Disney. Can this marriage be saved? 5.95.
   Macmillan
Popenoe, Paul. Marriage is what you make it. 1950. 3.95. Macmillan
Russell, Bertrand. Marriage and morals. 1929. 3.50. Liveright
Skidmore, Rex A., and Anthon S. Cannon. Building your marriage. 1958. 6.50.
   Harper
Van Buren, A. Dear Abby on marriage. 1962. 3.50. McGraw
MARRIAGE--U.S. (301.42)
Nimkoff, Meyer F. Marriage and the family. 1947. 6.75. Houghton
Sirjamaki, John. American family in the twentieth century. 1953. 4.25. Harvard
MARRIAGE, MIXED (301.42)
Bossard, J. H. S., and E. S. Boll. One marriage, two faiths. 1957. 3.50. Ronald
Pikem James A. If you marry outside your faith. 1962. 3.50? Harper

MARRIAGE COUNSELING (301.426)
Herbert, W. L., and F. V. Jarvis. Art of marriage counseling. 1959. 2.75.
    Emerson
Johnson, Dean. Marriage counseling. il. 1961. 7.65. Prentice-Hall
Mudd, Emily H., and others. Marriage counseling: A casebook. 1958. 6.50.
    Assn. Pr.
Vincent, Clark E. Readings in marriage counseling. 1957. 4.50. Crowell
MARRIAGE CUSTOMS AND RITES (392.5)
Fielding, William. Strange customs of courtship and marriage. 2.95. Doubleday
Fortes, Meyer. Marriage in tribal societies. 1962. 4.75. Cambridge U. P.
MARRIAGE LAW (347)
Fishman, Nathaniel. Married woman's bill of rights. 1943. 4.00. Liveright
Keezer, F. Marriage and divorce. 1946. with suppl. 15.00. Bobbs
MARS (PLANET) (523.4)
Ley, Willy, and Wernher Von Braun. Exploration of Mars. il. 1956. 5.95.
    Viking
Moore, Patrick. Guide to Mars. il. 1958. 3.50. Macmillan
Richardson, R. S. Exploring Mars. 1955. 4.50. McGraw
MARSHALL, JOHN, 1755-1835 (923.473)
Beveridge, Albert J. Life of John Marshall. il. 2 vols. set. 17.50. Houghton
MARSHALL, PETER, 1902-1949 (922)
Marshall, Catherine. Man called Peter. 1951. 4.00; special ed., 2.49. McGraw
MARSHES (631.6)
Errington, Paul L. Of men and marshes. 4.50. Macmillan
MARTYRDOM (272)
Rahner, Karl. On the theology of death. 1961. 2.25. Herder & Herder, N. Y. C.
MARTYRS (272)
Foxe, John. Foxe's book of martyrs. 3.00. Holt, Rinehart & Winston (R)
O'Connell, John B. Roman martyrology. 6.75. Newman
Ricciotti, Giuseppe. Age of martyrs. 1959. 4.95. Bruce
MARX, KARL, 1818-1883 (920.343)
Barzun, Jacques. Darwin, Marx, Wagner: Critique of a heritage. 3.00. Smith,
    Peter
Bober, M. M. Karl Marx's interpretation of history. 1948. 6.00. Harvard
Cornu, Auguste. Origins of Marxian thought. 1957. 3.75. Thomas, C. C
Engels, Friedrich. On Capital. 2.00. Int. Pubs.
Hook, Sidney. From Hegel to Marx. 1950. 6.00. Humanities
Mehring, Franz. Karl Marx: The story of his life. 5.00. Humanities
Riis, S. M. Karl Marx: Master of fraud. 3.00. Speller
Tucker, Robert C. Philosophy and myth in Karl Marx. 5.50. Cambridge U. P.
MARY I, QUEEN OF ENGLAND, 1516-1558 (923.142)
Prescott, Hilda F. M. Mary Tudor. il. 1962. 6.00. Macmillan
MARY STUART, QUEEN OF THE SCOTS, 1542-1587 (923.142)
Buchanan, George. Tyrannous reign of Mary Stuart. by W. A. Gatherer. il.
    1958. 5.00. Aldine
MacNalty, Arthur S. Mary, Queen of Scots. 1961. 4.50. Ungar
Morrison, N. Brysson. Mary, Queen of Scots. il. 1960. 5.50. Vanguard
Schiller, Friedrich von. Mary Stuart. tr. by Sophie Wilkins. 1959. bds. 2.95.
    Barron's
MARYLAND--HISTORY (975.2)
Crowl, Philip A. Maryland during and after the revolution. 1943. 2.50. Johns
    Hopkins
Manakee, Harold R. Maryland in the Civil War. il. 4.50. Maryland Hist. Soc.
MASONRY (693)
Dalzell, James Ralph. Simplified masonry planning and building. 1955. 6.75.
    McGraw
Graham, Frank D. Masons and builders guides. 4 vols. 9.00. Audel
Hawkins, R. R., and C. H. Abbe. Walks and paths, driveways, steps, curbs,
    and edgings. 2.50. Van Nostrand

MASS (264.02)
Amoit, Francois. History of Mass. 1959. 3.50. Hawthorn
Gassner, Jerome. Canon of the Mass: Its history, theology, and art. 1949. 5.00.
Herder
MASSACHUSETTS--HISTORY (974.4)
Morison, Samuel E. Maritime history of Massachusetts, 1783-1860. il. 1921. 6.50.
(Sentry 6) 1961. Houghton
Winslow, D. Kenelm. Mayflower heritage. 1957. 3.50. Funk
MASSACHUSETTS--HISTORY--COLONIAL PERIOD (974.4)
Bradford, William. Bradford's history of Plymouth Plantation, 1606-1646. by
W. T. Davis. 1908. 5.75. Barnes & Noble
Bradford, William. Of Plymouth plantation. il. by Samuel Eliot Morison. 1952.
6.75. Knopf
Hutchinson, Thomas. History of the Colony and Province of Massachusetts-Bay.
3 vols. by Lawrence Shaw Mayo. 1936. 15.00. Harvard
Winthrop, John. Journal, History of New England, 1630-1649. 2 vols. by J. K.
Hosmer. set 11.50. Barnes & Noble
MATERIALISM (140)
Lange, Friedrich A. History of materialism. 1950. 10.00. Humanities
Marx, Karl, and Friedrich Engels. German ideology. 4.00. Int. Pubs.
Taylor, F. Sherwood. Two ways of life. 1949. 2.00. Newman
MATERIALS (620.1)
Bacha, Charles P., and others. Elements of engineering materials. 1957. 7.25.
Harper
Brady, George S. Materials handbook. 1956. 15.00. McGraw (R)
Chorlton, F. Mechanics of materials for engineers. 1962. 4.50. Wiley
Kohn, Max, and Martin J. Starfield. Materials and processes. il. 1952. 4.68.
Macmillan
Mantell, Charles L. Engineering materials handbook. 1958. 25.00. McGraw (R)
Witty, M. B., and others. Dictionary of materials abbreviations. lib. bdg. 20.00.
Seti (R)
MATHEMATICAL ANALYSIS (510)
Altwerger, Samuel I. Modern mathematics, an introduction. il. 1960. 6.75.
Macmillan
Buck, R. Creighton. Advanced calculus. il. 1956. 8.75. McGraw
Camp, E. J. Mathematical analysis. 1956. 7.75. Heath
Crouch, Ralph B., and E. A. Walker. Introduction to modern algebra and analysis.
1962. 4.00. Holt, Rinehart & Winston
Federer, H., and B. Jonsson. Analytic geometry and calculus. 1961. 8.75. Ronald
Goursat, Edouard. Mathematical analysis. 2 vols. by Earle Hedrick and Dunkel.
vol. 1, 1904. 9.50; vol. 2, 2 pts. pt. 1, Functions of a complex variable; 1916;
pt. 2, Differential equations. 1945. 7.75 ea. Ginn
Jeager, Arno. Introduction to analytic geometry and linear algebra. 1960. 6.00.
Holt, Rinehart & Winston
Johnson, R. E., and others. Introduction to mathematical analysis. 7.00; answers
to even-numbered problems. 0.25. Holt, Rinehart & Winston
Kemeny, John G., and others. Introduction to finite mathematics. 1957. 10.60.
Prentice-Hall
Lass, Harry. Elements of pure and applied mathematics. 1957. 8.75. McGraw
Mostert, Paul S. Analytic trigonometry. il. 1960. 6.35. Prentice-Hall
Schaaf, William L. Basic concepts of elementary mathematics. il. 1960. 5.50.
Wiley
Sokolnikoff, Ivan S., and R. M. Redheffer. Mathematics of physics and modern-
engineering. 1958. 9.95. McGraw
MATHEMATICAL NOTATION (510)
Cajori, Florian. History of mathematical notations. 2 vols. 7.00 ea. Open Ct.
MATHEMATICAL PHYSICS (530.15)
Abro, A. d'. Rise of the new physics. 2 vols. il. 1953. pap. 2.00. ea. Dover

Cotton, Sidney J. Mathematics for communication engineers. il. 1959. 7.95.
Macmillan

Houston, William Vermillion. Principles of mathematical physics. il. 1948. 10.50. '
McGraw

Jackson, J. D. Mathematics for quantum mechanics. il. 1962. 6.00. Benjamin

Lambe, Cyril G. Applied mathematics for engineers and scientists. il. 1959. 8.95.
Macmillan

Menzel, Donald H. Fundamental formulas of physics. 2 vols. il. 1959. 2.00 ea;
set, pap. 4.00. Dover

Page, Leigh. Introduction to theoretical physics. il. 1952. 9.75. Van Nostrand

Sutton, Oliver G. Mathematics in action. il. 1959. 3.50. Dover

MATHEMATICAL RECREATIONS (793.74)

Bakst, Aaron. Mathematical puzzles and pastimes. il. 1954. 4.00. Van Nostrand

Bakst, Aaron. Mathematics--its magic and mastery. 1952. 7.50. Van Nostrand

Carroll, Lewis. Mathematical recreations of Lewis Carroll. Part I: Symbolic
logic, and Game of logic. Part II: Pillow problems, and Tangled tale. 1959.
pap. 1.50 ea. Dover

Court, Nathan A. Mathematics in fun and in earnest. 1958. 4.75. Dial

Gamow, George, and Marvin Stern. Puzzle-math. 1958. 2.75. Viking

Glenn, William H., and Donovan A. Johnson. Invitation to mathematics. il. 4.95.
Doubleday

Kasner, Edward, and James Newman. Mathematics and the imagination. 1940.
4.50. S. and S.

Langman, H. Play mathematics. 1961. 4.95. Hafner

Maxwell, Edwin A. Fallacies in mathematics. il. 1959. 2.95. Cambridge U. P.

Northrop, Eugene P. Riddles in mathematics: A book of paradoxes. il. 1944.
4.50. Van Nostrand

Rademacher, H., and O. Toeplitz: Enjoyment of mathematics: Selections from
mathematics for the amateur. 1957. 4.50. Princeton

Reichmann, W. J. Fascination of numbers. 1957. 4.00. Oxford U. P.

Scientific American. Scientific American book of mathematical puzzles and
diversions. by Martin Gardner. 2 bks. il. 1959. 3.50. 1961. 3.95. S. and S.

MATHEMATICAL STATISTICS (519.9)

Aitken, Alexander C. Statistical mathematics. il. 1952. 1.75. Wiley

Bailey, Norman T. J. Statistical methods in biology. 1959. 4.75. Wiley

Bennett, Carl A., and N. L. Franklin. Statistical analysis in chemistry and
the chemical industry. 1954. 9.75. Wiley

Birnbaum, Zygmunt W. Introduction to probability and mathematical statistics,
il. 1962. 6.50. Harper

Cramer, H. Mathematical methods of statistics. 1946. 7.50. Princeton

Freund, John E. Mathematical statistics. il. 1962. 10.00. Prentice-Hall

Hogben, Lancelot. Statistical theory. 1957. 12.00. Norton

Olkin, Ingram, and others. Contributions to probability, and statistics. 1960.
6.50. Stanford

Rietz, H. L. Mathematical statistics. 1927. 4.00. Open Ct.

Tintner, Gerhard. Mathematics and statistics for economists. 1953. 6.50.
Rinehart

Walker, Helen M., and Joseph Lev. Statistical inference. il. 1953. 7.25. Holt,
Rinehart & Winston

Wiener, Norbert. Cybernetics. 1961. 6.50. Wiley

MATHEMATICIANS (920)

Bell, Eric T. Men of mathematics. il. 1937. 6.50. S. and S. (R)

Hooper, Alfred. Makers of mathematics. pap. 1.45. Vintage

Sarton, George. Study of the history of mathematics and The study of the history
of science. 1957. pap. 1.25. Dover

Turnbull, Herbert W. Great mathematicians. by James R. Newman. il. 1961.
3.50. N. Y. U.

MATHEMATICS (510)

Adler, Irving. New mathematics. il. 1958. 4.00; exercises. 0.25. Day

Allendoerfer, C. B., and C. O. Oakley. Principles of mathematics. 1955. 6. 95. answers. 0. 50. McGraw

Brixey, John C., and Richard V. Andree. Fundamentals of college mathematics. 1961. 8. 95. Holt, Rinehart & Winston

Camm, F. J. Refresher course in mathematics. il. 1953. 2. 95. Emerson

Cooley, Hollis R., and others. Introduction to mathematics. 6. 50. Houghton

Courant, Richard, and Herbert Robbins. What is mathematics? il. 1941. 9. 00. Oxford U. P.

Crowhurst, Norman. Basic mathematics. 4 vols. il. vols. 1, 2, and 3. pap. 3. 90. ea; vol. 4, in prep. Rider

Currier, Clinton H., and others. Course in general mathematics. 1939. 6. 50. Macmillan

Denbow, Carl H. Foundations of mathematics. by Victor Goedicke. 1959. 6. 75. Harper

Dubisch, R. Nature of number. 1952. 5. 50. Ronald

Evans, Trevor. Fundamentals of mathematics. 6. 75. Prentice-Hall

Freund, John E. Modern introduction to mathematics. il. 1956. 8. 50. Prentice-Hall

Glenn, William H., and Donovan A. Johnson. Invitation to mathematics. il. 4. 95. Doubleday

Goodstein, R. L. Fundamental concepts of mathematics. 1962. 7. 50. Pergamon

Hogben, Lancelot. Mathematics for the million. il. 1951. 6. 95. Norton

Hooper, Alfred. Mathematics refresher. il. 5. 10. Holt, Rinehart & Winston

Howe, George. Mathematics for the practical man. il. 1957. 3. 50. Van Nostrand

James, Glenn. Tree of mathematics. il. 6. 00; 5. 50. cash with order. Digest Pr.

Kasner, Edward, and James Newman. Mathematics and the imagination. 1940. 4. 50. S. and S.

Kershner, R. B., and L. R. Wilcox. Anatomy of mathematics. 1950. 7. 50. Ronald

Kline, Morris. Mathematics: A cultural approach. il. 1962. 7. 75. Addison-Wesley

Korn, Granino A., and Thersa M. Mathematical handbook for scientists and engineers. 1961. 20. 00. McGraw (R)

Lapp, C. J., and others. Review of mathematics for college students. 1956. 2. 25. Scott

Logsdon, Mayme Irwin. Mathematician explains. il. 1936. 4. 00; (Phoenix PSS502) U. of Chicago

May, Kenneth O. Elements of modern mathematics. 1959. 9. 50. Addison-Wesley

Minnear, F. L., and Ruby M. Grimes. Review of mathematics: For beginning science and engineering students. 1960. 1. 65. Freeman

Pedoe, Daniel. Gentle art of mathematics. il. 1959. 3. 95. Macmillan

Rees, Paul K. Freshman mathematics. 6. 50. Prentice-Hall

Rider, Paul R. First-year mathematics for colleges. 1962. 7. 50. Macmillan

Rose, Israel H. Modern introduction to college mathematics. il. 1959. 6. 50. Wiley

Smith, Paul K., and H. F. Schroeder. College mathematics for freshman. il. 1959. 5. 00. Van Nostrand

Trimble, H. C., and others. Basic mathematics for general education. 1955. 10. 60. Prentice-Hall

Vance, Elbridge, P. Fundamentals of mathematics. il. 1960. 7. 75. Addison-Wesley

Vergara, William C. Mathematics in everyday things. il. 1959. 3. 95. Harper

Whitehead, Alfred North. Introduction to mathematics. 1959. pap. 1. 50. Oxford U. P.

MATHEMATICS--ADDRESSES, ESSAYS, LECTURES (510)

Court Nathan A. Mathematics in fun and in earnest. 1958. 4. 75. Dial

Fortune. New world of math. by George A. W. Boehm. 1959. 3. 00. Dial

Russell, Bertrand. Mysticism and logic. 1954. 2. 75. Barnes & Noble

Sawyer, W. W.   Prelude to mathematics. 1955. pap. 1.25. Penguin

Smith, Daivd E.   Poetry of mathematics. 1947. 1.25. Scripta Mathematica

Sutton, O. G.   Mathematics in action. il. 1959. 3.50. Dover

MATHEMATICS--APPLIED (510)

Benny, Leonard B.   Mathematics for students of engineering and applied science.
    1954. 6.10. Oxford U. P.

Defares, J. G., and I. N. Sneddon.   Introduction to the mathematics of medicine
    and biology. 1961. 14.00. Year Bk.

Fischer, Bernhard, and Herbert V. Jacobs.   Elements of mathematics for radio,
    television, and electronics. il. 1954. 5.60. Macmillan

Grazda, Edward E., and Martin E. Jansson.   Handbook of applied mathematics.
    il. 1955. 7.95. Van Nostrand (R)

Kuhn, Harry W., and Charles C. Morris.   Mathematics of finance. 6.00. Houghton

Maedel, George F.   Basic mathematics for television and radio. 1953. 6.44.
    Prentice-Hall

Rusinoff, S. E.   Mathematics for industry. il. 1949. 5.50. Am. Tech. Soc.

Sohon, Harry.   Engineering mathematics. 1944. 4.50. Van Nostrand

Stephenson, Geoffrey.   Mathematical methods for science students. 1961. 7.75.
    Wiley

MATHEMATICS--BIBLIOGRAPHY (510)

Parke, Nathan Grier, III.   Guide to the literature of mathematics and physics.
    1959. pap. 2.49. Dover

MATHEMATICS--COLLECTED WORKS (510)

Newman, James R.   World of mathematics. 4 vols. 1956. 25.00; 1960. 1962.
    vol. 1. Men and numbers. pap. 2.95; vol. 2. World of laws and the world
    of chance. pap. 2.75; vol. 3. Mathematical way of thinking. pap. 2.45;
    vol. 4. Machines, music and puzzles. pap. 2.25. S. and S. (R)

Smith, David E.   Source book of mathematics. 2 vols. il. 1959. pap. 1.85 ea.
    set, pap. 3.50. Dover (R)

MATHEMATICS--DICTIONARIES (510)

James, Glenn, and Robert C.   Mathematics dictionary. il. 1959. multilingual,
    15.00. Van Nostrand (R)

Witty, M. B., and others.   Dictionary of physics and mathematics abbreviations.
    lib. bdg. 20.00. Seti (R)

MATHEMATICS--EARLY WORKS TO 1800 (510)

Apollonius of Perga.   Treatise on conic sections. by T. L. Heath. 1961. 9.00.
    Barnes & Noble

Dijksterhuis, E. J.   Archimedes. 15.00. Humanities

MATHEMATICS--FORMULAE (510.8)

Burington, Richard Stevens.   Handbook of mathematical tables and formulas. il.
    1948. 3.75. McGraw (R)

Larsen, Harold.   Rinehart mathematical tables, formulas, and curves. 1953. 2.90;
    alternate ed. 1.75. Holt, Rinehart & Winston

Smith, Percey F., and W. R. Longley.   Mathematical tables and formulae. 1929.
    pap. 2.50. Wiley

MATHEMATICS--HISTORY (510.9)

Ball, W. W. Rouse.   Short account of the history of mathematics. pap. 2.00.
    Dover

Bell, Eric T.   Development of mathematics. 1945. 9.00. McGraw

Bell, Eric T.   Mathematics. queen and servant of science. 1951. 7.50. McGraw

Bell, Eric T.   Men of mathematics. il. 1937. 6.50. S. and S.

Cajori, Florian.   History of mathematics. 6.75. Macmillan

Eves, Howard.   Introduction to the history of mathematics. 1953. 7.00. Rinehart

Eves, Howard, and Carroll V. Newsom.   Introduction to the foundations and
    fundamental concepts of mathematics. 1957. 6.75. Rinehart

Felix, Lucienne.   Modern aspect of mathematics. tr. by Julius H. Hlavaty and
    Fancille H. Hlavaty. il. 1960. 5.00. Basic Books

Hogben, Lancelot.   Mathematics in the making. il. 9.95. Doubleday

Hogben, Lancelot. Mathematics for the million. il. 1951. 6.95. Norton

Kline, Morris. Mathematics in western culture. il. 1953. 8.50. Oxford U. P.

Kramer, Edna E. Main stream of mathematics. 1951. 7.75. Oxford U. P.

Sarton, George. Study of the history of mathematics and The study of the history of science. 1957. pap. 1.25. Dover

Smith, David Eugene. History of mathematics. 2 vols. 1951-1953. 12.00 ea. Ginn

Smith, David E. Number stories of long ago. il. 1955. pap. 0.75. Scripta

Turnbull, Herbert W. Great mathematicians. by James R. Newman. il. 1961. 3.50. N. Y. U.

MATHEMATICS--PHILOSOPHY (510.1)

Bentley, Arthur F. Linguistic analysis of mathematics. 1932. 4.40. Principia Press of Trinity U.

Black, Max. Nature of mathematics. 1950. 5.00. Humanities

Court, Nathan A. Mathematics in fun and in earnest. 1958. 4.75. Dial

Eves, Howard, and Carroll V. Newsom. Introduction to the foundations and fundamental concepts of mathematics. 1957. 6.75. Rinehart

Felix Lucienne. Modern aspect of mathematics. tr. by Julius H. Hlavaty and Fancille H. Hlavaty. il. 1960. 5.00. Basic Books

Lieber, Lillian R. Human values and science, art and mathematics. il. 1961. 3.95. Norton

Mays, Wolfe. Philosophy of Whitehead. 4.25. Macmillan

Richardson, Moses. Fundamentals of mathematics. il. 1958. 7.00. Macmillan

Russell, Bertrand. Introduction to mathematical philosophy. 1924. 3.25. Macmillan (R)

Russell, Bertrand. Principles of mathematics. 1938. 8.50. Norton

Stabler, E. R. Introduction to mathematical thought. il. 1953. 7.75. Addison-Wesley

Wedberg, A. Plato's philosophy of mathematics. 5.00. Humanities

MATHEMATICS--STUDY AND TEACHING (510.7)

Butler, Charles H., and F. Lynwood Wren. Teaching of secondary mathematics. 1961. 7.50. McGraw

Davis, David R. Teaching of mathematics. il. 1951. 7.50. Addison-Wesley

James, Edward J. Teaching of modern school mathematics. 1958. 3.40. Oxford, U. P.

National Council of Teachers of Mathematics. Growth of mathematical ideas, grades K-12. 24th yearbook. by Phillip S. Jones. 1959. 5.00. Nat. Council of Teachers of Math. (R)

National Council of Teachers of Mathematics. Learning of mathematics, its theory and practice. 21st yearbook. by Howard F. Fehr. 1953. 4.00. Nat. Council of Teachers, of Math. (R)

MATHEMATICS--TABLES, ETC. (510.8)

Attwood C. Six-figure logarithms: Antilogarithms and logarithmic trigonometrical functions. 1958. 2.00. Pergamon

Barlow, Peter. Tables, squares and cubes. 1948. 4.95. Powner

Burington, Richard Stevens. Handbook of mathematical tables and formulas. il. 1948. 3.75. McGraw (R)

Comrie, Leslie J. Barlow's tables of squares, square roots, cube roots and reciprocals of all integers up to 12,500. 1952. 4.75. Tudor (R)

Comrie, L. J. Chambers' six-figure mathematical tables. 2 vols. 1949. 12.00 ea. set. 1950. Van Nostrand

Davis, Harold T. Tables of mathematical functions: Arithmetical tables. 8.75. Principia Press of Trinity U.

Hodgman, Charles D., and others. C. R. C. standard mathematical tables. 1961. 4.00. Chemical Rubber (R)

Hodgman, Charles D., and others. Handbook of mathematical tables. 1962. 7.50. Chemical Rubber (R)

Lange, Norbert A. Handbook of chemistry. 1961. 11.00. McGraw (R)

MATHEMATICS, BABYLONIAN (510)
Van der Waerden, B. L. Science awakening. tr. by Arnold Dresden. 1961. 7.50.
Oxford U. P.
MATHEMATICS, CHINESE (510)
Mikami, Y. Development of mathematics in China and Japan. 3.95. Chelsea
MATHEMATICS, GREEK (510)
Euclid. Elements. bks 1-3, by H. S. A. Hall. 0.90. St. Martins
MATHER, COTTON, 1663-1728 (928)
Shryock, Richard H., and Otho T. Beall, Jr. Cotton Mather: The first significant
figure in American medicine. 1954. 4.00. Johns Hopkins
MATHER, INCREASE, 1639-1723 (922.4)
Murdock, Kenneth B. Increase Mather, the foremost American Puritan. il. 1925.
6.00. Harvard
MATISSE, HENRI, 1869-1954 (927.42)
Escholier, Raymond Matisse: A portrait of the artist and the man. il. 1960. 12.50.
Praeger
MATRICES (512.896)
Beaumont, Ross A., and Richard W. Ball. Introduction to modern algebra and
matrix theory. 1954. 6.00. Rinehart
Cooke, Richard G. Infinite matrices and sequence spaces. 1950. 9.50. St. Martins
Ferrar, William L. Algebra: A text-book of determinants, matrices, and alge-
braic forms. 1957. 3.40. Oxford U. P.
Finkbeiner, Daniel T. Introduction to matrices and linear transformations. 1960.
6.50. Freeman
Hohn, Franz E. Elementary matrix algebra. il. 1959. 7.50. Macmillan
Perlis, S. Theory of matrices. il. 1952. 7.75. Addison-Wesley
Thrall, R. M., and L. Thornheim. Vector spaces and matrices. 1957. 6.75.
Wiley
MATTER (530.1)
Fulk, Augustus Marion. Reincarnation. 1940. 4.00. Christopher
Gamow, George. Atom and its nucleus. il. 1961. pap. 1.95. Prentice-Hall
Miall, Stephen, and Laurence M. Chemistry, matter and life. 1937. 2.50. St.
Martins
MATTER--CONSTITUTION (530.1)
Cook, C. Sharp. Modern atomic and nuclear physics. il. 1961. 7.75. Van Nostrand
Fermi, E. Elementary particles. 1951. 3.00. Yale
Massey, Harrie S. W., and Arthur R. Quinton. Basic laws of matter. 1961. il.
3.75. Herald Bks.
Oldenberg, Otto. Introduction to atomic and nuclear physics. 1961. 7.95. McGraw
Rice, F. O., and E. Teller. Structure of matter. 1949. 7.75. Wiley
Wehr, Mentzer R., and James A. Richards, Jr. Physics of the atom. 1960. 9.75.
Addison-Wesley
MATTER--PROPERTIES (530.1)
Bragg, William. Concerning the nature of things. 3.50. Smith, Peter
Gamow, George. Matter, earth and sky. 1958. 10.60. Prentice-Hall
Oparin, A. I. Origin of life on the earth. 1957. 7.50. Academic Press
Smith, Clarence J. General properties of matter. (General degree physics, vol.1)
13.50. St. Martins
MATTHEW, SAINT, APOSTLE (922)
Goodspeed, Edgar J. Matthew, apostle and evangelist. 1959. 3.50. Winston
MATURATION (PSYCHOLOGY) (150)
Abrahamsen, David. Road to emotional maturity. 1958. 4.95. Prentice-Hall
MAUGHAM, WILLIAM SOMERSET, 1874- (928.2)
Brophy, John. Somerset Maugham. pap. 0.50. British Bk.
MAUPASSANT, GUY DE, 1850-1893 (840)
Sullivan, Edward. Maupassant the novelist. 1954. 4.00. Princeton
MAURIAC, FRANCOIS, 1885- (928)
Moloney, Michael F. Francois Mauriac: A critical study. 3.75. Swallow, A.

MAXIMILIAN, EMPEROR OF MEXICO, 1832-1867 (923.1)
Anderson, William M. American in Maximillian's Mexico, 1865-1866: The diaries of William Marshall Anderson. by Ramon E. Ruiz. 1959. 4.25. Huntington Lib.
MAXIMS (398.9)
Dobie, J. Frank. Spur-of-the-cock. 1933. 2.50. S. M. U.
Gracian, Balthasar. Art of worldly wisdom. tr. by Joseph Jacobs. 3.00. Ungar
Stevenson, Burton. Home book of proverbs, maxims and familiar phrases. 1948. boxed. 35.00. Macmillan (R)
MAYAS (972.015)
Gallenkamp, Charles. Maya: The riddle and rediscovery of a lost civilization. il. 1959. 5.50. McKay
Irwin, Constance. Fair gods and stone faces. in prep. St. Martins
Morley, Sylvanus G. Ancient Maya. by George W. Braninerd. 1956. 10.00. Stanford
Thompson, J. Eric S. Rise and fall of the Maya civilization. il. 1959. 5.00. U. of Okla.
Wauchope, Robert. Lost tribes and sunken continents. il. 1962. 3.95. U. of Chicago
MAYAS--ANTIQUITIES (972.015)
Radin, Paul. Story of the American Indian. il. 1944. 4.50. Liveright or Tudor
MAYFLOWER (SHIP) (973.17)
Simon, Philip J. Log of the Mayflower. 1956. 3.50. Priam
MAYO FAMILY (920)
Clapesattle, Helen. Doctors Mayo. il. 1954. 4.75. U. of Minn.
MAYO CLINIC, ROCHESTER, MINN. (616.075)
Wilder, Lucy. Mayo clinic. il. 1955. 3.75. Thomas, C. C.
MEANING (PSYCHOLOGY) (153.66)
Blandhard, Brand. Nature of thought. 2 vols. set. 9.00. Macmillan
Chase, Stuart. Tyranny of words. 1938. 4.50. 1959. Harcourt
Ogden, Charles K., and Ivor A. Richards. Meaning of meaning. 1959. 5.95. Harcourt
Osgood, Charles E., and others. Measurement of meaning. 1957. 7.50. U. of Ill.
Upton, Albert. Design for thinking. il. 1961. 5.00. Stanford
Wellman, Carl P. Language of ethics. 1961. 6.50. Harvard
MEASURING INSTRUMENTS (681.12)
Beckwith, Thomas G., and N. L. Buck. Mechanical measurements. 1961. 9.50. Addison-Wesley
Clason, W. E. Dictionary of automation, computers, control, and measuring. polyglot. 1962. 27.50; Russian suppl. 12.00. Am. Elsevier (R)
MECHANICAL DRAWING (744.422)
Anderson, Edwin P. Mechanical drawing and design. 3.00. Audel
Andrews, C. H. W. Introductory technical drawing. 1962. 3.50. St. Martins
Audels mechanical drawing guide. 2.50. Audel
Coover, Shriver L. Drawing, sketching and blueprint reading. il. 1954. 5.60. McGraw
Fleming, Joseph W., and others. Applied drawing and sketching. il. 1953. 3.50. Am. Tech. Soc.
Fuglsby, Glenn O., and others. General mechanical drawing. 1959. 3.20. Bruce
Giesecke, Frederick E., and others. Technical drawing. il. 1959. 8.25. Macmillan
MECHANICAL ENGINEERING--HANDBOOKS, MANUALS, ETC. (621)
American Society of Mechanical Engineers. ASME handbook of engineering tables. by Jesse Huckert. 1956. 17.50. McGraw (R)
American Society of Mechanical Engineers. ASME handbook of metals engineering: Design. il. by Oscar J. Horger. 1953. 12.00. McGraw (R)
Anderson, Edwin P. Millwrights and mechanics guide. 6.00. Audel (R)
Marks, Lionel S. Mechanical engineers' handbook. il. 1958. 25.00. McGraw (R)
MECHANICAL ENGINEERING--LABORATORIES (621)
Tuve, George L. Mechanical engineering experimentation. il. 1961. 8.00. McGraw

MECHANICAL MOVEMENTS (621.81)
Cowie, Alexander. Kinematics and design of mechanisma. il. 1961. 10.50. Int.
Textbook
Shigley, J. E. Theory of machines. combined vol. 11.50. McGraw
MECHANICS (531)
Broxon, James W. Mechanics. 8.50. Appleton
Galilei, Galileo. On motion, and On mechanics. tr. by I. E. Drabkin, and Stillman
Drake. il. 1960. 5.00. U. of Wis.
Stephenson, Reginald J. Mechanics and properties of matter. 1960. 7.50. Wiley
MECHANICS, ANALYTIC (531.017)
Faires, Virgil M., and Sherman D. Chambers. Analytic mechanics. 1952. 7.50.
Macmillan
MECHANICS, APPLIED (531)
Camm, F. J. Practical mechanics' handbook. 4.00. Transatlantic
Fairman, Selbert, and C. S. Cutshall. Engineering mechanics. 1946. 4.50. Wiley
Higdon, Archie. Mechanics of materials. il. 1960. 7.75. Wiley
Jensen, Alfred E. Statics and strength of materials. 1962. 8.00. McGraw
Key, Eugene G. Elementary engineering mechanics. il. 1960. 5.75. Wiley
Love, L. F. C. Problems in engineering science. 1958. 3.00. St. Martins
Poorman, Alfred P. Applied mechanics. il. 1949. 6.90. McGraw
MECHANIZATION, MILITARY (358.18)
Fuller, J. F. C. Armored warfare. il. 1955. 3.00. Stackpole
Ogorkiewicz, R. M. Armor: A history of mechanized forces. 1960. 8.50. Praeger
MEDAL OF HONOR (355.134)
Donovan, Frank. Medal: The story of the Medal of Honor. 1962. 3.50. Dodd
Schott, Joseph I. Above and beyond: The story of the Congressional Medal of
Honor. 4.95. Putnam
MEDICAL CARE (614)
Evang, Karl. Health service, society, and medicine. 1960. 5.00. Oxford U. P.
Ferguson, Thomas, and A. N. MacPhail, Hospital and community. 1954. 1.55.
Oxford U. P.
Huszar, George B. de. Fundamentals of voluntary health care. 1961. 6.00. Caxton
Potter, William H. You and your doctor. 1961. 5.00. Duell
Saunders, Lyle. Cultural difference and medical care. 1954. 4.50. Russell
Somers, Herman M., and Anne R. Doctors, patients, and health insurance. 1961.
7.50. Brookings
MEDICAL CARE, COST OF (614.253)
Anderson, Odin W., and J. J. Feldman. Family medical costs and voluntary health
insurance: A nationwide survey. 5.00. Harvard
Cunningham, Robert M. Hospitals, doctors, and dollars. 1961. 6.95. McGraw
Page, Earle. What price medical care? 1960. 3.50. Lippincott
Weeks, H. Ashley. Family spending patterns and health care. 1961. 3.50. Harvard
MEDICAL CENTERS (725.23)
Architectural Record. Hospitals, clinics, and health centers. il. 1960. 9.75.
McGraw
MEDICAL ECONOMICS (614.25)
Fein, Rashi. Economics of mental illness. 1958. 3.75. Basic Books
MEDICAL ETHICS (610.694)
DeWitt, Clinton. Privileged communications between physician and patient. 1958.
11.50. Thomas, C. C
Finney, Patrick, and Patrick O'Brien. Moral problems in hospital practice. 1956.
4.75. Herder
McFadden, Charles J. Medical ethics. 1961. 4.75. David
MEDICAL JURISPRUDENCE (340.6)
Brahdy, Leopold. Disease and injury. 1961. 12.50. Lippincott
Gradwohl, R. B. H. Legal medicine. il. 1954. 15.00. Mosby
Long, Rowland H. Physician and the law. 1959. 5.95. Appleton
Tracy, John Evarts. Doctor as a witness. 1957. 4.25. Saunders

MEDICAL MICROBIOLOGY (616. 01)
Brooks, Stewart M. Basic facts of medical microbiology. il. 1962. 5.00. Saunders
Neter, Erwin, and Dorotha R. Edgeworth. Medical microbiology. il. 1962. 7.50.
    Davis
MEDICAL PARASITOLOGY (616. 96)
Chandler, Asa C., and C. P. Read. Introduction to parasitology. 1961. 9.75.
    Wiley
Hegner, Robert, and others. Parasitology. il. 1938. 7.00. Appleton
Hoeppli, R. Parasites and parasitic infections in early medicine and science.
    1959. 14.50. Oxford U. P.
MEDICAL RESEARCH (610)
Bruner, H. Davis. Methods in medical research. vol. 8. 1960. 9.75. Year Bk.
Ciba Foundation. Significant trends in medical research. 1959. 9.50. Little
Ingle, Dwight J. Principles of research in biology and medicine. 1958. 4.75.
    Lippincott
Lush, Brandon. Concepts of medicine. il. 1961. 8.50. Pergamon
Quastel, J. H. Methods in medical research. vol. 9. 1961. 10.75. Year Bk.
Warren, James V. Methods in medical research. vol. 7. 1958. 7.50. Year Bk.
MEDICAL SOCIAL WORK (362.1)
Goldstine, Dora. Expanding horizons in medical social work. 1955. 5.00. U. of
    Chicago
Gruener, Jennette R., and Deborah M. Jensen. Community problems. il. 1954.
    4.00. Mosby
Sellew, Gladys, and Paul H. Furfey, Sociology and its use in nursing service.
    1962. 5.75. Saunders
MEDICAL TECHNOLOGISTS (610.69)
Bredow, Miriam. Medical assistant. 1958. 7.50. McGraw'
Miller, Besse M. Medical secretary's and assistant's handbook. 1960. 5.75.
    Prentice-Hall
Paul, Grace. Your future in medical technology. 2.95; lib. ed. 2.65. Richards
    Rosen
MEDICI, LORENZE DE, 1449-1492 (923.1455)
Ady, Cecilia M. Lorenzo dei Medici and Renaissance Italy. 1955. 2.50. Macmillan
MEDICI, HOUSE OF (920)
Schevill, Ferdinand. Medici. il. 1960. 3.50. Smith, Peter
MEDICINE (610)
Bollo, Louise E. Introduction to medicine and medical terminology. 1961. 5.00.
    Saunders
Mason, Mildred A. Basic medical-surgical nursing. il. 1959. 5.25. Macmillan
Speransky, A. D. Basis for the theory of medicine. 1944. 4.50. Int. Pubs.
MEDICINE--BIBLIOGRAPHY (610.016)
Kelly, E. C. Encyclopedia of medical sources. 1948. 7.50. Williams & Wilkins
    (R)
MEDICINE--BIOGRAPHY (926)
De Kruff, Paul. Men against death. il. 4.50. Harcourt
Williams, Harley. Between life and death. 1952. 4.50. Thomas, C. C
Williams, Harley. Healing touch. il. 1951. 6.75. Thomas, C. C
MEDICINE--COLLECTED WORKS (610)
Adams, Francis. Genuine works of Hippocrates. reprint 1946. 3.00. Williams &
    Wilkins
Spence, James. Purpose and practice of medicine. 1960. 9.50. Oxford U. P.
MEDICINE--DICTIONARIES (610.3)
Dorland, William A. N. Dorland's illustrated medical dictionary. il. 1957. thumb
    indexed, flexible bdg. 12.50. Saunders (R)
Fishbein, Morris. Handy home medical adviser and concise medical encyclopedia.
    il. 2.95. Doubleday (R)
Reference handbook and dictionary of nursing: Olson's Nurses' handbook, tenth
    edition, and Dorland's Pocket medical dictionary, twentieth edition. il. 1960.
    6.50. Saunders (R)

Stedman, Thomas L. Stedman's medical dictionary. by Isaac Asimov and others.
il. 1961. 14. 95. Williams & Wilkins (R)
Taber, Clarence W. Cyclopedic medical dictionary. il. 1962. 6. 00; thumb indexed,
flexible bdg. 6. 75. Davis (R)
Thomson, William A. R. Macmillan medical cyclopedia il. 1957. 7. 95. Macmillan
MEDICINE--HISTORY (610. 9)
Bankoff, G. Milestones in medicine. 1961. 3. 95. Pitman
Bett, W. R., and others. History and conquest of common diseases. 1954. 4. 00.
U. of Okla.
Castiglioni, Arturo. History of medicine. il. 1947. 17. 50. Knopf
Clendening, Logan. Source book of medical history. 4. 75. Smith, Peter
Glaser, Hugo. Road to modern surgery. il. 1962. 5. 75. Dutton
Guthrie, Douglas. History of medicine. il. 1958. with suppl. 10. 00. Lippincott (R)
Haggard, Howard W. Devils, drugs and doctors. il. 1945. 5. 00. Harper
Hemming, James. Mankind against the killers. 1956. 4. 75. McKay
Major, Ralph H. History of medicine. 2 vols. il. 1955. 14. 50. Thomas, C. C
Rapport, Samuel, and Helen Wright. Great adventures in medicine. 1961. 6. 95.
Dial
Schmidt, Jacob E. Medical discoveries. 1959. 14. 75? Thomas, C. C
Sigerist, Henry E. History of medicine. vol. 1, Primitive and archaic medicine.
1951. 12. 50; vol. 2, Early Greek, Hindu, and Persian medicine. 1961. 11. 00.
Oxford U. P. (R)
Singer, Charles. From magic to science. 1960. 4. 00. Smith, Peter
Singer, Charles. Short history of medicine: Introducing medical principles to
students and non-medical readers. il. 1928. 3. 50. Oxford U. P.
Stevenson, Lloyd G. Meaning of poison. 1959. 2. 00. U. of Kans.
Walker, Kenneth. Story of medicine. 1955. 6. 50. Oxford U. P.
MEDICINE--STUDY AND TEACHING (610. 7)
Allen, Raymond B. Medical education and the changing order. 1946. 1. 50. Harvard
Nourse, Alan E. So you want to be a doctor. 1957. 3. 00. Harper
Severinghaus, Aura E., and others. Preparation for medical education in the
liberal arts college: A restudy. il. 1961. 7. 95. McGraw
Wartman, William B. Medical teaching in western civilization. 1961. 7. 50.
Year Bk.
MEDICINE--TERMINOLOGY (610. 7)
Bollo, Louise E. Introduction to medicine and medical terminology. 1961. 5. 00.
Saunders
Jaeger, Edmund C. Source-book of medical terms. il. 1953. 5. 50. Thomas, C. C
Perkel, Louis L. Medical terminology simplified. 1958. 3. 85. Thomas, C. C
MEDICINE, CLINICAL (616)
Faddis, Margene O., and Joseph M. Hayman. Care of the medical patient. il.
1952. 6. 50. McGraw
Ryle, J. A. Natural history of disease. 1948. 6. 50. Oxford U. P.
Toohey, M. Medicine for nurses. il. 1960. 7. 00. Williams & Wilkins
MEDICINE, EXPERIMENTAL (619)
Beecher, Henry K. Experimentation in man. 1959. 3. 50. Thomas, C. C
Friedrich, Rudolph. Frontiers of medicine. il. 1961. 6. 95. Tudor
MEDICINE, POPULAR (610)
Banks, A. Leslie. Social aspects of disease. 1953. 4. 50. Williams & Wilkins
Brown, Ethan A., and others. Home health guide and medical encyclopedia. il.
1960. 4. 95. Home Lib. Pr. (R)
Bush, Lucius M. Common sense health. 1935. 3. 00. Liveright
Fishbein, Morris. Modern family health guide. il. 7. 50. Doubleday (R)
Fishbein, Morris. Popular medical encyclopedia. il. 4. 95. Doubleday
Miller, Benjamin F. Complete medical guide. 1955. 5. 95. S. and S.
MEDICINE, PREVENTIVE (614. 4)
Hilleboe, Herman E., and Granville W. Larimore. Preventive medicine. il. 1959.
12. 00. Saunders

Hubbard, John P.   Early detection and prevention of disease. il. 1957. 9.50.
  McGraw
Rodale, Jerome I.   Health finder. 1954. 6.95. Rodale (R)
Smillie, Wilson G.   Preventive medicine and public health. 7.50. Macmillan
MEDICINE, PSYCHOSOMATIC (616)
Alexander, Franz.   Psychosomatic medicine. 1950. 5.50. Norton
Goldberg, E. M.   Family influences and psychosomatic illness. 7.50. Humanities
Hamilton, M.   Psychosomatics. 1955. 4.75. Wiley
Inglis, Brian.   Emotional stress and your health. 1959. 4.95. Criterion
Winter, J. A.   Origins of illness and anxiety. 1962. 4.95. Wehman
MEDICINE AND RELIGION (201)
Barton, Richard Thomas.   Religious doctrine and medical practice. 1958. 3.75.
  Thomas, C. C
Boggs, Wade H., Jr.   Faith healing and the Christian faith. 1956. 3.50. John Knox
Wise, Carroll A.   Psychiatry and the Bible. 1956. 3.50. Harper
MEDICINE AS A PROFESSION (610.695)
Garland, Joseph, and Joseph Stokes.   Choice of a medical career. 1961. 5.50.
  Lippincott
Nourse, Alan E.   So you want to be a doctor. 1957. 3.50. Harper
MEDITATIONS (242)
Anderson, Stuart L.   Faith to live by. 1959. 2.75. Oxford U. P.
Cushman, Ralph S.   Meditations and verse. 1952. 2.00. Abingdon
Daskam, Max F.   Flaming spirit. 1961. 3.00. Abingdon
Kuyper, Abraham.   Near to God. 1961. 2.00. Eerdmans
Marshall, Peter.   Keepers of the springs and other messages from Mr. Jones,
  meet the Master. 1962. 1.00. Revell
MEETINGS (301.15)
Case, Lambert J.   How to reach group decisions. 1958. 1.00. Bethany
Hegarty, E. J.   How to run better meetings. 1957. 6.00. McGraw
Snell, Frank.   How to hold a better meeting. il. 1958. 2.95. Harper
MELANCHOLY (157)
Burton, Robert.   Anatomy of melancholy. 1955. 3.95. Tudor
MELVILLE, HERMAN, 1819-1891 (813.3)
Arvin, Newton.   Herman Melville. 1950. 4.75. Sloane
Bowen, Merlin.   Long encounter: Self and experience in the writings of Herman
  Melville. 1960. 5.00. U. of Chicago
Chase, Richard.   Melville: A collection of critical essays. 1962. 3.95. Prentice-
  Hall
Gleim, William.   Meaning of Moby Dick. 1962. 5.00. Russell
Leyda, Jay,   Melville log. Subtitle: A documentary biography of Herman Melville.
  2 vols. 12.50. Harcourt
Matthiessen, F. O.   American renaissance; Art and expression in the age of
  Emerson and Whitman. il. 1941. 10.00. Oxford U. P.
Metcalf, E. M.   Herman Melville: Cycle and epicycle. il. 1953. 5.50. Harvard
Miller, James E.   Reader's guide to Herman Melville. 1962. 4.95. Farrar, Straus
Sedgwick, William E.   Herman Melville, the tragedy of mind. 1962. 6.50. Russell
MEMORY (154)
Bartlett, Frederic C.   Remembering: A study in experimental and social psychology
  1932. 9.50. Cambridge U. P.
Freud, Sigmund.   Psychopathology of everyday life. 3.75. Macmillan
Katona, G.   Organizing and memorizing. 1940. 4.25. Columbia
Kohler, Wolfgang.   Dynamics in psychology. 1940. 3.00. Liveright
Mullaly, C., Sister.   Retention and recognition of information. 1952. 1.25.
  Catholic U. of Am. Pr.
Nielsen, J. M.   Memory and amnesia. il. 1958. 6.00. Univ. Pub.
Paul, I. H.   Studies in remembering. 1959. 3.50. Int. Univs.
Rapaport, David.   Emotions and memory. 1950. 4.00. Int. Univs.
Russell, W. Ritchie.   Brain, memory, learning: A neurologist's view. 1959. 5.00.
  Oxford U. P.

MENCKEN, HENRY LOUIS, 1880-1956 (928)
Angoff, Charles. H. L. Mencken: A portrait from memory. 3.95. Yoseloff
Mencken, H. L. H. L. Mencken on music. by Louis Cheslock. il. 1961. 4.50.
   Knopf
MENDEL, GREGOR JOHANN, 1822-1884 (925)
Sootin, Harry. Gregor Mendel: Father of the science of genetics. il. 1958. 3.00.
   Vanguard
MENDEL'S LAW (575.1)
Colin, Edward C. Elements of genetics. 1956. 7.75. McGraw
Ford, Edmund B. Mendelism and evolution. 1945. 2.25. Wiley
MENDELSOHN, ERICH, 1887-1953 (927)
Von Eckardt, Wolf. Eric Mendelsohn. il. 1960. 4.95. Braziller
MENDELSSOHN-BARTHOLDY, FELIX, 1809-1847 (927)
Radcliffe, Philip. Mendelssohn. 1954. 3.50. Farrar, Straus
MENNONITES (289.7)
Bender, Harold S., and C. Henry Smith. Mennonite encyclopedia. 4 vols. vol. 1,
   1955. 11.00; vol. 2, 1956, 11.00; vol. 3, 1957. 12.00; vol. 4. 1959. 12.00. set,
   42.50. Herald
Schreiber, William I. Our Amish neighbors. il. 1962. 5.95. U. of Chicago
MENTAL DEFICIENCY (132.2)
Earl, C. J. C. Subnormal personalities. 1961. 7.00. Williams & Wilkins
Mautner, Hans. Mental retardation, its care, treatment and physiological base.
   1959. 5.50. Pergamon
O'Connor N., and J. Tizard. Social problem of mental deficiency. 1957. 5.00.
   Pergamon
Rothstein, Jerome H. Mental retardation: Readings and resources. il. 1961. 6.75.
   Holt, Rinehart & Winston
MENTAL DISCIPLINE (159)
Kolesnik, Walter B. Mental discipline in modern education. 1958. 3.50. U. of Wis.
Overstreet, Harry A. Mature mind. 1949. 4.50. Norton
MENTAL HEALTH (131.3)
Alvarez, Walter C. Live at peace with your nerves. 1958. 4.95. Prentice-Hall
Anderson, Camilla M. Beyond Freud: A creative approach to mental health. 1957.
   4.50. Harper
Beers, Clifford W. Mind that found itself. 1948. 3.95. Doubleday
Bernard, Harold W. Toward better personal adjustment. il. 1957. 6.50; instructor's
   manual, 0.50. McGraw
Blaine, Graham B., and Charles C. McArthur. Emotional problems of the student.
   1961. 4.95. Appleton
Bonney, Marl E. Mental health in education. il. 1960. 8.65. Allyn & Bacon
Burnham, William H. Wholesome personality. 4.00. Appleton
Cannon, Walter B. Bodily changes in pain, hunger, fear and rage. 5.00. Bran-
   ford
Crow, Lester D., and Alice. Mental hygiene. 1951. 6.75. McGraw
Farnsworth, Dana L. Mental health in college and university. 1957. 5.00. Harvard
Glasser, William. Mental health or mental illness? il. 1961. 3.95. Harper
Gurin, Gerald, and others. Americans view their mental health. 1960. 7.50.
   Basic Books
Jahoda, Marie. Current concepts of positive mental health. 1958. 3.50. Basic
   Books
Johnson, Wendell. People in quandaries: The semantics of personal adjustment.
   1946. 6.50. Harper
Kaplan, Louis. Mental health and human relations in education. il. 1959. 5.50.
   Harper
Kaplan, Louis, and Denis Baron. Mental hygiene and life. 1952. 4.50. Harper
Katz, B., and G. F. J. Lehner. Mental hygiene in modern living. 1953. 6.00.
   Ronald
Klein, David B. Mental hygiene. 1956. 9.45. Holt, Rinehart & Winston

Lindgren, Henry Clay. Mental health in education. 1954. 6.50. Holt, Rinehart
& Winston
Menninger, Karl. Human mind. 1945. 6.75. Knopf
Menninger, W. C., and Munro Leaf. You and psychiatry. 1948. 2.95. Scribner
Miller, Zelma B., and Benjamin F. Good health: Personal and community. il.
1960. 6.00. Saunders
Ridenour, Nina. Mental health in the United States: A fifty-year history. 1961.
3.50. Harvard
Robinson, Reginald, and others. Community resources in mental health. 1960.
8.50. Basic Books
Shaffer, Laurance F., and Edward A. Shoben, Jr. Psychology of adjustment.
9.75. Houghton
Strecker, Edward A., and others. Discovering ourselves. il. 1958. 4.75.
Macmillan
Terhune, William B. Emotional problems and what you can do about them:
First aid to wiser living. 1955. 3.50. Morrow
Thorpe, Louis P. Mental hygiene and personality. 2.50. Lucas Bros.
Thorpe, Louis P. Psychology of mental health. 1960. 7.00. Ronald
Vaughan, Wayland F. Personal and social adjustments. il. 1952. 4.25. Odyssey
Wedge, Bryant M. Psychosocial problems of college men. il. 1958. 6.50. Yale
MENTAL ILLNESS (132.1)
Beutner, Karl E., and Nathan G. Hale, Jr. Emotional illness: How families can
help. 1957. 2.75. Putnam
Fein, Rashi. Economics of mental illness. 1958. 3.75. Basic Books
Katz, B., and L. P. Thorpe. Understanding people in distress. 1955. 4.50. Ronald
Lang, G. E. Mental health. 1958. 2.00. Wilson
Nunnally, Jum C. Popular conceptions of mental health. il. 1961. 5.00. Holt,
Rinehart & Winston
Oates, Wayne E. Religious factors in mental illness. 1955. 4.00. Assn. Pr.
Ridenour, Nina. Mental health in the United States: A fifty-year history. 1961.
3.50. Harvard
Shipley, Joseph T. Mentally disturbed teacher. 1961. 5.00. "Chilton
Stern, Edith M. Mental illness. 1957. 2.50. Harper
Szasz, Thomas. Myth of mental illness. 1961. 7.50. Hoeber
Terruwe, A. A. A. Psychopathic personality and neuroses. 1958. 3.95. Kenedy
MENTAL ILLNESS--PERSONAL NARRATIVES (616.89)
Alvarez, Walter C. Minds that came back. 1961. 5.95. Lippincott
Kruger, Judith. My fight for sanity. 1959. 4.95. Chilton
MENTAL SUGGESTION (134)
Atkinson, W. W. Mind power. 3.95. Wehman
Curtis, David. Learn while you sleep. 1960. 3.00. Libra
Hull, Clark L. Hypnosis and suggestibility. il. 1933. 6.00. Appleton
Winn, Ralph. Scientific hypnotism. 2.00. Borden
MENTAL TESTS (371.26)
Anastasi, Anne. Psychological testing. 1954. 7.00. Macmillan
Brueckner, Leo J., and Ernest O. Melby. Diagnostic and remedial teaching.
6.25. Houghton
Cronbach, Lee J. Essentials of psychological testing. 1960. 7.00. Harper
Goodenough, Florence L. Mental testing: Its history, principles, and applications.
1949. 7.75. Holt, Rinehart & Winston
Gulliksen, H. Theory of mental tests. 1950. 8.50. Wiley
Peterson, Harvey A., and others. Educational psychology. il. 6.00. Macmillan
Pinneau, S. R. Changes in the intelligence quotient: Infancy to maturity. 4.60.
Houghton
Stoddard, George D. Meaning of intelligence. 7.50. Macmillan
Thorndike, Robert L., and Elizabeth P. Hagen. Measurement and evaluation in
psychology and education. 1961. 7.75. Wiley
Tiegs, Ernest W. Tests and measurements in the improvement of learning. 1939.
5.50. Houghton

Traxler, Arthur E. Techniques of guidance. 1957. 6.00. Harper

Wechsler, David. Measurement and appraisal of adult intelligence. il. 1958.
5.00. Williams & Wilkins

MENTALLY HANDICAPPED (131.335)

Davies, Stanley P., and Katharine G. Ecob. Mentally retarded in society. 1959.
6.00. Columbia

Denhoff, Eric, and Isabel Robinault. Cerebral palsy and related disorders. 12.00.
McGraw

Gunzburg, Herbert C. Social rehabilitation of the subnormal. 1961. 6.50. Williams
& Wilkins

Stacey, Chalmers L., and Manfred DeMartino. Counseling and psychotherapy
with the mentally retarded. 1957. 7.50. Free Press

Tizard, J., and Jacqueline C. Grad. Mentally handicapped and their families.
1961. 6.50. Oxford U. P.

MENTALLY HANDICAPPED CHILDREN (131.335)

Blodgett, Harriet E., and Grace J. Warfield. Understanding mentally retarded
children. il. 1959. pap. 1.35. Appleton

Burt, Cyril L. Subnormal mind. 1955. 3.20. Oxford U. P.

Fernald, Grace M. Remedial techniques in basic school subjects. 1943. 6.25.
McGraw

French, Edward L., and J. Clifford Scott. Child in the shadows. 1960. 3.50.
Lippincott

Heiser, Karl F. Our backward children. 1955. 4.50. Norton

Hutt, Max L., and Robert G. Gibby. Mentally retarded child. 1958. 5.50. Allyn
and Bacon

Kirk, Samuel A. Early education of the mentally retarded. 1958. 6.00. U. of Ill.

Kirk, S. A., and G. O. Johnson. Educating the retarded child. 5.00. Houghton

Pollock, Morris P., and Miriam. New hope for the retarded. il. 1953. 4.50.
Sargent

MENTALLY HANDICAPPED CHILDREN--EDUCATION (371.92)

Garton, Melinda. Teaching the educable mentally retarded, practical methods.
1960. 7.50. Thomas, C. C.

Haring, Norris G., and Ewing L. Phillips. Educating emotionally disturbed
children. 1962. 6.50. McGraw

Perry, Natalie. Teaching the mentally retarded child. il. 1960. 6.50. Columbia

Rosenzweig, Louis E., and Julia Long. Understanding and teaching the dependent
retarded child. 1960. 4.25. Teacher's Pub.

Wallin, J. E. Wallace. Education of mentally handicapped children. 1955. 5.00.
Harper

MENTALLY ILL (362.2)

Goffman, Erving. Asylums. 6.75. Aldine

MENTALLY ILL--CARE AND TREATMENT (362.2)

Barton, Russell. Institutional neurosis. 1959. 2.50. Williams & Wilkins

Deutsch, A. Mentally ill in America. 1949. 6.00. Columbia

Grimes, J. M. When minds go wrong. 1954. 3.50. Devin

Schneck, Jerome M. History of psychiatry. il. 1960. 5.50. Thomas, C. C

MENUS (642)

Crocker, Betty. Betty Crocker's dinner for two cook book. il. 1958. 1.89.
Golden Press

Elkon, Juliette, and Elaine Ross. Menus for entertaining. 1960. 6.95. Hastings

Turgeon, Charlotte. Time to entertain. 1954. 4.50. Little

Whitfield, Nella. Fun with food. il. 1959. 7.50. Transatlantic

MERCANTILE BUILDINGS (725.2)

Architectural Record. Design for modern merchandizing. by the Editors of
Architectural Record. 1954. 8.95. McGraw

MERCANTILE SYSTEM (330.151)

Schuyler, Robert L. Fall of the old colonial system: A study in British free trade,
1770-1870. 1945. 4.75. Oxford U. P.

MERCHANT MARINE (387.5)
Bross, Steward R. Ocean shipping. il. 1956. 7.00. Cornell Maritime
Cornell, Felix M., and Alan C. Hoffman. American merchant seaman's manual
il. 1960. 7.50. Cornell Maritime
MERCHANT MARINE--HISTORY (387.5)
Braynard, Frank O. Famous American ships. il. 1956. 5.50. Hastings
Durant, John and Alice. Pictorial history of American ships. il. 1953. 4.95.
Barnes, A. S.
Riesenberg, Felix, Jr. Sea war: The story of the U. S. Merchant Marine in World
War II. il. 1956. 5.00. Rinehart
MERCHANTS, AMERICAN (920)
Mahoney, Tom. Great merchants. 1955. 4.95. Harper
MEREDITH, GEORGE, 1828-1909 (928)
Lindsay, Jack. George Meredith, his life and work. 6.00. Humanities
Sitwell, Osbert. Novels of George Meredith and some notes on the English novel.
1947. 1.00. Oxford U. P.
MERTON, THOMAS, 1915- (923.7)
Merton, Thomas. Seven storey mountain. 1948. 3.95. Harcourt
MESOPOTAMIA--ANTIQUITIES (935)
Zehren, Erich. Crescent and the bull. il. 1962. 6.95. Hawthorn
MESSIAH (291.61)
Silver, Abba H. History of Messianic speculation in Israel from the first through
the seventeenth centuries. 1959. 3.75. Smith, Peter
Wallis, Wilson. Messiahs: Their role in civilization. 1943. 2.50. Pub. Affairs
METABOLISM (612.39)
Houssay, B. A. Enzymes and metabolism. il. 1956. 9.75. Am. Elsevier
Wagner, R. F., and H. K. Mitchell. Genetics and metabolism. 1955. 8.00. Wiley
METABOLISM, DISORDERS OF (612.39)
Duncan, Garfield G. Diseases of metabolism. il. 1959. 18.50. Saunders
METAL CASTINGS (671.25)
Heine, Richard W., and Philip C. Rosenthal. Principles of metal casting. 1955.
8.50. McGraw
METAL-WORK (669.09)
Aitchinson, L. History of metals. 2 vols. il. 1960. 30.00. Wiley
Bollinger, J. W. Fun with metalwork. 1958. 4.75. Bruce
Du Mond, Theodore C. Fabricated materials and parts. 1953. 6.50. Reinhold
Mattson, E. B. Creative metalworking. 1960. 3.25. Bruce
METALLOGRAPHY (669.95)
Barrett, Charles S. Structure of metals. il. 1952. 13.00. McGraw
Rolfe, R. T. Dictionary of metallography. 1955. 5.75. Tudor (R)
Smith, Cyril S. History of metallography. il. 1960. 8.50. U. of Chicago
METALLURGY (669)
Dennis, William H. Metallurgy in the service of man. il. 1961. 10.00. Pitman
Henderson, John Goulding, and Jack M. Bates. Metallurgical dictionary. 1953.
10.00. Reinhold (R)
Keyser, Carl A. Basic engineering metallurgy. 1959. 13.00. Prentice-Hall
Merriman, A. D. Dictionary of metallurgy. 1959. 25.00. Pitman (R)
Stoughton, Bradley, and others. Engineering metallurgy. il. 1953. 8.95. McGraw
METALS (669.2)
Parr, J. Gordon. Man, metals, and modern magic. il. 1958. 2.95. Iowa State
Pascoe, K, J. Introduction to the properties of engineering materials. il. 1961.
6.00. Wiley
Rogers, Bruce A. Nature of metals. il. 1951. 2.95. Iowa State
Verrill, A. Hyatt. Minerals, metals and gems. il. 1939. 3.75. Farrar, Straus
METALS AT HIGH TEMPERATURES (669)
Clark, Claude L. High temperature alloys. 1953. 8.25. Pitman
METAPHOR (808)
Turbayne, Colin M. Myth of metaphor. il. 1962. 6.00. Yale

METAPHYSICS (110)

Aristotle. Aristotle on his predecessors. tr. by A. E. Taylor. 2.00. Open Ct.

Aristotle. Metaphysics. 2 vols. by William D. Ross. 1924. 12.00. Oxford U. P. (R)

Bergson, Henri L. Creative evolution. il. 1944. 1.95. Modern Lib.

Brunton, Paul. Hidden teaching beyond Yoga. 5.95. Dutton

Burtt, Edwin A. Metaphysical foundations of modern physical science. 1952. 5.50. Humanities

Christian, William A. Interpretation of Whitehead's metaphysics. 1959. 6.00. Yale

DeGeorge, R. T. Classical and contemporary metaphysics. 1962. 6.50. Holt, Rinehart & Winston

Drennen, D. A. Modern introduction to metaphysics. 1962. 6.50. Free Press

Hawkins, D. J. B. Being and becoming. 1954. 3.00. Sheed

Hocking, William E., and Richard B. Types of philosophy. 1959. 5.50. Scribner

Kant, Immanuel. Prolegomena to any future metaphysics. 1954. 2.20. Barnes & Noble

Klubertanz, George P. Introduction to the philosophy of being. 1955. 3.50. Appleton

Maritain, Jacques. Degrees of knowledge. 1959. 7.50. Scribner

Pears, D. F. Nature of metaphysics. 1957. 2.50. St. Martins

Thomas, Aquinas, Saint. Introduction to the metaphysics of St. Thomas Aquinas. tr. by James F. Anderson. 1953. 3.00. Regnery

METEORITES (523.5)

Krinov, E. L. Principles of meteoritics. by M. Brown. tr. by I. Vidziunas. 12.00. Pergamon

METEOROLOGY (551.5)

Bates, D. R. Earth and its atmosphere. il. 1957. 6.75. Basic Books

Berry, F. A., and others. Handbook of meteorology. 1945. 21.50. McGraw

Bretz, J. H. Earth sciences. 1940. 3.00. Wiley

Forrester, Frank H. 1001 questions answered about the weather. il. 1957. 6.00. Dodd

Huschke, Ralph E. Glossary of meteorology. 1959. 12.00. Am. Meteorological Soc.

Kendrew, Wilfred G. Climatology. il. 1957. 7.20. Oxford U. P.

Koeppe, Clarence E., and George C. DeLong. Weather and climate. 1958. 7.95. McGraw

Petterssen, Sverre. Introduction to meteorology. 1958. 7.25. McGraw

Sutton, O. G. Challenge of the atmosphere. il. 1961. 5.95. Harper

Yates, Raymond. Weather for a hobby. il. 1946. 3.50. Dodd

METEOROLOGY AS A PROFESSION (551.5)

Berry, Frederick A., and Sidney Frank. Your future in meteorology. 1962. 2.95. Richards Rosen

METEORS (523.5)

Kaiser, T. R. Meteors. 1955. 8.50. Pergamon

Watson, Fletcher G. Between the planets. il. 1956. 5.00. Harvard

METHODISM (287)

Smith, Roy L. Why I am a Methodist. 1954. 2.95. Nelson

METHODISM--HISTORY (287)

Lee, Umphrey, and William Warren Sweet. Short history of Methodism. 1956. 2.00. Abingdon

METHODOLOGY (112)

Cohen, Morris R., and Ernest Nagel. Introduction to logic and scientific method. 1934. 5.50. Harcourt

Collingwood, R. G. Essay on philosophical method. 1933. 4.50. Oxford U. P.

Gilbert, Neal W. Renaissance concepts of method. 1960. 6.00. Columbia

Northrop, Filmer S. C. Logic of the sciences and the humanities. 1.55. Meridian

METRIC SYSTEM (389.152)

Green, Marvin H. International and metric units of measurement. 1961. 6.00.
  Tudor (R)
METTERNICH-WINNEBURG, CLEMENS LOTHAR WENZEL, FURST VON,
  1773-1859 (943)
May, Arthur. Age of Metternich: 1814-1848. 1933. pap. 1.60. Holt
Schroeder, Paul W. Metternich's diplomacy at its zenith, 1820-1823. 1962. 5.00.
  U. of Tex.
MEXICAN FICTION--HISTORY AND CRITICISM (860)
Brushwood, J. S. Romantic novel in Mexico. 1954. 2.50. U. of Missouri
MEXICAN LITERATURE--TRANSLATIONS INTO ENGLISH (860)
Underwood, Edna W. Mexican anthology. (in English) 6.00. Glenn
MEXICAN POETRY--TRANSLATIONS INTO ENGLISH (860)
Paz, Octavio. Anthology of Mexican poetry. tr. by Samuel Beckett. 1958. 3.50.
  Indiana
MEXICANS IN THE U. S. (301.45)
Burma, John Harmon. Spanish-speaking groups in the United States. 1954. 4.00.
  Duke
McWilliams, Carey. North from Mexico. 1961. 5.00. Monthly Review
MEXICO--ANTIQUITIES (972)
Covarrubias, Miguel. Indian art of Mexico and Central America. il. 1957. 17.50.
  Knopf
Covarrubias, Miguel. Mexico South: The Isthmus of Tehuantepec. il. 1946. 12.50.
  Knopf
Peterson, Frederick. Ancient Mexico. 1959. 7.95. Putnam
MEXICO--CIVILIZATION (972)
Chase, Stuart. Mexico. il. 1931. 4.95. Macmillan
Cline, Howard F. Mexico: From revolution to evolution. 1962. 6.75. Oxford U. P.
Ramos, Samuel. Profile of man and culture in Mexico. tr. by Peter G. Earle.
  1962. 4.50. U. of Tex.
MEXICO--DESCRIPTION AND TRAVEL (917.272)
Chase, Stuart. Mexico. il. 1931. 4.95. Macmillan
Clark, Sydney. All the best in Mexico. il. 1961. 4.95. Dodd
Crow, John A. Mexico today. il. 1957. 5.00? Harper
Dobie, J. Frank. Tongues of the Monte. 1947. 6.00. Little
Gregg, Josiah. Commerce of the prairies. 5.00. Franklin, B.
Strode, Hudson. Now in Mexico. il. 5.00. Harcourt
Hine, Duncan. Vacation guide. 1949. 1.50. Hines, D.
Liebes, Herman and Juanita. Guide to Mexico. 4.95. Rand McNally
Martin, Lawrence, and Sylvia. Standard guide to Mexico and the Caribbean. il.
  1956. 4.95. Funk
Wilhelm, John. John Wilhelm's guide to all Mexico. 1962. 4.95. McGraw
MEXICO--FOREIGN RELATIONS (972)
Clendenen, Clarence C. United States and Pancho Villa. il. 1961. 5.75. Cornell
Cronon, E. David. Josephus Daniels in Mexico. 1960. 6.00. U. of Wis.
Garber, Paul N. Gadsden Treaty. 1959. 4.00. Smith, Peter
Gregg, Robert. Influence of border disorders on relations between the United
  States and Mexico, 1876-1910. 1937. 3.00. Johns Hopkins
James, Daniel. Mexico and the U. S. A. 1962. 7.50. Praeger
Tannenbaum, Frank. Mexico: The struggle for peace and bread. 1950. 4.00.
  Knopf
MEXICO--HISTORY (972)
Cline, Howard Francis. United States and Mexico. il. 1953. 6.00. Harvard
Coe, Michael D. Mexico. il. 1962. 6.95. Praeger
Parkes, Henry B. History of Mexico. il. 1960. 5.75. Houghton
MEXICO--HISTORY--TO 1519 (972)
Gillmor, Frances. Flute of the smoking mirror. il. 4.00. U. of N. Mex.
MEXICO--HISTORY--CONQUEST, 1519-1540 (972)
Bel Castillo, Bernal Diaz. Discovery and conquest of Mexico. 1958. pap. 2.95.
  Grove

Leon, Portilla, Miguel. Broken spears; the Aztec account of the conquest of
   Mexico. tr. by Lysander Kemp. il. 1962. bds. 5.00. Beacon
MEXICO--HISTORY--1910-1946 (972)
Cline, Howard F. Mexico: From revolution to evolution. 1962. 6.75. Oxford
   U. P.
Cumberland, Charles C. Mexican Revolution: Genesis under Madero. 1952.
   5.00. U. of Tex.
Quirk, Robert E. Mexican revolution, 1914-1915. 1960. 6.75. Indiana
MEXICO--INDUSTRY (972)
Mosk, Sanford A. Industrial revolution in Mexico. 1954. 5.00. U. of Calif.
MEXICO--POLITICS AND GOVERNMENT (972)
Dulles, John W. F. Yeaterday in Mexico: A chronicle of the revolution 1919-
   1936. il. 1960. 8.50. U. of Tex.
Scott, Robert E. Mexican government in transition. 1959. 5.75. U. of Ill.
Tucker, William P. Mexican government today. 1956. 6.50. U. of Minn.
MEXICO--SOCIAL CONDITIONS (972)
Lewis, Oscar. Children of Sanchez. 1961. 5.60. Random
Senior, Clarence. Land reform and democracy. 1958. 6.75. U. of Fla.
Tannenbaum, Frank. Mexico: The struggle for peace and bread. 1950. 4.00. Knopf
MEXICO--SOCIAL LIFE AND CUSTOMS (972)
Anderson, William M. American in Maximillian's Mexico, 1865-1866: The
   diaries of William Marshall Anderson. by Ramon E. Ruiz. 1959. 4.25.
   Huntington Lib.
Calderon de la Barca, Frances E. Life in Mexico. 1931. 1.95. Dutton
MICE (599.3233)
Greenwood, Major. Epidemiology: Historical and experimental. 1932. 1.50.
   Johns Hopkins
MICHELANGELO (BUONARROTI, MICHELANGELO) 1475-1564 (927)
Ackerman, James S. Architecture of Michelangelo. 2 vols. il. 1961. 12.50 ea.
   Viking
Alexander, Sidney. Michelangelo the Florentine. 1957. 4.95. Random
Goldscheider, Ludwig. Michelangelo. il. 1962. 9.50. N. Y. Graphic
Michelangelo. Raphael and Michelangelo: Selected drawings. by A. E. Popham.
   il. 1954. 2.95. N. Y. Graphic
Symonds, John A. Life of Michelangelo. 1936. 1.95. Modern Lib.
MICHIGAN--DESCRIPTION AND TRAVEL (917.7)
Michigan: Guide to the wolverine state. 6.50. Oxford U. P.
MICROBIOLOGY (576)
Carpenter, Philip L. Microbiology. il. 1961. 6.75. Saunders
Clifton, Charles E. Introduction to bacteria. 1958. 8.50. McGraw
Frazier, William C. Food microbiology. 1958. 9.95. McGraw
Frobisher, Martin. Fundamentals of microbiology. il. in prep. Saunders
Gale, E. F., and R. Davies. Adaptation in micro-organisms. 1953. 6.50.
   Cambridge U. P.
Grant, Madeleine P. Microbiology and human progress. 1953. 7.95. Holt,
   Rinehart & Winston
Hawker, Lilian E., and others. Introduction to the biology of micro-organisms.
   il. 1961. 6.75. St. Martins
Jacobs, Morris B., and others. Dictionary of microbiology. 1957. 7.25. Van
   Nostrand (R)
Jacobs, Morris B., and Maurice J. Gerstein. Handbook of microbiology. 1960.
   8.50. Van Nostrand (R)
Picken, Laurence E. R. Organization of cells and other organisms. il. 1960.
   13.45. Oxford U. P.
Sarles, William B., and others. Microbiology: General and applied. 1956. 6.00.
   Harper
Umbreit, W. W. Modern Microbiology. 1962. 8.50. Freeman
MICROCHEMISTRY (544)
Chamot, Emile M., and Clyde W. Mason. Handbook of chemical microscopy.
   2 vols. vol. 1, 1958. 11.95; vol. 2, 1940. 9.25. Wiley (R)

MICROFILMS (778)
Hale, Richard W. Guide to photocopied historical materials in the United States and Canada. 1961. 5.00. Cornell
MICRONESIA (996.5)
Tetens, Alfred. Among the savages of the South Seas: Memoirs of Micronesia, 1862-1868. il. 1958. 3.75. Stanford
MICRO-ORGANISMS (589.95)
Bracken, Arthur. Chemistry of micro-organisms, 1955. 6.50. Pitman
DeKruif, Paul. Microbe hunters. il. 1932. 4.50. by Harry G. Grover. 2.60. Harcourt
Kluyver, A. J., and C. B. Van Niel. Microbe's contribution to biology. il. 1956. 4.00. Harvard
Meynell, G. G., and H. Gooder. Microbial reaction to environment. 1961. 7.50. Cambridge U. P.
Tanner, Fred W. Bacteriology: A textbook of microorganisms. 1948. 6.95. Wiley
Wedberg, Stanley E. Microbes and you. il. 1954. 5.50. Macmillan
MICROPHOTOGRAPHY (778.315)
Allen, Roy M. Photomicrography. il. 1958. 10.00. Van Nostrand
MICROSCOPE AND MICROSCOPY (578)
Allen, Roy M. Microscope. 1940. 4.75. Van Nostrand (R)
Beiser, Arthur. Guide to the microscope. il. 1957. 3.25. Dutton (R)
Clark, George L. Encyclopedia of microscopy. 1961. 25.00. Reinhold (R)
Corrington, Julian D. Exploring with your microscope. il. 1957. 5.95. McGraw
Corrington, Julian D. Working with the microscope. 1941. 6.95. McGraw
Francon, M. Progress in microscopy. 1962. 9.00. Harper
Needham, George Herbert. Practical use of the microscope. il. 1958. 15.50. Thomas, C. C (R)
MICROSCOPE AND MICROSCOPY--EARLY WORKS TO 1800 (578)
Hooke, Robert. Micrographia. il. 2.00. Dover
MICROSCOPE AND MICROSCOPY--TECHNIQUE (578)
Clayden, E. C. Practical section cutting and staining. 1949. 3.25. Tudor
Gray, Peter. Handbook of basic microtechnique. 1958. 6.95. McGraw (R)
MICROWAVES (537.12)
Atwater, H. A. Introduction to microwave theory. 1962. 8.75. McGraw
Muchmore, R. B. Essentials of microwaves. 1952. 7.50. Wiley
Shevchik, V. N. Fundamentals of microwave electronics. in prep. Pergamon
Slater, John C. Microwave electronics. il. 1950. 7.50. Van Nostrand
MIDDLE AGE (612)
Bard, Mary. Forty odd. 1952. 3.75. Lippincott
Blanton, Smiley, and Arthur Gordon. Now or never, the promise of the middle years. 1959. 4.95. Prentice-Hall
Davis, Maxine. Get the most out of your best years. 4.00. Dial
Howe, Reuel L. Creative years. 1958. 3.50. Seabury
Tibbitts, Clark, and Wilma Donahue. Aging in today's society. 1960. 7.00. Prentice-Hall
MIDDLE AGES (940.1)
Adams, Henry. Mont Saint Michel and Chartres. il. 6.00. Houghton
Agarian life of the Middle Ages (Cambridge economic history of Europe. vol. 1) in prep. Cambridge U. P. (R)
Carlyle, R. W., and A. J. History of medieval thought in the West. 6 vols. vol. 1, Roman lawyers of the second century to the political writers of the ninth, 1927 5.00; vol. 2, Political theory of Roman lawyers. and canonists from the tenth century to the thirteenth century. 1909, 5.00; vol. 3, Political theory from the tenth century to the thirteenth century, 1915, 5.00; vol. 4, Theories of relation of empire and papacy from the tenth to the twelfth century. 1922. 7.50; vol. 5, Political theory of the thirteenth century. 1928, 7.50; vol. 6, Political theory from 1300 to 1600, 1936. 7.50; set, 40.00. Barnes & Noble (R)
Clagett, Marshall, and others. Twelfth century Europe and the foundations of modern society. 5.00. U. of Wis.

Crump, C. G., and E. F. Jacob. Legacy of the Middle Ages. il. 1926. 6.00. Oxford U. P.

Heer, Friedrich. Medieval world: Europe 1100-1350. il. 1962. 7.50. World Pub.

Holmes, George. Later Middle Ages 1272-1485. vol. 3. 1962. 4.50. Nelson

Huizinga, Johan. Waning of the Middle Ages. 4.75. St. Martins

Kibre, Pearl. Scholarly privileges in the Middle Ages. 1962. 7.50. Mediaeval

Knowles, David. Saints and scholars: Twenty-six medieval characters. 1962. 3.95. Cambridge U. P.

La Monte, John L. World of the Middle Ages. il. 1949. 7.00. Appleton

Loomis, Laura H. Adventures of the Middle Ages. 1962. 9.50. Franklin, B.

Rank, Edward K. Founders of the Middle Ages. 3.75. Smith, Peter (R)

Southern, R. W. Making of the Middle Ages. 1953. 4.50. Yale

Taylor, Henry Osborn. Mediaeval mind: A history of the development of thought and emotion in the Middle Ages. 2 vols. 1949. 10.00. Harvard

MIDDLE AGES--HISTORY (940.1)

Coulton, George G. Medieval scene. il. 3.75. Smith, Peter

Painter, Sidney. History of the Middle Ages. il. 1953. 6.00. Knopf

Previte-Orton, Charles W. Shorter Cambridge Medieval history. 2 vols. by P. Grierson. 1952. 2 vols. boxed. 17.50. Cambridge U. P

Strayer, Joseph R., and Dana C. Munro. Middle Ages, 395-1500. il. 1959. 7.25. Appleton

MIDDLE AGES--HISTORY--SOURCES (940.1)

Coulton, George G. Life in the Middle Ages. 4 vols. vols. 1-3 o.p; vol. 4. Monks, friars and nuns. 3.00; 4 vols. in 1. 1955. 9.50. Cambridge U. P.

Downs, Norton. Basic documents in Medieval history. (Anvil 38) 1959. pap. 1.25. Van Nostrand

MIDDLE AGES--INTELLECTUAL LIFE (940.1)

Artz, Frederick B. Mind of the Middle Ages. il. 1954. 6.50. Knopf

MIDDLE CLASSES (323.3)

Barber, E. G. Bourgeoisie in 18th century France. 1955. 3.50. Princeton

Frazier, Edward F. Black bourgeoisie. 1956. 4.00. Free Press

Johnson, John J. Political change in Latin America. 1958. 5.00. Stanford

Mills, C. Wright. White collar: American middle classes. 1951. 6.50. Oxford U.P.

Trevor-Roper, H. R. Gentry 1540-1640. 1953. 1.00. Cambridge U. P.

Wright, Louis B. Middle-class culture in Elizabethan England. 1958. 7.50. Cronell

MIDDLE STATES--U.S. (917)

Look Magazine. Regional guide: Central Northeast. by the Editors of Look Magazine. il. 5.50. Houghton

Pownall, Thomas. Topgraphical description of the dominions of the United States of America. by Lois Mulkearn. il. 10.00. Brown Book

MIDDLE WEST--U.S. (917)

Atherton, Lewis. Main Street on the Middle Border. il. 1954. 6.00. Indiana

Glazer, Sidney. Middle West. 1962. 3.50. Twayne

McAvoy, Thomas T. Midwest: Myth or reality. 1961. 3.50. U. of Notre Dame

Merrill, Horace Samuel. Bourbon democracy of the Middle West, 1865-1896. 1953. 4.50. La. State

Murray, John J., and others. Heritage of the middle west. il. 1958. 4.00. U. of Okla.

Nye, Russel B. Midwestern progressive politics, 1870-1958. 1959. 5.00. Mich. State

MIDDLE WEST--DESCRIPTION AND TRAVEL (917)

Garland, John. North American Midwest. 1955. 6.95. Wiley

In the Midwest and South (Wonderful places to take children. vol. 2) Norman, Jane, and others. 2.95. Channel Pr., Manhasset, N. Y.

Look Magazine. Regional guide: The Midwest. by the Editors of Look Magazine. il. 5.50. Houghton

MIDWAY, BATTLE OF, 1942 (940.542)

Fuchida, Mitsuo, and Masatake Okumiya. Midway, the battle that doomed Japan: The Japanese navy's story. by Clarke Kawakami and Roger Pineau. il. 1955. U. S. Naval Inst.

Tuleja, Thaddeus V. Climax at Midway. il. 1960. 4.50. Norton

MIES VAN DER ROHE, LUDWIG, 1886- (927.2)
Drexler, Arthur. Ludwig Mies van der Rohe. il. 1960. 4.95. Braziller

MIGRANT LABOR (331.67)
National Education Association. Rural Education Department. Knowing and teaching the migrant child. 1960. 3.50. N. E. A.

Schwartz, Harry. Seasonal farm labor in the U. S. 1945. 2.75. Columbia

Shotwell, Louisa R. Harvesters. 1961. bds. 4.50. Doubleday

Shotwell, Louisa R. This is the migrant. 1958. pap. 0.60. Friendship

Stout, Ronald M. New York farm labor camps. 1953. 1.40. U. of Ala.

MILITARISM (355)
Ekirch, A. A. Civilian and the military. 1956. 6.00. Oxford U. P.

Franklin, John Hope. Militant South, 1800-1861. 1956. 5.00. Harvard

Howard, Michael, and others. Soldiers and governments. 1959. 3.75. Indiana

Huntington, S. P. Soldier and the state: The theory and politics of civil-military relations. 1957. 7.50. Harvard

Toynbee, A. J. War and civilization. by A. V. Fowler. 1950. 3.00. Oxford U. P.

MILITARY ADMINISTRATION (355.6)
Williams, T. Harry. Americans at war. 1960. 3.50. La. State

MILITARY ART AND SCIENCE (355)
Adcock, F. E. Greek and Macedonian art of war. 1957. 4.00. U. of Calif.

Adcock, Frank E. Roman art of war under the Republic. 1960. 3.00. Barnes & Noble

Clausewitz, Carl von. Principles of war. 2.75. Stackpole

Clausewitz, Karl, von. War, politics and power. 1962. pap. 1.95. Regnery

Dupuy, Richard E., and Trevor N. Military heritage of America. 1956. 11.50. McGraw

Falls, Cyril B. Art of war from the Age of Napoleon to the present day. il. 1962. 3.50. Smith, Peter

Frederick, the Great. Instructions to his generals. il. 1951. 2.25. Stackpole

Frontinus. Stratagems and aqueducts. 3.50. Harvard

Fuller, J. F. C. Armored warfare. il. 1955. 3.00. Stackpole

Henderson, George F. R. Civil War: A soldier's view. by Jay Luvaas. 1957. 6.75. U. of Chicago

Lanza, Conrad H. Napoleon and modern war. 1954. 3.00. Stackpole

Liddell Hart, B. H. Defence of the West. 1950. 4.00. Morrow

Miksche, F. O. Atomic weapons and armies. 1959. 5.00. Praeger

Muller, Hollis L. Technique of modern arms. il. 1940. 2.50. Stackpole

Pokrovsky, G. I. Science and technology in contemporary war. 1959. 4.50. Praeger

Quimby, Robert S. The background of Napoleonic warfare; The theory of military tactics in eighteenth-century France. 1957. 6.75. Columbia

Ropp, Theodore. War in the modern world. 1960. 10.00. Duke

Saxe, Maurice de. Reveries on the art of war. il. 1953. 2.25. Stackpole (R)

Von Clausewitz, Karl. On war. 3 vols. il. 1961. 13.50. Barnes & Noble

Worley, Marvin L., Jr. New developments in army weapons, tactics, organization and equipment. il. 1959. 3.95. Stackpole

Wright, Quincy. Study of war. 2 vols. il. 1942. 20.00. U. of Chicago

MILITARY ASSISTANCE, AMERICAN (338.91)
Jordan, Amos A., Jr. Foreign aid and the defense of Southeast Asia. il. 1962. 6.50. Praeger

Lyons, Gene M. Military policy and economic aid: The Korean case, 1950-1953. 4.50. Ohio State

McClellan, G. S. U. S. foreign aid. 1957. 2.00. Wilson

MILITARY DISCIPLINE (335)
Edwards, Morris O., and Charles L. Decker. Serviceman and the law. il. 1957. 4.00. Stackpole

Goodman, Samuel M. Curriculum implications of Armed Services educational
    programs. 1947. 1.25. A. C. E.
Tuttle, George P., and Cornelius P. Turner. Guide to the evaluation of edu-
    cational experiences in the Armed Services. 1954. 5.00. A. C. E.

MILITARY HISTORY (355)

Aron, Raymond. Century of total war. 1954. 5.00. Doubleday
Earle, Edward M. Makers of modern strategy. 1943. 10.00. Princeton
Fuller, J. F. C. Conduct of war, 1789-1960. 1961. 6.00. Rutgers
Fuller, J. F. C. Military history of the Western world. vol. 1, From the
    earliest times to the battle of Lepanto, il. 1954; vol. 2, From the defeat of
    Spanish Armada, 1558, to the Battle of Waterloo, 1815, il. 1955; vol. 3, From
    the Seven Day's Battle, 1862, to the Battle of Leyte Gulf, 1944, il. 1956. 6.00
    ea. 3 vols. boxed 16.50. Funk
Montross, Lynn. War through the ages. il. 1960. 10.00. Harper
Oakeshott, R. Ewart. Archaeology of weapons. il. 1960. 8.50. Praeger (R)
Ropp, Theodore. War in the modern world. 1960. 10.00. Duke
Vagts, Alfred. History of militarism. 7.50. Meridian

MILITARY POLICY (355)

Heymont, Irving. Combat intelligence in modern warfare. 1961. 6.00. Stackpole
Huntington, Samuel P. Changing patterns of military politics. 1962. 7.50. Free
    Press
McGovern, William M. Strategic intelligence and the shape of tomorrow. 1961.
    4.00. Regnery
Slessor, John. Strategy for the West. 1954. 3.00. Morrow
Slessor, John. What price coexistence? 1961. 4.50. Praeger
Snyder, G. H. Deterrence and defense. 1961. 6.50. Princeton
Townsend, Elias C. Risks: The key to combat intelligence. il. 1956. pap. 1.50.
    Stackpole
Vagts, A. Defense and diplomacy. 1956. 8.75. Columbia

MILITARY SERVICE, COMPULSORY (355)

Conference on Military Manpower, 1955, Washington, D. C. Proceedings. 1955.
    1.00. A. C. E.
Duggan, J. C. Legislative and statutory development of the federal concept of
    conscription for military service. 1946. 3.00. Catholic U. of Am. Pr.
Evers, Alf. Selective service: A guide to the draft. 1957. 3.25. Lippincott
Gleaves, S. Z., and L. T. Wertenbaker. You and the armed services. 1961.
    pap. 1.25. S. and S.

MILITARY SERVICE AS A PROFESSION (355.069)

Janowitz, Morris. Professional soldier. 1960. 6.75. Free Press

MILK (637)

American public Health Association. Standard methods for the examination of
    dairy products. 1960. 7.00. Am. Public Health (R)
Chalmers, C. H. Bacteria in relation to milk supply. 1955. 5.00. St. Martins
Hammer, Bernard W., and F. J. Babel. Dairy bacteriology. 1957. 9.50. Wiley
Jenness, Robert and Stuart Patton. Principles of dairy chemistry. 1959. 8.95.
    Wiley
Wilson, Graham S. Pasteurization of milk. 1942. 4.50. St. Martins

MILKY WAY (523.113)

Bok, Bart J., and Priscilla F. Milky Way. il. 1957. 5.50. Harvard
Bova, Ben. Milky Way galaxy: Man's exploration of the stars. 5.00. Holt, Rinehart
    & Winston
Shapely, Harlow. Galaxies. 1961. 5.00. Harvard
Shapely, H. Inner metagalaxy. 1957. 6.75. Yale

MILL, JOHN STUART, 1806-1873 (921.2)

Anschutz, Richard Paul. Philosophy of J. S. Mill. 1953. 3.40. Oxford U. P.
Borchard, R. John Stuart Mill the man. 3.75. Humanities
Mill, John S. Autobiography. 2.75. Oxford U. P.
Mill, John Stuart. Autobiography of John Stuart Mill. 1924. 2.50. Columbia

MILLER, ARTHUR, 1915- (928)
Welland, Dennis. Arthur Miller. 3.00. Smith, Peter
MILLER, SAMUEL FREEMAN, 1816-1890 (923.4)
Fairman, Charles. Mr. Justice Miller and the Supreme Court, 1862-1890. il.
1939. 4.50. Harvard
MILLES, CARL, 1875- (927)
Cornell, Henrik. Carl Milles and the Milles gardens. il. 12.50. Boston Bk.
MILLET, JEAN FRANCOIS, 1814-1875 (927)
Hurll, Estelle M. Millet. 1900. 2.00. Houghton
MILTON, JOHN, 1608-1674 (821.47)
Adams, Robert Martin. Ikon: John Milton and the modern critics. 1955. 3.75.
Cornell
Allen, Don Cameron. Harmonious vision: Studies in Milton's poetry. 1953. 3.00.
Johns Hopkins
Banks, T. H. Milton's imagery. 1950. 3.50. Columbia
Bowra, Cecil Maurice. From Virgil to Milton. 4.50. St. Martins
Brett, R. L. Reason and imagination. 1959. 2.90. Oxford U. P.
Broadbent, J. B. Milton: Camus and Samson Agonistes. 1961. 1.95. Barron's
Broadbent, John B. Some graver subject: An essay on Paradise Lost. il. 1960.
6.00. Barnes & Noble
Bush, Douglas. Paradise lost in our times. 2.50. Smith, Peter
Bush, Douglas. Renaissance and English humanism. 1939. 3.00. U. of Toronto
Cooper, Lane. Concordance of the Latin, Greek and Italian poems of John Milton.
1923. 4.00. Cornell
Curry, Walter C. Milton's ontology, cosmogony, and physics. 1957. 5.00. U. of
Ky.
Daiches, David. Milton. 2.50. Hillary
Diekhoff, John S. Milton's Paradise Lost: A commentary on the argument. 3.75.
Humanities
Fletcher, Harris Francis. Intellectual development of John Milton. 2 vols. 10.00.
U. of Ill.
Gilman, Wilbur E. Milton's rhetoric. 1939. pap. 1.25. U. of Missouri
Grierson, Herbert. Milton and Wordsworth. 1960. 3.25. Barnes & Noble
Hanford, J. H. Milton handbook. il. 1946. 4.00. Appleton (R)
Havens, Raymond D. Influence of Milton on English poetry. 1961. 12.50. Russell
Huckabay, Calvin. John Milton: A bibliographical supplement, 1929-1957. 6.25.
Duquesne (R)
Johnson, Samuel. Lives of the poets: Milton. by K. Deighton. 1.25. St. Martins
Macaulay, Thomas B. Essay on John Milton. 1.00. Houghton
Masson, Davis. Life of John Milton. 7. vols. 60.00. Smith, Peter
Myers, R. M. Handel, Dryden, and Milton. 5.00. Hillary
Peter, John. Critique of Paradise Lost. 1960. 3.50. Columbia
Pope, Elizabeth. Paradise regained: The tradition and the poem. 1961. 5.00.
Russell
Thorpe, James. Milton criticism: Selections from four centuries. 1950. 4.50.
Rinehart
Tillyard, E. M. W. Studies in Milton. 3.25. Macmillan
Tuve, Rosemond. Images and themes in five poems by Milton. 1957. 4.00. Harvard
Werblowsky, R. J. Zwi. Lucifer and Prometheus: A study of Milton's Satan.
3.50. Humanities
Whaler, J. Counterpoint and symbol: An inquiry into the rhythm of Milton's
epic style. pap. 5.00. Humanities
MIND AND BODY (130.1)
Ayer, A. J. Privacy. 1959. 0.85. Oxford U. P.
Bergson, Henri. Matter and memory. 1911. 2.75. Macmillan
Blum, Gerald S. Model of the mind. 1961. 6.95. Wiley
Carmichael, Leonard. Making of modern mind. 1956. 2.75. Van Nostrand
Cobb, Stanley. Borderlands of psychiatry. il. 1943. 2.50. Harvard

Hook, Sidney. Dimensions of mind. 1960. 5.00. N. Y. U.
Overstreet, Harry A. Mature mind. 1949. 4.50. Norton
Ryle, Gilbert. Concept of mind. 1950. 4.50. Barnes & Noble
Scheler, Max. Man's place in nature. 1961. 4.00. Beacon
Sherrington, Charles S. Man on his nature. 1951. 6.00. Cambridge U. P.
MINDSZENTY, JOZSEF, CARDINAL, 1892- (922)
Shuster, George N. In silence I speak. il. 1956. 4.50. Farrar, Straus
MINERAL INDUSTRIES (333.8)
Herfindahl, Orris C. Three studies in mineral economics. 1961. pap. 1.00. Johns
    Hopkins
Shimkin, Demitri B. Minerals: A key to Soviet power. il. 1953. 9.00. Harvard
Sullivan, John W. W. Story of metals. il. 1951. 2.95. Iowa State
MINERALOGY (549.1)
Berry, L. G., and Brian Mason. Mineralogy: Concepts, descriptions, determina-
    tions. il. 1959. 8.75. Freeman
Chambers, Mineralogical dictionary. il. 5.50. Tudor (R)
Dana, Edward S. System of mineralogy. 3 vols. Wiley
Dana, Edward S., and Cornelius S. Hurlbut. Manual of mineralogy. il. 1959.
    9.95. Wiley
Dennen, William H. Principles of mineralogy. il. 1960. 7.50. Ronald
English, George L., and D. E. Jensen. Getting acquainted with minerals. il.
    1958. 6.95. McGraw
Kraus, Edward H., and Walter F. Hunt. Tables for the determination of minerals.
    1930. 6.95. McGraw
Loomis, Frederic B. Field book of common rocks and minerals. il. 1948. 3.50.
    Putnam (R)
Niggli, Paul. Rocks and mineral deposits. tr. by Robert L. Parker. 1954. 12.00.
    Freeman
Pearl, Richard M. 1001 questions answered about the mineral kingdom. il. 1959.
    6.00. Dodd
Pearl, Richard M. Successful mineral collecting and prospecting. il. 1961. bds. 5.95.
    McGraw
Pearl, Richard M. How to know the minerals and rocks. 1955. 4.25. McGraw
Pough , Frederick H. Field guide to rocks and minerals. il. 1953. 4.95. Houghton
Reinfeld, Fred. Treasures of the earth. il. 1954. 3.95. Sterling
Smith, Orsino C. Identification and qualitative chemical analysis of minerals.
    il. 1953. 8.50. Van Nostrand
Tomkeieff, S. I. Coals and bitumens and related fossil carbonaceous substances.
    il. 1954. 3.00. Pergamon (R)
Wahlstrom, E. E. Igneous minerals and rocks. 1947. 7.50. Wiley
Wahlstrom, Ernest Eugene. Petrographic mineralogy. 1955. 7.95. Wiley
MINES AND MINERAL RESOURCES (622)
Bateman, A. M. Economic mineral deposits. 1950. 9.25. Wiley
Bidwell, Percy W. Raw materials: A study of American policy. 1958. 5.95.
    Harper
Leet, L. Don, and Sheldon Judson. Physical geology. 1954. 11.65. Prentice-Hall
Riley, Charles M. Our mineral resources. il. 1959. 6.95. Wiley
MINNESOTA (977.6)
Blegen, Theodore C., and Theodore L. Nydahl. Minnesota history. 5.00. U. of
    Minn.
Szarkowski, John. Face of Minnesota. il. 1958. 5.00. U. of Minn.
Writers' Project. Minnesota. 1954. 6.50. Hastings
MINORITIES (323.1)
American Council on Education, Committee on the Study of Teaching Materials
    in Intergroup Relations. Intergroup relations in teaching materials. 3.00.
    A. C. E.
Barron, Milton L. American minorities: A textbook of readings in intergroup
    relations. 1957. 5.75. Knopf

Brown, Francis J., and Joseph S. Roucek. One America. 1952. 10.00. Prentice-Hall

Calpin, G. H. South African way of life. 1953. 3.50. Columbia

Claude, I. L., Jr. National minorities: An international problem. 1955. 4.50. Harvard

Conquest, Robert. Soviet deportation of nationalities. 1960. 6.95. St. Martins

Dewey, Richard, and W. J. Humber. Development of human behavior. il. 1951. 6.95. Macmillan

Dexter, Harriet Harmon. What's right with race relations. 1958. 4.00. Harper

Gittler, Joseph B. Understanding minority groups. 1956. 3.50. Wiley

Glazer, Nathan, and Davis McEntire. Studies in housing and minority groups. il. 1960. 6.00. U. of Calif.

Handlin, Oscar. American people in the twentieth century. 1954. 3.75. Harvard

McDonagh, Edward C., and Eugene S. Richards. Ethnic relations in the United States. 1953. 4.50. Appleton

MacIver, R. M. Group relations and group antagonisms. 3.50. Smith, Peter

Marden, Charles F., and Gladys Meyer. Minorities in American society. 1962. 6.25. Am. Bk. Co.

Rose, Arnold, and Caroline. America divided: Minority group relations in the United States. 1949. 3.75. Knopf

Simpson, George Eaton, and J. Milton Yinger. Racial and cultural minorities: An analysis of prejudice and discrimination. 1958. 8.00. Harper

Smal-Stoki, Roman. Captive nations. 1960. 3.50. Twayne

Warner, W. L., and L. Srole. Social systems of American ethnic groups. 1945. 6.00. Yale

Williams, Robin M., Jr. Reduction in intergroup tensions: A survey of research on problems of ethnic, racial and religious group relations. 1947. pap. 1.75. Soc. Sci. Res.

MISSIONS (266)

Aberly, John. Outline of missions. 1945. 3.25. Muhlenberg

Bavinck, J. H. Introduction to missions. 1960. 4.95. Presbyterian & Reformed

Haitz, Linn. Juju gods. 1961. pap. 1.00. Concordia

Johnson, R. Park. Middle East pilgrimage. 1958. 2.95. Friendship

Levison, Wilhelm. England and the continent in the eighth century. 1946. 4.80. Oxford U. P.

Schweitzer, Albert. On the edge of the primeval forest, and More from the primeval forest. il. 5.00. Macmillan

Vaulx, Bernard de. History of the missions. 1961. 3.50. Hawthorn

MISSISSIPPI (976)

Botkin, Benjamin A. Treasury of Mississippi River folklore. 1955. 5.00. Crown

Carter, Hodding. Lower Mississippi. il. 1942. 5.00. Rinehart

Clemens, Samuel Langhorne. Life on the Mississippi. il. 4.50. il. 1960. Harper

Havighurst, Walter. Upper Mississippi. il. 1944. 4.50. Rinehart

Highsaw, Robert B., and Charles N. Fortenberry. Government and administration of Mississippi. 1954. 5.75. Crowell

Parkman, Francis. Discovery of the great west: La Salle. by William R. Taylor. 1956. 1.65. Holt, Rinehart & Winston

Smith, Frank E. Yazoo River. il. 1954. 4.00. Rinehart

Writers' Project. Mississippi. 1946. 6.50. Hastings

MISSISSIPPI VALLEY--HISTORY (976)

Bemis, Samuel F. Pinckney's Treaty: America's advantage from Europe's distress, 1783-1800. 1960. 6.00. Yale

Paxson, Frederic L. History of the American frontier. 1924. 6.50. Houghton

Riegel, Robert E. America moves West. 1956. 10.10. Holt, Rinehart & Winston

Turner, Frederick J. Rise of the new West. 1959. 6.00. Smith, Peter

Webb, Walter P. Great plains. 1931. 8.00. Ginn

MISSOURI (977.8)

Battaglia, Elio L. Face of Missouri. il. 1960. 7.50. U. of Missouri

Collins, Earl A., and Felix E. Snider. Missouri: Midland state. il. 1961. 5.00. Ramfre

Karsch, Robert. Government of Missouri. 1961. 3.25. Lucas Bros.

Moore, Glover. Missouri controversy, 1819-1821. 1953. 6.00. U. of Ky.

Writers' Project. Missouri. 1954. 6.50. Hastings

MNEMONICS (154.1)

Ennever, W. Your mind: How to use it. 2.00. Wehman

Henderson, J. Lowell. Learn and like it. 3.00. DeVorss

Laird, Donald A., and Eleanor C. Techniques for efficient remembering. il. 1960. bds. 5.00. McGraw

MOBS (301.158)

Caughey, John W. Their majesties, the mob. 1960. 5.00. U. of Chicago

MODELING (730)

Kenny, John B. Ceramic sculpture. il. 1959. 7.50. Chilton

MODERNISM (ART) (759.91)

Biddle, George. Yes and no of contemporary art: An artist's evaluation. 1957. 5.00. Harvard

Leepa, Allen. Challenge of modern art. 1957. 3.95. Yoseloff

Myers, Bernard S. Modern art in the making. il. 1959. 10.95. McGraw

Rathbun, Mary C., and Bartlett H. Hayes, Jr. Layman's guide to modern art. 1954. 2.75. Addison Gallery

Read, Herbert. Philosophy of modern art. 1955. pap. 1.55. Meridian

MODIGLIANI, AMEDEO, 1884-1920 (927)

Modigliani, Jeanne. Modigliani: Man and myth. il. 1958. 7.50. Orion

Roy, Claude. Modigliani. il. 1958. 5.75. World Pub.

MOHAMMED, THE PROPHET, 570-632 (922.97)

Andrae, Tor. Mohammed: The man and his faith. 1956. 3.50. Barnes & Noble

Watt, W. Montgomery. Mohammed, prophet and statesman. 1961. 4.50. Oxford U. P.

MOHAMMEDAN COUNTRIES (953)

Atlas of the Arab world and the Middle East. 1960. 9.00. St. Martins

Byford-Jones, W. Forbidden frontiers. il. 1959. 5.50. Transatlantic

Conaldson, Dwight M. Studies in Muslim ethics. 5.50. Seabury

Hitti, Philip K. Arabs: A short history. 1956. pap. 0.95. Regnery

Khadduri, Majid, and Herbert Liebesny. Law in the Middle East. 7.50. Middle East Inst.

Spuler, B. Muslim world. 2 vols. il. 13.00. Humanities

MOHAMMEDANISM (297)

Fitch, Florence. Allah: The God of Islam. 1950. 3.00. Lothrop

Smith, Wilfred C. Islam in modern history. 1959. pap. 0.50. New Am. Lib.

MOLDS (BOTANY) (589.25)

Henrici, A. T. Molds, yeasts and actinomycetes. 1947. 7.95. Wiley

Smith, George. Introduction to industrial mycology. 1960. 10.00. St. Martins

MOLECULES (541.22)

Arkel, Anton E. van. Molecules and crystals in inorganic chemistry. il. 1957. 6.50. Wiley

Blackwood, O. H., and others. Outline of atomic physics. 1955. 7.50. Wiley

Brand, S. C. D., and J. C. Speakman. Molecular structure, the physical approach. 1960. 6.50. St. Martins

Debye, Peter. Polar molecules. il. pap. 1.50. Dover

Hirschfelder, Joseph O., and others. Molecular theory of gases and liquids. 1954. 22.50. Wiley

Moelwyn-Hughes, Emyr A. States of matter. il. 1961. 3.50. Wiley

Pauling, Linus. Nature of the chemical bond and the structure of molecules and crystals: An introduction to modern structural chemistry. il. 1960. 8.85. Cornell

Setlow, Richard B., and Ernest C. Pollard. Molecular biophysics. il. 1962. 11.75. Addison-Wesley

Williams, Dudley. Molecular physics. il. 1962. 19.00. Academic Press

MOLIERE, JEAN BAPTISTE POQUELIN, 1622-1673 (928.424)
Fellows, Otis E. French opinion of Moliere, 1800-1850. 1937. 1.75. Brown U.
Hubert, J. D. Moliere and the comedy of intellect. 1962. 5.50. U. of Calif.
Turnell, Martin. Classical moment. 1948. 5.00. New Directions
MOLLUSKS (594)
Allan, J. Australian shells. 12.00. Branford
Keen, A. Myra. Sea shells of tropical west America. il. 1958. 12.50. Stanford
Morris, Percy A. Field guide to the shells of the Pacific coast and Hawaii.
    il. 1952. 4.50. Houghton (R)
Morton, J. E. Molluscs. 2.50. Hillary
Warmke, Germaine L., and R. Tucker Abbott. Caribbean seashells. il. 8.95.
    Livingston
Webb, Walter F. Handbook for shell collectors. 1959. 5.00. Lee Pub. (R)
Webb, Walter F. United States mollusca. 1959. 5.00. Lee Pub.
MONARCHY (321.61)
Figgis, J. N. Political thought from Gerson to Grotius. 4.00. Cambridge U. P.
Paine, Thomas. Common sense. bd. with Crisis. pap. 0.95. Doubleday
MONASTERIES (271)
Cook, G. H. English monasteries in the Middle Ages. 1961. 7.50. Macmillan
Nigg, Walter. Warriors of God: The great religious orders and their founders.
    1959. 6.95. Knopf
MONDRIAN, PIETER CORNELIUS, 1872-1944 (927)
Mondrian, Piet. Mondrian. 3.95. Abrams
MONET, CLAUDE, 1840-1926 (927.0944)
Monet, Claude. Monet. 3.95. Abrams
Rouart, Denis, and Leon Degand. Monet. 1958. 5.75. World Pub.
MONEY (332.4)
Barger, Harold. Money, banking and public policy. 7.00. Rand McNally
Bogen, Jules I., and others. Money and banking. 1953. 7.50. Prentice-Hall
Commission on Money and Credit. Money and credit. 1961. 3.95. Prentice-Hall
Committee on money and banking. Money and banking. 1957. 6.00. Pitman
Copeland, M. A. Study of moneyflows in the U. S. 1952. 7.50. Princeton
Croome, Honor. Introduction to money. 1957. 2.50. Barnes & Noble
Desmonde, William H. Magic, myth, and money: The origin of money in religious
    ritual. 1962. 5.00. Free Press
De Sola, Ralph, and Stephen Naft. International conversion tables. 1961. 7.50.
    Duell (R)
Einzig, P. Primitive money in its ethnological, historical and economic aspects.
    6.00. Humanities
Fielding, George T. European currency guide. 3.95. Fielding (R)
Gould, Clarence P. Money and transportation in Maryland, 1720-1765. 1915. 2.75.
    Johns Hopkins
Groseclose, Elgin. Money and man. 1961. 5.00. Ungar
Halm, George N. Economics of money and banking. 1961. 10.60. Irwin
Hart, Albert G., and P. B. Kenen. Money, debt and economic activity. 1961. 11.95.
    Prentice-Hall
Kent, Raymond P. Money and banking. 1961. 7.75. Holt, Rinehart & Winston
Keynes, John Maynard. General theory of employment, interest, and money.
    1936. 6.00. Harcourt
Keynes, John Maynard. Treatise on money. 2 vols. 1935. 12.00. Harcourt
Mason, Will E. Clarification of monetary standards. 1962. 5.00. Penn. State
Mises, Ludwig von. Theory of money and credit. 1953. 7.00. Yale
Myrdal, Gunnar. Monetary equilibrium. 1939. 6.00. Kelley
Prather, Charles L. Money and banking. 1961. 10.00. Irwin
Quiggin, A. Hinston. Survey of primitive money. 8.50. Humanities
Reeve, Joseph. Monetary reform movements. 1943. 4.50. Pub. Affairs
Stokes, Milton L., and C. T. Arlt. Money, banking, and the financial system.
    1955. 7.00. Ronald
Sutherland, Carol H. V. Coinage in Roman Imperial Policy: 31 B. C. -A. D. 68.
    4.50. Humanities

Timlin, Mabel F. Keynesian economics. 1948. 4.25. U. of Toronto
Trescott, Money, banking and economic welfare. 1960. 7.50. McGraw

MONGOLIA (951.7)
Dawson, Christopher. Mongol mission. 1955. 4.00. Sheed
Polo, Marco. Travels of Marco Polo. il. 1958. 6.00. Orion
Tang, Peter S. H. Russian and soviet policy in Manchuria and Outer Mongolia, 1911-1931. 1959. 10.00. Duke

MONGOLISM (616.444)
Benda, Clemens E. Child with Mongolism. 1960. 9.50. Grune
Stout, Lucille. I reclaimed my child. 1959. 2.75. Chilton

MONOLOGUES (808)
Howard, Vernon. Humorous monologues. il. 1955. 2.50. Sterling
Ireland, Norma Olin. Index to monologs and dialogs. 1949. 6.00 net. Faxon (R)
Langbaum, Robert. Poetry of experience. 1957. 4.50. Random
Murray, John. Modern monologues for young people. 1961. 3.95. Plays
Schell, S. Monologues of today. 1.50. Wehman
Schell, S. Monologues with music. 1.50. Wehman

MONOPOLIES (338.82)
Chamberlin, Edward H. Theory of monopolistic competition. 1934. 6.00. Harvard
Chamberlin, E. H. Towards a more general theory of value. 1957. 5.00. Oxford U. P.
Lindblom, C. E. Unions and capitalism. 1949. 3.75. Yale
Tarbell, Ida M. Nationalizing of business. 1878-1898. il. 1936. 6.75. Macmillan
Wells, Henry A. Monopoly and social control. 1952. 3.25. Pub. Affairs

MONOTHEISM (211.3)
Albright, William Foxwell. From the stone age to Christianity. 1957. 5.00. Johns Hopkins
Niebuhr, H. Richard. Radical monotheism and Western culture. 1960. 2.75. Harper

MONROE, JAMES, PRES. U.S., 1758-1831 (923.173)
Cresson, William Penn. James Monroe. 1946. 6.50. U. of N. C.

MONROE DOCTRINE (973)
Perkins, Dexter. History of the Monroe Doctrine. 1955. 6.00. Little
Whitaker, Arthur P. United States and the independence of Latin America, 1800-1830. 1962. 10.00. Russell

MONTAIGNE, MICHEL EYQUEM DE, 1533-1592 (928.443)
Frame, D. F. Montaigne's discovery of man. 1955. 3.50. Columbia

MONTANA (978.6)
Christopherson, Edmund. This here is Montana. il. 1.00. Earthquake
Writers' Project. Montana. 1955. 6.50. Hastings

MONTESQUIEU, CHARLES LOUIS DE SECONDAT, BARON DE LA BREDE ET DE, 1689-1755. (923.444)
Durkheim, D. Emile. Montesquieu and Rousseau: Forerunners of sociology. 1960. 3.95. U. of Mich.
Shackleton, Robert. Montesquieu: A critical biography. 1961. 7.20. Oxford U. P.
Stark, W. Montesquieu, pioneer of knowledge. 1961. 4.25. U. of Toronto

MONTESSORI, MARIA, 1870-1952 (923.7)
Standing, E. M. Maria Montessori, her life and work. il. 1959. 5.95. Academy Lib.
Standing, E. M. Montessori method: A revolution in education. 1962. 4.50. Academy Lib.

MOON (523.3)
Barabashov, N. P., and others. Atlas of the moon's far side. 1961. 7.00. Wiley
Barabashov, N. P., and others. Atlas of the other side of the moon. 1961. 7.00. Pergamon
Clarke, A. C. Exploration of the moon. 3.50. Wehman
Fielder, G. Structure of the moon's surface. 1961. 7.50. Pergamon
Firsoff, V. A. Strange world of the moon. il. 1959. 6.00. Basic Books

Firshoff, V. A. Moon atlas. il. 1962. 10.00. Viking
Kopal, Zdenek. Physics and astronomy of the moon. 1962. 16.50. Academic Press
Ley, Wily. Conquest of space. il. 1949. 5.75. Viking
Markov, A. V. Moon: A Russian view. il. 1962. 8.00. U. of Chicago
Whipple, Fred L. Earth, moon and planets. 2.95. Grosset
Wilkins, Percy H. Our moon. il. 1960. 3.50. Wehman
MOORE, GEORGE EDWARD, 1873- (921.2)
Geliner, Ernest. Words and things. il. 1960. 5.00. Beacon
White, A. R. G. E. Moore: A critical exposition. 5.00. Humanities
MORAL EDUCATION (377.2)
Bower, William C. Moral and spiritual values in education. 3.50. U. of Ky.
Brinton, Crane. History of Western morals. 1959. 7.50. Harcourt
Durkheim, Emile. Moral education. 1961. 6.00. Free Press
McCluskey, Neil G. Public schools and moral education, the influence of Horace
    Mann, William Torrey Harris, and John Dewey. 1958. 6.00. Columbia
Phenix, Philip H. Education and the common good. 1961. 5.00. Harper
Peaget, Jean. Moral judgement of the child. 6.00. Free Press
Russell, Bertrand. Education and the good life. 1931. 3.50. Liveright
MORE, SIR THOMAS, SAINT, 1478-1535 (923.242)
Chambers, R. W. On the continuity of English prose from Alfred to More and
    his school. 1932. 2.25. Oxford U. P.
Chambers, Raymond W. Thomas More. 1949. 5.00. Newman
Hogrefe, Pearl. Sir Thomas More circle: A program of ideas and their impact
    on secular drama. 1959. 5.75. U. of Ill.
Kautsky, Karl. Thomas More and his Utopia. 5.00. Russell
Reynolds, Ernest E. St. Thomas More. 1954. 6.00. Kenedy
MORMONS AND MORMONISM (289.3)
Mulder, William, and Russell A. Mortensen. Among the Mormons. 1958. 6.75.
    Knopf
West, Ray B., Jr. Kingdom of the saints: The story of Brigham Young and the
    Mormons. il. 1957. 6.00. Viking
MORPHOLOGY (612)
Frey-Wyssling, A. Submicroscopic morphology of protoplasm. 1953. 11.00.
    Am. Elsevier
Moore, Arthur R. Individual in simpler forms. 1945. pap. 1.25. U. of Ore.
MORPHOLOGY (ANIMALS) (591.4)
Hanson, Earl D. Animal diversity. 1961. 3.75. Prentice-Hall
Saunders, John T., and S. M. Manton. Manual of practical vertebrate morphology.
    1959. 8.50. Oxford U. P.
MORRIS, WILLIAM, 1834-1896 (928)
Hoare, Dorothy M. Works of Morris and Yeats in relation to early saga literature.
    1937. 3.50. Cambridge U. P.
Mackail, J. W. Life of William Morris. 2.75. Oxford U. P.
MORTALITY (312.2)
Dublin, Louis I., and others. Length of life. 1949. 10.00. Ronald
Wolfenden, Hugh H. Population statistics and their compilation. 1954. 7.50. U.
    of Chicago
MORTGAGES (332.7)
Fisher, E. M. Urban real estate markets. 1951. 3.00. Princeton
Jones, L. A., and D. Durand. Mortgage lending experience in agriculture. 1954.
    5.00. Princeton
MORTON, WILLIAM THOMAS GREEN, 1819-1868 (926)
Ludovici, L. J. Discovery of anaesthesia. 1962. 5.00. Crowell
Woodward, Grace S. Man who conquered pain. il. 1962. 4.95. Beacon
MOSAICS (729.7)
Demus, Otto. Byzantine mosaic decoration. il. 1955. 8.50. Boston Bk.
Jenkins, Louisa, and Barbara Mills. Art of making mosaics. 1957. 5.95. Van
    Nostrand

Schapiro, Meyer, and Michael Avi-Yonah. Israel, ancient mosaics. il. 1960. 18.00. N. Y. Graphic
Young, Joseph L. Course in making mosaics. 1957. 3.50. Reinhold
MOSCOW (947.31)
Cartier-Bresson, Henri. People of Moscow. 1955. 10.00. S. and S.
Hurlimann, Martin. Moscow and Leningrad. il. 1958. 6.00. Viking
Stanislavski, Constantin. My life in art. 6.75. Theatre Arts
Tolstoy, Leo. What then must we do? 2.75. Oxford U. P.
MOSES, ANNA MARY ROBERTSON, 1860-1962 (927)
Moses, Anna Mary Robertson. Grandma Moses: My life's history. by Otto Kallir. il. 1952. 5.50. Harper
MOSQUITOES (595.771)
Carpenter, Stanley J., and Walter J. La Casse. Mosquitoes of North America. il. 1955. 10.00. U. of Calif.
MOSSES (588.2)
Conrad, Henry S. How to know the mosses and liverworts. 1956. 3.00. Brown, W. C.
Sterling, Dorothy. Story of mosses, ferns, and mushrooms. il. 1955. 2.75. Doubleday
MOTHS (595.774)
Worthington, Stuart, Brian. Collecting and breeding butterflies and moths. il. 1952. 3.00. Warne
MOTION (115)
Broer, Marion R. Efficiency of human movement. il. 1960. 6.00. Saunders
Infeld, Leopold, and J. Plebanski. Motion and relativity. 1961. 6.00. Pergamon
MOTIVATION (PSYCHOLOGY) (159.4)
Allport, Gordon W., and others. Assessment of human motives. pap. 1.05. Grove
Atkinson, John W. Motives in fantasy, action, and society: A method of assessment and study. 1958. 9.75. Van Nostrand
Brown, Judson S., and others. Current theory and research in motivation: A symposium. vol. 1. 1953. pap. 2.00. U. of Nebr.
Ferber, Robert, and Hugh G. Wales. Motivation and market behavior. 1958. 9.25. Irwin
Hall, John F. Psychology of motivation. 1961. 8.95. Lippincott
Lichtenberg, Philip, and others. Motivation for child psychiatry treatment. il. 1960. 5.00. Russell
McClelland, David C., and others. Achievement motive. il. 6.50. Appleton
McClelland, David C. Studies in motivation. il. 1955. 6.50. Appleton
Madsen, Kristen B. Theories of motivation. 7.00. Allen, Howard
Maslow, A. H. Motivation and personality. 1954. 5.00. Harper
Nebraska symposium on motivation. vols. 1-10. U. of Nebr.
Schreier, Fred T. Human motivation. 5.00. Free Press
Smith, G. H. Motivation research in advertising and marketing. 1954. 6.50. McGraw
MOUNDS (571.9)
Fox, Cyril. Life and death in the Bronze Age. il. 1959. 8.50. Humanities
MOUNT EVEREST (949.4)
Hunt, John. Conquest of Everest. 1954. 6.95. Dutton
MOUNT McKINLEY NATIONAL PARK (979.83)
Pearson, Grant H., and Philip Newill. My life of high adventure. il. 1962. 4.95. Prentice-Hall
MOUNTAINEERING (796.52)
Brower, David R. Manual of ski mountaineering. 1962. 3.75. Sierra
Henderson, Kenneth A. Handbook of American mountaineering. il. 4.00. Houghton
Ullman, James R. Age of mountaineering. il. 1954. 7.50. Lippincott
MOUNTAINS (551.43)
Huxley, Anthony. Standard encyclopedia of the world's mountains. 1962. 10.95. Putnam (R)

Macartney, Clarence E. Mountains and mountain men of the Bible. 2.50.
   Abingdon
MOUTH (612.31)
Bunting, Russell W. Oral hygiene. il. 1957. 7.00. Lea & F
Jenkins, G. Neil. Physiology of the mouth. 1960. 7.50. Davis
Permar, Dorothy. Manual of oral embryology and microscopic anatomy. 5.50.
   Lea & F
MOVING-PICTURES (791.43)
Agee, James. Agee on film. 2 vols. il. vol. 1, 1958, 6.50; vol. 2, 1960, 7.50.
   Obolensky
Bluestone, George. Novels into film. 1957. 5.00. Johns Hopkins
Blum, Daniel C. Pictorial history of the talkies. il. 1958. 12.50. Putnam
Filmstrip guide. 1955-1958. Wilson (R)
Franklin, Joe. Classics of the silent screen: A pictorial treasury. 1959. 6.95.
   Citadel
Knight, Arthur. Liveliest art: A panoramic history of the movies. il. 8.50.
   Macmillan
Lindgren, Ernest. Art of the film. il. 1962. 7.50. Macmillan
Lindgren, Ernest. Picture history of the cinema. il. 7.00. Macmillan
Pudovkin, V. Film technique and acting. 7.50. Wehman
Seldes, Gilbert. Seven lively arts. 1957. 4.95. Sagamore
Tydings, Kenneth S. Guide to Kodak 8mm Brownie movie camera. il. 1959. pap.
   1.95. Chilton (R)
Waldron, G. Information film. 1949. 4.25. Columbia (R)
MOVING-PICTURES IN EDUCATION (374.27)
McDonald, Gerald D. Educational motion pictures and libraries. 1942. 2.75.
   A. L. A.
MOZART, JOHANN CHRYSOSTOM WOLFGANG AMADEUS, 1756-1791 (927)
Blom, Eric. Mozart. il. 1949. 3.50. Farrar, Straus
Davenport, Marcia. Mozart. il. 1956. 6.00. Scribner
Einstein, Alfred. Mozart: His character, his work. 1945. 10.00. Oxford U. P.
Rothschild, Fritz. Musical performance in the times of Mozart and Beethoven.
   4.80. Oxford U. P.
Valentin, Erich. Mozart, a pictorial biography. il. 1960. 6.50. Viking
MULTIPLE SCLEROSIS (616.834)
Hess, George H. Living at your best with multiple sclerosis. il. 1962. 4.00.
   Thomas, C. C.
McAlpine, Douglas, and others. Multiple sclerosis. il. 1955. 7.00. Williams &
   Wilkins
MUNICIPAL GOVERNMENT (352)
Adrian, Charles R. Governing urban America. 1961. 7.50. McGraw
American Municipal Association. Intergovernment cooperation. 3.00. Am.
   Municipal Assn.
Anderson, William, and Edward W. Weidner. American city government. 1950.
   7.00. Holt, Rinehart & Winston
Banfield, Edward C., and Morton Grodzins. Government and housing in metro-
   politan areas. 1958. 6.50. McGraw
Banfield, Edward C. Political influence. 1961. 6.00. Free Press
Banfield, Edward C. Urban government. 1961. 7.50. Free Press
Brown, William H., and Charles E. Gilbert. Planning municipal investment.
   1961. 6.00. U. of Pa.
Dahl, Robert A. Who governs? 1961. 7.50. Yale
Fisher, Marguerite J., and Donald G. Bishop. Municipal and other local govern-
   ments. 1950. 10.00. Prentice-Hall
Isard, Walter, and Robert Coughlin. Municipal costs and revenues. 1957. 5.00.
   Chandler-Davis
Kneier, Charles M. City government in the United States. 1957. 6.50. Harper
Macdonald, Austin F. American city government and administration. 1956.
   6.50. Crowell

Phillips Jewell C. Municipal government and administration in America. il. 1960. 6.95. Macmillan

Steffens, Joseph Lincoln. Shame of the cities. 1959. 3.50. Smith, Peter

Tenner, Irving, and Lynn. Municipal and governmental accounting. 11.95. Prentice-Hall

Williams, Oliver P., and Charles Press. Democracy in urban America. 1961. 5.95. Rand McNally

MURAL PAINTING AND DECORATION (729.4)

Bernal, Ignacio, and Jacques Soustelle. Mexico, pre-Hispanic paintings. il. 1958. 18.00. N.Y. Graphic

Comarescu, Petru. Frescoes from Voronetz. il. 1959. 7.50. Vanous

Feibusch, Hans. Mural painting. il. 5.25. Transatlantic

Gabriel, Mabel M. Masters of companian painting. il. 1952. 12.00. Boston Bk.

Giotto. Frescoes. il. 1950. 4.50. Oxford U. P.

Grabar, Andre. Byzantine painting. il. 1953. 20.00. World Pub.

Maiuri, Amedeo. Pompeian wall paintings. il. 1960. 2.00. Taplinger

Maiuri, Amedeo. Roman painting. il. 1953. 15.00. World Pub.

Merrifield, Mary P. Art of Fresco painting. il. 3.75. Transatlantic

Rodojcic, Svetozar, and Talbot Rice. Yugoslavia, medieval frescoes. il. 1955. 18.00. N.Y. Graphic

MUSCLES (611.73)

Adams, Raymond D., and others. Diseases of muscle. 1962. 22.00. Hoeber

Basmajian, J. V. Muscles alive: Their functions revealed by electromyography il. 1962. 8.50. Williams & Wilkins

Coers, C., and A. L. Woolf. Innervation of muscle. il. 1959. 8.50. Davis

Duchenne, G. B. Duchenne's psysiology of motion. by Emanuel B. Kaplan. il. 1959. 11.00. Saunders

Hettinger, Theodor. Physiology of strength. il. 1961. 4.50. Thomas, C. C.

Hollinshead, W. Henry. Functional anatomy of the limbs and back. il. 1960. 9.00. Saunders

Inkster, R. G., and others. Anatomy of the locomotor system. 1956. 4.80. Oxford U. P.

Kendall, Henry O., and Florence P. Muscles, testing and function. il. 1949. 7.50. Williams & Wilkins

Lockhart, R. D. Living anatomy. il. 1959. 4.00. Oxford U. P.

McMurrich, Kathleen I. Applied muscle action and co-ordination. il. 1957. 3.75. U. of Toronto

Nachmansohn, David. Molecular biology: Elementary processes of nerve conduction and muscle contraction: A symposium. 1960. 6.50. Academic Press

Rodahl, Kaare, and S. M. Horvath. Muscle as a tissue. 1962. 15.00. McGraw

Szent-Gyorgyi, A. Nature of life: A study on muscle. 1948. 3.00. Academic Press

Weber, H. Motility of muscle and cells. il. 1958. 3.50. Harvard

Wright, Wilhelmine G. Muscle functions. il. 1928. 6.50. Hafner

MUSHROOMS (589.222)

Atkins, Frederick C. Mushroom growing to-day. 1961. 5.00. Macmillan

Atkinson, G. F. Studies of American fungi. 1903. 15.00. Hafner

Christensen, C. M. Common edible mushrooms. 3.50. Branford

Hard, M. E. Mushroom, edible and otherwise. il. 16.00. Hafner

Pilat, A., and Usak. Mushrooms. il. 12.95. Tudor

Ramsbottom, John. Mushrooms and toadstools. il. 1953. 6.25. Macmillan

Thomas, William S. Field book of common mushrooms. 1948. 5.00. Putnam (R)

MUSIC (780)

Barzun, Jacques. Music in American life. 2.75. Smith, Peter

Copland, Aaron. Copland on music. 1960. 3.95. Doubleday

Hawkins, John. General history of the science and practice of music. 2 vols. 1962. 15.00. Dover

Hughes, David G. Instrumental music. 1959. 4.25. Harvard

Pettis, Ashley. Music: Now and then. 1955. 2.50. Coleman-Ross

Smith, Cecil. Worlds of music. 1953. 5.00. Lippincott
Spaeth, Sigmund. Common sense of music. 2.50. Liveright
Stravinskii, Igor F., and Robert Craft. Conversations with Igor Stravinsky. il. 1959. 4.00. Doubleday
Toch, Ernst. Shaping forces in music. 5.00. Wehman
Weber, Max. Rational and social foundations of music. 1958. 5.75. Southern Ill.

MUSIC--ADDRESSES, ESSAYS, LECTURES (780.04)

Barzun, Jacques. Pleasures of music. 1960. pap. 1.95. Viking
Berlioz, Hector. Evenings with the orchestra. 1956. 6.75. Knopf
Bernstein, Leonard. Joy of music. il. 1959. 5.95. S. and S.
Chavez, Carlos. Musical thought. il. 1961. 4.50. Harvard
Einstein, Alfred. Essays on music. 1956. pap. 1.65. Norton
Huxley, Aldous. On art and artists. 1960. 4.50. Harper
Kolodin, Irving. Musical life. 1958. 4.50. Knopf
Lang, Paul H. 100 years of music in America. 6.95. Grosset
Lang, Paul H. One hundred years of music in America. 1961. 6.95. Schirmer
Lang, Paul H. Problems of modern music. 1962. pap. 1.45. Norton
Rolland, Romain. Essays on music. 3.50. Smith, Peter
Spaeth, Sigmund. Fifty years with music. il. 1959. 4.95. Fleet
Tovey, D. F. Main stream of music and other essays. 1949. 6.00. Oxford U. P.

MUSIC--ANALYSIS, APPRECIATION (780)

Bauer, Marion, and Ethel Peyser. Twentieth century music. 1947. 6.00. Putnam
Bartholomew, Wilmer T. Acoustics of music. 1942. 6.60. Prentice-Hall
Bernstein, Martin. Introduction to music. 1951. 10.00. Prentice-Hall
Bockman, Guy A., and William J. Starr. Perceiving music: Problems in sight and sound. 1962. pap. 7.95; with six 7 in. records. Harcourt
Bockman, Guy Alan, and William J. Starr. Scored for listening: A guide to music. il. 1959. pap. 2.75. Harcourt
Boyden, David D. Introduction to music. il. 1956. 8.00. Knopf
Bruxner, Mervyn. Letters to a musical boy. 1954. 3.00. Oxford U. P.
Cohn, Arthur. Collector's twentieth-century music in the western hemisphere. 1961. pap. 1.95. Lippincott
Copland, Aaron. What to listen for in music. 1957. 4.95. McGraw
Culver, C. A. Musical acoustics. 1956. 7.00. McGraw
Dorian, Frederick. History of music in performance. il. 1943. 6.95. Norton
Ewen, D. Home book of musical knowledge. 1955. 5.95. Prentice-Hall
Ferguson, Donald N. History of musical thought. 1959. 6.00. Appleton
Ferguson, Donald N. Masterworks of the orchestral repertoire: A guide for listeners. il. 1954. 7.50. U. of Minn. (R)
Fleming, William, and Abraham Veinus. Understanding music: Style, structure and history. 1958. 6.00. Holt
Hansen, Peter S. Introduction to twentieth century music. il. 1961. 8.95. Allyn & Bacon
Kaufmann, Helen L. Joy in listening. 1960. 1.50. Grosset
Kolodin, Irving. Composer as listener. pap. 1.50. Collier
Liepmann, K. Language of music. 1953. 6.00. Ronald
Lowance, Kathleen. Much ado about music. 1953. 3.95. McKay
Machlis, Joseph. Enjoyment of music. il. 1955. 9.00. Norton
McKinney, Howard D., and W. R. Anderson. Discovering music, a course in music appreciation. 6.25. Am. Bk. Co.
Miller, William H. Everybody's guide to music. il. 1961. 7.50. Chilton
Moore, Douglas. Listening to music. il. 1937. 3.85. Norton
Newman, William S. Understanding music. 1961. 6.00. Harper
Ratner, Leonard G. Music: The listener's art. il. 1957. 8.75. McGraw
Scholes, Percy A. Complete book of the great musicians. il. 1949. 3. vols. in one. 5.00. Oxford U. P.
Scholes, Percy A. Listener's history of music. 3 vols. 8.50. Oxford U. P.
Siegmeister, Elie. Invitation to music. il. 1961. 4.95. Harvey

Spaeth, Sigmund. Guide to great orchestral music. 2.95. Modern Lib.
Stringham, Edwin J. Listening to music creatively. 10.00. Prentice-Hall
Taylor, Deems. Of men and music. 1937. 3.00. S. and S.
Taylor, Deems. Well-tempered listener. 1940. 3.00. S. and S.
Ulrich, Homer. Music: A design for listening. 1962. 6.50. Harcourt
Woodhouse, Frederick E. Art and theory of music. 1958. 4.50. Pitman
MUSIC--DICTIONARIES (780.3)
Apel, Willi. Harvard dictionary of music. il. 1944. 9.50. Harvard (R)
Barbour, Harriot B., and Warren S. Freeman. Story of music. 1958. 3.80. Summy
Clason, W. E. Dictionary of cinema, sound and music. 1956. 22.50. Am.
   Elsevier
Cohn, Arthur, Collector's twentieth-century music in the western hemisphere.
   1961. pap. 1.95. Lippincott
Cooper, Martin. Concise encyclopedia of music and musicians. il. 15.00.
   Hawthorn
Ewin, David. Encyclopedia of concert music. il. 1959. 7.50. Hill & Wang
Ewen, David. Musical masterworks. 1954. 3.95. Arco
Grove, George. Dictionary of music and musicians. il. 1948. 11.50. Macmillan (R)
Hughes, Rupert, and others. Music lovers' encyclopedia. 1957. 3.95. Doubleday'
Pratt, Waldo S. New encyclopedia of music and musicians. 12.50. Macmillan
Scholes, Percy A. Concise Oxford dictionary of music. 1953. 6.00. Oxford U. P.
   (R)
Scholes, Percy A. Oxford companion to music. 1955. 25.00. Oxford U. P. (R)
Scholes, Percy A. Oxford junior companion to music. 1954. 6.75. Oxford U. P.
Westrup, J. A., and F. L. Harrison. New college encyclopedia of music.
   il. 1960. 7.50. Norton
MUSIC--HISTORY AND CRITICISM (780)
Barzun, Jacques. Pleasures of music. 1960. pap. 1.95. Viking
Bauer, Marion, and Ethel Peyser. Music through the ages. 1946. 5.50. Putnam
Bauer, Marion, and Ethel Peyser. Twentieth century music. 1947. 5.00. Putnam
Bowra, Cecil M. Primitive song. il. 1962. 6.50. World Pub.
Britten, Benjamin, and Imogen Hoist. Wonderful world of music. il. 1958. 2.95.
   Doubleday
Brockway, Wallace, and Herbert Weinstock. Men of music. 1950. 6.95. S. and S.
Bukofzer, Manfred F. Music in the baroque era. il. 1947. 5.95. Norton
Bukofzer, Manfred F. Studies in Medieval and Renaissance music. 1950. 7.50.
   Norton
Burney, Charles. General history of music. 1955. 2 vols. set. 12.50. Dover
Carpenter, Nan C. Music in the medieval and Renaissance universities. il.
   1958. 6.00. U. of Okla.
Collaer, Paul. History of modern music. il. 1961. 7.50. World Pub.
Copland, Aaron. Music and imagination. 1952. 2.75. Harvard
Einstein, Alfred. Short history of music. 1947. 5.00. Knopf
Einstein, Alfred. Music in the romantic era. il. 1947. 6.70. Norton
Ewen, David. David Ewen introduces modern music. il. 1962. 4.95. Chilton
Ewen, David. New book of modern composers. 1961. 7.50. Knopf
Ferguson, Donald N. History of musical thought. 1959. 6.00. Appleton
Ferguson, Donald N. Short history of music. 1943. 5.00. Appleton
Finney, Theodore M. History of music. 1947. 7.50. Harcourt
Foss, Hubert J. Heritage of music. 1927. 3 vols. vols. 1 and 2, o.p; vol. 3,
   2.00. Oxford U. P.
Grout, Donald J. History of Western music. il. 1960. 9.65. Norton
Hansen, Peter S. Introduction to twentieth century music. il. 1961. 8.95. Allyn
   & Bacon
Hanson, Howard. Harmonic materials of modern music. il. 1960. 6.00. Appleton
Hadow, W. H. Music. 1949. 1.70. Oxford U. P.
Harman, Alec. Mediaeval and early Renaissance music. 1958. 7.00. Oxford U. P.
Harman, Alec, and Anthony Milner. Late Renaissance and Baroque music. 1959.
   7.00. Oxford U. P.

Hughes, Anselm, Dom. Early medieval music up to 1300. 1954. 12.50. Oxford
    U. P.
Lang, Paul H. Music in western civilization. il. 1941. 15.00. Norton
Lang, Paul. One hundred years of music in America. 1961. 6.95. Schirmer
Lang, Paul H., and Otto L. Bettmann. Pictorial history of music. il. 1960.
    10.00. Norton
Lang, Paul H. Problems of modern music. 1962. pap. 1.45. Norton
Leichtentritt, Hugo. Music, history, and ideas. 1938. 5.00. Harvard
Machlis, Joseph. Introduction to contemporary music. il. 1961. 10.00. Norton
Mellers, Wilfrid. Romanticism and the 20th century (from 1800). 1957. 7.00.
    Oxford U. P.
McKinney, Howard D., and William R. Anderson. Music in history. 7.25.
    Am. Bk. Co.
Parrish, Carl, and John F. Ohl. Masterpieces of music before 1750. il. 1951.
    4.95. Norton
Reese, Gustave. Music in the Middle Ages. il. 1940. 7.50. Norton
Reese, Gustave. Music in the Renaissance. il. 1954. 15.00. Norton
Sachs, Curt. Commonwealth of art. il. 1946. 7.95. Norton
Sachs, Curt. Our musical heritage. 1955. 8.65. Prentice-Hall
Sachs, Curt. Rise of music in the ancient world. il. 1943. 5.95. Norton
Scholes, Percy A. Romantic and nationalist schools of the nineteenth century. 3.00.
    Oxford. U. P.
Sparks, Edgar H. Cantus firmus in mass and motet, 1420-1520. 1962. 12.50.
    U. of Calif.
Strunk, Oliver. Source readings in music history. il. 1950. 10.00. Norton

MUSIC--PHILOSOPHY AND ESTHETICS (780.1)
Aristotle. On the art of poetry. tr. by Ingram Bywater. 1920. pap. 1.00. Oxford
    U. P.
Cooke, Deryck. Language of music. 1959. 4.80. Oxford U. P.
Hindemith, Paul. Composer's world. 3.00. Smith, Peter
Meyer, Leonard B. Emotion and meaning in music. 1956. 6.50. U. of Chicago
Zuckerkandl, Victor. Sound and symbol. 1956. 5.00. Pantheon

MUSIC--PSYCHOLOGY (781.15)
Gutheil, Emil A. Music and your emotions. 3.00. Liveright
Lundin, R. W. Objective psychology of music. 1953. 5.50. Ronald
Meyer, Leonard B. Emotion and meaning in music. 1956. 6.50. U. of Chicago
Seashore, Carl E. In search of beauty in music. 1947. 6.00. Ronald
Seashore, Carl E. Psychology of music. 1938. pap. 2.95. McGraw

MUSIC--THEORY (781)
Boatwright, Howard. Introduction to the theory of music. 1956. 5.20. Norton
Castellini, John. Rudiments of music. 11. 1962. 4.95. Norton
Dallin, Leon. Foundations in music theory. 1962. spiral bdg. 2.50. Wadsworth
Elliott, Raymond. Fundamentals of music. 1955. 6.60. Prentice-Hall
Ferguson, Donald N. History of musical thought. 1959. 6.00. Appleton
Schenker, Heinrich. Harmony. by Oswald Jonas. il. 1954. 8.50. U. of Chicago
Woodhouse, Frederick. Art and theory of music. 1958. 4.50. Pitman

MUSIC, AMERICAN (780.973)
Chase, Gilbert. America's music. 1955. 10.00. McGraw
Howard, John T. Our American music. 1955. 12.95. Crowell
Howard, John T., and George K. Bellows. Short history of music in America.
    il. 1957. 5.00. Crowell
Swan, Howard. Music in the Southwest, 1825-1950. il. 1952. 5.00. Huntington
    Lib.

MUSIC, PRIMITIVE (781.71)
Jones, A. M. Studies in African music. 2 vols. 1959. 23.55. Oxford U. P.
Nettl, Bruno. Music in primitive culture. 1956. 5.00. Harvard
Sachs, Curt. Rise of music in the ancient world. il. 1943. 5.95. Norton

MUSIC AS A PROFESSION (780.069)
Curtis, Robert E. Your future in music. 1962. 2.95. Richards Rosen

Johnson, Harriett, and Vocational Guidance Research. Your career in music. il. 1944. 3.95. Dutton

MUSIC THERAPY (615.837)

Dax, E. Cunningham. Experimental studies in psychiatric art. il. 1953. 5.00. Lippincott

Gutheil, Emil A. Music and your emotions. 3.00. Liveright

MUSICAL FORM (781.5)

Fiske, Roger. Score reading. 3 vols. vol. 1. Orchestration. 1958. 1.75; vol. 2. Musical form. 1958. 2.00; vol. 3. Concertos. 1960. 2.25. Oxford U. P.

Leichtentritt, Hugo. Musical form. 1951. il. 7.50. Harvard

Moore, Douglas. From madrigal to modern music. il. 1942. 5.50. Norton

Morris, Reginald O. Structure of music: An outline for students. 1935. 2.25. Oxford U. P.

MUSICAL INSTRUMENTS (781.91)

Baines, Anthony. Musical instruments through the ages. il. 4.00. Smith, Peter

Galpin, Francis W. European musical instruments, their origin, history, and character. 1956. 6.00. DeGraff

Geiringer, Karl. Musical instruments: Their history in western culture from the Stone Age to the present. 1945. 8.50. Oxford U. P.

Lang, Paul H., and Otto L. Bettmann. Pictorial history of music. il. 1960. 10.00. Norton

Paetkau, David H. Growth of instruments and instrumental music. 7.50. Vantage

Sachs, Curt. History of musical instruments. il. 1940. 10.00. Norton

MUSICAL NOTATION (781)

Boehm, Laszlo. Modern music notation. il. 1961. 2.50. Schirmer

Sachs, Carl. Notation of Medieval music. il. 1957. 7.50. Norton

MUSICIANS (780.071)

Berloiz, Hector. New letters of Berlioz, 1830-1868. tr. by J. Barzun. 1954. 4.50. Columbia

Chotzinoff, Samuel. Lost paradise: Early reminiscences. 1955. 4.50. Knopf

Ewen, David. Living musicians. il. 1957. 9.00. Wilson (R)

Gelatt, Roland. Music-makers: Some outstanding musical performers of our time. il. 1953. 4.50. Knopf

Hentoff, Nat, and Nat Shapiro. Jazz makers. 1958. pap. 1.95. Grove

Rowley, Alec. Do's and dont's for musicians. 1.25. Boosey

Scholes, Percy A. Complete book of the great musicians. il. 1949. 3. vols. in one. 5.00. Oxford U. P. (R)

Stravinskii, Igor F., and Robert Craft. Expositions and developments. il. 1962. 4.95. Doubleday

Who's Who in music: Musician's international directory. 1961. 7.50. Hafner

Wilson, John S. Collector's jazz: Modern. 1959. 3.50. Lippincott

Wilson, John S. Collector's jazz, traditional and swing. 1958. 3.00. Lippincott

MUSORGSKII, MODESTE PETROVICH, 1839-1881 (927)

Calvocoressi, M. D. Modeste Mussorgsky: His life and works. 1956. 9.75. Oxford U. P.

Calvocoressi, M. D. Mussorgsky, 1946. 3.50. Farrar, Straus

MUSSOLINI, BENITO, 1883-1945 (923.145)

Hibbert, Christopher. Il Duce; The life of Benito Mussolini. il. 1962. 6.00. Little

Villari, Luigi. Italian foreign policy under Mussolini. 1956. 6.00. Devin

MYCENAE (571)

Marinatos, S. Crete and Mycenae. il. 1960. 25.00. Abrams

MYCOLOGY (589.2)

Alexopoulos, C. J. Introductory mycology. 8.50. Wiley

Smith, George. Introduction to industrial mycology. 1960. 10.00. St. Martins

Snell, W. H., and E. A. Dick. Glossary of mycology. il. 1957. 5.00. Harvard

Vanbreuseghem, R. Mycoses of man and animals. tr. by J. Wilkinson. il. 1959. 10.50. Thomas, C. C.

MYSTERIES AND MIRACLE-PLAYS (822.1)

Adams, Joseph Q. Chief pre-Shakespearean dramas. 6.75. Houghton

Browne, E. Martin. Twenty-one medieval myster and morality plays. (Religious drama. vol. 2) 1959. 3.50. Smith, Peter
Craig, Hardin. English religious drama of the Middle Ages. 1955. 7.70. Oxford U. P.
Everyman's and medieval miracle plays. 1.95. 1959. Dutton
Frank, Grace. Medieval French drama. 1954. 6.10. Oxford U. P.
Malcolmson, Anne B. Miracle plays. il. 1959. 3.00. Houghton
Prosser, Eleanor. Drama and religion in the English mystery plays. 1961. 5.00. Stanford

MYSTICISM (149. 3)

Baumgardt, David. Great western mystics. 1961. 3.00. Columbia
Bergson, Henri. Two sources of morality and religion. 1954. pap. 0.95. Doubleday
Cayre, Fulbert. Spiritual writers of the early church. 1959. 3.50. Hawthorn
Colledge, Eric. Mediaeval mystics of England. 1961. 4.95. Scribner
Dasgupta, S. N. Hindu mysticism. 1960. 3.75. Ungar
Dunbar, H. Flanders. Symbolism in medieval thought. 1960. 12.50. Russell
Eliade, Mircea. Myths, dreams, and mysteries. tr. by Philip Mairet. 1960. 5.00. Harper
Gregg, Richard B. Self beyond yourself. 1956. 4.25. Lippincott
Hall, Manly P. Lectures on ancient philosophy. 6.00. DeVorss
Jung, Carl G. Psychology and religion: West and east. by Herbert Read, and others. 1958. 6.00. Pantheon
Nicholson, D. H. S., and A. H. E. Lee. Oxford book of English mystical verse. 1917. 5.00. Oxford U. P.
Otto, Rudolf. Mysticism east and west. pap. 1.45. Meridian
Schweitzer, Albert. Mysticism of Paul the Apostle. 1955. 5.00. Macmillan
Steiner, Rudolph. Mysticism, at the dawn of the modern age. tr. by Karl E. Zimmer. 1960. 5.00. Herman
Suzuki, D. T. Mysticism: Christian and Buddhist. 1957. 3.50. Harper
Underhill, Evelyn. Fruits of the spirit, Light of Christ, and Abba: Meditations based on the Lord's Prayer. 1956. 3.50. Mckay
White, Helen C. Metaphysical poets: A study in religious experience. pap. 1.50. Collier
Whiteman, J. H. M. Mystical life. 6.00. Humanities
Yeats, William Butler. Vision. 1956. 5.00. Macmillan
Zaehner, Robert C. Mysticism, sacred and profane. 1957. 7.20. Oxford U. P.
Zaehner, Robert C. Hindu and Muslim mysticism. 1960. 4.80. Oxford U. P.

MYTHOLOGY (291)

Agard, Walter R. Classical myths in sculpture. il. 1953. 5.00. U. of Wis.
Bulfinch, Thomas. Mythology. 1962. 5.95. Crowell
Campbell, Joseph. Oriental mythology. 7.50. Viking
Campbell, Joseph. Primitive mythology. 6.00. Viking
Cassirer, E. Language and myth. 3.00. Smith, Peter
Cassirer, E. Myth of the state. 1946. 5.00. Yale
Colum, Padraic. Myths of the world. il. 1959. pap. 1.75. Grosset
Goodrich, Norma L. Ancient myths. 1960. pap. 0.50. New Am. Lib.
Hamilton, Edith. Mythology. pap. 1.95. Grosset
Kramer, Samuel N. Mythologies of the ancient world. 1961. 7.50. Quadrangle
Larousse. Larousse encyclopedia of mythology. il. 1959. 15.00. Putnam (R)
Murray, Henry. Myth and mythmaking. 1960. 6.00. Braziller
Rank, Otto. Myth of the birth of the hero: A psychological interpretation of mythology. 1952. 3.00. Basic Books
Robinson, Herbert S., and Knox Wilson. Myths and legends of all nations. 2.95. Doubleday
Watts, Alan W. Myth and ritual in Christianity. il. 1954. 5.50. Vanguard

MYTHOLOGY--DICTIONARIES, INDEXES, ETC. (291.03)

Diehl, K. S. Religions mythologies, folklores. An annotated bibliography. 1962. 12.50. Scarecrow (R)

Eastman, Mary H. Index to fairy tales, myths and legends. 1926. 8.00. Faxon (R)
Jobes, Gertrude. Dictionary of mythology, folklore and symbols. 2 vols. 1961.
    40.00. Scarecrow (R)
Sykes, Egerton. Dictionary of non-classical mythology. 3.95. Dutton (R)
Werner, Edward T. C. Dictionary of Chinese mythology. 1961. 12.50. Julian

MYTHOLOGY, CLASSICAL (292)

Clark, R. T. Rundle. Myth and symbol in ancient Egypt. il. 1960. 5.00. Grove
Craig, Elizabeth. Men and myths of Ancient Greece. il. 1961. portfolio 18.00.
    Yoseloff
Gayley, Charles M. Classic myths in English literature and in art. 1939. 6.75.
    Ginn
Grant, Michael. Myths of the Greeks and Romans. il. 1962. 7.50. World Pub.
Graves, Robert. Greek myths. 1957. 5.00. Braziller
Guerber, Helene A. Myths of Greece and Rome. 3.75. British Bk.
Guthrie, William K. C. Religion and mythology of the Greeks. 1.25. Cambridge
    U. P.
Kerenyi, Carl. Gods of the Greeks. il. 6.00. Vanguard
Kerenyi, Karoly. Heroes of the Greeks. il. 1960. 6.50. Grove
Nilsson, M. P. Greek folk religion. il. 3.25. Smith, Peter
Nilsson, M. P. History of Greek religion. 1949. 4.50. Oxford U. P.
Norton, Daniel S., and Peters Rushton. Classical myths in English literature.
    1952. 7.30. Holt, Rinehart & Winston
Otto, Walter F. Homeric gods. tr. by Moses Hadas. il. 1954. 5.00. Pantheon
Rose, H. J. Handbook of Greek mythology. 6.95. 1959. Dutton (R)
Seznec, Jean. Survival of the pagan gods. il. 1953. 6.50. Pantheon
Warner, Rex. Vengeance of the gods. 1955. 3.50. Mich. State
Young, Arthur M. Legend builders of the West. 1958. 4.00. U. of Pittsburgh
Zimmer, Heinrich. Myths and symbols in Indian art and civilization. il. by Joseph
    Campbell. 1946. 4.50. Pantheon

N

NADELMAN, ELIE, 1885-1946 (927)
Nadelman, Elie. Sculpture of Elie Nadelman. by Lincoln Kirstein. 1948. pap.
    1.50. Mus. of Mod. Art

NAMES (929.4)
Barnhart, Clarence, and William D. Halsey. New Century cyclopedia of names.
    3 vols. 39.50. Meredith (R)
Kokeritz, Helge. Shakespeare's names: A pronouncing dictionary. 1959. 2.00.
    Yale (R)

NAMES, GEOGRAPHICAL (910.3)
Bolton, C. K. Real founders of New England. 1929. 4.00. net. Faxon
Ekwall, Eilert. Concise Oxford dictionary of English place-names. 1960. 8.80.
    Oxford U. P. (R)
Gannett, Henry. American names: Guide to the origin of place names in the
    U. S. 1947. 3.75. Pub. Affairs (R)
Irvine, Theodora U. Pronouncing dictionary of Shakespearean proper names.
    1944. 3.50. Barnes & Noble
Reaney, P. H. Origin of English place names. 6.50. Hillary
Shankle, George E. American nicknames. 1955. 7.50. Wilson (R)
Stewart, George R. Names on the land. il. 1958. 6.00. Houghton

NAMES, PERSONAL (929.4)
Lambert, Eloise, and Mario Pei. Our names, where they came from and what
    they mean. 1960. 3.00. Lothrop
Reaney, P. H. Dictionary of British surnames. 1958. 12.50. Hillary
Smith, Elsdon C. Dictionary of American family names. 1956. 4.50. Harper
Withycombe, E. G. Oxford dictionary of English Christian names. 1947. 4.25.
    Oxford U. P. (R)

NAPOLEON I, EMPEROR OF THE FRENCH, 1769-1821 (923.1)
Brookes, Mabel. St. Helena story. il. 1961. 5.00. Dodd
Butterfield, Herbert. Napoleon. il. 2.50. Macmillan
Chateaubriand, Francois Rene. Memoires d'outre tombe. by Alexander H.
Thompson. 1.50. Cambridge U. P.
Guerard, Albert. Napoleon I. 1956. 3.00. Knopf
Hales, Edward E. Y. Emperor and the Pope. 1961. 3.50. Doubleday
Holtman, Robert. Napoleonic propaganda. 1950. 4.00. La. State
Lockhart, J. G. Life of Napoleon. 1.95. Dutton
Ludwig, Emil. Napoleon. 4.50. Liveright.
Markham, F. M. H. Napoleon and the awakening of Europe. 1954. 2.50. Macmillan
Shulim, Joseph I. Old Dominion and Napoleon Bonaparte. 1952. 4.50. Columbia
Thompson, James M. Napoleon Bonaparte: His rise and fall. 1952. 8.00. Oxford
U. P.
NARCOTIC HABIT (616.863)
Anslinger, Harry J., and Will Oursler. Murderers. il. 1961. 4.95. Farrar,
Straus
Anslinger, Harry J., and William F. Tompkins. Traffic in narcotics. 1953.
4.95. Funk
Ausubel, David P. Drug addiction: Physiological, psychological, and sociological
aspects. 1958, pap. 0.95. Random
DeRopp, Robert S. Drugs and the mind. 1957. 4.50. St. Martins
Hoch, Paul H., and J. Zubin. Problems of addiction and habituation. 1958. 6.75.
Grune
Hughes, Helen M. Fantastic lodge: Autobiography of a drug addict. 1961. 3.75.
Houghton
Kolb, Lawrence. Drug addiction. il. 1962. 7.25. Thomas, C. C.
Murtagh, John M., and Sara Harris. Who live in shadow. 1959. 4.50. McGraw
Schmidt, Jacob E. Narcotics, lingo and lore. 1959. 4.25. Thomas, C. C.
NARRATIVE POETRY (808.1)
Hohn, Max T. Stories in verse. 1961. 3.00. Odyssey
Kroeber, Karl. Romantic narrative art. 1960. 5.75. U. of Wis.
Untermeyer, Louis. Story poems: An anthology of narrative verse. pap. 0.50.
Pocket Bks.
NATION, CARRY AMELIA, 1846-1911 (923.6)
Beals, Carleton. Cyclone Carry: The story of Carry Nation. 1962. 6.00.
Chilton
NATIONAL CHARACTERISTICS, AMERICAN (973)
Adams, Henry. United States in 1800. 1955. pap. 1.25. Cornell
Allen, Frederick Lewis. Big change: America transforms itself, 1900-1950.
1952. 4.50. Harper
Almond, Gabriel A. American people and foreign policy. 1960. 4.00. Praeger
Baldwin, Leland D. Meaning of America. 1955. 4.00. U. of Pittsburgh
Barzun, Jacques. God's country and mine. 1959. pap. 1.25. Vintage
Boorstin, Daniel J. America and the image of Europe. 3.35. Smith, Peter
Boorstin, Daniel J. Americans: The colonial experience. 1958. 6.00. Random
Boorstin, Daniel J. Image; or, What happened to the American dream. 1962.
5.00. Atheneum
Brogan, D. W. America in the modern world. 1960. 3.00. Rutgers
Brooks, Van Wyck. America's coming of age. 1959. 3.00. Smith, Peter
Brown, Herbert R. Sentimental novel in America, 1789-1860. 1959. 6.00.
Cooper
Buck, Pearl S., and Eslanda Goode Robeson. American argument. 1949. 3.00.
Day
Burlingame, Roger. American conscience. 1957. 6.75. Knopf
Chase, Stuart. American credos. 1962. 3.95. Harper
Commager, Henry Steele. American mind. 1950. 6.50. Yale
Frohock, Wilbur M. Strangers to this ground: Cultural diversity in contemporary
American writing. 1961. 4.50. S. M. U.

Griffith, Thomas. Waist-high culture. 1959. 4.50. Harper
Handlin, Oscar. American principles and issues: The national purpose. 1961. 6.00.
    Holt, Rinehart & Winston
Howard, Leon. Literature and the American tradition. 1960. 4.50. Doubleday
Kohn, Hans. American nationalism. 5.00. Macmillan
Kronenberger, Louis. Company manners. pap. 1.65. Bobbs
Lerner, Max. America as a civilization. 1957. 12.00. S. and S.
Miles, Leland. Americans are people. 3.00. Twayne
Riesman, D. Faces in the crowd. 1952. 10.00. Yale
Riesman, David. Lonely crowd. 1950. 7.50. Yale
Schlesinger, Arthur M. Paths to the present. 5.75. Macmillan
Sellers, Charles G. Southerner as American. 1960. 5.00. U. of N. C.
Spencer, Benjamin T. Quest for nationality. 1957. 5.00. Syracuse
Spiller, Robert E., and Eric Larrabee. American perspectives: The national
    self-image in the twentieth century. 1961. 4.75. Harvard
NATIONAL CHARACTERISTICS, ENGLISH (942)
Nicolson, Harold. Meaning of prestige. 0.75. Cambridge U. P.
Raleigh, Walter, and others. Shakespeare's England: An account of the life and
    manners of his age. 2 vols. il. 1917. 12.00. Oxford U. P.
Spinley, B. M. Deprived and the privileged. 1953. 4.00. Humanities
Wallace, Malcolm W. English character and the English literary tradition. il.
    1952. 3.50. U. of Toronto
NATIONAL CHARACTERISTICS, FRENCH (944)
Bertier de Sauvigny, Guillaume de. Some historical clues to French politics.
    1958. pap. 0.50. Antioch
NATIONAL CHARACTERISTICS, GERMAN (943)
Hafkesbrink, H. Unknown Germany. 1948. 4.00. Yale
NATIONAL PARKS AND RESERVES (719.32)
Abrahams, Harold M. Britain's national parks. il. 1959. 6.25. Transatlantic
Adams, Ansel, and Nancy Newhall. This is the American earth. 1960. 15.00.
    Knopf
Bolin, Luis A. National parks of the United States. il. 1962. 3.95. Knopf
Brockman, C. F. Recreational use of wild lands. 1959. 8.75. McGraw
Butcher, Devereaux. Exploring our national parks. il. 1954. 6.50. Houghton
Ise, John. Our national park policy. 1961. 10.00. Johns Hopkins
Resources for the future. Comparisons in resource management. by Henry Jarrett.
    il. 1961. 5.50. Johns Hopkins
NATIONAL SONGS (784.71)
Griffith, Eloise R. National anthems and how they came to be written. 1952. 1.50.
    Christopher
National anthems of the American republics. bilingual, English and Spanish, 2.00.
    1961. Pan American
Shaw, Martin, and Henry Coleman. National anthems of the world. il. 1960. 10.00.
    Pitman
NATIONALISM (320.158)
Ahmed, Jamal M. Intellectual origins of Egyptian nationalism. 1960. 4.00. Oxford
    U. P.
Armstrong, John A. Ukrainian nationalism. 1962. 6.50. Columbia
Barghoorn, F. C. Soviet Russian nationalism. 1956. 7.50. Oxford U. P.
Berdyaev, Nicolas. Fate of man in the modern world. 1935. 4.40. U. of Mich.
Brown, Delmer M. Nationalism in Japan: An introductory historical analysis.
    1955. 7.50. U. of Calif.
Carr, Edward H. Nationalism and after. 1.25. St. Martins
Carter, Gwendolen. Independence for Africa. 4.50. Praeger
Childers, Eiskine B. Common sense about the Arab world. 1960. 2.95. Macmillan
Davis, Jerome. Citizens of one world. 1961. 3.95. Citadel
Deutsch, K. W. Nationalism and social communication. 1953. 6.50. Wiley
Djambatan, World on the move. 1962. 4.95. Sterling

Duffy, James, and Robert A. Manners. Africa speaks. 1961. 4.95. Van Nostrand

Emerson, Rupert. From empire to nation. 1960. 7.75. Harvard

Hahn, Lorna. North Africa: Nationalism to nationhood. 1960. 6.00. Pub. Affairs

Haim, Sylvia G. Arab nationalism: An anthology. 1962. 6.00. U. of Calif.

Hatch, John. Africa today - and tomorrow. 1962. 5.00. Praeger

Hayes, Carlton J. H. Historical evolution of modern nationalism. 1931. 6.00. Macmillan

Hayes, Carlton J. H. Nationalism: A religion. 1960. 5.00. Macmillan

Hertz, Frederick. Nationality in history and politics. 1944. 6.00. Humanities

Ingrams, Harold. Uganda. il. 1960. 6.00. British Info. Services

Kahin, George McTurnan. Nationalism and revolution in Indonesia. il. 6.00. Cornell

Kedourie, Elie. Nationalism. 2.50. Hillary

Kohn, Hans. American nationalism. 5.00. Macmillan

Kohn, Hans. Idea of nationalism. 1945. 7.50. Macmillan

Kohn, Hans. Mind of Germany. il. 1960. 5.95. Scribner

Kohn, Hans. Nationalism and liberty: Swiss example. 3.25. Macmillan

Lattimore, Owen. Nationalism and revolution in Mongolia. 1955. 2.85. Oxford U. P.

Legum, Colin. Congo disaster. 1961. 2.85. Smith, Peter

Low, Alfred D. Lenin on the question of nationality. 1958. 4.00. Twayne

Manning, Helen T. Revolt of French Canada, 1800-1835. il. 1962. 10.00. St. Martins

Marcus, John T. Neutralism and nationalism in France. 1959. 4.50. Twayne

Noether, E. P. Seeds of Italian nationalism, 1700-1815. 1951. 3.00. Columbia

Panikkar, Kavalam M. Revolution in Africa. il. 1961. 6.50. Taplinger

Perham, Margery. Colonial reckoning: The end of imperial rule in Africa. 1962. 3.95. Knopf

Quinn, Herbert F. Union nationale, a study in Quebec's nationalism. 1961. 6.50. U. of Toronto

Romein, Jan, and Jan Erik. Asian century: A history of modern nationalism in Asia. 1962. 7.50. U. of Calif.

Schlesinger, Rudolf. Nationalities problem and Soviet administration. 1955. 6.00. Humanities

Schuman, Frederick L. International politics. 1958. 7.75. McGraw

Shafer, Boyd C. Nationalism: Myth and reality. 1955. 5.00. Harcourt

Smal-Stocki, Roman. Nationality problem of the Soviet Union and Russian communism imperialism. 1952. 6.00. Bruce

Stern, Fritz R. Politics of cultural despair: A study in the rise of the Germanic ideology. 1961. 8.00. U. of Calif.

Sulzbach, Walter. National consciousness. 1940. 2.50. Pub. Affairs

Taylor, Griffith. Environment and nation: Geographical factors in the cultural and political history of Europe. il. 1936. 4.50. U. of Toronto

Thayer, Philip W. Nationalism and progress in free Asia. 1956. 5.75. Johns Hopkins

Warner, Douglas. Ghana and the new Africa. il. 3.75. Int. Pub. Service

Whitaker, Arthur P. Nationalism in Latin America, past and present. 1962. 3.50. U. of Fla.

Wiggin, G. A. Education and nationalism. 1962. 7.50. McGraw

NATURAL HISTORY (574.9)

Andrews, Roy Chapman. This amazing planet. 3.50. Putnam

Barry, Gerald, and others. Doubleday pictorial library of nature. il. 9.95. Doubleday

Book of popular science. 10 vols. 89.50. Grolier

Bourliere, Francois, and others. Tropics. il. 1957. 12.50. Knopf

Copeland, Herbert F. Classification of lower organisms. 7.50. Pacific Bks.

Darwin, Charles Robert. Voyage of the Beagle. 1.95. 1961. Dutton

Freuchen, Peter, and Finn Salomonsen. Arctic year. il. 1958. 5.95. Putnam

Hearne, Samuel. Journey to the Northern Ocean. 1959. 8.50. St. Martins
Hillcourt, William. Field book of nature activities and conservation. il. 1961.
    4.95. Putnam
Henry, Thomas R. Strangest things in the world. 1958. 3.50. Pub. Affairs
Kieran, John. Introduction to nature. il. 1955. 6.00. Doubleday
Krutch, Joseph Wood. Best of two worlds. il. 1953. 3.00. Sloane
Klingel, Gilbert. Ocean island (Inagua) 1953. 3.50. Dodd
Leach, John A. Australian nature studies. by E. Byrne. 6.00. St. Martins
Long, Amelia Reynolds. Outdoor reference guide. 1959. 7.50. Stackpole
McCowan, D. Naturalist in Canada. 1946. 4.50. St. Martins
Milne, Lorus J., and Margery J. World of night. il. 1956. 4.95. Harper
Museum of Natural History. Illustrated library of natural sciences. 4 vols.
    1958. 25.00. S. and S. (R)
Olson, Sigurd. Listening point. il. by Francis L. Jaques. 1958. 4.50. Knopf
Olson, Sigurd. Singing wilderness. il. 1956. 4.50. Knopf
Peattie, Donald Culross, and Noel Peattie. Cup of sky. 1950. 3.00. Houghton
Peterson, Roger Tory. Wildlife in color. il. 1951. 4.00. Houghton
Pliny, the Elder. Natural history. 8 vols. 3.50 ea. Harvard
Ritter, William E. Charles Darwin and the golden rule. 5.00. Storm
Roedelberger, Franz A. Wonderful world of nature. il. 1962. 7.50. Viking
Roosevelt, Theodore. Theodore Roosevelt's America. by Farida A. Wiley
Saunders, John Richard. World of natural history. il. 1952. 6.00. Sheridan
Teale, Edwin Way. Adventures in nature. il. 1959. 4.00. Dodd
Teale, Edwin Way. Autumn across America. il. 1956. 5.95. Dodd
Teale, Edwin Way. Circle of the seasons. il. 1953. 5.00. Dodd
Teale, Edwin Way. Journey into summer. il. 1960. 5.75. Dodd
Teale, Edwin Way. North with the spring. il. 1951. 5.95. Dodd
White, Gilbert. Natural history of Selborne: In the county of Southampton. 2.75.
    Oxford U. P.
NATURAL HISTORY--U.S. (574.973)
Bartram, John, and William. John and William Bartram's America. 1.45.
    Doubleday
Douglas, William O. My wilderness: East to Katahdin. il. 1961. 4.95. Doubleday
Kieran, John. Natural history of New York City. il. 1959. 5.75. Houghton
Krutch, Joseph Wood. Desert year. 1952. 3.75. Sloane
Rand, A. L., and R. M. Midwestern almanac. 1961. 4.50. Ronald
NATURAL LAW (340.1)
Becker, Carl L. Declaration of Independence: A study in the history of political
    ideas. 1942. 4.00. Knopf
Gierke, Otto. Natural law. tr. by Ernest Barker. 2 vols. in 1.1950. 14.50.
    Cambridge U. P.
Hegel, G. W. F. Philosphy of right. 4.80. Oxford U. P.
Hobbes, Thomas. De cive or, The citizen. by Sterling P. Lamprecht. 1949. pap.
    1.25. Appleton
Locke, John. Essays on the law of nature. 1954. 6.10. Oxford U. P.
Maritain, Jacques. Rights of man. 1.50. Hillary
Rommen, Heinrich A. Natural law. 1947. 4.95. Herder
Windolph, F. L. Leviathan and natural law. 1951. 2.50. Princeton
NATURAL RESOURCES (339.49)
Adams, Ansel E., and Nancy Newhall. This is the American earth. il. 1960.
    15.00. Knopf
Brady, Robert A. Organization, automation, and society: The scientific revolution
    in industry. 1961. 8.00. U. of Calif.
Brown, Harrison, and others. Next hundred years. il. 1957. 4.75. Viking
Callison, C. H. America's natural resources. 1957. 4.00. Ronald
Coyle, David Cushman. Conservation: An American story of conflict and
    accomplishment. il. 1957. 5.00. Rutgers
Firey, Walter. Man, mind, and land: A theory of resource use. 6.00. Free Press
Gustafson, A. F., and others. Conservation in the United States. 5.00. Cornell

Huberty, M. R., and W. L. Flock. Natural resources. 1959. 11.00. McGraw

King, Judson. Conservation fight: From Theodore Roosevelt to the Tennessee
Valley Authority. 1959. 6.00. Pub. Affairs

Sears, Paul B. Deserts on the march. il. 1959. 2.75. U. of Okla.

Smith, Guy H. Conservation of natural resources. il. 1958. 8.50. Wiley

Van Royen, William. Atlas of the world's resources: 1952. 13.35. Prentice-Hall
(R)

Vogt, William. Road to survival. il. 4.50. Sloane

NATURAL SCIENCE (575)

Ashley, Montagu, M. F. Darwin: Competition and cooperation. 1952. 2.50. Abelard

Darlington, Cyril D. Darwin's place in history. 1961. pap. 2.00. Macmillan

Lasker, Gabriel. Processes of ongoing human evolution. 1960. 3.75. Wayne

Sheppard, P. M. Natural selection and heredity. 2.50. Hillary

NATURAL THEOLOGY (210)

Donceel, Joseph. Natural theology. 1962. 3.00. Sheed

Willey, Basil. Eighteenth century background: Studies on the idea of nature in the
thought of the period. 1961. 1.75. Beacon

NATURALISM (146)

Butler, J. Donald. Four philosophies and their practice in education and religion.
1957. 6.50. Harper

Dennes, William Ray. Some dilemmas of naturalism. 1960. 4.00. Columbia

McCarthy, J. W. Naturalism of Samuel Alexander. 1948. 2.50. Columbia

NATURE STUDY (372.3)

Collingwood, R. G. Idea of nature. 1945. 4.50. Oxford U. P.

Comstock, Anna Botsford. Handbook of nature study. 1939. 6.75. Cornell

Cruickshank, Helen G. John and William Bartram's America. il. 5.00. Devin

Hillcourt, William. Field book of nature activities and conservation. il. 1961.
4.95. Putnam

Krutch, Joseph Wood. Twelve seasons. 1949. 3.00. Sloane

MacMillan's nature class pictures. 62 plates. 16.00. St. Martins

Macmillan's nature class reference book. 1.75. St. Martins

Miller, Loye. Lifelong boyhood: Recollections of a naturalist afield. il. 1950.
S. M. U.

Terres, John K. Discovery: Great moments in the lives of outstanding naturalists.
1961. 6.50. Lippincott

NAVAL ART AND SCIENCE (359)

Brodie, Bernard. Guide to naval strategy. Naval War College ed. il. 1958. 6.00.
Princeton

Kerchove, René de. International maritime dictionary. il. 1961. 20.00. Van
Nostrand

Landstrom Bjorn. Ships: An illustrated history. il. 1961. 14.95. Doubleday.

Lloyd, Christopher. Ships and seamen, from the Vikings to the present day. il.
1961. 12.50. World Pub.

Lovette, Leland P. Naval customs, traditions and usage. il. 1959. 5.50. U. S.
Naval Inst.

Macintyre, Donald C. Thunder of the guns. il. 1959. 3.95. Norton

Noel, John V., Jr. Naval terms dictionary. il. 1952. 5.75. Van Nostrand (R)

Robison, S. S., and Mary L. History of naval tactics from 1530-1930. il. 1942.
6.50. U. S. Naval Inst.

Thursfield, H. G. Brassey's annual: The Armed Forces yearbook. il. 9.50.
Macmillan

NAVAL HISTORY (359)

Casson, Lionel. Ancient mariners. 1959. 6.95. Macmillan

Lewis, Archibald Ross. Naval power and trade in the Mediterranean, A.D. 500-
1100. 1951. 4.00. Princeton

Mahan, Alfred T. Influence of sea power upon history, 1660-1783. il. 1890. 7.50.
Little

Robison, S. S., and Mary L. History of naval tactics from 1530-1930, il. 1942.
6.50. U. S. Naval Inst.

Spectorsky, Auguste C. Book of the sea. il. 1958. 4.95. Grosset
Blackman, Raymond. Jane's fighting ships. 35.00. McGraw
NAVIGATION (527)
Ageton, Arthur A. Manual of celestial navigation. il. 1961. 4.25. Van Nostrand'
Bok, B. J., and F. W. Wright. Basic marine navigation. 1952. 7.25. Houghton
Chapman, Charles F. Piloting, seamanship and small boat handling. 5.00.
    Motor Boating
Collinder, Per. History of marine navigation. 1954. 4.25. St. Martins
Cugle, Charles H. Practical navigation. 17.50. Dutton
Farrell, Charles F., Jr. Fell's guide to small boat navigation. 1961. 2.95. Fell
Rabl, Samuel S. Star atlas and navigation encyclopedia. il. 1946. 5.00. Cornell
    Maritime
Taylor, Eva G. Haven-finding art: A history of navigation from Odysseus to
    Captain Cook. il. 1957. 6.00. Abelard
NEAR EAST (956)
Berger, Morroe. Arab world today. il. 1962. 4.50. Doubleday
Bullard, Reader. Middle East, a political and economic survey. 1958. 9.00.
    Oxford U. P.
Campbell, John C. Defense of the Middle East. 1960. 5.00. Harper
Coon, Carleton S. Caravan: Story of the Middle East. 1958. 6.55. Holt, Rinehart
    & Winston
Douglas, William O. Strange lands and friendly people. 1951. 6.00. Harper
Eddy, Samuel K. King is dead: Studies in the Near Eastern resistance to
    Hellenism, 334-31 B.C. il. 1961. 8.50. U. of Nebr.
Ellis, Harry B. Challenge in the Middle East. 1960. 4.00. Ronald
Ellis, H. B. Heritage of the desert. 1956. 5.00. Ronald
Fisher, Carol A., and Fred Drinsky. Middle East in crisis. 5.00. Syracuse
Fisher, Sydney N. Middle East: A history. il. 1959. 8.95. Knopf
Fisher, William Bayne. Middle East. 1961. 9.75. Dutton
Hitti, Philip K. Near East in history, a 5000 year story. il. 1961. 10.00. Van
    Nostrand
Hoskins, Halford L. Middle East. il. 1954. 5.00. Macmillan
Kedourie, E. England and the Middle East: The vital years 1914-1921. 6.00.
    Humanities
Kirk, George E. Contemporary Arab politics. 1961. 5.00. Praeger
Kirk, George E. Short history of the Middle East. 1959. 6.00. Praeger
Laqueur, Walter Z. Soviet Union and the Middle East. 1959. 6.00. Praeger
Lencqowski, George. Middle East in world affairs. 1956. 7.25. Cornell
Marlowe, John. Arab nationalism and British imperialism. 7.50. Praeger
Morris, James. Islam inflamed: A Middle East picture. 1957. 5.00. Pantheon
Sharabi, Hisham B. Government and politics of the Middle East in the twentieth
    century. il. 1962. 8.75. Van Nostrand
Stoakes, Frank. Middle eastern affairs. 1959. 3.50. Praeger
Thayer, Philip W. Tensions in the Middle East. 1958. 5.50. Johns Hopkins
Yale, William. Near East: A modern history. 1958. 7.50. U. of Mich.
NEBRASKA (978.2)
Breckenridge, Adam Carlyle. One house for two: Nebraska's unicameral leg-
    islature. 1957. 2.50. Pub. Affairs
Writers' Project. Nebraska. 1947. 6.50. Hastings
NEBULAE (523.12)
Aller, L. H. Gaseous nebulae. 1956. 12.00. Wiley
Eddington, A. S. Expanding universe. 1933. 2.50. Cambridge U. P.
NECK (611.93)
Cunningham, D. J. Head and neck, brain. 1958. 6.50. Oxford U. P.
Truex, R. C., and C. E. Kellner. Detailed atlas of the head and neck. 1948.
    19.75. Oxford U. P.
NEFERTETE, QUEEN OF EGYPT, 14th CENTURY B.C. (923.1)
Chubb, Mary. Nefertiti lived here. il. 1955. 4.50. Crowell

NEGROES (301. 451)

Aptheker, Herbert. Negro people in America. 1.25. Int. Pubs.
Aptheker, Herbert. To be free: Studies in American Negro history. 1948. 3.00. Int. Pubs.
Ashmore, Harry S. Negro and the schools. 1954. 2.75. U. of N. C.
Ashmore, Harry S. Other side of Jordan. il. 1960. 3.50. Norton
Baldwin, James. Nobody knows my name. 1961. 4.50. Dial
Baldwin, James. Notes of a native son. 3.25. Smith, Peter
Becker, Gary S. Economics of discrimination. 1957. 3.50. U. of Chicago
Bontemps, Arna. One hundred years of Negro freedom. 1961. 3.50. Dodd
Botkin, Benjamin A. Lay my burden down: A folk history of slavery. il. 1945. pap. 1.65. U. of Chicago
Brown, Ina Corrine. Story of the American Negro. 1957. 2.75. Friendship
Davie, Maurice R. Negroes in American society. 1949. 7.50. McGraw
Davis, Allison, and others. Deep South: A social anthropological study of caste and class. il. 1941. 8.00. U. of Chicago
Davis, Allison, and John Dollard. Children of bondage. 1940. pap. 2.00. A. C. E.
Dollard, John. Caste and class in a southern town. 3.25. Smith, Peter
Drachler, Jacob. African heritage. 1962. 3.95. Crowell-Collier
Drake, St. Clair, and Horace R. Cayton. Black metropolis: A study of Negro life in a northern city. il. 1945. 6.75. Harcourt
Dubois, William E. B. Black reconstruction in America. 7.50. Russell
Elkins, Stanley M. Slavery. 1959. 4.50. U. of Chicago
Franklin, John Hope. From slavery to freedom: A history of American Negroes. il. 1956. 7.50. Knopf
Frazier, Edward F. Black bourgeoisie. 1957. 4.00. Free Press
Frazier, E. Franklin. Negro in the United States. 1957. 6.75. Macmillan
Ginzberg, E. Negro potential. 1956. 3.00. Columbia
Greenberg, Jack. Race relations and American law. 1959. 10.00. Columbia
Hughes, Langston. African treasury. 3.50. Crown
Hughes, Langston, and Arna Bontemps. Poetry of the Negro, 1746-1949. 1949. 6.00. Doubleday
Johnson, James Weldon. American Negro poetry: An anthology. 4.00. Harcourt
Johnson, James Weldon. Autobiography of an ex-coloured man. 1927. 3.50. Knopf
Johnson, James Weldon, and J. Rosamond. Books of American Negro spirituals. 1940. 5.95. Viking
Karon, Bertram P. Negro personality. 1958. 4.50. Springer
Laurenti, Luigi. Property values and race. 1960. 6.00. U. of Calif.
Lincoln, Charles E. Black Muslims in America. 1961. 4.95. Beacon
Lomax, John A., and Alan. American ballads and folk songs. 8.95. Macmillan
Lomax, Louis E. Negro revolt. 1962. 3.50. Harper
Meyerson, Martin, and Edward Banfield. Politics, planning and the public interest. 1955. 5.00. Free Press
Myrdal, Gunnar. American dilemma: The negro problem and modern democracy. 1944. 10.00. Harper
Park, Robert E. Race and culture. 1950. 5.00. Free Press
Redding, Saunders. Lonesome road: The story of the Negro in America. 1958. 5.75. Doubleday
Rutherford, Peggy. African voices: An anthology of native African writings. 1959. 3.95. Vanguard
Reddick, Lawrence D. Crusader without violence: Martin Luther King, Jr. il. 1959. 3.95. Harper
Shannon, A. H. Racial integrity of the American Negro. 1953. 3.25. Pub. Affairs
Sutherland, Robert L. Color, class, and personality. 1.50. A. C. E.
Taper, Bernard. Gomillion versus Lightfoot; the Tuskegee gerrymander case. 1962. bds. 3.75. McGraw
Truman, Harry S. Freedom and equality. 1960. 2.95. U. of Missouri

Vose, Clement. Caucasians only: The supreme court, the N. A. A. C. P. , and the restrictive covenants. il. 1959. 6.00. U. of Calif.
Warner, W. Lloyd, and others. Color and human nature. 3.00. A. C. E.
Weyl, Nathaniel. Negro in American civilization. 1960. 6.00. Pub. Affairs

NEHRU, JAWAHARLAL, 1889- (923.1)
Brecher, Michael. Nehru, a political biography. il. 1959. 8.50. Oxford U. P.
Moraes, Frank. Jawaharlal Nehru. 1956. 8.50. Macmillan
Nehru, J. Toward freedom. pap. 1.95. Beacon
Nehru, Jawaharlal, and R. K. Karanjia. Mind of Mr. Nehru. 2.75. Int. Pub. Service
Sheean, Vincent. Nehru, the years.of power. 1959. 5.00. Random

NELSON, HORATIO NELSON, 1758-1805 (923.5)
Southey, Robert. Life of Nelson. 1.25. Nelson
Warner, Oliver. Victory: The life of Lord Nelson. il. 1958. 6.50. Little

NEOPLATONISM (186)
Harper, George M. Neoplatonism of William Blake. 1961. 7.50. U. of N. C.
Pistorius, P. V. Plotinus and neoplatonism. 4.50. Hillary

NEO-SCHOLASTICISM (149.2)
O'Brien, Thomas C. Metaphysics and the existence of God. 1960. pap. 3.50. Thomist
Wulf, Maurice de. An introduction to scholastic philosophy. 1956. 3.50. Dover

NEPAL (954.26)
Karan, Pradyumna P. Nepal: A pyysical geography. 1960. 10.00. U. of Ky.
Petech, L. Medieval history of Nepal. 1958. 11.00. Peragon

NERVES (612.81)
Eccles, John C. Physiology of nerve cells. 1957. 5.75. Hopkins, John
Nachmansohn, David. Chemical and molecular basis of nerve activity. 1959. 7.50. Academic Press
Tasaki, Ichiji. Nervous transmission. il. 1953. 7.50. Thomas, C. C.

NERVOUS SYSTEM (612.8)
Alvarez, Walter C. Live at peace with your nerves. 1958. 4.95. Prentice-Hall
Ariens, Kappers, C. U., and others. Comparative anatomy of the nervous system. of vertebrates, including man. 3 vols. il. 1936. 27.50. Hafner
Brodal, Alf. Cranial nerves. il. 1962. 3.00. Davis
Davis, Roland C. Ability in social and racial classes. il. 1932. 1.75. Appleton
Denhoff, Eric, and Isabel Robinault. Cerebral palsy and related disorders. 12.00. McGraw
Dethier, Vincent G., and Eliot Stellar. Animal behavior. 1961. 3.75. Prentice-Hall
Grayson, John. Nerves, brain and man. il. 1961. 5.00. Taplinger
Jacobson, Edmund. You must relax. 1957. 4.95. McGraw
Kuntz, Albert. Autonomic Nervous system. il. 1953. 10.00. Lea & F
Larsell, Olof. Anatomy of the nervous system. il. 1951. 9.00. Appleton
Maloy, B. S. Nervous and mental diseases. 1935. 7.50. Bobbs
Matthews, Arthur Guy. Take it easy: The art of conquering your nerves. il. 1945. 3.50. Sheridan
Neumann, John von. Computer and the brain. 1958. 4.00. Yale
Papez, James W. Comparative neurology. il. 1929. 12.00. Hafner
Schafer, Roy. Clinical application of psychological tests. 1952. 6.75. Int. Univs.
Windle, William F. Regeneration in the central nervous system. il. 1956. 9.50. Thomas, C. C.

NETHERLANDS (949.2)
Barnouw, Adriaan J. Pageant of Netherlands, history. 1952. 6.50. McKay
Clark, Sydney. All the best in Holland. 1961. 4.95. Dodd
Elias, E., and E. Wijk. Holland. il. 12.50. Lounz
Hyma, Albert. History of the Dutch in the Far East. 1953. 3.95. Wahr
Motley, J. L. Dutch republic. 3 vols. 1.95 ea. Dutton
Muirhead, L. Russell. Blue guide to Holland. 7.95. Rand McNally
Timmers, J. J. M. History of Dutch life and art. 1959. 15.00. Nelson

NEUROLOGY (616. 8)
Association for Research in Nervous and Mental Disease. Genetics and the
inheritance of integrated neurological and psychiatric patterns. by Davenport
Hooker, and Clarence C. Hare. il. 1954. 10.00. Williams & Wilkins
Bowman, P. W., and H. V. Mautner. Mental retardation: Proceedings of the
First International Congress on mental retardation. 1960. 12.50. Grune
Gardner, Ernest. Fundamentals of neurology. 1958. 5.75. Saunders
Parker, Harry Lee. Clinical studies in neurology. 1956. 6.50. Thomas, C. C.
Riese, Walther. History of neurology. il. 1959. 4.00. MD Pub.
Rushton, J. G. Neurology for nurses. 1959. 3.00. Burgess
Symposium on Evaluation of Drug Therapy in Neurologic and Sensory Diseases,
University of Wisconsin, 1960. Evoluation of drug therapy. Proceedings. by
Francis M. Forster. 1961. 4.00. U. of Wis.
NEUROSES (132. 15)
Andreev, B. V. Sleep therapy in the neuroses. by Joseph Wortis. 1960. pap. 8.50.
Consultants Bureau
Asher, Richard. Nerves explained . 1959. 2.75. Thomas, C. C.
Bergler, Edmund. Counterfeit sex. 1958. 6.75. Grune
Cattell, R. B., and I. H. Scheier. Meaning and measurement of neuroticism and
anxiety. 1961. 12.00. Ronald
Cobb, Stanley. Foundations of neuropsychiatry. 1958. 5.00. Williams & Wilkins
Deutsch, Helene. Psychoanalysis of the neuroses. 3.75. Hillary
English, Oliver S., and G. H. J. Pearson. Common neuroses of children and
adults. 1937. 6.50. Norton
English, Oliver S., and G. H. J. Pearson. Emotional problems of living. 1955.
6.95. Norton
Eysenck, H. J. Behaviour therapy and the neuroses. 1960. 10.00. Pergamon
Freud, Sigmund. Problem of anxiety. 1936. 3.00. Norton
Hoagland, Hudson. Hormones, brain function, and behavior: Proceedings of a
conference on neuroendocrinology. il. 1957. 8.00. Academic Press
Horney, Karen. Neurosis and human growth. 1950. 5.50. Norton
Horney, Karen Neurotic personality of our time. 1937. 4.50. Norton
Horney, Karen. Our inner conflicts. 1945. 4.50. Norton
Jung, C. G. Psychology of the unconscious. 5.00. Dodd
Lorand, Sandor. Technique of psychoanalytic therapy. 4.50. Int. Univs.
Saul, Leon J. Emotional maturity: The development and dynamics of personality.
il. 1960. 7.50. Lippincott
Schilder, Paul. Brain and personality. 1951. 2.50. Int. Univs.
Strecker, Edward A. Their mothers' sons. 1951. 3.75. Lippincott
NEUTRALITY (341. 5)
Martin, Laurence W. Neutralism and nonalignment: The new states in world
affairs. 1962. 6.00. Praeger
Oakes, John B. Edge of freedom: Eastern Europe and Africa. 1961. 3.50. Harper
Royal Institute of International Affairs. War and the neutrals. 1956. Oxford U. P.
NEUTRONS (539. 7213)
Curtiss, Leon F. Introduction to neutron physics. 1959. 9.75. Van Nostrand
Davison, B., and J. B. Sykes. Neutron transport theory. 1957. 12.00. Oxford U. P.
NEVADA (979. 3)
Federal Writers' Program. Nevada, the Silver State. il. 5.00. Binfords
Thompson, Thomas H., and A. A. West. History of Nevada. 1958. 20.00. Howell-
North
NEW ENGLAND (974)
Adams, J. T. New England in the republic. il. 1958. 6.00. Smith, Peter
Bailyn, B. New England merchants in the seventeenth century. il. 1955. 4.75.
Harvard
Barnes, Viola F. Dominion of New England: A study in British colonial policy.
5.00. Ungar
Brooks, Van Wyck. Flowering of New England. 2.95. Dutton
Brooks, Van Wyck. New England: Indian summer, 1865-1915. 2.95. Dutton

Chamberlain, Samuel. Ever New England. 4.50. Hastings
Knight, Journal of Madam Knight. 3.00. Smith, Peter
Miller, Perry G. E. New England mind from colony to province. 1953. 7.50.
    Harvard
McLaughlin, Andrew C. Foundations of American constitutionalism. 2.00.
    Smith, Peter
Morison, Samuel E. Intellectual life of colonial New England. 1956. 4.95. N. Y. U.
Mussey, Barrows. Old New England. il. 3.75. Wyn
Pownall, Thomas. Topographical description of the dominions of the United States
    of America. by Lois Mulkearn. il. 10.00. Brown Book
Schneider, Herbert W. Puritan mind. 1958. 4.40. U. of Mich.
Solomon, Barbara Miller. Ancestors and immigrants: A changing New England
    tradition. 1956. 4.75. Harvard
Winthrop, John. Journal, History of New England, 1630-1649. 2 vols. 11.50.
    Barnes & Noble

NEW GUINEA (995)
Bjerre, Jens. Last cannibals. il. 1957. 4.50. Morrow
Gardi, R. Tambaran: Cultures in decline in New Guinea. 6.00. Humanities
Mead, Margaret. Growing up in New Guinea. 1962. pap. 1.95. Apollo

NEW HAMPSHIRE (974.2)
Jennison, Keith. New Hampshire. il. 1961. 2.95. Smith, Richard R.
New Hampshire guide. 6.50. Houghton

NEW JERSEY (974.9)
Cunningham, John T. This is New Jersey. 1953. 6.00. Rutgers
Scott, A. Influence of the proprietors in founding New Jersey. 1885. 0.75.
    Johns Hopkins
Writers' Project. New Jersey. 1959. 6.50. Hastings

NEW MEXICO (978.9)
Davis, W. W. H. El Gringo: or, New Mexico and her people. 1962. 7.50.
    Swallow, A.
Mann, Edward B. and Fred Harvey. New Mexico: Land of enchantment. il. 1955.
    5.00. Mich. State
Writers' Project. New Mexico. 1962. 6.95. Hastings

NEW YORK (CITY) (974.71)
Bales, William A. Tiger in the streets. il. 1962. 4.00. Dodd
Garrett, Charles. La Guardia years: Machine and reform politics in New York
    City. il. 1961. 8.50. Rutgers
Grund, Francis J. Aristocracy in America. 1959. 3.75. Smith, Peter
Hugins, Walter. Jacksonian Democracy and the working class. 6.00. Stanford
Look Magazine. Regional guide: New York City. by the Editors of Look Magazine.
    il. 5.50. Houghton
Morris, Lloyd. Incredible New York. il. 1951. 5.00. Random
Wecter, Dixon. Saga of American society. il. 1957. 7.50. Scribner

NEW YORK (STATE) (974.7)
Danckaerts, Jasper. Journal, 1679-1680. 1913. 5.75. Barnes and Noble
Ellis, David, and others. New York: The Empire State. 1961. 6.40. Prentice-Hall
Irving, Washington. Knickerbocker's history of New York. 1959. 5.00. Ungar
New York: Guide to the empire state. 7.50. Oxford U. P.

NEW ZEALAND (993.1)
Beaglehole, John C. Discovery of New Zealand. 1961. 3.40. Oxford U. P.
Belshaw, Horace. New Zealand. il. 1947. 5.00. U. of Calif.
Bigwood, Kenneth, and Jean. New Zealand in color. by James K. Baxter. il.
    1962. 5.00. Wellington
McCormick, E. H. New Zealand literature, a survey. 1959. 3.60. Oxford U. P.
Miles, Beryl. Islands of contrast: Adventures in New Zealand. il. 1955. 4.50.
    Transatlantic
New Zealand official yearbook. 4.50. Int. Pub. Service
Sinclair, Keith. History of New Zealand. il. 1961. 4.00. Oxford U. P.

Stamp, L. D. Australia and New Zealand. 1961. 3.00. Wiley
NEWFOUNDLAND (971.8)
Fay, C. R. Life and labour in Newfoundland. 1956. 5.00. U. of Toronto
NEWSPAPERS (070)
Bond, F. Fraser. Introduction to journalism. 1961. 5.50. Macmillan
Garst, R. E., and T. M. Bernstein. Headlines and deadlines. 1961. 5.00.
    Columbia
Hutt, Allen. Newspaper design. il. 1960. 8.00. Oxford U. P.
MacDougall, Curtis D. Interpretative reporting. 1957. 6.00. Macmillan
Mallory, Walter H. Political handbook of the world. 1960. and 1961, 4.50 ea;
    1962, 4.95. Harper (R)
Neal, Robert M. News gathering and news writing. 1949. 9.00. Prentice-Hall
NEWTON, SIR ISAAC, 1642-1727 (925)
Andrade, E. N. da C. Sir Isaac Newton. 1958. pap. 0.95. Doubleday
Anthony, H. D. Sir Isaac Newton. 1960. 4.00. Abelard
Burtt, Edwin A. Metaphysical foundations of modern physical science. 1952.
    5.50. Humanities
NICHOLAS, I, EMPEROR OF RUSSIA, 1796-1855 (923.1)
Riasanovsky, Nicholas V. Nicholas I and official nationality in Russia, 1825-
    1855. 1959. 6.50. U. of Calif.
NICHOLAS II, EMPEROR OF RUSSIA, 1868-1918 (923.1)
Frankland, Noble. Imperial tragedy: Nicholas II, last of the tsars. 1960. 3.95.
    Coward
NIEBUHR, REINHOLD, 1892- (922.973)
Harland, Gordon. Thought of Reinhold Niebuhr. 1960. 6.00. Oxford U. P.
Hofmann, Hans. Theology of Reinhold Niebuhr. 1956. 3.95. Scribner
Odegard, Holtan P. Sin and science: Reinhold Niebuhr as political theologian.
    3.00. Antioch
NIETZSCHE, FRIEDRICH WILHELM, 1844-1900 (921.3)
Bentley, Eric. Century of hero-worship. 3.75. Smith, Peter
Brinton, Crane. Nietzsche. il. 1941. 4.00. Harvard
Heller, Erich. Disinherited mind. 1957. 3.75. Farrar, Straus
Jaspers, Karl. Reason and existenz. 1955. 3.50. Farrar, Straus
Steiner, Rudolph. Friedrich Nietzsche, fighter for freedom. 1960. 4.75. Herman
NIGERIA (966.9)
Barth, Heinrich. Travels in Nigeria. il. 6.10. Oxford U. P.
Buchanan, K. M., and others. Land and people in Nigeria. il. 8.75. Int. Pub.
Collis, Robert. African encounter: A doctor in Nigeria. il. 1961. 4.50. Scribner
Crowder, Michael. Short history of Nigeria. il. 1962. 5.75. Praeger
Rothchild, Donald S. Toward unity in Africa. 1959. 5.00. Pub. Affairs
NIGHTINGALE, FLORENCE, 1820-1910 (926)
Cope, Zachary. Florence Nightingale and the doctors. il. 1958. 5.00. Lippincott
Seymer, Lucy Ridgely. Florence Nightingale. il. 2.50. Macmillan
Strachey, Lytton. Eminent Victorians. 1.95. Modern Lib.
NIHILISM (149.8)
Polanyi, Michael. Beyond nihilism. 1960. pap. 0.75. Cambridge U. P.
Thielicke, Helmut. Nihilism, its origin and nature, with a Christian answer.
    1961. 5.00. Harper
NILE RIVER AND VALLEY (967.1)
Fairservis, Walter A., Jr. Ancient kingdoms of the Nile and the doomed
    monuments of Nubia. il. 1962. 6.95. Crowell
Moorehead, Alan. Blue Nile. il. 1962. 6.50. Harper
Moorehead, Alan. White Nile. il. 1961. 5.95. Harper
NINETEENTH CENTURY (909.81)
Goodwin, Michael. Nineteenth century opinion. pap. 0.95. Penguin
Kaye, Julian B. Bernard Shaw and the nineteenth-century tradition. il. 1958.
    4.00. U. of Okla.
Mosse, George L. Culture of western Europe. 6.50. Rand McNally

Somervell, D. C. English thought in the 19th century. 1947. 2.75. McKay
Willey, Basil. More nineteenth century studies. 1956. 4.50. Columbia
Willey, B. Nineteenth century studies. 1949. 4.50. Columbia
NITROGEN (546.71)
Asimov, Isaac. World of nitrogen. pap. 0.95. Collier
Duddington, C. L. Microorganisms as allies. 1961. 5.95. Macmillan
Fowler, Gilbert J. Introduction to the bio-chemistry of nitrogen conservation. 1934. 3.00. St. Martins
Hallsworth, E. G. Nutrition of the legumes: Proceedings of the University of Nottingham fifth Easter school in agricultural science, 1958. 1959. 10.50. Academic Press
Shriner, R. L. Sterochemistry of carbon and nitrogen compounds. 1962. 1.95. Reinhold
Webb, Harry W. Absorption of nitrous gases. 1923. 6.50. St. Martins
NKRUMAH, KWAME, PRES. GHANA, 1909- (923.1)
Ames, Sophia R. Nkrumah of Ghana. il. 1961. 3.50. Rand McNally
Phillips, John. Kwame Nkrumah and the future of Africa. 6.50. Praeger
NO (JAPANESE DRAMA) (895.62)
Noh drama: Ten plays from the Japanese. 1960. 4.75. Tuttle
Toki, Zemmaro. Japanese Noh plays. il. 3.25. Tuttle
NOBEL, ALFRED BERNHARD, 1833-1896 (926)
Bergengren, Erik. Alfred Nobel. 1962. 6.50. Nelson
NOBEL PRIZES (378.32)
Farber, Eduard. Nobel Prize winners in chemistry: 1901-1961. 1962. 6.50. Abelard
Hamalian, Leo, and Edmond L. Volpe. Great stories by Nobel prize winners. 1959. 5.00. Farrar, Straus
NOISE (614.78)
Freeman, J. J. Principles of noise. il. 1958. 9.25. Wiley
Van der Ziel, A. Noise. 1954. 13.35. Prentice-Hall
NOMOGRAPHY (MATHEMATICS)(510)
Epstein, L. Ivan. Nomography. il. 1958. 4.50. Wiley
Levens, Alexander S. Nomography. il. 1959. 7.75. Wiley
NONFERROUS METALS (620.18)
Dennis, W. H. Metallurgy of non-ferrous metals. 1961. 16.00. Pitman
Raudebaugh, Robert J. Non-ferrous physical metallurgy. 1952. 7.00. Pitman
Reinfeld, Fred. Uranium and other miracle metals. 1959. 3.95. Sterling
NONSENSE-VERSES (808.87)
Lear, Edward, and others. Book of nonsense. 1.95. 1961. Dutton
NORMANS (944.2)
Haskins, Charles H. Norman institutions. 6.00. Ungar
Haskins, Charles H. Normans in European history. 1959. 4.50. Ungar
Matthew, D. J. A. Norman monasteries and their English possessions. 1962. 4.40. Oxford U. P.
Povremoyne, Jehan le. Normandy. il. 1962. 4.95. Tudor
NORTH AMERICA (970)
Bolton, C. K. Terra nova. 1935. 5.00. Faxon
Bolton, Herbert E., and Thomas M. Marshall. Colonization of North America, 1492-1783. il. 7.50. Macmillan
Hoffman, James. Concerns of a continent. 1958. 2.95. Friendship
Ireland, Gordon. Boundaries, possessions, and conflicts in Central and North America, and the Caribbean. il. 1941. 4.50. Harvard
Lamb, Harold. New found world. 1955. 5.75. Doubleday
Miller, George J., and others. Geography of North America. 1954. 8.50. Wiley
Priestley, Herbert I. Coming of the white man. 1492-1848. 1929. 6.75. Macmillan
NORTH ATLANTIC TREATY ORGANIZATION (341.2)
Buchan, Alastair. NATO in the 1960's: The implication of interdependence. 1960. 3.50. Praeger
Knorr, Klaus. NATO and American security. 1959. 6.00. Princeton

Lowenstein, Huberius Prinz zu, and Volkmar von Zuhlsdorff. NATO and the defense of the West. 7.50. Praeger
Moore, Ben T. NATO and the future of europe. 1958. 4.50. Harper
Osgood, Robert E. NATO, the entangling alliance. 1962. 7.50. U. of Chicago
Schmidt, Helmut. Defense or retaliation. 1962. 7.00. Praeger
NORTH CAROLINA (975.6)
Lefler, Hugh T., and Albert Ray Newsome. North Carolina: The history of a southern state. 1954. 7.50. U. of N. C.
Rankin, Robert S. Government and administration of North Carolina. il. 1955. 5.75. Crowell
Robinson, Blackwell P. North Carolina guide. 1955. 3.50. U. of N. C.
NORTH DAKOTA (978.4)
North Dakota: Guide to the northern prairie state. 6.50. Oxford U. P.
NORTHWEST (973)
Briggs, H. E. Frontiers of the northwest: A history of the Upper Missouri Valley. il. 5.50. Smith, Peter
Douglas, William O. My wilderness: The Pacific West. il. 1960. 4.95. Doubleday
Freeman, Otis W., and Howard H. Martin. Pacific Northwest. 1954. 8.95. Wiley
Fuller, George W. History of the Pacific Northwest. il. 1931. 5.00. Knopf
Havighurst, Walter. Upper Mississippi. il. 1944. 4.50. Rinehart
Irving, Washington. Adventures of Captain Bonneville, U.S.A. by Edgeley W. Todd. il. 1961. 7.95. U. of Okla.
Irving, Washington. Astoria. 2 vols. set. 8.50. Lippincott'
Johansen, Dorothy O., and Charles M. Gates. Empire of the Columbia. il. 1957. 8.95. Harper
Look Magazine. Regional guide: The Central Northwest. by the Editors of Look Magazine. il. 5.50. Houghton
McDonald, Lucile S. Search for the Northwest Passage. il. 1958. 3.00. Binfords
McKinley, Charles. Uncle Sam in the Pacific Northwest: Federal management of natural resources in the Columbia River Valley. il. 1952. 7.50. U. of Calif.
Speck, Gordon. Northwest explorations. il. 1954. 5.00. Binfords
Stefansson, Vilhjalmur. Northwest to fortune. 1958. 6.00. Duell
NORWAY (948.1)
Beyer, Harald. History of Norwegian literature. by Einar Haugen. 1956. 6.50. N. Y. U.
Derry, T. K. Short history of Norway. 5.75. Macmillan
Lindgren, R. E. Norway-Sweden: Union, disunion, and Scandinavian integration. 1959. 5.00. Princeton
Rodnick, David. Norwegians: A study in national culture. 1955. 3.25. Pub. Affairs
Schneiders, Toni and others. Norway. 1962. 6.50. Hill & Wang
Snorri Sturluson. Heimskringla. 1948. 1.95. Dutton
Welle-Strand, Erling. Way of the Vikings. il. 1961. 6.50. Vanous
NOSE (611.21)
Ballenger, Howard C., and John J. Diseases of the nose, throat and ear. il. 1957. 17.50. Lea & F.
Hall, I. Simson. Diseases of the nose, throat and ear. 1959. 5.00. Williams & Wilkins
Howard, Robert. Nuclear physics. 1962. 9.00. Wadsworth
International Conference on the Peaceful Uses of Atomic Energy, 2nd, Geneva, 1958. Physics and mathematics. 3 vols. by D. J. Hughes and others. vol. 1, 1956. 12.00; vol. 2. 1958. 14.00; vol. 3. 1959. 15.00. Pergamon
Jukes, John D. Man-made sun: The story of Zeta. il. 1959. 2.75. Abelard
Lenihan, J. M. A. Atomic energy and its applications. 1954. 4.00. Pitman
Leprince-Ringuet. Louis. Atoms and men. 1961. 3.00. U. of Chicago
NUCLEAR PHYSICS AS A PROFESSION (539.7069)
Thompson, William E. Your future in nuclear energy fields. 1961. 2.95. Richards Rosen

Seltzer, Albert P. Your nasal sinuses and their disorders. il. 1949. 2.50.
  Assoc. Booksellers
NOVELISTS (928.3)
Beach, Joseph W. American fiction 1920-1940. 1960. 6.00. Russell
Heppenstall, Rayner. Fourfold tradition. 1961. 4.50. New Directions
Ludwig, Jack. Recent American novelists. 1962. pap. 0.65. U. of Minn.
McCullough, Bruce. Representative English novelists: Defoe to Conrad. 1946.
  4.50. Harper
NUCLEAR ENGINEERING (621.48)
Bradley, J. E. S., tr. Physics of nuclear fission. 1958. 9.00. Pergamon
Gurinsky, David H., and G. J. Dienes. Nuclear fuels. il. 1956. 9.50. Van
  Nostrand
Helvey, T. C. Effects of nuclear radiation on men and materials. il. 1959. pap.
  1.80. Rider
Lenihan, J. M. A. Atomic energy and its applications. 1954. 4.00. Pitman
Mills, Mark, and others. Modern nuclear technology. 1960. 9.95. McGraw
Sarbacher, Robert. Encyclopedic dictionary of electronics and nuclear
  engineering. 35.00. Prentice-Hall (R)
Stokley, James. New world of the atom. il. 1957. 5.50. Washburn
Wendt, Gerald. You and the atom. 1956. 1.95. Whiteside
NUCLEAR ENGINEERING AS A PROFESSION (621.48069)
Thompson, William E. Your future in nuclear energy fields. 1961. 2.95.
  Richards Rosen
NUCLEAR PHYSICS (539.7)
Ajzenberg-Selove, Fay. Nuclear spectroscopy. 2 vols. pts. A and B, 1960, 16.00
  ea. Academic Press
Baldin, A. M., and others. Kinematics of nuclear reactions. 1961. 6.10. Oxford
  U. P.
Berthelot, Andre. Radiations and matter. 1960. il. 5.75. Macmillan
Bohr, Niels. Atomic physics and human knowledge. 1958. 3.95. Wiley
Cork, James M. Radioactivity and nuclear physics. 1957. 7.75. Van Nostrand
Duquesne, Maurice. Matter and antimatter. il. 1960. 2.25. Harper
Friedlander, G., and J. Kennedy. Nuclear and radiochemistry. 1955. 7.50.
  Wiley
NUCLEAR REACTORS (621.483)
Beck, Clifford K. Nuclear reactors for research. il. 1957. 8.50. Van Nostrand
Braunbek, Werner. Pursuit of the atom. 1959. 3.95. Emerson
Bussard, R. W., and R. D. DeLauer. Nuclear rocket propulsion. 1958. 11.50.
  McGraw
Glasstone, Samuel. Principles of nuclear reactor engineering. il. 1955. 7.95.
  Van Nostrand
Jacobs, Alan M., and others. Basic principles in nuclear science and reactors.
  il. 1960. 6.50. Van Nostrand
Kopelman, B. Materials for nuclear reactors. 1959. 12.00. McGraw
Littler, D. J., and J. F. Raffle. Introduction to reactor physics. il. 1957. 5.50.
  Pergamon
Wilkinson, Walter D., and William F. Murphy. Nuclear reactor metallurgy. il.
  1958. 5.60. Van Nostrand
NUCLEIC ACIDS (547.596)
Brady, Roscoe O., and Donald B. Tower. Neurochemistry of nucleotides and
  amino acids. il. 1960. 10.00. Wiley
Chargaff, E., and J. N. Davidson. Nucleic acids: Chemistry and biology. 3 vols.
  Academic Press
Danielli, J. F., and R. Brown. Nucleic acid. 7.00. Cambridge U. P.
Solvay Institute of Chemistry. Nucleoproteins. il. 1960. 10.50. Wiley
NUMBERS (512.81)
Asimov, Isaac. Realm of numbers. il. 1959. 2.75. Houghton
Bates, Grace E., and Fred L. Kiokemeister. Real number system. 1960. pap.
  1.95. Allyn & Bacon

Bell, E. T. Last problem. 1961. 4.95. S. and S.

Bouvere, K. L. de. Method in proofs of undefinability. 1959. pap. 2.50. Humanities

Dantzig, Tobias. Number, the language of science. 1954. 6.50. Macmillan

Davenport, H. Higher arithmetic: An introduction to the theory of numbers. 1952. 2.50. Hillary

Deaux, R. Introduction to the geometry of complex numbers. 6.50. Ungar

Fraenkel, Abraham A. Integers and theory of numbers. 1955. 2.75. Scripta Mathematica

Friend, J. Newton. Numbers: Fun and facts. il. 1954. 3.50. Scribner

Landau, E. Elementary number theory. 4.95. Chelsea

Lehmer, D. N. List of prime numbers 1 to 10,006, 721. 1956. 15.00. Hafner

National Education Association, National Council of Teachers of Mathematics. Some ideas about number theory. 1961. 1.40. N. E. A.

Olmsted, John M. H. Real number system. il. 1962. 4.50. Appleton

Ore, Oystein. Number theory and its history. il. 1948. 7.00. McGraw

Osborn, Roger. Tables of all primitive roots of odd primes less than 1,000. 1961. 3.00. U. of Tex.

Perron, O. Irrationalzahlen. in German. 3.25. Chelsea

Piaget, Jean. Child's conception of number. 1952. 5.00. Humanities

Reid, Constance. From zero to infinity: What makes numbers interesting. 1960. 3.95. Crowell

Schwerdtfeger, Hans. Geometry of complex numbers. 1961. 4.95. U. of Toronto

Siegel, C. L. Transcendental numbers. 2.00. Princeton

Sierpinski, Waclaw. Cardinal and ordinal numbers. 1958. 8.50. Hafner

Smeltzer, Donald. Man and number. il. 1958. 2.50. Emerson

Stewart, B. M. Theory of numbers. 1952. 6.25. Macmillan

Vinogradov, Ivan M. Elements of number theory. pap. 1.60. Dover

Waismann, Friedrich. Introduction to mathematical thinking. 1951. 4.50. Ungar

NUMERICAL CALCULATIONS (517.6)

Buckingham, R. A. Numerical methods. 1962. 15.00. Pitman

Neumann, John Von. Design of computers, theory of automation and numerical analysis. 1961. 14.00. Pergamon

Scarborough, James B. Numerical mathematical analysis. 1962. 6.00. Johns Hopkins

Steffenson, John F. Interpolation. 4.95. Chelsea

Wilcox, Glade, and C. H. Butler. Industrial calculating devices. 1962. 6.95. Holt, Rinehart & Winston

NUMISMATICS (737)

Brown, Laurence. Coins through the ages. 1962. 2.95. Sterling

Coffin, Joseph. Complete book of coin collecting. 1959. 3.95. Coward

Grant, Michael. Roman history from coins. 1958. 2.75. Cambridge U. P.

Hobson, Burton. Getting started in coin collection. 2.50 net. Sterling

Linecar, H. W. A. Coins. 1955. 3.50. Oxford U. P.

Milne, J. G., and others. Coin collecting. 1950. 2.00. Oxford U. P.

NUREMBERG TRIAL OF MAJOR GERMAN WAR CRIMINALS, 1945-1946 (341.41)

Benton, Wilbourn E., and Georg Grimm. Nuremberg: German views of the war trials. 1955. 4.00. S. M. U.

Gallagher, Richard. Nuremberg: The third Reich on trial. 1961. Avon

Woetzel, Robert. Nuremberg trials in international law. 1962. 10.50. Praeger

NURSERY SCHOOLS (372.216)

Fletcher, Margaret I. Adult and the nursery school child. il. 1958. 2.75. U. of Toronto

Foster, Josephine C., and Marion L. Mattson. Nursery school education. il. 1939. 3.25. Appleton

Justin, Florence, and M. E. Snyder. Directed observation in child development. 3.00. Houghton

Moore, Sallie Beth, and Phyllis Richards. Teaching in the nursery school. il. 1959. 5.50. Harper

Read, Katherine H. Nursery school. il. 1960. 4.25. Saunders

Rudolph, Marguerita. Living and learning in nursery school. 1954. 3.50. Harper

NURSES AND NURSING (610.73)

Abdellah, Faye G., and others. Patient-centered approaches to nursing. 4.90. Macmillan

Altschul, A. Psychology for nurses. 3.00. Williams & Wilkins

Austin, Anne L. History of nursing source book. 1957. 9.50. Putnam (R)

Averill, Lawrence Augustus, and Florence C. Kempf. Psychology applied to nursing. 1956. 4.25. Saunders

Brown, Amy Frances. Medical and surgical nursing. il. 1959. 8.00. Saunders

Burrow, Brunettie. Angels in white. il. 1959. 3.50. Naylor

Cady, Elwyn E. Law and contemporary nursing. 1961. pap. 1.75. Littlefield

Cowan, M. Cordelia. Yearbook of modern nursing. 15.00. Putnam

Crossen, Robert J., and Ann J. Campbell. Gynecologic nursing. 1956. 4.25. Mosby

Dock, Lavinia L., and M. A. Nutting. History of nursing. il. 4 vols. 5.00 ea; set, 1750. Putnam (R)

Faddis, Margene O., and Joseph M. Hayman. Textbook of pharmacology for nurses. il. 1959. 5.50. Lippincott

Flitter, Hessel H. Introduction to physics in nursing. 1962. 3.90. Mosby

Foote, John A. State board questions and answers for nurses. 1947. 6.00. Lippincott

Frank, Charles Marie, Sister. Foundations of nursing. 1959. 4.50. Saunders

Gibson, John. Psychiatry for nurses. 1962. 3.00. Davis

Hansen, H. F. Encyclopedic guide to nursing. 1957. 6.50. McGraw (R)

Hayes, Wayland J., and Rena Gazaway. Human relations in nursing. 1959. 5.25. Saunders

Index to nursing literature. 1956-1960. 20.00. annual suppls. 10.00. Glendale (R)

Jamieson, Elizabeth M., and Mary B. Sewall. History of nursing note book. 1956. loose-leaf 3.75. Lippincott

Jamieson, Elizabeth M., and others. Trends in nursing history. 1959. 5.00. Saunders

Jensen, Deborah MacLurg. History and trends of professional nursing. 1959. 5.25. Mosby

Lesnik, Milton J., and Bernice E. Anderson. Nursing practice and the law. 1962. 7.00. Lippincott

Marshall, John. Neurological nursing. il. 1956. 3.75. Davis

Meeks, Dorothy, and Audrey Kalafatich. Maternal and child health. 1960. pap. 1.95. Littlefield

Miller, Norman F., and Hazel Avery. Gynecology and gynecologic nursing. 1959. 5.50. Saunders

Montag, Mildred L., and Ruth S. Swenson. Fundamentals of nursing care. il. 1959. 5.00. Saunders

Morrissey, Alice B. Rehabilitation nursing. 1951. 6.00. Putnam

Morton, Honnor. Nurse's dictionary. 3.00. Landau

Newton, Kathleen. Geriatric nursing. 1960. 6.75. Mosby

Nightingale, Florence. Notes on nursing: What it is, and what it is not. 1957. 5.00. Lippincott

Nightingale, Florence. Selected writings. 1954. 5.00. Macmillan

Oakes, Lois. Oakes' dictionary for nurses. 1961. 2.75. Williams & Wilkins (R)

O'Hara, Frank J. Psychology and the nurse. il. 1960. 3.75. Saunders

Peplau, Hildegarde E. Interpersonal relations. 1952. 4.50. Putnam

Reference handbook and dictionary of nursing: Olson's Nurses' handbook, tenth edition, and Dorland's Pocket medical dictionary, twentieth edition. il. 1960. 6.50. Saunders (R)

Roberts, Mary M. American nursing. il. 1954. 7.00. Macmillan

Rothweiler, Elia L., and others. Art and science of nursing. 1959. 5.50. Davis

Sense, Eleanora. Clinical studies in nutrition. 1960. 4.00. Lippincott

Seymer, Lucy Ridgely. Selected writings of Florence Nightingale. 1954. 5.75. Macmillan

Shryock, Richard H. History of nursing. 1959. 5.00. Saunders
Young, Helen, and others. Lippincott's quick reference book for nurses. 1962.
   4.75. Lippincott (R)

NURSES AND NURSING--STUDY AND TEACHING (610.73)
Abdellah, Faye G., and others. Patient-centered approaches to nurses. 4.90.
   Macmillan
Bridgman, Margaret. Collegiate education for nursing. 1953. 2.50. Russell
Brown, Esther Lucile. Nursing for the future. 1948. 2.00. Russell Sage
Cardew, Emily C. Study guide for clinical nursing. 1961. 6.50. Lippincott
Chamberlain, E. M. Orientation to nursing. 1962. 4.95. McGraw
Lambertsen, Eleanor C. Education for nursing leadership. 1958. 5.00.
   Lippincott
Macgregor, Frances M. C. Social science in nursing. il. 1960. 5.00. Russell
   Sage
Montag, M. L. Community college education for nursing. 1959. 6.00. McGraw
Sand, Ole. Curriculum study in basic nursing education. 1955. 5.00. Putnam
Sand, Ole, and Helen C. Belcher. Experience in basic nursing education. il.
   1958. 5.00. Putnam
Tschudin, Mary S., and others. Evaluation in basic nursing education. il. 1958.
   6.00. Putnam

NURSING AS A PROFESSION (610.73069)
Deming, Dorothy. Careers for nurses. 1952. 6.00. McGraw
Dietz, Lena D. Professional adjustments. 2 vols. vol. 1. 1957. 3.25; vol. 2.
   1959. 4.50. Davis
Kelly, Cordelia W. Dimensions of professional nursing. il. 1962. 6.95. Mac-
   millan
McFadden, Charles J. Medical ethics. 1961. 4.75. Davis
McKenna, Frances M. Thresholds to professional nursing practice. 1960. 5.25.
   Saunders
Spalding, Eugenia Kennedy. Professional nursing, trends and relationships. 1959.
   6.00. Lippincott

NUTRITION (612.3)
Anderson, Linnea, and John H. Browe. Nutrition and family health service. il.
   1960. pap. 5.00. Saunders
Batjer, Margaret, and Mimi A. Atwater. Meals for the modern family. 1961.
   4.95. Wiley
Bender, A. E. Dictionary of nutrition and food technology. 1960. 5.80. Academic
   Press (R)
Bogert, L. Jean. Nutrition and physical fitness. 1960. 6.00. Saunders
Bradley, Alice V. Tables of food values. 1956. 5.50. Bennett
Brock, J. F. Recent advances in human nutrition. 1961. 11.50. Little
Byrd, Oliver E. Nutrition sourcebook. 1955. 7.50. Stanford
Cooper, Lenna, and others. Nutrition in health and disease. 1958. 6.00.
   Lippincott
Cruickshank, Ernest W. H. Food and nutrition. 1951. 6.50. Williams & Wilkins
Davidson, Stanley, and others. Human nutrition and dietetics. il. 1960. 15.00.
   Williams & Wilkins
Gilbert, Frank, A. Mineral nutrition of plants and animals. il. 1953. 2.75.
   U. of Okla.
Herriott, Roger M. Symposium on nutrition: The physiological role of certain
   vitamins and trace elements. 1953. 6.00. Johns Hopkins
Kilander, Holger F. Nutrition for health. il. 1951. 5.64. McGraw
Leverton, Ruth. Food becomes you. il. 1960. 3.50. Iowa State
McCollum, E. V. History of nutrition. 6.00. Houghton
Mitchell, H. H. and Marjorie Edman. Nutrition and climatic stress, with
   particular reference to man. il. 1951. 6.75. Thomas, C. C.
Mowry, Lillian. Basic nutrition and diet therapy for nurses. 1962. 3.25. Mosby
Proudfit, Fairfax T. Normal and therapeutic nutrition. il. 1961. 7.00. Macmillan

Rodale, Jerome I., and others. Complete book of food and nutrition. 1961. 6.95.
   Rodale
Sheehy, E. J. Animal nutrition. 1955. 7.50. St. Martins
Sherman, Henry C. Chemistry of food and nutrition. 1952. 7.00. Macmillan
Sherman, Henry C., and Caroline S. Lanford. Essentials of nutrition. 5.50.
   Macmillan
Sherman, Henry C. Nutritional improvement of life. 1950. 5.00. Columbia
Taylor, Clara Mae, and others. Foundations of nutrition. 6.50. Macmillan
Wohl, Michael G., and Robert S. Goodhart. Modern nutrition in health and
   disease. 1960. 18.50. Lea & F
NUTS (634.5)
Reed, C. A., and J. Davidson. Improved nut trees of North America. 1954.
   6.00. Devin
Smith, J. Russell. Tree crops. 6.00. Devin
NYASALAND (968.97)
Barber, William J. Economy of British Central Africa. il. 1961. 6.50. Stanford
Debenham, Frank. Nyasaland. il. 1955. 5.00. British Info. Services
Hanna, A. J. Story of the Rhodesias and Nyasaland. il. 1961. 4.50. Humanities

O

OBSCENITY (LAW) (343.1)
Paul, James C. N., and Murray L. Schwartz. Federal censorship. 1959. 7.50.
   Free Press
Pilpel, Harriet, and Theodora Zavin. Rights and writers. 1960. 7.50. Dutton
Spring, Samuel. Risks and rights in publishing, television, radio, motion pictures
   and the theater. 1956. 10.00. Norton
OBSTETRICS (618.2)
Bowes, K. Modern trends in obstetrics and gynecology. 12.00. Hoeber
Eianfrani, Theodore. Short history of obstetrics and gynecology. il. 1960. 12.50.
   Thomas, C. C.
DeLee, Joseph B. DeLee's obstetrics for nurses. il. 1962. 7.50. Saunders
Dewhurst, Christopher J. Student's guide to obstetrics and gynaecology. il.
   1960. 4.00. Lippincott
Eastman, Nicholson J. Expectant motherhood. il. 1957. 2.00. Little
Guttmacher, Alan F. Pregnancy and birth: A book for expectant parents. il.
   1957. 4.50. Viking
Mayes, Mary. Handbook for midwives and maternity nurses. il. 1959. 5.50.
   Williams & Wilkins
Wiedenback, Ernestine. Family-centered maternity nursing. il. 1958. 5.50.
   Putnam
Zabriskie, Louise. Zabriskie's obstetrics for nurses. 1960. 6.00. Lippincott
O'CASEY, SEAN, 1884- (928)
Hogan, Robert. Experiments of Sean O'Casey. 1960. 5.00. St. Martins
Krause, David. Sean O'Casey: The man and his work. il. 1961. 4.50. Macmillan
OCCULT SCIENCES (133)
Bromage, Bernard. Occult arts of ancient Egypt. 3.95. Wehman
Edmunds, Simeon. Hypnotism and the supernormal. 4.50. Llewellyn
Grillot de Givry, Emile. Pictorial anthology of witchcraft, magic and alchemy.
   il. 1958. 10.00. U.Books (R)
Hall, Manly P. Encyclopedia of Masonic, Hermetic, Qabbalistic and Rosicrucian
   symbolic philosophy. 13.50. DeVorss (R)
Hall, Manly P. Phoenix. 10.00. DeVorss
Ouspensky, P. D. New model of the universe. 1934. 7.50. Knopf
Rhine, J. B. New world of the mind. 1953. 4.00. Sloane
Spence, Lewis. Encyclopaedia of occultism. il. 1960. 15.00. U. Books (R)
OCCUPATIONAL THERAPY (615.8515)
Dunton, William Rush, Jr., and Sidney Licht. Occupational therapy: Principles
   and practice. 1956. 8.00. Thomas, C. C.

Johnstone, Rutherford T., and Seward E. Miller. Occupational diseases. il.
1960. 12.00. Saunders
MacDonald, E. M. Occupational therapy in rehabilitation. 1960. 8.50. Williams
& Wilkins
Watson, Donald P., and Alice W. Burlingame. Therapy through horticulture. il.
4.95. Macmillan
OCCUPATIONS (371.425)
Bennet, Carrie L. Defining the manager's job: The AMA manual of position
descriptions. 1958. 9.00. Am. Management Assn.
Bingham, Walter V. Aptitudes and aptitude testing. 1937. 6.00. Harper
Boynton, Paul W. Six ways to get a job. 1951. 3.50. Harper
Caplow, Theodore. Sociology of work. 1954. 5.00. U. of Minn.
Career Research Associates. What you can earn in 250 different careers. by
Ben S. Puchaski. 1959. 2.95. Chilton
Fortune. Adventures in small business. 1957. 4.50. McGraw
Hughes, Everett C. Men and their work. 4.00. Free Press
Myers, George E., and others. Planning your future. 1953. 4.96. McGraw
National and international employment handbook for specialized personnel. 1961.
17.50. World Trade Academy (R)
National directory of employment services. 25.00. Gale
Newman, Samuel Clayton. Employment problems of college students. 1942. 3.00.
Pub. Affairs
Reilly, William J. How to make your living in four hours a day: Without feeling
guilty about it. 1955. 2.95. Harper
Reis, Albert J., Jr. Occupations and social status. 1962. 6.00. Free Press
Science Research Associates Guidance Staff Editors. Handbook of job facts. 1948.
3.95. Sci. Res. Assoc.
Shartle, Carroll L. Occupational information: Its development and application.
10.00. Prentice-Hall
Thomas, L. G: Occupational structure and education. 1956. 9.00. Prentice-Hall
Thorndike, Robert L., and Elizabeth P. Hagen. Ten thousand careers. il. 1959.
8.95. Wiley (R)
Forrester, Gertrude. Occupational literature, an annotated bibliography. 1958.
6.50. Wilson (R)
OCEAN (551.46)
Bretz, J. H. Earth sciences. 1940. 3.00. Wiley
Carson, R. L. Sea around us. 1961. 5.00. Oxford U. P.
Cromie. Exploring the secrets of the sea. 1962. 3.95. Prentice-Hall
De Sales, W. A., and others. Sea. 17.50. Rand McNally (R)
Douglas, John Scott. Story of the oceans. 1952. 4.00. Dodd
Eckart, Carl. Hydrodynamics of oceans and atmospheres. 9.00. Pergamon
Emery, K. O. Sea off Southern California. il. 1960. 12.50. Wiley
Freuchen, Peter. Peter Freuchen's book of the seven seas. 1957. 8.95. Messner
Huxley, Anthony. Standard encyclopedia of the world's oceans and islands. 1962.
10.95. Putnam (R)
Pettersson, Hans. Ocean floor. 1954. 3.75. Yale
Russell, F. S., and C. M. Yonge. Seas: Our knowledge of life in the sea, and
how it is gained. il. 1928. 5.00. Warne
Spectorsky, Auguste C. Book of the sea. il. 1958. 4.95. Grosset
Walford, L. A. Living resources of the sea. 1958. 6.00. Ronald
Knight, Frank. Sea story. 1958. 5.50. St. Martins
OCEANICA (990)
Attenborough, David. People of Paradise. il. 1961. 3.95. Harper
Clark, Sydney. All the best in the South Pacific. il. 1961. 4.95. Dodd
Freeman, Otis W. Geography of the Pacific. 1951. 8.95. Wiley
Grattan, Clinton H. United States and the Southwest Pacific. 1961. 5.00. Harvard
Michener, James A., and A. Grove Day. Rascals in paradise. 1957. 4.75. Random
Michener, James A. Return to paradise. 1951. 3.95. Random

Sharp, Andrew. Discovery of the Pacific Islands. 1960. 7.70. Oxford U. P.
Smith, Bernard. European vision and the South Pacific, 1768-1850. il. 1960. 13.45.
Oxford U. P.

OCEANOGRAPHY (551.46)
Barnes, Harold. Oceanography and marine biology. il. 1959. 7.95. Macmillan
Bolin, Bert. Atmosphere and the sea in motion. 1959. 15.00. Oxford U. P.
Cowen, Robert C. Frontiers of the sea. il. 4.95. Doubleday
Defant, A. Physical oceanography. 2 vols. 1961. 35.00. Pergamon
Sears, Mary. Oceanography. 1961. 14.75. A.A.A.S.

ODES (292)
Maddison, Carol. Apollo and the Nine: A history of the Ode. 1960. 6.50. Johns
Hopkins

OEDIPUS (131.341)
Mullahy, Patrick. Oedipus: Myth and complex. 1955. pap. 2.45. Grove
Velikovsky, Immanuel. Oedipus and Akhnaton, myth and history. il. 1960. 4.95.
Doubleday

OFFICE MANAGEMENT (651)
Agnew, Peter L., and James R. Meehan. Clerical office practice. 1961. 4.12.
South-Western Pub.
Agnew, Peter L., and James R. Meehan. Secretarial office practice. 1960.
4.12. South-Western Pub.
Becker, Esther R., and Richard L. Lawrence. Success and satisfaction in your
office uob. 1954. 3.00. Harper
Delano, Margaret. How to be a top secretary. 1954. 4.95. McKay
Doris, Lillian, and Bessie M. Miller. Complete secretary's handbook. 5.95.
Prentice-Hall (R)
Fairbanks, Ralph W. Successful office automation. il. 1956. 10.00. Prentice-Hall
Fasnacht, Harold D., and Bauernfeind. How to use business machines. 1962.
2.28. McGraw
Fisher, Harrison. Today's business machines. il. 1959. 4.95. Am. Tech. Soc.
Friedman, Sherwood, and Jack Grossman. Secretarial practice. 1960. 4.20.
Pitman
Hoos, Ida R. Automation in the office. 1961. 4.50. Pub. Affairs
Hutchinson, Lois D. Standard handbook for secretaries. 1956. 5.95. McGraw
Lazzaro, V. Systems and procedures: A handbook for business and industry.
1959. 10.60. Prentice-Hall
Levin, H. S. Office work and automation. 1956. 5.95. Wiley
Mager, N. H., and S. K. Office encyclopedia. il. 0.50. Washington Square (R)
Neuner, John J. W. Office management. 1959. 7.00. South-Western Pub.
Pelo, William Joseph, and others. New secretary's desk book: A manual of
correct usage. il. 1959. 5.50. Holt, Rinehart & Winston (R)
Place, Irene, and Madeline S. Strony. Road to secretarial success. il. 1954.
5.75. McGraw
Savage, W. G., and others. Business review for professional secretaries. 1959.
6.00. Pitman
Taintor, Sarah A., and Kate M. Monro. Secretary's handbook. 5.95. Macmillan
(R)
Terry, George R. Office management and control. 1962. 10.60. Irwin
Wylie, H. L. Office management handbook. 1958. 12.00. Ronald

OHIO (977.1)
Collins, W. R. Ohio, the Buckeye State. 5.90. 1962. Prentice-Hall
Ohio guide. 6.50. Oxford U. P.
Roseboom, Eugene H., and Francis P. Weisenburger. History of Ohio. 1961.
7.50. Ohio Hist. Soc.

OIL FIELDS (553.28)
Cole, Frank W. Reservoir engineering manual. il. 1961. 11.50. Gulf
Illing, V. C. World's oilfields: The Eastern hemisphere. 1953. 25.00. Oxford
U. P. (R)

Thompson, Arthur Beeby. Black gold: The story of an oil pioneer. il. 1961.
  5.95. Doubleday
OILS AND FATS (665)
Andersen, Aage J. C. Refining of oils and fats for edible purposes. 1962.
  ' 10.00. Pergamon
Eckey, E. W., and L. P. Miller. Vegetable fats and oils. 1954. 17.50. Reinhold
Gunstone, Frank D. Chemistry of fats and fatty acids. il. 1958. 6.00. Wiley
Kirschenbauer, H. G. Fats and oils. 1960. 7.00. Reinhold
OKINAWA ISLAND (952.81)
Kerr, George H. Okinawa: The history of an island people. il. 1958. 6.75. Tuttle
Zabilka, Gladys. Customs and culture of Okinawa. 1958. 2.75. Tuttle
OKLAHOMA (976.6)
McReynolds, Edwin C. Oklahoma: History of the Sooner state. il. 1956. 4.95.
  U. of Okla.
Staff of the University of Oklahoma Press. Oklahoma: A guide to the Sooner state.
  5.95. U. of Okla. (R)
OLD AGE (301.435)
Albrecht, Ruth E. Aging in a changing society. 1962. pap. 3.75. U. of Fla.
Arthur, Julietta K. How to help older people: A guide for you and your family.
  1954. 4.95. Lippincott
Corson, John J., and John W. McConnell. Economic needs of older people. 1956.
  4.50. Twentieth Century
Dearing, Charles L. Industrial pensions. 1954. 3.75. Brookings
Donahue, Wilma T. Housing the aging. 1954. 3.75. U.of Mich.
Gerontological Congress. Old age in the modern world. il. 1955. 8.00. Williams
  & Wilkins
Gilbert, Jeanne G. Understanding old age. 1952. 6.00. Ronald
Kaplan, Oscar J. Mental disorders in later life. 1956. 8.50. Stanford
Kleemeier, Robert W. Aging and leisure. 1961. 5.75. Oxford U. P.
Lasser, Jacob K. Your social security. 1962. 1.95. S. and S.
McGill, Dan M. Fundamentals of private pensions. 1955. 5.50. Irwin
Patterson, Edwin W. Legal protection of private pension expectations. 1960.
  6.75. Irwin
Pilch, Michael, and Victor Wood. Pension schemes. 8.00. Humanities
Pinner, Frank A., and others. Old age and political behavior. 1959. 6.00. U.
  of Calif.
Sheldon, Joseph H. Social medicine of old age. il. 1948. 1.60. Oxford U. P.
Shock, Nathan W. Classified bibliography of gerontology and geriatrics. 1957.
  15.00. Stanford (R)
Shock, Nathan W. Trends in gerontology. 1957. 4.50. Stanford
Tibbitts, Clark. Living through the older years. 1949. 3.50. U. of Mich.
Webber, Irving L. Society and the health of older people. 1959. pap. 2.50.
  U. of Fla.
Whitman, Howard J. Brighter later life. 1961. 4.95. Prentice-Hall
Wolff, Kurt. Biological, sociological and psychological aspects of aging. 1959.
  3.75. Thomas, C. C.
OLYMPIC GAMES (796.48)
Kieran, John, and Arthur Daley. Story of the Olympic games, 776 B.C. to 1960,
  A.D. 1961. 6.95. Lippincott
Lechenperg, Harald. Olympic games, 1960. il. 4.95. Barnes, A. S.
U.S. Olympic Committee. United States Olympic book. 12.50. Hammond
O'NEILL, EUGENE GLADSTONE, 1888-1953 (928.973)
Alexander, Doris. Tempering of Eugene O'Neill. il. 1962. 5.95. Harcourt
Bowen, C., and S. O'Neill. Curse of the misbegotten. 1959. 5.00. McGraw
Cargill, Oscar, and others. O'Neill and his plays. 1961. 7.50. N. Y. U.
Falk, Doris V. Eugene O'Neill and the tragic tension. 1958. 4.50. Rutgers
Gelb, Barbara, and Arthur. O'Neill: A biography. 1962. 12.50. Harper
Miller, Jordan Y. Eugene O'Neill and the American critic, a summary and
  bibliographical checklist. 1962. 15.00. Shoe String (R)

Winther, Sophus. Eugene O'Neill. 1961. 7.50. Russell

ONTOLOGY (111)

Broad, C. D. Examination of McTaggart's philosophy. 1933. 7.50. Cambridge U. P.

Buber, Martin. I and thou. 1958. 1.75. Scribner

Heidegger, Martin. Introduction to metaphysics. 1959. 4.00. Yale

McTaggart, John M. E. Nature of existence. 1927. 9.50. Cambridge U. P.

Maritain, Jacques. Preface to metaphysics. 2.25. Sheed

Royce, Josiah. World and the individual: 2 vols. 8.50. Smith, Peter

Smith, Gerard, and Lottie E. Kendzierski. Philosophy of being: Metaphysics I. 5.75. Macmillan

Thomas, Aquinas, Saint. Concerning being and essence. 1937. 1.25. Appleton

Tillich, Paul. Courage to be. 1952. 3.75. Yale

OPERA (782.1)

Allen, Reginald. First night Gilbert and Sullivan. il. 7.50. Dial.

Bauer, Marion, and Ethel Peyser. How opera grew. il. 1956. 6.00. Putnam

Blum, Daniel. Pictorial treasury of opera in America. il. 1954. 10.00. Chilton

Cross, Milton J. Milton Cross' favorite arias from the great operas. il. 1960. 3.95. Doubleday

Cross, Milton J. Milton Cross' complete stories of the great operas. 1955. 3.95. Doubleday

Eaton, Quaintance. Opera production: A handbook. 1961. 6.50. U. of Minn. (R)

Ewen, David. Book of European light opera. 1962. 7.50. Holt, Rinehart & Winston

Ewen, David. Encyclopedia of concert music. il. 1959. 7.50. Hill & Wang (R)

Ewen, David. Encyclopedia of the opera. 1955. 7.50. Hill and Wang (R)

Fellner, Rudolph. Opera themes and plots. 1958. 5.95. S. and S.

Gilbert, William S., and Arthur Sullivan. Mikado and five other Savoy operas. pap. 0.95. Doubleday

Grout, D. J. Short history of opera. 1947. 6.00. Columbia

Howard, J. T. World's great operas. 1959. 1.95. Modern Lib.

Kerman, Joseph. Opera as drama. 1956. 5.00. Knopf

Kobbe, Gustav. Complete opera book. by Lord Harewood. 1954. 10.00. Putnam (R)

Krehbiel, Henry E. Book of operas: Histories, plots, and music. il. 2.95. Macmillan

Johnson, H. Earle. Operas on American subjects. 1962. 4.00. Coleman-Ross

Loewenberg, A. Annals of the opera. 2 vols. 1955. 55.00. Lounz

Marek, George R. Opera as theater. 1962. 5.00. Harper

Marek, George R. World treasury of grand opera. 1957. 7.50. Harper

Martin, George. Opera companion: Guide for the casual operagoer. il. 1961. 12.50. Dodd (R)

Moore, Frank L. Crowell's handbook of world opera. il. 1961. 7.50. Crowell (R)

Newman, Ernest. More stories of famous operas. 1943. 7.50. Knopf

Newman, Ernest. Seventeen famous operas. il. 1955. 7.50. Knopf

Pelz, Mary Ellis. Introduction to opera. 1962. 5.75. Barnes & Noble

Ross, Anne. Opera directory. il. 20.00. Sterling (R)

Samachson, Dorothy, and Joseph. Fabulous world of opera. 3.75. Rand McNally

Slonim, Marc. Russian theater, from the Empire to the Soviets. il. 1961. 7.50. World Pub.

Strauss, Richard. Stage works. 3.00. Boosey'

Turfery, Cossar, and King Palmer. Musical production. 1954. 6.50. Pitman

Wagner, Richard. Ring of the Nibelung. tr. by Stewart Robb. il. 1960. 4.50. Dutton

OPERATION SEA LION (940.548)

Ansel, Walter. Hitler confronts England. 1960. 7.50. Duke

Wheatley, Ronald. Operation Sea Lion: German plans for the invasion of England, 1939-1942. il. 1958. 7.00. Oxford U. P.

OPHTHALMOLOGY (617.7)

Adler, Francis Heed. Physiology of the eye. il. 1959. 16.00. Mosby

MacNalty, Arthur S. Preservation of eyesight. 1958. 3.00. Williams & Wilkins

Town, Arno E. Ophthalmology. il. 1951. 10.00. Lea & F

OPIUM (178. 8)

De Quincey, Thomas. Confessions of an English opium-eater. 2.25. Oxford U. P.

Lindesmith, A. R. Opiate addiction. 5.05. Principia Press of Trinity U.

Report to the Economic and Social Council on the work of the Permanent Central Opium Board. 1960. 1.00. U. N.

Reynolds, Albert K., and Lowell O. Randall. Morphine and allied drugs. il. 1957. 10.00. U. of Toronto

Willoughby, Westel W. Opium as an international problem: The Geneva conferences. 1925. 4.50. Johns Hopkins

OPTICS (535)

Boll, Richard H. Light-scattering functions. 1958. 9.50. U. of Mich.

Born, Max, and Emil Wolf. Principles of optics. 1959. 17.50. Pergamon

Boutry, Georges A. Instrumental optics. 1961. 27.50. Wiley

Frank, Nathaniel H. Introduction to electricity and optics. 1950. 7.50. McGraw

Herzberger, Max. Modern geometrical optics. il. 1958. 16.00. Wiley

Houstoun, Robert A. Physical optics. il. 1958. 6.25. Wiley

Palmer, C. Harvey. Optics: Experiments and demonstrations. 1962. 4.95. Johns Hopkins

Ronchi, Vasco. Optics, the science of vision. 1957. 10.00. N. Y. U.

OPTOMETRY (617. 75)

Gregg, James R. Your future in optometry. 1960. 2.95. Richards Rosen

ORATIONS (808. 85)

Braden, Waldo W., and Mary Louise Gehring. Speech practices: A resource book for student of public speaking. 1958. 3.00. Harper

Grossman, Richard L. Bold voices. 1960. bds. 5.95. Doubleday

Peterson, Houston. Treasury of the world's great speeches. 1954. 7.50. S. and S.

Werner, E. Ş. Famous modern orations. 1.50. Wehman

Woodson, Carter G. Negro orators and their orations. 1925. 5.25. Assoc. Publishers

ORCHESTRA (785. 1)

Bagar, Robert, and Louis Biancolli. Complete guide to orchestral music. 1960. 4.95. Grosset

Carse, Adam. Orchestra from Beethoven to Berlioz. il. 7.50. Saifer

Carse, Adam. Orchestra in the 18th century. 4.00. Saifer

Gilman, Lawrence. Orchestral music: An armchair guide. by Edward Cushing. 1951. 7.50. Oxford U. P.

Grabbe, Paul. Story of one hundred symphonic favorites. 1960. 1.50. Grosset

Grabbe, Paul. Story of orchestral music and its times. 1960. 1.50. Grosset

Korn, Richard. Orchestral accents. il. 1956. 3.50. Farrar, Straus

Mueller, John H. American symphony orchestra: A social history of musical taste. il. 1951. 6.95. Indiana

Noyes, Frank. Anthology of musical examples for instrumental conducting. pap. 6.50. Brown, W. C.

Scherchen, Hermann. Handbook of conduction. 1933. 5.50. Oxford U. P.

Spaeth, Sigmund. Guide to great orchestral music. 2.95. Modern Music

Ulrich, Homer. Symphonic music. 1952. 5.00. Columbia

ORCHIDS (584. 15)

Fennell, T. A., Jr. Orchids for home and garden. il. 1959. 3.95. Holt, Rinehart & Winston

Hawkes, Alex D. Orchids: Their culture and botany. il. 1960. 6.95. Harper

Northen, Rebecca T. Home orchid growing. il. 1962. 10.95. Van Nostrand

ORDINANCE (623. 4)

Bruce, Robert V. Lincoln and the tools of war. 1956. 6.00. Bobbs

Carman, W. Y. History of firearms. 1956. 3.25. St. Martins

O'Neil, Bryon H. St. J. Castles and cannon. il. 1960. 5.60. Oxford U. P.

Partington, J. R. A history of Greek fire and gunpowder. 1960. 15.00. Barnes & Noble

Pawle, Gerald. Secret war: 1939-1945. il. 1957. 5.00. Sloane

OREGON (979.5)

Brier, Howard M. Sawdust empire. il. 1958. 5.00. Knopf

Federal Writers' Program. Oregon, end of the trail. il. 5.00. Binfords

Gregg, Jacob Ray. History of the Oregon Trail, Santa Fe Trail and other trails. il. 1955. 5.00. Binfords

Tobie, Harvey Elmer. No man like Joe: Joe Meek the mountain man. il. 1949. 5.00. Binfords

Turner, Frederick J. Rise of the new West. 1959. 6.00. Smith, Peter

Neuberger, Richard L. Adventures in politics. 1954. 5.00. Oxford U. P.

ORGANICULTURE (635)

Organic Gardening and Farming. Encyclopedia of organic gardening, by the Staff of Organic Gardening and Farming magazine. il. 1959. 6.95. Rodale

Rodale, Jerome I. Complete book of composting. 6.95. Rodale

Rodale, Jerome I., and others. How to grow vegetables and fruits by the organic method. 1961. 6.95. Rodale

ORGANIZATION (658)

American Management Association. Executive committee control charts. 1960. 2.25. Am. Management Assn.

Argyris, Chris. Personality and organization. 1957. 5.00. Harper

Barnard, Chester Irving. Organization and management. 1948. 4.50. Harvard

Etzioni, Amitai. Comparative analysis of complex organizations. 1961. 8.50. Free Press

Krupp, Sherman R. Pattern in organization analysis: A critical examination. 1961. 5.00. Chilton

Pfiffner, John M., and Sherwood. Administrative organization. 10.60. 7.95. Prentice-Hall

Tannenbaum, R., and others. Leadership and organization: A behavioral science approach. 1961. 7.50. McGraw

Thompson, Victor A. Modern organization. 1961. 3.75. Knopf

ORGANIZATION OF AMERICAN STATES (341.187)

Dreier, John C. Organization of the American States. 1962. 2.95. Harper

Manger, William. Pan America in crisis. 1961. 3.25. Pub. Affairs

Mecham, J. Lloyd. United States and inter-American security, 1889-1960. 1961. 7.50. U. of Tex.

Thomas, Ann Van W., and A. J. Thomas, Jr. Organization of American States. 1962. 10.00. S. M. U.

ORIENTAL LITERATURE (890)

Arberry, Arthur J. Oriental essays. 4.75. Macmillan

De Bary, William T., Jr. Approaches to the oriental classics. 1959. 4.75. Columbia

Pritchard, James B. Ancient Near East: An anthology of texts and pictures. 1958. 6.00. Princeton

Pritchard, James Bennett. Ancient Near Eastern texts relating to the Old Testament. 1955. 17.50. Princeton

Yohannan, John D. Treasury of Asian literature. 1956. 7.50. Day

ORIGIN OF SPECIES (575)

Cain, A. J. Animal species and their evolution. 1954. 2.50. Hillary

Kerkut, G. A. Implications of evolution. 5.00. Pergamon

Lack, David L. Darwin's finches. il. 3.40. Smith, Peter

Rostand, Jean. Orion book of evolution. il. 1961. 6.95. Orion

ORPHEUS (882)

Bliss, A. J. Sir Orfeo. 1954. 2.40. Oxford U. P.

Freden, Gustav. Orpheus and the goddess of nature. 4.50. Hillary

Guthrie, W. K. C. Orpheus and the Greek religion. 6.00. Hillary

Sewell, Elizabeth. Orphic voice: Poetry and natural history. 1960. 7.50. Yale

Watmough, J. R. Orphism. 1934. 2.50. Cambridge U. P.

ORTHODOX EASTERN CHURCH (281)

Curtiss, John Shelton. Russian church and the Soviet state. 1953. 6.00. Little

Fedotov, G. P. Russian religious mind: Kievan Christianity, the 10th to the 13th centuries. 4.00. Smith, Peter

French, Reginald M. Eastern Orthodox Church. 2.50. Hillary

Iswolsky, Irene. Christ in Russia. 1960. 3.95. Bruce

Le Guillou, M. K. Spirit of eastern orthodoxy. 1962. 3.50. Hawthorn

Soloviev, Alexandre. Holy Russia: The history of a religious-social idea. 1959. 2.00. Humanities

Spinka, Matthew. Church in Soviet Russia. 1956. 3.50. Oxford U. P.

Zernov, Nicholas. Eastern Christendom. il. 1961. 7.50. Putnam

ORWELL, GEORGE, 1903-1950 (928)

Rees, Richard. George Orwell: Fugitive from the camp of victory. 1962. 4.50. Southern Ill.

Voorhees, Richard J. Paradox of George Orwell. 1961. pap. 1.95. Purdue

OSCILLATORS (621.3815)

Edson, W. A. Vacuum tube oscillators. 1953. 9.50. Wiley

Glasoe, G. N., and Jean V. Lebacqz. Pulse generators. 1948. 12.50. McGraw

Haag, Jules. Oscillatory motions. 1961. 10.00. Wadsworth

Kryloff, N., and N. Bogoliuboff. Introduction to mechanics. 1943. 2.00. Princeton

Minorsky, Nicholas. Non-linear oscillations. il. 1962. 16.75. Van Nostrand

Reich, Herbert J. Functional circuits and oscillators. il. 1961. 12.50. Van Nostrand

Strauss, Leonard. Wave generation and shaping. 1960. 12.50. McGraw

OSLER, SIR WILLIAM, BART, 1849-1919 (925)

Cushing, Harvey. Life of Sir William Osler. 2 vols. 1940. 16.50. Oxford U. P.

Noble, Iris. Doctor who dared: William Osler. 1959. 3.25. Messner

OUTDOOR LIFE (796.5)

Angier, Bradford. How to go live in the woods. il. 1959. 5.00. Stackpole

Kephart, Horace. Camping and woodcraft. il. 4.95. Macmillan

Kesting, Ted. Outdoor encyclopedia. il. 1957. 3.95. Barnes, A. S. (R)

Long, Amelia Reynolds. Outdoor reference guide. 7.50. Stackpole (R)

O'Reilly, John. Sports Illustrated book of the outdoors. il. 1959. 9.95. Golden Press

Outdoor Life. Great outdoor adventures. il. 1961. 4.50. Dutton

Outboard motor and boating guide. 1962. 4.00. Audel

Seton, Ernest T. Ernest Thompson Seton's America. by Farida Wiley. il. 1954. 5.00. Devin

Venk, Ernest. Complete outboard boating manual. il. 1958. 4.95. Am. Tech. Soc.

Vocational Guidance Research. Outdoor jobs for men. il. 1947. 3.95. Vanguard

Whelen, Townsend, and Bradford Angier. On your own in the wilderness. ill. 5.00. Stackpole

OUTER SPACE (629.1388)

Benson, O. O., and H. Strughold. Physics and medicine of the atmosphere and space. 1960. 12.50. Wiley

DuBridge, Lee A. Introduction to space. il. 1960. 2.50. Columbia

Ducrocq, Albert. Victory over space. tr. by Oliver Stewart. il. 1961. 4.95. Little

Godwin, Felix. Exploration of the solar system. il. 1960. 6.50. Consultants Bureau

Jastrov, Robert. Exploration of space. 1960. 5.95. Macmillan

Posin, Daniel Q. Out of this world. il. 1959. 3.95. Hawthorn

Ramo, Simon. Peacetime uses of outer space. il. 1961. 6.95. McGraw

OUTLAWS (923.41)

Adams, Ramon F. Six-guns and saddle leather: Bibliography of books and pamphlets on western outlaws and gunmen. il. 1954. 12.50. U. of Okla.

Hendricks, George. Bad man of the West. 5.00. Naylor

Horan, James D., and Paul Sann. Pictorial history of the wild West. il. 1954. 5.95. Crown

Keen, Maurice. Outlaws of medieval legend. il. 1961. 4.50. U. of Toronto

Kelly, Charles. Outlaw trail. 1958. 6.00. Devin

OVID (883)
Brewer, Wilmon. Ovid's Metamorphoses in European culture. 3 vols. 1.50 ea.
Jones, Marshall
Deferrari, R. J., and others. Concordance of Ovid. 1939. 20.00. Catholic U. of
Am. Pr. (R)
Frankel, Hermann. Ovid: A poet between two worlds. 1956. 5.00. U. of Calif.
Wilkinson, L. P. Ovid recalled. 1955. 7.50. Cambridge U. P.
OYSTERS (594.1)
Bolitho, Hecotr. Glorious oyster. il. 1961. 4.50. Horizon
Yonge, Charles M. Oysters. il. 1960. 4.50. Macmillan

P

PACIFIC OCEAN (990)
Danielsson, Bengt. From raft to raft. il. 1960. 4.50. Doubleday
Freeman, Otis W. Geography of the Pacific. 1951. 8.95. Wiley'
Grier, Mary C. Oceanography of the North Pacific Ocean, Bering Sea and Bering
Strait. 1941. 4.00. U. of Wash.
Hardy, V. O., and G. S. Dumke. History of the Pacific area in modern times.
1949. 7.50. Houghton
Heyerdahl, Thor. Kon-Tiki. 1950. 5.95. Rand McNally
Marshall, James S. and Carrie. Pacific voyages. 1960. 4.50. Binfords
Rakestraw, Norris W., and others. Oceanic observations of the Pacific. 2 vols.
1960. set 10.00. U. of Calif.
Rydell, Raymond A. Cape Horn to the Pacific: The rise and decline of an ocean
highway. 1952. 4.00. U. of Calif.
Willis, William. Gods were kind. il. 1955. 4.00. Dutton
Wood, Gordon L., and Patricia R. McBride. Pacific basin: A human and economic
geography. il. 1955. 2.05. Oxford U. P.
PACKAGING (658.7884)
American Management Association. Packaging for profits. 1960. 3.00. Am.
Management Assn.
Brown, Kenneth. Package design engineering. il. 1959. 8.50. Wiley
Cheskin, Louis. How to predict what people will buy. by Van Allan Bradley. 5.00.
Liveright
Fladager, Vernon L. Selling power of packaging. 1956. 4.00. McGraw
Friedman, Walter F., and Jerome J. Kipnees. Industrial packaging. il. 1960.
11.50. Wiley
Herdeg, Walter. Graphis packaging. il. 1960. 17.50. Praeger
Sutnar, Ladislav. Package design: The force of visual selling. il. 9.75. Arts
PAGANINI, NICCOLO, 1782-1840 (927)
Courcy, Geraldine I. C. de., Paganini, the Genoese. 2 vols. 1957. 12.50. Okla.
PAIN (152.5)
Bonica, John J. Management of pain. il. 1953. 20.00. Lea & F
Buytendijk, Frederik J. J. Pain, its modes and functions. tr. by Eda O'Shiel.
1962. 3.95. U. of Chicago
Ciba Foundation Study Groups. Pain and itch: Nervous mechanisms. 1959. 2.50.
Little
Seeman, Bernard. Man against pain: 3,000 years of effort to understand and
relieve physical suffering. 1962. 3.95. Chilton
Smith, Lucian A., and others. Atlas of pain patterns. il. 1961. 12.50. Thomas,
C. C.
Szasz, Thomas S. Pain and pleasure. 1957. 5.50. Basic Books
White, James C., and William H. Sweet. Pain: Its mechanisms and neurosurgical
control. il. 1955. 17.50. Thomas, C. C.
PAINE, THOMAS, 1737-1809 (923.2)
Aldredge, Alfred Owen. Man of reason: The life of Thomas Paine. 1959. 6.00.
Lippincott

Foner, Philip S.   Life and major writings of Thomas Paine. 1961. pap. 2.45.
Citadel
McKown, Robin.   Thomas Paine. 1962. 2.95. Putnam
Woodward, William E.   Tom Paine, America's godfather. il. 1945. 5.00. Dutton
PAINTERS (927.5)
Alloway, L.   Nine abstract artists. il. 1955. 2.75. Transatlantic
Baur, John I. H., and others.   New art in America. 1957. 22.50. N. Y. Graphic
Berenson, Bernard.   Italian painters of the Renaissance. 1959. 6.25. Oxford U. P.
Berenson, Bernhard.   Italian pictures of the Renaissance: The Venetian school.
2 vols. il. 1957. 20.00. N. Y. Graphic
Bizardel, Yvon.   American painters in Paris. 1960. 5.95. Macmillan
Craven, Thomas.   Treasury of art masterpieces. il. 1952. 12.50. S. and S.
Digeon, Aurelien.   English school of painting. il. 1959. 10.00. Universe
DuPont, Jacques, and Francois Mathey.   17th century: From Caravaggio to
Vermeer. il. 1951. 15.00. World Pub.
Frankenstein, Alfred.   After the hunt: William Harnett and other American still-
life painters, 1870-1900. il. 1953. 10.00. U. of Calif.
Genaille, Robert.   From Van Eyck to Brueghel. il. 1959. 10.00. Universe
Georges-Michel.   From Renoir to Picasso. il. 1957. pap. 2.50. Houghton
Godfrey, F. M.   Early Venetian painters, 1415-1495. il. 1955. 2.25. Transatlantic
Godfrey, F. M.   Student's guide to early Italian painting, 1250-1500. il. 5.75.
Transatlantic
Godfrey, Frederick M.   Student's guide to later Italian painting. 1500-1800. il.
1959. 5.75. Transatlantic
Goncourt, Edmond de, and Jules.   French eighteenth century painters. 2.95.
N. Y. Graphic
Haftmann, Werner.   Painting in the twentieth century. 2 vols. il. 42.50. Praeger
Hanson, Lawrence, and Elizabeth.   Impressionism: Golden decade. il. 1961. 5.00.
Holt, Rinehart & Winston
Heath, Adrian.   Abstract painting, its origins and meaning. il. 1953. 2.00.
Transatlantic
Johnson, Una E., and John Gordon.   Fourteen painter-printmakers. il. 1955. pap.
0.50. Brooklyn Mus.
Keller, Hiltgart, and Bodo Cichy.   Twenty centuries of great European painting.
il. 1960. 12.95. Sterling
Kent, Norman.   Seascapes and landscapes in watercolor. 7.50. Watson
Leymarie, Jean.   Impressionism. 2 vols. il. 1955. 6.50 ea. World Pub.
M. and M.   Karolik collection of American paintings, 1815-1865. 1951. 12.50.
Harvard
McKinney, Roland J.   Famous old masters of painting. 1951. 3.00. Dodd
McKinney, Roland J.   Famous American painters. il. 1955. 3.00. Dodd
Monro, Isabel S., and Kate.   Index to reproductions of American paintings. 1948.
8.50. Wilson
Myers, Bernard.   Encyclopedia of painting. il. 1955. 12.95. Crown (R)
Myers, Bernard S.   German expressionists. il. 1959. 17.50. Praeger
Nacenta, Raymond.   School of Paris. il. 1960. 25.00. N. Y. Graphic
Ottino della Chiesa, Angela.   Botticelli and his contemporaries. il. 1959. 7.95.
Crown
Raynal, Maurice.   Modern painting. il. 1956. 27.50. World Pub.
Raynal, Maurice.   19th century: From Goya to Gauguin. il. 1952. 15.00. World Pub.
Rewald, John.   Post-impressionism from Van Gogh to Gauguin. il. 1958. 20.00.
Doubleday
Ritchie, Andrew Carnduff.   Masters of British painting. 1800-1950. il. 1958. 5.50.
Doubleday
Seuphor, M.   Dictionary of abstract painting. il. 1957. 7.95. Tudor (R)
Thomas, Henry, and Dana Lee.   Living biographies of great painters. 1959. 2.50.
Doubleday
Tinker, Chauncey Brewster.   Painter and poet: Studies in the literary relationship
of English painting. il. 1938. 3.50. Harvard

Venturi, Lionello. Italian painters of today. il. 1959. 30.00. Universe
Venturi, Lionello, and Rosabianca Skira-Venturi. Italian painting. 3 vols. From
   Caravaggie to Modigliani. il. 1950. 1952. 17.50 ea. World Pub.
Wilenski, R. H. Flemish painters. 2 vols. il. 1960. 37.50. Viking
PAINTING (750)
Barr, Alfred H., Jr. What is modern painting? il. 1958. pap. 1.25. Doubleday
Belloni, G. Guido. Art of the western world: Prehistoric to classical painting.
   il. 1962. 5.00. Golden Press
Bethers, Ray. Art always changes: How to understand modern painting. 1958.
   4.50. Hastings
Bihalji-Merin, Oto. Modern primitives: Masters of naive painting. 1961. 15.00.
   Abrams
Blanshard, F. B. Retreat from likeness in the theory of painting. 1949. 4.50.
   Columbia
Fernau, Joachim. Encyclopedia of old masters. il. 6.75. Boston Bk. (R)
Freedman, Leonard. Looking at modern painting. il. 1961. 10.00. Norton
Friedlander, Max J. Landscape, portrait, still life. il. 6.00. Boston Bk.
Garland, Hamlin. Crumbling idols. by Jane Johnson. 1960. 3.50. Harvard
Hazan, F. Dictionary of modern painting. 7.95. Tudor (R)
Heath, Adrian. Abstract painting, its origins and meaning. il. 1953. 2.00.
   Transatlantic
Hulton, Nika. First steps in art appreciation. 1958. 3.75. Pitman
Huyghe, Rene. Ideas and images in world art: Dialogue with the visible. il. 1959.
   15.00. Abrams
Johnson, Charles. Language of painting. il. 1949. 3.50. Cambridge U. P.
Leepa, Allen. Challenge of modern art. 1957. 3.95. Yoseloff
Leonardo da Vinci. Genius of Leonardo da Vinci. by Andre Chastel. il. 1961.
   12.50. Orion
Merrifield, Mary P. Ancient art of painting. 2 vols. 1962. pap. 4.00. Dover
Myers, Bernard. Encyclopedia of painting. il. 1955. 12.95. Crown (R)
Rathbun, Mary C., and Bartlett H. Hayes, Jr. Layman's guide to modern art.
   1954. 2.75. Addison Gallery
Raynal, Maurice. Modern painting. il. 1956. in English or French. 27.50. World
   Pub.
Read, Herbert. Letter to a young painter. il. 1962. 5.75. Horizon
Seuphor, M. Dictionary of abstract painting. il. 1957. 7.95. Tudor (R)
Vasari, Giorgio. Vasari on technique. by B. Baldwin Brown. il. 4.00. Smith,
   Peter
PAINTING--HISTORY (759)
Barnes, Albert C. Art in painting. il. 6.95. Harcourt
Brill, Reginald. Modern painting. il. 1946. 3.00. Transatlantic
Diehl, Gaston. Moderns. il. 1961. 12.50. Crown
DuPont, Jacques, and Francois Mathey. 17th century: From Caravaggio to Vermeer.
   il. 1951. 15.00. World Pub.
Fosca, Francois. 18th century: From Watteau to Tiepolo. il. 1952. 15.00. World
   Pub.
Gaunt, William. History of painting. vols. 1-10. 30.00. Roy Pub.
Janson, Horst W. Picture history of painting. il. 1957. 15.00. Abrams
Levey, Michael. Concise history of painting from Giotto to Cezanne. il. 1962.
   7.50. Praeger
Maillard, Robert. History of painting in 1,000 color reproductions. il. 1961. 10.00.
   Tudor
Myers, Bernard S. Modern art in the making. il. 1959. 10.95. McGraw
Newmeyer, Sarah. Enjoying modern art. 1955. 2.50. Reinhold
Ponente, Nello. Modern painting: Contemporary trends. il. 1960. 27.50. World
   Pub.
Raynal, Maurice. 19th century: From Goya to Gauguin. il. 1952. 15.00. World
   Pub.

Read, Herbert E. Concise history of modern painting. il. 1959. 7.50. Praeger
Robb, David M., and J. J. Garrison. Art in the western world. il. 1953. 8.50.
  Harper
Robb, David M. Harper history of painting. il. 1951. 13.50. Harper
PAINTING--TECHNIQUE (751.4)
Abels, Alexander. Painting, methods and materials. 1959. pap. 1.00. Pitman
Bazzi, Maria. Artist's methods and materials. il. 1960. 6.00. Pitman
Birren, Faber. Creative color. il. 1961. 10.00. Reinhold
Brooks, Leonard. Oil painting, traditional and new. 1959. 7.95. Reinhold
Brooks, L. Watercolor: A challenge. 1957. 12.50. Reinhold
Carlson, Charles X. Color mixing. pap. 1.50. Sentinel
Carver, Michael. Painting in oil by the 5-color method. il. 1961. 8.95. McGraw
Chang, Shu-Chi, and Helen. Painting in the Chinese manner. il. 1960. 7.50.
  Viking
Clifton, Jack. Manual of drawing and painting. 5.95. Watson
Doener, Max. Materials of the artist. il. 1949. 5.75. Harcourt
Doust, Leonard A. Oil painting. il. 1960. 2.00. Warne
Fabry, Alois. Oil painting is fun. il. 1957. 3.75. Viking
Fitzgerald, and Edmund J. Painting and drawing in charcoal and oil. 1959. 4.95.
  Reinhold
Franklin-White, E. Beginner's book of oil painting. 1962. 2.95. Reinhold
Gasser, Henry. Oil painting: Methods and demonstrations. 1953. 10.00. Reinhold
Gasser, Henry M. Techniques of painting. il. 1958. 6.95. Reinhold
Guptill, Arthur L. Oil painting. step-by-step. 1953. 6.95. Watson
Herberts, Kurt. Complete book of artist's techniques. il. 1958. 15.00. Praeger
Hill, Adrian. Sketching and painting indoors. 1961. 2.75. Pitman
Itten, Johannes. Art of color. il. 1961. 30.00. Reinhold
Kerr, Alfred. Anyone can paint pictures. il. 1960. bds. 3.95. Pitman
Laidman, Hugh. How to make abstract paintings. il. 1961. 6.50. Viking
Lamb, Lynton. Preparation for painting. 1954. 3.40. Oxford U. P.
Leith-Ross, Harry. Landscape painter's manual. 1956. 4.95. Watson
Mayer, Ralph. Artist's handbook of materials and techniques. il. 1957. 6.75.
  Viking (R)
Mayer, Ralph. Painter's craft. il. 1948. 6.00. Van Nostrand
Mills, John. Oil painting. 1962. 3.95. Pitman
Nicholls, Bertram. Painting in oils. il. 1959. 6.00. Viking
Richmond, Leonard. Technique of oil painting. 1945. 10.95. Pitman
Taubes, Frederic. Amateur painter's handbook. il. 5.00. Dodd
Taubes, Frederic. New techniques in painting. il. 1962. 4.50. Dodd
Taubes, Frederic. Oil and tempera painting. 3.75. Watson
Taubes, Frederic. Oil painting for the beginner. 1944. 6.00. Watson
Taubes, Frederic. Quickest way to paint well. il. 1950. 4.95. Viking
Taubes, Frederic. Technique of oil painting. il. 1946. 3.75. Dodd
Zaidenberg, Arthur. Seeing with pencil and brush. il. 1962. 4.95. Harper
PAINTING, AMERICAN (750.973)
Barker, Virgil. American painting. 12.50. Macmillan
Barker, Virgil. From realism to reality in recent American painting. 1959. 4.00.
  U. of Nebr.
Contemporary American painting and sculpture. 3 vols: 1955; 1957; 1961. 3.50.
  ea. U. of Ill.
Eliot, Alexander, and Editors of Time. Three hundred years of American painting.
  1957. 13.50. Random
PAINTING, CHINESE (750)
Cahill, James. Chinese painting. il. 1960. 27.50. World Pub.
Lee, Sherman E. Chinese landscape painting. il. 1962. 7.50. Abrams
Rowley, G. Principles of Chinese painting. 1959. 7.50. Princeton
PAINTING, EUROPEAN (750)
Brion, Marcel. German painting. il. 1960. 10.00. Universe

Chiarelli, Reno, and others. European painting in the 15th century. il. 1961. 25.00. Viking

Dorival, Bernard. Twentieth century painters: vol. 1, Nabis, Fauves, Cubists. 1958. 10.00; vol. 2, From Cubism to abstract art. 1958. 10.00. Universe

Espezel, Pierre d', and Francois Fosca. Concise illustrated history of painting. il. 1961. pap. 0.90. Washington Square

Fosca, Francois. 19th century painters. 1960. 10.00. Universe

Friedlander, Max J. From Van Eyck to Bruegel. il. 1956. 8.50. N. Y. Graphic

Friedlaender, Walter. David to Delacroix. il. 1952. 6.00. Harvard

Lassaigne, Jacques, and Guilio C. Argan. 15th century: From Van Eyck to Botticelli. il. 1955. 20.00. World Pub.

Lassaigne, Jacques. Flemish painting. vol. 1. Century of Van Eyck. il. 1957. 25.00. World Pub.

Lassaigne, Jacques, and Robert Delevoy. Flemish painting. vol. 2, from Bosch to Rubens. il. 1958. 25.00. World Pub.

Leymarie, Jean. French painting. il. 1962. 29.50. World Pub.

Pesina, J. Painting of the Gothic and Renaissance periods. il. 1960. 12.60. Vanous

Selz, Peter Howard. German expressionist painting. il. 1957. 18.50. U. of Calif.

Serullaz, Maurice. Impressionist painters. 1960. 10.00. Universe

Sterling, Charles. Great French painting in the Hermitage. il. 1958. 25.00. Abrams

Wilenski, R. French painting. 8.50. Branford

PAINTING, GOTHIC (709.02)

Bunt, Cyril C. G. Gothic painting. il. 3.00. Transatlantic

DuPont, J., and Cesare Gnudi. Gothic painting. il. 1954. 20.00. World Pub.

PAINTING, ITALIAN (750)

DeWald, Ernest T. Italian painting: 1200-1600. 1961. 13.90. Holt, Rinehart & Winston

Francastel, Galienne. From the Byzantine masters to the Renaissance. il. 1959. 10.00. Universe

Gould, Cecil. Introduction to Italian Renaissance painting. il. 1957. 7.50. N. Y. Graphic

Levey, Michael. Painting in eighteenth century Venice. il. 1959. 6.50. N. Y. Graphic

Mather, Frank Jewett, Jr. History of Italian painting. il. 1923. 8.65. Holt, Rinehart & Winston

Meiss, M. Painting in Florence and Siena after the Black Death. 1951. 12.50. Princeton

Valsecchi, Marco. Art of the western world: Venetian painting. il. 1962. 5.00. Golden Press

PAINTINGS (750.759)

Clark, Kenneth. Looking at pictures. il. 1960. 10.00. Holt, Rinehart & Winston

Cogniat, Raymond. Century of the impressionists. 1960. 12.50. Crown

Craven, Thomas. Treasury of art masterpieces. il. 1952. 12.50. S. and S.

Freedman, Leonard. Looking at modern painting. il. 1961. 10.00. Norton

Great masterpieces. il. portfolio ed. 1.95. Abrams

Haftmann, Werner. Painting in the twentieth century. 2 vols. il. 1961. 42.50. Praeger (R)

Lassaigne, Jacques. Spanish painting. 2 vols. vol. 1. From the Catalan Frescos to El Greco; vol. 2. From Velazquez to Picasso. il. 1952. 17.50. ea. World Pub.

Monro, Isabel S., and Kate. Index to reproductions of American paintings. 1948. 8.50. Wilson

Monro, Isabel S., and Kate. Index to reproduction of European paintings. 1956. 12.50. Wilson

PAINTINGS, EUROPEAN (750.759)

Apollonio, Umbro. Fauves and cubists. il. 1959. 7.95. Crown

Bazin, Germain. Louvre: Masterpieces of Italian painting. il. 1956. 20.00. N. Y. Graphic

Davies, Martin. French school. il. 1957. 15.00. Abrams
Dell'Acqua, G. A. French impressionists. il. 1958. 7.95. Crown
Fosca, Francois. 19th century painters. 1960. 10.00. Universe
Keller, Hiltgart, and Bodo Cichy. Twenty centuries of great European painting.
    il. 1960. 12.95. Sterling
Maiuri, Amedeo, and Lionello Venturi. Painting in Italy. il. 1959. 20.00. World
    Pub.
MacLaren, Neil, comp. Dutch school, 17th to 19th century. 2 vols. il. 1958. 45.00.
    Abrams
Standen, Edith. Italian painting. il. 1956. 20.00. N. Y. Graphic
Wilenski, R. H. Flemish painters. 2 vols. il. 1960. 37.50. Viking
PAKISTAN (954.7)
Andrus, J. Russell, and Azizali F. Mohammed. Economy of Pakistan. 8.50.
    Stanford
Binder, Leonard. Religion and politics in Pakistan. 1961. 7.50. U. of Calif.
Brown, W. Norman. United States and India and Pakistan. 1953. 5.00. Harvard
Callard, Keith B., and others. Major governments of Asia. il. 1958. 7.25.
    Cornell
Husain, A. F. A. Human and social impact of technological change in Pakistan.
    2 vols. 1956. 2.65. Oxford U. P.
Ikram, A. M., and Percival Spear. Cultural heritage of Pakistan. 1955. 4.00.
    Oxford U. P.
Linck, Orville F. Passage through Pakistan. il. 1960. 5.95. Wayne
Tinker, Hugh. Politics of India and Pakistan. 1962. 4.50. Praeger
PALEOBOTANY (561)
Andrews, Henry N., Jr. Studies in paleobotany. il. 1961. 9.95. Wiley
Darrah, William C. Principles of paleobotany. il. 1960. 6.50. Ronald
Scott, Dukinfield H. Studies in fossil botany. 2 vols. il. 14.50. Hafner
PALEONTOLOGY (560)
Augusta, Josef, and Zdenek Burian. Prehistoric animals. il. 7.95. Tudor
Baker, Frank Collins. Life of the pleistocene. il. 1920. 5.00. U. of Ill.
Beerbower, James R. Search for the past: An introduction to paleontology.
    10.60. Prentice-Hall
Berckhemer, Fritz. Language of rocks. 4.50. Ungar
Bodenheimer, F. S. Animal and man in Bible lands. 1960. 11.50. Humanities
Carrington, Richard. Story of our earth. il. 1956, 3.50. Harper
Clark, Thomas H., and Colin W. Stearn. Geological evolution of North America.
    il. 1960. 7.50. Ronald
Clements, Thomas. Historical geology. 1.35. Lucas Bros.
Fenton, Carroll L., and Mildred A. Fossil book, a record of prehistoric life.
    il. 1958. 15.00. Doubleday
Hussey, Russell C. Historical geology. 1947. 7.50. McGraw
Huxley, Julian S. Wonderful world of life. il. 1958. 2.95. Doubleday
Kummel, Bernhard. History of the earth: An introduction to historical geology.
    il. 1961. 8.75. Freeman
Ley, Willy. Exotic zoology. il. 1959. 4.95. Viking
Simpson, George G. Life of the past: An introduction to paleontology. 1953. 6.00.
    Yale
Stirton, Ruben A. Time, life and man: The fossil record. il. 1959. 8.00. Wiley
Watson, D. M. S. Paleontology and modern biology. 1951. 4.00. Yale
PALESTINE (956.94)
Albright, William F. Archaelogy of Palestine. 3.00. Smith, Peter
Anati, Emmanuel. Palestine before the Hebrews. il. 1962. 8.95. Knopf
Baily, Albert E. Daily life in Bible times. il. 4.50. Scribner
Bouquet, A. C. Everyday life in New Testament times. 1954. 4.50. Scribner
Holley, Jasper E., and Carolyn F. Pictorial profile of the Holy Land. il. 1959.
    5.95. Revell
Morton, Henry C., and Fulton J. Sheen. This is the Holy Land: A pilgrimage in
    words and pictures. il. 1961. 4.95. Hawthorn

Nathan, Robert R., and others. Palestine: Problem and promise. 1946. 5.00. Pub. Affairs

Parkes, James. History of Palestine from 135 A.D. to modern times. 6.00. Oxford U. P.

Sharef, Zeev. Three days. 4.95. Doubleday

PANAMA (986.2)

Biesanz, John, and Mavis. People of Panama. 1955. 6.75. Columbia

Harding, Earl. Untold story of Panama. 6.00. Bookmailer

PAPACY (262.13)

Burn, Murdoch, H. Development of the Papacy. 8.50. Humanities

Brezzi, Paolo. Papacy: Its origins and historical evolution. 1958. 3.50. Newman

PAPER MAKING AND TRADE (676)

Adams, W. Calude. History of papermaking in the Pacific Northwest. 2.50. Binfords

Hardman, H., and E. J. Cole. Paper-making practice. il. 1960. 7.50. U. of Toronto

Hunter, Dard. Papermaking: The history and technique of an ancient craft. il. 1947 17.50. Knopf

Sutermeister, Edwin. Story of papermaking. 1954. 6.00. Bowker

PAPER WORK (793)

Adams, Ruth J. Kindergarten how-to-do-it book. il. 1962. 4.95. Denison

Ellis, Mary J. Creative handwork ideas. il. 1958. 3.50. Denison

Harrower, Dorothy. Decoupage: A limitless world in decoration. il. 1958. 10.00. Barrows

Rottger, Ernst. Creative paper design. il. 1959. 4.00. Reinhold

Severn, Bill. Magic with paper. il. 1962. 3.50. McKay

PARAGUAY (989.2)

Pendle, George. Paraguay. 1956. 2.40. Oxford U. P.

Raine, P. Paraguay. 1956. 8.50. Scarecrow

Warren, Harris G. Paraguay: An informal history. il. 1949. 5.00. U. of Okla.

PARASITES (616.961)

Baer, Jean G. Ecology of animal parasites. il. 1951. 5.00. U. of Ill.

Dogiel, V. A., and others. Parasitology of fishes. 1962. 17.50. Plenum

Levine, Norman D. Protozoan parasites of domestic animals and of man. il. 1961. 6.50. Burgess

Riley, William A., and Franklin G. Wallace. Introduction to the study of animal parasites and parasitism. 1959. 3.50. Burgess

Rogers, W. P. Nature of parasitism. 1962. 7.50. Academic Press

Rothschild, Miriam, and Theresa Clay. Fleas, flukes and cuckoos: A study of bird parasites. il. 5.95. Macmillan

Whitlock, John H. Diagnosis of veterinary parasitisms. il. 1960. 10.00. Lea & F

PARENT AND CHILD (136.7)

Andry, Robert G. Delinquency and parental pathology. il. 1960. 5.50. Thomas, C.C.

Armstrong, William H. 87 ways to help your child in school. il. 1961. 4.00. Barron's

Bandura, Albert, and Richard H. Walters. Adolescent agression. il. 1959. 7.50. Ronald

Bley, Edgar S. Have fun with your son. il. 1954. 2.50. Sterling

Buhler, Charlotte. Child and his family. 3.00. Humanities

Clark, Ann L. Leadership technique in expectant parent education. il. 1962. flexible bdg. 3.00. Springer

Egleson, Jim, and Janet Frank. Parents without partners. 1961. 4.50. Dutton

Gildewell, John C. Parental attitudes and child behavior. il. 1961. 8.50. Thomas, C. C.

Harris, Irving D. Normal children and mothers. 1958. 6.00. Free Press

Jameson, Marshall C. Helping your child succeed in elementary school. 1962. 3.50. Putnam

Kirk, Samuel A., and others. You and your retarded child. 1955. 4.95. Macmillan

Leonard, Edith M., and others. Counseling with parents. 1954. 4.75. Macmillan
Meek, Lois H. Preschool and parental education. NSSE, 28th yrbk. 5.00. U. of
Chicago
Post, Emily. Children are people. il. 1959. 3.50. Funk
Reich, Hanns. Children and their fathers. 1962. 3.50. Hill & Wang
Skala, John J. Dad and his teenagers. 1961. 2.00. Daughters of St. Paul
Strecker, Edward A., and Vincent T. Lathbury. Their mothers' daughters. 1956.
3.75. Lippincott
Thomas, R. C. Mother-daughter relationships and social behavior. 1955. 6.00.
Catholic U. of Am. Pr.
Weinstein, Edwin A. Cultural aspects of delusion. il. 1962. 5.00. Free Press
PARIS (944.36)
Barry, Joseph A. Left bank, right bank. 1951. 4.50. Norton
Ehrlich, Blake. Paris on the Seine. il. 1962. 12.50. Atheneum
Holmes, Urban T., Jr. Daily living in the Twelfth Century: Based on the obser-
vations of Alexander Neckam in London and Paris. il. 1952. 3.85. U. of Wis.
James, Henry. Parisian sketches. 1957. 5.00. N. Y. U.
Lacretelle, Jacques de. Paris. 1958. 6.50. Hastings
Life, Life guide to Paris. il. 1962. 4.95. Meredith
Muirhead, Russell. Blue guide to Paris. 3.95. Rand McNally
Otto-Wasow, Kurt. Paris. il. 1959. 5.95. Viking
PARIS, TREATY OF, 1783 (973.3)
Bemis, Samuel F. Diplomacy of the American Revolution. 1957. 3.75. Smith,
Peter
PARIS PEACE CONFERENCE, 1919 (973.9)
Baker, R. S. Woodrow Wilson and the world settlement. 3 vols. il. 1958. 20.00.
Smith, Peter
Birdsall, Paul. Versailles twenty years after. 1941. 8.50. Shoe String
PARLIAMENTARY PRACTICE (328.1)
Bridge, Lawrence W. Funk and Wagnalls' book of parliamentary procedure. 1954.
3.50. Funk
Robert, Henry M. Robert's rules of order. 1956. 3.00. Scott (R)
Sturgis, Alice F. Sturgis' standard code of parliamentary procedure. 1950. 5.95.
McGraw (R)
PARTICLES (NUCLEAR PHYSICS) (539.721)
Fermi, E. Elementary particles. 1951. 3.00. Yale
McConnell, James. Quantum particle dynamics. il. 1960. 6.50. Wiley
Williams, William S. C. Introduction to elementary particles. il. 1961. 11.00.
Academic Press
PARTNERSHIP (338.73)
Crane, J. A., and C. Magruder. Cases on the law of partnership and other
unincorporated business associations. 1951. 9.00. Bobbs
Frey, Alexander H. Cases and materials on corporations and partnerships. 1951.
9.75. Little
PASCAL, BLAISE, 1623-1662 (925)
Cailliet, Emile. Pascal, the emergence of genius. 3.85. Smith, Peter
Robert, James D. Faith and reason: A comparative study of Pascal, Bergson
and James. 1962. 3.00. Christopher
PASTERNAK, BORIS LEONIDOVICH, 1890-1960 (928)
Payne, Robert. Three worlds of Boris Pasternak. il. 4.50. Coward
PASTEUR, LOUIS, 1822-1895 (925)
Conant, James Bryant. Pasteur's and Tyndall's study of spontaneous generation.
1953. pap. 1.25. Harvard
Dolan, Edward F., Jr. Pasteur and the invisible giants. 1958. 3.00. Dodd
Dubos, Rene J. Louis Pasteur, free lance of science. il. 1950. 6.00. Little
Grant, M. Louis Pasteur: Fighting hero of science. 1959. 3.25. McGraw
Vallery-Radot, Pasteur. Louis Pasteur. 1958. 3.00. Knopf
PASTORAL COUNSELING (253.5)
Bier, W. C. Clergy and the teenager. 1962. 5.00. Fordham

Cavanagh, John R. Fundamental pastoral counseling. 1962. 6.00. Bruce
Hiltner, Seward, and Lowell G. Colston. Context of pastoral counseling. 1961. 4.50.
  Abingdon
Hulme, William E. Counseling and theology. 1956. 3.75. Muhlenberg
Moser, Leslie E. Counseling: A modern emphasis in religion. 1962. bds. 6.50.
  Prentice-Hall
PASTORAL THEOLOGY (250)
Fosdick, Harry Emerson. Book of public prayers. 1959. 3.00. Harper
Glover, Carl A. Prayers for Christian services. 1959. 2.25. Abingdon
Hofmann, Hans. Religion and mental health. 1961. 5.00. Harper
Jowett, John Henry. Preacher: His life and work. 1912. 2.50. Harper
Oglesby, Stuart R. Prayers for all occasions. 1940. 1.50. John Knox'
Stamm, Frederick Keller. So you want to preach. 1958. 2.00. Abingdon
Walker, Daniel D. Human problems of the minister. 1960. 3.95. Harper
Wise, Carroll A. Pastoral counseling: Its theory and practice. 1951. 2.75. Harper
PASTRY (641.631)
Amendola, Joseph. Bakers' manual. il. 1960. 6.00. Ahrens
D'Ermo, Dominique. Modern pastry chef's guide to professional baking. 1962.
  10.00. Harper (R)
PASTURES (636)
Pasture and range research techniques. il. 1962. 5.00. Cornell
PATENTS (608.7)
Amdur, Leon H. Patent fundamentals. 1959. 6.00. Boardman, Clark
Berle, Alf K., and L. Sprague de Camp. Inventions, patents and their manage-
  ment. 1959. 12.50. Van Nostrand
Brink, R. E., and others. Outline of United States patent law. 1959. 7.50. Wiley
Buckles, R. A. Ideas, inventions and patents. 1957. 5.95. Wiley
Diggins, Bartholomew, and Robert E. LeBlanc. What the businessman should
  know about patents and trademarks. 1958. pap. 1.00. Pub. Affairs
Naimark, George M. Patent manual for scientists and engineers. 1961. 5.50.
  Thomas, C. C.
Woodling, George A. Inventions and their protection. 1955. 10.00. Boardman,
  Clark
Yates, Raymond F. Yates' guide to successful inventing. 2.95. Funk
PATHOLOGY (616.07)
Anderson, William A. D. Pathology. il. 1961. 18.00. Mosby
Baker, Roger D. Essential pathology. 9.50. Williams & Wilkins
Cameron, Gordon R. Pathology of the cell. il. 1952. 22.50. Thomas, C. C.
Foster, William D. Short history of clinical pathology. il. 1962. 6.50. Williams
  & Wilkins
Goodale, Raymond H. Nursing pathology. il. 1956. 4.50. Saunders
Harrison, C. V. Recent advances in pathology. 1961. 12.00. Little
Manhold, John H., Jr., and Theodore E. Bolden. Outline of pathology. 1960. 4.75.
  Saunders
Muir, Ernest. Muir's textbook of pathology. il. 1958. 14.50. Williams & Wilkins
Perez-Tamayo, Ruy. Dynamics of disease. il. 1961. 14.00. Saunders
Virchow, Rudolf L. K. Disease, life, and man. 1958. 5.00. Stanford
Yardumian, Krikor Y. Illustrated outline of general pathology. il. 1960. 5.00. U.
  of Pittsburgh
PATRIOTISM (320.158)
Curti, Merle. Roots of American loyalty. 3.00. Brown Book
Davies, W. E. Patriotism on parade: The story of veterans' and hereditary
  organizations in America, 1783-1900. 1956. 6.00. Harvard
Grodzins, Morton. Loyal and the disloyal. 1956. 4.00. U. of Chicago
Morray, Joseph P. Pride of state, a study in patriotism and American national
  morality. 1959. 4.00. Beacon
PATTON, GEORGE SMITH, 1885-1945 (923.5)
Codman, Charles R. Drive. il. 1957. 5.00. Little

Wallace, Brenton G. Patton and his third army. il. 1951. 3.50. Stackpole

PAUL, SAINT, APOSTLE (922.22)

Baird, William. Paul's message and mission. 1960. 3.00. Abingdon

Beare, Frank W. St. Paul and his letters. 1962. 2.75. Abingdon

Conybeare, W. J., and J. S. Howson. Life and Epistles of St. Paul. 1949. 5.00. Eerdmans

Deissmann, Adolph. Paul, a study in social and religious history. tr. by William E. Wilson. 1958. 3.50. Smith, Peter

Ellis, E. Earle. Paul's use of the Old Testament. 1961. 3.75. Eerdmans

Goodspeed, Edgar J. Paul, a biography. 1947. 2.75. Winston

O'Brien, Isidore. Peter and Paul, apostles. 1950. 3.50. St. Anthony

Schweitzer, Albert. Paul and his interpreters. 4.50. Macmillan

PAVLOV, IVAN PETROVICH, 1849-1936 (925)

Babkin, Boris P. Pavlov. 1949. 6.00. U. of Chicago

Wells, Harry K. Pavlov and Freud. 2 vols. 7.50. Int. Pubs.

PEACE (341.1)

Carnegie Endowment for International Peace. Perspectives on peace, 1910-1960. 1960. bds. 3.00. Praeger

Einstein, Albert. Einstein on peace. by Otto Nathan, and Heinz Norden. 1960. 8.50. S. and S.

Eisenhower, Dwight D. Peace with justice. 1961. 4.00. Columbia

Etzioni, Amitai. Hard way to peace. 1962. 3.95. Crowell-Collier

Hershberger, Guy F. War, peace, and nonresistance. 1953. 3.50. Herald

Horowitz, Irving L. Idea of war and peace in contemporary philosophy. 1957. 8.50. Paine-Whitman

Kennedy, John F. Strategy of peace. 1960. 3.50. Harper

McClelland, Charles A. Nuclear weapons, missiles, and future war: Problem for the sixties. 1960. pap. 1.75. Chandler Pub.

Malik, Charles H. Man and the struggle for peace. 1962. 3.75? Harper

May, M. A. Social psychology of war and peace. 1943. 3.50. Yale

Millis, Walter, and others. World without war. 1961. pap. 0.45. Washington Square

Nitchie, E., and others. Pens for ploughshares. 1930. 2.00. Faxon

Perkins, Dexter. America's quest for peace. 1961. 3.00. Indiana

Wright, Quincy, and others. Preventing world war III: Some proposals. 1962. 7.00. S. and S.

PEACE OF MIND (131.3)

Allen, Charles L. Twelve ways to solve your problem. 1961. 1.25. Revell

Gockel, Herman W. Answer to anxiety. 1961. 3.00. Concordia

Holmes, Ernest S., and Willis H. Kinnear. New design for living. 1959. 3.95. Prentice-Hall

Liebman, Joshua Loth. Peace of mind. 1946. 3.50. S. and S.

Peale, Norman Vincent. Amazing results of positive thinking. 1959. 3.95. Prentice-Hall

Tillich, Paul. Courage to be. 1952. 3.75. Yale

PEALE, NORMAN VINCENT (922)

Gordon, A. Norman Vincent Peale: Minister to millions. 1958. 4.95. Prentice-Hall

PEARL HARBOR, ATTACK ON, 1941 (940.5453)

Burtness, Paul S., and Warren U. Ober. Puzzle of Pearl Harbor. 1962. 2.25. Harper

Kimmel, Husband E. Admiral Kimmel's story. 1955. 3.75. Regnery

Lord, Walter. Day of infamy. il. 1957. 3.95. Holt

Morgenstern, George. Pearl Harbor, the story of the secret war. 3.50. Devin

Trefousse, H. L. What happened at Pearl Harbor? 6.00. Twayne

PEASANTRY (323.33)

Bennett, Henry Stanley. Life on the English manor. 1937. 5.50. Cambridge U. P.

Blum, J. Lord and peasant in Russia from the 9th to the 19th century. 1961. 12.50. Princeton

De Young, John E. Village life in modern Thailand. il. 1958. 5.50. U. of Calif.
Engels, Friedrich. Peasant War in Germany. 1926. 2.50. Int. Pubs.
Jacoby, Erich H. Agrarian unrest in Southeast Asia. il. 1961. 7.25. Taplinger
Maynard, John. Russia in flux. 1948. 6.95. Macmillan
Mitrany, David. Marx against the peasant. 1952. 4.50. U. Of N. C.
Redfield, Robert. Peasant society and culture: An anthropological approach to
    civilization. 1956. 3.75. U. of Chicago
Ruopp, Ph. Approaches to community development. 4.00. Lounz
Tawney, R. H. Agarian problem in the sixteenth century. 16.50. Franklin, B.
Taylor, Carl C. Rural life in Argentina. 1948. 6.00. La. State
Thomas, William I., and Florian Znaniecki. Polish peasant in Europe and
    America. 2 vols. 12.50. Dover
Treadgold, D. W. The great Siberian migration. 1957. 5.00. Princeton
Trouton, Ruth. Peasant renaissance in Yugoslavia, 1900-1950. il. 1952. 6.00.
    Humanities
Tumin, M. Caste in a peasant society. 1952. 5.00. Princeton
Vakar, Nicholas P. Taproot of soviet society. 1962. 4.75. Harper
Whetten, Nathan L. Rural Mexico. il. 1948. 11.50. U. of Chicago
Wunderlich, Frieda. Farmers and farm labor in the Soviet Zone in Germany. 4.00.
    Twayne

PEDIATRICS (618.92)

Apley, John, and Ronald MacKeith. Child and his symptoms. 1962. 4.50. Davis
Holt, L. Emmett, Jr., and others. Pediatrics. il. 1961. 18.00. Appleton
Nadas, Alexander S. Pediatric cardiology. il. 1957. 12.00. Saunders
Silver, Henry K., and others. Handbook of pediatrics. il. 1961. 3.50. Lange
Watkins, A. G. Pediatrics for nurses. il. 1958. 3.75. Williams & Wilkins

PEIRCE, CHARLES SANTIAGO SANDERS, 1839-1914 (925)

Feibleman, James K. Introduction to Peirce's philosophy. il. 1960. 7.00. Hauser
Moore, Edward C. American pragmatism. 1961. 6.00. Columbia
Murphey, Murray G. Development of Peirce's philosophy. il. 1961. 7.50. Harvard

PEKING (950)

Bodde, Derk. Peking diary: A year of revolution. il. 1950. 3.75. Abelard
Fleming, Peter. Siege at Peking: The Boxer Rebellion. il. 1959. 4.00. Harper
Lin, Yu-t'ang. Imperial Peking. il. 1961. 10.00. Crown

PENCIL AND PEN DRAWING (741.24)

Guptill, A. Pencil drawing step-by-step. 1959. 7.95. Reinhold
Guptill, Arthur L. Drawing with pen and ink. 1961. 8.95. Reinhold
Hobbis, Charles I. Pencil drawing for the architect. il. 1954. 2.25. Transatlantic
Kautzky, Theodore. Pencil broadsides. il. 1960. 5.50. Reinhold
Kautzky, Theodore. Pencil pictures. 1947. 5.50. Reinhold
Loomis, Andrew. Fun with a pencil. il. 1939. 4.00. Viking
Pitz, Henry C. Ink drawing techniques. 1951. 6.75. Watson
Pitz, Henry C. Sketching with the felt-tip pen. il. 1959. 2.95. Viking
Taubes, Frederic. Pen and ink drawing. 3.50. il. 1956. Watson
Watson, Ernest W. Gallery of pencil techniques. 1958. 3.50. Reinhold

PENGUINS (598.44)

Kearton, Cherry. Penguin Island. il. 1960. 3.50. Branford
Pettingill, Eleanor R. Penguin summer. il. 1961. 5.00. Potter, C. N.

PENN, WILLIAM, 1644-1718 (923.2)

Buranelli, Vincent. King and the Quaker. 1961. 5.00. U. of Pa.
Peare, Catherine Owens. William Penn. il. 1956. 6.00. Lippincott

PENNSYLVANIA (974.8)

Crevecoeur, Saint John de. Eighteenth-century travels in Pennsylvania and
    New York. il. 1961. 5.00. U. of Ky.
Dunaway, Wayland F. History of Pennsylvania. 1948. 9.35. Prentice-Hall
Mittelberger, Gottlieb. Journey to Pennsylvania. 1960. 3.00. Harvard
Pennsylvania: Guide to the keystone state. 6.50. Oxford U. P.

PEPYS, SAMUEL, 1633-1703 (923. 2)
Hunt, Percival. Samuel Pepys in the diary. 1958. 5. 00. U. of Pittsburgh
Wilson, John Harold. Private life of Mr. Pepys. 1959. 4.75. Farrar, Straus
PERCEPTION (152. 7)
Allport, F. H. Theories of perception and the concept of structure. 1955. 8. 50.
  Wiley
Armstrong, D. Perception and the physical world. 5. 00. Humanities
Blake, Robert R., and Glenn V. Ramsey. Perception: An approach to personality.
  1951. 7. 50. Ronald
Boring, Edwin G. Sensation and perception in the history of experimental psychology.
  il. 6. 50. Appleton
Brain, Russell. Nature of experience. 1959. 2. 00. Oxford U. P.
Dember, William N. Psychology of perception. il. 1960. 6. 50. Holt, Rinehart &
  Winston
Kohler, Wolfgang. Dynamics in psychology. 1940. 3. 00. Liveright
Luce, Arthur A. Sense without matter of direct perception. 3. 25. Nelson
Taylor, James G. Behavioral basis of perception. 1962. 8. 50. Yale
PERENNIALS (635. 932)
Cumming, Roderick W., and Robert E. Lee. Contemporary perennials. 1960.
  6. 95. Macmillan
Hottes. Alfred C. Book of perennials. il. 1950. 4. 00. Dodd
Perry, F. Complete guide to hardy perennials. 5. 75. Branford
PERIODICALS (050)
Colegrove, Harriet. Index to little magazines. 3 vols. 2. 50 ea. Swallow, A.
Farber, Evan Ira. Classified list of periodicals for the college library. 1957.
  5. 00. Faxon
Graves, Eileen C. Ulrich's periodicals directory. 1962. 22. 50. net postpaid.
  Bowker
Industrial arts index. consult H. W. Wilson
International index. 6 vols. 1928-1960. service basis. Wilson
Osborn, Andrew D. Serial publications. il. 1955. 6. 00. A. L. A.
Poole's index to periodical literature. 6 vols. 15. 00 ea. Smith, Peter
Readers' guide to periodical literature. 22 vols. 1900-1961. 20. 00 ea. Wilson (R)
World list of scientific periodicals. 1952. 37. 00. Academic Press (R)
PERSECUTION (272)
Foxe, John. Christian martyrs of the world. 3. 95. Moody
Foxe, John. Foxe's book of martyrs. 3. 00. Holt, Rinehart & Winston
Myers, Gustavus. History of bigotry in the U. S. 1943. 3. 50. Random
Riccoitti, Giuseppe. Age of martyrs. 1959. 4. 95. Bruce
PERSHING, JOHN JOSEPH, 1860-1948 (923. 5)
O'Connor, Richard. Black Jack Pershing. 4. 95. Doubleday
Palmer, Frederick. John J. Pershing: General of the Armies. 1948. 4. 50.
  Stackpole
PERSONALITY (137)
Adorno, T. W., and others. Authoritarian personality. 1950. 8. 75. Harper
Allport, Gordon W. Pattern and growth in personality. 1961. 7. 50. Holt, Rinehart
  & Winston
Allport, Gordon W. Personality and the social encounter. 1960. 7. 50. Beacon
Baughman, E. Earl, and George S. Welsh. Personality: A behavioral science.
  1962. 7. 25. Prentice-Hall
Blos, Peter. Adolescent personality. 4. 00. Appleton
Blum, G. S. Psychoanalytic theories of personality. 1953. 5. 95. McGraw
Bogardus, Emory S. Leaders and leadership. 3. 75. Appleton
Bonner, Hubert. Psychology of personality. 1961. 7. 00. Ronald
Brand, H. Study of personality. 1954. 6. 95. Wiley
Brown, Lawrence Guy. Social pathology. 4. 75. Appleton
Cattell, Raymond B. Personality and motivation structure and measurement.
  10. 50. Harcourt

Cohen, Yehudi A. Social structure and personality. 1961. 7.50. Holt, Rinehart & Winston

Curran, Charles A. Personality factors in counselling. il. 1945. 6.00. Grune

Dalton, Robert H. Personality and social interaction. 1961. 6.00. Heath

Dudley, Geoffrey A. Your personality and how to cultivate it. il. 1962. 2.95. Emerson

Eaton, Joseph, and Robert J. Weil. Culture and mental disorders. 1955. 4.00. Free Press

English, Oliver S., and G. H. J. Pearson. Emotional problems of living. 1955. 6.95. Norton

Eysenck, H. J. Scientific study of personality. il. 5.00. Macmillan

Fisher, Margaret B., and Jeanne L. Noble. Collebe education as personal development. 1960. 4.95. Prentice-Hall

Garrison, Karl C. Psychology of adolescence. 1951. 6.95. Prentice-Hall

Guntrip, Henry J. S. Personality structure and human interaction. 1961. bds. 7.50. Int. Univ.

Hall, Calvin S. Primer of Freudian psychology. 1954. 2.50. World Pub.

Hall, C. S., and G. Lindzey. Theories of personality. 1957. 6.95. Wiley

Honigmann, John J. Culture and personality. 1954. 6.00. Harper

Horney, Karen. Neurotic personality of our time. 1937. 4.50. Norton

Howard, Vernon L. Word power. 1958. 4.95. Prentice-Hall

Hunt, J. McV. Personality and the behavior disorders. 2 vols. 1944. 16.00. Ronald

Jackson, Robert A. How to like people. 1962. 2.95. Crowell-Collier

Jennings, H. H. Leadership and isolation. 1950. 4.00. McKay

Johnson, Paul E. Personality and religion. 1957. 4.50. Abingdon

Johnson, Wendell. People in quandaries: The semantics of personal adjustment. 1946. 6.50. Harper

Jung, Carl G. Development of personality. 1954. 3.75. Pantheon

Klein, David B. Mental hygiene. 1956. 9.45. Holt, Rinehart & Winston

Kluckholn, Clyde K., and Henry A. Murray. Personality in nature, society, and culture. 1953. 8.75. Knopf

Kunkel, Fritz. In search of maturity. 1943. 3.95. Scribner

Lazarus, R. S. Adjustment and personality. 1961. 6.95. McGraw

Lecky, Prescott. Self-consistency. 1961. 4.25. Shoe String

Lindner, Robert M. Rebel without a cause. 1944. 6.00. Grune

Link, Henry C. Rediscovery of man. 1938. 3.75. Macmillan

Lundin, Robert W. Personality, an experimental approach. il. 1961. 5.75. Macmillan

Menninger, Karl. Human mind. 1945. 6.75. Knopf

Murphy, Gardner. Personality: A biosocial approach to origins and structure. 1947. 8.50. Harper

Myers, F. W. H. Human personality and its survival of bodily death. 1961. 10.00. U. Books

Newton, Roy, and F. G. Nichols. How to improve your personality. il. 1954. 5.50. McGraw

Overstreet, Harry, and Bonaro. Mind alive. 1954. 4.50. Norton

Overstreet, Harry, and Bonaro. Mind goes forth. 1956. 4.50. Norton

Patty, W. L., and Louise Snyder Johnson. Personality and adjustment. 1953. 6.50. McGraw

Presthus, Robert. Organizational society. 1962. 6.00. Knopf

Reiner, Beatrice S., and Irving Kaufman. Character disorders in parents of delinquents. 1959. pap. 2.75. Family Service Assn.

Roback, A. A. Psychology of character. 1952. 9.00. Sci-Art

Rogers, Carl R., and Rosalind F. Dymond. Psychotherapy and personality change. 1954. 8.50. U. of Chicago

Sarason, Irwin G. Contemporary research in personality. 1962. 7.00. Van Nostrand

Saul, Leon J. Emotional maturity: The development and dynamics of personality. il. 1960. 7.50. Lippincott
Schneider, Kurt. Psychopathic personalities. 1959. 3.75. Thomas, C. C.
Shacter, Helen. How personalities grow. il. 1958. 3.50. Taplinger
Shaffer, Laurance F., and Edward A. Shoben, Jr. Psychology of adjustment. 9.75. Houghton
Stagner, Ross. Psychology of personality. 1961. 7.50. McGraw
Strecker, Edward A. Their mothers' sons. 1951. 3.75. Lippincott
Thigpen, Corbett, H., and Hervey M. Cleckley. Three faces of Eve. il. 1957. 2.98. McGraw
Thorpe, Louis P., and Allen M. Schmuller. Personality: An interdisciplinary approach. il. 1958. 6.00. Van Nostrand
Way, Lewis. Adler's place in psychology. 1950. 4.50. Macmillan
White, Robert W. Abnormal personality. 1956. 7.50. Ronald
Young, Kimball. Personality and problems of adjustment. il. 6.50. Appleton

PERSONNEL MANAGEMENT (658.3)
Argyris, Chris. Executive leadership. 1953. 3.00. Harper
Argyris, Chris. Personality and organization. 1957. 5.00. Harper
Bellows, Roger M. Psychology of personnel in business and industry. 1961. 10.00. Prentice-Hall
Bittel, L. R. What every supervisor should know. 1959. 7.95. McGraw
Chruden, Herbert J., and Arthur W. Sherman, Jr. Readings in personnel management. 1961. 7.00. South-Western Pub.
Dyer, Frederick C. Executive's guide to handling people. 1958. 4.95. Prentice-Hall
Fleishman, Edwin A. Studies in personnel and industrial psychology. 1961. 9.35. Dorsey
Flippo, Edwin B. Principles of personnel management. 1961. 7.95. McGraw
Heckmann, I. L., and S. G. Huneryager. Human relations in management. 1960. 7.75. South-Western Pub.
Hodnett, Edward. Art of working with people. 1959. 3.95. Harper
Laird, Donald A., and Eleanor C. Technique of handling people. il. 1954. 4.50. McGraw
Luck, Thomas J. Personnel audit and appraisal. 1955. 0.75. McGraw
Maier, Norman R. F. Appraisal interview. il. 1958. 5.50. Wiley
Mee, J. F. Personnel handbook. 1951. 12.00. Ronald
Pond, John H. Your future in personnel work. 1962. 2.95. Richards Rosen
Poore, William D. Personnel practices in colleges and universities: Faculty and staff. 1958. 5.00. College & Univ. Pers. Assn.
Schell, Erwin H. Technique of executive control. 1957. 6.50. McGraw
Schrader, Albert W., and George S. Odiorne. Personnel management, new perspectives. 1961. pap. 4.50. Bur. of Ind. Rel., U. of Mich.
Spates, Thomas G. Human values where people work. 1960. 4.50. Harper
Spriegel, William R., and Joseph W. Towie. Retail personnel management. il. 1951. 6.95. McGraw
Wilson, Howard. Human relations. 1958. 0.75. Admin. Res. Associates
Wolf, William B. Management of personnel. 1961. 7.95. Wadsworth
Yoder, Dale. Personnel management and industrial relations. 1962. 10.60. Prentice-Hall

PERSONNEL SERVICE (371.422)
American Council on Education, Division on Child Development and Teacher Personnel. Helping teachers understand children. 3.50. A. C. E.
Arbuckle, Dugald S. Guidance and counseling in the classroom. 1957. 5.95. Allyn and Bacon
Arbuckle, Dugald S. Pupil personnel services in American schools. il. 1962. 8.95. Allyn & Bacon
Blaine, Graham B., Jr., and Charles C. McArthur. Emotional problems of the student. 1961. 4.95. Appleton

Chandler, John R., and others. Successful adjustment in college. 3.50. Prentice-Hall

Crow, Lester D., and Alice. Introduction to guidance. 1960. 5.90. Am. Bk. Co.

Dame, J. Frank, and Albert R. Brinkman. Guidance in business education. 1961. 4.00. South-Western Pub.

Davis, Frederick B. Utilizing human talent. 1.25. A. C. E.

Forrester, Gertrude. Methods of vocational guidance. 1951. 6.50. Heath

Froehlich, Clifford P. Guidance services in schools. 1958. 6.50. McGraw

Hahn, M. E., and M. S. Maclean. Counseling psychology. 1955. 5.95. McGraw

Humphries, J. Anthony, and others. Guidance services. il. 1960. 5.25. Sci. Res. Assoc.

Jones, Arthur J. Principles of guidance and pupil personnel work. 1951. 6.95. McGraw

Kaplan, Louis. Mental health and human relations in education. il. 1959. 8.50. Harper

Kefauver, Grayson N. Guidance in educational institutions. NSSE, 37th yrbk. pt. 1. 1938. 2.50. U. of Chicago

Roeber, Edward C., and others. Organization and administration of guidance services. 1955. 6.25. McGraw

Sifferd, Calvin S. College and you. il. 1958. 3.00. Taplinger

Strang, Ruth. Counseling technics in college and secondary school. 1949. 5.00. Harper

Strang, Ruth. Role of the teacher in personnel work. 1953. 4.00. T. C.

Taba, Hilda, and Deborah Elkins. With focus on human relations: A story of an eighth grade. 3.00. A. C. E.

Traxler, Arthur E. Techniques of guidance. 1957. 6.00. Harper

Wedge, Bryant M. Psychosocial problems of college men. il. 1958. 6.50. Yale

Williamson, Edmund G. Student personnel services in colleges and universities. 1961. 7.50. McGraw

Wrenn, C. G. Student personnel work in college. 1951. 6.75. Ronald

PERSPECTIVE (742)

Fuller, Wilfred H. How to draw perspectives to scale. il. 1952. 1.75. Viking

Kepes, Gyorgy. Language of vision. il. 1945. 10.50. Theobald

Morehead, James C., and James C., Jr. Handbook of perspective drawing. il. 1952. 6.50. Van Nostrand

Norling, Ernest R. Perspective made easy. il. 4.50. Macmillan

Watson, Ernest W. How to use creative perspective. 1955. 7.95. Reinhold

PERU (985)

Adams, Richard N. Community in the Andes: Problems and progress in Muquiyauyo. 1959. 4.75. U. of Wash.

Bushnell, G. H. S. Peru. il. 1957. 6.95. Praeger

Flornoy, Bertrand. World of the Inca. il. 4.50. Vanguard

Sitwell, Sacheverell. Golden wall and mirador, travels and observations in Peru. il. 1961. 7.50. World Pub.

PESTALOZZI, JOHANN HEINRICH, 1746-1827 (923.7)

Silber, K. Pestalozzi, the man and his work. 6.50. Humanities

Walch, M. R., Sister. Pestalozzi and the Pestalozzian theory of education. 1953. 3.75. Catholic U. of Am. Pr.

PETER, SAINT, APOSTLE (922.22)

Chevrot, Georges. Simon Peter. 1959. 3.25. Scepter

Cullmann, Oscar. Peter: Disciple, apostle, martyr. tr. by Floyd V. Filson. 1962. 5.00. Westminster

Guarducci, Margherita. Tomb of St. Peter. il. 1960. 4.95. Hawthorn

Winter, Michael M. St. Peter and the popes. 1960. 4.50. Taplinger

PETER I, THE GREAT, EMPEROR OF RUSSIA, 1672-1725 (923.147)

Grey, Ian. Peter the Great, Emperor of all Russia. 1960. 7.50. Lippincott

Klyuchevsky, Vasili. Peter the Great. 6.75. St. Martins

Sumner, B. H. Peter the Great and the emergence of Russia. 2.50. Macmillan

PETRARCH, FRANCESCO (FRANCESCO PETRARCA), 1304-1374 (921.9)
Petrarch. Triumphs of Petrarch. tr. by Ernest H. Wilkins. 1962. 5.00. U. of
    Chicago
Wilkins, Ernest Hatch. Life of Petrarch. 1961. 6.50. U. of Chicago
PETROLEUM (665.5)
Bartley, Ernest R. Tidelands oil controversy: Legal and historical analysis. 1953.
    5.00. U. of Tex.
Clark, James A., and Michel T. Halbouty. Spindletop. 1952. 3.95. Random
Hartshorn, J. E. Politics and world oil economics. il. 1962. 8.50. Praeger
Knowles, Ruth. Greatest gamblers: The epic of American oil exploration. 1959.
    6.00. McGraw
Pratt, Wallace Everett, and D. Good. World geography of petroleum. 1950. 9.00.
    Princeton
Rister, Carl Coke. Oil! Titan of the southwest. il. 1949. 6.95. U. of Okla.
Werner, Morris R., and John Starr. Teapot Dome. 1959. 5.00. Viking
Zimmermann, E. W. Conservation in the production of petroleum. 1957. 6.00.
    Yale
PETROLOGY (552)
Harker, A. Petrology for students. 1954. 4.25. Cambridge U. P.
Kemp, J. F. Handbook of rocks. il. 1940. 6.00. Van Nostrand
Spock, Leslie E. Guide to the study of rocks. 1962. 8.75. Harper
PHARMACY (615.1)
Biddle, Harry C., and Disa W. Sitler. Mathematics of drugs and solution. 1961.
    2.25. Davis
Burlage, Henry M., and others. Orientation to pharmacy. 1959. 6.95. McGraw
Musser, Ruth, and Joseph G. Bird. Modern pharmacology and therapeutics.
    1961. 7.00. Macmillan
Oldham, Frances, and others. Essentials of pharmacology. 1960. 7.75. Lippincott
Rouse, Sue H., and George M. Webber. Calculations in pharmacy. 1961. 5.00.
    Lippincott
Silverman, Milton. Magic in a bottle. 1948. 5.95. Macmillan
Wren, R. C. Potter's New cyclopaedia of botanical drugs and preparations. 1956.
    10.00. Pitman (R)
Wright, Harold N., and Mildred Montag. Pharmacology and therapeutics. 1959.
    5.00. Saunders
PHENOMENOLOGY (142.7)
Berg, J. H. van den. Phenomenological approach to psychiatry: An introduction
    to recent phenomenological psychopathology. 1955. 3.00. Thomas, C. C.
Farber, Marvin. Foundation of phenomenology: Edmund Hüsserl and the quest
    for a rigorous science of philosophy. 1962. 12.50. Paine-Whitman
Farber, Marvin. Naturalism and subjectivism. 1959. 9.50. Thomas, C. C.
Husserl, Edmund. Ideas: General introduction to pure phenomenology. 1931. 5.25.
    Macmillan
Jung, Carl G. Aion: Researches into the phenomenology of the self. 4.50. Pantheon
Luijpen, W. A. Existential phenomenology. 1960. 6.75. Duquesne
PHILADELPHIA (974.8)
Grund, Francis J. Aristocracy in America. 1959. 3.75. Smith, Peter
Historic Philadelphia: From the founding until the early nineteenth century. 1953.
    6.00. Am. Philos. Soc.
Tolles, Frederick B. Meeting house and counting house: The Quaker merchants
    of Colonial Pennsylvania. 1948. 5.00. U. of N. C.
PHILIPPINE ISLANDS (991.4)
Briggs, Donald S. Orient-Hawaii guide. 3.50. Crown
Forbes, William Cameron. Philippine Islands. 2 vols. 1928. il. 25.00. Houghton
Golay, Frank. Public policy and national economic development: The Philippines.
    1961. 6.75. Cornell
Grunder, Garel, and William E. Livezey. Philippines and the United States. il.
    1951. 4.00. U. of Okla.

Keith, Agnes Newton. Bare feet in the palace. 1955. 6.00. Little
PHILOSOPHERS (921)
Beardsley, Monroe C. European philosophers from Descartes to Nietzsche.
   2.95. Modern Lib.
Blackham, H. J. Six existentialist thinkers. 3.50. Macmillan
Blau, Joseph L. Men and movements in American philosophy. 1952. 9.25.
   Prentice-Hall
Burch, G. B. Early medieval philosophy. 1951. 2.25. Columbia
Crawford, William R. Century of Latin-American thought. 1961. 6.00. Harvard
Day, Clarence B. Philosophers of China: Classical and contemporary. 1962. pap.
   2.45. Citadel
Diogenes Laertius. Lives of eminent philosophers. 2 vols. 3.50 ea. Harvard
Fisch, Max H., and others. Classic American philosophers. 1951. 5.75. Appleton
Guthrie, W. K. C. Greek philosophers: From Thales to Aristotle. 1960. pap.
   0.95. Harper
Hough, Lynn Harold. Great humanists. 1952. 3.50. Abingdon
Marsak, Leonard M. French philosophers from Descartes to Sartre. 1961. pap.
   2.45. Meridan
Newman, James R. Science and sensibility. 2 vols. il. 1961. 10.00. S. and S.
Paul, L. English philosophers. 5.00. Hillary
Reinhardt, Kurt F. Existentialist revolt. 5.00. Ungar
Robinson, Daniel S. Crucial issues in philosophy. 1955. 5.00. Christopher
Runes, Dagobert D. World treasury of philosophy. 1959. pap. 3.45. Littlefield
Russell, Bertrand. Portraits from Memory. 1936. 3.50. S. and S.
Thomas, Henry. Understanding the great philosophers. 1962. bds. 5.95.
   Doubleday
Thomas, Henry, and Dana Lee. Living biographies of great philosophers. 1959.
   2.50. Doubleday
Van Wesep, H. B. Seven sages: The story of American philosophy. 1960. 6.95.
   McKay
Jones, Adam Leroy. Early American philosophers. 1958. 2.50. Ungar
PHILOSOPHY (100)
Boas, George. Limits of reason. 1961. 3.75. Harper
Bridgman, Percy W. Way things are. 1959. 5.75. Harvard
Bronstein, Daniel J. Basic problems of philosophy. 1955. 7.95. Prentice-Hall
Dampier, W. C. History of science. 1949. 4.95. Cambridge U. P.
Dewey, John. Experience and nature. 5.00. Open Ct.
Ducasse, Curt J. Nature, mind and death. 1951. 6.00. Open Ct.
Dunham, Barrows. Man against myth. 1962. 1.95. Hill & Wang
Durant, Will. Pleasures of philosophy. 1953. 5.00. S. and S.
Durant, Will. Story of philosophy. 1933. 5.00. S. and S.
Edman, Irwin. Philosopher's quest. 1947. 3.00. Viking
Edman, Irwin, and Herbert W. Schneider. Landmarks for beginners in philosophy.
   1941. 8.00. Holt
Ewing, A. C. Fundamental questions of philosophy. 1951. 4.25. Macmillan
Geiger, George R. Philosophy and the social order. 1947. 5.00. Houghton
Hall, Manly P. Twelve world teachers. 3.75. DeVorss
Heidegger, Martin. What is philosophy? 3.00. Twayne
Hocking, William E., and Richard B. Types of philosophy. 1959. 5.50. Scribner
Hocking, William Ernest, and others. Preface to philosophy. 6.00. Macmillan
James, William. Philosophy of William James. 1925. 1.95. Modern Lib.
James, William. Selected papers on philosophy. 1917. 1.95. Dutton
James, William. Some problems of philosophy. 1940. 2.25. McKay
James, William. Will to believe. bd. with Human immortality. pap. 1.65. Dover
Jeans, J. H. Physics and philosophy. 1942. 4.50. Cambridge U. P.
Joad, Cyril E. M. Guide to philosophy. 1956. pap. 2.00. Dover
Joad, C. E. M. Return to philosophy. 2.00. Humanities
Klubertanz, George P. Philosophy of human nature. 1953. 4.25. Appleton

Koestler, Arthur. Insight and outlook. An inquiry into the common foundations
  of science, art and social ethics. 1949. 5.50. Macmillan
Langer, Susanne Knauth. Philosophy in a new key: A study in the symbolism of
  reason, rite and art. 1957. 4.75. Harvard
Mayer, Frederick. Man, morals and education. 1962. 4.00. Twayne
Mayer, Frederick, and Frank E. Brower. Patterns of a new philosophy. 1955.
  3.25. Pub. Affairs
Perspectives on a troubled decade. Conference on Science, Philosophy and Religion.
  1950. 5.50. Harper
Reinchenbach, Hans. Rise of scientific philosophy. 1954. 6.50. U. of Calif.
Russell, Bertrand. Our knowledge of the external world. 4.00. Humanities
Russell, Bertrand. Outline of philosophy. pap. 1.55. Meridian
Russell, Bertrand R. Problems of philosophy. 1912. 1.70. Oxford U. P.
Santayana, George. Life of reason. 1954. 7.50. Scribner
Titus, Harold H. Living issues in philosophy. 6.00. Am. Bk. Co.
Von Hildebrand, Dietrich. What is philosophy? 1960. 4.25. Bruce
Weiss, Paul. Reality. 4.00. Smith, Peter
PHILOSOPHY--ADDRESSES, ESSAYS, LECTURES (104)
Berkeley, George. New theory of vision. 1.95. Dutton
Black, Max. Models and metaphors. 1962. 5.75. Cornell
Broad, C. D. Ethics and the history of philosophy. 1952. 4.50. Humanities
Buber, Martin. Pointing the way. tr. by Maurice Friedman. 1957. 4.50. Harper
Dewey, John. Influence of Darwin on philosophy and other essays. 3.75. Smith,
  Peter
Dewey, John. Philosophy of education. 1956. pap. 1.50. Littlefield
Durkheim, Emile. Sociology and philosophy. 1953. 3.50. Free Press
Frankel, Charles. Uses of philosophy. 1955. 3.50. S. and S.
Gruber, Frederick C. Emergence of the modern mind. 1958. 2.50. U. of Pa.
Hartshorne, Charles. Logic of perfection. 1962. 6.00. Open Ct.
Leclerc, Ivor. Relevance of Whitehead. 1961. 7.25. Macmillan
Lovejoy, Arthur O. Essays in the history of ideas. 1952. 5.50. Johns Hopkins
Lovejoy, Arthur O. Reason, the understanding and time. 3.95. Johns Hopkins
Maritain, J. On the use of philosophy: Three essays. 1961. 2.75. Princeton
Maritain, Jacques. Range of reason. 1952. 3.95. Scribner
Mayer, Frederick. Education and the good life. 1957. 2.50. Pub. Affairs
Mead, George Herbert. Philosophy of the present. 4.00. Open Ct.
Moore, George Edward. Some main problems of philosophy. 1953. 5.25. Mac-
  millan
Nelson, Leonard. Socratic method and critical philosophy. tr. by Thomas Brown.
  1949. 3.75. Yale
Ortega y Gasset, Jose. Modern theme. 3.35. Smith, Peter
Ortega y Gasset, Jose. What is philosophy? 1961. 4.50. Norton
Russell, Bertrand. Logic and knowledge: Essays 1901-1950. 4.50. Macmillan
Russell, Bertrand. Mysticism and logic. 1954. 2.75. Barnes & Noble
Russell, Bertrand. Unpopular essays. 1951. 3.50. S. and S.
Smith, Thomas V. Essays in philosophy. 4.00. Open Ct.
White, Morton G. Religion, politics, and the higher learning. 1959. 3.50. Harvard
Whitehead, Alfred North. Modes of thought. 3.75. Macmillan
Wild, John. Return to reason. 1953. 7.50. Regnery
PHILOSOPHY--COLLECTED WORKS (108)
Aristotle. Works: The Oxford translation. 12 vols. Oxford U. P.
Bacon, Francis. Selected writings. 1955. 1.95. Modern Lib.
Berkeley, George. Philosophical writing. 1960. 3.25. Nelson
Berkeley, George. Works. 9 vols. 7.50 ea. Nelson
Buber, Martin. Writings. by Will Herberg. 1958. 3.25. Smith, Peter
Descartes, Rene. Philosophical works. 2 vols. 1955. pap. 2.00 ea. Dover
Descartes, Rene. Philosophical writings. 1.95. Modern Lib.
Hulme, T. E. Speculations: Essays on humanism and the philosophy of art. 4.00.
  Humanities

Kant, Immanuel. Critique of pure reason. pap. 1.45. Doubleday
Kierkegaard, Soren. Living thoughts of Kierkegaard. by W. H. Auden. 1952. 2.50.
   McKay
Leibniz, Gottfreid Wilhelm von. Philosophical papers and letters tr. by LeRoy
   E. Loemker. 2 vols. set, 12.00 U. of Chicago
Maritain, Jacques. Social and political philosophy of Jacques Maritain. 1955. 5.00.
   Scribner
Montaigne, Michel E. de. Complete essays of Montaigne. 3 vols. pap. 1.45 ea.
   Doubleday
Sainte-Beuve, Augustine. Selections. 1918. 1.75. Cambridge U. P.
Spinoza, Benedict de. Works of Spinoza. 2 vols. 7.00. Smith, Peter
PHILOSOPHY--COLLECTIONS (108)
Alston, William P., and George Nakhnikian. Readings in twentieth-century
   philosophy. 1962. 7.50. Free Press
Clapp, James G., and others. Foundations of western thought. 1962. 10.75.
   Knopf
Commins, Saxe. Political philosophers. 1947. 3.95. Random
Commins, Saxe. Social philosophers. 1947. 3.95. Random
Commins, Saxe. Speculative philosophers. 1947. 3.95. Random
Commins, Saxe. World's great thinkers. 4 vols. 1947. 14.95.
Davidson, Robert F. Philosophies men live by. 1952. 5.50. Holt, Rinehart &
   Winston
Davidson, Robert F. Search for meaning in life. 1962. 5.50. Holt, Rinehart &
   Winston
Magill, Frank N. Masterpieces of world philosophy. 1961. 8.95. Harper (R)
Mourant, John A., and others. Essays in philosophy. 1962. 5.75. Penn. State
Runes, Dagobert D. World treasury of philosophy. 1959. pap. 3.45. Littlefield
Ryan, John K. Studies in philosophy and the history of philosophy. 1961. pap.
   5.00. Catholic U. of Am. Pr.
PHILOSOPHY--DICTIONARIES (103)
Baldwin, J. M. Dictionary of philosophy and psychology. 3 vols. 35.00. Smith, Peter
Runes, Dagobert D. Dictionary of philosophy. 1956. pap. 1.95. Littlefield
Selsam, Howard. Handbook of philosophy. 1949. 2.00. Int. Pubs.
Urmson, J. O. Concise encyclopedia of western philosophy and philosophers.
   il. 1960. 15.00. Hawthorn
PHILOSOPHY--HISTORY (109)
Allen, E. L. From Plato to Nietzsche, ideas that shape our lives. 1959. 3.75.
   Assn. Pr.
Clark, Gordon H. Thales to Dewey. 1957. 8.50. Houghton
Ferm, Vergilius. History of philosophical systems. 1958. pap. 2.25. Littlefield
Fuller, B. A. G., and Sterling M. McMurrin. History of philosophy. 8.75.
   Holt, Rinehart & Winston
Gilson, Etienne. Unity of philosophical experience. 1937. 4.50. Scribner
Glenn, Paul J. History of philosophy. 1929. 4.50. Herder
Hatch, Edwin. Influence of Greek ideas on Christianity. 1958. 3.50. Smith,
   Peter
Hegel, Georg Wilhelm Friedrich. Lectures on the history of philosophy. 3 vols.
   1954. 15.00. Humanities
Jaspers, Karl. Great philosophers. 1962. 8.50. Harcourt
Jones, William Thomas. History of Western philosophy. il. 1952. 9.75. Harcourt
Mayer, Frederick. History of philosophy. 2 vols. 6.25. ea. Am. Bk. Co.
Passmore, John. Hundred years of philosophy. 5.25. Macmillan
Radhakrishnan, Sarvepalli, and others. History of philosophy, eastern and
   western. 2 vols. 1962. 15.00. Barnes & Noble
Rogers, Arthur K. Student's history of philosophy. 1932. 5.50. Macmillan
Russell, Bertrand. History of western philosophy. 1945. 6.00. S. and S.
Russell, Bertrand A. Wisdom of the West. by Paul Foulkes. il. 1959. 12.50.
   Doubleday

Stallknecht, Newton P., and R. S. Brumbaugh. Spirit of western philosophy.
   1950. 6.00. McKay
Thilly, Frank, and Ledger Wood. History of philosophy. 1957. 6.75. Holt,
   Rinehart & Winston
Thomas, Henry. Understanding the great philosophers. 1962. bds. 5.95. Double-
   day
Tsanoff, Radoslav A. Great philosophers. 1953. 6.00. Harper
Whitehead, Alfred N. Adventures of ideas. 1933. 5.00. Macmillan
Windelband, Wilhelm. History of philosophy. 1901. 6.75. Macmillan

PHILOSOPHY, AMERICAN (191)
Brodbeck, May, and others. American non-fiction, 1900-1950. 1952. 3.00.
   Regnery
Fisch, Max H., and others. Classic American philosophers. 1951. 5.75.
   Appleton
Frankel, Charles. Golden age of American philosophy. 1960. 7.50. Braziller
Padover, Saul K. Genius of America. 1960. 6.50. McGraw
Padover, Saul K. World of the founding fathers. 3.95. Yoseloff
Parrington, Vernon Louis. Main currents in American thought. 1 vol. Harcourt
Riley, Woodbridge. American thought from puritanism to pragmatism. 5.50.
   Smith, Peter
Schneider, H. W. History of American philosophy. 1946. 6.00. Columbia
Van Wesep, H. B. Seven sages: The story of American philosophy. 1949. 7.00.
   McKay
Werkmeister, W. H. History of philosophical ideas in America. 1949. 7.00
   Ronald

PHILOSOPHY, ANCIENT (180)
Armstrong, Arthur H. Introduction to ancient philosophy. 1949. 3.25. Newman
Boas, George. Rationalism in Greek philosophy. 1961. 7.50. Johns Hopkins
Brady, Ignatius. History of ancient philosophy. 1959. 6.75. Bruce
Burnet, John. Early Greek philosophy. 6.00. Macmillan
Burnet, John. Greek philosophy from Thales to Plato. 4.50. St. Martins
Clarke, M. L. Roman Mind: Studies in the history of thought from Cicero to
   Marcus Aurelius. 1956. 3.75. Harvard
Confucius. Analects; or, The conversations of Confucius with his disciples and
   certain others. 1941. 2.25. Oxford U. P.
Confucius. Wisdom of Confucius. 1943. 1.95. Modern Lib.
Cornford, Francis M. Before and after Socrates. 1932. 3.50. Cambridge U. P.
Cornford, F. M. From religion to philosophy. 1958. 3.25. Smith, Peter
Creel, Herrlee G. Chinese thought from Confucius to Mao Tse-tung. 1953. 6.00.
   U. of Chicago
Creel, H. G. Sinism: A study of the evolution of the Chinese world-view. 1929.
   3.00. Open Ct.
Diogenes Laertius. Lives of eminent philosophers. 2 vols. 3.50 ea. Harvard
Fung, Yu-Lan. Short history of Chinese philosophy. 7.50. Macmillan
Guthrie, William K. C. Greek philosophers: From Thales to Aristotle. 1960.
   pap. 0.95. Harper
Hall, Manly P. First principles of philosophy. 3.75. DeVorss
Hall, Manly P. Lectures on ancient philosophy. 6.00. DeVorss
Hall, Manly P. Sages of China. 1.75. DeVorss
Mayer, Frederick. Ancient and medieval philosophy. 6.25. Am. Bk. Co.
Oates, Whitney J. Stoic and Epicurean philosophers. 3.75. Random
Pegis, Anton C. St. Thomas and the Greeks. 1939. 2.50. Marquette
Smith, Thomas V. Philosophers speak for themselves: From Aristotle to
   Plotinus. 1956. pap. 1.50. U. of Chicago
Smith, Thomas V. Philosophers speak for themselves: From Thales to Plato.
   1956. pap. 1.95. U. of Chicago
Snell, Bruno. Discovery of the mind: The Greek origins of European thought.
   1953. 5.50. Harvard

Stoic and Epicurean philosophers. 2.95. Modern Lib.
Waley, Arthur. Three ways of thought in ancient China. 3.00. Macmillan
Waley, Arthur. Way and its Power: Study of the Tao Te Ching and its place in Chinese thought. 3.50. Macmillan
Watts, Alan. Nature, man, and woman. 1958. 3.95. Pantheon
Wright, Arthur F. Studies in Chinese thought. il. 1953. 4.50. U. of Chicago
Zeller, Eduard. Outlines of the history of Greek philosophy. 4.50. Humanities
Zeller, Eduard. Plato and the Older Academy. 1962. 12.50. Russell
Zeller, Eduard. Stoics, Epicureans and Sceptics. 1962. 12.50. Russell

PHILOSOPHY, BRITISH (192)
Hume, David. Treatise of human nature. 2 vols. 1.95. ea. Dutton
Mace, C. A. British philosophy in the mid-century: A Cambridge symposium. 5.25. Macmillan
Metz, Rudolf. Hundred years of British philosophy. 1938. 5.25. Macmillan
Muirhead, John Henry. Contemporary British philosophy. 1953. 6.00. Macmillan
Tillyard, E. M. W. Elizabethan world picture. 1946. 2.25. Macmillan

PHILOSOPHY, COMPARATIVE (100)
Hall, Everett W. Philosophical systems. 1960. 4.00. U. of Chicago
Kraemer, Hendrik. World cultures and world religions. 1961. 6.50. Westminster
Radhakrishnan, Sarvepalli. Eastern religions and Western thought. 1940. 4.00. Oxford U. P.
Raju, P. T. Introduction to comparative philosophy. 1962. 7.50. U. of Nebr.

PHILOSOPHY, HINDU (181.4)
Bernard, T. Hindu philosophy. 4.50. Wehman
Dasgupta, S. Indian philosophy. 5 vols. Cambridge U. P.
Gokhale, Balkrishna G. Indian thought through the ages. 1961. 5.50. Taplinger
Hume, R. E. Upanishads. 1931. 3.75. Oxford U. P.
Keith, Arthur Berriedale. Religion and philosophy of the Veda and Upanishads. 2 vols. 1925. 10.00. Harvard
Radhakrishnan, Sarvepalli. Brahma sutra. 1960. 10.00. Harper
Radhakrishnan, Sarvepalli. Indian philosophy. 2 vols. 1923-27. 12.00. Macmillan
Radhakrishnan, S., and C. A. Moore. Sourcebook in Indian philosophy. 1957. 7.50. Princeton
Radhakrishnan, S., and J. H. Muirhead. Contemporary Indian philosophy. 1952. 6.00. Macmillan
Rolland, Romain. Life of Ramakrishna. 1952. 2.50. Vedanta Press
Zimmer, Heinrich. Philosophies of India. il. by Joseph Campbell. 1951. 6.00. Pantheon

PHILOSOPHY, MEDIEVAL (180)
Burch, G. B. Early medieval philosophy. 1951. 2.25. Columbia
Cassirer, Ernst, and others. Renaissance philosophy of man. 1948. 5.00. U. of Chicago
Delhaye, Philippe. Medieval Christian philosophy. 1960. 3.50. Hawthorn
Dunbar, H. Flanders. Symbolism in medieval thought. 1960. 12.50. Russell
Fuller, B. A. G., and Sterling M. McMurrin. Ancient and medieval philosophy. 5.50. Holt, Rinehart & Winston
Gilson, Etienne. Reason and revelation in the Middle Ages. 1938. 2.50. Scribner
Gilson, Etienne. Spirit of medieval philosophy. 1936. 3.50. Scribner
Maimonides, Moses. Guide for the perplexed. 3.85. Smith, Peter
Taylor, Henry Osborn. Mediaeval mind: A history of the development of thought and emotion in the Middle Ages. 2 vols. 1949. 10.00. Harvard
Unterman, Isaac. Light amid the darkness. 1959. 4.00. Twayne
Wulf, Maurice de. System of Thomas Aquinas. il. 1959. pap. 1.25. Dover

PHILOSOPHY, MODERN (190)
Aiken, Henry D. Age of ideology. 1957. 3.00. Houghton
Beardsley, Monroe C. European philosophers from Descartes to Nietzsche. 2.95. Modern Lib.
Boas, G. Dominant themes of modern philosophy. 1957. 7.50. Ronald

Cassirer, Ernst. Philosophy of the Enlightenment. 1959. 3.50. Smith, Peter
Collins, James. God in modern philosophy. 1959. 6.50. Regnery
Copleston, Frederick. Hobbes to Hume. 4.75. Newman
Copleston, Frederick. Wolff to Kant. 1960. 4.50. Newman
Fuller, B. A. G., and Sterling M. McMurrin. Modern philosophy. 6.00. Holt,
   Rinehart & Winston
James, William. Works. Essays in radical empiricism, and Pluralistic universe.
   by Ralph B. Perry. 1943. 4.50. McKay
Kaplan, Abraham. New world of philosophy. 1961. 4.95. Random
Kaufmann, W. From Shakespeare to existentialism. 1959. 5.95. Beacon
Klocker, Harry R. Thomism and modern thought. 1962. 4.00. Appleton
Koch, Adrienne. Philosophy for a time of crisis. 1959. 5.95. Dutton
Krutch, Joseph Wood. Measure of man. pap. 1.75. Bobbs
Randall, John H., Jr. Career of philosophy: From the Middle Ages to the
   Enlightenment. 1962. 13.95. Columbia
Santayana, George. Winds of doctrine, and Platonism and the spiritual life.
   1958. 3.50. Smith, Peter
Smith, Thomas Vernor. Philosophers speak for themselves: Berkeley, Hume,
   and Kant. pap. 1.95. U. of Chicago
White, M. G. Toward reunion in philosophy. 1956. 5.75. Harvard
Willey, B. Nineteenth century studies. 1949. 4.50. Columbia
Willey, B. Seventeenth century background. 1942. 5.00. Columbia

PHILOSOPHY AND RELIGION (201)
Beck, Lewis W. Six secular philosophers: Spinoza, Hume, Kant, Nietzche,
   James, Santayana. 1960. 2.75. Harper
Berdyaev, Nikolai. Destiny of man. 6.00. Hillary
Bewkes, Eugene G., and others. Experience, reason, and faith: A survey in
   philosophy and religion. 1940. 5.50. Harper
Brunner, H. Emil. Philosophy of religion. 1958. 3.50. Allenson
Ferre, Nels F. S. Faith and reason. 1946. 3.50. Harper
Frank, Erich. Philosophical understanding and religious truth. 1945. 4.00.
   Oxford U. P.
Hook, Sidney. Religious experience and truth. 1961. 5.00. N. Y. U.
Huxley, Aldous. Perennial philosophy. 1945. 5.00. Harper
Jaeger, Werner. Humanism and theology. 1943. 2.50. Marquette
James, William. Varieties of religious experience. 1.95. Modern Lib.
Kant, Immanuel. Religion within the limits of reason alone. 1960. 2.35. Harper
Lippmann, Walter. Preface to morals. 5.00. Macmillan
Otto, Rudolf. Mysticism east and west. pap. 1.45. Meridian
Radhakrishnan, Sarvepalli. Idealist view of life. 1932. 4.75. Macmillan
Royce, Josiah. Religious aspect of philosophy. 1958. 3.75. Smith, Peter
Unamuno, Miguel de. Tragic sense of life. 3.75. Smith, Peter
Wach, Joachim. Types of religious experience: Christian and non-Christian. 1941.
   4.50. U. of Chicago

PHONETICS (421.5)
Fletcher, Harvey. Speech and hearing in communication. il. 1953. 11.50. Van
   Nostrand
Jakobson, Roman, and Morris Halle. Fundamentals of language. 2.00. Humanities
Jones, Daniel. Pronunciation of English. 1950. 2.50. Cambridge U. P.

PHOSPHATES (631.85)
Pierre, W. H., and A. G. Norman. Soil and fertilizer phosphorus in crop
   nutrition. 1953. 9.00. Academic Press
Waggaman, William H. Phosphoric acid, phosphates and phosphatic fertilizers.
   1952. 15.00. Reinhold

PHOTOCHEMISTRY (541.35)
Bowen, E. J. Chemical aspects of light. il. 1946. 4.00. Oxford U. P.
Heidt, Lawrence J., and others. Photochemistry in the liquid and solid state.
   il. 1960. 6.00. Wiley

Leighton, Philip A. Photochemistry of air pollution. il. 1961. 11.00. Academic
    Press
PHOTOELECTRIC CELLS (537.42)
Ive, G. A. G. Photo-electric handbook. 4.50. Transatlantic
Summer, Walter. Photosensitors. il. 1958. 21.00. Macmillan
Zworykin, V. K., and Ramberg, E. G. Photoelectricity and its application. 1949.
    12.00. Wiley
PHOTOGRAPHY (770)
Adams, Ansel. Camera and lens. bk. 1. 1962. 3.95. Morgan
Adams, Ansel. Natural-light photography. 1959. 3.95. Morgan
Adams, Ansel. Print. 1961. 3.95. Morgan
Audels guide to creative photography. il. 1960. 3.95. Audel
Baines, Harry. Science of photography. il. 1958. 8.00. Wiley
Deschin, Jacob. 35mm photography. il. 1959. 5.00. Barnes, A. S.
Deschin, Jacob. Say it with your camera. il. 1960. 4.95. Barnes, A. S.
Eastman Kodak Company. How to make good pictures. 1957. 1.95. Random
Feininger, Andreas. Creative photographer. il. 1955. 4.95. Prentice-Hall
Feininger, Andreas. Successful photography. 1954. 4.95. Prentice-Hall
Focal encyclopedia of photography. 1957. 20.00. Macmillan (R)
Gernsheim, Helmut, and Alison. History of photography. 1955. 18.50. Oxford
    U. P.
Goldsmith, Arthur A. How to take better pictures. il. 1957. 2.50. Arco
Henle, Fritz, and H. M. Kinzer. Photography for everyone. il. 1959. 4.95.
    Viking
Larmore, Lewis. Introduction to photographic principles. 1959. 8.00. Prentice-
Hall
Miller, Thomas, and Wyatt Brummitt. This is photography: Its means and ends.
    1959. 3.50. Doubleday
Newhall, Beaumont. Daguerrotype in America. il. 1961. 12.50. Duell
Trorey, L. G. Aerial mapping and photogrammetry. 1952. 7.50. Cambridge U. P.
PHOTOGRAPHY AS A PROFESSION (770.069)
Abel, Charles. Photography: Careers and opportunities for you. 1961. 2.95.
    Chilton
PHOTOSYNTHESIS (581.13342)
Bassham, J. A., and Melvin Calvin. Path of carbon in photosynthesis. 1957.
    3.95. Prentice-Hall
Calvin, Melvin, and James A. Bassham. Photosynthesis of carbon compounds.
    il. 1962. 5.50. Benjamin
PHYSICAL EDUCATION AND TRAINING (371.73)
American Association for Health, Physical Education and Recreation. Current
    administrative problems in health, physical education and recreation. 1960.
    3.00. Am. Assn. for Health, Phys. Ed. & Rec.
Bucher, Charles. Foundations of physical education. il. 1960. 6.00. Mosby
Dayton, O. William. Athletic training and conditioning. 1960. 6.00. Ronald
Hughes, Williams L., and others. Administration of physical education for
    schools and colleges. 1962. 5.50. Ronald
Jenny, John H. Physical education, health education, and recreation. il. 1961.
    5.00. Macmillan
Larson, Leonard A., and others. Problems in health, physical , and recreation
    education. 1953. 9.00. Prentice-Hall
Morehouse, Laurence E., and Philip J. Rasch. Scientific basis of athletic
    training. il. 1958. 4.50. Saunders
National Education Association, American Association for Health, Physical
    Education, and Recreation. Evaluation standards and guide. 1959. 1.00.
    N. E. A.
National Education Association, American Association for Health, Physical
    Education and Recreation. Physical education for college men and women.
    1959. 1.00. N. E. A.

National Education Association, American Association for Health, Physical Education and Recreation. Physical education for high-school students. 1960. 3.00. N. E. A.

Nixon, Eugene W., and Frederick W. Cozens. Introduction to physical education. 1959. 4.25. Saunders

Rathbone, Josephine Langworthy. Corrective physical education. il. 1959. 5.00. Saunders

Rawlinson, Ken. Modern athletic training. il. 1961. 5.95. Prentice-Hall

Salt, Ellis B., and others. Teaching physical education in the elementary school. 1960. 6.00. Ronald

Sapora, Allen V., and E. D. Mitchell. Theory of play and recreation. 1961. 6.50. Ronald

Seaton, Don C., and others. Physical education handbook. 5.25. Prentice-Hall

PHYSICAL EDUCATION AS A PROFESSION (371.73069)

Duncan, Margaret M., and Ralph H. Johnson. Introduction to physical education, health education, and recreation. 1954. 6.50. Prentice-Hall

Johnson, Granville B., and others. Your career in physical education. 1957. 3.75. Harper

Smith, Hope M., and Marguerite A. Clifton. Physical education; exploring your future. il. 1962. 4.75. Prentice-Hall

PHYSICAL FITNESS (371.73)

Clarke, Henry H. Application of measurement to health and physical education. 1959. 7.25. Prentice-Hall

McCloy, C. H., and N. D. Young. Tests and measurements in health and physical education. il. 1954. 7.00. Appleton

Meyers, C. R., and T. E. Blesh. Measurement in physical education. 1962. 6.50. Ronald

National Education Association, American Association for Health, Physical Education and Recreation. Fit to teach, yearbook. 1957. 3.50. N. E. A.

Three hundred point physical skills contest for girls. 1961. 1.50. Assn. Pr.

Van Huss, Wayne, and others. Physical activity in modern living. il. 1960. pap. 3.25. Prentice-Hall

Vermes, Jean C. Girl's book of physical fitness. 1961. 1.95. Assn. Pr.

Willgoose, Carl E. Evaluation in health education and physical education. 1961. 7.50. McGraw

PHYSICAL GEOGRAPHY (551.4)

Beckinsale, R. P. Land, air and ocean. 1956. 4.00. Oxford U. P.

Carlson, Fred A. Geography of Latin America. 1951. 8.75. Prentice-Hall

Cram's unrivaled world atlas. 1958. 25.00. Cram

Debenham, Frank. Global atlas: A new view of the world from space. il. 1958. 5.95. Golden Press (R)

Fenneman, Nevin. Physiography of eastern United States. 1948. 13.00. McGraw

Fenneman, Nevin. Physiography of western United States. 1931. 11.00. McGraw

Mirov, N. T. Geography of Russia. 1951. 7.75. Wiley

Semple. E. C., and Clarence F. Jones. American history and its geographic conditions. 6.50. Houghton

Shabad, T. China's changing map. 7.50. Praeger

Shimer, John A. This sculptured earth: The landscape of America. il. 1959. bds. 7.50. Columbia

Sparks, B. W. Geomorphology. 1960. 6.75. Wiley

PHYSICAL MEASUREMENTS (530.8)

Beckwith, T. G., and N. L. Buck. Mechanical measurements. 1961. 9.50. Addison-Wesley

Lee, Oliver J. Measuring our universe. 1950. 4.50. Ronald

Moore, Mark B. Theory and application of mechanical engineering measurements. il. 1960. 6.75. Van Nostrand

Tyson, Forrest C. Industrial instrumentation. 1961. 10.00. Prentice-Hall

PHYSICAL THERAPY (615.83)

Bowley, Agatha H. Young handicapped child. il. 1957. 3.50. Williams & Wilkins

Buchwald, Edith. Physical rehabilitation for daily living. il. 1952. 9.50. McGraw

Colson, John H. C. Progressive exercise therapy in rehabilitation and physical therapy. il. 1959. 4.50. Williams & Wilkins

Garrett, James F., and Edna S. Levine. Psychological practices with the physically disabled. 1962. 8.75. Columbia

Heather, Arthur J. Manual of care for the disabled patient. 1961. 3.75. Macmillan

Kendall, Henry O., and others. Posture and pain. il. 1952. 7.00. Williams & Wilkins

Kessler, H. H. Rehabilitation of the physically handicapped. 1953. 5.50. Columbia

Levitt, Sphie. Physiotherapy in cerebral palsy. il. 1961. 6.50. Thomas, C. C.

Licht, Sidney. Massage, manipulation, and traction. 10.00. Licht

Licht, Sidney. Therapeutic exercise. 1961. 16.00. Licht

Schoenbohm, W. B. Planning and operating facilities for crippled children. il. 1962. 11.50. Thomas, C. C.

Shestack, Robert. Handbook of physical therapy. 1956. 4.25. Springer

Wright, Beatrice A. P. Physical disability, a psychological approach. 1960. 6.00. Harper

PHYSICIANS (610.6952)

Heiser, Victor G. American doctor's odyssey. il. 1936. 7.95. Norton

Lee, Roger I. Doctor speaks his mind. 1958. 3.00. Little

Monro, Thomas Kirkpatrick. Physician as a man of letters, science and action. 1951. 4.50. Williams & Wilkins

Munthe, Axel. Story of San Michele. 1936. 5.00. Dutton

Potter, William H. You and your doctor. 1961. 5.00. Duell

Pugh, Herbert L. Navy surgeon. il. 1959. 5.00. Lippincott

Rowntree, Leonard G. Amid masters of twentieth century medicine. il. 1958. 11.50. Thomas, C. C.

Sigerist, Henry. Great doctors. 1958. pap. 1.45. Doubleday

Sloop. Mary T., and L. Blythe. Miracle in the hills. 1953. 4.95. McGraw

Wylder, M. K. Rio Grande medicine man. 3.75. Rydal

PHYSICS (530)

Armitage, E. Basic practical physics. 1959. 1.25. Cambridge U. P.

Avery, Madalyn. Household physics. il. 1955. 6.75. Macmillan

Beiser, A. Basic concepts of physics. 1961. 7.75. Addison-Wesley

Beiser, Germaine, and Arthur. Physics for everybody. 1956. 3.50. Dutton

Black, Newton Henry, and Elbert P. Little. Introductory course in college physics. il. 6.95. Macmillan

Blanchard, Converse H., and others. Introduction to modern physics. 1958. 10.60. Prentice-Hall

Blass, Gerhard A. Theoretical physics. il. 1962. 8.50. Appleton

Broad, C. D. Scientific thought. 6.50. Humanities

Brown, Thomas B. Foundations of modern physics. 1949. 7.00. Wiley

Condon, Edward U., and Hugh Odishaw. Handbook of physics. 1958. 25.00. McGraw

Dampier, W. C. Matter and change. 1924. 1.75. Cambridge U. P.

Eubanks, H. L. Basic physics. 3.00. St. Martins

Faraday, Michael. On the various forces of nature. il. 1961. 2.75. Crowell

Fenyo, Eva. Guided tour through space and time. 3.50. Prentice-Hall

Fowler, Richard G., and Donald I. Meyer. Physics for engineers and scientists. 1961. 12.35. Allyn & Bacon

Gamow, George. Matter, earth and sky. 1958. 10.60. Prentice-Hall

Harnwell, Gaylord P., and W. E. Stephens. Atomic physics. 1955. 9.50. McGraw

Hausmann, E., and Edgar P. Slack. Physics. il. 1957. 8.00. Van Nostrand

Hodgman, Charles D. Handbook of chemistry and physics. 12.00. Chemical Rubber (R)

McCue, J. J. G. World of atoms. 1956. 7.00. Ronald

Pauli, W. Niels Bohr and the development of physics. 1955. 4.50. Pergamon

Rogers, E. M. Physics for the inquiring mind: The methods, nature, and philosophy of physical science. 1959. 8.50. Princeton

Sears, Francis W. Mechanics, wave motion and heat. 1958. 9.75. Addison-Wesley

Semat, Henry. Introduction to atomic and nuclear physics. 1962. 7.50. Holt, Rinehart & Winston

Shortley, George H., and Dudley E. Williams. Elements of physics. 1961. 14.00. Prentice-Hall

PHYSICS--DICTIONARIES (530.03)

Ballentyne, D. W. C., and L. E. Q. Walker. Dictionary of named effects and laws in chemistry. 1961. 6.75. Macmillan

Encyclopaedic dictionary of physics. 9 vols. 298.00. Collier-Macmillan

Gray, H. J. Dictionary of physics. 1958. 15.00. Wiley (R)

Hyman, Charles J. Dictionary of physics and allied sciences, German-English. 1959. 9.00. Ungar (R)

Idlin, Ralph. Dictionary of physics and allied sciences, English-German. 1961. 11.50. Ungar (R)

International dictionary of physics and electronics. il. 1961. 27.85. Van Nostrand

PHYSICS--HISTORY (530.09)

Aristotle. Physics. tr. by Richard Hope. il. 1961. 6.00. U. of Nebr.

Cajori, Florian. History of physics. 4.00. Smith, Peter

Einstein, Albert, and Leopold Infeld. Evolution of physics. il. 1938. 4.50. S. and S.

Fraser, Charles G. Half-hours with great scientists. 1948. 9.00. U. of Toronto

Galilei, Galileo. Dialogues concerning two new sciences. tr. by Henry Crew and Alfonso de Salvio. 3.50. Northwestern

Galilei, Galileo. On motion, and On mechanics. 1960. 5.00. U. of Wis.

Gamow, George. Biography of physics. il. 1961. 5.95. Harper

Holton, G., and D. H. D. Roller. Foundations of modern physical science. 1958. 8.75. Addison-Wesley

Lemon, Harvey B. From Galileo to the nuclear age. il. 1946. 9.50. U. of Chicago

Newton, Isaac. Newton's philosophy of nature - selected writings. 1953. 2.35. Hafner

Vries, Leonard, de. Book of the atom. tr. by E. G. Breeze. il. 1960. 3.95. Macmillan

Wilson, William. Hundred years of physics. 3.50. Macmillan

PHYSICS--PHILOSOPHY (530.101)

Bohr, Niels. Atomic physics and human knowledge. 1958. 3.95. Wiley

Bridgman, Percy Williams. Logic of modern physics. 1946. 4.50. Macmillan

Campbell, Norman Robert. Foundations of experimental science. (Formerly titled; Physics: The elements) 1957. pap. 2.95. Dover

Capek, Milio. Philosophical impact of contemporary physics. 1961. 7.50. Van Nostrand

De Broglie, Louis. Physics and microphysics. 1954. 4.50. Pantheon

Friedrich, Lawrence W. Nature of physical knowledge. 1960. 4.50. Indiana

Hutten, Ernest H. Language of modern physics: An introduction to the philosophy of science. 1956. 3.75. Macmillan

Jeans, J. H. New background of science. 1934. 4.50. Cambridge U. P.

Jeans, J. H. Physics and philosophy. 1942. 4.50. Cambridge U. P.

Millikan, R. A. Evolution in science and religion. 1927. 3.00. Yale

Schlegel, Richard. Time and the physical world. 1961. 7.50. Mich. State

Smith, Vincent E. Philosophy of physics. 1961. pap. 2.50. St. Johns

Watson, W. H. On understanding physics. 1938. 4.50. Cambridge U. P.

PHYSIOLOGICAL CHEMISTRY (540)

Fearon, William R. Introduction to biochemistry. by William J. E. Jessop. il. 1961. 8.00. Academic Press

Goodwin, Trevor W. Recent advances in biochemistry. 1960. 11.50. Little

Harper, Harold A. Review of physiological chemistry. il. 1961. 5.50. Lange
Kleiner, Israel S., and James M. Orten. Biochemistry. il. 1962. 9.75. Mosby
McElroy, William D. Cellular physiology and biochemistry. 1961. 3.75. Prentice-Hall
Walker, B. S., and others. Chemistry and human health. 1956. 6.50. McGraw
PHYSIOLOGY (612)
Anthony, Catherine P. Structure and function of the body. il. 1960. 3.00. Mosby
Baillif, Ralph N., and Donald L. Kimmel. Structure and function of the human body. il. 1945. 3.75. Lippincott
Best, Charles Herbert, and Norman Burke Taylor. Human body: Its anatomy and physiology. il. 1956. 7.95. Holt, Rinehart & Winston
Carlson, Anton J., and others. Machinery of the body. 1961. 6.50. U. of Chicago
Chase, Peter P. Your wonderful body. 1957. 5.95. Prentice-Hall
Clendening, Logan. Human body. il. 1945. 6.75. Knopf
D'Armour, Fred E. Basic physiology. 1961. 7.95. U. of Chicago
DeCoursey, Russell M. Human organism. 1961. 7.50. McGraw
Guyton, Arthur C. Function of the human body. il. 1959. 7.50. Saunders
Langley, L. L., and E. Cheraskin. Physiology of man. il. 1958. 7.95. McGraw
McDowall, Robert J. S. Handbook of physiology. il. 1960. 12.50. Lippincott (R)
Miller, Benjamin F., and Ruth Goode. Man and his body. 1960. 5.95. S. and S.
Pavlov, Ivan P. Selected works. 1955. 4.50. San Francisco
Riddle, Janet T. E. Elementary textbook of anatomy and physiology applied to nursing. 1961. 3.50. Williams & Wilkins
Rogers, Terence A. Elementary human physiology. il. 1961. 6.50. Wiley
Tallmadge, G. Kasten. Basic biology of man. 1952. 3.00. Random
Williams, Jesse F. Healthful living. il. 1957. 5.20. Macmillan
PICASSO, PABLO, 1881- (927)
Arnheim, Rudolf. Picasso's Guernica: The autobiography of a work of art. il. 10.00. U. of Calif.
Duncan, David Douglas. Private world of Pablo Picasso. 1958. 4.95. Harper
Horodisch, Abraham. Picasso as a book artist. il. 1962. 6.50. World Pub.
Picasso, Pablo. Ceramics of Picasso. il. 1960. 7.00. World Pub.
Picasso, Pablo. Pablo Picasso: Drawings. by Maurice Jardot. il. 1959. 15.00. Abrams
Picasso, Pablo. Picasso cubism to present. il. 3.95. Abrams
Picasso, Pablo. Picasso: 55 years of his graphic work. by Bernhard Geiser. il. 1955. 10.00. Abrams
Picasso, Pablo. Picasso's Picassos. by David D. Duncan. il. 1961. 30.00. Harper
PIGMENTS (751.2)
Fox, Harold M., and Gwyne Vevers. Nature of animal colours. 1960. 6.50. Macmillan
Martin, J. H., and W. M. Morgans. Glossary of pigments, varnish and lacquer constituents. 1959. 3.50. Tudor
Mayer, Ralph. Artist's handbook of materials and techniques. 1956. 6.75. Viking (R)
Mayer, Ralph. Painter's craft. il. 1948. 6.00. Van Nostrand
PILGRIMS AND PILGRIMAGES (248)
Jusserand, Jean J. English wayfaring life in the Middle Ages. 1950. 4.50. Barnes & Noble
Morton, Henry C., and Fulton J. Sheen. This is Rome: A pilgrimage in words and pictures. il. 1960. 4.95. Hawthorn
Morton, Henry C. V., and Fulton J. Sheen. This is the Holy Land: A pilgrimage in words and pictures. il. 1961. 4.95. Hawthorn
PISTOLS (623.443)
Askins, Charles. Pistol shooter's book. 1961. 8.50. Stackpole
Guns and Ammunition. Complete book of handgunning. 1961. 7.50. Prentice-Hall
Smith, Walter H. B. Book of pistols and revolvers. 10.00. Stackpole
Weston, Paul B. Combat shooting for police. il. 1961. 7.50. Thomas, C. C.

PLAGUE (616. 9232)

Bartel, Roland.   London in plague and fire, 1665-1666. 1957. pap. 1.40. Heath

Defoe, Daniel.   Journal of the plague year. 1.95. Dutton

Mullett, Charles F.   Bubonic plague and England: An essay in the history of public health. 1956. 9.00. U. of Ky.

Nohl, Johannes.   Black death. pap. 0.35. Ballantine

Politzer, R.   Plague. 10.00. Int. Doc. Service-Columbia

PLANETS (523.4)

Kopal, Zdenek.   Figures of equilibrium of celestial bodies. il. 1960. 3.00. U. of Wis.

Ley, Willy.   Conquest of space. il. 1949. 5.75. Viking

Moore, Patrick.   Planets. 1962. 5.95. Norton

Nourse, Alan E.   Nine Planets. il. 1960. 5.95. Harper

Velikovsky, Immanuel.   Worlds in collision. 1950. 4.50. Doubleday

Watson, Fletcher G.   Between the planets. pap. 1.25. Doubleday

PLANT CELLS AND TISSUES (581.4)

Allard, Robert W.   Principles of plant breeding. 1960. 9.75. Wiley

Crane, Morley B., and William J. C. Lawrence.   Genetics of garden plants. 1952. 4.00. St. Martins

Darlington, C. D., and Wylie, A. P.   Chromosome atlas of flowering plants 10.50. Macmillan

De Vries, Hugo.   Plant-breeding. il. 3.00. Open Ct.

Eames, Arthur, and Laurence MacDaniels.   An introduction to plant anatomy. 1947. 8.50. McGraw

Esau, Katherine.   Anatomy of seed plants. il. 1960. 6.95. Wiley

Esau, K.   Plant anatomy. 1953. 9.75. Wiley

Hayes, Herbert K., and others.   Methods of plant breeding. il. 1955. 10.50. McGraw

PLANT DISEASES (581.2)

Anderson, Harry W.   Diseases of fruit crops. 10.00. McGraw

Beaumont, A.   Diseases of garden plants. 6.50. Transatlantic

Chester, Kenneth S.   Nature and prevention of plant diseases. 1947. 8.95. McGraw

Dimock, A. E.   Gardener's ABC of pest and disease. 1953. 2.95. Barrows

Elliott, C.   Manual of bacterial plant pathogens. 1951. 6.50. Ronald

Headstrom, Richard.   Garden friends and foes. il. 1954. 3.50. Washburn

Lawfield, W. N., and J. Van Konynenburg.   Encyclopaedia of garden pests and diseases. 1959. 10.50. Transatlantic

Shurtleff, Malcolm.   How to control plant diseases in home and garden. il. 1962. 4.95. Iowa State

Walker, John Charles.   Plant pathology. il. 1957. 11.50. McGraw

Westcott, Cynthia.   Plant disease handbook. il. 1960. 15.00. Van Nostrand

PLANT LORE (581.508)

Lehner, Ernst, and Johanna.   Folklore and odysseys of food and medicinal plants. il. 1961. 4.95. Tudor

Lehner, Ernst, and Johanna.   Folklore and symbolism of flowers, plants and trees. il. 1960. 4.95. Tudor

Peattie, Donald Culross.   Natural history of trees of eastern and central North America. il. 1950. 6.00. Houghton (R)

PLANT PHYSIOLOGY (581.1)

Adriance, Guy W., and Fred R. Brison.   Propagation of horticultural plants. 1955. 7.95. McGraw

American Joint Committee on Horticultural Nomenclature.   Standardized plant names. 1942. 10.50. McFarland, J. Horace (R)

Baily, Liberty H.   Nursery manual. il. 1920. 7.50. Macmillan

Bonner, James, and Arthur W. Galston.   Principles of plant physiology. il. 1952. 6.50. Freeman

Carleton, R. Milton.   Index to common names of herbaceous plants. 1959. 10.00. Shoe String

Free, Montague. Plant propagation in pictures. il. 1957. 4.95. Doubleday

Godwin, H. Plant biology. 1945. 3.25. Cambridge U. P.

James, William O. Introduction to plant physiology. il. 1955. 3.20. Oxford
U. P.

Meyer, Bernard S., and Richard H. Bohning. Introduction to plant physiology.
il. 1960. 7.50. Van Nostrand

Milne, L., and M. Plant life. 6.95. Prentice-Hall

Scientific American. Plant life. 1957. 1.45. S. and S.

Sheat, Wilfred G. Propagation of trees, shrubs, and conifers. 1953. 5.00. St.
Martins

Singleton, W. Ralph. Nuclear radiation in food and agriculture. il. 1958. 9.50.
Van Nostrand

PLANTS (581)

Bassham, J. A., and Melvin Calvin. Path of carbon in photosynthesis. 1957.
3.95. Prentice-Hall

Bower, F. O. Origin of land flora. 1959. 10.00. Hafner

Crafts, A. S., and others. Water in the physiology of plants. 1949. 6.50. Ronald

Davies, D. D. Intermediary metabolism in plants. 1961. 4.00. Cambridge U.P.

Gilbert, Frank A. Mineral njtrition and the balance of life. il. 1957. 5.95. U.
of Okla.

Hillman, William S. Physiology of flowering. il. 1962. 4.50. Holt, Rinehart &
Winston

Squires, Mabel. Art of drying plants and flowers. il. 1958. 4.50. Barrows

Stebbins, G. L. Variation in plants. 1950. 10.00. Columbia

PLANTS, CULTIVATED (581.5)

Bold, Harold C. Morphology of plants. 1957. 9.25. Harper

Eastwood, T., and others. Soilless growth of plants. 1947. 6.50. Reinhold

Jordan, Emil L., and others. Hammond's Encyclopedia of pets, plants, and
animals. il. 1959. 7.50. Hammond

Kramer, Paul J. Plant and soil water relationships. 1949. 8.50. McGraw

Stiles, W., and W. Leach. Respiration in plants. 1952. 2.25. Wiley

Veen, R. van der, and G. Meijer. Light and plant growth. il. 1960. 10.25.
Macmillan

PLASTICS (547.843)

Allcott, Arnold. Plastics today. 1960. 2.90. Oxford U. P.

Cope, D. W. Plastics book. il. 1960. 4.50. Goodheart

Corey, E. Raymond. Development of markets for new materials. 1956. 4.00.
Harv. Bus. School

Groneman, Chris H. Plastics made practical. 1948. 4.50. Bruce

Redfarn, C. A., and J. Bedford. Experimental plastics for students. il. 1960.
4.25. Wiley

Simonds, Herbert R. Concise guide to plastics. 1957. 6.95. Reinhold

PLATO, 427?-347 B.C. (921.94)

Barker, Ernest. Greek political theory: Plato and his predecessors. 1947.
4.00. Barnes & Noble

Brumbaugh, Robert S. Plato for the modern age. 1962. 3.95. Crowell-Collier

Crossman, Richard H.S. Plato today. 1959. 4.00. Oxford U. P.

Cushman, Robert E. Therapeia: Plato's conception of philosophy. 1958. 6.00.
U. of N. C.

Field, G. C. Philosophy of Plato. 1949. 1.70. Oxford U. P.

Gulley, Norman. Plato's theory of knowledge. 1962. 4.50. Barnes & Noble

Lodge, Rupert C. Philosophy of Plato. 5.50. Humanities

Lodge, R. C. Plato's theory of art. 5.00. Humanities

Lynch, William F. Integrating mind: An exploration into Western thought. 1962.
3.95. Sheed

Mahdi, Muhsin. Alfarabi's Philosophy of Plato and Aristotle. 1962. 4.75.
Free Press

Murphy, N. R. Interpretation of Plato's Republic. 1951. 4.00. Oxford U. P.

Nettleship, R. L. Lectures on the Republic of Plato. 1901. 3.50. St. Martins
Nettleship, R. L. Theory of education in Plato's Republic. 1935. 1.40. Oxford
    U. P.
Robinson, Richard. Plato's earlier dialectic. 1953. 4.80. Oxford U. P.
Ross, W. D. Plato's theory of ideas. 1951. 4.00. Oxford U. P.
Shorey, Paul. What Plato said. 1957. 11.50. U. of Chicago
Taylor, Alfred E. Commentary on Plato's Timaeus. 1928. 9.60. Oxford U. P.
Taylor, A. E. Mind of Plato. 1960. 4.40. U. of Mich.
Taylor, Alfred E. Plato, the man and his work. 4.50. Humanities
Winspear, Alban Dewes. Genesis of Plato's thought. 5.00. Russell
PLAY (790)
Axline, Virginia M. Play therapy. 1947. 6.00. Houghton
Butler, George D. Playgrounds, their administration and operation. 1960. 7.00.
    Ronald
Caillois, Roger. Man, play, and games. 1961. 5.00. Free Press
Hartley, Ruth E., and Robert M. Goldenson. Complete book of children's play.
    il. 1957. 5.95. Crowell
Neumeyer, Martin H., and E. S. Leisure and recreation. 1958. 6.00. Ronald
Page, Hilary. Playtime in the first five years. il. 1954. 3.50. Lippincott
Sapora, A. V., and E. D. Mitchell. Theory of play and recreation. 1961. 6.50.
    Ronald
Williams, Wayne R. Recreation places. 1958. 6.50. Reinhold
PLOTS (DRAMA, NOVEL, ETC.) (808.2)
Armstrong, Spencer. 101 of the world's greatest books. il. 1954. 5.50. Hawthorn
Gillett, Margaret, and E. A. Grozier. Plot outlines of 101 best novels. 1962.
    4.95. Barnes & Noble
Goodman, Paul. Structure of literature. 1954. 5.00. U. of Chicago
Harris, William. Basic patterns of plot. 1959. 3.95. U. of Okla. (R)
Haydn, Hiram, and Edmund Fuller. Thesaurus of book digests. 1949. pap.
    1.95. Crown (R)
Heath, Eric. Story plotting simplified. 1941. 3.00. Writer
Holzknecht, Karl J. Outlines of Tudor and Stuart plays, 1497-1642. il. 1952.
    3.75. Barnes & Noble
PLUMBING (696)
Babbitt, Harold E. Plumbing. 1960. 13.50. McGraw
Davis, Paul. Plumbing, heating, and piping estimator's guide. 1960. 7.00.
    McGraw
Manas, Vincent T. National plumbing code handbook: Standards and design
    information. il. 1957. 12.50. McGraw
POE, EDGAR ALLAN, 1809-1849 (928.13)
Allen, Hervey. Israfel: Life and times of Edgar Allan Poe. il. 1949. 8.50.
    Rinehart
Baudelaire, Charles P. On Poe: Critical papers. 1952. 4.00. Bald Eagle
Bittner, William. Poe: A biography. 1962. 6.50. Little
Bonaparte, Marie. Life and works of Edgar Allan Poe. 8.50. Hillary
Buranelli, Vincent. Edgar Allan Poe. 3.50. Twayne
Campbell, Killis. Mind of Poe, and other studies. 1962. 6.50. Russell
Davidson, Edward H. Poe: A critical study. 1957. 4.75. Harvard
Levin, Harry. Power of blackness. 1958. 4.00. Knopf
Quinn, Arthur H. Edgar Allan Poe: A critical biography. il. 1941. 10.00. Meredith
Winwar, Frances. Haunted palace, a life of Edgar Allan Poe. il. 1959. 6.00.
    Harper
POETRY (808.1)
Arnold, Matthew. Essays in criticism: Second series. 1.50. St. Martins
Baldwin, C. S. Ancient rhetoric and poetic. 1959. 4.25. Smith, Peter
Baldwin, C. S. Medieval rhetoric and poetic to 1400. 1959. 4.50. Smith, Peter
Baldwin, C. S. Renaissance literary theory and practice. 1959. 4.25. Smith,
    Peter

Baxter, James K. Fire and the anvil. 1.50. Cambridge U. P.

Bloom, Edward A., and others. Order of poetry: An introduction. 1961. pap. 1.50. Odyssey

Boulton, M. Anatomy of poetry. 2.50. Hillary

Bowra, Cecil Maurice. Heritage of symbolism. 4.25. St. Martins

Bradley, Andrew C. Oxford lectures on poetry. 4.00. St. Martins

Coleridge, Samuel Taylor. Biographia literia. 2 vols. 1907. 4,80. Oxford U. P.

Cooper, Charles W., and John Holmes. Preface to poetry. 1946. 5.50. Harcourt

Crane, R. S. Languages of criticism and the strucutre of poetry. il. 1953. 5.50. U. of Toronto

Daiches, David. Critical approaches to literature. 1956. 9.00. Prentice-Hall

Deutsch, Babette. Poetry handbook: A dictionary of terms. 1962. 3.95. Funk (R)

Dodds, A. E. Romantic theory of poetry. 1962. 7.50. Russell

Doubleday, Neal Frank. Studies in poetry: An introduction to the critical reading of poems. 1949. 3.50. Harper

Drew, Elizabeth. Poetry: A modern guide. 1959. 3.95. Norton

Eastman, Max. Enjoyment of poetry, and Anthology for the enjoyment of poetry. 7.50. Scribner

Eliot, T. S. On poetry and poets. 1957. 4.50. Farrar, Straus

Eliot, T. S. Three voices of poetry. 1954. 1.75. Cambridge U. P.

Empson, William. Seven types of ambiguity. 4.50. New Directions

Gibson, Robert. Modern French poets on poetry. 1961. 7.50. Cambridge U. P.

Gokak, Vinayak K. Poetic approach to language. 1952. 3.95. Oxford U. P.

Graves, Robert. Oxford addresses on poetry. 4.95. Doubleday

Graves, Robert. White goddess. 1958. pap. 1.65. Vintage

Hamilton, G. R. Poetry and contemplation. 2.50. Cambridge U. P.

Hamilton, Ann. Seven principles of poetry. 4.00. Writer

Hamm, Victor M. Language, truth and poetry. 1960. 2.50. Marquette

Heller, Erich. Hazard of modern poetry. 1953. 6.00. Saifer

Highet, Gilbert. Powers of poetry. 1960. 6.00. Oxford U. P.

Hillyer, Robert. First principles of verse. 1938. 3.00. Writer

James, David G. Scepticism and poetry. 1960. 5.00. Barnes & Noble

Kreuzer, James R. Elements of poetry. 1955. 3.25. Macmillan

Krieger, Murray. New apologists for poetry. 1956. 4.00. U. of Minn.

Lieder, Paul R., and Robert Withington. Art of literary criticism. 1941. 4.00. Appleton

MacLeish, Archibald. Poetry and experience. 1961. 4.00. Houghton

Maritain, Jacques. Art and scholasticism and the frontiers of poetry. by Joseph W. Evans. 1962. 5.00. Scribner

Millett, Fred. Reading poetry. 1950. 3.00. Harper

Perrine, Laurence. Sound and sense: An introduction to poetry. 1956. pap. 2.50. Harcourt

Pound, Ezra. Literary essays. by T. S. Eliot. 1953. 6.00. New Directions

Pratt, John C. Meaning of modern poetry. 5.95. Doubleday

Rukeyser, Muriel. Life of poetry. 3.00. Wyn

Santayana, George. Interpretations of poetry and religion. 1958. 3.50. Smith, Peter

Schlauch, Margaret. Modern English and American poetry. 1959. 4.50. Hillary

Sen Gupta, S. C. Towards a theory of the imagination. 1959. 3.35. Oxford U. P.

Dewell, Elizabeth. Orphic voice: Poetry and natural history. 1960. 7.50. Yale

Sitwell, Edith. Poet's notebook. 1950. 4.00. Little

Spender, Stephen. Making of a poem. 1962. 4.00. Norton

Stauffer, Donald A. Nature of poetry. 1946. 3.90. Norton

Tate, Allen. On the limits of poetry. 4.00. Swallow, A.

Tillyard, E. M. W. Poetry direct and oblique. 1959. 2.50. Barnes & Noble

Untermeyer, Louis, and others. Doorways to poetry. 1938. 3.16. Harcourt

Untermeyer, Louis. Forms of poetry: A pocket dictionary of verse. 1926. 2.95. Harcourt

Viereck, Peter. Dream and responsibility: Tension between poetry and society. 1953. 2.00. U. Pr. of Wash., D. C.

Whalley, George. Poetic process. 4.50. Hillary

POETRY--COLLECTIONS (808.81)

Burnshaw, Stanley. Poem itself. pap. 2.25. Meridian

Cook, Roy J. One hundred and one famous poems. 2.00. Reilly & Lee

Creekmore, Hubert. Little treasury of world poetry. il. 1955. 5.00. Scribner

Doubleday, Neal Frank. Studies in poetry: An introduction to the critical reading of poems. 1949. 3.50. Harper

Engle, Paul, and Joseph Langland. Poet's choice. 1962. 6.95. Dial

Huxley, Aldous. Texts and pretexts. 1933. 3.95. Harper

Lowell, Robert. Imitations. 1961. 4.50. Farrar, Straus

Ross, David. Poet's gold. 5.00. Devin

Van Doren, Mark. Anthology, of world poetry. 8.75. Harcourt

Van Doren, Mark and Garibaldi M. Lapolla. World's best poems. 4.95. World Pub.

Wells, Henry W. 1001 Poems of mankind. 1953. 5.00. McKay

POETRY--HISTORY AND CRITICISM (809.1)

Aristotle. Art of poetry: A Greek view of poetry and drama. by W. H. Fyfe. 1940. 1.60. Oxford U. P.

Aristotle. On poetry and style. tr. by G. M. A. Grube. 1958. 3.00. Bobbs

Aristotle. Poetics. bd. with Longinus' On the sublime, and Demetrius' On style. 3.50. Harvard

Aristotle. Poetics. tr. by S. H. Butcher. 1961. 3.50. Hill & Wang

Aristotle. Rhetoric and poetics. 1.95. Modern Lib.

Arnstein, Flora J. Adventure into poetry. 1951. 3.00. Stanford

Baldwin, Michael. Poetry without tears. 1959. 3.00. Hillary

Bernhardt, W. F. Granger's index to poetry. 1962. 65.00. Columbia (

Blair, Walter, and W. K. Chandler. Approaches to poetry. 1953. 4.75. Appleton

Bowra, Cecil Maurice. Creative experiment. 4.00. Smith, Peter

Bowra, Cecil M. Inspiration and poetry. 4.25. St. Martins

Brewer, Wilmon. Talks about poetry. 2.00. Jones, Marshall

Brooks, Cleanth. Modern poetry and the tradition. 1939. 3.75. U. of N. C.

Burnshaw, Stanley. Poem itself: 45 modern poets in a new presentation. 1960. 6.90. Holt, Rinehart & Winston

Day, Lewis, C. Poetic image. 1947. 2.70. Oxford U. P.

Day, Lewis, Cecil. Poet's task. 1951. 0.75. Oxford U. P.

Drew, Elizabeth. Discovering poetry. 1933. 3.95. Norton

Dryden, John. Of dramatic poesy, and other critical essays. 2 vols. 1.95 ea. Dutton

Durham, Willard H. Critical essays of the eighteenth century. 8.50. Russell

Eliot, T. S. Use of poetry and the use of criticism. 1955. 3.00. Barnes & Noble

Flores, Angel. Anthology of medieval lyrics. 1.95. Modern Lib.

Gilbert, Allan H. Literary criticism: Plato to Dryden. 1962. 6.50. Wayne

Gurrey, Percival. Appreciation of poetry. 1935. 1.20. Oxford U. P.

Hastings, Henry C. Spoken poetry on records and tapes. 1957. pap. 1.75. A. L. A. (R)

Hillyer, Robert S. In pursuit of poetry. 1960. 4.75. McGraw

Housman, A. E. Name and nature of poetry. 1933. 1.75. Cambridge U. P.

Jarrell, Randall. Poetry and the age. 1953. pap. 1.45. Vintage

Lowell, Amy. Poetry and poets. 1930. 2.25. Houghton

MacLeish, Archibald. Poetry and experience. 1961. 4.00. Houghton

Murray, Gilbert. Classical tradition in poetry. 1927. 3.00. Harvard

Neff, Emery. Revolution in European poetry, 1660-1900. 1940. 3.50. Columbia

New anthology of modern poetry. 2.95. Modern Lib.

Pound, Ezra. Literary essays. by T. S. Eliot. 1953. 6.00. New Directions

Pound, Ezra. Spirit of romance. 1952. 4.00. New Directions

Press, John. Chequer'd shade. 1958. 5.75. Oxford U. P.

Sansom, Clive. World of poetry. 1960. 4.50. Writer
Shapiro, Karl J. In defense of ignorance. 1960. 4.00. Random
Shapiro, Karl. Prose keys to modern poetry. 1962. pap. 2.25. Harper
Sitwell, Edith. Poet's notebook. 1950. 4.00. Little
Tate, Allen. Language of poetry. 1960. 4.50. Russell
Viereck, Peter. Dream and responsibility: Tension between poetry and society. 1953. lib. bdg. 2.00. U. Pr. of Wash., D.C.
Pope, Alexander. Essay on criticism. by J. Churton Collins. 1.00. St. Martins

POETS (808.1092)

Bowra, C. Maurice. Greek lyric poetry from Aleman to Simonides. 1961. 7.20. Oxford U. P.
Brereton, Geoffrey. Introduction to the French poets: Villon to the present day. 1957. 5.00. Oxford U. P.
De Quincey, Thomas. Reminiscences of the English lake poets. 1.95. Dutton
Emden, Cecil S. Poets in their letters. 1959. 3.40. Oxford U. P.
Johnson, Samuel. Lives of the English poets. 2 vols. 2.25 ea. Oxford U. P.
Johnson, Samuel. Lives of the poets. 2 vols. 1.95 ea. Dutton
Poggioli, Renato. Poets of Russia, 1890-1930. 1960. 8.75. Harvard
Thomas, Henry, and Dana Lee. Living biographies of great poets. 1959. 2.50. Doubleday
Wilson, Robert N. Man made plain. 1959. 3.75. Allen, Howard

POISONS (615.9)

Bensley, E. H., and G. E. Joron. Handbook of treatment of acute poisoning. 1958. 4.00. Williams & Wilkins (R)
Kaye, Sidney. Handbook of emergency toxicology. il. 1961. 10.75. Thomas, C. C.
Lucas, G. H. W. Symptoms and treatment of acute poisoning. 1953. 4.00. Macmillan
Wickenden, Leonard. Our daily poison. 3.50. Devin

POLAND (943.8)

Galbraith, John K. Journey to Poland and Yugoslavia. 1958. 3.00. Harvard
Halecki, Oscar. History of Poland. 4.25. Roy Pub.
Oakes, John B. Edge of freedom: Eastern Europe and Africa. 1961. 3.50. Harper
Stern, H. Peter. Struggle for Poland. 1953. 2.00. Pub. Affairs

POLICE (351.74)

Ashenhust, Paul H. Police and the people. 1957. 5.50. Thomas, C. C.
Clowers, Norman L. Patrolman patterns, problems, and procedures. 1962. 8.75. Thomas C. C.
Germann, A. C. Police executive development. 1962. 5.00. Thomas, C. C.
Hazelet, John C. Police report writing. il. 1960. 8.00. Thomas, C. C.
Holman, Mary. Police officer and the child. il. 1962. 5.50. Thomas, C. C.
Kenney, John P., and John B. Williams. Police operations. 1961. 7.50. Thomas, C. C.
Millspaugh, A. C. Local democracy and crime control. 1936. 2.00. Brookings
Morrish, Reginald. Police and crime-detection today. il. 1955. 2.40. Oxford U. P.
Smith, Bruce. Police systems in the United States. 1960. 6.00. Harper
Soderman, Harry, and John J. O'Connell. Modern criminal investigation. by Charles E. O'Hara. il. 1962. 7.50. Funk

POLIOMYELITIS (616.835)

Debre, R., and others. Poliomyelitis. 8.00. Int. Doc. Service-Columbia
Kenny, Elizabeth, Sister, and Martha Ostenso. And they shall walk: The life story of Sister Elizabeth Kenny. il. 1943. 4.00. Dodd
Trueta, Josep, and others. Handbook on poliomyelitis. il. 1956. 3.75. Davis

POLISH LITERATURE (891.85)

Kridl, Manfred. Anthology of Polish literature. 1957. 8.50. Columbia
Kridl, M. Survey of Polish literature and culture. 1957. 9.50. Columbia

POLITICAL PARTIES (329.9)

Barron, Richard. Parties and politics in modern France. 1958. 4.50. Pub. Affairs

Comfort, George O. Professional politicians. 1958. 1.00. Pub. Affairs
David, Paul T., and others. Politics of national party conventions. 1960. 10.00.
  Brookings
Duverger, M. Political parties. 1954. 6.95. Wiley
Hodgkin, Thomas. African political parties. 3.00. Smith, Peter
LaPonce, J. A. Government of the Fifth Republic. 1961. 7.50. U. of Calif.
Leiserson, Avery. Parties and politics: An institutional and behavioral approach.
  1958. 5.75. Knopf
McDonald, Neil A. Study of political parties. 1955. pap. 0.95. Random
Mallory, Walter H. Political handbook of the world. 1963. 4.95. Harper (R)
Michels, Robert. Political parties. 6.00. Free Press
Neumann, Sigmund. Modern political parties. 1955. 8.50. U. of Chicago
Pollock, James K., and others. German democracy at work. 1955. 4.50.
  U. of Mich.
Ruggiero, Guido de. History of European liberalism. 4.50. Smith, Peter
Scalapino, Robert, and Junnosuke Masumi. Parties and politics in contemporary
  Japan. 1962. 3.75. U. of Calif.
Taylor, Lily R. Party politics in the age of caesar. 1962. 4.00. Smith, Peter
Weiner, M. Party politics in India. 1957. 5.00. Princeton
POLITICAL PARTIES--U.S. (329)
Agar, Herbert. Price of union. 1950. 8.50. Houghton
Binkley, Wilfred E. American political parties. 1958. 5.75. Knopf
Bone, Hugh A. American politics and the party system. 1955. 7.25. McGraw
Bowles, Chester. Coming political breakthrough. 1959. 4.00. Harper
Charles, Joseph. Origins of the American party system. 3.25. Smith, Peter
Cunningham, Noble E., Jr. Jeffersonian Republicans: The formation of party
  organization, 1789-1801. 1958. 6.00. U. of N. C.
Ewing, Cortez A. M. Congressional elections, 1896-1944. 1947. 2.00. U. of
  Okla.
Goodman, William. Two-party system in the United States. il. 1960. 6.85.
  Van Nostrand
Hesseltine, William. Rise and fall of third parties. 2.50. Smith, Peter
Key, V. O., Jr. Politics, parties, and pressure groups. il. 1958. 6.50.
  Crowell
Lazarsfeld, P. F., and others. People's choice. 1948. 3.75. Columbia
Lipset, Seymour M. Political man: The social bases of politics. 1959. 4.95.
  Doubleday
Lockard, Duane. New England state politics. il. 1959. 6.00. Princeton
Millspaugh, Arthur C. Party organization and machinery in Michigan since
  1890. 1917. 3.00. Johns Hopkins
Nash, Howard P. Third parties in American politics. il. 1958. 6.00. Pub.
  Affairs
Patterson, C. Perry. Presidential government in the United States. 1947. 4.00.
  U. of N. C.
Porter, Kirk H., and Donald B. Johnson. National party platforms, 1840-1956.
  1956. 10.00. U. of Ill.
Ranney, Austin, and Willmoore Kendall. Democracy and the American party
  system. 1956. 9.75. Harcourt
Truman, David Bicknell. Congressional party. 1959. 7.50. Wiley
Vorees, Edith. Political parties in the United States. 1960. 2.75. Pageant
Westerfield, H. B. Foreign policy and party politics: Pearl Harbor to Korea.
  1955. 6.00. Yale
POLITICAL SCIENCE (320)
Adam, Thomas R. Elements of government: An introduction to political
  science. 1960. 6.75. Random
Aristotle. Politics. 1932. 3.50. Harvard
Bagehot, Walter. Physics and politics. 1959. 3.25. Smith, Peter
Barker, Ernest. Principles of social and political theory. 1951. 4.80. Oxford
  U. P.

Beard, Charles A. Economic basis of politics and related writings. 1957. pap. 1.45. Vintage

Bentham, Jeremy. Bentham's handbook of political fallacies. 1952. 4.75. Johns Hopkins

Binder, Leonard. Iran: Political development in changing society. 1962. 7.50. U. of Calif.

Bosanquet, Bernard. Philosophical theory of the state. 1899. 4.25. St. Martins

Burke, Edmund. Philosophy of Edmund Burke. 1961. 5.95. U. of Mich.

Calhoun, John C. Disquisition on government. 1958. 2.50. Smith, Peter

Canavan, Francis P. Political reason of Edmund Burke. 1960. 5.00. Duke

Cantril, Hadley. Human nature and political systems. 1961. 3.00. Rutgers

Carter, Gwendolen M., and John H. Herz. Government and politics in the twentieth century. 1961. 4.75. Praeger

Cassirer, E. Myth of the state. 1946. 5.00. Yale

Catlin, George E. G. Systematic politics. 1962. 7.50. U. of Toronto

Collingwood, R. G. New leviathan; or, Man, society, civilization and barbarism. 1942. 6.10. Oxford U. P.

Corry, J. A., and Henry J. Abraham. Elements of democratic government. 1958. 6.50. Oxford U. P.

Dahl, Robert A., and Charles E. Lindbolm. Politics, economics, and welfare. 1953. 6.50. Harper

Dillon, Conley H., and others. Introduction to political science. il. 1958. 4.85. Van Nostrand

Easton, David. Political system. 1953. 5.00. Knopf

Ebenstein, William. Modern political thought: The great issues. 1960. 8.00. Holt, Rinehart & Winston

Eisenstadt, S. N. Political systems of empires. 1962. 10.00. Free Press

Friedrich, Carl J. Constitutional government and democracy. 8.75. Ginn

Halle, L. J. Men and nations. 1962. 4.75. Princeton

Hegel, G. W. F. Philosophy of right. by T. M. Knox. 1942. 4.80. Oxford U. P.

Hermens, Ferdinand A. Introduction to modern politics. 1959. 5.00. U. of Notre Dame

Hobbes, Thomas. Leviathan. 1950. 2.95. Dutton

Jefferson, Thomas. Political writings. 1955. pap. 1.00. Bobbs

Laski, Harold J. Grammar of politics. 1957. 6.00. Humanities

Laslett, Peter. Philosophy, politics and society. 3.00. Macmillan

Lasswell, Harold D. Political writings. 3 vols. in 1. 1951. 7.50. Free Press

Lasswell, Harold D., and Abraham Kaplan. Power and society. 1950. 6.50. Yale

Lippmann, Walter. Good society. 1943. 5.00. Little

Lippmann, Walter. Public philosophy. 1955. 4.00. Little

Lipson, Leslie. Great issues of politics. 1960. 5.75. Prentice-Hall (R)

Locke, John. On politics and education. 1947. 1.75. Van Nostrand

Locke, John. Second treatise of government. 2.75. Bobbs

Locke, John. Two treatises of civil government. 1.95. Dutton

Loewenstein, Karl. Political power and the governmental process. 1957. 6.00. U. of Chicago

Mabbott, John D. State and the citizen: An introduction to political philosophy. 2.50. Hillary (R)

McDonald, Lee C. Western political theory: The modern age. 6.95. Harcourt

Machiavelli, Niccolo. Prince. 1.95. Dutton

Machiavelli, Niccolo. Prince, and Discourses. 1.95. Modern Lib.

MacIver, R. M. Modern state. 1926. 6.10. Oxford U. P.

MacIver, R. M. Web of government. 1947. 7.00. Macmillan

Malthus, Thomas R. Occassional papers on population and political economy. by Bernard Semmel. 1962. 8.50. Franklin, B.

Mannheim, Karl. Ideology and Utopia. pap. 1.35. Harcourt

Maritain, Jacques. Scholasticism and politics. pap. 0.95. Doubleday

Merriam, Charles E. Systematic politics. 1945. 5.00. U. of Chicago
Michels, Roberto. First lectures in political sociology. tr. by Alfred De
   Grazia. 1949. 2.75. U. of Minn.
Mill, James. Essay on government. 1955. pap. 0.60. Bobbs
Mises, Ludwig von. Bureaucracy. 1962. 4.50. Yale
Morgenthau, Hans J. Scientific man vs. power politics. 1946. 5.00. U. of
   Chicago
Neumann, Franz. Democratic and the authoritarian state. 1956. 6.00. Free
   Press
Niebuhr, Reinhold. Reinhold Niebuhr on politics. 6.50. Scribner
Paine, Thomas. Common sense, and other political writings. 1953. 3.25.
   Bobbs
Plato, Republic. 2 vols. 3.25 ea. Harvard
Plato. Statesman. tr. by J. B. Skemp. 1957. pap. 0.80. Bobbs
Ranney, Austin. Essays on the behavioral study of politics. 1962. 5.00. U. of
   Ill.
Riemer, Neal. Revival of democratic theory. 1962. pap. 1.95. Appleton
Rienow, Robert. Introduction to Government. 1956. 5.75. Knopf
Rogow, Arnold A. Government and politics. 1961. pap. 4.25. Crowell
Rousseau, Jean Jacques. Political writings. 1953. 3.00. Nelson
Rousseau, Jean J. Social contract. 1954. 2.75. Regnery
Rousseau, Jean Jacques. Social contract and Discourses. 1950. 2.95. Dutton
Rubinstein and Thumm. Challenge of politics: Ideas and issues. 1961. 6.00.
   Prentice-Hall
Sait, Edward McC. Political institutions: A preface. 1938. 5.00. Appleton
Santayana, George F. Dominations and powers. 1951. 7.50. Scribner
Simon, Yves. Philosophy of democratic government. 1951. 1.95. U. of Chicago
Spinoza, Benedict de. Political works. 1958. 10.10. Oxford U. P.
Strauss, Leo. Political philosophy of Hobbes. 1952. 6.00. U. of Chicago
Strauss, Leo. What is political philosophy, and other studies. 1959. 6.00.
   Free Press
Thomas Aquinas, Saint. Selected political writings. 2.75. Macmillan
Voegelin, Eric. New science of politics. 1952. 4.00. U. of Chicago
POLITICAL SCIENCE--HISTORY (320.9)
Barker, Ernest. Greek political theory: Plato and his predecessors. 1947.
   4.00. Barnes & Noble
Barker, Ernest. From Alexander to Constantine. 1956. 8.80. Oxford U. P.
Bowle, John. Western political thought. 1948. 4.00. Oxford U. P.
Brecht, A. Political theory: The foundations of twentieth-century political
   thought. 1959. 12.00. Princeton
Brinton, Crane. English political thought in the nineteenth century. 1962. pap.
   1.85. Harper
Brinton, Crane. Political ideas of the English romanticists. 1962. 6.50. Russell
Burns, Edward M. Ideas in conflict. 1960. 7.35. Norton
Butz, Otto. Of man and politics: An introduction to political science. 1960. 4.00.
   Holt, Rinehart & Winston
Davidson, William Leslie. Political thought in England: Utilitarians from Bentham
   to Mill. 1915. 1.70. Oxford U. P.
Figgis, John N. Political thought from Gerson to Grotius. 4.00. Cambridge U. P.
Fink, Zera S. Classical Republicans. 1962. 5.00. Northwestern U.
Foster, Michael B. Masters of political thought. 4.50. Houghton
Gettell, Raymond G. Gettell's history of political thought. 1953. 5.50. Appleton
Gooch, G. P. Political thought in England: From Bacon to Halifax. 1946. 1.70.
   Oxford U. P.
Hammond, Mason. City-state and world state: In Greek and Roman political theory
   until Augustus. 1951. 4.00. Harvard
Heimann, Eduard. Reason and faith in modern society. 1961. 6.50. Wesleyan U. P.
Jones, William T. Masters of political thought, vol. 2: Machiavelli to Bentham.
   1941. 5.25. Houghton

Lancaster, Lane W. Hegel to Dewey. 1959. 4.75. Houghton
Laski, H. J. Political thought in England: Locke to Bentham. 1.70. Oxford U. P.
Laski, Harold J. Rise of European liberalism. 3.00. Humanities
Lewis, Ewart. Medieval political ideas. 2 vols. 1954. 15.00. Knopf
Mayer, J. P. Political thought in France from the Revolution to the Fourth
  Republic. 1949. 3.25. Humanities
Maxey, Chester C. Political philosophies. 1948. 6.75. Macmillan
McGovern, William M. From Luther to Hitler: History of Fascist-Nazi political
  theory. 1941. 7.75. Houghton
McIlwain, Charles H. Growth of political thought in the West. 1932. 6.75.
  Macmillan
Morrall, John B. Political thought in medieval times. 2.50. Hillary
Morris, Christopher. Political thought in England: Tyndale to Hooker. 1953.
  1.70. Oxford U. P.
Parkinson, C. Northcote. Evolution of political thought. 1958. 5.00. Houghton
Pollock, Frederick. Introduction to the history of the science of politics. 3.25.
  Smith, Peter
Sabine, George H. History of political theory. 1961. 7.50. Holt, Rinehart &
  Winston
Soltau, Roger H. French political thought in the 19th century. 7.50. Russell
Vaughan, Charles E. Studies in the history of political philosophy before and
  after Rousseau. 1960. 12.50. Russell
POLITICAL SCIENCE--HISTORY--U. S. (320.973)
Boorstin, Daniel J. Genius of American politics. 1953. 4.00. U. of Chicago
Crick, Bernard. American science of politics. 1959. 5.75. U. of Calif.
Easton, David. Political system. 1953. 5.00. Knopf
Grimes, Alan P. American political thought. 1960. 6.50. Holt, Rinehart & Winston
Haile, Pennington, Eagle and the bear. 1950. 3.00. Washburn
Haraszti, Zoltan. John Adams and the prophets of progress. 1952. il. 5.00.
  Harvard
Hyneman, Charles S. Study of politics. 1959. 4.50. U. of Ill.
Jacobson, Jacob M. Development of American political thought. 7.50. Appleton
Rossiter, Clinton. Seedtime of the republic. 1953. 7.50. Harcourt
Scott, Andrew M. Political thought in America. 1959. 8.50. Holt, Rinehart &
  Winston
Weinberg, A. K. Manifest destiny: A study of Nationalist expansion in American
  history. 1958. 7.50. Smith, Peter
Van Dyke, Vernon. Political science: A philosophical analysis. 1960. 5.00.
  Stanford
Wilson, Francis Graham. American political mind. 1949. 7.25. McGraw
POLITICAL SCIENCE--YEARBOOKS (320.02)
International yearbook and statesman's who's who. annual. 25.00. Int. Pub. Service
  (R)
POLK, JAMES KNOX, PRES. U. S., 1795-1849 (923.173)
McCoy, Charles A. Polk and the presidency. il. 1960. 4.50. U. of Tex.
Sellers, C. G., Jr. James K. Polk: Jacksonian, 1795-1843. 1957. 7.50. Princeton
POLLOCK JACKSON, 1912-1956 (927)
O'Hara, Frank. Jackson Pollock. il. 1959. 4.95. Braziller
POLO, MARCO, 1254-1323 (923.9)
Komroff, Manuel. Travels of Marco Polo. 3.50. Liveright
Olschki, Leonardo. Marco Polo's Asia. 1960. 10.00. U. of Calif.
Shor, Jean. After you, Marco Polo. 1955. 5.95. McGraw
POLYNESIA (996)
Heyerdahl, Thor, and Edwin N. Ferdon, Jr. Archaeology of Easter Island.
  25.00. Rand McNally
Heyerdahl, Thor. American Indians in the Pacific: The theory behind the Kon-
  Tiki expedition. il. 1953. 15.00. Rand McNally
Keesing, Felix M. Social anthropology in Polynesia. 1953. 3.60. Oxford U. P.
Melville, Herman. Omoo. il. 1924. 4.50. Dodd

Rockefeller, James. Man on his island. il. 1957. 3.95. Norton
POMPEII (937)
Brion, Marcel. Pompeii and Herculaneum: The glory and the grief. 10.00. Crown
Tanzer, Helen H. Common people of Pompeii. 1939. 3.00. Johns Hopkins
POOR (362.5)
Harrington, Michael. Other America: Poverty in the United States. 1962. 4.00.
  Macmillan
POPE, ALEXANDER, 1688-1744 (928.21)
Beljame, Alexandre. Men of letters and the English public in the eighteenth
  century. 1948. 6.50. Humanities
Boyce, Benjamin. Character-sketches in Pope's poems. il. 1962. 5.00. Duke
Brower, Reuben A. Alexander Pope, the poetry of allusion. 1959. 6.10. Oxford
  U. P.
Felps, Jettie I. Pope's common sense. 1958. 2.00. Forum
Knight, G. Wilson. Laureate of peace: On the genius of Alexander Pope. 1955.
  4.00. Oxford U. P.
Tillotson, Geoffrey. On the poetry of Pope. 1950. 2.40. Oxford U. P.
POPES (922.21)
Aradi, Zsolt. Popes: History of how they are chosen, elected and crowned. 1955.
  4.00. Farrar, Straus
Brusher, Joseph. Popes through the ages. il. 1959. 14.95. Van Nostrand
Sugrue, Francis. Popes in the modern world. il. 1961. 5.95. Crowell
POPULATION (301.32)
Bates, Marston. Prevalence of people. 1955. 3.95. Scribner
Coontz, Sidney. Population theories and the economic interpretation. 5.00.
  Humanities
Darwin, Charles. Problems of world population. 1958. 0.75. Cambridge U. P.
Fagley, Richard M. Population explosion and Christian responsibility. 1960. 4.25.
  Oxford U. P.
Glass, D. V. Introduction to Malthus. 1953. 2.95. Wiley
Landis, Paul H., and Paul K. Hatt. Population problems. 1954. 7.00. Am. Bk. Co.
Malthus, Thomas. On population. 1.95. Modern Lib.
Myrdal, Gunnar. Population, a problem for democracy. 3.75. Smith, Peter
Osborn, Fairfield. Limits of the earth. 1953. 3.75. Little
Pearl, Raymond. Natural history of population. 1939. 3.50. Oxford U. P.
Sauvy, Alfred. Fertility and survival. 1961. 7.50. Criterion
Sax, Karl. Standing room only: The world's exploding population. 1960. 3.75.
  Smith, Peter
Stuart, Alexander J. Overpopulation: Twentieth century nemesis. 1958. 4.00.
  Exposition
Thompson, Warren S. Population problems. il. 1953. 7.50. McGraw
Vogt, William. People? Challenge to survival. 1960. 4.50. Sloane
Wolfenden, Hugh H. Population statistics and their compilation. 1954. 7.50. U.
  of Chicago
POPULIST PARTY (329.8)
Rochester, Anna. Populist movement in the United States. 1944. 1.50. Int. Pubs.
PORTER, WILLIAM SYDNEY, 1862-1910 (928.973)
Langford, Gerald. Alias O. Henry: A biography of William Sidney Porter. il.
  5.00. Macmillan
Long, E. H. O. Henry, the man and his work. 3.50. Smith, Peter
PORTRAITS (757)
Auerbach, Erna. Tudor artists. 1954. 11.20. Oxford U. P.
Carr, Henry. Portrait painting. il. 1959. 6.50. Viking
Degas, Hilaire. Portraits. by Jean S. Boggs. il. 1962. 15.00. U. of Calif.
Gwynne-Jones, Allan. Portrait painters: European portraits to the end of the
  19th century; and English 20th century portraits. il. 1955. 6.00. Transatlantic
Karsh, Yousuf. Portraits of greatness. 1959. 20.00. Nelson
Parker, Barbara Neville, and Anne Bolling Wheeler. John Singleton Copley. il.
  1938. 7.50. Harvard

Renoir, Pierre Auguste. Renoir gallery of portraits. il. 3.95. Abrams
PORTUGAL (946.9)
Ambriere, Francis. Portugal. 1960. 6.75. Hastings
Chapman, Charles E. Colonial Hispanic America. 1933. 6.50. Macmillan
Nowell, Charles E. History of Portugal. il. 1952. 5.75. Van Nostrand
POSITIVISM (146.4)
Comte, Auguste. General view of positivism. 5.00. Speller
Mises, Richard von. Positivism: A study in human understanding. 1956. 4.95.
    Braziller
Windolph, F. L. Leviathan and natural law. 1951. 2.50. Princeton
POST-IMPRESSIONISM (ART) (759.06)
Rewald, John. Post-impressionism: From Van Gogh to Gauguin. il. 15.00. Double-
    Day
POSTAGE-STAMPS (383.2)
Cabeen, Richard McP. Standard handbook of stamp collecting. il. 1957. 7.95.
    Crowell
Curle, Richard. Stamp-collecting. il. 1947. 4.00. Knopf
Denhof, William C., and Robert Denhof. Denhof's new complete United States
    stamp album. 1959. 6.50. Ungar
Easton, John. De La Rue history of British and foreign postage stamps. il. 1958.
    15.00. Van Nostrand
Mueller, Barbara. United States postage stamps. il. 1958. 6.95. Van Nostrand
Patrick, Douglas, and Mary. International guide to stamps and stamp collecting.
    il. 1962. 6.00. Dodd
POSTAL SERVICE--U.S. (383.1)
Baratz, Morton S. Economics of the postal service. 1962. 3.25. Pub. Affairs
Doherty, William C. Mailman, U.S.A. 1960. 4.50. McKay
Rogers, Lindsay. Postal power of Congress. 1916. 2.50. Johns Hopkins
POSTURE (613.78)
Kelly, E. D. Teaching posture and body mechanics. 1949. 4.00. Ronald
Lane, Janet. Your carriage, madam. 1947. 3.95. Wiley
Rathbone, Josephine Langworthy. Corrective physical education. il. 1959. 5.00.
    Saunders
POTTERY (738.1)
Cushion, J. P., and W. B. Honey. Handbook of pottery and porcelain marks.
    1957. 10.95. Pitman
Dalton, W. B. Craftsmanship and design in pottery. 1957. 10.00. Pitman
Eberlein, Harold D., and Roger W. Ramsdell. Practical book of chinaware. 1948.
    10.00. Lippincott
Gray, Basil. Early Chinese pottery and porcelain. 1953. 6.75. Pitman
Kenny, John B. Complete book of pottery making. il. 1959. 7.50. Chilton
POULTRY (636.5)
Bailey, J. W. Poultryman's manual. il. 1957. 4.50. Springer
Barger, Edgar H., and others. Diseases and parasites of poultry. il. 1958. 5.00.
    Lea & F
Jull, Morley A. Poultry husbandry. il. 1951. 7.75. McGraw
Rice, James E., and H. E. Botsford. Practical poultry management. 1956. 4.75.
    Wiley
Winter, A. R., and E. M. Funk. Poultry: Science and practice. 1960. 7.25.
    Lippincott
POUND, EZRA LOOMIS, 1885- (928.11)
Emery, Clark. Ideas into action: A study of Pound's cantos. 4.50. U. of Miami
Leavis, Frank R. New bearings in English poetry. 1960. 4.40. U. of Mich.
Norman, Charles. Ezra Pound. il. 1960. 6.95. Macmillan
O'Connor, William Van, and Edward Stone. Casebook on Ezra Pound. 1959. 2.50.
    Crowell
Wright, George T. Poet in the poem: The personae of Eliot, Yeats, and Pound.
    1960. 3.50. U. of Calif.

POVERTY (339.46)
Hoffman, Paul G. World without want. 1962. 3.75. Harper
POWER (MECHANICS) (621)
Atteberry, Pat H. Power mechanics. il. 1961. 2.35. Goodheart
Gibson, A. H. Natural sources of energy. 1913. 1.75. Cambridge U. P.
Marcus, Abraham, and Rebecca. Power unlimited. 3.50. Prentice-Hall
Nevins, Allan, and others. Energy and man, a symposium. 1960. 3.75. Appleton
POWER--SOCIAL SCIENCES (351.9)
Handlin, Oscar, and Mary F. Dimensions of liberty. 1961. 3.75. Harvard
Lasswell, Harold D., and Abraham Kaplan. Power and society. 1950. 6.50. Yale
Russell, Bertrand. Power: New analysis. 1962. pap. 0.95. Barnes & Noble
Sorokin, Pitirim A., and Walter A. Lunden. Power and morality. 3.50. Sargent
Westin, Alan F., and others. Uses of power. il. 1962. 5.95. Harcourt
POWER RESOURCES (301.155)
DeCamp, Sprague. Man and power. il. 1961. 4.95. Golden Press
Putnam, Palmer. Energy in the future. il. 1953. 15.00. Van Nostrand
Schurr, Sam H., and others. Energy in the American economy, 1850-1975. 1960.
    12.50. Johns Hopkins
PRAGMATISM (144.3)
Butler, J. Donald. Four philosophies and their practice in education and religion.
    1957. 6.50. Harper
Childs, John L. American pragmatism and education. 1956. 5.00. Holt
James, William. Essays in pragmatism. 1957. Hafner
James, William. Philosophy of William James. 1925. 1.95. Modern Lib.
James, William. Works. Essays in radical empiricism, and Pluralistic universe.
    1943. 4.50. McKay
Vaihinger, Hans. Philosophy of As If. 1935. 7.00. Barnes & Noble
Van Wesep, H. B. Seven sages: The story of American philosophy. 1960. 6.95.
    McKay
Wiener, Philip Paul. Evolution and the founders of pragmatism. 1949. 5.00.
    Harvard
PRAYER (291.3)
Barth, Karl. Prayer. 1952. 1.50. Westminster
Bishop, Shelton H. Wonder of prayer. 1959. 2.25. Seabury Press
Buttrick, George A. Prayer. 3.50. Abingdon
Chaing Kai-shek, Madame. Sure victory. 1955. 1.50. Revell
Gerturde, Sister. Christian prayer. 1959. 1.00. Assn. Pr.
Harkness, Georgia. Prayer and the common life. 1948. 3.50. Abingdon
Lauback, Frank C. Prayer, the mightiest force in the world. 1946. 1.00. Revell
Morgan, G. Campbell. Practice of prayer. 1961. 2.00. Revell
Rahner, Karl. Happiness through prayer. 1958. 2.25. Newman
PRAYERS (291.3)
Barclay, William. Book of everyday prayers. 1959. 2.50. Harper
Calvin, John, Devotions and prayers of John Calvin. 1.50. Baker Bk.
Donne, John. Prayers. 1962. 3.00. Twayne
Harris, Edward G. Prayers for a university. 1961. 2.75. U. of Pa.
Kjerkegaard Soren. Prayers. 3.50. U. of Chicago
Marshall, Catherine. Prayers of Peter Marshall. 1954. 4.50. McGraw
Marshall, Peter. Mr. Jones, meet the Master. 2.95. Revell
PREACHING (251.09)
Doughty, William L. John Wesley, preacher. 1955. 3.50. Allenson
PRECIOUS STONES (553.8)
Anderson, Basil W. Gem testing. il. 1959. 11.50. Emerson
Kraus, Edward H., and Chester B. Slawson. Gems and gem materials. 1947. 7.25.
    McGraw
Liddecoat, Richard T., Jr. Handbook of gemstone indentification. 7.50.
    Gemological Inst.
Pearl, Richard M. Popular gemology. 4.00. Swallow, A.
Spencer, Leonard J. Key to precious stones. il. 3.95. Emerson

PREDESTINATION (234.9)

Berkouwer, Gerrit C. Divine election. 1958. 5.00. Eerdmans

Buis, H. Historical Protestantism and predestination. 1958. 2.75. Presbyterian & Reformed

Calvin, John. On God and man. 1.75. Ungar

PREGNANCY (618.2)

Castallo, Mario A. Getting ready for parenthood: Manual for espectant mothers and fathers. il. 1957. 3.95. Macmillan

Davis, Adelle. Let's have healthy children. il. 1959. 3.75. Harcourt

Goodrich, F. W. Natural childbirth. 3.50. Prentice-Hall

Malmnaes, C. Immunity in pregnancy. 1959. 4.00. Lounz

PREJUDICES AND ANTIPATHIES (301.45)

Allport, Gordon W. Nature of prejudice. 1954. 7.50. Addison-Wesley

Baruch, Dorothy W. Glass house of prejudice. 1946. 3.50. Morrow

Hirsh, Selma. Fears men live by. 1955. 3.50. Harper

Marney, Carlyle. Structures of prejudice. 1961. 4.50. Abingdon

Marrow, Alfred J. Changing patterns of prejudice. il. 1962. 6.95. Chilton

Powdermaker, Hortense. Probing our prejudices. 1944. 1.95. Harper

PRESIDENTS--U.S. (353)

Binkley, Wilfred E. Man in the White House: His powers and duties. 1959. 6.00. Johns Hopkins

Corwin, Edward S., and Louis W. Koenig. Presidency today. 1956. 3.00. N. Y. U.

Corwin, Edward S. President: Office and powers. 1957. 6.50. N. Y. U.

Coyle, David C. Ordeal of the presidency. 1960. 6.00. Pub. Affairs

Durant, John, and Alice. Pictorial history of American presidents. il. 1959. 7.95. Barnes, A. S.

Finer, Herman. Presidency: Crisis and regeneration. 1960. 5.00. U. of Chicago

Hamilton, Holman. White House images and realities. 1958. 3.50. U. of Fla.

Jensen, Amy L. White House and its thirty-two families. 1958. 12.50. McGraw

Kane, Joseph N. Facts about the Presidents. il. 1959. 6.00. Wilson (R)

Koenig, Louis. Invisible presidency: The behind-the-scenes story of seven presidential confidants from Hamilton to Sherman Adams. 1960. 6.95. Holt, Rinehart & Winston

Neustadt, R. E. Presidential power. 1960. 5.50. Wiley

Parks, Lillian R., and Frances S. Leighton. My thirty years backstairs at the White House. pap. 0.75. Avon

Rossiter, Clinton. American presidency. 1960. pap. 1.95. Harcourt

Truman, Harry S. Truman speaks. il. 1960. 3.00. Columbia

Tugwell, Rexford G. Enlargement of the Presidency. 1960. 6.95. Doubleday

PRESIDENTS--U.S.--ELECTION (324.2)

Burnham, W. Dean. Presidential ballots, 1836-1892. 1954. 10.00. Johns Hopkins

Campbell, Angus, and others. Voter decides. 1954. 4.75. Harper

Hamilton, Charles G. Lincoln and the Know Nothing movement. 1954. pap. 1.00. Pub. Affairs

Hesseltine, William B. Three against Lincoln. 1960. 6.00. La. State

LaFollette, Robert M. LaFollette's autobiography. 1960. 6.00. U. of Wis.

Lazarsfeld, P. F., and others. People's choice. 1948. 3.75. Columbia

MacBride, Roger Lea. American electoral college. 1953. pap. 0.75. Caxton

Moos, Malcolm C., and Stephen Hess. Hats in the ring. il. 1960. 3.50. Random

Morgan, H. Wayne. Eugene V. Debs: Socialist for president. il. 1962. 5.75. Syracuse

Petersen, Svend. Statistical history of our presidential elections. 15.00. Ungar

Roseboom, Eugene H. History of presidential elections. 9.50. Macmillan

Ross, George E. Know your presidents and their wives. il. 1961. 2.95. Rand McNally

Stone, Irving. They also ran. 4.95. Doubleday

White, Theodore H. Making of the president, 1960. 1961. 6.95. Atheneum

Wilmerding, Lucius, Jr. Electoral college. 1958. 5.00. Rutgers

PRESS--U.S. (070.1973)

Cater, Douglass. Fourth branch of government. 1959. 3.50. Houghton

Ickes, Harold L. Freedom of the press today. 1941. 2.75. Vanguard

Pope, John Keith. Handbook of police-press relations. 1954. 3.75. Academy Lib.

Schlesinger, Arthur M. Prelude to independence. 1958. 6.00. Knopf

PRESSURE GROUPS (301.43)

Banfield, Edward C. Political influence. 1961. 6.00. Free Press

Eckstein, Harry. Pressure group politics. il. 1960. 3.75. Stanford

PRICES (338.5)

Abramovitz, Moses, and others. Allocation of economic resources. il. 1959. 6.00. Stanford

American Assembly. Wages, prices, profits and productivity. il. 1959. 2.00. Am. Assembly

Backman, J. Price practices and price policies. 1953. 8.00. Ronald

Bain, Joe S. Pricing, distribution, and employment: Economics of an enterprise system. 1953. 9.50. Holt, Rinehart & Winston

Bezanson, Anne, and others. Prices and inflation during the American Revolution. Pennsylvania, 1770-1790. 1951. 6.75. U. of Pa.

Cole, Arthur Harrison. Wholesale commodity prices in the United States, 1700-1861. pt. 1. 1938. 4.00. Harvard

Commodity year book. 14.95. Commodity Res. Bur.

Galbraith, John Kenneth. Theory of price control. 1952. 1.50. Harvard

Jasny, Naum. Soviet prices of producers' goods. 2.00. Stanford

National Bureau Committee for Economic Research. Business concentration and price policy. 1955. 9.00. Princeton

Papandreou, Andreas G., and John T. Wheeler. Competition and its regulation. 1954. 10.60. Prentice-Hall

Scitovsky, Tibor. Welfare and competition. 1951. 9.35. Irwin

Stigler, George J., and Kenneth E. Boulding. Readings in price theory. 1952. 6.75. Irwin

Stigler, George J. Theory of price. 1952. 5.25. Macmillan

Thin, Tun. Theory of markets. il. 1960. 5.00. Harvard

Wasserman, Paul. Sources of commodity prices. 5.00. S.L.A.

Weintraub, Sidney. Classical Keynesianism, monetary theory and the price level. 1961. 4.00. Chilton

PRINTING (655)

Allen, Agnes. Story of the book. il. 1953. 3.50. Macmillan

Ballinger, R.A. Layout. 1956. 15.00. Reinhold

Hostettler, Rudolf. Technical terms of the printing industry. il. 1959. 3.50. Wittenborn

Lee, Marshall. Books for our time. il. 1951. 5.50. Oxford U.P.

McMurtrie, D. C. Book: Story of printing and bookmaking. 1943. 11.00. Oxford U.P.

McMurtrie, Douglas C. Invention of printing. 1942. 25.00. Franklin, B.

Melcher, Daniel, and Nancy Larrick. Printing and promotion handbook. il. 1956. 9.00. McGraw

Morison, Stanley. Four centuries of fine printing. il. 1960. 3.95. Barnes & Noble

Polk, Ralph W. Practice of printing. 1952. 4.75. Bennett

Skillin, Marjorie E., and Robert M. Gay. Words into type. 5.00. Meredith

Steinberg, S. H. Five hundred years of printing. il. 1959. 6.95. Criterion

Updike, Daniel B. Printing types: Their history, forms and use. 2 vols. il. 1951. 15.00. Harvard

PRINTING AS A GRAPHIC ART (760)

Carlsen, Darvey E. Graphic arts. 1958. 3.80. Bennett

Jackson, H.E. Printing: A practical introduction to the graphic arts. 1957. 5.36. McGraw

McLean, Ruari. Modern Book design, From William Morris to the present day. 1959. 4.75. Oxford U.P.

PRISONS (365)
Cohen, Elie A. Human behavior in the concentration camp. 1953. 7.50. Norton
Cressey, Donald. Prison: Studies in institutional organization and change. 1961.
    6.00. Holt, Rinehart & Winston
DeFord, Miriam A. Stone walls: Prisons from fetters to furloughs. 1962. 5.00.
    Chilton
Korn, Richard R., and Lloyd W. McCorkle. Criminology and penology. 1959. 6.50.
    Holt, Rinehart & Winston
Tannenbaum, F. Crime and the community. 1938. 4.50. Columbia
Tappan, Paul W. Crime, justice and correction. 1960. 10.95. McGraw
PRIVATE SCHOOLS--DIRECTORIES (370)
Bunting, James E., and others. Private independent schools, a directory. il.
    1962. 7.50. Bunting
Lovejoy, Clarence E. Lovejoy's prep school guide. 1958. 4.50. Harper
Sargent, Porter. Handbook of private schools. 10.00. Sargent (R)
PROBABILITIES (519.1)
Adler, Irving. Probability and statistics for everyman. il. 1962. 4.75. Day
Boole, George. Laws of thought. 4.00. Smith, Peter
Carnap, Rudolf. Logical foundations of probability. 1962. 10.00. U. of Chicago
David, F. N. Probability theory for statistical methods. 1949. 4.50. Cambridge
    U.P.
Fisher, Ronald A. Statistical methods and scientific inference. 1956. 3.00.
    Hafner
Fry, Thornton C. Probability and its engineering uses. il. 1928. 9.75. Van
    Nostrand
Hogben, Lancelot. Statistical theory. 1957. 12.00. Norton
Keynes, John Maynard. Treatise on probability. 1952. 4.25. St. Martins
Lee, Y. W. Statistical theory of communication. 1960. 15.00. Wiley
Neyman, Jerzy. First course in probability and statistics. il. 1950. 6.50. Holt,
    Rinehart & Winston
Parratt, Lyman G. Probability and experimental errors in science. 1961. 6.50.
    Wiley
PROBATION (364.63)
Adler, Alfred. Problem child. 1960. 2.50. Putnam
Bettelheim, Bruno. Love is not enough: The treatment of emotionally disturbed
    children. 1950. 5.00. Free Press
Despert, J. Louise. Children of divorce. 1953. 3.95. Doubleday
Keve, Paul W. Prison, probation, or parole? 1954. 3.75. U. of Minn.
Newman, Charles L. Sourcebook on probation, parole, and pardons. 1958. 7.50.
    Thomas, C. C.
Radinowicz, Leon. Results of probation. 1959. 5.50. St. Martins
Redl, Fritz, and David Wineman. Aggressive child: Children who hate, and
    Controls from within. 1957. 7.50. Free Press
PRODUCE TRADE (631.18)
Bowring, James, and others. Marketing policies for agriculture. 1960. 7.95.
    Prentice-Hall
Food and Agriculture Organization. Trade yearbook, 1960. 3.50. Int. Doc.
    Service-Columbia
PRODUCTION CONTROL (658.56)
Eilon, Samuel. Elements of production planning and control. il. 1962. 9.75.
    Macmillan
Koepke, Charles A. Plant production control. 1961. 8.95. Wiley
Magee, J. F. Production planning and inventory control. 1958. 8.50. McGraw
Timms, Howard L. Production function in business. 1962. 10.00. Irwin
PROFESSIONAL EDUCATION (378.99)
Anderson, G. Lester. Education for the professions. NSSE 61st yrbk. pt. 2. 4.50.
    U. of Chicago
McGrath, Earl J. Liberal education in the professions. 1959. pap. 1.50. T.C.

PROFIT (339.2)
Cottle, Sidney, and Tate Whitman. Corporate earning power and market valuation, 1935-1955. 1959. 12.50. Duke
Knight, Frank H. Risk, undertainty and profit. 6.00. Kelley
Nourse, E. G. Basic criteria of price policy. 1943. pap. 0.25. Brookings
Prentice-Hall Editorial Staff. How to set up a successful profit-sharing plan. 1954. 18.00 Prentice-Hall
PROGRAMMI.G (658.51)
Chapin, Ned. Programming computers for business applications. il. 1961. 7.50. McGraw
Green, E. . Learning process and programmed instruction. 1962. 4.00. Holt, Rinehart & Winston
Leeds, H., and G. Weinberg. Computer programming fundamentals. 1961. 8.50. McGraw
Margulies, S., and L. D. Eigen. Programmed instruction applied. 1962. 6.95. Wiley
PROGRESS (301.245)
Becker, Carl L. Progress and power. 1949. 3.00. Knopf
Bury, J. B. Idea of progress. 1960. 3.75. Smith, Peter
Childe, V. Gordon. Man makes himself. 1952. pap. 0.60. New Am. Lib.
Marck, Kurt W. Yestermorrow: Notes on man's progress. 1961. 3.50. Knopf
PROGRESSIVISM (U. S. POLITICS) (329.6)
Hofstadter, Richard. Age of reform: From Bryan to F.D.R. 1955. 5.00. Knopf
PROPAGANDA (301.1523)
Berelson, Bernard, and Morris Janowitz. Reader in public opinion and communication. 1953. 7.50. Free Press
Bernays, Edward L. Propaganda. 1928. 3.50. Liveright
Carlson, John Roy. Under cover: My four years in the Nazi underworld of America. il. 5.95. Dutton
Christenson, Reo M., and R. O. McWilliams. Voice of the people. 1962. 4.95. McGraw
Davidson, Philip G. Propaganda and the American Revolution. 1941. 5.00. U. of N. C.
Dunham, Donald C. Kremlin target: U.S.A. 1961. 4.50. Washburn
George, Alexander L. Propaganda analysis, a study of inferences made from Nazi propaganda in World War II. 1959. 6.00. Harper
Houn, Franklin W. To change a nation. 1961. 6.50. Free Press
Huxley, Aldous. Brave new world revisited. 1958. 3.50. Harper
Kris, Ernst, and others. German radio propaganda. il. 4.00. Cornell
Reisky de Dubnic, Fladimir. Communist propaganda methods. 1961. 6.00. Praeger
Shackford, R. H. Truth about soviet lies. 1962. 4.50. Pub. Affairs
PROPHETS (291.63)
Caiger, S. L. Lives of the prophets. 3.00. Seabury
Hamilton, Edith. Spokesmen for God. 1949. 3.95. Norton
Lewinsohn, Richard. Science, prophecy and prediction. il. 1961. 4.95. Harper
Nostradamus. Nostradamus' complete prophesies. by Henry Roberts. 5.00. Crown
Nostradamus. Oracles of Nostradamus. 1.95. Modern Lib.
Smart, James D. Servants of the word: The prophets of Israel. 1961. 1.50. Westminster
Smith, John M. Powis. Prophets and their times. 1941. 5.00. U. of Chicago
Young, Edward J. My servants the prophets. 1952. 3.00. Eerdmans
PROSE LITERATURE (800)
Boulton, M. Anatomy of prose. 2.50. Hillary
Douglas, Wallace. Character of prose. 1959. pap. 2.25. Houghton
Fidell, Ideas in prose. 1961. 2.75. Prentice-Hall
PROTEINS (547.75)
Allison, James B., and William H. Fitzpatrick. Dietary proteins in health and disease. il. 1960. 4.50. Thomas, C.C.

Anfinson, Christian B. Molecular basis of evolution. 1959. 7.00. Wiley

Fox, S. W. , and J. Foster. Introduction to protein chemistry. 1957. 9.95. Wiley

Haurowitz, Felix. Chemistry and biology of proteins. 1950. 6.80. Academic Press

Wormell, R. L. New fibres from proteins. 1954. 5.80. Academic Press

PROTESTANT CHURCHES (284)

Brauer, Jerald C. Protestantism in America. 1953. 3.50. Westminister

Callahan, Daniel. Christianity divided: Protestant and Roman Catholic theological issues. 1961. 6.00. Sheed

Hardon, John A. Protestant churches of America. 1958. 5.00. Newman

Hudson, Winthrop S. American Protestantism. 1961. 3.95. U. of Chicago

Miller, Robert M. American Protestantism and social issues, 1919-1939. 1958. 6.00. U. of N. C.

Rian, Edwin H. Christianity and American education. 1949. 3.00. Naylor

Weigel, Gustave. Churches in North America. 1961. 3.95. Taplinger

Weigel, Gustave. Faith and understanding in America. 1959. 3.75. Macmillan

PROTESTANTISM (284)

Batten, J. Minton. Protestant backgrounds in history. 1951. pap. 1.50. Abingdon

Bouyer, Louis. Spirit and forms of Protestantism. 1956. 3.75. Newman

Loyer, Merle William. Luther in Protestantism today. 1957. 3.50. Assn. Pr.

Brown, Robert M. Spirit of Protestantism. 1961. 4.75. Oxford U. P.

Flew, R. Newton, and Rupert E. Davies. Catholicity of Protestantism. 1954. 1.75. Muhlenberg

Forell, Protestant faith. 1960. 7.35. Prentice-Hall

Hall, Thomas Cuming. Religious background of American culture. 1959. 5.75. Ungar

Nichols, James H. Short primer for Protestants. 1957. pap. 0.50. Assn. Pr.

Woods, Henry M. Our priceless heritage. 1957. 3.50. Christian Lib. Crusade

PROTOZOA (593)

Dobell, Clifford. Antony Van Leeuwenhoek and his "Little Animals." 10.00. Russell

Jahn, Theodore L. How to know the protozoa. by Harry E. Jaques. 1949. 3.25. Brown, W. C.

Richardson, U. F. , and S. B. Kendall. Veterinary protozoology. il. 1958. 4.50. Macmillan

PROUST, MARCEL, 1871-1922 (928)

Barker, Richard H. Marcel Proust: A biography. il. 1958. 6.50. Criterion

Girard, Rene. Proust: A collection of critical essays. 1962. 3.95. Prentice-Hall

Green, F. C. Mind of Proust. 1949. 6.50. Cambridge U. P.

Krutch, Joseph W. Five masters, a study in the mutations of the novel. 1959. 3.75. Smith, Peter

March, Harold. Two worlds of Marcel Proust. 1948. 4.00. U. of Pa.

Piroue, Georges. Proust's way, an essay in descriptive criticism. 1958. 4.00. Oxford U. P.

PROVERBS (398.9)

Browning, D. C. Dictionary of quotations and proverbs. 1952. 4.25. Dutton (R)

Hart, Henry H. , tr. Seven hundred Chinese proverbs. 1937. 3.00. Stanford

Smith, William G. , and Paul Harvey. Oxford dictionary of English proverbs. 1948. 7.20. Oxford U. P.

Stevenson, Burton. Home book of proverbs, maxims and familiar phrases. 1948. 35.00. Macmillan

Taylor, Archer, and Bartlett J. Whiting. Dictionary of American proverbs and phrases. 1820-1880. 1959. 9.50. Harvard

Tilley, Morris P. Dictionary of the proverbs in England in the sixteenth and seventeenth centuries. il. 1950. 25.00. U. of Mich.

PRUSSIA (943.1)

Adams, Henry M. Prussian-American relations, 1775-1871. 4.50. Western Reserve

Carsten, Francis L. Origins of Prussia. 1954. 5.60. Oxford U. P.

PSYCHIATRY (616.89)

Ackerknecht, Erwin H. Short history of psychiatry. il. 1959. 3.50. Hafner

Alexander, Franz, and Helen Ross. Dynamic psychiatry. 1952. 11.50. U. of Chicago

Bellak, Leopold. Contemporary European psychiatry. 7.50. 1961. Grove
Boisen, Anton T. Out of the depths. 1960. 4.00. Harper
Cohen, Mabel B. Advances in psychiatry. 1959. 5.50. Norton
Chapman, James C. Abnormal psychology and modern life. 1956. 7.50. Scott
Dunlap, Jane. Exploring inner space. 1961. 3.75. Harcourt
Eissler, K. R. Psychiatrist and the dying patient. il. 1955. 5.00. Int. Univs.
Felix, Robert H. Mental health and social welfare. 1961. 3.75. Columbia
Galdston, Iago. Ministry and medicine in human relations. 1956. 3.50. Int.
    Univs.
Gorman, Mike. Every other bed. 1956. 4.00. World Pub.
Hinsie, Leland E., and Robert J. Campbell. Psychiatric dictionary. 1960. 17.50.
    Oxford U. P. (R)
Hoch, Paul H., and Joseph Zubin. Future of psychiatry. il. 1962. 8.75. Grune
Jung, Carl G. Psychiatric studies. by Herbert Read, and others. 1957. 3.75.
    Pantheon
Kraepelin, Emil. One hundred years of psychiatry. 1962. 1.75. Citadel
Laing, Ronald D. Divided self: A study of sanity and madness. 1960. 5.00.
    Quadrangle
Lemkau, Paul V. Basic issues in psychiatry. 1958. 3.50. Thomas, C. C.
Linton, Ralph. Culture and mental disorders. 1956. 4.50. Thomas, C. C.
McKown, Robin. Pioneers in mental health. 1961. 3.25. Dodd
Masserman, Jules. Practice of dynamic psychiatry. 1955. 12.00. Saunders
May, Rollo, and others. Existence. 7.50. Basic Books
Menninger, W. C., and Munro Leaf. You and psychiatry. 1948. 2.95. Scribner
Menninger, Karl A. Man against himself. 6.00. 1956. Harcourt
Menninger, Karl. Psychiatrist's world: The selected papers of Karl Menninger.
    1959. 10.00. Viking
Menninger, Karl A. Guide to psychiatric books. 1956. 5.00. Grune
Mezer, Robert R. Dynamic psychiatry in simple terms. 1960. 2.75. Springer
Meyer, Adolf. Collected papers of Adolf Meyer. 4 vols. 7.50 ea. set 30.00.
    Johns Hopkins
Moore, Thomas Verner. Nature and treatment of mental disorders. 1951. 6.50.
    Grune
Mullahy, Patrick. Study of interpersonal relations. 1949. 6.50. Nelson
Murphy, Gardner. Challenge of psychical research: A primer of parapsychology.
    il. 1961. 6.00. Harper
Noyes, Arthur P., and Lawrence C. Kolb. Modern clinical psychiatry. 1958. 8.00.
    Saunders
Pavlov, I. Essays in psychology and psychiatry: With a special section on sleep
    and hypnosis. 1962. pap. 1.95. Citadel
Reed, Charles F., and others. Psychopathology: A sourcebook. il. 1958. 9.75.
    Harvard
Rennie, Thomas A. C., and L. E. Woodward. Mental health in modern society.
    il. 1948. 4.00. Harvard
Rodger, T. Ferguson, and others. Topics in psychiatry. 1959. 4.00. Thomas, C.C.
Rogers, Carl R., and Rosalind F. Dymond. Psychotherapy and personality change.
    1954. 8.50. U. of Chicago
Schwartz, Herman S. Home care for the emotionally. ill. 5.00. Sessions
Sechehaye, M. A. Symbolic realization. 1952. 3.25. Int. Univs.
Sheldon, William H. Varieties of delinquent youth. il. 1949. 10.00. Harper
Strecker, Edward A. Basic psychiatry. 1952. 3.95. Random
Sullivan, Harry S. Conceptions of modern psychiatry. 1953. 6.50. Norton
Sullivan, Harry S. Interpersonal theory of psychiatry. 1953. 6.50. Norton
Valentine, Max. Introduction to psychiatry. 1962. 5.00. Williams & Wilkins

PSYCHICAL RESEARCH (133)
Garrett, Eileen, J. Beyond the five senses. 1957. 4.95. Lippincott
Rhine, J. B., and J. G. Pratt. Parapsychology. il. 1957. 4.75. Thomas, C.C.
Rhine, J. B. Reach of the mind. 1961. Apollo

Tauber, Edward S., and Maurice R. Green. Prelogical experience: An inquiry into dreams and other creative processes. 1959. 4.50. Basic Books

Walker, Kenneth M. Extrasensory mind. 1961. 3.95. Emerson

PSYCHOANALYSIS (131.34)

Academy of Religion and Mental Health. Religion, culture, and mental health. 1961. 3.50. N. Y. U.

Academy of Religion and Mental Health. Religion in the developing personality. 1960. 3.00. N. Y. U.

Academy of Religion and Mental Health. Religion, science, and mental health. 1959. 3.00. N. Y. U.

Ackerman, Nathan W. Psychodynamics of family life. il. 1958. 6.75. Basic Books

Adler, Alfred. Individual psychology. by Heinz L. and Rowena R. Ansbacher. 1956. 8.50. Basic Books

Alexander, Franz. Psychoanalysis and psychotherapy. 1956. 5.50. Norton

Berg, Charles. Psychotherapy: Practice and theory. 1948. 5.00. Norton

Blum, G. S. Psychoanalytic theories of personality. 1953. 5.95. McGraw

Brenner, Charles. Elementary textbook of psychoanalysis. 1957. 4.00. Int. Univs.

Brown, Norman O. Life against death: The psychoanalytical meaning of history. 1959. 6.50. Wesleyan U. P.

Campbell, Joseph. Hero with a thousand faces. 1949. 4.00. Pantheon

Erikson, Eri, H. Childhood and society. 1950. 5.95. Norton

Fenichel, Otto. Psychoanalytic theory of neurosis. 1945. 10.00. Norton

Fliess, Robert. Psycho-analytic reader. 1962. 7.50. Int. Univs.

Flugel, John C. Man, morals, and society. 1957. 4.50. Int. Univs.

Freeman, Lucy. Fight against fears. 1951. 3.50. Crown

Freud, Anna. Ego and the mechanisms of defense. 1957. 4.00. Int. Univs.

Freud, Sigmund. Autobiographical study. tr. by James Strachey. 1952. 3.00. Norton

Freud, Sigmund. Basic writings. 2.95. Modern Lib.

Freud, Sigmund. Beyond the pleasure principle. 2.75. Liveright

Freud, Sigmund. Collected papers. by Ernest Jones. 5 vols. 1959. boxed, 25.00. Basic Books

Freud, Sigmund, and D. E. Oppenheim. Dreams in folklore. 1958. 3.00. Int. Univs.

Freud, Sigmund. Future of an illusion. 2.75. Liveright

Freud, Sigmund. General introduction to psychoanalysis. 4.50. Liveright

Freud, Sigmund. Group psychology and the analysis of the ego. 2.75. Liveright

Freud, Sigmund. Interpretation of dreams. by James Strachey. 1955. 8.50. Basic Books

Freud, Sigmund. Outline of psychoanalysis. 1949. 3.00. Norton

Fromm, Erich. Forgotten language. 1957. pap. 1.75. Grove

Fromm, Erich. Psychoanalysis and religion. 1950. 3.00. Yale

Groddeck, Georg. Exploring the unconscious. 1950. 2.75. Funk

Hendrick, Ives. Facts and theories of psychoanalysis. 1958. 6.00. Knopf

Hoch, P. H., and J. Zubin. Current approaches to psychoanalysis. 1960. 6.50. Grune

Horney, Karen. Are you considering psychoanalysis? 1946. 4.50. Norton

Horney, Karen. Neurotic personality of our time. 1937. 4.50. Norton

Horney, Karen. Self-analysis. 1942. 4.50. Norton

Jung, C. G. Basic writings of C. G. Jung. 1959. 1.95. Modern Lib.

Jung, Carl G. Modern man in search of a soul. 5.75. Harcourt

Jung, Carl G. Two essays on analytical psychology. 1953. 3.75. Pantheon

Klein, Melanie, and others. Developments in psychoanalysis. 6.00. Hillary

Lorand, Sandor. Psychoanalysis today. 1950. 6.00. Int. Univs.

Marcuse, Herbert. Eros and civilization. 1956. 3.95. Beacon

Menninger, Karl. Human mind. 1945. 6.75. Knopf

Menninger, Karl. Theory of psychoanalytic technique. 1958. 4.75. Basic Books

Munroe, Ruth L. Schools of psychoanalytic thought. 1955. 8.00. Holt, Rinehart & Winston

Outline of psychoanalysis. 1. 95. Modern Lib.
Rank, Otto. Will therapy. bd. with Truth and reality. 1945. 5. 00. Knopf
Reik, Theodor. Listening with the third ear: The inner experience of a psychoana-
   lyst. 1948. 6. 50. Farrar, Straus
Reik, Theodor. Myth and guilt. 1957. 5. 75. Braziller
Reik, Theodor. Search within. 1956. 7. 50. Farrar, Straus
Saul, Leon J. Technic and practice of psychoanalysis. 1958. 8. 00. Lippincott
Schilder, Paul. Psychoanalysis: Man and society. 1951. 5. 50. Norton
Stekel, Wilhelm. Technique of analytical psychotherapy. 4. 95. Liveright
Thompson, Clara. Psychoanalysis: Evolution and development. 1950. 3. 00. Nelson
Wittels, Fritz. Freud and his time. 1931. 4. 50. Liveright
Wolberg, Lewis R. Hypnoanalysis. 1945. 6. 00. Grune
PSYCHOLOGY (150)
Adler, Alfred. Understanding human nature. pap. 0. 50. Fawcett
Adler, Alfred. What life should mean to you. 1959. pap. 1. 25. Putnam
Allport, Gordon W. Becoming. 1955. 3. 75. Yale
Averill, Lawrence Augustus, and Florence C. Kempf. Psychology applied to
   nursing. 1956. 4. 25. Saunders
Bernhardt, Karl S. Practical psychology. il. 1953. 6. 25. McGraw
Boring, Edwin G. , and others. Foundations of psychology. 1948. 7. 95. Wiley
Broad, C. D. Mind and its place in nature. 7. 00. Humanities
Broudy, H. S. , and E. L. Freel. Psychology for general education. 1956. 5. 50.
   McKay
Brown, Roger, and others. New directions in psychology. 1962. 3. 00. Holt,
   Rinehart & Winston
Cantril, Hadley. Why of man's experience. il. 4. 75. Macmillan
Carmichael, Leonard. Basic psychology. 1957. 3. 95. Random
Cattell, General psychology. 1947. 5. 50. Sci-Art
Crow, Lester, and Alice. Understanding our behavior. 1956. 6. 50. Knopf
Cruze, Wendell W. General psychology for college students. 1951. 6. 95. Prentice-
   Hall
Dollard, John, and Neal E. Miller. Personality and psychotherapy. 1950. 7. 50.
   McGraw
Fromm, Erich. Man for himself: An inquiry into the psychology of ethics. 3. 75.
   1947. Rinehart
Gates, Arthur I. , and others. Educational psychology. 6. 25. Macmillan
Goodenough, Florence L. , and Leona E. Tyler. Developmental psychology. il.
   1959. 6. 00. Appleton
Grabbe, Paul. We call it human nature. il. 1939. 5. 00. Harper
Grinker, Roy R. Toward a unified theory of human behavior. 6. 50. Basic Books
Guilford, J. P. Fields of psychology. 1950. 7. 00. Van Nostrand
Guilford, J. P. Fundamental statistics in psychology and education. 1956. 7. 25;
   Elementary statistical exercises, workbook. 2. 50; Intermediate statistical
   exercises, workbook. 2. 95. McGraw
Hahn, John F. Introduction to psychology. 1. 45. Doubleday'
Hall, Calvin S. Primer of Freudian psychology. 1954. 2. 50. World Pub.
Hall, Calvin S. Psychology. 1960. 5. 50. Allen, Howard
Hartley, Eugene L. , and Ruth E. Outside readings in psychology. 1957. bds.
   2. 50. Crowell
Hilgard, Ernest R. Introduction to psychology. il. 1962. 7. 75. Harcourt
James, William. Principles of psychology. 2 vols. 9. 00. Smith, Peter
James, William. Psychology. il. 1950. 1. 95. World Pub.
Katshoff, Louis O. Design of human behavior. 1953. 5. 00. Educ. Pubs. Inc.
Koren, Henry J. Introduction to the philosophy of animate nature. 1955. 4. 00.
   Herder
Krech, David, and Richard S. Crutchfield. Elements of psychology. il. 1958.
   9. 50. Knopf
Levine, Albert J. Current psychologies. 1940. 5. 00. Sci-Art

Lindgren, Henry C. Psychology of personal and social adjustment.
Logan, F., and others. Behavior theory and social science. 1955. 3.00. Yale
McDougall, William. Psychology: The study of behaviour. 1947. 1.70. Oxford U.P.
Mandler, George, and William Kessen. Language of psychology. 1959. 6.75.
　Wiley
Marcuse, F. L. Areas of psychology. 1954. 6.00. Harper
Marx, Melvin H. Psychological theory: Contemporary readings. 1951. 6.25.
　Macmillan
Miller, George A. Psychology: The science of mental life. il. 1962. 6.95.
　Harper
Morgan, Clifford T. Introduction to psychology. 1961. 7.95. McGraw
Murphy, Gardner. Historical introduction to modern psychology. 1949. 8.25. Harcourt
Murphy, Gardner. Introduction to psychology. 1951..5.00. Harper
O'Hara, Frank J. Psychology and the nurse. 1960. pap. 3.75. Saunders
Overstreet, Harry A. Great enterprise. 1952. 4.50. Norton
Painter, George S. Fundamental psychology. 1938. 3.75. Liveright
Pressey, S. L., and Raymond G. Kuhlen. Psychological development through
　the life span. 1957. 6.50. Harper
Reith, H. R. Introduction to philosophical psychology. 8.35. Prentice-Hall
Roback, A. A. Story of psychology and psychiatry. il. 1961. 7.50. Sci-Art
Royce, James E. Personality and mental health. 1955. 3.50. Bruce
Russell, Bertrand. Analysis of mind. 1921. 3.50: Macmillan
Sartain, A. Q., and others. Psychology: Understanding human behavior. 1958.
　6.75. McGraw
Sheldon, William H. Psychology and the Promethean will. 4.50. Harper
Smeltzer, C. H. Psychology for student nurses. il. 1962. 6.50. Macmillan
Strecker, Edward A., and others. Discovering ourselves. 1958. 4.75. Macmillan
Symonds, Percival M. Dynamic psychology. 1949. 5.25. Appleton
Symonds, Percival M. Dynamics of human adjustment. 1946. 6.00. Appleton
Tussing, Lyle. Psychology for better living. il. 1959. 5.95. Wiley
Weisskopf, Walter. Psychology of economics. 1955. 4.00. U. of Chicago
Young, Paul T. Motivation and emotion. 1961. 8.95. Wiley
PSYCHOLOGY--ADDRESSES, ESSAYS, LECTURES (150)
Aristotle. Parva naturalia. by David Ross. 1955. 8.00. Oxford U. P.
Baldwin, J. M. Dictionary of philosophy and psychology. 3 vols. 10.00 ea. Smith,
　Peter (R)
Boring, Edwin G. Sensation and perception in the history of experimental
　psychology. il. 6.50. Appleton
Brett, George S. History of psychology. by R. S. Peters. 1953. 8.75. Macmillan
Chaplin, J. P., and T. S. Krawiec. Systems and theories of psychology. 1960.
　6.50. Holt, Rinehart & Winston
Doniger, Simon. Nature of man. 1962. 6.00. Harper
English, Horace B., and Ava C. Comprehensive dictionary of psychological and
　psychoanalytical terms. iL 1958. 10.75. McKay (R)
Fairchild, Johnson E. Personal problems and psychological frontiers. 4.00.
　Sheridan
Flugel, J. C. Hundred years of psychology. 3.75. Macmillan
Garrett, Henry E. Great experiments in psychology. 1951. 4.00. Appleton
Heidbreder, Edna. Seven psychologies. 1933. 4.75. Appleton
Kohler, Wolfgang. Dynamics in psychology. 1940. 3.00. Liveright
Murphy, Gardner. Historical introduction to modern psychology. 1949. 8.25.
　Harcourt
Sykes, Gerald. Hidden remnant. 1962. 4.00. Harper
Tolman, Edward Chace. Behavior and psychological man. 1958. pap. 1.95. U.
　of Calif.
Warren, Howard B. Dictionary of psychology. 5.75. Houghton
PSYCHOLOGY, APPLIED (150.13)
Alder, Vera S. Humanity comes of age. 2.50. Wehman

Berrien, F. K. Practical psychology. 1952. 6.75. Macmillan
Brooke, Esther Eberstadt. You and your personality. 1949. 3.00. Harper
Burtt, Harold. Applied psychology. 1957. 7.50. Prentice-Hall
Burtt, H. E. Psychology of advertising. 5.50. Houghton
Carnegie, Dale. How to win friends and influence people. 1946. 3.50. S. and S.
Chesser, Eustace. Outline of human relationships. 1960. 5.95. Hawthorn
Duvall, Sylvanus M. Art and skill of getting along with people. 1961. 4.95.
   Prentice-Hall
Gray, John Stanley, and others. Psychology applied to human affairs. il. 1954.
   7.25. McGraw
Havighurst, R. J. Human development and education. 1953. 4.00. McKay
Hepner, Harry W. Psychology applied to life and work. 1957. 11.35. Prentice-Hall
Kunkel, Fritz. In search of maturity. 1943. 3.95. Scribner
Laird, Donald A., and Eleanor. Dynamics of personal efficiency. il. 1961. 4.95.
   Harper
Laird, Donald A., and Eleanor C. Practical business psychology. 1961. 7.75.
   McGraw
Laird, Donald A., and Eleanor C. Technique of handling people. 1954. 4.50. McGraw
Lehner, George F. J., and E. Kube. Dynamics of personal adjustment. 1955. 10.00.
   Prentice-Hall
Lehner, George F. J. Explorations in personal adjustment. 1957. 3.95. Prentice-
   Hall
McKinney, F. Psychology of personal adjustment. 1960. 6.75. Wiley
May, Rollo. Man's search for himself. 1953. 4.50. Norton
Minnick, Wayne C. Art of persuasion. 1958. 6.50. Houghton
Overstreet, Harry A. Influencing human behavior. 1925. 4.50. Norton
Overstreet, Harry, and Bonaro. Mind goes forth. 1956. 4.50. Norton
Peale, Norman Vincent. Guide to confident living. 1948. 3.95. Prentice-Hall
Peale, Norman Vincent. Power of positive thinking. 1952. 3.95. Prentice-Hall
Peale, Norman Vincent. Stay alive all your life. 1957. 3.95. Prentice-Hall
Steckle, Lynde C. Problems of human adjustment. il. 1957. 6.00. Harper
Tead, Ordway. Art of leadership. 1935. 5.95. McGraw
Viteles, Morris S. Industrial psychology. il. 1932. 7.25. Norton
PSYCHOLOGY, PATHOLOGICAL (616.89)
Adler, Alfred. Individual psychology. by Heinz L. and Rowena R. Ansbacher. 1956.
   8.50. Basic Books
Adler, Alfred. Theory and practice of individual psychology. 1951. 5.00.
   Humanities
Bowlby, John. Personality and mental illness. 3.00. Emerson
Cameron, Norman. Psychology of behavior disorders. 7.25. Houghton
Davis, D. R. Introduction to psychopathology. 1957. 7.50. Oxford U. P.
Eysenck, Hans, J. Handbook of abnormal psychology. il. 1961. 18.00. Basic Books
Freeman, Lucy, and Wilfred Hulse. Children who kill. pap. 0.50. Berkley
Freud, Sigmund. Psychopathology of everyday life. 3.75. Macmillan
Garrison, K. C., and D. G. Force, Jr. Psychology of exceptional children. 1959.
   6.50. Ronald
Guthrie, E. R. Psychology of human conflict. 4.25. Smith, Peter
Jung, C. G., and W. Pauli. Interpretation of nature and the psyche. 1955. 3.00.
   Pantheon
Jung, C. G. Psychology of the unconscious. 5.00. Dodd
Jung, Carl G. Symbols of transformation (Collected works, vol. 5) by Herbert
   Read, and others. 1956. 5.00. Pantheon
Levine, Maurice. Psychotherapy in medical practice. 4.50. Macmillan
Maslow, Abraham H., and Bela Mittelmann. Principles of abnormal psychology.
   1951. 7.00. Harper
Menninger, Karl. Human mind. 1945. 6.75. Knopf
Page, James D. Abnormal psychology. il. 1947. 6.95. McGraw
Prince, Morton. Clinical and experimental studies in personality. il. 1939. Sci-
   Art

Rank, Otto. Myth of the birth of the hero: A psychological interpretation of mythology. 1952. 3.00. Basic Books

Rapaport, David. Emotions and memory. 1950. 4.00. Int. Univs.

Rogers, Carl R. Clinical treatment of the problem child. 1939. 6.00. Houghton

Stekel, Wilheim. Technique of analytical psychotherapy. 4.95. Liveright

Thorpe, Louis P. Abnormal psychology. 2.50. Lucas Bros.

Tomkins, Silvan Samuel. Contemporary psychopathology: A source book. il. 1943. 5.00. Harvard

Weinberg, Henry, and A. William Hire. Case book in abnormal psychology. 1956. 4.50. Knopf

PSYCHOLOGY, PHYSIOLOGICAL (131)

Anastasi, Anne. Differential psychology. il. 7.50. Macmillan

Bartlett, Frederic C. Remembering: A study in experimental and social psychology. 1932. 9.50. Cambridge U. P.

Beach, Frank. Hormones and behavior. 6.95. Cooper

Boring, Edwin G. History of experiemntal psychology. 6.50. Appleton

Buhler, Charlotte. From birth to maturity. 4.00. Humanities

Coleman, James. Personality dynamics and effective behavior. 1960. 6.00. Scott

Crafts, Leland W., and others. Recent experiments in psychology. 1950. 5.75. McGraw

Garrett, Henry E. Great experiments in psychology. il. 1951. 4.00. Appleton

Hebb, D. O. Organization of behavior. 1949. 5.95. Wiley

Kantor, Jacob Robert. Problems of physiological psychology. 1947. 6.00. Principia Press, Inc.

Korzbski, Alfred. Science and sanity. 1958. 11.00. Inst. of Gen. Semantics

Lashley, Karl S. Neuropsychology of Lashley. 1960. 9.50. McGraw

Lewin, Kurt. Dynamic theory of personality. 1945. 6.95. McGraw

Maier, Norman R. F. Frustration: The study of behavior without a goal. 1961. 4.40. U. of Mich.

Morgan, Clifford T., and Eliot Stellar. Physiological psychology. 1950. 7.95. McGraw

Munn, N. L. Evolution and growth of human behavior. 1955. 7.50. Houghton

Postman, Leo, and James P. Egan. Experimental psychology. 1949. 5.50. Harper

Stevens, S. S. Handbook of experiemntal psychology. 1951. 18.50. Wiley

Wenger, Marion A., and others. Physiological psychology. il. 1956. 6.75. Holt, Rinehart & Winston

PSYCHOLOGY, RELIGIOUS (201)

Alcoholics Anonymous Fellowship. Alcoholics anonymous. 1955. 4.50. A.A. World Services

Allport, Gordon W. Individual and his religion. 3.25. Macmillan

Anderson, George C. Man's right to be human. 1959. 3.50. Morrow

Boisen, Anton T. Out of the depths. 1960. 4.00. Harper

James, William. Varieties of religious experience. 1.95. Modern Lib.

Johnson, Paul E. Psychology of religion. 1959. 5.00. Abingdon

Jung, C. G. Psychology and religion. 1938. 3.00. 1960. Yale

Kierkegaard, Soren. Concept of dread. tr. by Walter Lowrie. 1944. 4.00. Princeton

Oates, Wayne E. Religious dimensions of personality. 1957. 4.50. Assn. Pr.

Pratt, James Bissett. Religious consciousness. 1920. 5.00. Macmillan

Strunk, Orlo, Jr. Readings in the psychology of religion. 1959. 4.50. Abingdon

Thouless, Robert H. Introduction to the psychology of religion. 1935. 3.95. Cambridge U. P.

Wach, Joachim. Types of religious experience: Christian and non-Christian. 1951. 4.50. U. of Chicago

PSYCHOLOGY AS A PROFESSION (150.069)

Hirt, M. Psychology as a profession and career. 1.00. Bellman

PSYCHOTHERAPY (615.851)

Alexander, Leo. Objective approaches to treatment in psychiatry. il. 1958. 4.50. Thomas, C. C.

Bernstein, Arnold. On the nature of psychotherapy. 1954. pap. 0.85. Random
Bromberg, Walter. Mind of man. 1959. pap. 1.95. Harper
Bromberg, Walter. Nature of psychotherapy. 1961. 4.50. Grune
Buhler, Charlotte. Values in psychotherapy. 1962. 5.25. Free Press
Bychowski, Gustav, and J. Louise Despert. Specialized techniques in psycho-
    therapy. 1952. 6.00. Basic Books
Dollard, John, and Neal E. Miller. Personality and psychotherapy. 1950. 7.50.
    McGraw
Hofmann, Hans. Religion and mental health. 1961. 5.00. Harper
May, Rollo, and others. Existence. 7.50. Basic Books
Mowrer, O. H., and others. Psychotherapy: Theory and research. 1953. 12.00.
    Ronald
Peris, Frederick. Gestalt therapy. 1951. 6.50. Julian
Rogers, Carl R. On becoming a person. 1961. 6.75. Houghton
Seward, G. Psychotherapy and culture conflict. 1956. 7.50. Ronald
Stein, Morris I. Contemporary psychotherapies. 1961. 7.50. Free Press
Stendal, Stanley W., and Raymond J. Corsini. Critical incidents in psychotherapy.
    1959. 7.50. Prentice-Hall
Watkins, John G. General psychotherapy. 1960. 9.25. Thomas, C. C.

PUBLIC ADMINISTRATION (350)

Dimock, Marshall E. Philosophy of administration. 1958. 4.00. Harper
Dimock, Marshall E., and others. Public administration. 1958. 7.00. Holt,
    Rinehart & Winston
Lepawsky, Albert. Administration: The art and science of organization and
    management, 1949. 6.00. Knopf
Pfiffner, J. M., and R. V. Presthus. Public administration. 1960. 7.50. Ronald
Rowat, Donald C. Basic issues in public administration. 5.95. Macmillan
Sweeney, Stephen B. Education for administrative careers in government service.
    1958. 5.00. U. of Pa.
White, Leonard D. Introduction to the study of public administration. 1955. 6.75.
    Macmillan

PUBLIC HEALTH (614)

Anderson, Carl L., and Clair V. Langton. Health principles and practice. 1961.
    5.75. Mosby
Burn, John L. Recent advances in public health. 1959. 10.00. Little
Freeman, Ruth B. Public health nursing practice. 1957. 5.00. Saunders
Hanlon, John J. Principles of public health administration. il. 1960. 10.50. Mosby
Hobson, W. Theory and practice of public health. 1961. 14.00. Oxford U. P.
Johnson, W. R., and others. Health concepts for college students. 1962. 5.00.
    Ronald
Leff, S., and Vera. From witchcraft to world health. il. 4.50. Macmillan
Miller, Zelma B., and Benjamin F. Good health: Personal and community. il.
    1960. 6.00. Saunders
Mills, Clarence A. Air pollution and community health. 1954. 2.75. Christopher
Mustard, Harry S. Government in public health. il. 1945. 1.50. Harvard
Mustard, Harry S., and Ernest L. Stebbins. Introduction to public health. 5.00.
    Macmillan
Newsholme, Arthur. Public health and insurance: American addresses, 1920.
    2.50. Johns Hopkins
Roberts, Llewelyn. Aids to public health. 1958. 3.00. Williams & Wilkins
Rogers, Edward S. Human ecology and health. 1960. 7.75. Macmillan
Schifferes, Justus J. Essentials of healthier living. il. 1960. 5.75. Wiley
Smillie, Wilson G. Preventive medicine and public health. 7.50. Macmillan
Turner, Clair E. Personal and community health. il. 1959. 5.75. Mosby
Wilbur, Muriel B. Community health services. 1962. 5.00. Saunders
Wilson, Graham S. Pasteurization of milk. 1942. 4.50. St. Martins
World Health Organization. Publications of WHO, a bibliography. 3.25. Int. Doc.
    Service-Columbia (R)

PUBLIC OPINION (301.154)
Albig, W. Modern public opinion. 1956. 7.50. McGraw
Almond, Gabriel A. American people and foreign policy. 1960. 4.00. Praeger
Berelson, Bernard, and Morris Janowitz. Reader in public opinion and communication. 1953. 7.50. Free Press
Buchanan, William, and Hadley Cantril. How nations see each other. 1953. 5.00. U. of Ill.
Christenson, R. M., and R. O McWilliams. Voice of the people. 1962. 4.95. McGraw
Ernst, Morris, and David Loth. People know best. 1949. 2.50. Pub. Affairs
Fenton, John M. In your opinion. 1960. 3.95. Little
Inkeles, Alex. Public opinion in Soviet Russia: A study in mass persuasion. 1950. 5.50. Harvard
Jordan, Elijah. Theory of legislation: An essay on the dynamics of public mind. 1952. 7.00. U. of Chicago
Key, Valdimer O., Jr. Public opinion and American democracy. 1961. Knopf
Kracauer, S., and P. L. Berkman. Satellite mentality. 1956. 4.50. Praeger
MacDougall, Curits D. Understanding public opinion. 6.50. Macmillan
McPhee, William N., and William A. Glasser. Public opinion and congressional elections. 1962. 6.00. Free Press
Roper, Elmo. You and your leaders: Their actions and your reactions, 1936-1956. 1958. 3.95. Morrow
Schettler, Clarence. Public opinion in American society. 1960. 7.50. Harper
Smith, Bruce L., and others. Propaganda, communication, and public opinion. 1946. 6.00. Princeton
Stephan, Frederick F., and Philip J. McCarthy. Sampling opinions. 1958. 12.50. Wiley
Truman, David B. Governmental process: Political interests and public opinion. 1951. 5.50. Knopf
Tumin, M. Desegration: Resistance and readiness. 1958. 5.00. Princeton
Weinberg, A. K. Manifest destiny: A study of Nationalist expansion in American history. 1958. 7.50. Smith, Peter
Wilson, Francis G. Theory of public opinion. 1962. 7.00. Regnery
PUBLIC RELATIONS (659.111)
Bernays, Edward L. Crystallizing public opinion. 1961. 3.95. Liveright
Center, Allen H. Public relations ideas in action: 500 tested public relations programs and techniques. 1957. 6.00. McGraw
Lundborg, Louis B. Public relations in the local community. 1950. 3.50. Harper
Samstag, Nicholas. Persuasion for profit. il. 1958. 3.75. U. of Okla.
Steinberg, Charles S. Mass communicators. 1958. 5.25. Harper
Stephenson, H. Handbook of public relations. 1960. 12.50. McGraw
PUBLIC RELATIONS AS A PROFESSION (659.111069)
Bernays, Edward L. Your future in public relations. 1961. 2.95. Richards Rosen
PUBLIC SCHOOLS (379.1)
Cremin, Lawrence A., and Merle L. Borrowman. Public schools in our democracy. il. 1956. 4.00. Macmillan
Cubberley, Ellwood P. Public education in the United States. 1919. 7.75. Houghton
Grieder, C., and S. Romine. American public education. 1955. 5.00. Ronald
Hansen, K. H. Public education in American society. 8.35. Prentice-Hall
PUBLIC SPEAKING (808.5)
Arnold, Carroll C., and others. Speakers resource book. 1961. 2.95. Scott
Avery, Elizabeth, and others. First principles of speech training. il. 4.00 Appleton
Baird, A. Craig, and Franklin H. Knower. General speech: An introduction. 1957. 5.50. McGraw
Barnes, Harry G. Speech handbook. 1959. 3.25. Prentice-Hall
Becker, Mortimer. Speaking for all occasions. 1949. 4.68. Prentice-Hall

Borcners, Gladys L. Living speech. 1949. 2.72. Harcourt
Braden, Waldo W. , and Mary Louise Gehring. Speech practices: A resource
   book for student of public speaking. 1958. 3.00. Harper
Brigance, W. N. Speech communication: Brief textbook. 1955. 3.25. Appleton
Brigance, W. N. Speech compositions. 1953. 3.75. Appleton
Brigance, W. Norwood. Speech: Its techniques and disciplines in a free society.
   1961. 5.50. Appleton
Bryant, Donald C. and Karl R. Wallace. Oral communication. 1961. 3.75. Appleton
Craig, Alice E. Speech arts. il. 1941. 5.16. Macmillan
Crocker, Lionel G. , and Louis M. Eich. Oral reading. 1955. 6.95. Prentice-Hall
Dolman, John, Jr. Handbook of public speaking. 1944. 2.25. Harcourt
Eisenson, Jon. Basic speech. il. 1950. 5.00. Macmillan
Friedman, Edward L. Speechmaker's complete handbook. 1955. 4.95. Harper
Gerber, Philip L. Effective English. 1959. 5.50. Random
Gilman, Wilbur E. , and others. Fundamentals of speaking. il. 1954. 5.95.
   Macmillan
Hedde, Wilhelmina G. , and William N. Brigance. American speech. 1955. 4.84.
   Lippincott
Jones, E. Winston. Guide to effective speech. 1961. 3.75. McKay
Lowrey, Sara, and Gertrude E. Johnson. Interpretative reading. 4.50. Appleton
Monroe, Alan H. Principles and types of speech. 1962. 5.75. Scott
Monroe, Alan H. Principles of speech. 1958. 3.75. Scott
Muehl, William. Road to persuasion. 1956. 4.25. Oxford U. P.
Norvelle, Lee, and others. Speaking effectively. il. 1957. 3.75. Holt, Rinehart
   & Winston
Oliver, Robert T. Psychology of persuasive speech. 1957. 5.00. McKay
Prochnow, Herbert V. , comp. Complete toastmaster. 1960. bds. 4.95. Prentice-
   Hall
Prochnow, Herbert. Successful speaker's handbook. 1951. 4.95. Prentice-Hall
Sarett, Lew, and others. Basic principles of speech. 1946. 5.75. Houghton
Simmons, Harry. Executive public speaking techniques. 1959. 5.00. Chilton
Soper, Paul L. Basic public speaking. 1956. 4.50. Oxford U. P.
Von Hesse, Elisabeth. So to speak. il. 1959. 4.75. Lippincott
Weaver, Andrew T. , and Ordean G. Ness. Introduction to public speaking. 1961.
   3.75. Odyssey
Whiting, Percy H. How to speak and write with humor. 1959. 4.95. McGraw
Zetler, Robert L. , and W. George Crouch. Successful communication in science
   and industry: Writing, reading and speaking. 1961. 7.95. McGraw
PUBLIC UTILITIES (380)
Clemens, Eli Winston. Economics and public utilities. il. 1950. 6.50. Appleton
Daley, Robert. World beneath the city. il. 1959. 4.50. Lippincott
PUBLIC WELFARE (360)
Bisno, Herbert. Philosophy of social work. 1952. 3.25. Pub. Affairs
Bornet, Vaughn D. Welfare in America. il. 1960. 4.95. U. of Okla.
Bremner, Robert H. From the depths: The discovery of poverty in the United
   States. il. 1956. 5.50. N. Y. U.
Burns, E. M. Social security and public policy. 1956. 6.95. McGraw
Cohen, Social work in the American tradition. 5.00. Holt, Rinehart & Winston
Felix, Robert H. Mental health and social welfare. 1961. 3.75. Columbia
Fleisher, Wilfrid. Sweden: The welfare state. il. 1956. 4.00. Day
Friedlander, Walter. Introduction to social welfare. 1961. 7.95. Prentice-Hall
Hall, M. Penelope. Social services of modern England. 1953. 5.00. Humanities
Turnbull, J. G. , and others. Economic and social security. 1962. 8.00. Ronald
Vasey, Wayne. Government and social welfare. 1958. 5.50. Holt
PUBLICITY (301.1523)
Baus, Herbert M. Publicity in action. 1954. 4.75. Harper
Griswold, Glenn, and Denny. Your public relations, the standard public relations
   handbook. il. 1948. 7.50. Funk

Loizeaux, Marie D. Publicity primer. 1959. pap. 1.50. Wilson
Lyle, Guy R. College library publicity. 1935. 2.00 net. Faxon
Stahl, Le Roy. Art of publicity. 1962. 3.95. Denison
PUBLISHERS AND PUBLISHING (655.5)
Burack, Abraham S. Writer's handbook. 1944. 6.95. Writer (R)
Gross, Gerald, comp. Publishers on publishing. 1961. 5.00. Bowker
Hicks, Tyler G. Successful technical writing. 1959. 5.95. McGraw
Rosenthal, Richard. Writer's market. 1962. 5.95. Writer's Digest (R)
Schick, Frank. Paperbound book in America. 1958. 7.50 net postpaid. Bowker
Richter, Anne J. Literary market place, 1962-63: The business directory of
     American book publishing. 7.45. Bowker
PUERTO RICO (972.95)
Brameld, Theodore A. Remaking of a culture: Life and education in Puerto Rico.
     1959. 7.50; with Cultural foundations of education, 11.50. Harper
Clark, Victor S., and others. Porto Rico and its problems. 1930. 5.00. Brookings
Friedrich, Carl J. Puerto Rico, middle road to freedom. 1959. pap. 2.00.
     Holt, Rinehart & Winston
Hancock, Ralph H. Puerto Rico, a travelers' guide. 1962. 5.95. Van Nostrand
Marvel, Evalyn. Guide to Puerto Rico and the Virgin Islands. 3.50. Crown
Rand, Christopher. Puerto Ricans. 1958. 3.75. Oxford U. P.
PUNIC WARS (937.04)
Cottrell, Leonard. Hannibal, enemy of Rome. il. 1961. 5.00. Holt, Rinehart &
     Winston
Donauer, F. Swords against Carthage. 1961. 3.50. Biblo & Tannen
PUNISHMENT (343.2)
Bok, Curtis. Problems in criminal law. 1955. 2.00. U. of Nebr.
Playfair, Giles, and Derrick Sington. Offenders: The case against legal vengeance.
     1957. 3.95. S. and S.
Rolph, C. H. Common sense about crime and punishment. 1961. 2.95. Macmillan
Zilboorg, Gregory. Psychology of the criminal act and punishment. 1954. 3.50.
     Harcourt
PUPPETS AND PUPPET-PLAYS (791.53)
Batchelder. Marjorie. Puppet theatre handbook. il. 1947. 5.00. Harper
Boehn, M. von. Dolls and puppets. 7.50. Branford
McCrea, Lilian. Puppets and puppet plays. il. 1949. 1.20. Oxford U. P.
Speaight, George. History of the English puppet theatre. 1955. 6.00. De Graff
PURCELL, HENRY, 1658-1695 (927)
Holst, Imogen. Henry Purcell, 1659-1695, essays on his music. 1959. 5.00.
     Oxford U. P.
Moore, Robert E. Henry Purcell and the Restoration theatre. il. 1961. 5.25.
     Harvard
Westrup, J. A. Purcell. 1949. 3.50. Farrar, Straus
PURITANS (973)
Haller, William. Rise of Puritanism. 1938. 6.50. Columbia
Miller, Perry. American Puritans, their prose and poetry. 1959. 3.25. Smith,
     Peter
Miller, Perry G. E. New England mind from colony to province. 1953. 7.50.
     Harvard
Miller, P. G. E. New England mind: The seventeenth century. 1954. 7.50. Harvard
Miller, Perry. Orthodoxy in Massachusetts, 1630-1650. 4.00. Smith, Peter
Morison, Samuel E. Intellectual life in colonial New England. 1956. 4.95. N. Y. U.
Perry, Ralph B. Puritanism and democracy. 1944. 7.50. Vanguard
PUSHKIN, ALEKSANDR SERGEEVICH, 1799-1837 (928.917)
Simmons, Ernest Joseph. Pushkin. 1937. 6.00. Harvard
PYRAMIDS (913)
Cottrell, Leonard. Mountains of Pharoah. il. 1956. 5.00. Rinehart
Davidson, D. Great pyramid. 17.50. Wehman

Edwards, Iorwerth E. S. Pyramids of Egypt. 1961. 8.50. Pitman
Reisner, George Andrew. Mycerinus. il. 1931. 35.00. Harvard

Q

QUACKS AND QUACKERY (615.856)
Consumers Report. Medicine show. by the Editors of Consumers' Report. 1961.
    3.95. S. and S.
Holbrook, Stewart H. Golden age of quackery. 4.95. Macmillan
Lasagna, Louis. Doctor's dilemmas. 1962. 4.95. Harper
Palmer, Rachel Lynn, and Sarah K. Greenberg. 40,000,000, guinea pig children.
    1937. 2.50. Vanguard
QUALITY CONTROL (658.562)
Allan, Douglas H. W. Statistical quality control. il. 1959. 3.50. Reinhold
Duncan, Acheson J. Quality control and industrial statistics. 1959. 13.35. Irwin
Feigenbaum, Armand V. Total quality control. 1961. 11.00. McGraw
Juran, J. M. Quality control handbook. il. 1951. 16.50. McGraw
QUANTUM CHEMISTRY (541.383)
Daudel, Raymond, and others. Quantum chemistry. il. 1960. 14.50. Wiley
Eyring, H. , and others. Quantum chemistry. 1944. 7.95. Wiley
Karagounis, G. Introductory organic quantum chemistry. 1962. 6.50. Academic
    Press
Linnett, J. W. Wave mechanics and valency. 1960. 4.00. Wiley
Moelwyn-Hughes, E. A. Physical chemistry. il. 1961. 17.50. Pergamon
QUANTUM THEORY (530.12)
Abro, A. d'. Rise of the new physics. 2 vols. il. 1953. pap. 2.00 ea Dover
Bergman, Peter G. Basic theories of physics - heat and quanta. 3.75. Smith,
    Peter
Bohr, Niels. On the application of quantum theory to atomic structure. pt. 1. 1953.
    0.40. Cambridge U. P.
Born, Max. Mechanics of the atom. 1959. 6.50. Ungar
Broglie, Louis de. Revolution in physics: A non-mathematical survey of quanta.
    pap. 1.75. Farrar, Straus
Dicke, Robert H. , and J. P. Wittke. Introduction to quantum mechanics. 1960.
    9.50. Addison-Wesley
Einstein, Albert, and Leopold Infled. Evolution of physics. il. 1938. 4.50. S. and
    S.
Eisberg, Robert M. Fundamentals of modern physics. il. 1961. 10.50. Wiley
French, A. P. Principles of modern physics. il. 1958. 6.95. Wiley
Gamow, G. Mr. Tompkins in Wonderland. 1939. 2.95. Cambridge U. P.
Henley, E. M. , and W. Thirring. Elementary quantum theory. 1962. 8.95.
    McGraw
Pauling, Linus. Nature of the chemical bond and the structure of molecules and
    crystals: An introduction to modern structural chemistry. 1960. 8.85. Cornell
Rice, F. O. , and E. Teller. Structure of matter. 1949. 7.75. Wiley
Slater, J. C. Quantum theory of matter. il. 1951. 8.95. McGraw
QUEBEC (PROVINCE) (972)
Chapin, Miriam. Quebec now. 1955. 3.75. Oxford U. P.
Hughes, Everett C. French Canada in transition. 1943. 5.00. U. of Chicago
Lloyd, C. P. Quebec, 1759; the siege and the battle. 1959. 6.50. St. Martins
QUMRAN COMMUNITY (221.4)
Black, Matthew. Scrolls and Christian origins. il. 1961. 3.95. Scribner
Cross, Frank M. , Jr. Ancient library of Qumran and modern biblical studies.
    il. 1958. 4.50. Doubleday
Howie, Carl G. Dead Sea Scrolls and the living church. 1958. 4.50. John Knox
Rabin, Chaim. Qumran studies. 1957. 3.40. Oxford U. P.
QUOTATIONS (808.88)
Adams, Franklin P. FPA's book of quotations. 1952. 5.95. Funk (R)
Bartlett, John. Familiar quotations. 1955. 10.00. Little

Browning, D. C. Dictionary of quotations and proverbs. 1952. 4.25. Dutton (R)
Chapin, John. Book of Catholic quotations. 1956. 8.50. Farrar, Straus (R)
Edwaras, Tryon. New dictionary of thoughts. 1955. 10.00. Doubleday (R)
Esar, Evan. Dictionary of humorous quotations. 4.95. Horizon
Fadiman, Clifton, and Charles Van Doren. American Treasury, 1455-1955. 1955.
    8.95. Harper
Flesch, Rudolf. Book of unusual quotations. 1957. 4.95. Harper
Henry, Lewis C. 5000 quotations for all occasions. 1956. 2.50. Doubleday
Jones, Hugh P. Dictionary of foreign phrases and classical quotations. 6.00.
    Spencer (R)
King, W. Francis H. Dictionary of classical and foreign quotations. 1958. 6.50.
    Ungar (R)
Mencken, Henry L. New dictionary of quotations on historical principles from
    ancient and modern sources. 1942. 10.00. Knopf
Oxford dictionary of quotations. 1953. 10.50. Oxford U. P.
Prochnow, Herbert V., and Herbert V., Jr. Dictionary of wit, wisdom and satire.
    1962. 4.95. Harper (R)
Prochnow, Herbert V. Speaker's handbook of epigrams and witticisms. 1955. 4.95.
    Harper
Roberts, Kate Louise. Hoyt's new cyclopedia of practical quotations. 1940. 7.50.
    Funk (R)
Stevenson, Burton. Home book of quotations. 1959. 25.00. Dodd (R)
Taylor, Archer, and Bartlett J. Whiting. Dictionary of American proverbs and
    proverbial phrases 1820-1880. 1959. 9.50. Harvard (R)
Van Buren, Maud. Quotations for special occasions. 1938. 3.00. Wilson

R

RABELAIS, FRANCOIS - ca. 1490-1553? (843)
Lewis, D. B. Wyndham, Dom. Doctor Rabelais. 1957. 4.00. Sheed
Screech, M. A. Rabelaisian marriage: Aspects of Rabelais's religion, ethics,
    and comic philosophy. 5.50. St. Martins
RACE (301.451)
American Academy of Arts and Sciences. Ethnic groups in American life. 1961.
    1.75. Am. Acad. of Arts & Sci.
Barnett, Richard. Where the States stand on civil rights. 1961. 2.95. Sterling
Bibby, Cyril. Race, prejudice and education. 1960. 2.50. Praeger
Boas, Franz. Race, language and culture. 7.25. Macmillan
Garn, Stanley M. Human races. 1960. 5.50. Thomas, C. C.
Garn, Stanley M. Readings on race. il. 1959. 6.75. Thomas, C. C.
Greenberg, Jack. Race relations and American law. 1959. 10.00. Columbia
Symposium on Race and Race relations, London, 1959. Man, race, and Darwin.
    by Philip Mason. 2.90. Oxford U. P.
UNESCO. Race and science: A scientific analysis from UNESCO. 1961. 5.00.
    Columbia
UNESCO. Race question in modern sicence: A symposium. 1956. 5.00. Whiteside
RACE PROBLEMS (301.45)
Benedict, Ruth. Race: Science and politics. 1959. pap. 1.25. Viking
Boas, Franz. Mind of primitive man. 5.50. Macmillan
Browne, Robert S. Race relations in international affairs. 1961. 1.00. Pub. Affairs
Campbell, Ernest Q., and Thomas F. Pettigrew. Christians in racial crisis. 1959.
    3.50. Pub. Affairs
Conant, Melvin. Race issues on the world scene. 4.00. U. of Hawaii
Frazier, E. Franklin. Race and culture contacts in the modern world. 1957. 5.00.
    Knopf
Haselden, Kyle. Racial problem in Christian perspective. 1959. 3.50. Harper
Linton, Ralph. Science of man in the world crisis. 1945. 4.75. Columbia
McWilliams, Carey. Brothers under the skin. 1951. 5.50. Little

Park, Robert E. Race and culture. 1950. 5.00. Free Press
Stonequist, Everett V. Marginal man: A study in personality and culture conflict. 1962. 6.50. Russell
Thompson, E. T., and Everett C. Hughes. Race: Individual and collective behavior. 7.50. Free Press
Walter, Paul. Race and culture relations. il. 1952. 6.95. McGraw

RACHMANINOFF, SERGEI, 1873-1943 (927)
Bertensson, Sergei, and Jay Leyda. Sergei Rachmaninoff: A lifetime of Music. 1955. 6.50. N. Y. U.

RACINE, JEAN BAPTISTE (1639-1699 (928)
Muir, Kenneth. Last periods of Shakespeare, Racine, Ibsen. 1961. 4.50. Wayne
Stendhal, M. de. Racine and Shakespeare. 1962. 3.95. Crowell-Collier

RADAR (621.3848)
AGARD. Avionics research: Satellites and problems of long range detection and tracking. by E. V. D. Glazier and others. 1960. 10.00. Pergamon
Battan, Louis J. Radar meteorology. 1959. 6.00. U. of Chicago
Boulding, R. S. H. Radar pocket book. il. 1962. 4.50. Van Nostrand
Dunlap, Orrin E., Jr. Radar: What radar is and how it works. 1948. 3.95. Harper
Maclanachan, W. Television and radar encyclopaedia. 1954. 6.75. Pitman
Oudet, L. Radar and collision. il. 1960. 3.00. Van Nostrand
Penrose, Harold E., and R. S. H. Boulding. Principles and practice of radar. 1959. 15.00. Van Nostrand
Wylie, F. J. Use of radar at sea. 1958. 7.95. Van Nostrand

RADIATION (539.7)
Frisch, Otto R., and others. Trends in atomic physics. il. 1959. 7.50. Wiley
Harvey, E. Newton. History of luminescence from the earliest times until 1900. 1957. 6.00. Am. Philos. Soc.
Harwood, J. J., and others. Effects of radiation on materials. 1958. 10.50. Reinhold
Holter, Marvin R., and others. Fundamentals of infrared technology. 1962. 12.50. Macmillan
Reinfeld, Fred. Rays: Visible and invisible. il. 1958. 3.95. Sterling
Shilling, C. W. Radiation: Use and control in industrial application. il. 1960. 6.75. Grune

RADIATION--PHYSIOLOGICAL EFFECT (612.01448)
American Public Health Association. Public exposure to ionizing radiations. 1958. 1.35. Am. Public Health
Barnes, D. E., and Denis Taylor. Radiation hazards and protection. 1959. 6.75. Pitman
Blatz, Hanson. Radiation hygiene handbook. 1959. 27.50. McGraw
Braestrup, Carl B., and Harold D. Wyckoff. Radiation protection. il. 1958. 10.50. Thomas, C. C.
Gleason, Sterling. Ultra violet guide to minerals. il. 1960. 7.95. Van Nostrand
Brobman, Arnold. Our atomic heritage. il. 1951. 2.95. U. of Fla.
Loutit, John F. Irradiation of mice and men. il. 1962. 5.00. U. of Chicago
Schubert, Jack, and Ralph E. Lapp. Radiation: What it is and how it affects you. 1957. 3.95. Viking
Williams, Katharine, and others. Radiation and health. 1962. 7.00. Little
World Health Organization. Effect of radiation on human heredity. 4.00. Int. Doc. Service-Columbia

RADICALS (CHEMISTRY)(544.1)
Minkoff, G. J. Frozen free radicals. il. 1960. 5.50. Wiley
Waters, W. A. Chemistry of free radicals. il. 1948. 5.20. Oxford U. P.

RADIO (621.38413)
Albert, Arthur L. Radio fundamentals. il. 1948. 6.00. McGraw
American Radio Relay League. Radio amateur's handbook. 3.50. Am. Radio
Chester, Giraud, and Garnet R. Garrison. Television and radio: An introduction. 6.50. Appleton

Collins, A. Frederick. Radio amateur's handbook. il. 1957. 3.95. Crowell
Henney, Keith. Radio engineering handbook. 1959. 25.00. McGraw
McCleery, D. K. Radio today. il. 1961. 3.40. Oxford U. P.
Manly, Harold P. Radio-television-electronic dictionary. 1960. 5.00. Drake, F. J. (R)
Tyler, Poyntz. Television and radio; 1961. 2.50. Wilson

RADIO BROADCASTING (384.54)
Barnhart. Radio and television announcing. 1953. 7.25. Prentice-Hall
Bender, James F. NBC handbook of pronunciation. 1962. 5.75. Crowell
Carboni, Erberto. Radio and television publicity. il. 1959. 10.00. N. Y. Graphic
Codding, George A., Jr. Broadcasting without barriers. il. 1959. 4.50. Int. Doc. Service-Columbia
Henneke, Ben Graf, and Edward S. Dumit. Announcer's handbook. 1959. pap. 4.25. Holt, Rinehart & Winston
Holt, Robert T. Radio free Europe. 1958. 5.00. U. of Minn.
Hyde, Stuart W. Television and radio announcing. il. 1951. 8.50. Houghton
Seehafer, Eugene F., and J. W. Laemmar. Successful television and radio advertising. il. 1959. 9.95. McGraw
Seldes, Gilbert. Public arts. 1957. pap. 1.50. S. and S.
Smead, Elmer E. Freedom of speech by radio and television. 1951. 6.50. Rinehart
Wolfe, Charles H. Modern radio advertising. 1953. 7.50. Funk

RADIOACTIVITY (539.752)
Abbatt, John D., and others. Protection against radiation. il. 1961. 6.50. Thomas, C. C.
Brues, Austin M. Low-level irradiation. 1959. 3.75. A. A. A. S.
Burton, Milton, and others. Comparative effects of radiation. il. 1960. 8.50. Wiley
Calder, Rithcie. Living with the atom. il. 1962. 5.95. U. of Chicago
Cork, James M. Radioactivity and nuclear physics. il. 1957. 7.75. Van Nostrand
Fowler, John M. Fallout. il. 1960. 5.50. Basic Books
Glassner, Alvin. Introduction to nuclear sicence. il. 1961. 3.75. Van Nostrand
Hines, Neal O. Proving ground: An account of the radio-biological surveys in the Pacific, 1946-1961. il. 1962. 6.00. U. of Wash.
Keil, Andrew A. Radiation control. il. 1960. 4.75. Nat. Fire Protection
Sacks, J. Isotopic tracers in biochemistry and physiology. il. 1953. 8.50. McGraw
Taylor, Denis. Measurement of radio isotopes. 1958. 2.00. Wiley
Teller, Edward, and Albert L. Latter. Our nuclear future: Facts, dangers, and opportunities. il. 1958. 3.50. Criterion

RAILROADS (625)
Allen, Cecil J. Modern railways. 1960. 9.00. Macmillan
Beebe, Lucius, and Charles Clegg. Hear the train blow: A pictorial epic of America in the railroad age. il. 12.75. Dutton
Clark, Ira G. Then came the railroads. il. 1958. 5.75. U. of Okla.
Moore, William. Reorganization of railroad corporations. 1941. 3.00. Pub. Affairs
Weller, Walter W., and Charles J. Fagg. Fundamentals of transportation. including problem sheets 5.50. Traffic

RAILROADS--U.S. (625.973)
Baker, George P. Formation of the New England railroad systems. il. 1937. 4.50. Harvard
Black, Robert C. Railroads of the Confederacy. 1952. 6.00. U. of N. C.
Collias, Joe G. Last of steam. 1960. 10.00. Howell-North
Grodinsky, Julius. Iowa pool. A study in railroad competition 1870-84. il. 1950. 4.00. U. of Chicago
Howard, Robert W. Great iron trail. 1962. 5.95. Putnam
Hultgren, T. American transportation in prosperity and depression. 1948. 5.00. Princeton

Josephson, Matthew. Robber barons. 1934. 4.75. Harcourt
Locklin, David Philip. Economics of transportation. 1960. 11.35. Irwin
Moody, Linwood W. Maine two-footers. il. 6.00. Howell-North
Nelson, James C. Railroad transportation and public policy. il. 1959. 7.50.
    Brookings
Stover, John F. American railroads. 1961. 5.00. U. of Chicago
Tyler, Poyntz. Outlook for the railroads. 1960. 2.50. Wilson
RALEIGH, SIR WALTER, 1552?-1618 (923.9)
Irwin, Margaret E. F. That great Lucifer: A portrait of Sir Walter Raleigh. 1960.
    4.50. Harcourt
Oakeshott, Walter F. Queen and the poet. il. 1961. 5.00. Barnes & Noble
Rowse, Alfred L. Sir Walter Raleigh. il. 1962. 6.95. Harper
Wallace, W. M. Sir Walter Raleigh. 1959. 6.00. Princeton
RANCH LIFE (630.1)
Adams, Ramon F. Best of the American cowboy. il. 1957. 4.95. U. of Okla.
Adams, Ramon F. Old-time cowhand. il. 1961. 7.50. Macmillan
Atherton, Lewis E. Cattle kings. il. 1961. 6.95. Indiana
Lea, Tom. King ranch. il. 2 vols. 1957. 20.00. Little
Wyman, Walker D. Nothing but prairie and sky: Life on the Dakota range, in early
    days. il. 1954. 3.75. U. of Okla.
RAND, AYN (928)
Branden, Nathaniel. Who is Ayn Rand? 1962. 3.95. Random
RAPHAEL (RAFFAELO SANZIO D'URBINO) 1483-1520 (927)
Berti, Luciano. Raphael. il. 1961. 3.95. Norton
Raphael. Raphael. il. collectors ed. 3.95. Abrams
RASPUTIN, GRIGORI EFIMOVICH, 1871-1916 (922)
Fulop-Miller, Rene. Rasputin: The holy devil. 5.00. Ungar
Liepman, Heinz. Rasputin and the fall of Imperial Russia. 3.95. Rolton
RATIONALISM (149.7)
Brophy, Brigid. Black ship to hell. 1962. 8.50. Harcourt
Bury, John B. History of freedom of thought. 1952. 1.70. Oxford U. P.
Heimann, Eduard. Reason and faith in modern society. 1961. 6.50. Wesleyan U.P.
Lecky, William E. H. Rise and influence of rationalism in Europe. 1955. 5.00.
    Braziller
Paine, Thomas. Age of Reason. 2.00. Ottenheimer
RATS (599.323)
Chitty, Dennis, and H. N. Southern. Control of rats and mice. 1954. 16.80. Oxford
    U. P.
Munn, N. L. Handbook of psychological research on the rat. 8.75. Houghton
RAVEL, MAURICE, 1875-1937 (927)
Demuth, Norman. Ravel. 1949. 3.50. Farrar, Straus
Myers, Rollo H. Ravel: Life and works. il. 1961. 1.95. Yoseloff
READING (428.4)
Adler, Mortimer J. How to read a book. 1956. pap. 1.75. S. and S.
Bond, Guy L., and Miles A. Tinker. Reading difficulties: Their diagnosis and
    correction. il. 1957. 5.50. Appleton
Bullock, Harrison. Helping the non-reading pupil in the secondary school. 1956.
    4.00. T. C.
Cleary, Florence Damon. Blueprints for better reading. 1957. 3.00. Wilson
Gilbert D. W. Breaking the reading barrier. 1959. 3.95. Prentice-Hall
Gilbert D. W. Power and speed in reading. 5.25. Prentice-Hall
Gray, William S., and Bernice Rogers. Maturity in reading, its nature and
    appraisal. 1956. 5.75. U. of Chicago
Gray, William S. Promoting growth toward maturity in interpreting what is read.
    1951. pap. 3.85. U. of Chicago
Hildreth, Gertrude H. Teaching reading. 1958. 6.50. Holt, Rinehart & Winston
Leedy, P. D. Reading improvement for adults. 1956. 6.95. McGraw
Lewis, Norman. How to read better and faster. 1958, 4.95. Crowell

Newton, John R. Reading in your school. 1960. 5.95. McGraw

Robinson, Helen M. Evaluation of reading. 1958. 3.50. U. of Chicago

Robinson, Helen M. Materials for reading. 1957. 3.50. U. of Chicago

Robinson, Helen M. Sequential development of reading abilities. 1960. 3.50. U. of Chicago

Robinson, Helen M. Why pupils fail in reading. 1946. 4.50. U. of Chicago

Simpson, Elizabeth A. Helping high school students read better. il. 1954. 3.70. Sci. Res. Assoc.

Simpson, Elizabeth A. SRA better reading. 3 bks. il. 1962. 2.50 ea. Sci. Res. Assoc.

Smith, Nila B. Read faster and get more from your reading. 1958. 5.95. Prentice-Hall

Spache, George D., and Paul C. Berg. Faster reading for business. 1958. 3.95. Crowell

Strang, Ruth, and others. Improvement of reading. 1961. 6.75. McGraw

Strang, Ruth, and Dorothy K. Bracken. Making better readers. 1957. 6.00. Heath

Witty, Paul A. Development in and through reading. 5.00. U. of Chicago

Witty, Paul. How to improve your reading. 1962. 4.95. Sci. Res. Assoc.

READING (ELEMENTARY) (372.41)

Betts, Emmett A. Foundations of reading instruction: With emphasis on differentiated guidance. 8.00. Am. Bk. Co.

Bond, Guy L., and Eva Bond Wagner. Teaching the child to read. 1960. 5.75. Macmillan

Broom, M. E., and others. Effective reading instructions in the elementary school. il. 1951. 6.50. McGraw

De Boer, John J., and Martha Dallmann. Teaching of reading. il. 1960. 5.00. Holt, Rinehart & Winston

Durrell, Donald D. Improving reading instruction. 4.95. Harcourt

Flesch, Rudolf. Teaching Johnny to read. 1956. 1.50. Grosset

Flesch, Rudolf. Why Johnny can't read - and what you can do about it. 1955. 3.95. Harper

Gates, Arthur I. Improvement of reading. 1947. 5.75. Macmillan

Gray, L., and D. Reese. Teaching children to read. 1957. 6.00. Ronald

Harris, Albert J. Effective teaching of reading. 1962. 6.00. McKay

McKee, Paul. Teaching of reading in the elementary school. 5.00. Houghton

Monroe, Marion. Children who cannot read. 1932. 4.50. U. of Chicago

Russell, David H. Children learn to read. 1961. 6.25. Ginn

Strang, Ruth M. Helping your child improve his reading. il. 1962. 4.50. Dutton

Tinker, Miles A., and C. McCullough. Teaching elementary reading. il. 1961. 6.50. Appleton

Tooze, Ruth. Your children want to read: A guide for teachers and parents. 1957. 7.00. Prentice-Hall

READING (HIGHER EDUCATION) (378)

Altick, Richard D. Preface to critical reading. 1960. 3.75. Holt, Rinehart & Winston

Baker, William D. Reading skills. 1953. 1.95. Prentice-Hall

Barnhart, T. A., and others. Viewpoints: Readings for analysis. 1954. 5.25. Prentice-Hall

Carter, Homer L. J., and Dorothy J. McGinnis. Effective reading for college students. 1957. 4.25. Holt, Rinehart & Winston

Case, Keith E., and George T. Vardaman. Mature reading and thinking. 1959. pap. 3.95. Burgess

Cuomo, George. Becoming a better reader. 1960. pap. 1.00. Holt, Rinehart & Winston

Hayford, Harrison, and H. P. Vincent. Reader and writer. 5.25. Houghton

Jones, Everett L. Approach to college reading. 1959. 2.50. Holt, Rinehart & Winston

Price, Jacob M. Reading for life: Developing the college student's lifetime reading interest. 1959. 6.00. U. of Mich.

Smith, Donald E. P. Learning to learn. il. 1961. pap. 1.95. Harcourt
READING, PSYCHOLOGY OF (428.4)
Center, Stella. Art of book reading. 1952. 4.50. Scribner
Gray, William S. Reading in the high school and college. NSSE, 47th yrbk. pt. 2.
    1948. 4.50. U. of Chicago
Harris, Albert J. How to increase reading ability. 1961. 6.00. McKay
Henneke, Ben Graf. Reading aloud effectively. 1955. 9.10. Holt, Rinehart & Winston
Lee, Charlotte I. Oral interpretation. 1959. 5.50. Houghton
Parrish, W. M. Reading aloud. 1953. 5.50. Ronald
Robinson, Helen Mansfield. Oral aspects of reading. 1955. 3.50. U. of Chicago
Smith, Henry P., and E. V. Dechant. Psychology in teaching reading. 1961. 10.00.
    Prentice-Hall
REAL ESTATE (333.33)
Atkinson, H. G., and L. E. Frailey. Fundamentals of real estate practice. 1957.
    9.35. Prentice-Hall
Brown, Robert K., and A. H. Sturgess. Real estate primer. il. 1961. 7.50.
    Prentice-Hall
Case, Frederick E. Real estate. il. 1962. 10.95. Allyn & Bacon
Davies, Pearl J. Real estate in American history. 1958. 5.00. Pub. Affairs
Dykstra, Gerald O., and Lillian G. Business law of real estate. 1956. 7.50.
    Macmillan
Doris, Lillian. Real estate office secretary's handbook. 1953. 5.95. Prentice-Hall
Friedman, Edith Judity. Encyclopedia of real estate appraising. 22.50. Prentice-
    Hall
Friedman, Edith J. Handbook of real estate forms. 8.50. Prentice-Hall
Husband, William H., and Frank Ray Anderson. Real estate. 1960. 10.60. Irwin
J. K. Lasser Tax Institute. Lasser's successful tax-planning for real estate.
    1961. 7.50. Citadel
Kratovil, Robert. Real estate law. 1958. 11.00. Prentice-Hall
Lusk, Harold F. Law of the real estate business. 1958. 9.25. cases. 1961. pap.
    3.35. Irwin
McMichael, Stanley L. How to operate a real estate business. 7.35. Prentice-
    Hall
Prentice-Hall Editorial Staff. Prentice-Hall treasury of money-making real
    estate ideas and practices. 1962. 15.00. Prentice-Hall
Teckemeyer, Earl B. How to value real estate: The foremost factor in selling.
    1956. 5.35. Prentice-Hall
Teckemeyer, Earl B. Techemeyer on selling real estate. il. 1962. 5.95.
    Prentice-Hall
Ungar, M. A. Real estate. 1959. 6.75. South-Western Pub.
Weimer, Arthur M., and Homer Hoyt. Principles of real estate. 1960. 7.50.
    Ronald
REALITY (153.66)
Chiari, Joseph. Realism and imagination. 1961. 6.00. Macmillan
Dewey, John. Essays in experiemntal logic. 3.75. Smith, Peter
Kant, Immanuel. Inaugural dissertation, and Early writings on space. 2.00.
    Open Ct.
Renard, Henri. Philosophy of being. 1943. 2.75. Bruce
Royce, Josiah. World and the individual: ser. 1 and 2. 2 vols. 8.50. Smith, Peter
Vogel, Arthur. Reality, reason and religion. 3.00. Morehouse
Wheelwright. Philip E. Metaphor and reality. 1962. 5.00. Indiana
Wild, John. Introduction to realistic philosophy. 1948. 5.00. Harper
REASONING (153.6)
Ferre, Nels F. S. Faith and reason. 1946. 3.50. Harper
Gerrish, Brian A. Grace and reason: A study in the Theology of Luther. 1962.
    6.75. Oxford U. P.
Joad, Cyril E. M. Return to philosophy. 2.00. Humanities
Keyes, Kenneth S. How to develop your thinking ability. 1950. 5.95. McGraw
Passmore, John A. Philosophical reasoning. 1962. 3.50. Scribner

Templin, Mildred C. Development of reasoning in children with normal and defective hearing. 1950. 3.00. U. of Minn.

RECONSTRUCTION (973.8)

Bowers, Claude G. Tragic era: The revolution after Lincoln. il. 1929. 6.00. Houghton

Buck, Paul. Road to reunion, 1865-1900. 1959. 3.25. Smith, Peter

Carter, Hodding. Angry scar: The story of reconstruction 1865-1890. 1958. 5.95. Doubleday

Daniels, Jonathan. Prince of carpetbaggers. 6.00. Lippincott

Fleming, Walter L. Documentary history of Reconstruction. 12.50. Smith, Peter

Franklin, John H. Reconstruction after the Civil War. 1961. 5.00. U. of Chicago

Hesseltine, William B. Tragic conflict. 1962. 8.50. Braziller

Rozwenc, Edwin C. Reconstruction in the South. 1952. pap. 1.50. Heath

Trowbridge, John T. Desolate South: 1865-1866. 1956. 6.00. Duell

Welles, Gideon. Civil War and Reconstruction. 1959. 4.50. Twayne

Welles, Gideon. Diary of Gideon Welles. by Howard K. Beale. 3 vols. il. 1960. 30.00. Norton

Welles, Gideon. Lincoln's administration. 4.50. Twayne

Woodward, C. Vann. Reunion and reaction. 3.00. Smith, Peter

Woolfolk, George R. The cotton regency. 1958. 5.00. Twayne

RECREATION (790)

Brightbill, Charles K., and Harold D. Meyer. Community recreation. il. 1956. 9.25. Prentice-Hall

Butler, George D. Introduction to community recreation. 1959. 7.75. McGraw

Butler, George D. Recreation areas: Their design and equipment. 1958. 8.00. Ronald

Cleaver, Nancy. Treasury of family fun. il. 1960. 4.95. Revell

Corbin, Hayman D. Recreation leadership. 1959. 6.95. Prentice-Hall

Danford, Howard G. Recreation in the American community. 1953. 5.50. Harper

Durant, Clement A. Program encyclopedia. 1955. 7.95. Assn. Pr.

Gabrielsen, M. Alexander, and Caswell M. Miles. Sports and recreation facilities for school and community. il. 1958. 10.60. Prentice-Hall

Harbin, E. O. Recreation leader. 1952. 1.50. Abingdon

Kraus, Richard G. Recreation leader's handbook. 1955. 6.95. McGraw

Leavitt, N. M., and H. D. Price. Intramural and recreational sports for high school and college. 1958. 5.00. Ronald

Nash, Jay B. Philosophy of recreation and leisure. 1960. 3.50. Brown, W. C.

National Education Association, American Association for Health, Physical Education and Recreation. Research methods in health, physical education, and recreation. 1959. 6.00. N. E. A.

School recreation. 1960. 1.50. Am. Assn. for Health, Phys. Ed. & Rec.

Thompson, Nellie Zetta. High times: 700 suggestions for social activity. 2.50. Dutton

Trow, William Clarke, and others. Recreation and leisure. 1951. 1.32. McGraw

REFERENCE BOOKS (028.7)

Alexander, Carter, and Arvid J. Burke. How to locate educational information and data. 1958. 6.25. T. C.

Barton, Mary N., and Marion V. Bell. Reference books. 1962. 1.25; 10 or more, 1.00 ea. Enoch Pratt

Hoffman, Hester R. Reader's adviser and bookman's manual. 1960. 15.00. Bowker

Murphey, R. W. How and where to look it up. 1958. 15.00. McGraw (R)

Russell, Harold, and others. Use of books and libraries. 1958. 1.75. U. of Mich.

Shores, Louis. Basic reference sources. 1954. 6.25. A. L. A. (R)

Subscription books bulletin reviews: 1956-1960. 1961. 5.00. A. L. A. (R)

Williams, Cecil B., and Allan H. Stevenson. Research manual: For college studies and papers. 1951. 2.75. Harper

Winchell, Constance M. Guide to reference books. 1951. 10.00. A. L. A.

REFORMATION (940.23)

Aulen, Gustaf. Reformation and Catholicity. 1961. 3.75. Muhlenberg

Bainton, Roland. Reformation of the sixteenth century. 3.75. Smith, Peter

Beard, Charles. Reformation of the 16th century. 4.40. U. of Mich.

Belloc, Hilaire. Characters of the Reformation. 1958. pap. 0.85. Doubleday

Belloc, Hilaire. How the Reformation happened. 3.50. Dodd

Butterworth, Charles C. English primers. 1953. 6.00. U. of Pa.

D'Aubigne, J. H. Merle. Life and times of Martin Luther. 1950. 3.50. Moody

Durant, Will. Reformation. 12.00. S. and S.

Fosdick, Harry Emerson. Great voices of the Reformation. 2.95. Modern Lib.

George, Charles, and Katharine. Protestant mind of the English Reformation, 1570-1640. 1961. 8.50. Princeton

Grimm, Harold J. Reformation era. 1500-1650. il. 1954. 6.75. Macmillan

Harbison, E. Harris. Christian scholar in the age of the reformation. 1956. 3.00. Scribner

Hughes, Philip. Popular history of the Reformation. 1957. 4.00. Doubleday

Latourette, Kenneth Scott. Three centuries of advance: A.D. 1500-1800. (History of the expansion of Christianity, vol. 3) 6.00. Harper

Lucas, Henry S. Renaissance and the Reformation. 1960. 8.50. Harper

Mackinnon, J. Calvin and the Reformation. 1962. 7.50. Russell

Reformation. 8.50. Cambridge U. P.

Schaff, Philip. German Reformation (History of the Christian church, vol. 7) 6.00. Eerdmans

Smith, Preserved. Age of the Reformation. 1920. 8.00. Holt

Spinka, Matthew. Advocates of reform: From Wyclif to Erasmus. 1953. 5.00. Westminster

Tanner, Emmeline M. Renaissance and the Reformation: A textbook of European history, 1494-1610. 1908. 2.40. Oxford U. P.

Tillmanns, Walter G. World and men around Luther. 1959. 5.95. Augsburg

REFRIGERATION AND REFRIGERATING MACHINERY (621.56)

Jennings, B. H., and S. R. Lewis. Air conditioning and refrigeration. 1958. 10.50. Int. Textbook

Sharpe, Norman. Refrigerating principles and practices. 1949. 7.50. McGraw

REGIONAL PLANNING (309.24)

Chapin, F. Stuart, Jr. Urban land use planning. 1957. 8.00. Harper

Freeman, T. W. Geography and planning. 2.50. Hillary

Higbee, Edward C. Squeeze: Cities without space. 1960. 5.95. Morrow

MacKaye, Benton. New exploration: A philosophy of regional planning. 1962. pap. 1.75. U. of Ill.

Mumford, Lewis. Culture of cities. il. 1938. 7.50. Harcourt

REHABILITATION (331.868)

Bettelheim, Bruno. Truants from life: The rehabilitation of emotionally disturbed children. 1955. 6.00. Free Press

Heather, Arthur J. Manual of care for the disabled patient. 1961. 3.75. Macmillan

Johnston, N., and Norman B. Sociology of punishment and correction. 1962. 6.50. Wiley

Kiernander, Basil. Physical medicine and rehabilitation. il. 1953. 12.50. Davis

Ling, Thomas M., and C. J. S. O'Malley. Rehabilitation after illness and accident. 1958. 3.50. Williams & Wilkins

Meyer, Henry J., and Edgar F. Borgatta. Experiment in mental patient rehabilitation. il. 1959. 2.50. Russell Sage

Soden, W. H., and others. Rehabilitation of the handicapped. 1949. 6.50. Ronald

Terry, Florence J., and others. Principles and technics of rehabilitation nursing. il. 1961. 6.00. Mosby

RELATIVITY (PHYSICS) (530.11)

Abro, A. d'. Evolution of scientific thought from Newton to Einstein. 3.75. Smith, Peter

Barnett, Lincoln. Universe and Dr. Einstein. 1957. 3.50. Sloane

Born, Max. Einstein's theory of relativity. pap. 2.00. Dover

Coleman, James A. Relativity for the layman. il. 3.75. Macmillan

Eddington, Arthur S. Mathematical theory of relativity. 5.50. Cambridge U. P.
Eddington, Arthur S. Space, time and gravitation. 1960. 5.50. Cambridge U. P.
Einstein, Albert. Meaning of relativity. 1956. 3.75. Princeton
Einstein, Albert. Relativity: The special and general theory. 3.00. Crown
Einstein, Albert, and Leopold Infled. Evolution of physics. il. 1938. 4.50. S. and S.
Lieber, Lillian R. Einstein theory of relativity. il. 1945. 3.95. Rinehart
Moller, C. Theory of relativity. 1952. 7.20. Oxford U. P.
Recent developments in general relativity. 1962. 8.00. Pergamon
Reichenbach, Hans. Philosophy of space and time. pap. 2.00. Dover
Russell, Bertrand. ABC of relativity. 1959. 3.75. Oxford U. P.
Stephenson, G., and C. W. Kilmister. Special relativity for physicists. 1958. 3.25. Wiley

RELIGION (200)
Basilius, Harold A. Contemporary problems in religion. il. 1956. 3.50. Wayne
Benson, Purnell H. Religion in contemporary culture. 1960. 8.00. Harper
Browne, Thomas. Religion medici. 1.50. Nelson
Chesterton, G. K. Everlasting man. 1955. pap. 0.95. Doubleday
Dewey, John. Common faith. 1934. 3.00. Yale
Eliade, Mircea. History of religion: Essays in methodology. 1959. 5.00. U. of Chicago
Ferm, Vergilius. Encyclopedia of religion. 1959. pap. 2.95. Littlefield
Hastings, James. Encyclopedia of religion and ethics. 13 vols. 1951. 195.00. Scribner
Huxley, Julian. Religion without Revelation. 1959. pap. 0.50. New Am. Lib.
James, William. Varieties of religious experience. 1.95. Modern Lib.
Kraemer, Hendrik. Religion and the Christian faith. 1957. 6.00. Westminster
Mencken, Henry L. Treatise on the gods. 1946. 4.50. Knopf
Mill, John Stuart. Nature and utility of religion. 1958. pap. 0.80. Bobbs
Radhakrishnan, Sarvepalli. Recovery of faith. 1955. 3.95. Harper
Santayana, George. Interpretations of poetry and religion. 1958. 3.50. Smith, Peter
Schleiermacher, Friedrich. On religion. by E. Graham Waring. 2.25. Ungar
Tagore, Rabindranath. Religion of man. 1961. pap. 1.65. Beacon
Thurman, Howard. Creative encounter: An interpretation of religion and the social witness. 1954. 2.00. Harper
Tolstoy, Leo. On life, and Essays on religion. 2.75. Oxford U. P.
Toynbee, Arnold. Historian's approach to religion. 1956. 5.00. Oxford U. P.
Whitehead, Alfred N. Religion in the making. 1926. 3.95. Macmillan

RELIGION, PHILOSOPHY (201)
Bertocci, Peter A. Introduction to the philosophy of religion. 1951. 9.65. Prentice-Hall
Bertocci, Peter A. Religion as creative insecurity. 1958. 2.50. Assn. Pr.
Brightman, Edgar S. Philosophy of religion. 1940. 11.00. Prentice-Hall
Burtt, Edwin Arthur. Types of religious philosophy. 1951. 5.00. Harper
Butler, J. Donald. Four philosophies and their practice in education and religion. 1957. 6.50. Harper
Garnett, A. C. Religion and the moral life. 1955. 4.00. Ronald
Hegel, G. W. F. Lectures on the philosophy of religion. 3 vols. 17.50. Humanities
Herberg, Will. Four existentialist theologians. 1958. pap. 1.45. Doubleday
Herschel, Abraham Joshua. God in search of man: A philosophy of Judaism. 1955. 5.00. Farrar, Straus
Huxley, Aldous. Perennial philosophy. 1945. 5.00. Harper
Kierkegaard, Soren A. Philosophical fragments. 1962. 6.50. Princeton
MacGregor, Geddes. Introduction to religious philosophy. 6.75. Houghton
Radhakrishnan, S. East and West in religion. 1950. 2.50. Macmillan
Smart, Ninian. Historical selections in the philosophy of religion. 1962. 7.00. Harper

Trueblood, Elton. Philosophy of religion. 1957. 5.00. Harper
Wells, Donald A. God, man, and the thinker: Philosophies of religion. 1962. 8.95.
　Random
RELIGION, PRIMITIVE (290)
Albright, William Foxwell. From the Stone Age to Christianity. 1957. pap. 1.45.
　Doubleday
Goode, William J. Religion among the primitives. 1951. 6.00. Free Press
Howells, William White. Heathens: Primitive man and his religions. il. 1948.
　4.00. Doubleday
James, Edwin O. Beginnings of religion. 2.50. Hillary
James, Edwin O. Prehistoric religion. 1961. 6.50. Barnes & Noble
Lowie, Robert H. Primitive religion. 1947. 3.95. Liveright
Maringer, Johannes. Gods of prehistoric man. il. 1960. 5.75. Knopf
Radin, Paul. Primitive religion. 3.85. Smith, Peter
Swanson, Guy E. Birth of the gods. 1960. 4.95. U. of Mich.
RELIGION AND SCIENCE (215)
Compton, Arthur H. Human meaning of science. 1940. 1.00. U. of N. C.
De Vries, John. Beyond the atom. 1948. 2.50. Eerdmans
Du Nouy, Lecomte. Human destiny. pap. 0.60. New Am. Lib.
Ferre, Nels F. S. Faith and reason. 1946. 3.50. Harper
Haber, Francis C. Age of the world: Moses to Darwin. 1959. 5.00. Johns Hopkins
Heim, Karl. Christian faith and natural science. 3.25. Smith, Peter
Heim, Karl. World: Its creation and consummation. 1962. 3.00. Muhlenberg
Koestler, Arthur. Sleepwalker. 1959. 6.95. Macmillan
Lecomte du Nouy, Pierre. Human destiny. 1947. 5.00. McKay
Millikan, R. A. Evolution in science and religion. 1927. 3.00. Yale
Morrison, A. Cressy. Seven reasons why a scientist believes in God. 1962. 1.00.
　Revell
Neuman, Abraham A., and others. In search of God and immortaltiy. 1961. 3.95.
　Beacon
Orr, James. God's image in man. 1948. 3.00. Eerdmans
Richardson, Alan. Bible in the age of science. 1961. 3.50. Westminster
Rimmer, Harry. Theory of evolution and facts of science. 1935. 2.50. Eerdmans
Russell, Bertrand. Religion and science. 1935. 1.70. Oxford U. P.
Shapley, Harlow. Science ponders religion. 5.00. Meredith
Smethurst, Arthur F. Modern science and Christian beliefs. 1957. 4.00. Abingdon
White, Andrew D. History of the warfare of science with theology in Christendom.
　1955. 7.50. Braziller
RELIGIONS (290)
Anderson, James N. D. World's religions. 1950. 3.00. Eerdmans
Archer, John Clark, and C. E. Purinton. Faiths men live by. 1958. 6.00. Ronald
Bach, Marcus. Had you been born in another faith. 1961. 3.95. Prentice-Hall
Bach, Marcus. Major religions of the world. 1959. 1.00. Abingdon
Bach, Marcus. Strange sects and curious cults. 1961. 4.50. Dodd
Bouquet, Alan C. Christian faith and non-Christian religions. 1959. 7.00. Harper
Braden, Charles Samuel. World's religions. 1954. 3.00. Abingdon
Braswell, William. Melville's religious thought. 1959. 3.00. Cooper
Browne, Lewis. This believing world: A simple account of the great religions of
　mankind. il. 3.95. Macmillan
　Burtt, Edwin Arthur. Man seeks the divine. 1957. 6.50. Harper
Fairchild, Johnson E. Basic beliefs: The religious philosophies of mankind.
　4.00. Sheridan
Ferm, Vergilius, T. A. Living schools of religions. 1956. pap. 2.25. Littlefield
Gaer, Joseph. How the great religions began. 1956. 3.95. Dodd
Grant, Frederick C. Hellenistic religions. 1953. pap. 1.75. Bobbs
Hopper, Stanley R. Spiritual problems in contemporary literature. 1958. 3.50.
　Smith, Peter
Hume, Robert E. World's living religions. 1959. 3.50. Scribner

James, Edwin O. Ancient gods. il. 1960. 7.50. Putnam
Jurji, E. J. Great religions of the modern world. 1946. 6.00. Princeton (R)
Knight, G. Wilson. Christian renaissance. 1962. 4.95. Norton
Landis, Benson Y. World religions. 1957. 2.95. Dutton
Life. World's great religions. by the Editors of Life. 1958. 5.00. Golden Press
Long, Valentine. Not on bread alone. 1954. 2.00. St. Anthony
Lyon, Q. M. Great religions. 5.50. Odyssey
Martin, Walter R. Rise of the cults. 1955. 1.95. Zondervan
Parrinder, Geoffrey. Comparative religion. 3.75. Macmillan
Potter, Charles F. Faiths men live by. 1954. 3.95. Prentice-Hall
Potter, Charles Francis. Great religious leaders. 1958. 7.50. S. and S.
Prosser, Eleanor. Drama and religion in the English mystery plays. 1961. 5.00.
    Stanford
Reinach, Salomon. Orpheus: A history of religions. il. 1933. 3.95. Liveright
Smith, Huston. Religions of man. 1958. 5.75. Harper
Soper, Edmund D. Religions of mankind. 1951. 3.50. Abingdon
Speaight, Robert. Christian theatre. 1960. 3.50. Hawthorn
Spiegelberg, F. Living religions of the world. 1956. 8.75. Prentice-Hall
Toynbee, Arnold. Christianity among the religions of the world. 1957. 2.95.
    Scribner
Weales, Gerald. Religion in modern English drama. 1961. 7.50. U. of Pa.
White, Helen C. Metaphysical poets: A study in religious experience. pap. 1.50.
    Collier
Zaehner, R. C. Concise encyclopedia of living faith. il. 1959. 15.00. Hawthorn

RELIGIOUS EDUCATION (268)

Benson, Clarence H. History of Christian education. 3.50. Moody
Buttrick, George A. Biblical thought and the secular university. 1960. 2.50. La.
    State
Fallaw, Wesner. Church education for tomorrow. 1960. 3.75. Westminster
Foster, Virgil E. How a small church can have good Christian education. 1956.
    2.00. Harper
Gable, Lee J. Encyclopedia for church group leaders. 1959. 7.95. Assn. Pr.
Gaebelein, Frank E. Christian education in a democracy. 1951. 4.50. Oxford U.P.
Gauss, C. Teaching of religion in American higher education. 1951. 3.25. Ronald
Little, Lawrence C. Foundations for a philosophy of Christian education. 1962.
    4.00. Abingdon
Meadows, Thomas. Psychology of learning and teaching Christian education. 1957.
    4.50. Pageant
Smart, James D. Creed in Christian teaching. 1962. 4.50. Westminster
Wyckoff, D. Campbell. Theory and design of Christian education curriculum. 1961.
    4.50. Westminster

RELIGIOUS THOUGHT (800)

Brown, Carleton. Religious lyrics of the 14th century. 1952. 4.00. Oxford U. P.
Cecil, David, Lord. Oxford book of Christian verse. 1940. 5.50. Oxford U. P.
Clark, Thomas Curtis. One thousand quotable poems. 1937. 5.00. Harper
DeWolf, L. Harold. Trends and frontiers in religious thought. 1955. bds. 1.50.
    Methodist Student
Hill, Caroline M. World's great religious poetry. 1938. 5.50. Macmillan
Kauffman, Donald T., comp. Treasury of religious verse. 1962. 2.49. Revell
Kepler, Thomas S. Contemporary religious thought: An anthology. 1941. 5.00.
    Abingdon
Manning, Stephen. Wisdom and number: Toward a critical appraisal of the Middle
    English religious lyric. 1962. 4.50. U. of Nebr.
Maus, Cynthia Pearl. Church and the fine arts. il. 1960. 6.95. Harper
McGiffert, Arthur C. History of Christian thought. vol. 1, Early and Eastern;
    vol. 2, West from Tertullian to Erasmus. 3.50 ea. Scribner
Morrison, James Dalton. Masterpieces of religious verse. 1948. 7.95. Harper
Tawney, R. H. Religion and the rise of capitalism. pap. 0.50. New Am. Lib.

Viner, J. Religious thought and economic society: The European background. by
J. W. Smith, and A. L. Jamison. 1961. 6.00. Princeton
Wallis, Charles L. Treasury of poems for worship and devotion. 1959. 4.95.
Harper
Willey, Basil. More nineteenth century studies. 1956. 4.50. Columbia
Willey, B. Nineteenth century studies. 1949. 4.50. Columbia
Williams, Daniel D. What present-day theologians are thinking. 1959. 3.00. Harper
White, Helen C. Prayer and poetry. 2.50. Univ. Pub.
Woods, Ralph L. Poems of prayer. 1962. 5.00. Hawthorn
REMBRANDT HERMANSZOON VAN RIJN, 1606-1669 (927)
Pierpont, Morgan Library. Rembrandt drawings from American collections:
Exhibition catalog. il. 1960. 6.00. Morgan, Pierpont
Rembrandt. Rembrandt. by Wilhelm Koehler. il. 1961. 7.50. Abrams
Rembrandt, Rembrandt. by F. R. Meijer. 2.95. Yoseloff
Roger-Marx, Claude. Rembrandt. 1960. 20.00. Universe
Van Loon, Hendrik Willem. Life and times of Rembrandt. il. 1942. 4.50. Liveright
RENAISSANCE (940. 21)
Ady, Cecilia M. Lorenzo dei Medici and Renaissance Italy. 1955. 2.50. Macmillan'
American Heritage. Horizon book of the Renaissance. by the Editors of American
Heritage. il. 17.50. Doubleday
Atkins, John W. H. English literary criticism: 17th and 18th centuries. 1952. 6.00.
Barnes & Noble
Burckhardt, Jacob. Civilization of the Renaissance in Italy. 1.95. Modern Lib.
Buxton, John. Sir Philip Sidney and the English Renaissance. 1954. 4.75. St.
Martins
Craig, Hardin. Enchanted glass: The Elizabethan mind in literature. 1952. 4.00.
Oxford U. P.
Durant, Will. Renaissance (Story of civilization. vol. 5) 10.00. S. and S.
Haydn, Hiram. Counter-Renaissance. 5.00. Smith, Peter
Hoopes, Robert. Right reason in the English Renaissance. 1962. 5.75. Harvard
Horizon. Golden book of the Renaissance. by Irwin Shapiro. il. 1962. 5.00. Golden
Press
Pater, Walter. Renaissance. 1.95. Modern Lib.
Renaissance. (New Cambridge modern history. vol. 1) 8.50. Cambridge U. P.
Symonds, John A. Renaissance in Italy. 3 vols. il. vol. 1. Age of the despots,
3.75; vol. 2, Revival of learning. 3.50; vol. 3, Fine arts. 3.75. Smith, Peter
Tillyard, E. M. W. English Renaissance: Fact or fiction. 1952. 3.00. Johns
Hopkins
Watson, Curtis B. Shakespeare and the Renaissance concept of honor. 1960. 7.50.
Princeton
Wright, L. B. Middle-class culture in Elizabethan England. 1958. 7.50. Cornell
RENOIR, PIERRE AUGUSTE, 1841-1919 (927)
Fosca. Renoir: His life and work. 1962. 6.95. Prentice-Hall
Renoir, Jean. Renoir, my father. il. 1962. 8.95. Little
Renoir, Auguste. Renoir. by Walter Pach. il. 1950. 15.00. Abrams
Renoir, Pierre Auguste. Renoir drawings. 7.50. Yoseloff
REPORT WRITING (029)
Anderson, Chester Reed, and others. Business reports: Investigation and pre-
sentation. il. 1957. 6.95. McGraw
Brown, Leland. Effective business report writing. 7.95. Prentice-Hall
Doremus, Robert B. Writing college themes. 1960. pap. 1.50. Oxford U. P.
Dugdale, Kathleen. Manual of form for theses and term reports. 1962. 2.00.
Dugdale
Hook, Lucyle, and Mary Gaver. Research paper. 1.95. 1962. Prentice-Hall
Sigband, Norman B. Effective report writing. 1960. 6.75. Harper
Yaggy, Elinor. How to write your term paper. 1958. 1.75. Chandler Pub.
REPRESENTATIVE GOVERNMENT AND REPRESENTATION (321. 8)
De Grazia, Alfred, Jr. Public and republic: Political representation in America.
1951. 3.75. Knopf

Graham, George A. America's capacity to govern. 1960. 3.00. U. of Ala.

Mill, John S. On liberty; Representative government; The subjection of women. 2.25. Oxford U. P.

Mill, John Stuart. Utilitarianism, Liberty and representative government. 2.95. Dutton

REPTILES (598.1)

Bellairs, Angus d'A. Reptiles. 1957. 2.50. Hillary

Conant, Roger. Field guide to reptiles and amphibians. il. 1958. 4.50. Houghton

Ditmars, Raymond L. Reptiles of North America. 1936. 8.50. Doubleday

Ditmars, Raymond L. Reptiles of the world. 1935. 6.95. Macmillan

Mertens, Robert. World of amphibians and reptiles. il. 1960. 15.00. McGraw

Pope, Clifford H. Reptile world. il. 1955. 7.50. Knopf

Pope, Clifford H. Reptiles round the world. il. 1957. 3.50. Knopf

Schmidt, Karl P., and Robert F. Inger. Living reptiles of the world. il. 1957. 9.95. Doubleday

REPUBLICAN PARTY (329.6)

Crandal, A. W. Early history of the Republican Party. 5.00. Smith, Peter

Hoyt, Edwin P., Jr. Jumbos and jackasses: A popular history of the political wars. 5.95. Doubleday

Larson, Arthur. Republican looks at his party. 1956. 2.95. Harper

Moos, Malcolm. Republicans: A history of their party. 1956. 5.95. Random

Schnapper, M. B. Grand old party: A pictorial history of the first 100 years of the Republican Party. 1955. 6.00. Pub. Affairs

RESEARCH (029)

Fortune. Mighty force of research. 1956. 4.75. McGraw

Freedman, Paul. Principles of scientific research. 1960. 4.50. Pergamon

Good, Carter V., and Douglas E. Scates. Methods of research: Educational, psychological, and sociological. 1954. 7.00. Appleton

Hillway, Tyrus. Introduction to research. 1956. 5.75. Houghton

Marvin, Philip R. Top management and research. 1953. 5.00. Research Pr.

Whitney, Frederick L. Elements of research. 1950. 9.00. Prentice-Hall

Wilson, E. Bright. Introduction to scientific research. 1952. 7.50. McGraw

RESPIRATION (612.2)

Cherniack, Reuben M., and Louis. Respiration in health and disease. il. 1961. 10.50. Saunders

Luchsinger, Peter C., and Kenneth M. Moser. Respiration. il. 1960. 15.75. Mosby

Knowles, John H. Respiratory physiology and its clinical application. il. 1959. 5.25. Harvard

RETAIL TRADE (658.87)

Fortune. Why do people buy: A close look at selling. by the Editors of Fortune. 1953. 3.95. McGraw

Goldenthal, Irving. How to take the physical inventory and its relation to profits. il. 1959. pap. 1.25. Chilton

Hahn, Lew. Stores, merchants and customers. 1952. 5.00. Fairchild

Levy, Leon, and others. Basic retailing. 1960. 3.60. Pitman

Mahoney, Tom. Great merchants. 1955. 4.95. Harper

Robinson, O. Preston, and Kenneth B. Haas. How to establish and operate a retail store. 1952. 6.50. Prentice-Hall

Robinson, O. Preston, and others. Store organization and operation. 1957. 7.25. Prentice-Hall

Scott, George A. Your future in retailing. 1961. 2.95. Richards Rosen

Scott, Wesley E., and others. Everyday consumer business. 1959. 4.04; combined workbooks, 2.32; tests, 0.96. Prentice-Hall

Tobe, lectures in retail distribution. 4 vols. 1957-58; 1958-59; 1959-60; 1960-61. 3.00 ea. Harv. Bus. School

Wingate, John W., and others. Problems in retail merchandising. 1961. pap. 4.95. Prentice-Hall

Wingate, John W., and J. Dana Weiner. Retail merchandising. 1957. 4.20. South-Western Pub.

Wingate, John W. , and Elmer D. Schaller. Techniques of retail merchandising. 1950. 6. 95. Prentice-Hall

RHETORIC (808)

Baldwin, C. S. Renaissance literary theory and practice. 1959. 4. 25. Smith, Peter
Howell, W. S. Problems and styles of communication. 1945. 2. 50. Appleton
Thonssen, Lester. Selected readings in rhetoric and public speaking. 1942. 3. 50. Wilson
Wood, Frederick T. Training in thought and expression. 1. 25. St. Martins
Miriam Joseph, Sister. Shakespeare's use of the arts of language. 1947. 3. 75. Columbia
Wallace, Karl R. Francis Bacon on communication and rhetoric. 1943. 5. 00. U. of N. C.
Aristotle. Art of rhetoric. 3. 50. Harvard
Aristotle. Poetics. On the sublime, and Demetrius. On style. 3. 50. Harvard
Aristotle. Rhetoric and poetics. 1. 95. Modern Lib.

RHEUMATIC FEVER (616. 991)

Thomas, Lewis. Rheumatic fever: A symposium. il. 1952. 6. 50. U. of Minn.

RHEUMATISM (616. 742)

Crain, Darrell G. Help for ten million. il. 1959. 3. 50. Lippincott
Traut, Eugene F. Rheumatic diseases. il. 1952. 10. 00. Mosby

RHODES, JAMES FORD, 1848-1927 (923. 3)

Cruden, Robert. James Ford Rhodes, the man, the historian, and his work. 6. 00. Western Reserve

RHODESIA (968. 9)

Clegg, Edward M. Race and politics. 1960. 4. 80. Oxford U. P.
Hanna, A. J. Story of the Rhodesias and Nyasaland. il. 1961. 4. 00. Humanities
Mason, Philip. Birth of a dilemma, the conquest and settlement of Rhodesia. il. 1958. 4. 80. Oxford U. P.
Waugh, Evelyn. Tourist in Africa. 1960. 3. 75. Little

RICHARD II, KING OF ENGLAND, 1367-1400 (923.142)

Hutchison, Harold F. Hollow crown: A life of Richard II. il. 1961. 5. 50. Day

RICHARD III, KING OF ENGLAND, 1452-1485 (923.142)

Kendall, Paul Murray. Richard III. il. 1956. 7. 50. Norton

RICHELIEU, ARMAND JEAN DU PLESSIS, CARDINAL, DU DE, 1585-1642 (923. 2)

Cox, Cynthia. Talleyrand's successor. il. 1960. 5. 95. Vanguard
Wedgwood, C. V. Richelieu and the French monarchy. 2. 50. Macmillan

ROBINSON, EDWIN ARLINGTON, 1869-1935 (928)

Coxe, Louis O. Edwin Arlington Robinson. 1962. pap. 0. 65. U. of Minn.
Neff, Emery. Edwin Arlington Robinson. 1948. 4. 75. Sloane

ROCKEFELLER, JOHN DAVISON, 1839-1937 (923. 3)

Nevins, Allan. John D. Rockefeller. il. 1959. 5. 95. Scribner

ROCKETS (629.1338)

Adams, Carskie C. , and W. von Braun. Careers in astronautics and rocketry. in prep. McGraw
Baar, James, and William E. Howard. Spacecraft and missiles of the world, 1962. il. 1962. 5. 95. Harcourt
Bergaust, Erik. Reaching for the stars. il. 1960. 4. 95. Doubleday
Berkner, L. V. Rockets and satellites. 25. 00. Pergamon
Boyd, R. L. F. Space research by rocket and satellite. il. 1961. 2. 25. Harper
Clarke, Arthur C. Interplanetary flight. 1960. 3. 50. Harper
Herrick, John, and Eric Burgess. Rocket encyclopedia illustrated. il. 1959. 12. 50. Aero
Huzel, Dieter K. Peenemunde to Canaveral. 1962. 4. 95. Prentice-Hall
Newell, Homer E. Express to the stars. il. 1961. 5. 75. McGraw
Parkin, Charles M. , Jr. Rocket handbook for amateurs. il. 1959. 5. 95. Day
Stine, G. Harry. Rocket power and space flight. il. 1957. 3. 75. Holt, Rinehart & Winston

ROCKS (552)

Bates, Robert L. Geology of the industrial rocks and minerals. 1960. 10. 00. Harper

Fenton, Carroll L., and Mildred A. Rock book. il. 1940. 8.95. Doubleday
Fritzen, D. K. Rock-hunter's field manual. pap. 1.00. Cornerstone
Gilbert, Miriam. Starting a rock and mineral collection. il. 1961. 1.00. Hammond
Harker, Alfred. Metamorphism: A study of the transformations of rockmasses.
    il. 1932. 5.50. Dutton
Pearl, Richard M. Rocks and minerals. 1956. pap. 1.75. Barnes & Noble
Pettijohn, Francis J. Sedimentary rocks. 1957. 13.50. Harper
Random, Jay E. Rock-hunter's range guide. il. 1962. 4.95. Harper
RODIN, AUGUSTE, 1840-1917 (927)
Elsen, Albert E. Rodin's Gates of hell. 7.50. U. of Minn.
Rodin, Auguste. Rodin; Sculptures. by Sommerville Story. il. 1956. 4.75. N. Y.
    Graphic
RONTGEN, WILHELM CONRAD, 1845-1923 (925)
Glasser, Otto. Dr. W. C. Rontgen. 1958. 4.50. Thomas, C. C.
ROMAN LAW (349.37)
Daube, David. Forms of Roman legislation. 1956. 4.00. Oxford U. P.
Jolowicz, H. F. Roman foundations of modern law. 1957. 6.10. Oxford U. P.
Lissner, Ivar. Caesars: Might and madness. il. 1958. 5.95. Putnam
Schulz, Fritz. Principles of Roman law. 1936. 4.00. Oxford U. P.
Schulz, Fritz. History of Roman legal science. 1946. 5.60. Oxford U. P.
Suetonius. Lives of the Caesars. 2 vols. 3.50 ea. Harvard
Suetonius. Twelve caesars. 4.50. Penguin
ROMANTICISM (809.9)
Abrams, Meyer H. English romantic poets: Modern essays in criticism. 4.50.
    Smith, Peter
Abrams, Meyer Howard. Mirror and the lamp. 1953. 7.50. Oxford U. P.
Babbitt, Irving. Rousseau and romanticism. 1919. 6.00. Houghton
Barzun, Jacques. Classic, romantic and modern. 1961. 5.00. Little
Bate, Walter J. From Classic to Romantic. 3.35. Smith, Peter
Battenhouse, Henry. English romantic writers. 3.50. Barron's
Bernbaum, E. Anthology of romanticism. 1948. 7.50. Ronald
Bernbaum, Ernest. Guide through the Romantic Movement. 1949. 5.00. Ronald
Bloom, Harold. Visionary company: English Romantic poetry. 4.50. Doubleday
Bowra, C. Maurice. Romantic imagination. 1961. pap. 1.75. Oxford U. P.
Brinton, Crane. Political ideas of the English romanticists. 1962. 6.50. Russell
Campbell, Oscar J., and others. Poetry and criticism of the Romantic movement.
    6.50. Appleton
Cizevskie, Dmytro. On romanticism in Slavic literatures. pap. 1.50. Humanities
Dodds, A. E. Romantic theory of poetry. 1962. 7.50. Russell
Einstein, Alfred. Music in the romantic era. il. 1947. 6.90. Norton
Evans, David O. Social romanticism in France, 1830-1848. 1951. 2.90. Oxford U. P.
Fairchild, Hoxie N. Romantic quest: Romantic movement in English poetry. 1931.
    6.00. Saifer
Hough, Graham G. Romantic poets. 2.50. Hillary
Kroeber, Karl. Romantic narrative art. 1960. 5.75. U. of Wis.
Lucas, F. L. Decline and fall of the romantic ideal. 1948. 4.00. Cambridge U. P.
Noyes, Russell. English romantic poetry and prose. 1956. 8.50. Oxford U. P.
Praz, Mario. Hero in eclipse in Victorian fiction. 1956. 7.20. Oxford U. P.
Praz, Mario. Romantic agony. 1951. 5.60. Oxford U. P.
Reiss, H. S. Political thought of the German romantics. 1956. 2.50. Macmillan
Thorpe, Clarence D., and others. Major English romantic poets: A symposium in
    reappraisal. 1957. 5.50. Southern Ill.
Varma, Devendra P. Gothic flame. 1950. 8.75. British Bk.
Woods, George B. English poetry and prose of the romantic movement. 1950. 9.50.
    Scott
Carter, Marion E. Role of the symbol in French Romantic poetry. 1946. 1.75.
    Catholic U. of Am. Pr.
ROME (945.632)
Adcock, Frank E. Roman art of war under the Republic. 1960. 3.00. Barnes &
    Noble

Burckhardt, Jacob. Age of Constantine the Great. 1956. pap. 1.45. Doubleday

Cheesman, George L. Auxilia of the Roman imperial army. 1962. 5.00. Barnes & Noble

Frazer, James George. Greece and Rome. 1.50. St. Martins

Geer, Russel M. Classical civilization: Rome. 1950. 7.50. Prentice Hall

Grose-Hodge, H. Roman panorama. 1944. 3.50. Cambridge U. P.

Hamilton, Edith. Roman way. 1932. 4.50. Norton

Heichelheim, Fritz M., and Cedric A. Yeo. History of the Roman people. 1961. 10.60. Prentice-Hall

Heyden, A. A. M. van der, and H. H. Scullard. Atlas of the classical world. il. 1960. 15.00. Nelson

Kennedy, Eberhard C., and George W. White. S.P.Q.R.: History and social life of ancient Rome. 2.00. St. Martins

Petrie, Alexander. Introduction to Roman history, literature, and antiquities. il. 1930. 1.20. Oxford U. P.

Rostovtzeff, M. Social and economic history of the Roman empire. 2 vols. 1957. 26.90. Oxford U. P.

Rowell, Henry T. Rome in the Augustan age. 1962. 2.75. U. of Okla.

Showerman, Grant. Rome and the Romans. il. 1931. 6.60. Macmillan

Stobart, John C. Grandeur that was Rome. by W. S. Maguinness and H. H. Scullard. il. 1962. 8.50. Hawthorn

ROME--HISTORY (937)

Augustan Empire, 44 B.C. - A.D. 70. (Cambridge ancient history, vol. 10). 13.50. Cambridge U. P.

Caesar, Alexandrian, African and Spanish wars. 3.50. Harvard

Caesar. Civil wars. 3.50. Harvard

Caesar, Julius. Gallic War and other writings. 1.95. Modern Lib.

Caesar, Julius. War commentaries. 1.85. Dutton

Clarke, M. L. Roman Mind: Studies in the history of thought from Cicero to Marcus Auerlius. 1956. 3.75. Harvard

Gibbon, Edward. Decline and fall of the Roman Empire. 3 vols. 1962. pap. 2.95. Washington Square

Gibbon, Edward. Portable Gibbon. by Dero A. Saunders. 1952. 2.95. Viking

Imperial crisis and recovery, A.D. 193-324. (Cambridge ancient history, vol. 12) 13.50. Cambridge U. P.

Imperial peace, A.D. 70-192. (Cambridge ancient history. vol. 11) 13.50. Cambridge U. P.

Lewis, Naphtali, and Meyer Reinhold. Roman civilization. 2 vols. 7.50 ea. Columbia

Lissner, Ivar. Caesars: Might and madness. il. 1958. 5.95. Putnam

Livy, History of Rome: Selections. 1.95. Modern Lib.

Mommsen, Theodor. History of Rome. 5 vols. 1957. 17.50. Free Press

Reinhold, Meyer. Classics, Greek and Roman: A guide to the humanties. 3.50. Barron's

Roman Republic, 133-44 B.C. (Cambridge ancient history. vol. 9) 13.50. Cambridge U. P.

Rome and the Mediterranean, 218-133 B.C. (Cambridge ancient history. vol. 8) 13.50. Cambridge U. P.

Scullard, H. H. Roman world, 753-146 B.C. 1962. 7.95. Barnes & Noble

Stobart, John C. Grandeur that was Rome. il. 1962. 8.50. Hawthorn

Tacitus, Histories. 2 vols. 3.40. Oxford U. P.

Tappan, Eva March. Story of the Roman people. 1960. 3.04. Houghton

ROME (CITY)--SOCIAL LIFE AND CUSTOMS (937)

Carcopino, Jerome. Daily life in ancient Rome. by Henry T. Rowell. tr. by E. O. Lorimer. il. 1960. 6.50. Yale

ROMMEL, ERWIN, 1891-1944 (923.5)

Young, Desmond. Rommel: The desert fox. il. 1951. 4.95. Harper

ROOSEVELT, ELEANOR (ROOSEVELT) 1884- (923.6)

Roosevelt, Eleanor. Autobiography. il. 1961. 7.50. Harper

Steinberg, Alfred. Mrs. R.: The life of Eleanor Roosevelt. il. 1958. 5.00.
    Pubnam
ROOSEVELT, FRANKLIN DELANO, PRESIDENT U.S., 1882-1945 (923.1?3)
Beard, C. A. President Roosevelt and the coming of the war, 1941. 1948. 7.50.
    Yale
Bestor, Arthur, and others. Three Presidents and their books: The reading of
    Jefferson, Lincoln, and Franklin D. Roosevelt. 1955. 2.50. U. of Ill.
Burns, James M. Roosevelt: The lion and the fox. 1956. 6.75. Harcourt
Flynn, John T. Roosevelt myth. 4.50. Devin
Gunther, John. Roosevelt in retrospect. 1950. 6.00. Harper
Hickock, Lorena A. Road to the White House: F.D.R., the pre-presidential years.
    il. 1962. 3.95. Chilton
Roosevelt, Eleanor. This I remember. il. 1949. 6.50. Harper
Roosevelt, James, and Sidney Shalett. Affectionately, F. D. R. il. 1959. 5.75.
    Harcourt
Schary, Dore. Sunrise at Campobello. 1958. 3.95. Random
Sherwood, Robert E. Roosevelt and Hopkins. 1960. pap. 2.95. Grosset
Walker, Turnley. Roosevelt and the Warm Springs sotry. 1953. 3.50. Wyn
ROOSEVELT, THEODORE, PRES. U.S. 1858-1919 (923.1)
Beale, Howard K. Theodore Roosevelt and the rise of America to world power.
    1956. 6.00. Johns Hopkins
Blum, John Morton. Republican Roosevelt. 1954. 3.50. Harvard
Mowry, George E. Era of Theodore Roosevelt, 1900-1912. 1958. 5.00. Harper
Mowry, George. Theodore Roosevelt and the progressive movement. 1960. 5.00.
    Hill & Wang
Roosevelt, Theodore. Autobiography of Theodore Roosevelt. 1958. 4.95. Scribner
Wagenknecht, E. Seven worlds of Theodore Roosevelt. 1958. 6.50. McKay
ROUAULT, GEORGES, 1871-1958 (927)
Soby, James Thrall, Georges Rouault: Paintings and prints. il. 3.75. 1958. Doubleday
Venturi, Lionello. Rouault. il. 1959. 5.75. World Pub.
ROUSSEAU, JEAN JACQUES, 1712-1778 (921.4)
Babbitt, Irving. Rousseau and romanticism. 1919. 8.00. Houghton
Winwar, Frances. Jean Jacques Rousseau. 1961. 6.00. Random
ROYCE, JOSIAH, 1855-1916 (921.1)
Marcel, Gabriel. Royce's metaphysics. 1956. 4.50. Regnery
Smith, John E. Royce's social infinite: The community of interpretation. 1950.
    2.75. Bobbs
RUBBER (620.194)
Barron, Harry. Modern rubber chemistry. il. 1948. 8.50. Van Nostrand
Huke, D. W. Natural and synthetic rubbers. il. 1961. 5.00. Tudor
Polhamus, L. G. Rubber. il. 1962. 14.50. Wiley
RUBENS, SIR PETER PAUL, 1577-1640 (927)
Burckhardt, Jacob. Recollections of Rubens. il. 2.95. N. Y. Graphic
Rubens, Peter Paul. Rubens. il. collectors ed. 3.95. Abrams
RUMANIA (949.8)
Roberts, Henry L. Rumania. 1951. 6.50. Yale
RUSKIN, JOHN, 1819-1900 (923.142)
Fain, John T. Ruskin and the economists. 4.50. Vanderbilt
Rosenberg, J. D. Darkening glass: A portrait of John Ruskin's genius. 1961. 5.00.
    Columbia
RUSSELL, BERTRAND RUSSEL, 3d EARL, 1872- (921.2)
Schilpp, Paul A. Philosophy of Bertrand Russell. 6.95. Tudor
Wood, Alan. Bertrand Russell: The passionate skeptic. 1958. 3.50. S. and S.
RUSSELL, CHARLES MARION, 1864-1925 (927.973)
Garst, Shannon.. Cowboy-artist: Charles M. Russell. 1960. 3.25. Messner
Shelton, Lola. Charles Marion Russell. il. 1962. 4.00. Dodd
RUSSIA (947)
Conquest, Robert. Common sense about Russia. 1960. 2.95. Macmillan

Florinsky, Michael. McGraw-Hill encyclopedia of Russia and the Soviet Union. il. 1961. 23.50. McGraw
Gunther, John. Inside Russia today. 1958. 6.50. Harper
Stevenson, Adlai. Friends and enemies. il. 1959. 3.50. Harper
Stipp, John L. Soviet Russia today. 1957. 4.00. Harper
RUSSIA--CIVILIZATION (947)
Balzak, S. S., and others. Economic geography of the USSR. American ed. by Chauncy D. Harris. tr. by R. M. Hankin, and O. A. Titelbaum. 10.50. Macmillan
Blinoff, Marthe. Life and thought in old Russia. 1961. 5.95. Penn State
Campbell, Robert W. Soviet economic power. il. 1960. 5.00. Houghton
Cressey, George B. Soviet potentials. il. 1962. 5.75. Syracuse
Douglas, William O. Russian journey. il. 1956. 4.50. Doubleday
Dumas, Alexandre. Adventures in Czarist Russia. tr. by Alma E. Murch. 1961. 3.50. Chilton
Fischer, Louis. Russia revisited: A new look at Russia and her satellites. 1957. 4.00. Doubleday
Harriman, W. Averell. Peace with Russia? 1959. 3.00. S. and S.
Hindus, Maurice. House without a roof: Russia after forty-three years of revoltuion. 6.95. Doubleday
Mead, Margaret. Soviet attitudes toward authority. 1955. 5.00. Morrow
Perlo, Victor. How the Soviet economy works. 1961. 1.50. Int. Pubs.
Rama Rau, Santha. My Russian journey. 1959. 4.95. Harper
Rounds, Frank Jr. Window on Red Square. 1953. 4.50. Houghton
Vakar, Nicholas P. Taproot of Soviet society. 1962. 4.75. Harper
Wolfe, Bertram D. Communist totalitarianism. 1961. 5.50. Beacon
RUSSIA--FOREIGN RELATIONS (947)
Allen, Robert L. Soviet economic warfare. 1960. 5.00. Pub. Affairs
Baldwin, Hanson. Great arms race. 2.95. Praeger
Barghoorn, Frederick C. Soviet cultural offensive. 1960. 7.50. Princeton
Beloff, Max. Soviet policy in the Far East, 1944-1951. 1953. 4.00. Oxford U. P.
Bouscaren, Anthony T. Soviet foreign policy. 1962. 5.00. Fordham
Campaigne, Jameson G. American might and Soviet myth. 1960. 2.00. Regnery
Carr, Edward H. German-Soviet relations between the two world wars, 1919-1939. 1951. 3.00. Johns Hopkins
Dallin, David J. Changing world of Soviet Russia. 1956. 6.00. Yale
Dallin, Alexander. Soviet conduct in world affairs. 1960. 4.50. Columbia
Dallin, David J. Soviet foreign policy after Stalin. 1961. 7.95. Lippincott
Deutscher, Isaac. Great contest: Russia and the West. 1960. 2.75. Oxford U. P.
Fleming, Denna F. Cold war and its origins, 1917-1960. 2 vols. 1961. vol. 1, 1917-1950; vol. 2, 1950-1960. set, boxed, 15.00. Doubleday
Freund, Gerald. Unholy alliance. 1957. 6.00. Harcourt
Gilbert, Rodney. Competitive coexistence. 1956. 3.00. Bookmailer
Hudson, G. F., and others. Sino-Soviet dispute. 5.00. Praeger
Kennan, George F. American diplomacy: 1900-1950. 1951. 3.50. U. of Chicago
Kennan, George F. Russia and the West under Lenin and Stalin. 1961. 5.75. Little
Khrushchev, Nikita. Conquest without war. 1961. 7.50. S. and S.
Kovner, Milton. Challenge of coexistence. 1961. 3.25. Pub. Affairs
Lippman, Walter. Coming tests with Russia. 1961. 2.50. Little
Millis, Walter, and John C. Murray. Foreign policy and the free society. 1958. 2.75. Oceana
Overstreet, Harry A., and Bonard. War called peace: Khrushchev's communism. 1961. 4.50. Norton
Rubinstein, Alvin Z. Foreign policy of the Soviet Union. 1960. 6.50. Random
Schuman, Frederick L. Cold War: Retrospect and prospect. 1962. 3.00. La. State
Smith, Walter Bedell. My three years in Moscow. il. 1950. 5.00. Lippincott
Weinberg, G. L. Germany and the Soviet Union, 1939-1941. 1954. 6.50. Lounz
Werth, Alexander. Russia under Khrushchev. 1962. 5.00. Hill & Wang
Zeman, Z. A. B. Germany and the Revolution in Russia, 1915-1918: Documents from the Archives of the German Foreign Ministry. 1958. 4.00. Oxford U. P.

RUSSIA--HISTORY (947)
Armour, Richard. It all started with Marx. 1958. 3.50. McGraw
Black, Cyril E.., and John M. Thompson. American teaching about Russia. 1959.
   4.50. Indiana
Carmichael, Joel. Illustrated history of Russia. by Georges and Rosamond Bernier.
   il. 20.00. Reynal
Chamberlin, William Henry. Russia revolution. 1917-1921. 2 vols. il. 15.00.
   Macmillan
Crankshaw, Edward. Khrushchev's Russia. 1960. 2.75. Smith, Peter
Duncan, David D. Kremlin. il. 1960. 25.00. N. Y. Graphic
Florinsky, Michael T. Russia: A history and interpretation. 2 vols. 1953. 15.75.
   Macmillan
Jorre, G., and E. D. Laborde. Soviet Union. 1961. 7.25. Wiley
Kerner, Robert Joseph. Urge to the sea: The course of Russian history. il. 1946.
   5.00. U. of Calif.
Koestler, Arthur. Darkness at noon. 5.00. Macmillan
Lamb, Harold. City and the tsar. il. 1948. 4.50. Doubleday
Lawrence, John W. History of Russia. 1960. 6.50. Farrar, Straus
Masaryk, Thomas G. Spirit of Russia. 2 vols. by Slavik. 1955. vol. 1, 4.25;
   vol. 2, 6.00. Macmillan
Moorehead, Alan. Russian Revolution. il. 1958. 5.00. Harper
Pares, Bernard. History of Russia. il. 1953. 8.00. Knopf
Rauch, George von. History of Soviet Russia. 1954. 7.50. Praeger
Reed, John. Ten days that shook the world. 1919. 1.95. Modern Lib.
Salisbury, Harrison E. American in Russia. il. 1955. 5.50. Harper
Schuman, Frederick L. Russia since 1917: Forty years of Soviet politics. 1957.
   6.50. Knopf
Schwartz, Harry. Red phoenix: Russia since World War II. 6.00. Praeger
Seeger, Elizabeth. Pageant of Russian history. 1950. 6.50. McKay
Seton-Watson, Hugh. Decline of imperial Russia. il. 1952. 7.50. Praeger
Sholokhov, Mikhail. Silent Don. 2 vols. vol. 1, And quiet flows the Don. 1934,
   5.00; vol. 2, Don flows home to the sea. 1940. 5.75; 1 vol ed. 10.00. Knopf
Spector, Ivar. First Russian revolution. 1962. 3.95. Prentice-Hall
Treadgold, Donald W. Twentieth century Russia. il. 1959. 7.00. Rand McNally
Trotsky, Leon. History of the Russian Revolution. 1957. 12.50. U. of Mich.
Vernadsky, George. Origins of Russia. 1959. 6.10. Oxford U. P.
Walsh, Warren B. Russia and the Soviet Union: A modern history. 1958. 10.00.
   U. of Mich.
Warth, Robert D. Allies and the Russian Revolution. 1954. 6.00. Duke
Yarkovsky, Jan M. It happened in Moscow. 3.95. Vantage
RUSSIA--POLITICS AND GOVERNMENT (947)
Armstrong, John A. Ideology, politics, and government in the Soviet Union. 1962.
   4.00. Praeger
Conquest, Robert. Power and politics in the USSR. 1961. 7.95. St. Martins
Crankshaw, Edward. Russia without Stalin: The emerging pattern. il. 1956. 3.75.
   Viking
Dallin, D. J. New Soviet empire. 1951. 4.00. Yale
Daniels, Robert V. Conscience of the revolution. 1960. 10.00. Harvard
Fischer, George. Russian liberalism: From gentry to intelligentsia. il. 1958.
   4.50. Harvard
Fischer, Louis. Russia revisited: A new look at Russia and her satellites. 1957.
   4.00. Doubleday
Hazard, John N. Soviet system of government. 1960. 4.00. U. of Chicago
Lenin, Vladimir I. What is to be done? 2.00. Int. Pubs.
Levine, Irving R. Main Street, U.S.S.R. il. 1959. 4.50. Doubleday
McClosky, H., and J. Turner. Soviet dictatorship. 1960. 10.95. McGraw
Miller, Wright W. Russians as people. il. 1961. 3.95. Dutton
Mosby, Aline. View from Number 13 People's Street. 1962. 3.95. Random

Norton, Howard. Only in Russia. 1961. 4.95. Van Nostrand
Rounds, Frank, Jr. Window on Red Square. 1953. 4.50. Houghton
Schlesinger, Rudolf. Changing attitudes in Soviet Russia: The family. 6.00.
 Humanities
Schuman, Frederick L. Government in the Soviet Union. 1961. 2.95. Crowell
Stalin, Joseph. Selected writings. 2.75. Int. Pub.
Trotsky, Leon. My life. 1960. pap. 2.45. Grosset
Wolfe, Bertram D. Communist totalitarianism. 1961. 5.50. Beacon
Yarmolinsky, Avrahm. Road to revolution. il. 1959. 5.95. Macmillan

RUSSIAN DRAMA (891.7)
Houghton, Narris. Great Russian plays. pap. 0.75. Dell
Magarshack, David. Storm, and other Russian plays. 1960. 4.50. Hill & Wang
Noyes, G. R. Masterpieces of the Russian drama. 2 vols. 8.00. Smith, Peter
Reeve, F. D. Anthology of Russian plays. pap. 1.45. Vintage

RUSSIAN FICTION (891.7)
Rahv, Philip. Great Russian short novels. 1951. 6.00. Dial
Yarmolinsky, Avrahm. Treasury of great Russian short stories. 1944. 9.75.
 Macmillan

RUSSIAN LITERATURE (891.7)
Cournos, John. Treasury of classic Russian literature. 1962. pap. 2.45. Putnam
Eng-Liedmeier, A. M., van der. Soviet literary characters. 1959. 5.00. Humanities
Guerney, Bernard G. Portable Russian reader. 1947. 2.95. Viking
Guerney, Bernard Guibert. Treasury of Russian literature. il. 7.50. Vanguard
Masaryk, Thomas G. Spirit of Russia. 2 vols. 16.00. Macmillan
Mathewson, R. W., Jr. Positive hero in Russian literature. 1958. 6.00. Columbia
Mirsky, Dmitrii S. History of Russian literature. 1949. 5.75. Knopf
Slonim, Marc. Modern Russian literature from Chekhov to the present. 1953.
 8.00. Oxford U. P.
Slonim, Marc. Outline of Russian literature. 1958. 5.00. Oxford U. P.
Spector, Ivar. Golden age of Russian literature. il. 1952. 6.00. Caxton
Stender-Petersen, A., and S. Congrat-Butler. Anthology of old Russian literature.
 1955. 8.50. Columbia
Trotsky, Leon. Literature and revolution. 3.75. Russell

S

SACRED BOOKS (SELECTIONS: EXTRACTS, ETC.) (291.82)
Ballou, Robert O. Bible of the world. 1939. 10.00. Viking
Ballou, Robert O. Portable world Bible. 1944. 2.95. Viking
Browne, Lewis. World's great Scriptures. il. 7.50. Macmillan

SAGAS (398.22)
Hallberg, Peter Icelandic saga. 1962. 4.50. U. of Nebr.
Jones, Gwyn. Eirik the Red and other Icelandic sagas. 2.75. Oxford U. P.

SAHARA (966.11)
Briggs, Lloyd C. Tribes of the Sahara. il. 1960. 6.00. Harvard
Gerster, Georg. Sahara: Desert of destiny. tr. by Stewart Thomson. 1960. 5.00.
 Coward
Ward, Edward. Sahara story. il. 1962. 4.50. Norton

SAILING (797.124)
Baker, William A. Colonial vessels. il. 1962. 7.50. Barre
Brown, Alan. Invitation to sailing. 1962. 5.95. S. and S.
Fowle, Leonard. Guide to sailing. il. 1960. 2.95. Chilton
Laing, Alexander. American sail. il. 1961. 15.00. Dutton
Short, Vincent, and Edmund Sears. Sail and steam along the Maine coast. il. 1955.
 5.00. Wheelwright
Villiers, Alan. Way of a ship. il. 10.00. Scribner
Warner, Oliver. Sailing ships. 1958. 10.00. De Graff
Whipple, A. B. C. Tall ships and great captains. il. 1960. 4.95. Harper

SAINT EXUPERY, ANTOINE DE, 1900-1944 (928.144)
Migeo, M. Saint-Exupery. 1960. 5.59. McGraw
Rumbold, Richard, and Lady Margaret Stewart. Winged life: A portrait of Antoine de Saint-Exupery, poet and airman. 1955. 3.50. McKay
SAINTS (922.22)
Coulson, John. Saints: A concise biographical dictionary. il. 1958. 12.95. Hawthorn
Douillet, Jacques. What is a saint? tr. by Donald Attwater. 1958. 3.50. Hawthorn
Englebert, Omer. Lives of the saints. 1951. 6.50. McKay
Ward, Maisie. Saints who made history. 1959. 4.50. Sheed
SALES LETTERS (658.824)
Buckley, Earle A. How to increase sales with letters. 1961. 5.00. McGraw
SALES MANAGEMENT (658.81)
Biglow, Burton. Human side of sales management. 1961. 12.50. Prentice-Hall
DeVoe, Merrill. How of successful sales management. 1957. 6.35. Prentice-Hall
DeVoe, Merrill. How to be an effective sales manager. 1958. 5.65. Prentice-Hall
Fortune. Why do people buy: A close look at selling. by the Editors of Fortune. 1953. 3.95. McGraw
SALESMEN AND SALESMANSHIP (658.85)
Bell, Hugh S. Championship selling. 1959. 4.95. Prentice-Hall
Bell, Hugh S. How to be a winner in selling. 1957. 4.95. Prentice-Hall
Fernald, Charles H. Salesmanship. 1942. 10.65. Prentice-Hall
Frank, William W., and Charles L. Lapp. How to outsell the born salesman. 1959. 4.95. Macmillan
Hattwick, M. S. New psychology of selling. 1960. 5.95. McGraw
Hill, Napoleon. How to sell your way through life. 1946. 2.95. DeVorss
Laird, Donald A., and Eleanor C. Practical sales psychology. 1952. 4.95. McGraw
Lapp, C. L. Successful selling strategies. 1957. 6.95. McGraw
Lohse, Charles F. Creative selling. il. 4.95. Scribner
Roth, Charles B. 1000 ways a slaesman can increase his sales. 1950. 4.95. Prentice-Hall
Simmons, Harry. How to develop your sales ability. 3.00. Brown Book
Small, Richard L. Salesmanship. 1952. 4.50. Macmillan
Thompson, Joseph W., and Steven J. Shaw. Salesmanship. 1960. 5.75. Holt, Rinehart & Winston
Wheeler, Elmer. Sizzlemanship: New tested selling sentences. 1940. 4.95. Prentice-Hall
Wheeler, Elmer. Tested selling tips from around the world. 1961. 4.95. Prentice-Hall
Whiting, Percy H. Five great rules of selling. 1957. 4.95. McGraw
Wilson, John McGregor. Open the mind and close the sale; the key to success in selling. il. 1953. 4.25. McGraw
Wingate, John W., and Carroll A. Nolan. Fundamentals of selling. 1959. 4.12. South-Western Pub.
SALMON (597.5)
Jones, J. W. Salmon. il. 1961. 4.50. Harper
Netboy, Anthony. Salmon of the Pacific Northwest. il. 3.50. Binfords
SALT-WATER FISHING (799.16)
Farrington, S. Kip, Jr. Fishing the Atlantic. il. 7.50. Coward
Salt-water game fishes. 1.50. Stackpole
SALVAGE (387.55)
Brady, Edward M. Marine salvage operations. il. 1959. 12.50. Cornell Maritime
Masters, David. Epics of salvage. 1954. 4.75. Little
SALVATION ARMY (267.15)
Neal, Harry E. Hallelujah army. 4.95. Chilton
Nygaard, Norman E. Trumpet of salvation: The story of William and Catherine Booth. 1961. bds. 2.50. Zondervan
SAMOAN ISLANDS (996.13)
Gray, J. A. C. Amerika Samoa: A history of American Samoa and its United States Naval administration. il. 1960. 6.00. U.S. Naval Inst.

Stevenson, Fanny, and Robert Louis Stevenson. Our Samoan adventure. il. 1955. 4.00. Harper

West, Francis J. Political advancement in the South Pacific: A comparative study of colonial practice in Fiji, Tahiti and American Samoa. 1961. 4.55. Oxford U. P.

SAMPLING (STATISTICS) (311.21)

Cochran, W. G. Sampling techniques. 1953. 7.50. Wiley

Cyert, and Davidson. Statistical sampling for accounting information. il. 1962. 7.95. Prentice-Hall

Deming, William E. Sample designs in business research. 1960. 12.00. Wiley

Deming, W. E. Some theory of sampling. 1950. 10.75. Wiley

Heiland, R., and W. J. Richardson. Work sampling. 1957. 7.50. McGraw

SAN FRANCISCO (979.461)

Beebe, Lucius, and Charles Clegg. San Francisco's golden era. il. 1960. 5.95. Howell-North.

Fritz, Jean. San Francisco. 2.75. Rand McNally

Writers' Project. San Francisco. 1947. 6.50. Hastings

SAND, GEORGE, PSEUD OF MME. DUDEVANT, 1804-1876 (928)

Maurois, Andre. Lelia: The life of George Sand. il. 1953. 6.95. Harper

SANDBURG, CARL, 1878- (928)

Golden, Harry. Carl Sandburg. il. 1961. 5.00. World Pub.

SANITARY ENGINEERING (628)

Mitchell, George Eric. Sanitation, drainage, and water supply. 1959. 7.50. Transatlantic

Sawyer, Clair N. Chemistry for sanitary engineers. 1960. 9.95. McGraw

SANSKRIT LANGUAGE (491.2)

Keith, A. B. History of Sanskrit literature. 1928. 7.20. Oxford U. P.

Keith, A. Berriedale. Sanskrit drama in its origin, development, theory, and practice. 1924. 4.00. Oxford U. P.

Woodroffe, John. Hymns to the goddess. 1952. 3.00. Vedanta Press

SANTAYANA, GEORGE, 1863-1952 (921.1)

Arnett, W. E. Santayana and the sense of beauty. 1960. 3.25. Smith, Peter

Kirkwood, M. M. Santayana: Saint of the imagination. 1961. 5.00. U. of Toronto

Schilpp, Paul A. Philosophy of George Santayana. 1951. 6.95. Tudor

SARTRE, JEAN PAUL (1905- (921.4)

Greene, Norman N. Jean-Paul Sartre: The Existentialist ethic. 1960. 3.95. U. of Mich.

Stern, Alfred. Sartre: His philosophy and psychoanalysis. 4.50. Bobbs

Thody, Philip. Jean-Paul Sartre. 1961. 4.50. Macmillan

SATELLITES (ARTIFICIAL) (629.13882)

Burgess, Eric. Satellites and spaceflight. il. 1958. 4.50. Macmillan

Caidin, Martin. Vanguard: The story of America's scientific satellite program. il. 1957. 4.95. Dutton

Clarke, Arthur C. Making of a moon. 3.50. Wehman

Marcus, Abraham, and Rebecca. Tomorrow the moon. 3.50. Prentice-Hall

Moore, Patrick, and Irving Geis. Earth satellites. 1958. 3.95. Norton

Van Allen, James A. Scientific uses of earth satellites. 1958. 10.00. U. of Mich.

Woodbury, David O. Around the world in 90 minutes. il. 1958. 5.75. Harcourt

SATIRE (808.7)

Carlisle, Henry C., Jr. American satire in prose and verse. 1962. 6.95. Random

Elliott, Robert C. Power of satire. 1960. 6.00. Princeton

Highet, G. Anatomy of satire. 1962. 5.00. Princeton

Kernan, Alvin B. Modern satire. 1962. pap. 2.45. Harcourt

Knox, E. V. Mechanism of satire. 1951. 0.35. Cambridge U. P.

Peter, John. Complaint and satire in early English literature. 1956. 7.20. Oxford U. P.

Wedgwood, C. V. Poetry and politics under the Stuarts. 1960. 4.75. Cambridge U. P.

SAUDI ARABIA (953.8)

Butler, Grant C. Kings and camels. il. 1960. 4.50. Devin

Lipsky, George A. Saudi Arabia: Its people, its society, its culture. 1959. 7.00. Taplinger

Twitchell, Karl S. Saudi Arabia. 1958. 5.00. Princeton
SAVING AND INVESTMENT (332.6)
Duesenberry, J. S. Business cycles and economic growth. 1958. 6.50. McGraw
Haavelmo, Trygve. Study in the theory of investment. il. 1960. 5.00. U. of Chicago
Hansen, Alvin H. Business cycles and national income. 1951. 6.90. Norton
Ulmer, Melville J. Capital in transportation, communications, and public utilities.
    1960. 12.00. Princeton
SCANDINAVIA (948)
De Mare, Eric. Scandinavia. il. 1955. 5.00. Hastings
Fodor, Eugene. Scandinavia. 4.95. McKay
Hovde, Bryn J. Scandinavian countries, 1720-1865: The rise of the middle classes.
    1943. 2. vols. 7.00. Cornell
Scott, Franklin Daniel. United States and Scandinavia. il. 1950. 4.50. Harvard
SCHILLER, JOHANN CHRISTOPH FRIEDRICH VON, 1759-1805 (928)
Stahl, E. L. Friedrich Schiller's drama. 1954. 4.00. Oxford U. P.
SCHIZOPHRENIA (132.1982)
Arieti, Silvano. Interpretation of schizophrenia. 1955. 7.50. Basic Books
Auerback, A. Schizophrenia. 1959. 6.00. Ronald
Davis, John Eisele. Recovery from schizophrenia: The Roland method. 1957. 4.75.
    Thomas, C. C.
Dawson, Joseph G. , and others. Psychotherapy with schizophrenics. 1960. 5.00.
    La. State
Scheflen, Albert E. Psychotherapy of schizophrenia: Direct analysis. 1961. 8.50.
    Thomas, C. C.
Sullivan, Harry S. Schizophrenia as a human process. 1962. 6.50. Norton
SCHOLARSHIPS (378.34)
Brownstein, Samuel C. , and others. You can win a scholarship. 1958. 4.95. Barron's
Feingold, S. Norman. Scholarships, fellowships and loans. 4 vols. 10.00. Bellman
National register of scholarships and fellowships. 2 vols. vol. 1, Register of
    scholarships and loans; vol. 2, Register of fellowships and grants. 1962-63 ed.
    15.00 ea. World Trade Academy
UNESCO. Study abroad. vol. 13. 1962. pap. 3.00. Int. Doc. Service-Columbia
SCHOLASTICISM (149.2)
Gilson, Etienne. Spirit of medieval philosophy. tr. by A. C. Downes. 1936. 3.50.
    Scribner
Maritain, Jacques. St. Thomas Aquinas. pap. 1.45. Meridian
Robson, John A. Wyclif and the Oxford schools. 1961. 6.50. Cambridge U. P.
Sheen, Fulton J. God and intelligence in modern philosphy. 1958. pap. 1.25.
    Doubleday
Wuellner, Bernard. Dictionary of scholastic philosophy. 1955. 4.25. Bruce
Wulf, Maurice de. Introduction to scholastic philosophy. 1956. 3.50. Dover
SCHOOL LIBRARIES (027.82)
Douglas, Mary P. Teacher-librarian's handbook. 1949. 2.75. A. L. A.
Fargo, Lucile F. Library in the school. 1947. 4.00. A. L. A.
Independent Schools Education Board. 3,000 books for secondary school libraries.
    1961. pap. 3.00. Bowker
McAllister, Mariana K. Basic book collection for high schools. 1957. 2.75. A. L. A.
Rossoff, Martin. Library in high school teaching. 1961. 3.00. Wilson
Trinkner, Charles L. Better libraries make better schools. 1962. 6.00. Shoe
    String
Wofford, Azile. School library at work. 1959. 3.50. Wilson
SCHOOL MANAGEMENT AND ORGANIZATION (371.2)
Bartky, John A. Supervision as human relations. 1953. 5.50. Heath
Dudley, Lofton Leland. School and the community. 1933. 2.50. Harvard
Gross, Neal. Who runs our schools? 1958. 4.95. Wiley
Hand, Harold C. What people think about their schools. 3.50. Harcourt
Mickelson, P. P. , and K. H. Hansen. Elementary school administration. 1957. 5.95.
    McGraw
Puffer, K. Hart. How your school should be run - since you ask me! 1962. 4.75.
    Wheelwright

Reavis, William C. Critical issues in educational administration. 1938. pap. 3.50.
    U. of Chicago
Wiles, Kimball. Supervision for better schools. 1955. 6.95. Prentice-Hall
Yauch, Wilbur A. Helping teachers understand principals. 1957. pap. 1.10. Appleton
Yeager, William A. Administration of the noninstructional personnel and services.
    1959. 5.50. Harper
SCHOOL SUPERINTENDENTS AND PRINCIPALS (371.1)
Burton, William H., and Leo J. Brueckner. Supervision: A social process.
    il. 1955. 6.75. Appleton
Hansford, B. W. Guidebook for school principals. 1961. 5.00. Ronald
Hicks, Hanne J. Educational supervision in principal and practice. il. 1960.
    6.25. Ronald
Kyte, George C. How to supervise. 5.50. Houghton
National Education Association, National Association of Secondary-School
    Principals. Annual proceedings. Forty-fifth, 1961. 2.00; Forty-sixth, 1962.
    2.00. N. E. A.
Swearingen, Mildred E. Supervision of instruction: Foundations and dimensions.
    1962. 6.50. Allyn & Bacon
Wilson, Robert E. Modern school superintendent. il. 1960. 4.50. Harper
Woellner, Mrs. Robert C., and M. Aurilla Wood. Requirements for certification
    of teachers, counselors, librarians, administrators for elementary schools,
    secondary schools, junior colleges. pap. 3.50. U. of Chicago
SCHUBERT, FRANZ PETER, 1797-1828. (927)
Brown, Maurice J. E. Schubert: A biography with critical digressions. 1958. 6.75.
    St. Martins
Deutsch, Otto Erich. Schubert: Memoirs by his friends. il. 10.00. Macmillan
Einstein, Alfred. Schubert: A musical portrait. 1951. 7.50. Oxford U. P.
Hutchings, Arthur. Schubert. il. 1949. 3.50. Farrar, Straus
SCHUMANN, ROBERT ALEXANDER, 1810-1856 (927)
Abraham, Gerald. Schumann: A symposium. 1952. 7.00. Oxford U. P.
Chissell, Joan. Schumann. 1949. 3.50. Farrar, Straus
SCHUMPETER, JOSEPH ALOIS, 1883-1950. (923.7)
Harris, Seymour Edwin. Schumpeter, social scientist. il. 1951. 4.75. Harvard
SCHWEITZER, ALBERT, 1875- (923.6)
Anderson, Erica, and Eugene Exman. World of Albert Schweitzer. il. 1955.
    6.00. Harper
Cousing, Norman. Dr. Schweitzer of Lambarene. il. 1960. 3.95. Harper
Gollomb, Joseph. Albert Schweitzer: Genius of the jungle. 1949. 3.00. Vanguard
Hagedorn, Hermann. Prophet in the wilderness: The story of Albert Schweitzer.
    1954. 4.95. Macmillan
Joy, Charles R. Music in the life of Albert Schweitzer, with selections from his
    writings. 3.75. Smith, Peter
Ostergaard-Christensen, L. At work with Albert Schweitzer. il. 1962. 3.50.
    Beacon
Payne, Robert. Three worlds of Albert Schweitzer. 1957. 3.50. Nelson
Roback, A. A. Albert Schweitzer jubilee book. il. 8.50. Sci-Art
Roback, A. A. In Albert Schweitzer's realms. il. 1962. 10.00. Sci-Art
SCIENCE (500)
Ashford, Theodore A. From atoms to stars: An introduction to the physical sciences.
    1960. 8.50. Holt, Rinehart & Winston
Asimov, Isaac. Intelligent man's guide to science. 2 vols. il. 1960. 15.00. Basic
    Books
Barber, Bernard. Science and the social order. 1952. 5.00. Free Press
Bates, Marston. Nature of natural history. 4.50. Scribner
Bonner, F. T., and M. Phillips. Principles of physical science. 1957. 8.75.
    Addison Wesley
Brinckerhoff, Richard, and others. Physical world. il. 1958. 5.04. Harcourt
Brown, Harry B., and Sydney Jones. Introductory applied science. 2 vols. 1940.
    2.00 ea. St. Martins

Cohen, I. Bernard. Science, servant of man: A layman's primer for the age of science. 1948. 5.00. Little

Compton, Arthur H. Human meaning of science. 1940. 1.00. U. of N. C.

Elbers, Gerald W., and Paul Duncan. Scientific Revolution: Challenge and promise. 1959. 6.00. Pub. Affairs

Fortune. Great American scientists. 1961. 3.50. Prentice-Hall

Gamow, George. One two three...infinity. il. 1961. 5.00. Viking

Gray, Dwight E., and John W. Coutts. Man and his physical world. 1958. 7.00. Van Nostrand

Hildebrand, Joel H. Science in the making. 1957. 3.00. Columbia

Hogben, Lancelot. Science for the citizen. il. 1957. 12.50. Norton

Holton, Gerald J. Introduction to concepts and theories in physical science. il. 1952. 8.75. Addison-Wesley

Hutchings, Edward M., Jr. Frontiers in science. 1958. 6.00. Basic Books

Jean, Frank C., and others. Man and his physical universe. 1958. 7.25. Ginn

Joslin, I. C. General science. 1937. 2.50. St. Martins

Korzybski, Alfred. Science and sanity. 1958. 11.00. Inst. Of Gen. Semantics

Krauskopf, K. B. Fundamentals of physical science. 1959. 7.95. McGraw

McCorkle, Paul. Physical world. 1956. 6.95. McGraw

Newmann, James R. What is science? 5.95. 1958. S. and S.

Platt, John R. Excitement of science. 1962. 3.50. Houghton

Scientific American. Scientific American book of projects. by C. L. Strong. 1960. 5.95. S. and S.

Shapley, Harlow, and others. Treasury of science. 1959. 6.95. Harper

Slabaugh, Wendell H., and Alfred Butler. College physical science. 1958. 8.75. Prentice-Hall

Swenson, H. N., and J. E. Woods. Physical science for liberal arts students. 1957. 6.75. Wiley

Vergara, William C. Mathematics in everyday things. il. 1959. 3.95. Harper

Vergara, William C. Science in everyday things. il. 1958. 4.50. Harper

Wistar, R. Man and his physical universe. 1953. 5.50. Wiley

SCIENCE--ADDRESSES, ESSAYS, LECTURES (504)

Ashley, Montagu, M. F. Studies and essays in the history of science and learning. 1947. 12.00. Abelard

Asimov, Isaac. Fact and fancy. 3.95. Doubleday

Beadle, George W., and others. Science and resources. il. 1959. 5.00. John Hopkins

Calder, Ritchie. Science in our lives. 1954. 3.00. Mich. State

Conant, James B. Modern science and modern man. 1952. 2.75. Columbia

Dubos, R. Dreams of reason: Science and utopias. 1961. 5.00. Columbia

Eddington, Arthur. New pathways in science. 1959. pap. 1.95. U. of Mich.

Ginger, Ray. Spectrum: The world of science. il. 1959. 3.95. Holt, Rinehart & Winston

Jeans, James H. Mysterious universe. 1931. 1.95. Cambridge U. P.

Knickerbocker, William S. Classics of modern science. 1962. pap. 2.25. Beacon

Oppenheimer, J. Robert. Open mind. 1960. pap. 1.00. S. and S.

Platt, John R. Excitement of science. 1962. 3.50. Houghton

Rhys, Hedley H. Seventeenth century science and arts. il. 1961. 3.00. Princeton

Russell, Bertrand. Mysticism and logic. 1954. 2.75. Barnes & Noble

Schrodinger, E. Science and humanism. 1951. 2.50. Cambridge U. P.

Shapley, H. Of stars and men. 1958. 3.50. Beacon

Shapley, Harlow, and others. Readings in the physical sciences. 1948. 3.00. Appleton

Whitehead, Alfred N. Science and the modern world. 1926. 6.00. Macmillan

SCIENCE--DICTIONARIES (503)

DeVries, Louis. French-English science dictionary. 1951. 10.00. McGraw

DeVries, Louis. German-English science dictionary. 1959. 7.00. McGraw

Evans, R. Our new age: Illustrated science dictionary. il. 1962. 3.95. McKay

Flood, Walter E. Scientific words: Their structure and meaning. 1960. 3.50. Meredith

Hechtlinger, A. Modern science dictionary. 1959. 10.00. Franklin Pub.

McGraw-Hill. McGraw-Hill encyclopedia of science and technology. 16 vols. including index and 1962 yearbook. 1960. set only, 219.50; limited deluxe ed. 285.00; teacher's guide. 1961. Renner, and others, 0.64. McGraw

Newman, James R. Harper encyclopedia of science. 4 vols. 1962. 30.00. Harper

Tver, David F. Dictionary of business and scientific terms. 1961. 10.00. Gulf

Van Nostrand. Van Nostrand's scientific encyclopedia. 1958. 29.75. Van Nostrand

SCIENCE--HISTORY (509)

Anthony, Herbert D. Science and its background. 1957. 4.50. St. Martins

Bell, Whitfield, J., Jr. Early American science. 1955. 1.50. U. of N. C.

Boas, Marie. Scientific Renaissance: 1450-1630. il. 1962. 6.00. Harper

Butterfield, Herbert. Origins of modern science, 1300-1800. 4.00. Macmillan

Conant, James Bryant. Science and common sense. 1951. 5.00. Yale

Conant, James Bryant, and others. Harvard case histories in experimental science. 2 vols. il. 1957. 10.00. Harvard

Crombie, Alistair. C. Augustine to Galileo. 2 vols. il. 1961. set, 5.50. Harvard

Campier, W. C. History of science. 1949. 4.95. Cambridge U. P.

Dampier, W. C., and Margaret. Readings in the literature of science. 3.50. Smith, Peter

Evans, Herbert M. Men and moments in the history of science. il. 1959. 4.50. U. of Wash.

Fuller, Elizabeth M., and Mary J. Ellis. Springboards to science. 3.00. Denison

Hindle, Brooke. Pursuit of science in revolutionary America, 1735-1789. 1956. 7.50. U. of N. C.

Jaffe, Bernard. Men of science in America. 1958. 6.95. S. and S.

Jeans, James. Growth of physical science. pap. 0.50. Fawcett

Mason, Stephen S. Main currents of scientific thought. 1953. 6.00. Abelard

Newton, Isaac. Isaac Newton's papers and letters on natural philosophy, and related documents. by I. Bernard Cohen. 1958. 12.50. Harvard

Pledge, H. T. Science since 1500: A short history of mathematics, physics, chemistry and biology. 3.50. Smith, Peter

Porta, John Baptista. Natural magick. 1957. 8.50. Basic Books

Sarton, George. Appreciation of ancient and medieval science during the Renaissance. 1957. 6.00. U. of Pa.

Sarton, G. Guide to the history of science. 1952. 7.50. Ronald

Sarton, George A. History of science: Hellenistic science and culture in the last three centuries B.C. il. 1959. 11.00. Harvard

Sarton, George. Life of science. 1960. 4.50. Indiana

Sarton, George. Six wings: Men of science in the Renaissance. il. 1956. 6.75. Indiana

Sarton, George. Study of the history of mathematics and The study of the history of science. 1957. pap. 1.25. Dover

Schwartz, George I., and Philip W. Bishop. Moment of discovery. 2 vols. il. vol. 1. Origins of science; vol. 2. Development of modern science. boxed. 15.00. Basic Books

Sedgwick, W. T., and others. Short history of science. 6.90. Macmillan

Singer, Charles. From magic to science. 1960. 4.00. Smith, Peter

Taylor, F. Sherwood. Short history of science and scientific thought. il. 1949. 6.00. Norton

Thorndike, L. History of magic and experimental science. 8 vols. 1923-1956. vol. 1-6, 8.50 ea; vols. 7-8, 10.00 ea. Columbia

Turner, D. M. Book of scientific discovery. 3.95. Ungar

Voigt, Melvin J. Scientists' approaches to information. 1961. 2.50. A.L.A.

White, Andrew D. History of the warfare of science with theology in Christendom. 2 vols. pap. 1.85 ea; set, pap. 3.70. Dover

Wolf, Abraham. History of science, technology, and philosophy in the 16th and 17th centuries. 2 vols. il. 1959. 1.95 ea. 18th century. 2 vols. il. 1961. 2.50 ea. Harper

SCIENCE--METHODOLOGY (500.018)

Abro, A. d', Evolution of scientific thought from Newton to Einstein. 3.75. Smith, Peter

Bacon, F. Essays, Advancement of learning, New Atlantis, and other pieces. 2.50. Odyssey

Bacon, Francis. New Organon. 1960. 3.50. Bobbs

Blake, R. M., and others. Theories of scientific method: Renaissance to nineteenth century. 1960. 6.50. U. of Wash.

Conant, James Bryant. Science and common sense. 1951. 5.00. Yale

Descartes, Rene. Discourse on method; Meditations on the first philosophy; and Principles of philosophy. 2.95. Dutton

Hall, A. R. Scientific revolution, 1500-1800. 1954. 5.00. Longmans

Mill, John Stuart. John Stuart Mill's philosophy of scientific method. by Ernest Nagel. 1950. pap. 1.95. Hafner

Popper, Karl K. Logic of scientific discovery. 1959. 8.50. Basic Books

SCIENCE--PHILOSOPHY (501)

Beck, William S. Modern science and the nature of life. 1957. 5.75. Harcourt

Bridgman, P. W. Way things are. 1959. 5.75. Harvard

Bronowski, J. Common sense of science. 1953. 2.00. Harvard

Butler, J. A. V. Science and human life. 3.95. Basic Books

Butterfield, Herbert. Origins of modern science, 1300-1800. 4.00. Macmillan

Conant, James B. Modern science and modern man. 1952. 2.75. Columbia

Danto, Arthur, and Sidney Morgenbesser. Philosophy of science. pap. 1.75. Meridian

Eddington, Arthur. Nature of the physical world. 1958. pap. 1.95. U. of Mich.

Eddington, Arthur. New pathways in science. 1959. pap. 1.95. U. of Mich.

Feigi, Herbert, and May Brodbeck. Readings in the philosophy of science. 1953. 7.00. Appleton

Frank, Philipp. Modern science and its philosophy. 1955. 3.00. Braziller

Gatland, Kenneth W., and Derek D. Dempster. Inhabited universe. il. 1958. 3.95. McKay

Gillispie, Charles C. Edge of objectivity. il. 1960. 7.50. Princeton

Hall, A. R. Scientific revolution, 1500-1800. 1954. 5.00. Longmans

Harris, Errol E. Nature, mind and modern science. 1954. 6.00. Macmillan

Holton, G. Science and the modern mind. 1958. 3.95. Beacon

Kemeny, John G. Philosopher looks at science. il. 1959. 6.50. Van Nostrand

MacIver, Robert M. Life: Its dimensions and its bounds. 1960. 3.50. Harper

Melsen, A. G. van. Science and technology. 6.95. Duquesne

Polanyi, Michael. Study of man. 1959. 1.75. U. of Chicago

Price, Derek. Science since Babylon. il. 1961. 4.50. Yale

Reichenbach, H. Modern philosophy of science. 5.50. Humanities

Weyl, Hermann. Philosophy of mathematics and natural science. 1949. pap. 1.95. Princeton

Whitehead, A. N. Concept of nature. 1919. 3.50. Cambridge U. P.

Whitehead, Alfred North. Process and reality. 1960. 6.50. Macmillan

Whittaker, Edmund T. From Euclid to Eddington. 1959. Dover

Wiener, Philip P. Readings in philosophy of science. 6.75. Scribner

SCIENCE--STUDY AND TEACHING (375.5)

Blough, Glenn O., and Marjorie H. Campbell. Making and using classroom science materials in the elementary school. 1954. 3.95. Holt, Rinehart & Winston

Haun, R. R. Science in general education. 1960. 4.50. Brown, W. C.

Richardson, John S. Science teaching in secondary schools. 1957. 10.00. Prentice-Hall

UNESCO. 700 science experiments for everyone. il. 1958. 3.00. Doubleday

UNESCO. Source book for science teaching. 3.00. Int. Doc. Service-Columbia

SCIENCE AND THE HUMANITIES (507)

American Academy of Arts and Sciences. Education in the age of science. 1959. 1.75. Am. Acad. of Arts & Sci.

Glass, Bentley. Science and liberal education. 1960. 3.00. La. State
Snow, C. P. Two cultures and the scientific revolution. 1959. 1.75. Cambridge U. P.
SCIENCE AS A PROFESSION (500.069)
Nourse, Alan Edward. So you want to be a scientist. il. 1960. 3.50. Harper
Science Research Associates. Jobs in science. il. 1958. Sci. Res. Assoc.
SCIENTIFIC APPARATUS AND INSTRUMENTS (681.2)
Davis, Helen Miles. Scientific instruments you can make. 1954. 2.00. Science
    Service.
Heldman, Julius D. Techniques of glass manipulation in scientific research. 1946.
    5.35. Prentice-Hall
Moore, William. Science equipment. 1962. 2.50. Putnam
SCIENTISTS (920)
Berland, Theodore. Scientific life. 1962. 5.75. Coward
DeKruif, Paul. Microbe hunters. il. 1932. 4.50. Harcourt
Firth, Margaret A. Handbook of scientific and technical awards in the United States
    and Canada, 1900-1952. 1956. 3.00. S. L. A.
Fortune. Great American scientists. by the Editors of Fortune. 1961. 3.50. Prentice-
    Hall
Haller, Albert von. Vitamin hunters. 1962. 5.95. Chilton
Jaffe, Bernard. Men of science in America. 1958. 6.95. S. and S.
Lenard, Phillip. Great men of science. il. 4.50. British Bk.
Levitan, Tina N. Laureates: Jewish winners of the Nobel Prize. 4.50. Twayne
Poole, Lynn, and Gray. Scientists who changed the world. il. 1960. 3.00. Dodd
Thomas, Henry, and Dana Lee. Living biographies of great scientists. 1959.
    2.50. Doubleday
Williams, Greer. Virus hunters. 1959. 6.50. Knopf
SCOTLAND (941)
Bain, Robert. Clans and tartans of Scotland. 3.00. Collins
Boswell, James. Journal of a tour to the Hebrides. bd. with Samuel Johnson's
    Journey to the western islands of Scotland. by R. W. Chapman. 1930. 4.50.
    Oxford U. P.
Campbell, Grace. Highland heritage. il. 1962. 4.95. Meredith
Glover, Janet R. Story of Scotland. 1960. 5.95. Roy Pub.
Lacaille, A. D. Stone Age in Scotland. 1954. 8.80. Oxford U. P.
Leyburn, James G. Scotch-Irish: A social history. 1962. 7.00. U. of N. C.
Porter, Jane. Scottish chiefs. ill. 1921. 5.00. Scribner
Scott-Moncrieff, George. Mirror and the cross. il. 1961. 3.95. Taplinger
Smith, Edwin, and G. S. Fraser. Scotland. il. 1955. 12.00. Viking
SCOTT, SIR WALTER, BART, 1771-1832 (928)
Davie, Donald. Heyday of Sir Walter Scott. 1961. 4.50. Barnes & Noble
Pearson, Hesketh. Sir Walter Scott: His life and personality. il. 1955. 4.00. Harper
SCREEN PROCESS PRINTING (655.316)
Clemence, Will. Screen process printing. 1961. 2.75. Pitman
SCREENS (764.8)
Chiba, Reiko. Japanese screens in miniature. il. 1960. 4.50. Tuttle
Grilli, Elise. Golden screen paintings of Japan. il. 1959. pap. 1.25. Crown
SCULPTORS (927)
Richter, Gisela M. A. Sculpture and sculptors of the Greeks. 1960. 20.00. Yale
Roditi, Edouard. Dialogues on art. il. 1961. 4.95. Horizon
Turnbull, Grace H. Chips from my chisel. il. 1953. 5.00. Smith, Richard R.
SCULPTURE (730)
Album of Japanese sculpture. vols. 2-6, 5.00 ea. Tuttle
Auerbach, Arnold. Modelled sculpture and plaster casting. il. 1962. 6.95. Barnes,
    A. S.
Bilk, Urs. Sculpture on buildings. 1961. 12.00. Universe
Contemporary American painting and sculpture. 3 vols: 1955; 1957; 1961; 3.50 ea.
    U. of Ill.
Desroches-Noblecourt, Christine. Ancient Egypt. il. 1961. ods. 8.95. N. Y. Graphic

581

Dodd, Loring Holmes. Golden age of American sculpture. il. 5.00. Chapman

Eliscu, Frank. Sculpture: Techniques in clay, wax, slate. il. 1959. 7.50. Chilton

Gadd, C. J. Stones of Assyria. il. 12.50. Boston Bk.

Gardner, Arthur. English medieval sculpture. 1951. 12.50. Cambridge U. P.

Gardner, A. T. Yankee stonecutters. 1947. 5.00. Columbia

Giedion-Welcker, Carola. Contemporary sculpture, an evolution in volume and space. 1960. 16.50. Wittenborn

Gunnis, R. Dictionary of British sculptors, 1660-1851. il. 1954. 12.50. Harvard (R)

Hoffman, Malvina. Sculpture inside and out. 2.98. Crown

Hunter, Samuel. Modern American painting and sculpture. 1959. pap. 0.95. Dell

Kidder, J. Edward. Masterpieces of Japanese sculpture. il. 1951. 27.50. Tuttle

Louis-Frederic. Art of India. tr. by Eva M. Hooykaas and A. H. Christie. il. 1960. 17.50. Abrams

Lynch, John. How to make mobiles. il. 1953. 3.50. Viking

Matt, Leonard von, and Valerio Mariani. Baroque art in Rome. 1961. 4.75. Universe

Munsterberg, Hugo. Art of the Chinese sculptor. 1960. pap. 2.50. Tuttle

Noguchi, Isamo, and others. il. 12.50. Tuttle

Paulme, Denise. African sculpture. il. 1962. 5.00. Viking

Pope-Hennessy, John. Italian Gothic sculpture. il. 1955. 8.50. N. Y. Graphic

Pope-Hennessy, John. Italian High-Renaissance and Braoque sculpture. 1962. 3 vols. 13.50 ea. N. Y. Graphic

Pope-Hennessy, John. Italian Renaissance sculpture. il. 1958. 20.00. N. Y. Graphic

Radin, Paul, and James J. Sweeney. African folktales and sculpture. il. 1952. 10.00. Pantheon

Read, Herbert. Art of sculpture. 1961. 7.50. Pantheon

Rich, J. C. Materials and methods of sculpture. il. 1947. 12.50. Oxford U. P.

Ritchie, Andrew Carnduff. Sculpture of the twentieth century. il. 1958. 7.50. Mus. of Mod. Art.

Robb, David M., and J. J. Garrison. Art in the western world. 1953. 8.50. Harper

Savini, Roberto. Modern Italian sculpture. il. 1962. 20.00. Abrams

Schaefer-Simmern, Henry. Sculpture in Europe today. il. 1955. 8.50. U. of Calif.

Segy, Ladislas. African sculpture speaks. 1952. il. 6.95. Hill & Wang

Seuphor, Michel. Sculpture of this century. tr. by Haakon Chevalier. il. 1960. 15.00. Braziller

Slobodkin, Louis. Sculpture: Principles and practice. 1949. 7.50. World Pub.

Struppeck, Jules. Creation of sculpture. il. 1952. 12.40. Holt, Rinehart & Winston

Trier, Eduard. Form and space. il. 15.00. Praeger

Vasari, Giorgio. Vasari on technique. by B. Baldwin Brown. il. 4.00. Smith, Peter

Watson, William. Sculpture of Japan. 15.00. Boston Bk.

Zaidenberg, Arthur. Anyone can sculpt. il. 1952. 4.50. Harper

Zorach, W. Zorach explains sculpture - what it means and how it is made. il. 1960. 4.95. Tudor

SCULPTURE, GREEK (571.73)

Bieber, Margarete. Sculpture of the Hellenistic Age. 1961. 27.00. Columbia

Carpenter, Rhys. Greek sculpture. il. 1960. 6.95. U. of Chicago

Devambez, Pierre. Greek sculpture. tr. by Barbara M. Bell. il. 1960. 5.95. Tudor

Lullies, Reinhard. Greek sculpture. 1957. 15.00. Abrams

Richter, Gisela M. A. Sculpture and sculptors of the Greeks. 1950. 20.00. Yale

Yalouris, Nikolas. Classical Greece. il. 1961. bds. 8.95. N. Y. Graphic

SEA-POWER (359)

Eliot, George Feilding. Victory without war - 1957-1961. 1958. 2.00. U.S. Naval Inst.

Lewis, David D. Fight for the sea. il. 1961. 6.00. World Pub.

Mahan, Alfred T. Influence of sea power upon history. 1660-1783. il. 1890. 7.50.
    Little
Richmond, Herbert. Statesmen and sea power. 1946. 4.50. Oxford U. P.
Sokol, Anthony E. Seapower in the nuclear age. 1961. 6.00. Pub. Affairs
SEA STORIES (808.8)
Aymar, Gordon. Treasury of sea stories. 1948. 5.00. Barnes, A. S.
Belloc, Hilaire. On sailing the sea. 2.95. De Graff
French, Joseph Lewis. Great sea stories. 1955. 2.49. Tudor
Mason, Van Wyck. Sea Venture. 5.75. Doubleday
Snow, Edward Rowe. Great sea rescues. il. 1958. 4.00. Dodd
SEAFARING LIFE (910.45)
Campbell, A. B. Great moments at sea. 2.50. Roy Pub.
Chapman, Charles F. Seamanship: A practical manual. 1960. 2.00. Motor Boating
Carse, Robert. Moonrakers: The story of the clipper ship men. il. 1961. 4.00.
    Harper
Conrad, Joseph. Mirror of the sea, and A. personal record. 1.45. Doubleday
Dana, Richard H. Two years before the mast. il. 3.50. Dodd
Hartle, Maurice C., and others. Elementary seamanship. il. 1958. 2.00. U. S.
    Naval Inst.
Healey, James C. Foc's'le and glory-hole: A study of the Merchant seaman and
    his occupation. 1936. 2.50. Oxford U. P.
Knight, F. Beginners guide to the sea. 2.75. St. Martins
Olson, Louis B. Olson's small boat seamanship. il. 1956. 7.50. Van Nostrand
Robberson, Elbert. Seamanship simplified. il. 1959. 4.95. Barnes, A. S.
Sawyer, E. O., Jr. America's sea saga. il. 7.50. Pageant
Spectorsky, A. C. Book of the sea. 1958. 4.95. Grosset
Villiers, Alan J. Give me a ship to sail. il. 1959. 4.95. Scribner
Villiers, Alan. Sons of Sinbad. il. 1940. 6.00. Scribner
SEASHORE BIOLOGY (574.92)
Barrett, John, and C. M. Yonge. Pocket guide to the sea shore. il. 6.00. Collins
Berrill, N. J., and Jacquelyn. 1001 questions answered about the seashore. il.
    1957. 5.00. Dodd
Carson, Rachel. Edge of the sea. 1955. 3.95. Houghton
Gaul, Albro. Wonderful world of the seashore. il. 1955. 5.00. Meredith
Richards, Horace G. Animals of the seashore. 3.00. Humphries
Van Reine, W. J. Prud'homme. Plants and animals of the seashore. 2.75.
    Transatlantic
Yonge, C. M. Sea shore. il. 6.00. Collins
SECESSION (973.713)
Perkins, Howard C. Northern editorials on secession. 2 vols. 1942. 10.00. Appleton
Phillips. Ulrich B. Course of the South to secession. 3,50. Smith, Peter
Stampp, Kenneth. And the war came. 1950. 4.50. La. State
Wooster, Ralph A. Secession conventions of the South. 1962. 6.50. Princeton
SECRET SERVICE (351.742)
Baughman, Urbanus E., and Leonard Robinson. Secret service chief. il. 1962.
    4.95. Harper
Bowen, Walter S., and Harry E. Neal. United States secret service. 1960. 4.95.
    Chilton
Kane, Harnett T. Spies for the blue and gray. il. 1954. 3.95. Doubleday
Hutton, Bernard. School for spies. 1962. 3.95. Coward
Monas, Sidney. Third Section: Police and society in Russia under Nicholas I.
    1961. 6.75. Harvard
Wolin, S., and R. Slusser. Soviet secret police. 1957. 9.25. Praeger
SECRETARIES (651.3741)
Becker, Esther R. How to be an effective executive secretary. 1962. bds. 4.50.
    Harper
Becker, Esther R. Secretaries who succeed. 1947. 2.95. Harper
Becker, Esther R., and Richard L. Lawrence. Success and satisfaction in your
    office job. 1954. 3.00. Harper

Bredow, Miriam. Handbook for the medical secretary. 1959. 7.75. McGraw
Bredow, Miriam. Medical assistant. il. 1958. 7.50. McGraw
Burke, Marylin C. Executive secretary. 1959. bds. 3.95. Doubleday
Coffin, Kenneth B. , and Forrest Colwell. Medical secretary. il. 1959. 5.95.
    Macmillan
Delano, Margaret. How to be a top secretary. 1954. 4.95. McKay
Epstein, Abraham, and Morris White. Shorthand, typewriting and secretarial
    training. 1.00. Grosset
Frederick, Portia M. , and Carol Towner. Office assistant in medical practice.
    1960. 5.25. Saunders
Mayo, Lucy S. Communications handbook for secretaries. 7.95. workbook 1,
    2.75; workbook 2, 3.00; teacher's manual and key. 4.00. McGraw
Miller, Besse M. Medical secretary's and assistant's handbook. 1960. 5.75.
    Prentice-Hall
Parsons, Esther Jane. In the doctor's office: The art of the medical assistant. 1956.
    2.75. Lippincott
Place, Irene, and Madeline S. Strony. Road to secretarial success. il. 1954. 5.75.
    McGraw
Root, K. B. , and E. E. Byers. Medical secretary. 1960. 5.50. McGraw
Smith, John Allan. School secretary's handbook. 1962. 6.95. Prentice-Hall
Turner, David R. School secretary. 1961. pap. 4.00. Arco
SECTIONALISM (U.S.) (973.7)
Craven, Avery O. Growth of southern nationalism. 1953. 7.50. La. State
Sydnor, Charles. Development of Southern sectionalism, 1819-1848. 1948.
    7.50. La. State
Turner, Frederick J. Frontier and section: Selected essays. 1961. 3.95. Prentice-
    Hall
Turner, F. J. Significance of sections in American history. 4.25. Smith, Peter
SECTS (291.9)
Algermissen, Konrad. Christian sects. 1962. 3.50. Hawthorn
Bach, Marcus. They have found a faith. 3.50. Bobbs
Bach, Marcus. Strange sects and curious cults. 1961. 4.50. Dodd
Hawks, E. F. Pedigree of Protestantism. 1936. 1.25. Reilly, P.
Mathison, Richard R. Faiths, cults, and sects of America. 1960. 5.00. Bobbs
Mayer, Frederick E. Religious bodies of America. by A. C. Piepkoin. 1961. 8.50.
    Concordia
Mead, Frank S. Handbook of denominations in the United States. 1961. 2.95.
    Abingdon (R)
Neve, J. L. Churches and sects of Christendom. 1952. 5.00. Lutheran
Potter, Charles F. Faiths men live by. 1954. 3.95. Prentice-Hall
Rosten, Leo. Guide to the religions of America. 1955. 3.95. S. and S.
Spence, Hartzell. Story of America's religions. 1960. 4.00. Holt, Rinehart &
    Winston
Stuber, Stanley I. Denominations: How we got them. 1958. pap. 0.50. Assn. Pr.
Stuber, Stanley I. How we got our denominations. 1959. 3.50. Assn. Pr.
Weigel, Gustave. Churches in North America. 1961. 3.95. Taplinger
Williams, John Paul. What Americans believe and how they worship. 1962. 7.50.
    Harper
Wilson, Bryan R. Sects and society. 1960. 5.75. U. of Calif.
SECURITIES (332.6)
Badger, Ralph E. , and Harry Guthmann. Investment principles and practices.
    1961. 11.95. Prentice-Hall
Barnes, Leo. Your investments. 1961. pap. 3.95. Citadel
Bellemore, Douglas. Investments. 1960. 10.00. Simmons-Boardman
Clendenin, John C. Introduction to investments. 1960. 7.95. McGraw
Effinger, R. C. ABC of investing. 1953. 1.95. Harper
Feyler, Sherman F. Income growth with security: The formula-plan solution.
    il. 1958. 4.95. Macmillan

Finley, Harold M. Everybody's guide to the stock market. 1959. 4.95. Regnery
Gellermann, Henry. How to make money make money. il. 1957. 4.50. Crowell
Graham, Benjamin. Intelligent investor. 1959. 4.95. Harper
Kamm, Jacob O. Investor's handbook. 4.95. World Pub.
Kamm, Jacob O. Making profits in the stock market. 1958. 3.50. World Pub.
Mundt, Carlos S. Easy-to-use guide to successful investment. 1961. 1.95. Grosset
Plum, Lester V. Investing in American industries. 1960. 6.95. Harper
Robbins, Sidney M. Managing securities. 1954. 7.25. Houghton
SECURITY, INTERNATIONAL (341.1)
Hogan, Willard N. International conflict and collective security. 1955. 3.50. U. of
    Ky.
Mecham, John L. United States and inter-American security, 1889-1960. il. 1961.
    7.50. U. of Tex.
Rockefeller Brothers Fund. International security, the military aspect. 1958. pap.
    0.50. Doubleday
Streit, Clarence K. Union now: A proposal for an Atlantic federal union of the free
    postwar ed. 3.00. Harper
SEEDS (581.467)
Crocker, W., and L. V. Barton. Physiology of seeds. 1953. 8.00. Ronald
Martin, Alexander C., and William D. Barkley. Seed identification manual. il.
    1961. 10.00. U. of Calif. (R)
SEGREGATION (301.45)
Bates, D. Long shadow of Little Rock. 1962. 4.95. McKay
Blaustein, Albert, and Clarence C. Ferguson. Desegregation and the law. 1957.
    5.00. Rutgers
Blossom, Virgil T. It has happened here. 1959. 2.95. Harper
Brickman, William W., and Stanley Lehrer. Countdown on segregated education.
    1960. 3.50. Soc. for the Advancement of Educ.
Campbell, Ernest Q., and Thomas F. Pettigrew. Christians in racial crisis. 1959.
    3.50. Pub. Affairs
Campbell, Ernest Q., and others. When a city closes its schools. 1960. 2.00. U.
    of N. C. Inst. for Res. in Soc. Sci.
Cook, James G. Segregationists. 1962. 4.95. Meredith
Hays, Brooks. Southern moderate speaks. 1959. 1.00. U. of N. C.
Kilpatrick, James J. Southern case for school segregation. 1962. 3.95. Crowell-
    Collier
Knapp, Robert B. Social integration in urban communities. 1960. 5.75. T.C.
Maston, T. B. Segregation and desegregation: A Christian approach. 3.50.
    Macmillan
McGill, Ralph E. Church, a school. 1959. 2.00. Abingdon
Miller, Arthur S. Racial discrimination and private education. 3.50. U. of N. C.
National Conference of Social Work. Minority groups: Segregation and integration.
    1955. 2.25. Columbia
O'Neill, Joseph E. Catholic case against segregation. 3.95. Macmillan
Tilson, Charles Everett. Segregation and the Bible. 1958. 2.50. Abingdon
Ziegler, Benjamin M. Desegregation and the Supreme Court. pap. 1.50. Heath
SELF (171.3)
Dorsey, John M. Growth of self-insight. 1962. 5.00. Wayne
Dorsey, John M., and Walter H. Seegers. Living consciously: The science of
    self. 1960. 4.95. Wayne
Harding, M. E. Journey into self. 1956. 5.00. McKay
Jung, G. G. Undiscovered self. 1958. 3.50. Little
Mead, George H. Mind, self, and society: From the standpoint of a social be-
    haviorist. by Charles W. Morris. 1934. 6.75. U. of Chicago
Moustakas, Clark E. Self: Explorations in personal growth. 1956. 5.00. Harper
Niebuhr, Reinhold. Self and the dramas of history. 1955. 3.75. Scribner
Strauss, Anselm. Mirrors and masks: The search for identity. 1959. 4.00.
    Free Press
Symonds, Percival M. Ego and the self. 1951. 2.50. Appleton

Sypher, Wylie. Loss of the self in modern literature and art. 1962. 4.00. Random
Wylie, Ruth C. Self concept: A critical survey of pertinent research literature.
    4.50. U. of Nebr.
SELF-GOVERNMENT (IN EDUCATION) (371.59)
Carr, A. J. Student participation in college policy determination and administration.
    1959. 1.25. Am. Assn. of Colleges for Teacher Educ.
Klopf, Gordon John. College student government. 1960. 3.50. Harper
Lunn, Harry H., Jr. Student's role in college policy-making. 1957. 1.00. A.C.E.
National Education Association, American Association of Colleges for Teacher
    Education. Student participation in college policy determination and administra-
    tion. 1959. 1.25. N.E.A.
SELF-INCRIMINATION (323.4)
Griswold, Erwin N. 5th Amendment today. 1955. 2.00. Harvard
Harding, Arthur L. Fundamental law in criminal prosecution. 1959. 3.00. S.M.U.
Maguire, John M.. Evidence of guilt. 1959. 12.50. Little
Rogge, O. John. First and the fifth, with some excursions into others. 1960. 8.50.
    Nelson
SEMANTICS (422)
Berlo, David K. Process of communication: An introduction to theory and practice.
    1960. 4.25. Holt, Rinehart & Winston
Black, Max. Language and philosophy: Studies in method. il. 1949. 3.50. Cornell
Carnap, Rudolf. Introduction to semantics and formalization of logic. 1959. 7.00.
    Harvard
Garey, Doris B. Putting words in their places. 1957. 3.75. Scott
Johnson, Wendell. People in quandaries: The semantics of personal adjustment.
    1946. 6.50. Harper
Johnson, Wendell. Your most enchanted listener. 1956. 4.50. Harper
Keene, Geoffrey B. Language and reasoning. 1961. 2.75. Van Nostrand
Linsky, Leonard. Semantics and the philosophy of language. 1952. 4.50. U. of Ill.
Morris, Charles. Signs, languages, and behavior. 1955. 5.00. Braziller
Naess, A. Democracy, idealogy and objectivity. pap. 4.50. Humanities
Nesbit, Francis F. Language, meaning and reality. 1955. 3.00. Exposition
Schaff, A. Introduction to semantics. 1962. 10.00. Pergamon
Searles, Herbert L. Logic and scientific methods. 1956. 4.50. Ronald
Sherwood, John C. Discourse of reason. 1960. pap. 1.25. Harper
Sondel, Bess. Humanity of words: A primer of semantics. 4.00. World Pub.
Tarski, Alfred. Logic, semantics, metamathematics. tr. by J. H. Woodger. 1956.
    9.60. Oxford U. P.
Thurman, Kelly. Semantics. 1960. pap. 1.75. Houghton
Ullmann, Stephen. Semantics: Introduction to the science of meaning. 1962. 6.50.
    Barnes & Noble
Upton, Albert. Design for thinking. il. 1961. 5.00. Stanford
Wilson, John. Language and the pursuit of truth. 1956. 1.95. Cambridge U. P.
Ziff, Paul. Semantic analysis. 1960. 5.00. Cornell
SEMICONDUCTORS (537.622)
Dunlap, W. C. Introduction to semiconductors. 1957. 11.75. Wiley
Gottieb, I. Fundamentals of transitor physics. il. pap. 3.90. Rider
Hannay, Norman B. Semiconductors. il. 1959. 15.00. Reinhold
Hunter, L. P. Handbook of semiconductor electronics. 1962. 18.50. McGraw
Schwartz, S. Selected semiconductor circuits handbook. 13.00. Wiley
Shepherd, Alan D. Introduction to the theory and practice semiconductors. il.
    1959. 4.75. Ungar
Shive, J. N. Properties, physics, and design of semiconductor devices. il. 1959.
    9.75. Van Nostrand
Turner, Rufus P. Semiconductors devices. il. 1961. 7.50. Holt, Rinehart & Winston
Valdes, L. B. Physical theory of transitors. 1961. 10.50. McGraw
Warschauer, Douglas M. Semiconductors and transitors. 1959. 7.50. McGraw
SEMIOLOGY (616.072)
Birch, C. Allan. Common symptoms described and explained for nurses. il. 1953.
    2.50. Williams & Wilkins

Chamberlain, E. Noble. Symptoms and signs of clinical medicine. 1961. 9.00. Williams & Wilkins

MacBryde, Cyril M. Signs and symptoms: Applied pathologic physilogy and their clinical interpretation. il. 1957. 12.00. Lippincott

Modell, Walter. Relief of symptoms. 1961. 11.50. Mosby

SENSES AND SENSATION (612.8)

Armstrong, D. M. Bodily sensations. 3.00. Humanities

Buddenbrock, Wolfgang von. Senses. il. 1958. 4.00. U. of Mich.

Carthy, J. D. Introduction to the behavior of invertebrates. il. 1959. 8.00. Macmillan

Geldard, F. A. Human senses. 1953. 6.50. Wiley

Pieron, Henri. Sensations: Their functions, processes, and mechanisms. tr. by M. H. Pirenne, and B. C. Abbott. il. 1952. 6.50. Yale

Rosenblith, W. Sensory communication. 1961. 16.00. Wiley

Wyburn, G. M. Nervous system. il. 1960. 5.00. Academic Press

SERBIA (949.71)

Vucinich, Wayne S. Serbia between East and West. 1954. pap. 4.75. Stanford

West, Rebecca. Black lamb and grey falcon. il. 1941. 6.95. Viking

SERMONS (252)

Butler, G. Paul. Best sermons. 1962. 5.95. Van Nostrand

Frost, S. E., Jr. World's great sermons. 2.95. Doubleday

McArthur, Harvey K. Understanding the Sermon on the Mount. 1960. 3.50. Harper

Pink, Arthur W. Sermon on the Mount. 4.95. Baker Bk.

SERVOMECHANISMS (629.83)

Ahrendt, William R., and C. J. Savant, Jr. Servomechanism practice. 1960. 13.00. McGraw

Davis, Sidney A., and Byron K. Legerwood. Electromechanical components for servomechanisms. 1961. 11.50. McGraw

Gibson, J. E., and F. Tuteur. Control system components. 1958. 13.00. McGraw

Gille, J. C., and others. Feedback control systems. 1959. 17.00. McGraw

James, Hubert M., and others. Theory of servomechanisms. il. 1947. 9.50. McGraw

Lauer, Henri, and others. Servomechanism fundamentals. 1960. 10.00. McGraw

Murphy, Gordon J. Basic automatic control theory. il. 1957. 10.75. Van Nostrand

Truxal, J. G. Control engineer's handbook. 1958. 22.50. McGraw (R)

Tyers, A., and R. B. Miles. Principles of servomechanisms. il. 1960. 6.50. Pitman

SETON, ERNEST THOMPSON, 1860-1946 (925)

Garst, Shannon, and Warren. Ernest Thompson Seton, naturalist. 1959. 3.25. Messner

SEVENTEENTH CENTURY (909.6)

Clark, G. N. War and society in the 17th century. 1958. 3.50. Cambridge U. P.

Coleridge, Samuel Taylor. Coleridge on the seventeenth century. 1955. 12.50. Duke

Cruttwell, P. Shakespearean moment and its place in the poetry of the seventeenth century. 1955. 3.75. Columbia

Mazzeo, Joseph A. Reason and the imagination. il. 1962. 6.50. Columbia

Nussbaum, Frederick L. Triumph of science and reason: 1660-1685 (Rise of modern Europe) il. 1953. 6.00. Harper

Rhys, H. Seventeenth-century science and the arts. 1961. 3.00. Princeton

Willey, B. Seventeenth century background. 1942. 5.00. Columbia

SEWAGE DISPOSAL (628.74)

American Public Health Association. Standard methods for the examination of water and wastewater. 1960. 10.00. Am. Pub. Health

Babbitt, Harold E. Sewerage and sewage treatment. 1958. 11.25. Wiley

Steel, Ernest W. Water supply and sewerage. 1960. 11.00. McGraw

SEWING (646.2)

Bishop, Edna B., and others. Fashion sewing by the Bishop method. il. 2.75. Lippincott

Carter, Meg. McCall's 1001 questions on sewing. il. 1961. 2.95. Putnam
Duncan, Ida Riley. American woman's complete sewing book. 3.95. Tudor
Hollen, Norma R. Flat pattern methods with selected sewing suggestions. il. 1961. 3.60. Burgess
McCalls. McCall's new complete book of sewing and dressmaking. il. 1957. 5.95. Hawthorn
Picken, Mary B. Singer sewing book. 4.95. Grosset
Ryan, Mildred Graves. Sew smartly. il. 1956. 3.50. Scribner
Spears, R. W. Home decoration with fabric and thread. 1940. 3.50. Barrows
Talbot, C., and Isabelle Stevenson. Complete book of sewing. 1955. 4.95. Hawthorn

SEX (136.1)
Baruch, Dorothy. New ways in sex education. il. 1959. 4.75. McGraw
Child Study Association. What to tell your children about sex. 1961. 1.50. Arco
Crow, Lester D., and Alice. Sex Education for the growing family. 1959. 4.00. Christopher
Davis, Maxine. Sex and the adolescent. 1958. 5.00. Dial
Dickerson, Roy E. So youth may know. 1948. 3.00. Assn. Pr.
Dreyfus, Alfred. Information, please: For women only. 1960. 7.50. Vantage
Duvall, Evelyn M. Facts of life and love. 1956. 3.50. Assn. Pr.
Duvall, Sylvanus M. Before you marry. 1959. 3.50. Assn. Press
Ellis, Albert. American sexual tragedy. 5.00. Twayne
Ellis, Havelock. Psychology of sex. 3.95. Emerson
Jung, G. G. Psychology of the unconscious. 5.00. Dodd
Jung, Carl G. Symbols of transformation. 1956. 5.00. Pantheon
Kinsey, Alfred C., and others. Sexual behavior in the human female. il. 1953. 8.00. Saunders
Kinsey, Alfred C., and others. Sexual behavior in the human male. il. 1948. 7.50. Saunders
Lawrence, D. H. Sex, literature, and censorship. 3.00. Twayne
Malinowski, B. Sex and repression in savage society. 4.50. Humanities
Menninger, William C., and others. How to understand the opposite sex. 1956. 2.95. Sterling
Reik, Theodor. Sex in man and woman. 1960. 4.50. Farrar, Straus
Shultz, Gladys Denny. Letters to Jane. 1960. 3.95. Lippincott
Stone, Hannah M., and Abraham. Marriage manual. 1952. 4.95. S. and S.
Strain, Frances B. New patterns in sex teaching. 1951. 2.95. Meredith

SHAKESPEARE, WILLIAM, 1564-1616 (822.33)
Adams, J. Q. Life of William Shakespeare. 6.00. Houghton
Barber, Cesar L. Shakespeare's festive comedy. 1959. 5.00. Princeton
Bartlett, Terrell. Man of Stratford: A defense of Shakespeare's authorship. 3.50. Nay
Benezet, Louis P. Six loves of Shakespeare. 1958. 3.00. Pageant
Bentley, Gerald E. Shakespeare: A biographical handbook. 1961. 4.00. Yale
Blumenthal, Walter H. Paging Mr. Shakespeare. 1961. 6.00. Univ. Pub.
British Academy. Aspects of Shakespeare. 1933. 4.00. Oxford U. P.
Brown, J. R. Shakespeare and his comedies. 3.75. Hillary
Campbell, Lily B. Shakespeare's tragic heroes - slaves of passion. 1960. 4.00. Smith, Peter
Chambers, E. K., and Charles Williams. Short life of Shakespeare: With the sources. il. 1933. 2.00. Oxford U. P.
Chambers, Edmund K. William Shakespeare: A study of facts and problems. il. 2 vols. 1930. 12.00. Oxford U. P.
Chute, Marchette. Shakespeare of London. 5.95. Dutton
Clark, E. T. Satirical comedy: Love's Labour's Lost. 2.50. Smith, Richard R.
Coe, Charles N. Shakespeare's villains. 3.00. Twayne
Coles, Blanche. Shakespeare's four giants. 3.00. Smith, Richard R.
Craig, Hardin. Interpretation of Shakespeare. pap. 4.00. Lucas Bros.
Craig, Hardin. New look at Shakespeare's quartos. 1961. 3.50. Stanford
Drinkwater, John. Shakespeare. il. 1.50. Macmillan

Ebisch, Walther, and L. L. Schucking. Shakespeare bibliography. 1931. 4.50.
  Oxford U. P.
Evans, Bertrand. Shakespeare's comedies. 1960. 7.20. Oxford U. P.
Feuillerat, A. Composition of Shakespeare's plays. 1953. 5.00. Yale
Friedman, William F., and Elizebeth S. Shakespearean ciphers examined. 1957.
  5.00. Cambridge U. P.
Gibson, H. N. Shakespeare claimants. 1962. 6.00. Barnes & Noble
Goldsmith, Robert H. Wise fools in Shakespeare. 1955. 3.50. Mich. State
Gordon, George S. Shakespearian comedy, and other studies. 1944. 2.00. Oxford
  U. P.
Granville-Barker, H., and G. B. Harrison. Companion to Shakespeare studies.
  1934. 5.50. Cambridge U. P.
Halliday, F. E. Life of Shakespeare. il. 1961. 5.00. Yoseloff
Halliday, F. E. Shakespeare: A pictorial biography. il. 1957. 5.95. Viking
Halliday, F. E. Shakespeare and his critics. 1952. 6.50. Bentley
Harbage, A. Shakespeare's audience. 1941. 3.00. Columbia
Harrison, G. B. Introducing Shakespeare. 1939. pap; 0.85. Penguin
Hazlitt, William. Characters of Shakespeare's plays. 1.95. Dutton
Holzknecht, Karl J. Backgrounds of Shakespeare's plays. 6.00. Am. Bk. Co.
Jaggard, William. Shakespeare bibliography. il. 1959. 12.50. Ungar
Jepsen, Laura. Ethical aspects of tragedy. 1953. 3.75. U. of Fla.
 Kirschbaum, Leo. Character and characterization in Shakespeare. 1962. 4.00.
  Wayne
Knight, G. Wilson. Sovereign flower. 1953. 6.00. Barnes & Noble
Lamborn, E. A. G., and G. B. Harrison. Shakespeare, the man and his stage.
  1924. 1.40. Oxford U. P.
Lawrence, William W. Shakespeare's problem comedies. 1959. 5.00. Ungar
Lewis, Benjamin Roland. Shakespeare documents. Facsimiles, transliterations,
  translations, and commentary. 2 vols. 35.00. Stanford
McCurdy, H. G. Personality of Shakespeare. 1953. 5.00. Yale
McMichael, George, and Edgar M. Glenn. Shakespeare and his rivals. 1962. pap.
  1.95. Odyssey
Ogburn, Dorothy, and Charlton, Jr. Shake-Speare: The real man behind the name.
  il. 1962. 4.50. Morrow
Ornstein, Robert. Discussions of Shakespeare's problem comedies. 1961. pap. 1.40.
  Heath
Palmer, John. Comic characters of Shakespeare. 3.50. St. Martins
Palmer, John. Political and comic characters of Shakespeare. 1962. pap. 4.75.
  St. Martins
Palmer, John. Political characters of Shakespeare. 1945. 4.75. St. Martins
Parrott, Thomas Marc. William Shakespeare: A handbook. 1955. Scribner (R)
Parrott, Thomas M. William Shakespeare: A handbook. 1955. 3.50. Smith, Peter
Pearson, Hesketh. Life of Shakespeare. 1961. 5.00. Walker
Pitcher, Seymour M. Case for Shakespeare's authorship of the famous victories.
  il. 1960. 6.00. Univ. Pub.
Priestley, J. B., and O. B. Davis. Four English biographies. il. 1961. 3.60.
  teacher's manual gratis on request. Harcourt
Ralli, A. History of Shakesperian criticism. 2 vols. 17.50. Humanities
Reese, Max M. Shakespeare: His world and his work. 1953. 7.50. St. Martins
Schucking, L. L. Character problems in Shakespeare's plays. 4.00. Smith, Peter
Smith, David N. Shakespeare criticism: A selection. 2.75. Oxford U. P.
Smith, Gordon R. Classified Shakespeare bibliography. vol. 1. 1962. 12.50. Penn.
  State
Spencer, Theodore. Shakespeare and the nature of man. 1949. 5.00. Macmillan
Spivack, B. Shakespeare and the allegory of evil. 1958. 7.50. Columbia
Stokes, F. G. Dictionary of the characters and proper names in the works of
  Shakespeare. 6.75. Smith, Peter
Tillyard, Eustace M. W. Nature of comedy and Shakespeare. 1958. 1.00. Oxford
  U. P.

Traversi, Derek. Shakespeare: The early comedies. 1960. pap. 0.50. British Bk.
Wadsworth, Frank W. Poacher from Stratford. il. 1958. 4.50. U. of Calif.
Wilson, John Dover. Essential Shakespeare. 1932. 2.50. Cambridge U. P.
Wilson, John Dover. Fortunes of Falstaff. 1943. 3.00. Cambridge U. P.
SHAKESPEARE, WILLIAM--CRITICISM AND INTERPRETATION (822.33)
Bartlett, John. Complete concordance of Shakespeare. 22.50. St. Martins
Bradbrook, M. C. Shakespeare and Elizabethan poetry. 1952. 3.40. Oxford U. P.
Brown, Ivor. Shakespeare in his time. il. 1960. 4.50. Nelson
Bradley, Andrew C. Oxford lectures on poetry. 4.00. St. Martins
Bush, Geoffrey. Shakespeare and the natural condition. 1956. 3.00. Harvard
Chambers, Edmund K. William Shakespeare: A study of facts and problems. il. 2 vols. 1930. 12.00. Oxford U. P.
Chambers, E. K. Shakespeare, a survey. 4.50. Macmillan
Charlton, H. B. Shakespearian comedy. 4.50. Macmillan
Charlton, Henry B. Shakespearian tragedy. 1948. 4.75. Cambridge U. P.
Coleridge, Samuel Taylor. Shakespearean criticism. 1.95 ea. Dutton
Cragi, Hardin. Introduction to Shakespeare. 1952. 2.95. Scott
Crane, Milton. Shakespeare's prose. 1951. 3.50. U. of Chicago
Cruttwell, P. Shakespearean moment and its place in the poetry of the seventeenth century. 1955. 3.75. Columbia
Dean, Leonard F. Shakespeare, modern essays in criticism. 4.25. Smith, Peter
Dowden, Edward. Shakespeare, his mind and art. 1962. pap. 1.45. Putnam
Draper, John W. Stratford to Dogberry: Studies in Shakespeare's earlier plays. 1961. 3.00. U. of Pittsburgh
Goddard, Harold C. Meaning of Shakespeare. 1951. 10.00. U. of Chicago
Granville-Barker H., and G. B. Harrison. Companion to Shakespeare studies. 1934. 5.50. Cambridge U. P.
Granville-Barker, H. Prefaces to Shakespeare. 2 vols. 1947. 6.00 ea. Princeton
Halliday, F. E. Enjoyment of Shakespeare. 1952. 2.00. Bentley
Harbage, Alfred E. Shakespeare and the rival traditions. 1952. 6.00. Macmillan
Harrison, G. B. Shakespeare at work, 1592-1603. 1958. pap. 1.75. U. of Mich.
Holzknecht, Karl J. Backgrounds of Shakespeare's plays. 6.00. Am. Bk. Co.
Johnson, Samuel. Johnson on Shakespeare. 1908. 1.70. Oxford U. P.
Knights, Lionel C. Some Shakespearean themes. 1960. 3.50. Stanford
Lanier, Sidney. Shakespeare and his forerunners. by Kemp Malone. 6.00. Johns Hopkins
Lawrence, William W. Shakespeare's problem comedies. 1959. 5.00. Ungar
Neilson, William A., and A. H. Thorndike. Facts about Shakespeare. 1.95. Macmillan
Nicoll, Allardyce. Shakespeare. 1952. 1.20. Oxford U. P.
Nicol, Allardyce. Shakespeare survey. 1949-1962. vols. 3-10 5.50 ea. Cambridge U. P.
Parker, M. D. H. Slave of life: Shakespeare and the idea of justice. 4.00. Hillary
Quiller-Couch, Arthur T. Shakespearean workmanship. 1931. 2.50. Cambridge U. P.
Ralli, Augustus. History of Shakesperian criticism. 2 vols. 17.50. Humanities
Ridley, M. R. William Shakespeare: A commentary. 1936. 1.45. Dutton
Rossiter, A. P. Angel with horns and other lectures on Shakespeare. 1961. 5.50. Theatre Arts
Sewell, Arthur. Character and society in Shakespeare. 1951. 2.90. Oxford U. P.
Shaw, George Bernard. Shaw on Shakespeare. 1961. 4.50. Dutton
Simpson, Percy. Studies in Elizabethan drama. 4.50. Oxford U. P.
Stoll, Elmer E. Shakespeare studies. 1959. 6.50. Ungar
Tillyard, Eustace M. W. Shakespeare's last plays. 2.00. Hillary
Tillyard, Eustace M. W. Shakespeare's problem plays. il. 1949. 2.50. U. of Toronto
Traversi, Derek A. Approach to Shakespeare. 1956. pap. 0.95. Doubleday
Van Doren, Mark. Shakespeare. 1953. pap. 0.95. Doubleday
Wilson, John Dover. Essential Shakespeare. 1932. 2.50. Cambridge U. P.
Wilson, John Dover. Life in Shakespeare's England. 1913. 2.00. Cambridge U. P.
Wilson, John Dover. Through Elizabethan eyes. 1939. 0.90. Cambridge U. P.

SHAKESPEARE, WILLIAM--DICTIONARIES, INDEXES, ETC. (822.33)
Baker, Arthur E. Shakespeare commentary. 2 vols. 1957. 15.00. Ungar
Browning, D. C. Dictionary of Shakespeare quotations. 1954. 3.95. Dutton (R)
Cowden-Clarke, Charles, and Mary. Shakespeare key. 2 vols. 12.50. Ungar
Partridge, Eric. Shakespeare's bawdy. 1947. 5.00. Dutton
Stokes, F. G. Dictionary of the characters and proper names in the works of
    Shakespeare. 6.75. Smith, Peter
SHAKESPEARE, WILLIAM--SOURCES (822.33)
Armour, Richard. Twisted tales from Shakespeare. 1957. 3.50. McGraw
Baldwin, Thomas W. On the literary genetics of Shakespeare's plays, 1592-1594.
    1959. 8.50. U. of Ill.
Beckerman, Bernard. Shakespeare at the Globe, 1599-1609. 1962. 5.95. Macmillan
Blackmur, R. P., and others. Riddle of Shakespeare's sonnets. 1962. 5.75. Basic
    Books
Bullough, Geoffrey. Narrative and dramatic sources of Shakespeare. 4 vols.
    vol. 1. Early comedies, poems, Romeo and Juliet. 1957; vol. 2. Comedies,
    1597-1603, 1958; vol. 3. Histories. 1958; vol. 4. Later English history play.
    7.50 ea. Columbia
Campbell, Lily B. Shakespeare's histories: Mirrors of Elizabethan policy. 1958.
    7.50. Huntington Lib.
Clarkson, Paul S., and Clyde T. Warren. Law of property in Shakespeare and the
    Elizabethan drama. 1942. 3.50. Johns Hopkins
Clemen, W. H. Development of Shakespeare's imagery. 1951. 3.25. Harvard
Curry, Walter Clyde. Shakespeare's philosophical patterns. 1959. 5.00. La.
    State
Deutsch, Babette. Reader's Shakespeare. 1946. 5.00. Messner
Harbage, Alfred. As they liked it, a study of Shakespeare's moral artistry. 3.50.
    Smith, Peter
Harbage, A. Shakespeare's audience. 1941. 3.00. Columbia
Holinshed, Raphael. Holinshed's chronicle as used in Shakespeare's plays. 1.95.
    Dutton
Hubler, Edward L. Sense of Shakespeare's sonnets. pap. 1.25. Hill & Wang
Joseph, Bertram. Acting Shakespeare. 4.75. Theatre Arts
Jorgensen, Paul A. Redeeming Shakespeare's words. 1962. 3.50. U. of Calif.
Kokeritz, Helge. Shakespeare's pronunciation. 1953. 8.50. Yale (R)
Lamborn, E. A. G., and G. B. Harrison. Shakespeare, the man and his stage.
    1924. 1.40. Oxford U. P.
Lanier, Sidney. Shakespeare and his forerunners. by Kemp Malone. 6.00. Johns
    Hopkins
Leishman, J. B. Themes and variations in Shakespeare's sonnets. 6.00. Hillary
Lewis, William D. Shakespeare said it. 1961. 6.50. Syracuse
McSpadden, J. Walker. Shakespearean synopses. 1959. 2.95. Crowell
McSpadden, J. Walker. Shakespeare's plays in digest form. pap. 1.25. Apollo
Magill, Lewis M., and N. A. Ault. Synopses of Shakespeare's plays. 1952. pap.
    1.25. Littlefield
Mahood, M. M. Shakespeare's wordplay. 3.75. Hillary
Miriam Joseph, Sister. Shakespeare's use of the arts of language. 1947. 3.75.
    Columbia
Moulton, Richard G. Shakespeare as a dramatic artist. 1906. pap. 1.50. Dover
Muir, K. Shakespeare's sources: Vol. 1. Comedies and tragedies. 5.00. Hillary
Nagler, Alois M. Shakespeare's stage. il. 1958. 2.00. Yale
Reese, Max M. Cease majesty: A study of Shakespeare's history plays. 1962.
    8.00. St. Martins
Sanders, Gerald. Shakespeare primer. 1960. pap. 2.00. Holt, Rinehart & Winston
Shackford, Martha H. Shakespeare, Sophocles. 3.00. Twayne
Speaight, Robert. Nature in Shakespearian tragedy. pap. 0.95. Collier
Spencer, T. J. B. Tyranny of Shakespeare. 1959. 0.85. Oxford U. P.
Spurgeon, C. Shakespeare's imagery. 1952. 7.50. Cambridge U. P.

Stoll, Elmer E. Art and artifice in Shakespeare. 1962. 3.75. Barnes & Noble
Thorndike, Ashley H. Shakespeare's theatre. il. 1916. 5.50. Macmillan
Tillyard, E. M. W. Shakespeare's history plays. 1946. 4.50. Macmillan
Watson, C. B. Shakespeare and the Renaissance concept of honor. 1960. 7.50. Princeton
Webster, Margaret. Shakespeare without tears. 1955. 4.50. World Pub.
Whitaker, Virgil K. Shakespeare's use of learning: An inquiry into the growth of his mind and art. 1953. 6.50. Huntington Lib.
Willcock, G. D. Language and poetry in Shakespeare's early plays. 1954. 0.85. Oxford U. P.
Wilson, John Dover, and Thomas C. Worsley. Shakespeare's histories at Stratford. 1951. il. 3.75. Theatre Arts

SHAKESPEARE, WILLIAM--TRAGEDIES (822.33)
Bradley, Andrew C. Shakespearean tragedy. 1956. 4.75. St. Martins
Conklin, Paul S. History of Hamlet criticism, 1601-1821. 5.00. Humanities
Grebanier, Bernard D. Heart of Hamlet. 1960. pap. 3.75. Crowell
Hankins, John Erskine. Character of Hamlet and other essays. 1941. 3.50. U. of N. C.
Halliday, F. E. Poetry of Shakespeare's plays. 1954. 4.00. Bentley
Harrison, G. B. Shakespeare's tragedies. 1952. 4.00. Oxford U. P.
Kitto, Humphrey D. F. Form and meaning in drama. 1957. 6.00. Barnes & Noble
Knight, George Wilson. Wheel of fire: Interpretation of Shakespeare's tragedies. 5.00. Macmillan
Knights, Lionel C. Approach to Hamlet. 1961. 2.75. Stanford
Lawlor, John. Tragic sense in Shakespeare. 1960. 3.75. Harcourt
Leavenworth, Russell E. Interpreting Hamlet. 1960. pap. 2.25. Chandler Pub.
Levenson, Jacob C. Discussions of Hamlet. 1960. pap. 1.40. Heath
Levin, Harry. Question of Hamlet. 1959. 3.75. Oxford U. P.
Lokse, O. Outrageous fortune; critical studies in Hamlet and King Lear. pap. 3.75. Humanities
McCutchan, J. Wilson. Macbeth. 1962. pap. 1.95. Barnes & Noble
Markels, Julian. Shakespeare's Julius Caesar. 1961. pap. 1.95. Scribner
Muir, Kenneth. Shakespeare and the tragic pattern. 1959. 0.85. Oxford U. P.
Ribner, Irving. Patterns in Shakespearian tragedy. 1960. 4.50. Barnes & Noble
Rosen, William. Shakespeare and the craft of tragedy. 1960. 4.75. Harvard
Rosenberg, Marvin. Masks of Othello. 1961. 5.00. U. of Calif.
Siegel, Paul N. Shakespearean tragedy and the Elizabethan compromise. 1957. 5.00. N. Y. U.
Stirling, B. Unity in Shakespearian tragedy. 1956. 3.75. Columbia
Wilson, Harold S. On the design of Shakespearian tragedy. 1957. 5.00. U. of Toronto
Wilson, John Dover. What happens in Hamlet. 1951. 5.50. Cambridge U. P.

SHARKS (597.31)
Helm, Thomas. Shark: Unpredictable killer of the sea. il. 4.00. Dodd
Senning, W. C. Laboratory studies in comparative anatomy. 1937. 4.25; outline drawings, 4.75. McGraw

SHAW, GEORGE BERNARD, 1856-1950 (928.23)
Bentley, Eric. Bernard Shaw. 1947. pap. 1.25. New Directions
Ervine, St. John. Bernard Shaw: His life, work and friends. il. 1956. 7.50. Morrow
Henderson, Archibald. George Bernard Shaw: Man of the century. 1956. 12.00. Meredith
Kozelka, Paul. Glossary to the plays of Bernard Shaw. 1959. pap. 1.50. T. C.
Kronenberger, Louis. G. B. Shaw: A critical survey. 1957. 6.00. World Pub.
Norwood, Gilbert. Euripides and Shaw. 2.50. Humphries
Pearson, Hesketh. G. B. S.: A full length portrait, and G. B. S.: A postscript. 1952. il. 6.00. Harper
Shenfield, Margaret. Bernard Shaw: A pictorial biography. il. 1962. 5.95. Viking

SHEEP (636.3)

Kammlade, William G., and William G., Jr. Sheep science. il. 1955. 7.95.
   Lippincott
McKinney, John. Sheep book. il. 1959. 4.96. Wiley

SHEET-METAL WORK (671.82)

Anderson. Problems in elementary sheet metalwork. il. 1959. 3.80. Taplinger
Betterley, M. L. Sheet metal drafting. 1961. 6.50. McGraw
Blackburn, R. G., and J. Cassidy. Sheet metal work: vol. 1, Geometry and pattern
   development, 4.00; vol. 2, Calculations and science, 1957. 3.00. St. Martins
Broemel, Louis, and J._S. Daugherty. Sheet metal workers' manual. 5.00. Drake,
   F. J.
Bruce, Leroy F. Sheet metal shop practice. il. 1959. 4.50; study guide, 1.25.
   Am. Tech. Soc.
Daugherty, James S. Sheet metal drafting and shop problems. 1959. 6.00. Bennett
Giachino, J. W. Basic sheet-metal practice. il. 1952. 5.00. Van Nostrand
Meyer, Leo A. Sheet metal layout. 1961. 5.25. McGraw
Smith, Robert E. Sheet metalwork. 1959. pap. 1.40. Taplinger
Stieri, Emanuele. Sheet metal principles and procedures. 1953. 7.28. Prentice-
   Hall
Strasser, Federico. Practical design of sheet metal stampings. il. 1959. 10.00.
   Chilton

SHELLEY, PERCY BYSSHE, 1792-1822 (928)

Baker, Carlos. Shelley's major poetry. 1961. 7.50. Russell
Bloom, Harold. Shelley's mythmaking. 1959. 5.00. Yale
King-Hele, Desmond. Shelley: The man and the poet. 2.95. Yoseloff
Marshall, William H. Byron, Shelley, Hunt, and the Liberal. 1960. 5.00. U. of Pa.
Maurois, Andre. Ariel: The life of Shelley. 3.75. Ungar
Rogers, Neville. Keats, Shelley and Rome. il. 1961. 2.75. Ungar
Rogers, Neville. Shelley at work: A critical inquiry. 1956. 6.10. Oxford U. P.
White, Newman Ivey. Portrait of Shelley. 1945. 5.75. Knopf

SHELLS (594)

Abbott, R. Tucker. Sea shells of the world. by Herbert S. Zim. il. 1962. 3.50.
   Golden Press
Cameron, Roderick. Shells. 1961. 3.95. Putnam
Morris, Percy A. Field guide to the shells of our Atlantic and Gulf coasts. il.
   1951. 4.50. Houghton (R)
Robert, Paul A. Wonders of the sea shells. il. 1945. 4.00. Oxford U. P.
Rogers, Julia E. Shell book. 1951. 8.50. Branford
Verrill, A. Hyatt. Shell collector's handbook. il. 1950. 4.00. Putnam
Verrill, A. Hyatt. Strange sea shells and their stories. 1936. 4.00. Farrar, Straus

SHERIDAN, PHILIP HENRY, 1831-1888 (923.5)

Rister, Carl Coke. Border command: General Phil Sheridan in the West. il. 1944.
   3.75. U. of Okla.
Stackpole, Edward James. Sheridan in the Shenandoah: Jubal Early's disaster.
   il. 1961. 5.95. Stackpole

SHERIDAN, RICHARD BRINSLEY BUTLER, 1751-1816 (923.5)

Gibbs, Lewis. Richard Brinsley Sheridan. il. 5.00. Saifer
Sherwin, Oscar. Uncorking old sherry: Richard Brinsley Sheridan. 6.00. Twayne

SHERMAN, WILLIAM TECUMSEH, 1820-1891 (923.5)

Athearn, Robert G. William Tecumseh Sherman and the settlement of the West.
   il. 1956. 5.00. U. of Okla.
Lewis, Lloyd. Sherman, fighting prophet. il. 1958. 6.95. Harcourt
Sherman, William T. Memoirs of General William T. Sherman. 1957. 8.00.
   Indiana

SHERMAN'S MARCH THROUGH THE CAROLINAS (973.738)

Barrett, John G. Sherman's march through the Carolinas. 1956. 6.00. U. of N. C.
Gibson, John M. Those 163 days: A Southern account of Sherman's march from
   Atlanta to Raleigh. il. 5.75. Coward

SHIPPING (387.54)

Gorter, Wytze, and George H. Hildebrand. Pacific coast maritime shipping industry, 1930-1948. 2 vols. il. vol. 1. An economic profile. 1952. 2.50; vol. 2. Analysis of performance. 1954. 5.00. U. of Calif.

Horn, Paul V., and Henry Gomez. International trade principles and practices. 10.60. Prentice-Hall

McDowell, Carl E., and Helen M. Gibbs. Ocean transportation. il. 1954. 8.95. McGraw

McPhedran, Marie. Cargoes on the Great Lakes. 2.75. Bobbs

Newell, Gordon, and Joe Williamson. Pacific steamboats. il. 10.00. Superior Pub. Co.

Rydell, Raymond A. Cape Horn to the Pacific: The rise and decline of an ocean highway. 1952. 4.00. U. of Calif.

Scull, Penrose. Great ships around the world. il. 1960. 5.95. Barnes, A.S.

Tute, Warren. Atlantic conquest: The men and ships of the glorious age of steam. il. 1962. 5.95. Little

Villiers, Alan. Way of a ship. il. 10.00. Scribner

SHIPS (387)

Bloomster, E. L. Sailing and small craft down the ages. il. 1957. 6.50. U.S. Naval Ins

Church, Albert C. Whale ships and whaling. il. 1960. 8.50. Norton

Dunn, Laurence. Ship recognition: Merchant ships. 1961. 3.50. De Graff

Ellis, C. Hamilton. Picture history of ships. il. 6.95. Macmillan

Landstrom, Bjorn. Ship: An illustrated history. il. 1961. 14.95. Doubleday

SHIPS IN ART (743.8)

Aylward, William A. Ships and how to draw them. 1950. pap. 1.00. Pitman

Leszczynski, Michal. How to draw sail and sea. il. 1944. 1.70. Viking

Soderberg, Y. E. Drawing boats and ships. 1959. pap. 1.00. Pitman

Watson, Ernest W. Boats and harbors (vol. 3. Course in pencil sketching). 1957. 2.95. Reinhold

SHIPWRECKS (910.453)

Duffy, J. Shipwreck and empire: Being an account of Portuguese maritime disasters in a century of decline. il. 1955. 4.00. Harvard

Hoehling, Adolf A. They sailed into oblivion. 1959. 2.95. Yoseloff

Porges, Irwin. Many brave hearts: True tales of heroism at sea. il. 1962. 3.95. Chilton

Ratigan, William. Great Lakes shipwrecks and survivals. 1960. 6.00. Eerdmans

Singer, Kurt D., and Jane Sherrod. Great adventures of the sea. 1962. 4.95. Denison

Villiers, Alan. Posted missing. il. 1956. 4.75. Scribner

SHOP MATHEMATICS (510)

Camm, F. J. Workshop calculations, tables and formulae. 1959. 3.00. Transatlantic

Felker, Charles A. Shop mathematics. 1955. 3.60. answer book. 0.30. Bruce

Graham, Frank D. Machinists and toolmakers handbook. 6.00. Audel

McMackin, Frank J., and John H. Shaver. Mathematics of the shops. il. 1947. 4.20. Van Nostrand

Stout, C. E. Shop mathematics. 1955. 4.00. Wiley

Wilson, J. Douglas, and Clell M. Rogers. Carpentry mathematics. il. 1949. 4.40. McGraw

Wolfe, John H., and E. R. Phelps. Practical shop mathematics. 2 vols. vol. 1. Elementary. 1959. 5.20; vol. 2. Advanced. 5.20; answer keys. 0.50 ea. McGraw

SHORT STORIES (808.831)

Ashmun, Margaret. Modern short stories. 4.50. Macmillan

Barrows, Herbert. 15 stories. 1950. 2.20; suggestions for teaching 15 stories. pap. 0.40. Heath

Blair, Thomas M. H. Fifty modern stories. 1960. 5.25. Harper

Booth, Michael R., and Clinton S. Burhans, Jr. Thirty-one stories. 1960. pap. 3.95. Prentice-Hall

Brewster, Dorothy. Book of modern short stories. pap. 3.25. Macmillan
Brooks, Cleanth, Jr., and Robert Penn Warren. Scope of fiction. 1960. 2.75.
   Appleton
Buckler, William E., and Arnold Sklare. Stories from six authors. 1960. 4.25.
   McGraw
Burnett, Whit, and Hallie. Story: Magazine of the short story in book form.
   Story no. 1. 1951; no. 2. 1952; no. 3. 1952; no. 4. 1953. 3.00 ea. Wyn
Canby, Henry Seidel, and Robeson Bailey. Book of the short story. 3.50. Appleton
Cerf, Bennett. Great modern short stories. pap. 1.45. Vintage
Clark, Barrett H., and Maxim Lieber. Great short stories, of the world. 5.75.
   World Pub.
Cook, Dorothy E., and Isabel S. Monro. Short story index. 1953. 14.00. suppl.
   1950-1954. 1956. 5.00; suppl. 1955-58. 1960. 6.00. Wilson (R)
Current-Garcia, Eugene, and Walton R. Patrick. What is the short story? 1961.
   softbound 2.95. Scott
Davis, Robert Gorham. Ten modern masters. 1959. 4.25; instructor's manual,
   gratis on request. Harcourt
Eaton, Harold T. Short stories for study and enjoyment. 1960. 3.00. Odyssey
Elwood, Maren. Write the short short. 1947. 4.50. Writer
Fidell, Estelle A., and Esther B. Flory. Short story index supplement 1955-1958.
   1960. 6.00. Wilson (R)
Foley, Martha, and David Burnett. Best American short stories, 1961. 5.50.
   Houghton
Frakes, R., and I. Traschen. Short fiction, a critical collection. 1959. 3.95.
   Prentice-Hall
Fumento, Rocco. Introduction to the short story: An anthology. 1962. 4.75. Ronald
Gettmann, Royal A., and Bruce Harkness. Book of stories. 1955. 2.00. Rinehart
Gilkes, Lillian, and Warren Bower. Short story craft. 4.50. Macmillan'
Goodman, Roger. 75 short masterpieces. pap. 0.60. Bantam
Gordon, Caroline, and Allen Tate. House of fiction. pap. 3.25. Scribner
Great Jewish short stories. pap. 0.75. Dell
Great modern short stories. 1.95. Modern Lib.
Hamalian, Leo, and Edmond L. Volpe. Great stories by Nobel prize winners. 1959.
   5.00. Farrar, Straus
Hart, Nina, and Edna M. Perry. Representative short stories. by Moffet. il. 1930.
   2.56. Macmillan
Haydn, Hiram, and John Cournos. World of great stories. 1947. pap. 1.95. Crown
Heilman, Robert B. Modern short stories: A critical anthology. 1950. 8.95.
   Harcourt
Hemingway, Ernest. Men at war. pap. 0.75. Berkley
Hopkins, Joseph G. E. Scribner treasury. 1953. 6.00. Scribner
Jaffe, Adrian H., and Virgil Scott. Studies in the short story. 1960. pap. 3.25.
   Holt, Rinehart & Winston
Jarrell, Randall. Anchor book of stories: An anthology. 1958. pap. 1.45. Doubleday
Kesten, Hermann. Blue Flower. 5.00. Roy Pub.
Kielty, Bernardine. Treasury of short stories. 1947. 6.00. S. and S.
Kimball, R. A. Short story reader. 1961. 3.00. Odyssey
Laughton, C. Tell me a story. 1957. 6.00. McGraw
Lynskey, Winifred. Reading modern fiction. 1957. pap. 2.95. Scribner
McClennen, Joshua. Masters and masterpieces of the short story. 1957. pap. 2.50.
   2nd series. 1960. pap. 2.85. Holt, Rinehart & Winston
Male, Roy R. Types of short fiction. 1962. pap. 3.95. Wadsworth
Millett, Fred. Reading fiction. 1950. 3.00. Harper
Mizener, Arthur. Modern short stories. 1962. 2.95. Norton
Neider, Charles. Short stories from the world's literature. 1950. pap. 3.75. Holt,
   Rinehart & Winston
O'Faolain, Sean. Short stories: Study in pleasure. 1961. pap. 2.95. Little
Peden, William. Twenty-nine stories. 1960. pap. 2.25. Houghton
Perrine, Laurence. Story and structure. 1959. 2.95. Harcourt

Pugh, Cynthia Ann. Book of short stories. 1941. 4.25. Macmillan
Schorer, Mark. Story: A critical anthology. 1950. 6.00. Prentice-Hall
Schramm, Wilbur. Great short stories. 1950. 2.64. Harcourt
Schweikert, H. C. Short stories. 1934. 2.40. Harcourt
Short, Raymond W., and Richard B. Sewall. Short stories for study. 1956. 4.25.
 Holt, Rinehart & Winston
Short stories - tradition and direction: An anthology. 3.00. New Directions
Short story. 3 vols. 1958. 4.50; 1959. 4.50; 1960. 4.50. Scribner
Singleton, Ralph. Two and twenty: A collection of short stories. 1962. 4.00.
 St. Martins
Stegner, Wallace, and others. Writer's art: A collection of short stories. 1950.
 3.65. Heath
Summers, Richard. Craft of the short story. 1948. 5.50. Rinehart
Thurston, Jarvis A. Reading modern short stories. 1955. 2.95. Scott
Walker, Warren S. Twentieth-century short story explication. 1961. 9.00. Shoe
 String
West, Ray B., Jr., and Robert Wooster Stallman. Art of modern fiction. 1949. 5.75.
 Holt, Rinehart & Winston
Winter's tales. 7 vols. vol. 1, o.p; vols. 2 and 4, 3.75 ea; vol. 3. 4.50; vol. 5,
 4.25; vol. 6, 4.75; vol. 7, Stories from modern Russia. by C. P. Snow and
 Pamela H. Johnson. 4.95. St. Martins

SHORT STORIES, AMERICAN (808.831)

Baudin, Maurice, Jr. Contemporary short stories. 3 vols. 4.00. Bobbs
Burrell, Angus, and Bennett Cerf. Anthology of famous American stories. 1953.
 2.95. Modern Lib.
Cerf, Bennett. Encyclopedia of modern American humor. il. 1954. 3.95. Doubleday
Cerf, Bennett. Modern American short stories. 3.50. World Pub.
Current-Garcis, Eugene, and Walton R. Patrick. American short stories. 1952.
 2.95. Scott
Day, A. Grove. Greatest American short stories. il. 1953. 4.75. McGraw
Fenton, Charles A. Best short stories of World War II: An American anthology.
 1957. 5.95. Viking
First prize stories: From the O. Henry memorial awards 1919-1960. 3.95. Double-
 day
Foley, Martha, and David Burnett. Best American short stories: 1961. pap. 0.75.
 Ballantine
Foley, Martha, and David Burnett. Best of the best. 1952. 5.00. Houghton
Gold, Herbert. Fiction of the Fifties. pap. 0.95. Doubleday
Great tales of the American West. 1.95. Modern Lib.
Hathaway, Baxter, and John A. Sessions. Writers for tomorrow. series. 3.00.
 Cornell
Havighurst, Walter E. Masters of the modern short story. 1945. 5.50. Harcourt
Hopper, Vincent F. Classic American short stories. 2.95. Barron's
Linscott, R. N. Best American humorous short stories. 1.95. Modern Lib.
Ludwig, Jack B., and W. Richard Poirier. Stories: British and American. 3.50.
 Houghton
Mikels, Rosa Mary. Short stories for English courses. study guides by Helen
 T. Munn. 1960. 3.00. Scribner
New Yorker. Fifty-five short stories from the New Yorker. 1940-1949. 1949. 5.00.
 S. and S.
New Yorker. Stories from the New Yorker. 1950-1960. 1960. 7.50. S. and S.
Pattee, Fred Lewis. American short stories. 1936. 3.50. Dodd
Pattee, Fred Lewis. Century readings in the American short story. 1927. 5.50.
 Appleton
Rideout, Walter B., and James K. Robinson. College book of modern fiction.
 1961. 6.50. Harper
Ross, Danforth R. American short story. 1961. pap. 0.65. U. of Minn.
Saturday Evening Post. Saturday Evening Post stories. 2 vols. 1962 7.45.
 Doubleday

Simpson, Claude M. Local colorists: American short stories, 1857-1900. 1960.
   pap. 2. 95. Harper
Stegner, Mary, and Wallace. Great American short stories. pap. 0. 75. Dell
Turner, Arlin. Southern stories. 1960. pap. 1. 25. Holt, Rinehart & Winston
Waite, Harlow O., and Benjamin P. Atkinson. Stories from Literature for our
   time. 1959. pap. 2. 50. Holt, Rinehart & Winston
Warren, Robert Penn, and Albert Erskine. Short story masterpieces. pap. 0. 75.
   Dell'
West, Ray B., Jr. American short stories. 1960. 5. 95. Crowell
West, Ray B. Short story in America. pap. 1. 25. Regnery
Wood, William R., and John D. Husband. Short stories as you like them. 1940.
   2. 28. Harcourt
Wright, Austin M. American short story in the twenties. 1961. 7. 50. U. of Chicago
SHORT STORIES, ENGLISH - -TRANSLATIONS (823. 08)
Anthology of famous British stories. 2. 95. Modern Lib.
Bree, Germaine. Great French short stories. pap. 0. 50. Dell
English short stories. 15th to 20th Centuries. 1. 95. Dutton
French, J. L. Great Russian short stories. 1960. 5. 95. Tudor
French short stories of the 19th and 20th centuries. 1. 95. 1961. Dutton
Geist, Stanley. French stories and tales. 1961. pap. 0. 45. Washington Square
Graham, Stephen. Great Russian short stories. 1960. 5. 95. Liveright
Great Spanish stories. 1. 95. Modern Lib.
Howe, Irving, and Eliezer Greenberg. Treasury of Yiddish stories. il. 1954.
   5. 95. Viking
Isherwood, Christopher. Great English short stories. 1957. pap. 0. 50. Dell
Johnson, Ben. Stories of modern Italy. 1. 95. Modern Lib.
Kahn, Sholom J. Whole loaf. Stories from Israel. 1962. 4. 95. Vanguard
Kamen, Isai. Great Russian stories. pap. 1. 25. Vintage
Kapp, Yvonne. Short stories of Russia today. 1958. 3. 50. Houghton
Lu, Hsun. Old tales retold. 1961. pap. 1. 00. China
Morris, Ivan. Modern Japanese stories, an anthology. 6. 50. Tuttle
Onis, Harriet de. Spanish stories and tales. 1954. 4. 50. Knopf
Ordon, Edmund. Ten contemporary Polish stories. 1958. 5. 00. Wayne
Yarmolinsky, Avrahm. Soviet short stories. pap. 1. 45. Doubleday
SHORT STORIES, FRENCH (843. 08)
Eyer, Cortland. Contemporary French short stories. 1949. 3. 50. Houghton
Fowlie, Wallace. French stories. bilingual, in French and English. pap. 0. 75.
   Bantam
French short stories of the 19th and 20th centuries. 1. 95. 1961. Dutton
Hall, Marie-Louise M. Nouvelles francaises. 1959. 2. 50. Odyssey
March, Harold. Types of French short story. 1941. 2. 75. Ronald
Meras, Edmond, and Andre Celieres. Contes populaires. 1938. 2. 56. Houghton
SHORT STORIES, GERMAN (833. 08)
Fleissner, Otto S., and E. M. Fleissner. Die Kunst der Prosa. 1941. 3. 25.
   Appleton
Lange, Victor. Great German short novels and stories. 1952. 1. 95. Modern Lib.
Puckett, Hugh W. Intermediate readings in German. 1938. 3. 75. Macmillan
Spender, Stephen. Great German short stories. pap. 0. 50. Dell
Steinhauer, Harry. Die deutsche Novelle. expanded ed. 1880-1950. 1958. 4. 50.
   Norton
SHORT STORIES, IRISH (891. 63)
Garrity, Devin. 44 Irish short stories. 5. 00. Devin
SHORT STORIES, LATIN AMERICAN (808. 831)
Arratia, Alejandro, and Carlos D. Hamilton. Diez cuentos hispanoamericanos.
   il. by Marjorie Auerbach. 1958. pap. 2. 75. Oxford U. P.
Colford, William E., tr. Classic Spanish-American short stories. 1962. 2. 95.
   Barron's
Eoff, Sherman H., and Paul C. King. Spanish American short stories. il. 1944.
   pap. 2. 00. Macmillan

Vazquez, Alberto. Cuentos de la America Espanola. 1952. 3. 00. McKay
Walsh, Donald D. Seis relatos americanos. 1943. pap. 2. 00. Norton
SHORT STORIES, RUSSIAN (891. 73)
Guerney, B. G. New Russian stories. 1952. 3. 75. New Directions
Seltzer, Thomas. Best Russian short stories. 1. 95. Modern Lib.
Townsend, Rochelle. Russian short stories. 1. 95. 1961. Dutton
Yarmolinsky, Avrahm. Treasury of great Russian short stories. 1944. 9. 75.
    Macmillan
SHORT STORIES, SPANISH (863. 08)
Anderson, Imbert, Enrique, and Lawrence B. Kiddle. Veinte cuentos espanoles
    del siglo xx. 1961. pap. 2. 75. Appleton
Arjona, Doris K. , and Edith Helman. Cuentos contemporaneos. pap. 2. 30. Norton
Ashburn, Robert R. Selected Spanish short stories. 1943. 3. 50. Crowell
Ashburn, Robert R. , and Francisco Herrera Y Sanchez. Selected Spanish short
    stories. 1957. 3. 50. Crowell
Cardona, Rodolfo. Novelistas espanoles de hoy. 1959. 3. 50. Norton
Olmsted, Richard H. , and Raymond L. Grismer. Spanish short stories. 1942.
    3. 75. Ronald
Tatum, Terrell. Cuentos recientes de Espana. 1960. 3. 35. Scribner
SHORT STORY (808. 31)
Barrows, Herbert. Reading the short story. (Introduction to literature, pt. 1)
    1959. pap. 2. 00. Houghton
Barry, Keith. Writing for profit. 1955. 1. 25. Assoc. Booksellers
Bates, H. E. Modern short story. 3. 50. Writer
Blackiston, Elliott. Short story writing for profit. 3. 00. Writer
Burnett, Whit, and Hallie. Makers of the modern short story. 1962. 5. 00.
    Hawthorn
Elwood, Maren. Write the short short. 1947. 4. 50. Writer
Gavin, Marian. Writing short stories for pleasure and profit. 3. 95. Writer
Kempton, Kenneth Payson. Short stories for study. 1953. 4. 75. Harvard
McCleary, Dorothy. Creative fiction writing. 3. 00. Writer
Mirrielees, Edith R. Story writing. 1947. 4. 00. Writer
O'Faolain, Sean. Short story. 3. 75. Devin
Thurston, Jarvis, and others. Short fiction criticism: A checklist of interpretation
    since 1925 of stories and novelettes (American, British, continental) 1800-1958.
    1959. 4. 00. Swallow, A.
Uzzell, Thomas H. , and Camelia W. Narrative technique: A practical course in
    literary psychology. 4. 75. Harcourt
SHORTHAND (653)
Epstein, Abraham, and Morris White. Shorthand, typewriting and secretarial
    training. 1. 00. Grosset
Gregg, John Robert, and others. Gregg speed building for colleges, simplified.
    1958. 5. 00. McGraw
Gregg, John Robert, and others. Gregg speed building simplified. 1957. 3. 88.
    McGraw
Gregg, John R. Gregg shorthand dictionary. 1930. 4. 00. McGraw
Gregg, John Robert, and others. Most-used shorthand words and phrases.
    simplified ed. 1949. 1. 64. McGraw
Gregg, John Robert, and others. Gregg speed building simplified: One-year
    course. 1951. 5. 36. McGraw
Horne, Berry H. Stenotype-stenograph reporting. 1962. 10. 00. Smith, Richard R.
Hosler, Russell J. , and others. Gregg transcription for colleges, simplified.
    1959. 4. 40; teacher's handbook, 1. 75; student's transcript. 1. 80. McGraw
Leslie, Louis A. , and Charles E. Zoubek. Graded transcribing tests in Gregg
    shorthand simplified. 1955. 1. 36; key. 1. 50. McGraw
Leslie, Louis A. Methods of teaching Gregg shorthand. 1953. 6. 75. McGraw
Leslie, Louis A. , and Charles E. Zoubek. Dictation for mailable transcripts.
    1950. 4. 50. McGraw

Linton, J. D., and L. J. Porter. Introduction to court reporting in Thomas natural shorthand. 1951. 5.00. Prentice-Hall

Modern business dictation. (Pitman shorthand) 1954. 3.00. Pitman

Pitman shorthand, new basic course. 1961. 3.00. Pitman

Pitman medical dictation. (Pitman shorthand) 1954. 3.00. Pitman

Practice in legal stenography. (Pitman shorthand) 1953. 3.00. Pitman

Smither, Effie B. Gregg medical shorthand manual and dictionary. 1953. 5.25. McGraw

Swem, Charles L., and John Robert Gregg. Gregg shorthand reporting course. il. 1936. 14.50. McGraw

Zoubek, Charles E., and Morris W. Rifkin. Gregg reporting shortcuts. 1959. 7.50. McGraw

SHOULDER (611.717)

Bateman, James. Shoulder and its environs. il. 1955. 12.50. Mosby

Saha, A. K. Theory of shoulder mechanism-descriptive and applied. il. 1961. 5.50. Thomas, C.C.

SHRUBS (635.976)

Benson, Lyman and Robert Darrow. Trees and shrubs of the Southwestern Deserts. il. 1954. pap. 8.50. U. of New Mex., or U. of Ariz.

Boltz, Howard O. Landscape use of shrubs and vines. 1958. 6.00. Educ. Pubs. Inc.

Cloud, Katharine M. P. Evergreen and flowering shrubs for your home. il. 1957. 4.95. Chilton

Cox, E.H.M., and P. S. Modern shrubs. 1959. 6.25. Nelson

Graves, Arthur Harmount. Illustrated guide to trees and shrubs. 1956. 6.50. Harper

Grimm, William C. Book of shrubs. 10.00. Stackpole

Hottes, Alfred C. Book of shrubs. il. 1952. 4.95. Dodd

Mathews, F. Schuyler. Field book of American trees and shrubs. il. 1915. 3.95. Putnam

Petrides, George A. Field guide to the trees and shrubs. il. 1958. 4.50. Houghton

Rehder, Alfred. Manual of cultivated trees and shrubs hardy in North America. 1940. 13.95. Macmillan

Whitehead, Stanley B. Book of flowering trees and shrubs. 3.50. Warne

SIBELIUS, JEAN, 1865-1957 (927)

Abraham, Gerald. Music of Sibelius. il. 1947. 4.50. Norton

Johnson, Harold E. Jean Sibelius. il. 1959. 5.00. Knopf

Ringbom, Nils-Eric. Jean Sibelius. tr. by G.I.C. DeCourcy. il. 1954. 3.75. U. of Okla.

SIBERIA (957)

Collins, Perry M. Siberian journey: Down the Amur to the Pacific, 1856-1857. 1962. 6.00. U. of Wis.

Golder, Frank A. Russian expansion on the Pacific: 1641-1850. 6.00. Smith, Peter

Kennan, George. Siberia and the exile system. 1958. 5.00. U. of Chicago

Lensen, George A. Russian push toward Japan: Russo-Japanese relations, 1697-1875. il. 1959. 10.00. Princeton

Sutzkevee, Abraham. Siberia. il. 1961. 5.00. Abelard

SICILY (945.8)

Brea, L. B. Sicily before the Greeks. il. 1958. 6.95. Praeger

Guercio, Francis M. Sicily. il. 1954. 7.50. Transatlantic

Levi, Carlo. Words are stones, impressions of Sicily. 1958. 3.75. Farrar, Straus

Matt, Leonard von, and Luigi Pareti. Ancient Sicily. 1960. 12.50. Universe

Runciman, Steven. Sicilian vespers. 1958. 5.50. Cambridge U. P.

SIDNEY, SIR PHILIP, 1554-1586 (923.8)

Judson, Alexander C. Sidney's appearance; A study in Elizabethan portraiture. il. 4.50. Indiana

SIGHT-READING (MUSIC) (780.77)

Berkowitz, Sol, and others. New approach to sight singing. 1960. 4.95. Norton

Deutsch, Leonhard. Piano sight-reading. 6.95. Nelson-Hall

Lieberman, Maurice. Ear training and sight singing. 1959. 5.25. Norton

McHose, Allen I., and Ruth N. Tibbs. Sight-singing manual. 1957. 3.75. Appleton

SIGNS AND SYMBOLS (419)

Koch, Rudolf. Book of signs. 1955. pap. 1.00. Dover

Lehner, Ernst. American symbols: A pictorial history. 1957. 3.50. Tudor

Lehner, Ernst. Picture book of symbols. 1956. 3.50. Tudor

Morris, Charles W. Foundations of the theory of signs. 1938. pap. 1.50. U. of Chicago

SILICON (546.683)

Berezhnoi, A. S. Silicon and its binary systems. 1960. 8.50. Consultants Bureau

Eaborn, C. Organosilicon compounds. 1959. 15.00. Academic Press

Eitel, Wilhelm. Physical chemistry of the silicates. il. 1954. 45.00. U. of Chicago

Hauser, Ernst. Colloidal phenomena. 1954. pap. 5.00. M.I.T.

Hauser, Ernst A. Silicic science. il. 1955. 6.75. Van Nostrand

Iler, Ralph K. Colloid chemistry of silica and silicates. il. 1955. 5.50. Cornell

Marshall, C. Edmund. Colloid chemistry of the silicate minerals. 1949. 6.80. Academic Press

Meals, Robert N., and Frederick M. Lewis. Silicones. 1959. 5.95. Reinhold

Rochow, Eugene G. Introduction to the chemistry of the silicones. 1951. 6.95. Wiley

SILVERSMITHING (739.23)

Abbey, Staton. Goldsmith's and silversmith's handbook. 1953. 5.00. Van Nostrand

Kovel, Ralph, and Terry H. Directory of American silver, pewter and silver plate. 5.95. Crown

Maryon, Herbert. Metalwork and enameling. il. 1955. 8.00. Dover

Stow, Millicent. American silver. 1950. 2.00. Barrows

SINGING (784.9)

Dodds, George. Voice placing and training exercises. 2 vols. 1927. Contralto and baritone pap. 2.00; Soprano and tenor pap. 2.00. Oxford U. P.

Fields, V. A. Training the singing voice. 1947. 6.00. Columbia

Gould, Herbert. Handbook for voice students. 2.75. Lucas Bros.

Greene, Harry Plunket. Interpretation in song. 3.50. St. Martins

Kagen, Sergius. On studying singing. pap. 1.25. Dover

Lawless, Ray M. Folksingers and folksongs in America. 1960. 10.00. Duell

Litante, Judith. Natural approach to singing. 1959. 4.00. Brown, W. C.

Mackworth-Young, Gerard. What happens in singing. 1956. 3.75. Pitman'

Matz, Jane M. Opera stars in the sun. 1955. 3.95. Farrar, Straus

Moore, Gerald. Singer and accompanist. 1954. 4.50. Macmillan

Reid, Cornelius L. Bel canto: Principles and practices. il. 1950. 4.50. Coleman-Ross

Scott, Charles K. Fundamentals of singing. 1954. 8.95. Pitman

Siegel, Al. How to become a professional singer. 4.95. Citadel

SINGLE TAX (336.226)

George, Henry. More progress and less poverty. by Joseph S. Thompson. 0.50. Schalkenbach

George, Henry. Progress and poverty. 1938. 1.95 Modern Lib.

George, Henry. Social problems. 1953. 1.50. Schalkenbach

Slocomb, Whitney. H. Mass production and money. 15.00. Forum

SIXTEENTH CENTURY (909.5)

Taylor, Henry O. Thought and expression in the sixteenth century. 2 vols. 1959. 9.00. Ungar

SKELETON (591.47)

Inkster, R. G.; and others. Anatomy of the locomotor system. 1956. 4.80. Oxford U. P.

Schlossberg, Leon. Human skeleton. 22.50. Johns Hopkins

SKEPTICISM (121.5)

Baumer, Franklin L. Religion and the rise of scepticism. 1960. 5.95. Harcourt

Bevan, Edwyn. Stoics and sceptics. 1959. 4.50. Barnes & Noble

Popkin, Richard H. History of scepticism and from Erasmus to Descartes. 6.00.
Humanities
Zeller, Eduard. Stoics, Epicureans and Sceptics. 1962. 12.50. Russell
SKIN (611.77)
Andrews, George C. Diseases of the skin. il. 1954. 13.00. Saunders
Behrman, Howard T., and Oscar L. Levin. Your skin and its care. il. 1948. 3.50.
Emerson
Montagna, William, and others. Advances in biology of skin. 2 vols. vol. 1,
Cutaneous innervation. 1960; vol. 2, Blood vessels and circulation. 1961. 10.00
ea; vol. 3. Eccrene sweat glands and eccrene sweating. in prep. Pergamon
Ormsby, Oliver S., and Hamilton Montgomery. Diseases of the skin. il. 1954.
22.00. Lea & F
Rothman, Stephen. Human integument. il. 1959. 6.75. A.A.A.S.
Sauer, Gordon C. Manual of skin diseases. 1959. 9.75. Lippincott
Solomons, Bethel, Jr. Synopsis of skin diseases. 1959. 6.75. Williams & Wilkins
Sutton, Richard L., Jr. Diseases of the skin. il. 1956. 29.50. Mosby
Wilkinson, Darrell S. Nursing and management of skin diseases. il. 1959. 5.75.
Macmillan
Wittkower, E., and B. Russell. Emotional factors in skin diseases. 4.00. Hoeber
Zelickson, Alvin S. Electron microscopy of human skin and oral mucous mem-
brane. in prep. Thomas, C.C.
SKIS AND SKIING (796.93)
Bracken, W. R. Handbook on skiing. 2.50. Branford
Bradley, David, and others. Expert skiing. il. 1960. 12.50. Holt, Rinehart &
Winston
Brown, Conrad. Skiing for beginners. il. 3.50. Scribner
Day, Frank. If you can walk, you can ski. 3.95. Crowell-Collier
Georg, Hans. Modern ski systems. il. 1954. 3.75. Hastings
Kramer, Franz. Ski the new way. il. 1960. 2.95. Sterling
Polasek, Ollie. Skiing. 3.95. Barnes, A.S.
Sports Illustrated. Sports Illustrated book of skiing. by the Editors of Sports
Illustrated. il. 1960. 2.95. Lippincott
SKITS, STUNTS, ETC. (793)
Brings, Lawrence M. Master stunt book. 1957. 3.95. Denison
Depew, Arthur M. Cokesbury stunt book. 1953. 2.95. Abingdon
Eisenberg, Helen and Larry. Fun with skits, stunts and stories. 1955. 2.95.
Assn. Pr.
Eisenberg, Helen and Larry. Handbook of skits and stunts. 1953. 2.95. Assn. Pr.
Howard, Vernon. Pantomimes, charades and skits. il. 1959. 2.50. Sterling
Ireland, Norma O. Index to skits and stunts. 1958. 8.00. Faxon
SKULL (611.714)
Brock, Samuel. Injuries of the brain and spinal cord. il. 1960. 18.50. Springer
Young, Barton R. Skull, sinuses and mastoids: A handbook of Roentgen diagnosis.
1948. 7.00. Year Bk.
SLAVERY (326)
Bancroft, Frederic. Slave trading in the old south. il. 1959. 7.00. Ungar
Barnes, G. H. Anti-slavery impulse (1830-1844) 4.00. Smith, Peter
Buckmaster, Henrietta. Let my people go. 1959. 4.00. Smith, Peter
Craven, Avery. Coming of the Civil War. 1957. 6.50. U. of Chicago
Davidson, Basil. Black Mother: The years of African slave trade. 1961. 6.50.
Little
Douglass, Frederick. Narrative of the life of Frederick Douglass, an American
slave. by Benjamin Quarles. il. 1960. 3.50. Harvard
Dumond, Dwight L. Antislavery origins of the Civil War in the United States. 1959.
4.40. U. of Mich.
Dumond, Dwight L. Antislavery: The crusade for freedom in America. il. 1961.
20.00. U. of Mich.
Elkins, Stanley M. Slavery. 1959. 4.50. U. of Chicago

Filler, Louis. Crusade against slavery. 1830-1860. il. 1960. 5.00. Harper
Fitzhugh, George, and Hinton R. Helper. Ante-bellum: Three classic writings on
    slavery in the old South. by Harvey Wish. 1960. 2.50. Putnam
Furnas, J. C. Goodbye to Uncle Tom. il. 1956. 6.00. Sloane
Furnas, J. C. Road to Harpers Ferry. 1959. 6.00. Sloane
Gara, Larry. Liberty line: The legend of the Underground Railroad. 1961. 5.00.
    U. of Ky.
Graebner, Norman A. Politics in the crisis of 1860. 1961. 3.00. U. of Ill.
Greenidge, C. W. W. Slavery. 4.50. Hillary
Howard, Warren S. American slavers and the federal law: A study in crime and
    punishment, 1837-1864. 1963. 6.50. U. of Calif.
Jenkins, William S. Pro-slavery thought in the old South. 1959. 5.50. Smith, Peter
Jernegan, Marcus W. Laboring and dependent classes in Colonial America, 1607-
    1783. 3.75. Ungar
Lader, Lawrence. Bold Brahmins. il. 1961. 5.00. Dutton
Mannix, Daniel P., and Malcolm Cowley. Black cargoes: A history of the Atlantic
    slave trade. il. 1962. 6.95. Viking
Mendelsohn, Isaac. Slavery in the ancient Near East. 1949. 5.00. Oxford U. P.
Muelder, Hermann R. Fighters for freedom. 6.50. Columbia
O'Callaghan, Sean. Slave trade today. 1962. bds. 3.95. Crown
Olmstead, Frederick Law. Cotton kingdom. by Arthur M. Schlesinger. 1953.
    7.50. Knopf
Olmstead, Frederick L. Slave states: Before the Civil War. 1959. 2.50. Putnam
Phillipps, U. B. American Negro slavery. 6.00. Smith, Peter
Phillips, Ulrich B. Life and labor in the old South. il. 1929. 6.00. Little
Sherrard, Owen A. Freedom from fear: The slave and his emancipation. 1961.
    3.95. St. Martins
Soulsby, Hugh G. Right of search and the slave trade in Anglo-American relations,
    1814-1862. 1933. 2.75. Johns Hopkins
Stowe, Harriet Beecher. Uncle Toms' cabin: Or, Life among the lowly. 1962.
    5.00. Harvard
Wertenbaker, Thomas J. Planters of colonial Virginia. 5.00. Russell
Williams, Eric. Capitalism and slavery. 6.50. Russell
Woodson, Carter G. Mind of the Negro as reflected in letters written during the
    crisis, 1800-1860. 1926. 10.00. Assoc. Publishers
Wookman, John. Journal. 1.95. Dutton
SLAVS (936.7)
Chubb, Thomas. Slavic peoples. il. 1962. 3.50. World Pub.
Dvornik, Francis. Slavs in European history and civilization. 1962. 15.00. Rutgers
Dvornik, Francis. Slavs: Their early history and civilization. (Survey of Slavic
    civilizations, vol. 2) 1956. 6.00. Am. Acad. of Arts & Sci.
SLEEP (612.8217)
Ciba Foundation. Nature of sleep. 1961. 10.00. Little
SLIDE-RULE (510.7823)
Arnold, J. N. Complete slide rule handbook. Principles and applications. 1962.
    2.45. Prentice-Hall
Arnold, Joseph N. Slide rule. 5.25. Prentice-Hall
Clark, John J. Slide rule and logarithmic tables. 1957. 3.00. Drake, F. J.
SLUMS (711.59)
Hemdahl, Reuel. Urban renewal. 1959. 8.00. Scarecrow
Kerr, Madeleine. People of Ship Street. 4.50. Humanities
Lubove, Roy. Progressives and the slums: Tenement house reform in New York
    City, 1890-1917. 1962. 6.00. U. of Pittsburgh
Millspaugh, Martin, and Gurney Breckenfeld. Human side of urban renewal. il.
    1960. 4.50. Washburn
Riis, Jacob A. How the other half lives. 1959. 3.25. Smith, Peter
SMALL BUSINESS (658.9)
Alexander-Frutschi, Marian Crites. Annotated bibliography on small industry
    development. 1959. 6.00. Free Press

Broom, H. N., and J. G. Longenecker. Small business management. 1961. 7.75. South-Western Pub.

Bunzel, John H. American small businessman. 1962. 3.95. Knopf

Carpenter, Walter H., and Edward Handler. Small business and pattern bargaining. 1961. pap. 3.00. Babson

Ellis, Jessie C. Small business bibliography. 1951. 6.00 net. Faxon

Grimshaw, Austin. Problems of the independent businessman. 1955. 6.95. instructors manual, 1.00. McGraw

Kahm, Harold S. Small business of your own. 1952. bds. 1.00. Ottenheimer

Lasser, Jacob K. How to run a small business. 1955. 6.00. McGraw

Liggett, Donald R. Small industry development organizations. 1959. 10.00. Free Press

Ostlund, Harry J., and Stanley C. Hollander. Small business is big business. 1956. pap. 1.00. U. of Minn.

Stepanek, Joseph E. Managers for small industry. il. 1960. 6.00. Free Press

Zeigler, Harmon, Jr. Politics of small business. 1961. 3.25. Pub. Affairs

SMALL GROUPS (301.151)

Cartwright, Dorwin, and Alvin Zander. Group dynamics: Research and theory. 1960. 7.25. Harper

Hare, A. Paul. Handbook of small group research. 1961. 10.00. Free Press

Hare, A. Paul, and others. Small groups: Studies in social interaction. 1955. 6.50. Knopf

Hoffmann, Randall W., and Robert Plutchik. Small-group discussion in orientation and teaching. 1959. 4.00. Putnam

King, Charles E. Sociology of small groups. 5.00. Pageant

National Education Association, Adult Education Service and National Association of Public School Adult Educators. Group development. 1961. 2.00. N. E. A.

National Education Association, Adult Education Service, and National Association of Public School Adult Educators. Issues in human relations training. 1962. 2.00. N. E. A.

Olmsted, Michael. Small group. 1.59. Random

Solomon, Herbert. Mathematical thinking in the measurement of behavior. 1959. 7.50. Free Press

Verba, Sidney. Small groups and political behavior. 1961. 6.00. Princeton

SMITH, ADAM, 1723-1790 (923)

Fay, C. R. Adam Smith and the Scotland of his day. 1956. 4.75. Cambridge U. P.

Franklin, Burt, and Francesco Cordasco. Adam Smith: A bibliographical checklist. 1950. 6.50. Franklin, B.

Johnson, Edgar A. J. Predecessors of Adam Smith: The growth of British economic thought. 1937. 8.50. Kelley

Montgomery, George S. Return of Adam Smith, 1949. 2.50. Caxton

Rae, John. Life of Adam Smith. 1895. 10.00. Kelley

SMITH, ALFRED EMMANUEL, 1873-1944 (923.2)

Farley, James A., and James C. G. Conniff. Governor Al Smith. il. 1959. 2.25. Farrar, Straus

Handlin, Oscar. Al Smith and his America. 1958. 3.75. Little

Silva, Ruth C. Rum, religion, and votes: 1928 re-examined. 1962. 5.00. Penn. State

SMITH, JOHN, 1580-1631 (923.9)

Smith, Bradford. Captain John Smith. 1956. 5.00. Lippincott

Wharton, Henry. Life of John Smith, English soldier. tr by Laura Polanyi Striker. 1957. 4.00. U. of N. C.

SMUTS, JAN CHRISTIAAN, 1870-1950. (923.2)

Smuts, J. C. Jan Christian Smuts: A biography. il. 1952. 6.00. Morrow

SNAKES (598.12)

Aymar, Brandt. Treasury of snake lore. 1956. 5.00. Chilton

Ditmars, Raymond L. Fieldbook of North American snakes. il. 1939. 4.95. Doubleday (R)

Ditmars, Raymond L. Snakes of the world. il. 1931. 6.95. Macmillan (R)

Kauffeld, Carl. Snakes and snake hunting. il. 1957. 3.95. Doubleday

Pope, Clifford H. Giant snakes. il. 1961. 6.95. Knopf

Pope, Clifford H. Snakes alive, and how they live. il. 1937. 4.50. Viking

Schmidt, Karl P. , and D. Dwight Davis. Field book of snakes of United States and Canada. il. 1941. 3.50. Putnam (R)

Wright, Albert Hazen, and Anna Allen. Handbook of snakes of the United States and Canada. 2 vols. il. 1957. 14.75. Cornell (R)

SOCIAL CASE WORK (301.24)

Aptekar, H. H. Dynamics of casework and counseling. 1955. 4.50. Houghton

Junker, Buford H. Field work: An introduction to the social sciences. 1960. pap. 3.50; U. of Chicago

National Conference on social Welfare: Casework papers. annual. pap. 2.50. Family Service Assn.

Nicholds, Elizabeth. Primer of social casework. 1960. 4.50. Columbia

Voiland, Alice L. , and others. Family casework diagnosis. 1962. 8.50. Columbia

SOCIAL CHANGE (301.24)

Allen, Francis R. , and others. Technology and social change. il. 7.00. Appleton

Bailey, Frederick G. Tribe, caste, and nation. il. 1960. 6.50. Humanities

De Vries, Egbert. Man in rapid social change. 4.50. Doubleday

Doob, Leonard W. Becoming more civilized: psychological exploration. 1960. 6.75. Yale

Erasmus, Charles J. Man takes control: Cultural development and American aid. 1961. 6.50. U. of Minn.

Ginzberg, Eli. Family and social change. 4.50. Columbia

Hagen, Everett E. On the theory of social change. 1962. 10.00. Dorsey

Hagbin, H. Ian. Social change. 1958. 4.50. Humanities

Loomis, Charles P. Social systems. 1960. 6.50. Van Nostrand

Mair, Lucy. Studies in social anthropology. 2.75. Humanities

Martindale, Don A. Social life and cultural change. 1962. 9.00. Van Nostrand

Millikan, Max F. , and Donald L. M. Blackmer. Emerging nations: Their growth and the U.S. policy. 1961. 4.50. Little

Nordskog, John E. Social change. il. 1960. 7.50. McGraw

Spicer, Edward H. Human problems in technological change. 1952. 4.00. Russell Sage

SOCIAL CLASSES (323.3)

Barber, Bernard. Social stratification: A comparative analysis of structure and process. 1957. 6.95. Harcourt

Bendix, Reinhard, and Seymour M. Lipset. Class, status and power: A reader in social stratification. 1953. 7.50. Free Press

Bergel, Egon E. Social stratification. 1962. 7.95. McGraw

Caplow, Theodore. Sociology of work. 1954. 5.00. U. of Minn.

Centers, Richard. Psychology of social classes. 1961. 6.00. Russell

Cole, G. D. H. Studies in class structure. 1955. 4.00. Humanities

Cuber, John F. , and William F. Kenkel. Social stratification in the United States. il. 1954. 4.00. Appleton

Edmonson, Munro S. Status terminology and the social structure of North American Indians. 1958. 3.00. U. of Wash.

Gordon, Milton M. Social class in American sociology. 1958. 6.00. Duke

Gough, J. W. Social contract. 1957. 4.80. Oxford U. P.

Halbwachs, Maurice. Psychology of social classes. 1958. 4.00. Free Press

Hollingshead, August B. , and Frederick C. Redlich. Social class and mental illness: A community study. 1958. 6.95. Wiley

Hughes, Everett C. Men and their work. 1958. 4.00. Free Press

Kahl, Joseph A. American class structure. 1957. 6.55. Holt, Rinehart & Winston

Kolko, Gabriel. Wealth and power in America: An analysis of social class and income distribution. 4.85. Praeger

Landis, Paul H. Social control. 1956. 6.95. Lippincott

Landtman, G. Origin of the inequality of the social classes. 5.50. Humanities

Montague, Joel B., Jr. Class and nationality. 1962. 4.00. Twayne
Pakcard, Vance O. Status seekers. 1959. 5.50. McKay'
Reissman, Leonard. Class in American society. 1959. 6.75. Free Press
Rousseau, Jean Jacques. Political writings. 1953. 3.00. Nelson
Rousseau, Jean Jacques. Social contract, and Discourses. 1950. 2.95. Dutton
Spiller, Robert E. Social control in a free society. 1960. 4.50. U. of Pa.
Warner, W. L. Social class in America. 1960. 3.75. Smith, Peter
Warner, W. L., and P. S. Lunt. Status system of a modern community. 1942.
  6.00. Yale
Warner, W. Lloyd, and others. Who shall be educated? 1944. 3.50. Harper
SOCIAL ETHICS (177)
Angell, Robert Cooley. Free Society and moral crisis. 1958. 6.00. U. of Mich.
Durkheim, Emile. Professional ethics and civic morals. 5.00. Free Press
Ginsberg, Morris. Essays in sociology and social philosophy. 3 vols. vol. 1,
  On diversity of morals; vol. 2, Reason and unreason in society; vol. 3,
  Evolution and progress. 1961. 4.00 ea. Macmillan
Habas, Ralph. Morals for moderns. 1939. 3.00. Liveright
Harris, Robert. Social ethics. 1962. 7.95. Lippincott
Niebuhr, Reinhold. Moral man and immoral society. 1932. 3.95. Scribner
Sorokin, Pitirim, and Walter Lunden. Power and morality. 3.50. Sargent
SOCIAL GROUPS (301.151)
Beal, George M., and others. Leadership and dynamic group action. il. 1962.
  6.00. Iowa State
Bion, W. R. Experiences in groups. 1961. 3.95. Basic Books
Bonner, Hubert. Group dynamics. 1959. 6.50. Ronald
Bowden, Edwin T. Dungeon of the heart. 3.75. Macmillan
Campbell, Angus, and Homer C. Cooper. Group differences in attitudes and votes.
  1956. 3.00. U. of Mich., Inst. for Soc. Res.
Cantril, Hadley. Politics of despair. 1958. 5.00. Basic Books
Caudwell, C. Studies in a dying culture. 3.00. Hillary
Coulton, George G. Medieval village, manor and monastery. 4.50. Smith, Peter
Coyle, Grace Longwell. Group work with American youth. 1948. 4.00. Harper
Dalton, Robert H. Personality and social interaction. 1961. 6.00. Heath
Dean, John P., and Alex Rosen. Manual of intergroup relations. 1955. 4.50. U.
  of Chicago
Elliott, Grace L. How to help groups make decisions. 1959. 1.00. Assn. Pr.
Ginger, Ray. American social thought. 1961. 4.00. Hill & Wang
Glanz, Edward C. Groups in guidance. il. 1962. 8.75. Allyn & Bacon
Gutkind, E. A. Revolution of environment. il. 1946. 6.00. Humanities
Homans, George C. Social behavior. il. 1961. 7.50. Harcourt
Hoselitz, Bert F. Sociological aspects of economic growth. 1959. 5.00. Free
  Press
Klein, Josephine. Study of groups. 5.00. Humanities
Knowles, Malcolm, and Hulda. Introduction to group dynamics. 1959. 2.50.
  Assn. Pr.
Lang, Kurt, and Gladys E. Collective dynamics. 1961. 7.25. Crowell
Leavis, Frank R. Culture and environment. 2.00. Hillary
Lifton, Walter M. Working with groups. 1961. 6.50. Wiley
Lowy, Louis. Adult education and group work. 1955. 4.50. Whiteside
Mumford, Lewis. Technics and civilization. 1934. 6.00. Harcourt
Reynolds, Robert L. Europe emerges: Transition toward an industrial world
  wide society. 600-1750. 1961. 7.50. U. of Wis.
Rose, Arnold. Human behavior and social processes. 1962. 7.25. Houghton
Sherif, Muzafer, and Carl I. Hovland. Social judgment. 1961. 6.00. Yale
Shibutani, Tamotsu. Society and personality. 1961. 7.95. Prentice-Hall
Smelser, Neil J. Theory of collective behavior. 1962. 6.50. Free Press
Thibaut, John W., and Harold H. Kelley. Social psychology of groups. il. 1959.
  6.00. Wiley
Trecker, Audrey R., and Harleigh B. How to work with groups. 1952. 3.50.
  Assn. Pr.

Trecker, Harleigh B. Group work: Foundations and frontiers. 1955. 5.00. Assn. Pr.

Warters, Jane. Group guidance. 1960. 6.50. McGraw

Webb, Walter Prescott. Great frontier. 1952. 6.00. Houghton

White, Ralph K., and Ronald O. Lippitt. Autocracy and democracy. 1960. 6.00. Harper

Wood, Margaret M. Paths of loneliness. 1953. 3.75. Columbia

SOCIAL PROBLEMS (301)

Banks, A. Leslie. Social aspects of disease. 1953. 4.50. Williams & Wilkins

Barnes, Harry Elmer. Society in transition. 1952. 7.00. Prentice-Hall

Barnes, Harry Elmer. Social institutions. 1942. 7.25. Prentice-Hall

Bernard, Jessie. Social problems at midcentury. 1957. 8.75. Holt, Rinehart & Winston

Bernard, Jessie, and Deborah N. Jensen. Sociology. 1962. 6.00. Mosby

Brandeis, Louis Dembitz. Social and economic views of Mr. Justice Brandies. 1930. 6.00. Vanguard

Bredemeier, Harry C., and Jackson Toby. Social problems in America: Costs and casualties in an acquisitive society. il. 1960. 6.75. Wiley'

Carlyle, Thomas. Past and present, John Knox, and Miscellanies. il. 3.50. Farrar, Straus

Chase, Stuart. Proper study of mankind. 1956. 4.50. Harper

Cuber, John F., and others. Problems of American society: Values in conflict. 1956. 5.50. Holt

Elliott, Mabel A., and Francis E. Merrill. Social desorganization. 1961. 8.50. Harper

Furfey, Paul H., and Mary E. Walsh. Social problems and social action. 1958. 6.95. Prentice-Hall

Galdston, Iago. Meaning of social medicine. 1954. 2.75. Harvard

Groves, Ernest R., and Gladys H. Contemporary American family. 1947. 6.00. Lippincott

Guerard, Albert Leon. Testament of a Liberal. 1956. 4.50. Harvard

Hayek, Friedrich A. von. Constitution of liberty. 1960. buck. 7.50. U. of Chicago

Hoyle, Fred. Man and materialism. 1956. 3.50. Harper

Huxley, Aldous. Ends and means. 1937. 5.50. Harper

Kane, John J. Social problems. il. 1962. 9.25. Prentice-Hall

Landis, Paul H. Social control. 1956. 6.95. Lippincott

Landis, Paul H. Social problems in nation and world il. 1959. 6.95. Lippincott

Lee, Elizabeth B., and Alfred M. Social problems in America: A source book. pap. 5.50. 1955. Holt, Rinehart & Winston

Lippmann, Walter. Good society. 1943. 5.00. Little

Lippmann, Walter. Preface to politics. 1962. 4.40. U. of Mich.

Millikan, Max F., and Donald L. M. Blackmer. Emerging nations: Their growth and the U.S. policy. 1961. 4.50. Little

Newcomb, Theodore M. Personality and social change. 1957. 4.25. Holt, Rinehart & Winston

Niebuhr, Reinhold. Love and justice: Selections from the shorter writings. by D. B. Robertson. 1957. 6.00. Westminster

Nordskog, John E., and others. Analyzing social problems. 1956. 6.50. Holt, Rinehart & Winston

Patterson, S. Howard, and others. Problems in American democracy. il. 1961. 5.32. Macmillan

Raab, Earl, and Gertrude Selznick. Major social problems. 1959. 6.50. Harper

Robinson, James Harvey. Mind in the making. 1921. 1.40. Harper

Sellew, Gladys, and Paul H. Furfey. Sociology and its use in nursing service. il. 1962. 5.75. Saunders

Sinclair, Upton. Cry for justice. 1962. 10.00. Stuart, Lyle

Tawney, Richard H. Acquisitive society. 1946. 3.00. Harcourt

Tolstoy, Leo. What then must we do? 2.75. Oxford U. P.

Toynbee, Philip. Underdogs: Anguish and anxiety. 1962. 4.50. Horizon

Weinberg, Samuel K. Social problems in our time. il. 1960. 6.95. Prentice-Hall
SOCIAL PSYCHOLOGY (301.15)
Arnold, Thurman W. Folklore of capitalism. 1937. 4.50. Yale
Barker, Roger G., and others. Adjustment to physical handicap and illness. 1953.
    Soc. Sci. Res.
Bogardus, Emory S. Leaders and leadership. 3.75. Appleton
Cartwright, Dorwin, and Alvin Zander. Group dynamics: Research and theory.
    1960. 7.25. Harper
Davis, Allison. Psychology of the child in the middle class. 1960. 1.85. U. of
    Pittsburgh
Dewey, John. Human nature and conduct. 1930. 1.95. Modern Lib.
Doob, Leonard W. Social psychology. 1952. 10.90. Holt, Rinehart & Winston
Follett, M.. Creative experience. 4.25. Smith, Peter
Freud, Sigmund. Civilization and its discontents. 1961. 3.75. Norton
Freud, Sigmund. Group psychology and the analysis of the ego. 2.75. Liveright
Fromm, Erich. Escape from freedom. 3.75. 1941. Rinehart
Fromm, Erich. Sane society. 1955. 5.00. Rinehart
Gordon, Richard E., and others. Split-level trap. 1961. 4.95. Random
Hoffer, Eric. True believer: Thoughts on the nature of mass movements. 1951.
    2.50. Harper
Homans, George C. Human group. il. 1950. 7.75. Harcourt
Jaspers, Karl. Man in the modern age. 3.00. Humanities
Klineberg, Otto. Social psychology. 1954. 9.45. Holt, Rinehart & Winston
Landis, Paul H. Social control. 1956. 6.95. Lippincott
Leighton, Alexander H. Introduction to social psychiatry. 1960. 4.75. Thomas, C.C.
Lewin, Kurt. Resolving social conflicts. by Gertrude Weiss Lewin. 1948. 4.00.
    Harper
Lindesmith, Alfred R., and Anselm Strauss. Social psychology. 1956. 6.25. Holt,
    Rinehart & Winston
Mackay, Charles. Extraordinary popular delusions and the madness of crowds.
    7.00. McGraw
Mannheim, Karl. Man and society in an age of reconstruction. 4.50. Harcourt
Marcel, Gabriel. Man against mass society. 1962. 1.95. Regnery
Marcuse, Herbert. Eros and civilization. 1956. 3.95. Beacon
Mead, George H. Mind, self, and society: From the standpoint of a social be-
    haviorist. by Charles W. Morris. 6.75. U. of Chicago
Newcomb, T. M. Social psychology. 1950. 6.95. Holt, Rinehart & Winston
Opler, Marvin K. Culture and mental health. 1959. 8.75. Macmillan
Robinson, James Harvey. Mind in the making. 1921. 1.40. Harper
Rose, Arnold. Mental health and mental disorder. 1955. 6.95. Norton
Sargent, Stephen S., and R. C. Williamson. Social psychology. 1958. 7.00. Ronald
Sherif, Muzafer, and Carolyn W. Outline of social psychology. 1956. 7.75. Harper
Sorokin, P. A. Man and society in calamity. 1942. 5.00. Dutton
Stoodley, Bartlett H. Society and self: A reader in social psychology. 1962. 7.50.
    Free Press
Tournier, Paul. Escape from loneliness. tr. by John S. Gilmour. 1962. 4.00.
    Westminster
Young, Kimball. Personality and problems of adjustment. il. 6.50. Appleton
Young, Kimball. Social psychology. il. 6.50. Appleton
SOCIAL SCIENCES (300)
Bonner, Thomas N., and others. Contemporary world: The social sciences in
    historical perspective. 1960. 8.75. Prentice-Hall
Chamberlin, Jo H. Careers for social scientists. il. 1961. 3.50. Walck
Chase, Stuart. Proper study of mankind. 1956. 4.50. Harper
Festinger, Leon, and Daniel Katz. Research methods in the behavioral sciences.
    1953. 6.75. Holt, Rinehart & Winston
Gross, Richard E., and Leslie D. Zeleny. Educating citizens for democracy.
    1958. 6.00. Oxford U. P.

Hunt, Elgin F. , and Jules Karlin. Society today and tomorrow: Readings in social science. 1961. pap. 3.95. Macmillan

Lazarsfeld, Paul F. , and Morris Rosenberg. Language of social research. 1955. 7.50. Free Press

Lerner, Daniel. Human meaning of the social sciences. 3.50. Smith, Peter

Lewin, Kurt. Field theory in social science. 1951. 5.00. Harper

McCormick, Thomas, and Roy G. Francis. Methods of research in the behavioral science. 1958. 4.50. Harper

Manis, Jerome G. , and Samuel I. Clark. Man and society. il. 1960. 7.50. Macmillan

Mayhew, Lewis B. Social science in general education. 1960. 4.50. Brown, W.C.

Seligman, Edwin B. A. , and Alvin Johnson. Encyclopedia of the social sciences. 8 vols. 110.00. Macmillan (R)

Tawney, R. H. Equality. 1961. pap. 1.35. Putnam

Weber, Max. From Max Weber: Essays in sociology. by Hans, H. Gerth, and C. Wright Mills. pap. 2.25. Oxford U. P.

Weinberg, O. , and M. Shabat. Society and man. 11.95. Prentice-Hall

White, Morton. Social thought in America. 3.75. Smith, Peter

Whitehead, Alfred North. Whitehead's American essays in social philosophy. by A. H. Johnson. 1959. 4.00. Harper

Zadrozny, John T. Dictionary of social science. 1958. 6.00. Pub. Affairs (R)

SOCIAL SURVEYS (309.1)

Hollingshead, A. B. Elmtown's youth. 1949. 5.50. Wiley

Warren, Roland L. Studying your community. 1955. 3.00. Russell Sage

SOCIALISM (335)

Beer, M. General history of Socialism and social struggles. 2 vols. 7.50. Russell

Blodgett, Ralph H. Comparative economic systems. 7.75. Macmillan

Cannon, James P. America's road to socialism. 0.35. Pioneer Publishers

Cheyney, Edward P. Modern English reform, from individualism to socialism. 1962. pap. 1.95. Barnes, A.S.

Colbert, Evelyn S. Left wing in Japanese politics. 1952. 4.50. Inst. of Pac. Rel.

Cole, George D. H. Socialist thought. 5 vols. vol. 1, Forerunners, 1789-1850. 6.50; vol. 2, Marxism and anarchism, 1850-1890. 1954. 6.75; vol. 3, Second international. 2 pts. 1956. 16.00; vol. 4, Communism and social democracy. 1914-1931. 2 pts. 14.50; vol. 5, Socialism and fascism, 1931-1939. 1960. 8.00. St. Martins

Cole, Margaret I. Story of Fabian socialism. il. 1961. 6.50. Stanford

Dorfman, Joseph. Thorstein Veblen and his America. 1934. 8.50. Kelley

Durkheim, Emile. Socialism. pap. 0.95. Collier

Durkheim, Emile. Socialism and Saint-Simon. 5.00. Antioch

Eastman, Max. Reflections on the failure of socialism. 1955. 3.00. Devin

Egbert, Donald D. , and S. Persons. Socialism and American life. 2 vols. 10.00 ea. Princeton

Engels, Friedrich. Socialism, utopian and scientific. 1935. 1.50. Int. Pubs.

Foster, William Z. Historic advance of world socialism. 1960. pap. 0.50. Int. Pubs.

Gay, Peter. Dilemma of democratic socialism: Eduard Bernstein's challenge to Marx. pap. 0.95. Collier

Haimson, L. H. Marxists and the origins of Bolshevism. il. 1955. 5.50. Harvard

Hook, Sidney. Marx and the Marxists. 1955. pap. 1.25. Van Nostrand

Hook, Sidney. Political power and personal freedom. 1959. 7.50. Criterion

Hoover, Calvin B. Economy, liberty, and the state. 1959. 5.00. Twentieth Century

Lenin, Vladimir I. State and revolution. pap. 0.75. Int. Pub.

Lichtheim, George. Marxism: A historical and critical study. 8.50. Praeger

Lipset, S. M. Agrarian socialism: The cooperative Commonwealth Federation in Saskatchewan. 1959. 5.50. U. of Calif.

Mackenzie, Norman. Socialism: A short history. 2.50. Hillary
Marx, Karl, and Friedrich Engels. Basic writings on politics and philosophy. by
    L. S. Feuer. 3.50. Smith, Peter
Marx, Karl. Communist manifesto. pap. 0.65. Regnery
Marx, Karl, and Friedrich Engels. German ideology. 4.00. Int. Pubs.
Mills, C. Wright. Marxists. pap. 0.75. Dell
Mises, Ludwig von. Socialism: An economic and social analysis. tr. by J. Kahane.
    1959. 10.00. Yale
Noyes, J. H. History of American socialisms. 12.50. Hillary
Perlman, Selig. Theory of the labor.movement. 1949. 3.50. Kelley
Pigou, Arthur C. Socialism versus capitalism. 1939. 2.00. St. Martins
Schapiro, J. Salwyn. Movements of social dissent in modern Europe. 1962. pap.
    1.25. Van Nostrand
Shaw, Bernard, and others. Fabian essays in socialism. 3.95. Macmillan
Sternberg, Fritz. Capitalism and socialism on trial. 1952. 7.00. Day
Sweezy, Paul M. Theory of capitalist development. 6.00. Monthly Review
Taylor, Overton H. Classical liberalism, Marxism, and the twentieth century.
    1960. 3.50. Harvard
Thomas, Norman. Socialist's faith. 1951. 5.50. Norton
Ulam, Adam B. Unfinished revolution. 1960. 5.00. Random
Wilson, Edmund. To the Finland station, a study in the writing and acting of
    history. 1959. 3.25. Smith, Peter
SOCIETY, PRIMITIVE (572)
Benedict, Ruth. Patterns of culture. 4.00. 1961. Houghton
Calas, Nicholas, and Margaret Mead. Primitive heritage. 1953. 5.00. Random
Engels, Friedrich. Origin of the family, private property and the state. 2.00.
    Int. Pubs.
Goldschmidt, Walter. Man's way. 1959. 4.00. World Pub.
Herskovits, Melville Jean. Cultural anthropology. il. 1955. 5.50. Knopf
Kardiner, A. Individual and his society. 1939. 6.50. Columbia
Lissner, Ivar. Man, God and magic. 1961. 5.95. Putnam
Lowie, Robert H. Primitive society. 1947. 3.95. Tudor
Malinowski, B. Crime and custom in savage society. 4.00. Humanities
Malinowski, B. Sex and repression in savage society. 4.50. Humanities
Mead, Margaret. Cooperation and competition among primitive peoples. 1961.
    pap. 2.95. Beacon
Mead, Margaret. From the South Seas: Studies of adolescence and sex in primitive
    societies. 1939. 5.00. Morrow
Mead, Margaret, and Frances C. Macgregor. Growth and culture. il. 1951. 7.50.
    Putnam
Murdock, George P. Our primitive contemporaries. il. 1934. 6.25. Macmillan
Radin, Paul. World of primitive man. 1953. 5.00. Abelard
Service, Elman R. Profile of primitive culture. 1958. 6.00. Harper
SOCIOLOGY (301)
American Sociological Society. Sociology today, problems and prospects. by
    Robert K. Merton, and others. il. 1959. 7.50. Basic Books
Arendt, Hannah. Human condition. 1958. 5.50. U. of Chicago
Ashley, Montagu, M. F. Direction of human development: Biological and social
    bases. 1955. 5.00. Harper
Ashley, Montagu, M. F. On being human. 1950. 2.50. Abelard
Bain, Read. Sociology, introductory readings. 1962. 4.75. Lippincott
Barnes, Harry E. Introduction to the history of sociology. 1948. 10.00. U. of
    Chicago
Barnes, Harry Elmer. Social institutions. 1942. 7.25. Prentice-Hall
Becker, Howard, and Alvin Boskoff. Modern sociological theory. 1957. 8.50.
    Holt, Rinehart & Winston
Bell, Earl H. Social foundations of human behavior. 1961. 7.00. Harper
Bierstedt, R. Social order. 1957. 7.25. McGraw

Biesanz, John B. , and Mavis. Modern society. 8.75. Prentice-Hall

Bogardus, E. S. Development of social thought. 1960. 6.00. McKay

Bogardus, Emory S. Sociology. 6.50. Macmillan

Brown, Francis J. Sociology: With application to nursing and health education. 1957. 10.00. Prentice-Hall

Cooley, Charles H. Social organization, and Human nature and the social order. 1955. 7.50. Free Press

Cuber, John F. Sociology, a synopsis of principles. il. 1959. 6.50. workbook and readings. by Theodore I. Lenn. pap. 2.40. Appleton

Cuber, John F. , and Peggy B. Haroff. Readings in sociology. 1962. pap. 1.95. Appleton

Durkheim, Emile. Sociology and philosophy. 1953. 3.50. Free Press

Elliott, Mabel A. , and Francis E. Merrill. Social disorganization. 1961. 8.50. Harper

Fairchild, Henry Pratt. Dictionary of sociology. 1956. pap. 1.95. Littlefield (R)

Gillin, John L. , and others. Social problems. 1952. 4.75. Appleton

Ginger, Ray. American social thought. 1961. 4.00. Hill & Wang

Gittler, J. B. Review of sociology. 1957. 10.95. Wiley

Green, Arnold W. Sociology. 1960. 7.50. McGraw

Hofstadter, Richard. Social Darwinism in American thought. 1959. 4.00. Braziller

Johnson, Harry Morton. Sociology. 1960. 7.25. Harcourt

Kimball, E. P. Sociology and education. 1932. 4.50. Columbia

Koenig, Samuel, and others. Sociology: A book of readings. 1953. 3.95. Prentice-Hall

Landis, P. H. Introductory sociology. 1958. 7.00. Ronald

Levy, Marion Joseph. Structure of society. 1952. 6.00. Princeton

Loomis, Charles P. Social systems. 1960. 6.50. Van Nostrand

Mannheim, Karl. Essays on the sociology of culture. 1956. 4.50. Oxford U. P.

Mannheim, Karl. Freedom, power and democratic planning. 1950. 6.50. Oxford U. P.

Mercer, Blaine E. Introduction to the study of society. il. 1959. 7.25. instructor's manual, gratis on request. Harcourt

Mills, C. Wright. Images of man. 1960. 7.50. Braziller

Mills, C. Wright. Sociological imagination. 1959. 6.00. Oxford U. P.

Nadel, S. F. Foundations of social anthropology. 1953. 7.50. Free Press

Nadel, S. F. Theory of social structure. 1957. 6.00. Free Press

O'Brien, R. W. , and others. Readings in general sociology. 3.75. Houghton

Ogburn, William F. , and Meyer F. Nimkoff. Sociology. 7.50. Houghton

Park, Robert E. Society. 1955. 5.00. Free Press

Parsons, Talcott. Social system. 1951. 7.50. Free Press

Parsons, Talcott. Structure of social action. 1958. 10.00. Free Press

Parsons, Talcott, and others. Theories of society. 2 vols. 1961. 25.00. Free Press

Quinn, James A. Living in social groups. il. 1962. 5.40. Lippincott

Ross, Eva J. Sociology and social problems. 1960. 3.96. Bruce

Roucek, Joseph S. Readings in contemporary American Sociology. 1962. pap. 2.25. Littlefield

Sellew, Gladys, and Paul H. Furfey. Sociology and its use in nursing service. il. 1962. 5.75. Saunders

Sorokin, Pitirim. Fads and foibles in modern sociology. 1956. 10.00. Regnery

Sorokin, Pitirim. Social and cultural mobility. 1959. 7.50. Free Press

Spencer, Herbert. Study of sociology. 4.40. 1961. U. of Mich.

Sutherland, Robert L. , and others. Introductory sociology. il. 1956. 6.50. Lippincott

Weber, Max. Basic concepts in sociology. 1961. 1.50. Citadel

Whitehead, Alfred N. Adventures of ideas. 1933. 5.00. Macmillan

Young, Kimball, and Raymond W. Mack. Sociology and social life. il. 6.00. Am. Bk. Co.

Young, Kimball, and Raymond W. Mack. Principles of sociology: A reader in theory and research. 3.75. Am. Bk. Co.

SOCIOLOGY, RURAL (301)

Bertrand, Alvin L. Rural sociology. 1958. 7.95. McGraw

Duncan, O. D., and A. J. Reiss. Social characteristics of urban and rural communities. 1950. 1956. 7.95. Wiley

Hatch, D. S. Toward freedom from want: From India to Mexico. il. 1949. 2.25. Oxford U. P.

Kolb, John H. Emerging rural communities: Group relations in rural society, a review of Wisconsin research in action. 1959. 4.50. U. of Wis.

Kolb, John H., and Edmund de S. Brunner. Study of rural society. 7.50. Houghton

Loomis, Charles P. Rural social systems and adult education. il. 1953. 5.00. Mich. State

Loomis, Charles P., and J. Allan Beegle. Rural sociology: The strategy of change. 1957. 9.65. Prentice-Hall

Rogers, Everett M. Social change in rural society. il. 1960. 6.75. Appleton

Slocum, Walter L. Agricultural sociology. 1962. 7.50. Harper

Smith, T. Lynn. Sociology of rural life. 1953. 6.50. Harper

Yang, M. C. Chinese village: Taitou, Shantung Province. 4.50. Columbia

SOCIOMETRY (370.193)

Evans, K. M. Sociometry and education. 3.75. Humanities

Gronlund, Norman E. Sociometry in the classroom. 1959. 4.50. Harper

Thorpe, Louis P., and others. Studying social relationships in the classroom. 1959. pap. 1.25. Sci. Res. Assoc.

SOCRATES (921.9)

Chroust, Anton-Hermann. Socrates, man and myth: The two Socratic apologies of Xenophon. 1958. 6.75. U. of Notre Dame

Levin, Richard. Question of Socrates. pap. 2.25. Harcourt

Plato. Portrait of Socrates: Being the Apology, Crito and Phaedo. by R. W. Livingstone. 1938. 2.00. Oxford U. P.

Plato, Trial and death of Socrates. 1903. 2.25. St. Martins

Taylor, Alfred E. Socrates. 1959. pap. 0.95. Doubleday

SOFTBALL (796.3578)

American Association for Health, Physical Education, and Recreation, Division for Girls' and Women's Sports. Official softball rules and guide. 1.00. Am. Assn. for Health, Phys. Ed., & Rec.

Kneer, Marian. Softball. 1962. 1.95. Sterling

Mitchell, A. V. Softball for girls. 1952. 2.95. Ronald

National Education Association, American Association for Health, Physical Education and Recreation. Softball-track and field: Sports guide. 1.00. N.E.A.

Noren, A. T. Softball. 1959. 3.50. Ronald

SOIL CONSERVATION (631.45)

Archer, Sellers G. Soil conservation. il. 1960. 3.75. U. of Okla.

Baver, L. D. Soil physics. 1956. 7.75. Wiley

Beasley, R. P., and J. C. Wooley. Farm water management for erosion control. 4.75. Lucas Bros.

Brinhart, Betty. Soil management and improvement. il. 1962. pap. 0.35. T.F.H.

Colman, Edward A. Vegetation and watershed management. 1953. 7.50. Ronald

Cook, Ray L. Soil management for conservation and production. il. 1962. 9.95. Wiley

Frevert, R. K., and others. Soil and water conservation engineering. 1955. 8.50. Wiley

Hough, B. K. Basic soils engineering. 1957. 9.50. Ronald

Hubbard, Alice H. This land of ours. 1960. 4.95. Macmillan

Jumikis, Alfred R. Soil mechanics. 1962. 12.50. Van Nostrand

Karol, Reuben H. Soils and soil engineering. 1960. 11.95. Prentice-Hall

Osborn, Fairfield. Our plundered planet. 1948. 3.75. Little

Scarseth, George D. Man and his earth. il. 1962. 4.50. Iowa State

Stallings, J. H. Soil conservation. 1957. 13.00. Prentice-Hall

SOILS (631.4)

Bear, Firman E. Earth, the stuff of life. 1962. 3.95. U. of Okla.

Bear, F. E. Soils and fertilizers. 1953. 6.95. Wiley

Cook, J. Gordon. Our living soil. 1960. 3.50. Dial

Donahue, R. L. Soils: An introduction to soils and plant growth. 1958. 9.25. Prentice-Hall

Gustafson, A. F. Using and managing soils. il. 1948. 4.96. McGraw

Kellogg, Charles E. Soils that support us. 1941. 6.95. Macmillan

Lutz, H. J., and R. F. Chandler. Forest soils. 1946. 7.95. Wiley

Lyon, T. L., and others. Nature and properties of soils. il. 6.25. 1960. Macmillan

Millar, C. E., and others. Fundamentals of soil science. 1958. 7.75. Wiley

Spangler, Merlin G. Soil engineering. 1951. 9.75. Int. Textbook

Waksman, S. A. Soil microbiology. 1952. 8.00. Wiley

Woodruff, Understanding our soils. 3.00. Lucas Bros.

Alexander, M. Introduction to soil microbiology. 1961. 9.75. Wiley

SOLAR SYSTEM (523.2)

Alfven, H. On the origin of the solar system. 1954. 5.60. Oxford U. P.

Blanco, V. M., and S. W. McCuskey. Basic physics of the solar system. 1961. 7.50. Addison-Wesley

Cook, James, Gordon. We live by the sun. 1957. 3.50. Dial

Galilei, Galileo. Dialogue concerning the two chief world systems. Ptolemaic and Copernican. 1953. 10.00. U. of Calif.

Galilei, Galileo. Dialogue on the great world systems. il. 1953. 12.50. U. of Chicago

Konzo, Seichi, and others. Summer air conditioning. il. 1958. 8.00. Industrial Pr.

Kurth, Rudolf. Introduction to mechanics of the solar system. 1959. 6.50. Pergamon

Leighton, Philip A. Photochemistry of air pollution. il. 1961. 11.00. Academic Press

Moore, Patrick. Guide to the planets. il. 1960. 6.50. Norton

Pickering, James S. Captives of the sun. 1961. 4.95. Dodd

Russell, Henry N., and others. Astronomy. 2 vols. 1955. 8.50 ea. Ginn

Threlkeld, James L. Thermal environmental engineering. 1962. 16.00. Prentice-Hall

SOLIDS (531)

Aigrain, P. R., and others. Electronic processes in solids. il. 1960. 4.00. Wiley

Azaroff, Leonid V. Introduction to solids. 1960. 9.95. McGraw

Bueren, Hendrik G. van. Imperfections in crystals. il. 1960. 16.75. Wiley

Crandall, S. H., and N. C. Dahl. Introduction to the mechanics of solids. 1959. 8.95. McGraw

Cusack, N. E. Electrical and magnetic properties of solids. 1958. 8.25. Wiley

Dekker, Adrianus J. Solid state physics. 1957. 13.35. Prentice-Hall

Frechette, V. D. Non-crystalline solids. 1960. 15.00. Wiley

Kallman, H. P., and M. Silver. Electrical conductivity in organic solids. 1962. 12.50. Wiley

Kittel, Charles. Introduction to solid state physics. 1956. 10.75. Wiley

Koerber, George G. Properties of solids. 1962. 13.00. Prentice-Hall

Peierls, R. E. Quantum theory of solids. 1955. 5.60. Oxford U.P.

SOLUTION (CHEMISTRY) (540)

Allen, Augustine O. Radiation chemistry of water and aqueous solutions. il. 1961. 6.00. Van Nostrand

Hamer, Walter J. Structure of electrolytic solutions. il. 1959. 18.50. Wiley

Harned, Herbert Spencer, and B.B. Owen. Physical chemistry of electrolytic solutions. 1958. 20.00. Reinhold

Hildebrand, Joel H., and Robert L. Scott. Regular solutions. 1962. 7.00. Prentice-Hall

King, Edward J. Qualitative analysis and electrolytic solutions. 7.50. 1959. Harcourt

Prigogine, I. Molecular theory of solutions. il. 1957. 13.75. Wiley

Silverstein, J. M., and A. Nicholson. Structure and properties of solid solutions. 1962. 4.50. Pergamon

SONGS (784)

Auden, W. H., and others. Elizabethan songbook: Lute songs, madringals and rounds. il. 1955. pap. 1.45. Doubleday

Engel, Lyle K. America's greatest song hits. 1962. 6.95. Grosset

Fuld, James J. American popular music: 1875-1950. il. 7.50. Saifer

Hall, James Husst. Art song. 1953. 4.50. U. of Okla.

Moore, Gerald. Singer and accompanist. 1954. 4.50. Macmillan

Stevens, Denis W. History of song. il. 1960. 7.50. Norton

SOPHOCLES, 496?-406 B:C. (882.2)

Adams, S. M. Sopholcles the playwright. 1957. 4.75. U. of Toronto

Bowra, C. M. Sophoclean tragedy. 1944. 4.80. Oxford U.P.

Falk, Eugene H. Renunciation as a tragic focus: A study of five plays. 1954. 3.00. U. of Minn.

Goheen, R. Imagery of Sopholcles' Antigone. 1951. 3.00. Princeton

Kitto, H.D.F. Sophocles, dramatist and philosopher. 1958. 1.20. Oxford U.P.

Knox, B.M.W. Oedipus at Thebes. 1957. 5.00. Yale

Opstelton, S. C. Sophocles and Greek pessimism. 6.00. Humanities

Waldock, A.J.A. Sophocles the dramatist. 1951. 3.75. Cambridge U.P.

Whitman, Cedric Hubbell. Sophocles: A study of heroic humanism. 1951. 5.25. Harvard

SOUND (534)

Beranek, L. L. Acoustics. il. 1954. 11.50. McGraw

Beranek, L. L. Acoustic measurements. 1949. 12.50. Wiley

Beranek, Leo L. Noise reduction. 14.50. McGraw

Colby, Malcolm Y. College course in sound waves and acoustics. il. 1938. 5.75. Holt, Rinehart & Winston

Fletcher, Harvey. Speech and hearing in communication. il. 1953. 11.50. Van Nostrand

Frayne, John G., and H. Wolfe. Elements of sound recording. 1949 12.75. Wiley

Friedlander, F. G. Sound pulses. 1958. 7.50. Cambridge U.P.

Griffin, Donald R. Echoes of bats and men. 1959. pap. 0.95. Doubleday

Hueter, Theodor F., and R. H. Bolt. Sonics. 1955. 10.75. Wiley

Hunter, Joseph L. Acoustics. 1957. 11.35. Prentice-Hall

Johns, R. V., and others. Heat, light, and sound. 1.50. St. Martins

Kinsler, L. E., and A.R. Frey. Fundamentals of acoustics. 1950. 7.75. Wiley

Lamb, Horace. Dynamical theory of sound. 3.50. Smith, Peter

Mason, Warren P. Physical acoustics and the properties of solids. il. 1958. 9.00. Van Nostrand

Molloy, E. High fidelity sound reproduction. 5.50. Transatlantic

Morse, Philip M. Vibration and sound. 1948. 9.00. McGraw

Nesbett, Alex. Technique of the sound studio. il. 1962. 10.50. Hastings

Officer, Charles B. Introduction to the theory of sound transmission. 1958. 10.00. McGraw

Parkin, Peter H., and H. R. Humphreys. Acoustics, noise and buildings. il. 1958. 16.50. Praeger

Richardson, Edward G. Acoustics for architects. 1945. 1.25. St. Martins

Sands, Leo G. Commerical sound installer's handbook. pap. 4.95. Bobbs

Sears, Francis W. Mechanics, heat, and sound. il. 1950. 9.75. Addison-Wesley

Tremaine, Howard M. Audio cyclopedia. 19.95. Bobbs (R)

SOUTH AMERICA (980)

Davies, Howell. South American handbook. 4.00. Rand McNally (R)

Hanke, Lewis. South America: Modern Latin America, continent in ferment. vol. 2. 1959. pap. 1.25. Van Nostrand

Ireland, Gordon. Boundaries, possessions, and conflicts in South America. il. 1938. 4.50. Harvard

Matthiessen, Peter. Cloud forest: A chronicle of the South American wilderness. 6.50. Viking

Peck, A. M. Pageant of South American history. 1958. 6.50. McKay

Whitaker, Arthur Preston. United States and South America: The northern republics. il. 1948. 4.75. Harvard

SOUTH CAROLINA (975.7)

Crane, Verner W. Southern frontier, 1670-1732. 1956. pap. 1.75. U. of Mich.

Lander, Ernest McP. History of South Carolina, 1865-1960. 1960. 5.00. U. of N.C.

Lawson, John. History of Carolina. il. 4.00. Garrett

South Carolina: Guide to the palmetto state. 6.50. Oxford U. P.

SOUTH DAKOTA (978.3)

Schell, Herbert S. History of South Dakota. il. 1961. 5.50. U. of Nebr.

Writers' Project. South Dakota. 1952. 6.50. Hastings

SOUTH POLE (999)

Scott, Robert S. Scott's last expedition. il. 1951. 4.25. Transatlantic

Siple, Paul A. 90 degrees South: The story of the American South Pole expedition. il. 1959. 5.75. Putnam

SOUTHERN STATES (975.976)

Abernethy, Thomas P. South in the new nation, 1789-1819. 1961. 7.50. La. State

Alden, John R. First South. 1961. 3.50. La. State

Alden, John R. South in the Revolution, 1763-1789. 1957. 7.50. La. State

Ashmore, Harry S. Epitaph for Dixie. 1958. 3.75. Norton

Bartram, William. Travels of William Bartram. by Francis Harper. il. 1958. 8.50. Yale

Botkin, B. A. Treasury of Southern folklore. 1949. 5.00. Crown

Carter, Hodding. Southern legacy. 1950. 3.00. La. State

Cash, Wilbur J. Mind of the South. 1960. 4.50. Knopf

Clark, Thomas D. Emerging South. 1961. 6.00. Oxford U. P.

Coulter, E. Merton. South during reconstruction. 1947. 7.50. La. State

Craven, Avery O. Growth of southern nationalism. 1953. 7.50. La. State

Craven, Wesley. F. Southern colonies in the seventeenth century. 1949. 7.50. La. State

Dabbs, James M. Southern heritage. 1958. 4.00. Knopf

Daniels, Jonathan. Devil's backbone. il. 1962. 6.95. McGraw

Davis, Allison, and others. Deep South: A social anthropological study of caste and class. il. 1941. 8.00. U. of Chicago

Dollard, John. Caste and class in a southern town. 3.25. Smith, Peter

Eaton, Clement. Growth of Southern civilization, 1790-1860. 1961. 6.00. Harper

Eaton, Clement. History of the Old South. il. 6.25. Macmillan

Franklin, John Hope. Militant South, 1800-1861. 1956. 5.00. Harvard

Henry, Robert. Story of Reconstruction. 6.00. Smith, Peter

Hesseltine, William B. Confederate leaders in the new South. 1950. 2.50. La. State

Hesseltine, William B., and Smiley. South in American history. 1960. 8.00. Prentice-Hall

Howard, Robert W. This is the South. 1959. 7.50. Rand McNally

I'll take my stand: The South and the agrarian tradition. 4.50. Smith, Peter

Kane, Harnett. Gone are the days. il. 1960. 12.50. Dutton

Kane, Harnett T. Romantic South. il. 1961. 12.50. Coward

Maclachlan, John M., and Joe S. Floyd. This changing South. 1956. 4.00. U. of Fla.

Nicholls, William H. Southern tradition and regional progress. 1960. 5.00. U. of N.C.

Osterweis, R. G. Romanticism and nationalism in the Old South. 1949. 3.75. Yale

Overdyke, W. D. Know-nothing party of the South. 1950. 4.00. La. State

Overy, David H. Wisconsin carpetbaggers in Dixie. 1961. 3.00. Wis.State Hist. Soc.

Phillips, Ulrich B. Course of the South to secession. 3.50. Smith, Peter

Rand, Clayton. Sons of the South. 1961. 7.60. Holt, Rinehart & Winston
Randall, James G. Lincoln and the South. 1946. 1.50. La. State
Rubin, Louis Jr., and James Jackson Kilpatrick. Lasting South. 1957. 5.50.
    Regnery
Russel, Robert R. Economic aspects of Southern sectionalism. 1960. 7.50. Russell
Russell, William Howard. My diary, North and South. by Fletcher Pratt. il. 1954.
    4.00. Harper
Savage, Henry, Jr. Seeds of the Time. Holt. 4.50.
Simkins, Francis B. History of the South. il. 1953. 6.50. Knopf
Smith, Lillian E. Killers of the dream. 1961. 4.50. Norton
Stephenson, Wendell. Basic history of the Old South. 1959. pap. 1.25. Van Nostrand
Stephenson, Wendell H. South lives in history: Southern historians and their legacy.
    1955. 3.00. La. State
Strother, David H. Old South illustrated. by Cecil D. Eby. 6.00. U. of N.C.
Sydnor, Charles. Development of Southern sectionalism, 1819-1848. 1948. 7.50.
    La. State
Taylor, William R. Cavalier and Yankee. 6.00. Braziller
Trowbridge, John T. Desolate South: 1865-1866. 1956. 6.00. Duell
Van Noppen, Ina W. South: A documentary history. il. 1958. 6.75. Van Nostrand
Westmoreland, Frank E. South: Last bulwark of America. 3.50. Vantage
Woodward, C. Vann. Burden of Southern history. 1960. 3.50. La. State
Woodward, C. Vann. Origins of the new South, 1877-1913. 1951. 7.50. La. State
Workman, William D., Jr. Case for the South. 1960. 5.00. Devin
SOUTHEY, ROBERT, 1774-1843 (928)
Carnall, Geoffrey. Robert Southey and his age: The development of a conservative
    mind. 1960. 4.80. Oxford U. P.
Cobban, Alfred. Edmund Burke and the revolt against the eighteenth century. 1961.
    3.75. Barnes & Noble
SOUTHWEST, NEW (979)
Bolton, Herbert E. Spanish exploration in the Southwest, 1542-1706. 1916. 5.75.
    Barnes & Noble
Dobie, J. Frank. Coronado's children. 1.95. Grosset
Gladwin, Harold S. History of the ancient Southwest. il. 1957. 8.50. Wheelwright
Gregg, Josiah. Commerce of the prairies. 5.00. Franklin, B.
Magoffin, Susan S. Down the Sante Fe Trail and into Mexico. il. 1962. 7.50.
    Yale
Major, Mabel, and others. Southwest heritage. 1948. 2.00. U. of N. Mex.
Peyton, Green. America's heartland: The Southwest. il. 1948. 3.75. U. of Okla.
Stone, Irving. Men to match my mountains: The story of the opening of the Far
    West 1840-1900. 1956. 5.95. Doubleday
Wellman, Paul I. Glory, God and gold. il. 1955. 5.75. Doubleday
Wellman, Paul I. Indian wars of the West. il. reprinted. 1954. 5.95. Doubleday
SOUTHWEST, OLD (976)
Peyton, Green. America's heartland: The Southwest. il. 1948. 3.75. U. of Okla.
Whitaker, Arthur P. Spanish American frontier, 1783-1795. 4.75. Smith, Peter
SOVEREIGNTY (320.157)
Laski, Harold J. Grammar of politics. 1957. 6.00. Humanities
Sheppard, Paul. Sovereignty and state-owned entities. 6.50. Twayne
Wilkinson, H. A. American doctrine of state succession. 1934. 2.25. Johns
    Hopkins
SPACE FLIGHT (629.1388)
Berman, Arthur I. Physical principles of astronautics. il. 1961. 8.50. Wiley
Burgess, Eric. Satellites and spaceflight. il. 1958. 4.50. Macmillan
Caidin, Martin. Rendezvous in space: The story of Projects Mercury, Gemini,
    Dyna-Soar and Apollo. il. 4.95. Dutton
Carter, L. J. Realities of space travel. 1957. 8.50. McGraw
Clarke, Arthur C. Exploration of the moon. il. 1955. 2.50. Harper
Cox, Donald W. Space race: From Sputnik to Aplool...and beyond. 1962. 6.95.
    Chilton

Eddington, Arthur S. Space, time and gravitation. 1960. 5.50. Cambridge U. P.
Fenyo, Eva. Guided tour through space and time. 3.50. Prentice-Hall
Gartmann, Heinz. Space travel. il. 1962. 5.00. Viking
Hobbs, Marvin. Basics of missile guidance and space techniques. 2 vols. il.
    1959. pap. 3.90 ea. set, pap. 7.80. Rider
Jammer, M. Concepts of space: The history of theories of space in physics. 1954.
    3.75. Harvard
Ley, Willy. Conquest of space. il. 1949. 5.75. Vikins
Von Braun, Wernher. First men to the moon. il. 1960. 3.95. Holt, Rinehart &
    Winston
Von Braun, Wernher. Mars project. 1962. pap. 0.95. U. of Ill.
Williams, Kenneth G. New frontier: Man's survival in the sky, il. 1960. 5.50.
    Thomas, C.C.

SPACE MEDICINE (616)
Abraham, Lewis H. Structural design of missiles and spacecraft. il. 12.50.
    McGraw
Baar, James, and William E. Howard. Spacecraft and missiles of the world,
    1962. il. 1962. 5.95. Harcourt
Benson, O. O., and H. Strughold. Physics and medicine of the atmosphere and
    space. 1960. 12.50. Wiley
Hobbs, Marvin. Fundamentals of rockets, missiles, and spacecraft. il. 1962.
    8.95. Rider
Lent, Henry B. Man alive in outer space. il. 3.00. Macmillan
Seifert, Howard S., and Kenneth Brown. Ballistic missile and space vehicle
    systems. il. 1961. 12.00. Wiley

SPAIN (946)
Altamira, Rafael. History of Spain. tr. by Muna Lee. 1949. 9.00. Van Nostrand
Adams, Nicholson B. Heritage of Spain. il. 1959. 6.00. Holt, Rinehart & Winston
Baedeker, Karl. Baedeker's autoguide: Spain and Portugal. il. 1959. 6.75.
    Macmillan
Bemis, Samuel F. Pinckney's Treaty: America's advantage form Europe's
    distress, 1783-1800. il. 1960. 6.00. Yale
Bertrand, Louis, and Charles Petrie. History of Spain. 6.00. Macmillan
Bolton, Herbert E., and Thomas M. Marshall. Colonization of North America,
    1492-1783. il. 7.50. Macmillan
Bourne, Edward G. Spain in America. 5.00. Barnes & Noble
Brenan, Gerald. Face of Spain. 1951. 4.50. Farrar, Straus
Brenan, Gerald. Spanish labyrinth. 1950. 6.50. Cambridge U. P.
Clark, Sydney. All the best in Spain and Portugal. 1958. 4.95. Dodd
Chapman, Charles E. Colonial Hispanic America. 1933. 6.50. Macmillan
Chapman, Charles E. History of Spain. 1918. 7.25. Macmillan
Cleugh, James. Image of Spain. il. 1961. 5.95. Pitman
Croft-Cooke, Rupert. Through Spain with Don Quixote. il. 1960. 5.00. Knopf
Davies, R. Trevor. Golden century of Spain, 1501-1621. 1954. 5.00. St. Martins
Dumas, Alexandre. Adventures in Spain. tr. by A. E. Murch. il. 1959. 3.50.
    Chilton
Fodor, Eugene. Spain and Portugal. il. 4.95. McKay'
Foster, George M. Culture and conquest: America's Spanish heritage. il. 1960.
    6.00. Quadrangle
Fuller, Hubert B. Purchase of Florida. in prep. U. of Fla.
Hamilton, Arthur. Study of Spanish manners, 1750-1800, from the plays of
    Ramon de la Cruz. 1927. pap. 1.00. U. of Ill.
Hanke, Lewis. Aristotle and the American Indians. 1959. 3.50. Regnery
Holiday. Travel guide to Spain. by the editors of Holiday. il. 1960. pap. 1.45.
    Random
Hurlimann, Martin. Spain. il. 1952. 12.00. Viking
Kirkpatrick, F. A. Spanish conquistadores. pap. 1.95. Meridian
McLachlan, J. O. Trade and peace with Old Spain. 1940. 6.50. Cambridge U. P.
Madariaga, Salvador de. Spain: A modern history. 8.25. Praeger

Mariejol, Jean H. Spain of Ferdinand and Isabella. 1961. 7.50. Rutgers
Marx, Karl, and Friedrich Engels. Revolution in Spain. 1939. 3.50. Int. Pubs.
Merriman, Roger B. Rise of the Spanish empire in the old world and in the new. 4 vols. 35.00. Cooper
Orwell, George. Homage to Catalonia. 1952. 3.50. Harcourt
Payne, Robert. Civil war in Spain, 1936-1939. 1962. 5.75. Putnam
Payne, Stanley G. Falange: History of Spanish Fascism. 1961. 6.00. Stanford
Priestley, Herbert I. Coming of the white man, 1492-1848. 1929. 6.75. Macmillan
Sitwell, Sacheverell. Spain. il. 1955. 4.50. Hastings
Taylor, F. Jay. United States and the Spanish Civil War. 5.00. Twayne
Thomas, Hugh. Spanish Civil War. il. 1961. 8.95. Harper
Trend, J. B. Civilization of Spain. 1944. 1.70. Oxford U. P.
Ugarte, Francisco. Espana y su civilizacion. il. 1952. 3.00. Odyssey
Way, Ruth. Geography of Spain and Portugal. il. 7.95. Dutton
Whitaker, Arthur P. Spain and the defense of the West. pap. 2.25. Praeger
Whitaker, Arthur P. Spanish American frontier, 1783-1795. 4.75. Smith, Peter
Wright, Richard. Pagan Spain. 1957. 4.00. Harper

SPANISH DRAMA (862)

Alpern, Hymen, and Jose Martel. Diez comedias del Siglo de Oro. 1939. 6.00. Harper
Bentley, Eric. Six Spanish plays. 3.50. Smith, Peter
Eoff, Sherman. Modern Spanish novel. 1961. 6.00. N. Y. U.
Hill, John M., and Mabel M. Harlan. Cuatro comedias. 1941. 6.50. Norton

SPANISH LANGUAGE (460)

Brady, Agnes M., and Laurel H. Turk. Cuentos y comedias de Espana. 3.75. Houghton
Cano, Juan. La vida de un picaro. il. 2.45. Macmillan
Cassell's Spanish dictionary: Spanish-English, English-Spanish. 1959. 7.50. Funk (R)
Castillo, Carlos, and Otto F. Bond. University of Chicago Spanish dictionary. Spanish-English and English-Spanish. 1948. 5.50. U. of Chicago (R)'
Cuyas, Arturo, and others. Appleton's revised Cuyas dictionary: English-Spanish and Spanish-English. 1960. 7.50. Appleton
Garcia Lorca, L. R. de. Cuentos de Clarin. 2.50. Houghton
Grismer, R. L., and M. B. Mac Donald. El tesoro enterrado y otros cuentos. 1952. 2.00. Houghton
Kasten, L. A., and Eduardo Neale-Silva. Lecturas escogidas. 1945. 3.75. Harper
Marmol, Jose. Amalia. 1.00. Houghton
Oteyza, Luis de. El tesoro de Cuautemoc. il. 1956. pap. 3.25. Ginn
Perez Galdos, Benito. Marianela. by Nicholson B. Adams. pap. 3.00. Ginn
Piper, Anson C. Asi es la vida! 1958. 2.75. Norton
Rogers, Paul, and Augusto Centeno. Patterns of Spanish conversation. 1951. 1.50. Houghton
Rogers, Paul, and Charles W. Butler. Florilegio de cuentos espanoles. 1961. 3.25. Macmillan
Sacks, N. P. Cuentos de hoy y de ayer. 1956. 3.50. Ronald
Turk, Laurel H., and Agnes M. Brady. Cuentos y comedias de America. 1950. 3.95. Houghton
Valdes, Palacio. Marta y Maria. 1961. 2.20. Odyssey
Vazquez, Alberto. Cuentos de la America espanola. 1952. 3.00. McKay
Wast, Hugo. 1937. 1.80. Odyssey
Wilkins, Lawrence A. Omnibus of modern Spanish prose. 3.00. Odyssey

SPANISH LITERATURE (860)

Adams, Nicholson, and John E. Keller. History of Spanish literature. 1960. pap. 1.95. Littlefield
Brenan, G. Literature of the Spanish people. 1953. 10.00. Cambridge U. P.
Chandler, R. E., and Kessel Schwartz. New history of Spanish literature. 1961. 10.00. La. State'

Fitzmaurice-Kelly, James, and J. B. Trend. Oxford book of Spanish verse: 13th century to 20th century. 1940. 5.00. Oxford U. P.

Guillen, Jorge. Language and poetry: Some poets of Spain. 1961. 5.50. Harvard

Martinez-Lopez, Ramon. Image of Spain. il. 1961. 4.00. U. of Tex.

Northup, George T. Introduction to Spanish literature. 1960. 6.00. U. of Chicago

Peers, E. Allison. Spain: A companion to Spanish studies. 1957. 6.00. Pitman

SPECTRUM (535.84)

Ajzenberg-Selove, Fay. Nuclear spectroscopy. 2 vols. pts. A and B, 1960, 16.00 ea. Academic Press

Bak, B. Elementary introduction to molecular spectra. 1962. 6.00. Wiley

Brugel, Werner. Introduction to infrared spectroscopy. 1962. 9.00. Wiley

Clark, George L. Encyclopedia of spectroscopy. il. 1960. 25.00. Reinhold

Lawson, Katheryn E. Intrared abosrption of inorganic substances. 1961. 6.75. Reinhold

Saidel, A. N., and others. Tables of spectrum lines. 1961. 14.00. Pergamon (R)

Szymanski, H. A. Infrared band handbook. 1962. 35.00. Plenum (R)

SPEECH (808.5)

Abernathy, E. Fundamentals of speech. 1959. pap. 3.50. Brown, W. C.

Adams, Martin H., and Thomas C. Pollock. Speak up! il. 1956. 4.40. teacher's manual. 1957. pap. 1.60. Macmillan

Avery, Elizabeth, and others. First principles of speech training. il. 4.00. Appleton

Baird, A. Craig, and Franklin H. Knower. General speech: An introduction. 1957. 5.50; teacher's manual. 1.00. McGraw

Barbara, Dominick A. Your speech reveals your personality. 1958. 5.50. Thomas, C. C.

Barrick, Augusta I. Power of effective speech. 1959. 5.00. Twayne

Barrows, Sarah T., and Ida M. Case. Speech drills in form of play. 1.00. Expression

Black, J. W., and W. E. Moore. Speech. 1955. 5.95. McGraw

Brigance, William N., and Florence Henderson. Drill manual for improving speech. il. 1955. 5.00. Lippincott

Cass, Carl B. Manner of speaking. 1961. 4.50. Putnam

Craig, Alice E. Speech arts. il. 1941. 5.16. Macmillan

Eisenson, Jon. Basic speech. il. 1950. 5.00. Macmillan

Eisenson, Jon. Psychology of speech. 1938. 3.00. Appleton

Gray, Giles W., and Claude Merton Wise. Bases of speech. 1959. 7.00. Harper

Griffith, Francis J., and others. Your speech. 1955. 4.08. Harcourt

Hedde, Wilhelmina G., and William N. Brigance. New American speech. il. 1957. 4.84. Lippincott

Johnson, Wendell, and others. Speech handicapped school children. 1956. 5.50. Harper

Judson, L. S., and A. T. Weaver. Voice science. il. 4.50. Appleton

Kaplan, Harold M. Anatomy and physiology of speech. 1960. 8.50. McGraw

Levin, Nathaniel M. Voice and speech disorders. il. 1962. 27.50. Thomas, C. C.

McBurney, James H., and E. J. Wrage. Guide to good speech. 1960. 5.75. Prentice-Hall

Manser, Ruth B. Speech improvement on the contract plan. 1961. 5.00. Chilton

Oliver, Robert T., and others. Communicative speech. 1962. 5.25. Holt, Rinehart & Winston

Pierce, John R., and Edward E. David, Jr. Man's world of sound. il. 1958. 5.00. Doubleday

Raubicheck, Letitia, and others. Your voice and speech. 1953. 4.40. Prentice-Hall

Sandford, William P., and Willard Hayes Yeager. Effective business speech. 1960. 6.95. McGraw

Stinchfield-Hawk, Sara M. Psychology of speech. 3.00. Expression

Thonssen, Lester, and Howard Gilkinson. Basic training in speech. 1953. 5.50. Heath

Van Riper, Charles. Speech correction: Principles and methods. 1954. 7.95. Prentice-Hall

Van Riper, Charles, and John Irwin. Voice and articulation. il. 1958. 7. 95. Pren-
tice-Hall
Weaver, Andrew T. , and Ordean G. Ness. Fundamentals and forms of speech. 4. 25.
Odyssey
Wood, Alice L. Sound games: Speech correction for your very young. 2. 00. Dutton
SPEECHES, ADDRESSES, ETC. (808. 5)
Baird, A. Craig. American public addresses. 1956. 5. 50. McGraw
Baird, A. C. Representative American speeches. 7 vols. 1943-1944; 1944-1945.
1. 25 ea; 1949-1950; 1950-1951; 1951-1952. 1. 75 ea; 1957-1958. 2. 00; 1958-1959.
2. 50. Wilson
Copeland, Lewis. World's great speeches. 1957. pap. 2. 49. Dover
Edgerton, Alice. Speech for every occasion. 1949. 3. 60. Noble
Hastings, William T. Man thinking: A third volume of representative Phi Beta
Kappa orations, 1915-1959. 1962. 5. 75. Cornell
Lincoln, Abraham. Gettysburg address, bd. with George Washington's Farewell
address and Daniel Webster's Bunker Hill oration. 1. 16. Houghton
Lott, Davis Newton. Inaugural addresses of the American presidents: From
Washington to Kennedy. 8. 95. Holt, Rinehart & Winston
Sutton, Roberta B. Speech index, 1935-1955. 1956. 8. 50; suppl. in prep. Scarecrow
Wright, C. W. Better speeches for all occasions. 3. 00. Crown
SPENSER, EDMUND, 1552?-1599 (821. 31)
Arthos, John. On the poetry of Spenser and the form of romances. 1962. 4. 00.
Barnes & Noble
Bennett, Josephine W. Evolution of the Faerie Queene. 1960. 8. 50. Franklin, B.
Bradner, Leicester. Edmund Spenser and the Faerie queen. 1948. 5. 00. U. of
Chicago
Davis, Bernard. Edmund Spenser. 1962. 7. 50. Russell
Greenlaw, Edwin. Studies in Spenser's historical allegory. 1932. 4. 00. Johns
Hopkins
Hamilton, Albert C. Structure of the Faerie Queene. 1961. 5. 60. Oxford U. P.
Jones, Harry S. V. Spenser handbook. il. 1930. 4. 00. Appleton
Judson, Alexander Corbin. Life of Edmund Spenser. 1945. 4. 50. Johns Hopkins
Mohl, Ruth. Studies in Spenser, Milton, and the theory of monarchy. 1949. 2. 50.
Columbia
SPICES (641. 3383)
Hayes, Elizabeth S. Spices and herbs around the world. il. 1961. 5. 95. Doubleday'
Parry, John W. Spices: Their morphology, histology and chemistry. 1961. 8. 00.
Tudor
Parry, John W. Story of spices. 1953. 4. 50. Tudor
SPIDERS (595. 44)
Emerton, James H. Common spiders of the United States. 3. 50. Smith, Peter
Gertsch, Willis J. American spiders. il. 1949. 7. 95. Van Nostrand
SPIES (341. 31)
Bakeless, Katherine, and John. Spies of the revolution. 1962. 3. 95. Lippincott
De Gramont, Sanche. Secret war. 1962. 5. 95. Putnam
Koeston, Joachim. They call it intelligence. 1962. 5. 00. Abelard
Kane, Harnett T. Spies for the blue and gray. il. 1954. 3. 95. Doubleday
Singer, Kurt D. Spies for democracy. 1960. 3. 95. Denison
SPINAL CORD (611. 82)
Austin, George. Spinal cord. il. 1961. 26. 50. Thomas, C. C.
Brock, Samuel. Injuries of the brain and spinal cord. il. 1960. 18. 50. Springer
Dillon, John B. Spinal anesthesia. il. 1957. 3. 00. Thomas, C. C.
Stelmasiak, M. Anatomical atlas of the human brain and spinal cord. il. 1956.
12. 50. Hafner
SPINOZA, BENEDICTUS DE, 1632-1677 (921. 9)
Hallett, H. F. Benedict de Spinoza: The elements of his philosophy. 1957. 4. 00.
Oxford U. P.
Parkinson, George H. R. Spinoza's theory of knowledge. 1954. 3. 40. Oxford U. P.

SPORTS (796)

Ainsworth, Dorothy, and others. Individual sports for women. il. 1955. 4. 75. Saunders

American Association for Health, Physical Education, and Recreation. Special events in the girls sports program. 1961. 1. 50. Am. Assn. for Health, Phys. Ed., & Rec.

American Association for Health, Physical Education and Recreation. Division for Girls' and Women's Sports. Girls sports organization handbook. 1961. 0. 75. Am. Assn. for Health, Phys. Ed. & Rec.

Boyden, E. Douglas, and Roger G. Burton. Staging successful tournaments. 1957. 4. 75. Assn. Pr.

Cummings, P. Dictionary of sports. 1949. 7. 50. Ronald (R)

De Witt, Raymond T. Teaching individual and team sports. 1953. 10. 00. Prentice-Hall

Durant, John, and Otto Bettmann. Pictorial history of American sports. il. 4. 95. Barnes, A. S.

Esquire. Esquire's great men and moments in sports. il. 1961. 8. 50. Harper

Forsythe, Charles E. Athletic director's handbook. il. 1956. 9. 00. Prentice-Hall

Gardiner, E. N. Athletics of the ancient world. il. 1930. 8. 80. Oxford U. P.

Hirshberg, Al, and Joe McKenney. Famous American athletes of today. 1947. 3. 95. Farrar, Straus

Jordan, Emil L. Sports atlas of America. il. 1955. 2. 95. Hammond

Ley, Katherine, and Donna M. Miller. Individual and team sports for women. 1955. 9. 25. Prentice-Hall

Menke, Frank G. Encyclopedia of sports. 1953. 12. 00. Barnes, A. S. (R)

Meyer, Margaret H., and Marguerite M. Schwarz. Team sports for girls and women. 1957. 4. 50. Saunders

Paxton, Harry. Sport, U. S. A. 1961. 7. 50. Nelson

Thorndike, Augustus. Athletic injuries. 1962. 5. 00. Lea & F

Tunis, J. R. Sport for the fun of it. 1958. 4. 00. Ronald

Vannier, Maryhelen, and Hally B. Poincexter. Individual and team sports for girls and women. il. 1960. 6. 50. Saunders

SQUARE DANCING (793. 34)

Gowing, Gene. Square dancers' guide. 1957. 3. 95. Crown

Kraus, R. Square dances of today and how to teach and call them. 1950. 4. 00. Ronald

McNair, Ralph J. Square dance! il. 1951. 2. 00. Doubleday

STAGE LIGHTING (792)

Bowman, Wayne. Modern theatre lighting. il. 1958. 5. 00. Harper

Selden, Samuel, and Hunton D. Sellman. Stage scenery and lighting. il. 1959. 7. 95. Meredith

STALIN, JOSEPH (IOSIF STALIN) 1879-1953 (923. 1)

Avtorkhanov, Abdurakhman. Stalin and the Soviet Communist Party. 1959. 6. 00. Praeger

Deutscher, Isaac. Stalin: A political biography. il. 1949. 8. 75. Oxford U. P.

STAMMERING (371. 927)

Ainsworth, Stanley H. Speech correction methods. 1948. 5. 75. Prentice-Hall

Eisenson, Jon. Stuttering, a symposium. il. 1958. 7. 00. Harper

Johnson, Wendell. Stuttering and what you can do about it. 1961. 3. 95. U. of Minn.

Van Riper, Charles, and Leslie Gruber. Casebook in stuttering. 1957. 2. 50. Harper

Van Riper, Charles. Speech correction: Principles and methods. 1954. 7. 95. Prentice-Hall

STANLEY, SIR HENRY MORTON, 1841-1904 (923. 9)

Sterling, Thomas. Stanley's way: A sentimental journey through central Africa. 4. 00. Atheneum

STARS (523. 8)

Baade, Walter. Evolution of stars and galaxies. by Cecilia Payne-Gaposchkin. in prep. Harvard

Callatay, V. de. Atlas of the sky. tr. by Harold S. Jones. 1958. 12.50. St. Martins
Kopal, Zdenek. Close binary systems. il. 1959. 17.50. Wiley
Kruse, W., and W. Dieckvoss. Stars. il. 1957. 5.00. U. of Mich.
Payne-Gaposchkin, Cecilia. Stars in the making. il. 1952. 4.75. Harvard
Payne-Gaposchkin, Cecilia. Variable stars and galactic structure. 1954. 3.40.
    Oxford U. P.
Pickering, James Sayre. Stars are yours. il. 4.95. Macmillan
Schatzman, E. White dwarfs. il. 1958. 6.75. Wiley
Schwarzchild, M. Structure and evolution of the stars. 1958. 6.00. Princeton
Sobolev, V. V. Moving envelopes of stars. il. 1960. 4.75. Harvard
Velikovsky, Immanuel. Worlds in collision. 1950. 4.50. Doubleday
Woolley, R. v. d. R., and D. W. N. Stibbs. Outer layers of a star. 1953. 8.00.
    Oxford U. P.

STATE, THE (321)

Barker, Ernest. Social contract: Essays by Locke, Hume, and Rousseau. 1951.
    2.75. Oxford U. P.
Carr, Edward H. New society. 1957. 2.00. St. Martins
Cassirer, E. Myth of the state. 1946. 5.00. Yale
Chodorov, Frank. Rise and fall of society. 1959. 3.95. Devin
Dewey, John. Public and its problems. 1957. 2.50. Swallow, A.
Engels, Friedrich. Origin of the family, private property and the state. 2.00.
    Int. Pubs.
Hobbes, Thomas. Leviathan. 1950. 2.95. Dutton
Hobhouse, L. T. Metaphysical theory of the state: Criticism. 1960. 3.00. Barnes
    & Noble
Joad, Cyril E. M. Introduction to modern political theory. 1924. 1.20. Oxford U. P.
Laski, Harold J. Grammar of politics. 1957. 6.00. Humanities
Lowie, Robert. Origin of the state. 1961. 5.00. Russell
MacIver, R. M. Modern state. 1926. 6.10. Oxford U. P.
Maritain, Jacques. Man and the state. 1951. 4.00. U. of Chicago
Niebuhr, Reinhold. Structure of nations and empires. 1959. 5.95. Scribner
Schuman, Frederick L. International politics. il. 1958. 7.75. McGraw
Spencer, Herbert. Man versus the state. by Albert Jay Nock. 1940. 3.50. Caxton
Willoughby, W. F. Government of modern states. 5.00. Appleton

STATE GOVERNMENTS (350)

Adrian, C. R. State and local governments. 1960. 7.50. McGraw
Allen, Robert S. Our sovereign state. 5.00. Vanguard
Anderson, William and others. Government in the fifty states. il. 1960. 6.50.
    Holt, Rinehart & Winston
Babcock, Robert S. State and local government and politics. 1962. pap. 5.50.
    Random
Betters, Paul V. State centralization on North Carolina. 1932. 2.00. Brookings
Burns, James M., and Jack W. Peltason. Government by the people. 1960.
    national ed. 7.95; national, state, and local ed. 8.25. Prentice-Hall
Calvocoressi, Peter. World order and new states. 1962. 4.25. Praeger
Clark, Glenn. World's greatest debate. 3.50. Macalester
Corwin, Edward S. Commerce power versus states rights. 1959. 4.00. Smith,
    Peter
Frost, Richard T. Cases in state and local government. 1961. pap. 4.25. Prentice-
    Hall
Gosnell, Cullen B., and Lynwood M. Holland. State and local government in the
    United States. 1951. 9.00. Prentice-Hall
Jensen, Merrill. American union: Its interpretation and its historic origins. 1950.
    0.35. Oxford U. P.
Johnson, Claudius O. American state and local government. 1961. pap. 3.50.
    Crowell
Kautsky, J. H. Political change in underdeveloped countries: Nationalism and
    communism. 1962. 3.95. Wiley

Key, V. O., Jr. American state politics. 1956. 4. 50. Knopf
Kilpatrick, James Jackson. Sovereign states. 1957. 6.00. Regnery
MacDonald, Austin F. American state government and administration. il. 1960.
   7.00. Crowell
Maddox, Russell W., and Robert F. Faquay. State and local governments. il. 1962.
   7. 75. Van Nostrand
Morlan, Robert. Capitol, courthouse, and city hall. pap. 3.50. Houghton
Neuberger, Richard L. Adventures in politics. 1954. 5.00. Oxford U. P.
Ogg, Frederic A., and P. Orman Ray. Essentials of American government. by
   William H. Young, il. 1959. 6.50. Appleton
Ogg, Frederic A., and R. Orman Ray. Introduction to American Government.
   by William H. Young. il. 8.00. Appleton
Owsley, Frank L. State rights in the Confederacy. 4.50. Smith, Peter
Peel, Roy. State government today. 1948. 1.00. U. of N. Mex.
Snider, Clyde F. American state and local government. 1950. 6.00. Appleton
Swarthout, John M., and Ernest R. Bartley. Principles and problems of state
   and local government. 1958. pap. 4.50. Oxford U. P.
Theobald, Robert. New nations of West Africa. 1960. 2.50. Wilson
Wilcox, Thomas. States' rights vs. the Supreme Court. 1960. 3.00. Forum
Workman, William D., Jr. Case for the South. 1960. 5.00. Devin

STATICS (531. 2)

Beer, Ferdinand P., and E. Russell Johnston, Jr. Statics (Mechanics for engineers
   vol. 1) 5.00; solutions manual. 0.50. McGraw
Housner, George W., and Donald E. Hudson. Applied mechanics: Statics. il. 1961.
   5. 75. Van Nostrand
Jensen, Alfred E. Statics and strength of materials. 1962. 8.00. McGraw
Lamb, Horace. Statics. 6.50. Cambridge U. P.

STATISTICS (310)

Adams, J. K. Basic statistical concepts. 1955. 6.95. McGraw
Blalock, Hubert M. Social statistics. 7.95. McGraw
Bryant, Edward C. Statistical analysis. il. 1960. 6.95; volutions manual, 1.50.
   McGraw
Croxton, Frederick E., and D. J. Cowden. Applied general statistics. 1955.
   11. 95; Prentice-Hall
Garrett, Henry E. Statistics in psychology and education. 1958. 5.75. McKay
Huff, Darrell, and Irving Geis. How to lie with statistics. il. 1954. 2.95. Norton
Johnson, Palmer O., and Robert W. B. Jackson. Modern statistical methods.
   il. 1959. 8.00. Rand McNally
McCarthy, P. J. Introduction to statistical reasoning. 1957. 6.95. McGraw
Mood, Alexander M. Introduction to the theory of statistics. 1950. 7.50; answers,
   0. 50. McGraw
Neiswanger, William A. Elementary statistical methods. il. 7.50. Macmillan
Smith, C. Frank, and D. A. Leabo. Basic statistics for business economics.
   1960. 8. 65. Irwin
Statesman's year-book. 9.50. St. Martins (R)
Tippett, L. H. Methods of statistics. 1952. 7.50. Dover

STEAM ENGINEERING (621)

Duncan, John. Steam and other engines. 1950. 2.50. St. Martins
Gaffert, Gustaf A. Steam power stations. il. 1952. 9.75. McGraw
Graham, Frank Duncan. Power plant engineers guide. 6.00. Audel
Lee, John F. Theory and design of steam and gas turbines. il. 1953. 10.75.
   McGraw
Wootton, W. R. Steam cycles for nuclear power plant. 1958. 2.75. Simmons-
   Boardman
Zerban, A. H., and E. P. Nye. Power plants. 1952. 9.50. Int. Textbook

STEEL (620.17)

Bullens, D. K., and Battelle Memorial Institute, Metallurgical Staff. Steel and
   its heat treatment. 3 vols. vol. 1, Principles, 1948. 10.50; vol. 2, Tools,
   processes, control, 1948. 7.00; vol. 3, Engineering and special purpose tools.
   1949. 11.50. Wiley

Conway, C. G. Heat-resisting steels and alloys. il. 1953. 5.75. Van Nostrand
Dearden, John. Iron and steel today. 1956. 2.40. Oxford U. P.
Lothers, John E. Design in structural steel. 1953. 13.00. Prentice-Hall
Parker, Harry E. Simplified design of structural steel. 1955. 5.25. Wiley
Wertime, Theodore A. Coming of the age of steel. il. 1962. 6.95. U. of Chicago
STEIN, GERTRUDE, 1874-1946 (928)
Brinnin, John Malcolm. Third rose: Gertrude Stein and her world. il. 1959. 6.00.
    Little
Reid, B. L. Art by subtraction: A dissenting opinion of Gertrude Stein. il. 1958. 4.00.
    U. of Okla.
Sutherland, Donald. Gertrude Stein: A biography of her work. 1951. 5.00. Yale
STEINBECK, JOHN ERNST, 1902- (928)
French, Warren. John Steinbeck. 3.50. Twayne
Lisca, Peter. Wide world of John Steinbeck. 1957. 5.00. Rutgers
Tedlock, Ernest W., Jr., and C. V. Wicker. Steinbeck and his critics. 1957. 6.00.
    U. of N. Mex.
STENDHAL (MARIE HENRI BEYLE) 1783-1842 (928)
Alams, Robert M. Stendhal: Notes on a novelist. 1959. 4.00. Farrar, Straus
Brombert, Victor H. Stendhal: A collection of critical essays. 1962. pap. 1.95.
    Prentice-Hall
Krutch, Joseph W. Five masters, a study in the mutations of the novel. 1959. 3.75.
    Smith, Peter
STEREOPHONIC SOUND SYSTEMS (534)
Crowhurst, Norman. Stereo high fidelity handbook. il. 1959. 5.95. Crown
Gardner, Douglas. Stereo and hi-fi as a pastime. il. 1960. 3.00. Taplinger
Tardy, David. Guide to stereo sound. il. 4.95. Hawthorn
STEVENS, THADDEUS, 1792-1868 (923.2)
Brodie, Fawn M. Thaddeus Stevens, scourge of the south. il. 1959. 8.50. Norton
Korngold, Ralph. Thaddeus Stevens. 1955. 6.00. Harcourt
STEVENS, WALLACE (928)
Brown, Ashley, and Robert S. Haller. Achievement of Wallace Stevens. 1962. 5.00.
    Lippincott
STEVENSON, ADLAI EWING, 1900- (923.2)
Brown, Stuart G. Conscience in politics: Adlai E. Stevenson in the 1950's il. 1961.
    5.00. Syracuse
STEVENSON, ROBERT LOUIS, 1850-1894 (928)
Caldwell, Elsie. Last witness for Robert Louis Stevenson, il. 1960. 5.00. U. of Okla.
Chesterton, G. K. Robert Louis Stevenson. 2.50. Sheed
Daiches, David. Robert Louis Stevenson. 2.00. New Directions
McGaw, M. Martha, Sister. Stevenson in Hawaii. 1950. 3.75. U. of Hawaii
STILL-LIFE PAINTING (758)
Richmond, Leonard. Technique of still life painting in oil colors. 1936. 7.95. Pitman
Sterling, Charles. Still life painting. il. 1959. 17.50. Universe
Walter, Start. Beginner's book of still life painting. il. 1961. 2.95. Reinhold
Watson, Ernest W. Composition in landscape and still life. 12.50. Watson
STIMSON, HENRY LEWIS, 1867-1950. (923.2)
Morison, Elting E. Turmoil and tradition: A study of the life and times of Henry
    L. Stimson. 1960. 7.50. Houghton
STOCK AND STOCK-BREEDING (636)
Ashbrook, Frank G. Raising small animals for pleasure and profit. 1951. 4.75.
    Van Nostrand
Briggs, Hilton M. Modern breeds of livestock. 8.50. Macmillan
Garrigus, Wesley P. Introductory animal science. il. 1960. 7.95. Lippincott
Gilfillan, Archer B. Sheep: Life on the South Dakota range. 1957. 4.00. U. of
    Minn.
Kays, John M. Basic animal husbandry. 1958. 10.00. Prentice-Hall
Park, R. D. Animal husbandry. il. 1961. 2.90. Oxford U. P.
Rice, Victor Arthur, and others. Breeding and improvement of farm animals.
    il. 1957. 8.90. McGraw

Smith, William W. Elements of live'stock-judging. 1946. 4.20. Lippincott
Trimberger, George W. Dairy cattle judging techniques. 1958. 8.35. Prentice-Hall
Vaughn, H. W. Breeds of live stock in America. 4.75. Long's College Bk.
Vaughn, H. W. Types and market classes of live stock, 1941. 4.75. Long's College Bk.
Winters. L. M. Animal breeding. 1954. 6.75. Wiley
STOCKS (332.6)
Bernhard, Arnold. Evaluation of common stocks. 1959. 3.95. S. and S.
Bishop, George W. Charles H. Dow and the Dow theory. 1960. 6.00. Appleton
Brooks, John Nixon. Seven fat years: Chronicles of Wall Street. 1958. 4.00. Harper
Cowee, George A. Ups and downs of common stocks. 3.00. Vantage
Dice, Charles A., and Wilford J. Eiteman. Stock market. 1952. 9.50. McGraw
Gilbert, Lewis D. Dividends and democracy. 3.95. Citadel
Grant, Edwin S. Lifetime investing for security and growth. 1959. 3.50. Exposition
Hedges, Joseph Edward. Commercial banking and the stock market before 1863. 1938. 2.50. Johns Hopkins
Leffler, G. L. St ock market. 1957. 7.50. Ronald
Livingston, J. A. American stockholder. 4.95. Lippincott
Magee, John. General semantics of Wall Street. il. 12.00. Magee
Rosenberg, Claude N., Jr. Stock market primer. 1962. 12.50. Prentice-Hall
Shultz, Birl E. Securities market: And how it works. 1946. 7.50. Harper
Smith, Edgar L. Common stocks and business cycles. il. 1959. 10.00. William-Frederick
Willner, Sidney H. What the businessman should know about regulation of securities. 1958. pap. 0.50. Pub. Affairs
Yield and interest tables, bonds and stocks. 2.00. Financial
STOICS (188)
Bevan, Edwyn. Stoics and sceptics. 1959. 4.50. Barnes & Noble
Hicks, Robert. Stoic and Epicurean. 1961. 7.50. Russell
Mates, Benson. Stoic logic. 3.50. Smith, Peter
Sambursky, Samuel. Physics of the stoics. 1959. 3.50. Macmillan
Zeller, Eduard. Stoics. Epicureans and Sceptics. 1962. 12.50. Russell
STOMACH (611.33)
Magee, D. F. Gastro-intestinal physiology. il. 1962. 11.50. Thomas, C. C.
Montague, J. F. Nervous stomach trouble. 4.95. Nelson-Hall
STONE, HARLAN FISKE, 1872-1945 (923.4)
Mason, Alpheus Thomas. Harlan F. Stone: Pillar of the law. 1956. 8.75. Viking
STONE AGE (571)
Burkitt, M. C. Old stone age: A study of Palaeolithic times. il. 1956. 3.75. N. Y. U.
Burkitt, M. C. Our early ancestors. 1926. 4.50. Cambridge U. P.
Coon, C. S. Cave explorations in Iran: 1949. 1951. 1.50. U. Museum
Forde-Johston, J. L. Neolithic cultures of North Africa. il. 1959. 7.50. Humanities
Leakey, L. S. B. Stone Age cultures of Kenya Colony. 1931. 9.50. Cambridge U. P.
Leakey, Louis S. B. Adam's ancestors, the evolution of man and his culture. 3.50. Smith, Peter
Mewhinney, H. Manual for Neanderthals. il. 1957. 3.50. U. of Tex.
Michael, Henry N. Neolithic age in eastern Siberia. 1958. 2.50. Am. Philos. Soc.
Peake, Harold, and H. J. Fleure. Hunters and artists. 1927. 2.40. Oxford U. P.
STORMS (551.55)
Battan, Louis J. Nature of violent storms. pap. 0.95. Doubleday
Fisher, John. Storms. 1959. 3.50. De Graff
Sloane, Eric. Book of storms. il. 1956. 3.50. Duell
STORY-TELLING (027.6251)
Droke, Maxwell. Speaker's handbook of humor. 1956. 4.95. Harper

Emerson, Laura S. Storytelling. 1959. 3.50. Zondervan
Goodreds, V. Spencer. Good stories and how to tell them. il. 3.95. Denison
Olcott, Frances Jenkins. Good stories for great holidays. il. 4.50. Houghton
Sawyer, Ruth. Way of the storyteller. 1962. 4.00. Viking
Shedlock, Marie L. Art of the story-teller. 1951. pap. 1.50. Dover
Tooze, Ruth. Storytelling. 1959. 5.65. Prentice-Hall
STOWE, HARRIET ELIZABETH (BEECHER) 1811-1896 (928)
Foster, Charles H. Rungless ladder: Harriet Beecher Stowe and New England
    Puritanism. 1954. 6.00. Duke
Furnas, J. C. Goodbye to Uncle Tom. il. 1956. 6.00. Sloane
STRACHEY, GILES LYTTON, 1880-1932 (928)
Sanders, C. R. Lytton Strachey: His mind and art. 1957. 6.00. Yale
STRADIVARI, ANTONIO, d. 1737 (927)
Hill, William H., and others. Antonio Stradivari, his life and his work. 1962.
    2.00. Dover
STRAINS AND STRESSES (531.38)
Deyarmond, Albert, and Albert Arsian. Fundamentals of stress analysis. 1960.
    5.75. Aero
Harris, Charles O. Introduction to stress analysis. 1959. 7.75. Macmillan
Parker, Harry E. Simplified design of roof trusses for architects and builder.
    1953. 4.75. Wiley
STRATEGY (355.43)
Brodie, Bernard. Strategy in the missile age. 1959. 6.50. Princeton
Fryklund, Richard. 100 million lives: Maximum survival in nuclear war. 1962.
    3.95. Macmillan
Higgins, Trumbull. Winston Churchill and the second front, 1940-1943. 1957.
    6.00. Oxford U. P.
Kingston-McCloughry, E. J. Global strategy. 4.50. Praeger
Liddell Hart, Basil H. Strategy. 5.95. Praeger
Turner, Gordon B., and Richard D. Challener. National security in the nuclear
    age. 6.00. Praeger
STRAVINSKII, IGOR FEDOROVICH, 1882- (927)
Stravinsky, Igor. Autobiography. 1962. pap. 1.45. Norton
Vlad, Roman. Stravinsky. tr. by Frederick and Ann Fuller. 1960. 7.00.
    Oxford U. P.
STRENGTH OF MATERIALS (620.1)
Bassin, M., and S. Brodsky. Statics and strength of materials. 7.00. McGraw
Breneman, John W. Strength of materials. 1952. 3.50. McGraw
Jensen, Alfred. Applied strength of materials. il. 1957. 5.75. McGraw
Olsen, G. Elements of mechanics of materials. 1958. 12.00. Prentice-Hall
Parker, Harry E. Simplified design of structural steel. 1955. 5.25. Wiley
STRIKES AND LOCKOUTS (331.89)
Adamic, Louis. Dynamite, the story of class violence in America. il. 1959.
    6.00. Smith, Peter
Crook, Wilfrid. Communism and the general strike. 1960. 8.75. Shoe String
Karsh, Bernard. Diary of a strike. 1958. 3.50. U. of Ill.
Kornhauser, Arthur, and others. Industrial conflict. 1954. 7.95. McGraw
Ross, A. M., and P. Hartman. Changing patterns of industrial conflict. 1960.
    6.50. Wiley
Sorel, Georges. Reflections on violence. 4.00. Smith, Peter
Warner, W. L., and J. O. Low. Social system of the modern factory. 1947. 5.00.
    Yale
STRUCTURES, THEORY OF (624)
Carpenter, Samuel T. Structural mechanics. il. 1960. 9.50. Wiley
Lucy, T. A. Practical design of structural members. 1957. 12.00. McGraw
Neal, B. G. Plastic methods of structural analysis. 1957. 8.00. Wiley
Timoshenko, S. History of the strength of materials. 1953. 12.00. McGraw
STUART, GILBERT, 1755-1828 (927)
Flexner, James Thomas. Gilbert Stuart. 1955. 3.00. Knopf

STUART, JAMES EWELL BROWN, 1833-1864 (923. 5)
Davis, Burke. Jeb Stuart, the last cavalier. il. 6. 00. Rinehart
Thomason, John W. Jeb Stuart. il. 7. 50. Scribner
STUART, JESSE, 1907- (928)
Stuart, Jesse. Thread that runs so true. 1958. 4. 50. Scribner
STUDENT ACTIVITIES (371. 8)
Green, H. H. Activities handbook for business teachers: Clubs, plays, and
    projects. 1958. 5. 75. McGraw
McKown, Harry C. Extracurricular activities. 7. 50. Macmillan
Miller, F. A. , and others. Planning student activities. 1957. 6. 75. Prentice-Hall
Strang, Ruth. Group work in education. 1958. 5. 50. Harper
Williamson, E. G. , and others. Study of participation in college activities. 1954.
    pap. 2. 25. U. of Minn.
STUDENT TEACHING (370. 733)
Neal, Charles D. Student teacher at work. 1959. 3. 25. Burgess
STUDENTS (378)
Alsop, Gulielma F. , and Mary F. McBride. She's off to college: A girl's guide
    to college life. 3. 00. Vanguard
Beach, Waldo. Conscience on campus. 1958. 2. 50. Assn. Pr.
Bennett, Margaret E. College and life. 1952. 4. 95. McGraw
Bennett, M. E. Getting the most out of college. 1957. 4. 75. McGraw
Bragdon, Helen D. , and others. Educational counseling of college students. 0. 50.
    A. C. E.
Carpenter, Marjorie. Larger learning. 1960. 3. 00. Brown, W. C.
Carter, Homer L. J. , and Dorothy J. McGinnis. Building a successful college
    career. 1950. pap. 2. 50. Brown, W. C.
Coleman, James, and others. Success in college. 1960. 2. 75. Scott
Craig, W. Bradford. How to finance a college education. 1959. pap. 1. 95. Holt,
    Rinehart & Winston
Eddy, Edward D. College influence on student character. 1959. 3. 00. A. C. E.
Eldridge, Elizabeth. Co-ediquette: Poise and popularity for every girl. 3. 50.
    Dutton
Evans, M. Stanton. Revolt on the campus. 1961. 4. 50. Regnery
Farnsworth, Dana L. Mental health in college and university. 1957. 5. 00. Harvard
Goldsen, Rose K. , and others. What college students think. 1960. 5. 95. Van
    Nostrand
Hoffmann, Randall W. , and Robert Plutchik. Small-group discussion in orientation
    and teaching. 1959. 4. 00. Putnam
Jacob, Philip E. Changing values in college. 1958. 3. 50. Harper
McKinney, F. Psychology of personal adjustment. 1960. 6. 75. Wiley
Mechanic, David. Students under stress: A study in the social psychology of
    adaptation. 1962. 5. 00. Free Press
Mueller, Kate H. , and others. Counseling for mental health. 1947. 1. 00. A. C. E.
Murphy, Lois, and Esther Rauschenbush. Achievement in the college years. 1960.
    4. 95. Harper
Shacter, Helen. How personalities grow. il. 1958. 1. 00. Taplinger
Sharpe, Russell T. , and others. Financial assistance for college students. 1946.
    1. 00. A. C. E.
Sifferd, Calvin S. College and you. il. 1958. 3. 00. Taplinger
Straus, Robert, and Selden D. Bacon. Drinking in college. 1953. 4. 00. Pacific
    Bk. Supply
Wedge, Bryant M. Psychosocial problems of college men. il. 1958. 6. 50. Yale
Willis, Ellen. Questions freshman ask. il. 1962. 3. 50. Dutton
Wise, W. Max. They come for the best of reasons: College students today. 1958.
    1. 00. A. C. E.
STUDENTS, FOREIGN (371. 39)
Du Bois, Cora. Foreign students and higher education in the United States. 1956.
    3. 50. A. C. E.

STUDY, METHOD OF (371.3)

Armstrong, William H. Study is hard work. 1957. 3.50. Harper
Bennett, Margaret E. College and life. 1952. 4.95. McGraw
Dudycha, George J. Learn more with less effort. 1957. 3.00. Harper
Ehrlich, Eugene H. How to study better and get higher marks. 1961. 4.95. Crowell
Flesch, Rudolf, and others. How you can be a better student. 1957. 2.95. Sterling
Frederick, Robert W., and others. Guide to college study. 1947. 2.50. Appleton
Hook, Julius N. How to take examinations in college. 1958. pap. 1.25. Barnes & Noble
Huff, Darrell. Score: The strategy of taking tests. il. 1961. 3.75. Meredith
Jones, Edward S. Improvement of study habits. pap. 1.25. Stewart
Kalish, Richard A. Making the most of college. 1959. 2.95. Wadsworth
Morgan, C. T., and J. Deese. How to study. 1957. 1.50. McGraw
Pauk, Walter. How to study in college. 1962. 1.95. Houghton
Robinson, Francis P. Effective reading. 1962. pap. 1.35. Harper
Robinson, Francis P. Effective study. 1961. 4.50. Harper
Weigand, George, and Walter S. Blake, Jr. College orientation. 1955. 3.95. Prentice-Hall

STYLE, LITERARY (808)

Aristotle. On poetry and style. tr. by G.M.A. Grube. 1958. 3.00. Bobbs
Aristotle. Poetics. bd. with Longinus' On the sublime, and Demetrius' On style 3.50. Harvard
Artz, Frederick B. From the Renaissance to romanticism. 1962. 5.00. U. of Chicago
Lucas, F. L. Style. 1955. 4.75. Macmillan
Spitzer, Leo. Linguistics and literary history. 1962. 6.50. Russell
Vallins, George H. Best English. 1960. 3.50. Oxford U. P.

STYLE, MUSICAL (780.92)

Artz, Frederick B. From the Renaissance to romanticism. 1962. 5.00. U. of Chicago
Cannon, Beekman C., and others. Art of music. il. 1960. 8.50. Crowell
Dorian, Frederick. History of music in performance. il. 1943. 6.95. Norton
Moore, Douglas. From madrigal to modern music. il. 1942. 5.50. Norton

SUBCONSCIOUSNESS (153.8)

Broad, C. D. Mind and its place in nature. 7.00. Humanities
Freud, Sigmund. Jokes and their relation to the unconscious. 1960. 4.50. Norton
Jung, C. G. Psychology of the unconscious. 5.00. Dodd
Lesser, S. Fiction and the unconscious. 1957. 3.00. Beacon
Murphy, Joseph. Miracles of your mind. 3.00. DeVorss
Wickes, Frances G. Inner world of man. il. 1959. 5.50. Ungar

SUBJECT HEADINGS (025.33)

Ball, Miriam Ogden. Subject headings for the information file. 1956. 3.00. Wilson
Bliss, Henry E. Organization of knowledge in libraries. 1939. 4.00. Wilson (R)
Frarey, Carlyle J. Subject headings. 1960. 8.00. Rutgers (R)
Metcalfe, John. Information indexing and subject cataloging. 1957. 6.75. Scarecrow
Metcalfe, John. Subject classifying and indexing of libraries and literature. 1959. 7.50. Scarecorw
Pettee, Julia. Subject headings. 1946. 2.75. Wilson (R)
Sears, Minnie E. Sears list of subject headings. by Bertha M. Frick. 1959. 6.00. Wilson

SUBMARINES (359.32)

Cross, Wilbur. Challengers of the deep. il. 1959. 5.00. Sloane
Lewis, David D. Fight for the sea. il. 1961. 6.00. World Pub.
Rush, C. W., and others. Complete book of submarines. 4.95. World Pub.
Whitehouse, Arthur G. J. Subs and submariners. il. 1961. 4.95. Doubleday

SUBVERSIVE ACTIVITIES (323.2)

Buckley, William F., and L. Brent Bozell. McCarthy and his enemies. 1954. pap. 2.00. Regnery

Mowery, Edward J. HUAC and FBI: Targets for abolition. 1.00. Bookmailer
Murray, Robert K. Red scare: A study in national hysteria. il. 1955. 4.75.
U. of Minn.
SUCCESS (174)
Albert, Dora. You're better than you think. 1957. 4.95. Prentice-Hall
Burkhart, Roy A. Freedom to become yourself. 1956. 4.95. Prentice-Hall
Carnegie, Dale. How to win friends and influence people. 1936. 3.50. S. and S.
Clark, Charles H. Brainstorming: The dynamic way to create successful ideas.
1958. 4.50. Doubleday
Davies, Daniel R., and Robert Teviot Livingston. You and management. 1958.
4.50. Harper
Duvall, Sylvanus M. Art and skill of getting along with people. 1961. 4.95. Prentice-
Hall
Fortune. Adventures in small business. 1957. 4.50. McGraw
Goldner. Success through creative thinking. 1962. 4.95. Prentice-Hall
Hart, Hornell. Autoconditioning: The new way to a successful life in selling.
1956. 4.95. Prentice-Hall
Hubbard, Elbert. Message to Garcia, and other essays. 1959. 1.00. Revell
Laird, Donald A., and Eleanor C. Sizing up people. 1951. 4.95. McGraw
Laird, Donald A. Technique of getting things done. 1947. 4.95. McGraw
Laird, Donald A., and Eleanor C. Technique of handling people. 1954. 4.50.
McGraw
MacGibbon, Elizabeth G. Fitting yourself for business. 1961. 5.50. McGraw
Maltz, Maxwell. Psycho-cybernetics. 1960. 4.95. Prentice-Hall
Murphy, Thomas P. Business of your own. 1956. 4.95. McGraw
Reilly, William J. In search of a working philosophy of life. 1959. 2.95. Harper
Roosevelt, Eleanor. You learn by living. 1960. 3.95. Harper
Wardlaw, Jack. Top secrets of successful selling. 1952. 3.50. Funk
Warner, W. Lloyd, and James Abegglen. Big business leaders in America. 1955.
3.95. Harper
Wetherill, Richard W. Dyanmics of human relations. 3 vols. 1948. 4.75 ea. Van
Nostrand
SUDAN (962.4)
Holt, Peter M. Modern history of the Sudan. il. 1961. 5.95. Grove
SUEZ CANAL (962.15)
Lauterpacht, Elihu. Suez canal settlement. 1960. 2.50. Praeger
SUFFRAGE (324)
Campbell, Ernest H., and George D. Smith. United States citizenship and
qualifications for voting in Washington. 1951. pap. 1.50. U. of Wash.
De Grazia, Alfred, Jr. Public and republic: Political representation in America.
1951. 3.75. Knopf
Riess, L. History of the English electoral law. 1940. 3.00. Cambridge U. P.
Williamson, C. American suffrage from property to democracy, 1760-1860. 1960.
6.00. Princeton
SUGAR (664.1)
Edson, B. H. Sugar: From scarcity to surplus. 5.00. Tudor
Mintz, Sidney W. Worker in the cane. il. 1960. 5.00. Yale
Swerling, B. C., and Vladimir P. Timoshekno. World's sugar: Progress and
policy. 7.50. Stanford
SUICIDE (179)
Allen, George N., and Edward R. Ellis. Traitor within: Our suicide problem.
3.95. Doubleday
Durkheim, Emile. Suicide. 1951. 6.00. Free Press
Williams, Glanville. Sanctity of life and the criminal law. 1957. 5.00. Knopf
SULLIVAN, SIR ARTHUR SEYMOUR, 1842-1900 (927)
Hughes, Gervase. Music of Arthur Sullivan. 1960. 7.00. St. Martins
Moore, Frank Ledlie. Crowell's handbook of Gilbert and Sullivan. il. 1962. 4.95.
Crowell

Power-Waters, Alma. Melody maker: The life of Sir Arthur Sullivan. 1959. 3.25.
    Dutton
SULLIVAN, LOUIS HENRY, 1856-1924 (927)
Bush-Brown, Albert. Louis Sullivan. il. 1960. 4.95. Braziller
Morrison, Hugh. Louis Sullivan, prophet of modern architecture. il. 1958. 6.00.
    Smith, Peter
SULPHUR (553.6)
Haynes, Williams. Brimstone: The stone that burns. il. 1959. 5.95. Van Nostrand
Pryor, William A. Mechanisms of sulfur reactions. il. 1962. 9.75. McGraw
Young, Leslie, and George A. Maw. Metabolism of sulphur compounds. 1958.
    3.00. Wiley
SUMNER, CHARLES, 1811-1874 (923.2)
Donald, David. Charles Sumner and the coming of the civil War. il. 1960. 6.75.
    Knopf
SUN, YAT-SEN, 1866-1925 (923.2)
Leng, Shao Chuan, and Norman D. Palmer. Sun Yat-sen and communism. 1960.
    6.00. Praeger
Linebarger, Paul M. A. Political doctrines of Sun Yat-sen: Exposition of the San
    Min Chu I. 1937. 4.50. Johns Hopkins
SUN (523.7)
Ellison, M. A. Sun and its influence. il. 1956. 5.00. Macmillan
Gamow, George. Birth and death of the sun. il. 1940. 4.75. Viking
Harrison, Lucia C. Earth, sun, time, and man. 4.50. Rand McNally
Hawkes, Jacquetta. Man and the sun. 1962. 5.00. Random
Kiepenheurer, Karl. Sun. il. 1959. 5.00. U. of Mich.
Kuiper, Gerard P. Sun. il. 1953. 12.50. U. of Chicago
Menzel, Donald Howard. Our sun. 1959. 7.50. Harvard
Stetson, Harlan T. Sunspots in action. 1947. 5.00. Ronald
Willson, Robert Wheeler. Times of sunrise and sunset in the United States. il.
    1908. 1.25. Harvard
SUPERSTITION (133)
Budge, Ernest A. Amulets and talismans. il. 1961. 10.00. U. Books
Elworthy, Frederick T. Evil eye. 7.50. Wehman
Read, C. Man and his superstitions. 1925. 6.50. Cambridge U. P.
Tabori, Paul. Natural science of stupidity. 1959. 4.50. Chilton
SUPERVISION OF EMPLOYEES (658.3124)
Brown, Milon. Effective supervision. il. 1956. 4.95. Macmillan
Carroll, Phil. Better wage incentives. 1957. 6.00. McGraw
Cooper, Alfred M. How to supervise people. 1958. 4.95. McGraw
Franseth, Jane. Supervision as leadership. 1961. 5.00. Harper
Kay, Brian R. , and Stuart Palmer. Challenge of supervision. 1961. 6.95. McGraw
Van Dersal, William R. Successful supervisor in government and business. il.
    1962. 3.95. Harper
Williamson, Margaret. Supervision: New patterns and processes. 1961. 4.00.
    Assn. Pr.
SUPPLY AND DEMAND (331.112)
Douglas, Paul H. Theory of wages. 8.50. Kelley
Henderson, Hubert. Supply and demand. 1958. pap. 1.35. U. of Chicago
Hicks, J. R. Revision of demand theory. 1956. 4.25. Oxford U. P.
Norris, R. T. Theory of consumer's demand. 1952. 3.75. Yale
SURGERY (614.255)
Felter, Robert K. , and West. Surgical nursing. il. 1958. 5.50. Davis
Frantz, Virginia K. , and Harold D. Harvey. Introduction to surgery. 1959. 6.00.
    Oxford U. P.
Glaser, Hugo. Road to modern surgery. il. 1962. 5.75. Dutton
Harlow, F. W. Atlas of surgery for students and nurses. il. 1959. 10.25. Grune
Moroney, James. Surgery for nurses. il. 1959. 7.00. Williams & Wilkins
Richardson, Robert G. Surgeon's tale. il. 1959. 4.95. Scribner
Riedman, Sarah R. Masters of the scalpel. il. 1962. 4.25. Rand McNally

Sholtis, Lillian A., and Jane S. Bragdon. Art of clinical instruction. 1961. 5.75. Lippincott

SURREALISM (709.04)

Fowlie, Wallace. Age of Surrealism. 1960. 3.50. Smith, Peter
Jean, Marcel. History of Surrealist painting. il. 1960. 17.50. Grove
Josephson, Matthew. Life among the surrealists. 1961. 6.00. Holt, Rinehart & Winston
Waldberg, Patrick. Surrealism. il. 1962. 6.50. World Pub.

SURVEYING (526.9)

Breed, C. B. Surveying. 1957. 6.00. Wiley
Brinker, Russel C., and W.C. Taylor. Elementary surveying. 9.50. Int. Textbook
Clark, Frank E. Clark on surveying and boundaries. 1959. 12.50. Bobbs
Davis, Raymond E. Elementary plane surveying. 1955. 6.95. McGraw
Gurden, R. L. Traverse tables. 1949. 15.00. Van Nostrand
Kissam, Philip. Surveying. 1956. 6.95. McGraw
Laurila, Simo. Electronic surveying and mapping. il. 1960. 6.00. Ohio State
Legault, Adrian R., and others. Surveying: An introduction to engineering measurements. il. 1956. 10.00. Prentice-Hall
Parker, Harry E., and J. W. MacGuire. Simplified site engineering. 1954. 4.95. Wiley

SWEDEN (948.5)

Abrahamsen, Samuel. Sweden's foreign policy. 1957. 2.50. Pub. Affairs
Andersson, Ingvar, and others. Introduction to Sweden. il. 1962. 5.50. Bedminster
Childs, Marquis W. Sweden: The middle way. 1960. il. 5.00. Yale
Heckscher, E. F. Economic history of Sweden. il. 1954. 5.00. Harvard
Strode, Hudson. Sweden: Model for a world. il. 6.75. Harcourt

SWIFT, JONATHAN, 1667-1745 (928)

Bullitt, John M. Jonathan Swift and the anatomy of satire: A study of satiric technique. 1953. 4.50. Harvard
Case, A. E. Four essays on Gulliver's travels. 1958. 3.25. Smith, Peter
Ehrenpreis, I. Personality of Jonathan Swift. 1958. 3.00. Harvard
Ferguson, Oliver W. Jonathan Swift and Ireland. 1962. 5.00. U. of Ill.
Goldgar, Bertrand A. Curse of party: Swift's relations with Addison and Steele. 1961. 4.00. U. of Nebr.
Paulson, Ronald. Theme and structure in Swift's Tale of a tub. 1960. 5.00. Yale
Quintana, Ricardo. Swift: An introduction. pap. 1.50. Oxford U. P.
Williams, Harold. Text of Gulliver's Travels. 1952. 4.50. Cambridge U. P.

SWIMMING (797.2)

Armbruster, David A., Sr., and others. Swimming and diving. il. 1958. 5.00. Mosby
Kauffman, Carolyn. How to teach children to swim. il. 1960. 3.50. Putnam
Kiphuth, R., and H. M. Burke. Basic swimming. 1950. 3.95. Yale
Moriarty, Phil. Springboard diving. il. 1959. 4.00. Ronald
Scharff, Robert. Swimming pool book. il. 1958. 3.50. Barrows
Silvia, Charles E. Lifesaving and water safety.instruction. 1958. 4.50. Assn. Pr.
Spears, Betty. Beginning synchronized swimming. 1958. 3.00. Burgess
Sports Illustrated. Sports Illustrated book of diving. il. 1961. 2.95. Lippincott
Sports Illustrated. Sports Illustrated book of swimming. il. 1961. 2.95. Lippincott
V-Five Association of America. Swimming and diving. 1962. 4.50. U.S. Naval Inst.
Yates, Fern, and T. W. Anderson. Synchronized swimming. 1958. 5.00. Ronald

SWINE (636.4)

Cunha, T. J. Swine feeding and nutrition. il. 1957. 5.75. Wiley
Leone, Charles A. Fetal pig manual. il. 1960. 2.50. Burgess
Patten, Bradley M. Embryology of the pig. 1948. 5.75. McGraw
Towne, Charles W., and Edward N. Wentworth. Pigs: From cave to corn belt. il. 1950. 4.00. U. of Okla.

SWITZERLAND (949.4)

Bonjour, E., and others. Short history of Switzerland. il. 1952. 6.75. Oxford U. P.

Clark, Sydney. All the best in Switzerland. 1961. 4.95. Dodd

Codding, George A., Jr. Federal government of Switzerland. 1961. pap. 1.95. Houghton

Dumas, Alexandre. Adventures in Switzerland. 1960. 3.50. Chilton

Hurlimann, Martin. Switzerland. il. 1960. 12.00. Viking

Lloyd, William B., Jr. Waging peace: The Swiss experience. 1958. 2.50. Pub. Affairs

Muirhead, Russell. Blue guide to Switzerland. 7.94. Rand McNally

Soloveytchik, George. Switzerland in perspective. 1954. 4.00. Oxford U. P.

SYMBOLISM (704.946)

American Academy of Arts and Sciences. Symbolism in religion and literature. 1958. 1.75. Am. Acad. of Arts & Sci.

Art Directors Club of New York. Symbology. il. 1960. 6.95. Hastings

Cassirer, Ernst. Essay on man. 1944. 5.00. Yale

D'Alviella, Eugene Goblet. Migration of symbols. 1956. 5.00. U. Books

Digby, G. W. Symbol and image in William Blake. 1957. 6.10. Oxford U. P.

Eliade, Mircea. Images and symbols. 1961. 3.50. Sheed

Gaskell, G. A. Dictionary of all scriptures and myths. 1960. 15.00. Julian

Haight, E. H. Aspects of symbolism in the Latin anthology and in classical and Renaissance art. 1952. 2.00. McKay

Jung, Carl G. Psychology and religion: West and east. by Herbert Read, and others. 1958. 6.00. Pantheon

Jung, C. G. Psychology of the unconscious. 5.00. Dodd

Langer, Susanne Knauth. Philosophy in a new key: A study in the symbolism of reason, rite and art. 1957. 4.75. Harvard

May, Rollo. Symbolism in religion and literature. 1962. 5.00. Braziller

Whitehead, Alfred N. Symbolism: Its meaning and effect. 1958. 2.50. Macmillan

SYMBOLISM, LITERATURE (809.91)

Beebe, Maurice. Literary symbolism. 1960. 1.95. Wadsworth

Bell, Eric T. Numerology: Magic of numbers. 2.50. Wehman

Bowra, Cecil Maurice. Heritage of symbolism. 4.25. St. Martins

Cheiro, Cheiro's book of numbers. 3.50. Wehman

Dunbar, H. Flanders. Symbolism in medieval thought. 1960. 12.50. Russell

Feidelson, Charles, Jr. Symbolism and American literature. 1959. pap. 1.85. U. of Chicago

Musurillo, Herbert. Symbol and myth in ancient poetry. 1960. 5.00. Fordham

Stalnaker, Leo. Mystic symbolism in Bible numerals. 1956. 3.50. Assoc. Booksellers

Tindall, William Y. Literary symbol. 1959. 3.75. Smith, Peter

Wilson, Edmund. Axel's castle. 1931. 4.50. Scribner

SYMPHONIES (785.11)

Mueller, John H. American symphony orchestra: A social history of musical taste. il. 1951. 6.95. Indiana

Spaeth, Sigmund. Great symphonies: How to recognize and remember them. il. 3.50. Carlton

Tovey, Donald F. Symphonies. 5.00. Oxford U. P.

Tovey, Donald F. Symphonies, variations and orchestral polyphony. 5.00. Oxford U. P.

SYNGE, JOHN MILLINGTON, 1871-1909 (928)

Greene, David H., and Edward M. Stephens. J. M. Synge, 1871-1909. il. 1959. 6.95. Macmillan

SYRIA (956.91)

Hitti, Philip K. Syria: A short history. 1959. 6.50. Macmillan

Macurdy, Grace Harriet. Hellenistic queens: A study of woman-power in Macedonia, Seleucid Syria, and Ptolemaic Egypt. il. 1932. 4.00. Johns Hopkins

Stark, Freya. Letters from Syria. il. 2.25. Transatlantic

T

TAFT, ROBERT ALPHONSO, 1889-1953 (923.2)

White, William S. Taft story. il. 1954. 6.00. Harper
TAGORE, SIR RABINDRANATH, 1861-1941 (923.7)
Elmhirst, L.K. Sir Rabindranath Tagore, pioneer in education. il. 3.75. Transatlantic
Kripalani, Krishna. Rabindranath Tagore. 1962. 8.75. Grove
Sinha, Sasadhar. Social thinking of Rabindranath Tagore. 1962. 6.75. Taplinger
TAHITI (996.211)
Conrad, Barnaby. Tahiti. il. 1962. 6.50. Viking
TANGANYIKA (967.82)
Cairns, John C. Bush and boma. il. 1959. 4.50. Transatlantic
Cloete, Rehna. Nylon safari. 1956. 3.50. Houghton
TAOISM (299.514)
Legge, James. Texts of taoism. 7.50. Julian
Soothill, W. E. Three religions of China. 1930. 2.40. Oxford U. P.
Weber, Max. Religion of China. 1951. 6.00. Free Press
Welch, Holmes. Parting of the way: Lao Tzu and the Taoist movement. 1961.
    5.00. U. Books
TARIFF (337)
Bidwell, Percy W. What the tariff means to American industries. 1956. 5.00.
    Harper
Humphrey, Don D. American imports. 1955. 6.00. Twentieth Century
Lloyd, Lewis E. Tariffs: The case for protection. 3.50. Devin
Summers, Festus P. William L. Wilson and tariff reform. 1953. 5.00. Rutgers
Taft, Charles P. Trade barriers and the national interest. 1955. 1.50. S.M.U.
Vaccara, Beatrice N. Employment and output in protected manufacturing industries.
    1960. pap. 2.00. Brookings
Wright, H. R. C. Free trade and protection in the Netherlands, 1816-30. 1955.
    6.50. Cambridge U. P.
TARKINGTON, BOOTH (928)
Woodress, James. Booth Tarkington, Gentleman from Indiana. il. 1955. 6.00.
    Lippincott
TASMANIA (994.6)
Emmett, E. T. Tasmania by road and track. 2.75. Cambridge U. P.
Hartwell, R. M. Economic development of Van Diemen's land, 1820-1850. 1954.
    6.00. Cambridge U. P.
TAXATION (336.2)
Adams, Henry Carter. Taxation in the United States. 1.25. Johns Hopkins
Bickford, Hugh C. Successful tax practice. 1956. 10.00. Prentice-Hall
Blough, Roy. Federal taxing process. 1952. 7.35. Prentice-Hall
Eisenstein, L. Ideologies of taxation. 1961. 5.00. Ronald
Floyd, Joe S. , Jr. Effects of taxation on industrial location. 1952. 3.00. U. of
    N. C.
Groves, Harold M. Financing government. 1958. 7.00. Holt
Groves, H. M. Trouble spots in taxation. 1948. 2.00. Princeton
Hollander, Jacob H. Studies in state taxation. 1900. 3.50. Johns Hopkins
Holzman, Franklyn D. Soviet taxation: The fiscal and monetary problems of a
    planned economy. 1955. 8.00. Harvard
Lasser, J. K. Standard handbook of business tax techniques. 1957. 4.95. McGraw
Mitchell, Sydney K. Taxation in Medieval England. by S. Painter. 1951. 5.00.
    Yale
Mortenson, Ernest R. Federal tax fraud law. 1958. 12.50. Bobbs
Moulton, Harold G. , and Others. Capital expansion, employment and economic
    stability. 1940. 3.50. Brookings
Parkinson, Cyril N. Law and the profits. il. 1960. 3.50. Houghton
Pigou, Arthur C. Study in public finance. 1947. 4.00. St. Martins
Shehab, F. Progressive taxation. 1953. 5.60. Oxford U. P.
Shultz, William J. , and Clement L. Harriss. American public finance. 1959.
    10.60. Prentice-Hall
Smith, D. T. Federal tax reform. 1961. 7.00. McGraw

Strayer, Paul J. Fiscal policy and politics. 1958. 4.50. Harper
TCHAIKOVSKY, PETER, 1840-1893 (927)
Abraham, Gerald. Music of Tchaikovsky. il. 1946. 4.50. Norton
Bowen, Catherine Drinker. Beloved friend. 1961. 6.00. Little
Gee, John, and Elliot Selby. Triumph of Tchaikovsky. il. 1960. 5.00. Vanguard
Weinstock, Herbert. Tchaikovsky. il. 1943. 6.75. Knopf
Wheeler, Opal. Peter Tschaikowsky and the Nutcracker Ballet. il. 1959. 3.50.
   Dutton
TEACHERS (371.1)
Abraham, Willard. Handbook for the new teacher. 1960. pap. 1.00. Holt, Rinehart
   & Winston
Adams, Loyce. Three T's: Teach, travel and tell. il. 1960. 3.00. Christopher
American Association for Health, Physical Education and Recreation. Fit to
   teach, yearbook. 1957. 3.50. Am. Assn. for Health, Phys. Ed. & Rec.
American Council on Education, Commission on Teacher Education. Teachers
   for our times. 2.00. A.C.E.
Bell, Terrell H. Effective teaching: How to recognize and reward it. 1962. 3.50.
   Exposition
Burrup, Percy E. Teacher and the public school system. 1960. 5.75. Harper
Chamberlain, Leo M., and Leslie W. Kindred. Teacher and school organization.
   10.00. Prentice-Hall
Cronkhite, Bernice B. Handbook for college teachers. 1950. 3.75. Harvard
Fisher, Dorothy Canfield. Learn or perish. 1930. 2.00. Liveright
Gauerke, Warren E. Legal and ethical responsibilities of school personnel. 1959.
   4.95. Prentice-Hall
Grande, Luke, Brother. Twelve virtues of a good teacher. 1962. 3.50. Sheed
Herold, Amos L. I chose teaching. il. 1958. 5.00. Naylor
Huggett, Albert J., and T. M. Stinnett. Professional problems of teachers. il.
   5.50. Macmillan
Lasser, J. K. Teachers' income tax. 1960. 1.95. S. and S.
Mead, Margaret. School in American culture. 1951. 1.50. Harvard
National Education Association, Educational Research Service. Teacher-aides:
   Current practices and experiments. 1960. 0.75. N.E.A.
National Education Association. Research Division. Teacher supply and demand
   in public schools, 1962. 1962. 1.00. N.E.A.
National Education Association, American Association of Colleges for Teacher
   Education. Source book on accreditation of teacher education. 1962. 0.50.
   N.E.A.
National Education Association, Teacher Education and Professional Standards
   Commission and others. Education of teachers: Certification. 1961. 3.50.
   N.E.A. (R)
National Education Association, Teacher Education and Professional Standards
   Commission, and others. Manual on certification requirements for school
   personnel in the United States. 1961. 4.00. N.E.A.
National Education Association, Research Division. Economic status of teachers
   in 1961-62. 1962. 0.75. N.E.A.
National Education Association, Research Division. Salaries paid and salary
   practices in universities, colleges, and junior colleges, 1961-62. 1962. 1.00.
   N.E.A. (R)
National Education Association, Research Division. Tenure and contracts: School
   law summaries. 1960. 50 states and D.C. 2.00. N.E.A.
Ryans, David G. Characteristics of teachers. 1960. 7.50. A.C.E.
Shipley, Joseph T. Mentally disturbed teacher. 1961. 5.00. Chilton
Sibley, Agnes. Exchange teacher. 1961. pap. 2.50. Caxton
Woellner, Mrs. Robert C., and M. Aurilla Wood. Requirements for certification
   of teachers, counselors, librarians, administrators for elementary schools,
   secondary schools, junior colleges. pap. 3.50. U. of Chicago (R)
Wynne, John P. Qualities of experience and educational philosophy. 1962. pap.
   1.65. College & Univ.

Borrowman, Merle L. Liberal and technical in teacher education: A historical survey of American thought. 1956. 5.00. T.C.

Corey, Stephen M. In-service education for teachers, supervisors and administrators. 1957. 4.50. U. of Chicago

Foundations for excellence. yearbook. 1962. 3.00. Am. Assn. of Colleges for Teacher Educ.

Hodenfeld, G.R., and T. M. Stinnett. Education of teachers: Consensus and conflict. 1961. pap. 1.95. Prentice-Hall

Jeffreys, M.V.C. Revolution in teacher training. 1961. 2.50. Pitman

Kelly, Fred J. Improving college instruction. 1950. 1.75. A.C.E.

National Education Association, American Association of Colleges for Teacher Education. Foundations for excellence. 15th yearbk. 3.00. N.E.A.

National Education Association, American Association of Colleges for Teacher Education. Student evaluation of teaching and learning. 1962. 0.50. N.E.A.

National Education Association, American Association of School Administrators. Who's a good teacher? 1961. 2.00. N.E.A.

National Education Association, Teacher Education and Professional Standards Commission, and others. Education of teachers; Curriculum programs. 1959. 3.50. N.E.A.

Recent research and developments and their implications for teacher education. yearbook. 1960. 2.50. Am. Assn. of Colleges for Teacher Educ.

Sarason, S.B., and others. Preparation of teachers. 1962. 3.95. Wiley

Stabler, Ernest. Education of the secondary school teacher. 5.00. Wesleyan U.P.

TEACHING (371)

Alexander, William M., and Paul M. Halverson. Effective teaching in secondary schools. 1956. 6.75. Holt, Rinehart & Winston

Barzun, Jacques. Teacher in America. 1945. 5.00. Little

Brembeck, Cole S. Discovery of teaching. 1962. pap. 3.95. Prentice-Hall ·

Buckley, William F., Jr. God and man at Yale: The superstitions of "academic freedom". 1951. 3.50. Regnery

Bush, Robert Nelson. Teacher-pupil relationship. 1954. 7.00. Prentice-Hall

Cantor, Nathaniel. Teaching-learning process. 1953. 4.50. Holt, Rinehart & Winston

Chandler, B.J. Education and the teacher. 1960. 5.50. Dodd

Filbin, Robert L., and Stefan Vogel. So you're going to be a teacher. 1961. 2.95. Barron's

Fine, Benjamin. Teaching machines. 3.95. Sterling

Fleming, Charlotte M. Teaching, a psychological analysis. il. 1958. 5.00. Wiley

Haskew, L.D. This is teaching. 1962. 5.75. Scott

Highet, Gilbert. Art of teaching. 1950. 4.50. Knopf

Hofstadter, Richard. Academic freedom in the age of the college. 1961. pap. 1.75. Columbia

Hyde, William Dewitt. Teacher's philosophy in and out of school. 1.50. Houghton

Kelley, Earl C., and Marie I. Rasey. Education and the nature of man. 1952. 3.75. Harper

Kirk, Russell. Academic freedom. 1955. 4.50. Regnery

Klausmeier, Herbert J., and Katharine Dresden. Teaching in the elementary school. 1962. 8.00. Harper

Lazarsfeld, Paul F., and Wagner Thielens. Academic mind. 1958. 7.50. Free Press

Lieberman, Myron. Education as a profession. 1956. 9.35. Prentice-Hall

Massey, Harold W., and Edwin E. Vineyard. Profession of teaching. 1961. 4.00. Odyssey

Miel, Alice. Creativity in teaching. 1961. 4.95. Wadsworth

Mills, H. H., and H. R. Douglass. Teaching in high school. 1957. 6.50. Ronald

Murphy, Garner. Freeing intelligence through teaching. 1961. 2.95. Harper

Mursell, James L. Successful teaching. il. 1954. 5.75. McGraw

National Education Association, Association for Supervision and Curriculum Development. Learning and the teacher, yearbk. 1959. 3.75. N.E.A.

National Education Association, NEA-Magazine Publishers Joint Committee. Controversial issues.in the classroom. 1961. 0.50. N.E.A.

National Education Association, Audiovisual Instruction Department, Current teaching machine programs and programming techniques. 1961. 2.00. N.E.A.

National Education Association, Audio-Visual Instruction Department. Teaching machines and programmed learning: A source book. 1960. 7.50. N.E.A.

Nordberg, H. Orville, and others. Secondary school teaching. il. 1962. 6.00. Macmillan

Philps, William Lyon. Excitement of teaching. 1931. 2.00. Liveright

Ragan, W. B. Teaching America's children. 1961. 4.50. Holt, Rinehart & Winston

Redefer, Frederick L., and Dorothy Reeves. Careers in education. 1960. 4.00. Harper

Sharp, Louise. Why teach? 1957. 4.00. Holt, Rinehart & Winston

Shockley, Robert J. Your future in elementary school teaching. 1961. 2.95. Richards Rosen

Spindler, G.D. Transmission.of American culture. 1959. 1.50. Harvard

Staton, Thomas F. How to instruct successfully. 1960. 6.50. McGraw

Stinnett, T. M., and Laurence D. Haskew. Teaching in American schools: A handbook for the future teacher. 1962. 2.00. Harcourt

Tead, O. College teaching and college learning. 1949. 2.75. Yale

Van Dalen, Deobold B., and Robert W. Brittell. Looking ahead to teaching. 1959. 7.95. Allyn & Bacon

Waller, Willard. Sociology of teaching. 1961. 8.50. Russell

Woofter, T. J. Teaching in rural schools. 1917. 4.00. Houghton

Wynn, Richard. Careers in education. 1960. 4.95. McGraw

TECHNICAL ASSISTANCE (336.185)

Brown, William Adams, Jr., and Redvers Opie. American foreign assistance. 1954. 6.00. Brookings

Curti, Merle. American philanthropy abroad. 1962. 12.50. Rutgers

Curti, Merle, and Kendall Birr. Prelude to Point Four: American technical missions overseas, 1838-1938. 1954. 5.00. U. of Wis.

Erasmus, Charles J. Man takes control: Cultural development and American aid. 1961. 6,50. U. of Minn.

Humphrey, Richard A. Education without boundaries. 1959. 1.00. A.C.E.

Mair, Lucy. Studies in social anthropology. 2.75. Humanities

Shonfield, Andrew. Attack on world poverty. 1960. 5.00. Random

Teaf, Howard M., Jr., and Peter G. Franck. Hands across frontiers. 5.50. Cornell

Wiggins, James W., and Helmut Schoek. Foriegn aid reexamined. 1958. 5.00. Pub. Affairs

TECHNICAL WRITING (808.066)

Baker, J.C.Y. Guide to technical writing. 1961. 3.50. Pitman

Comer, David B., III, and Ralph R. Spillman. Modern technical and industrial reports. 1962. 7.95. Putnam

Emberger, Meta R., and Marian R. Hall. Scientific writing. 1955. 4.95. Harcourt

Gilman, William. Language of science. 1961. 4.95. Harcourt

Godfrey, James W., and Geoffrey Parr. Technical writer. il. 1959. 8.50. Wiley

Henn, Thomas R. Science in writing. 1961. 4.75. Macmillan

Hicks, Tyler G. Successful technical writing. 1959. 5.95. McGraw

Jennings, H. L., and R. C. Tracy. Handbook for technical writers. il. 3.50. Am. Tech. Soc.

Kapp, Reginald O. Presentation of technical information. 1959. 2.95. Macmillan

Marder, Daniel. Craft of technical writing. 1960. 5.25. Macmillan

Menzel, Donald, and others. Writing a technical paper. 1961. 3.25. McGraw

Zetler, Robert L., and W. George Crouch. Successful communication in science and industry: Writing, reading and speaking. 1961. 7.95. McGraw

TECHNOLOGY (600)

Applied science and technology index. 3 vols. 1958-1960. Wilson (R)

Beadle, George W., and others. Science and resources. by Henry Jarrett. il. 1959. 5.00. Johns Hopkins

Bennett, Harry. Concise chemical and technical dictionary. 1962. 15.00. Tudor

Crispin, Frederic S. Dictionary of technical terms. 1961. 5.00. Bruce

Derry, T. K., and Trevor I. Williams. Short history of technology from the
earliest times to A.D. 1900. il. 1961. 8.50. Oxford U. P.

Foster, George M. Traditional cultures, and the impact of technological change.
1962. 6.50. Harper

Guinle, R. L. Modern Spanish-English and English-Spanish technical and
engineering dictionary. 7.00. Dutton (R)

Habakkuk, H. J. American and British technology in the nineteenth century:
Search for labour-saving inventions. 1962. 6.00. Cambridge U. P.

Industrial arts index. H. W. Wilson Company

Johnston, Edgar G. Preserving human values in an age of technology. il. 1961.
4.00. Wayne

Melsen, Andreas G. M. van. Science and technology. 1961. 6.95. Duquesne

Nevins, Allan, and others. Energy and man, a symposium. 1960. 3.75.
Appleton

Oliver, J. W. History of American technology. 1956. 7.50. Ronald

Ropke, Wilhelm T. Humane economy: The social framework of the free market.
tr. by Elizabeth Henderson. 1960. 5.00. Regnery

Singer, Charles, and others. History of technology: vol. 1, From early times
to fall of ancient empires, 1954; vol. 2, Mediterranean civilizations and the
Middle Ages, c. 700 B.C. to c. A.D. 1500, 1956; vol. 3, From the Renaissance
to the Industrial Revolution, c. 1500 to c. 1750. 1957; vol. 4, Industrial Revolution,
c. 1750. to c. 1850. 1958; vol. 5. Late Nineteenth Century, c. 1850. to c. 1900.
26.90 ea. Oxford U. P. (R)

Taube, Mortimer. Men and machines. 1961. 3.75. Columbia

Trelease, Sam F. How to write scientific and technical papers. 1958. 3.25.
Williams & Wilkins

Tweney, C. F., and L. E. C. Hughes. Chamber's technical dictionary. 1958.
7.95. Macmillan (R)

Walker, Charles R. Modern technology and civilization. il. 1962. 7.50. McGraw

White, Lynn, Jr. Medieval technology and social change. 1962. 6.00. Oxford U. P.

TEETH (611.314)

Bunting, Russell W. Oral hygiene. il. 1957. 7.00. Lea & F

Dunning, James M. Principles of dental public health. il. 1962. 11.00. Harvard

Orban, Balint. Oral histology and embryology. il. 1962. 10.50. Mosby

Stoll, Frances A. Dental health education. 5.50. Lea & F

TELECOMMUNICATION (621.38)

Beranek, L. L. Acoustics. il. 1954. 11.50. McGraw

Carson, Ralph S. Principles of applied electronics. il. 1961. 9.95. McGraw

Dunlap. Orrin E., Jr. Communications in space: From wireless to satellite
relay. il. 1962. 4.95. Harper

Hershberger, W. D. Principles of communication systems. 1955. 8.00. Prentice-
Hall

Pierce, John R. Electrons, waves and messages. 1956. 5.00. Doubleday

Shrader, Robert L. Electronic communication. il. 1959. 13.99. McGraw

Visser, A. Telecommunication dictionary. 1960. 27.50. Am. Elsevier

TELEOLOGY (210)

Kant, Immanuel. Critique of judgement. tr. by J. C. Meredith. 1952. 4.50.
Oxford U. P.

Lecomte du Nouy, Pierre. Human destiny. 1947. 5.00. McKay

TELESCOPE (522.2)

Fassero, James S. Photographic giants of Palomar. 1953. 1.50. Westernlore

Kuiper, Gerard P., and Barbara M. Middlehurst. Telescopes. il. 1960. 8.50.
U. of Chicago

Reichert, Robert J., and Elsa. Binoculars and scopes and their use in photography. il. 1960. 2.95. Chilton

Texereau, Jean. How to make a telescope. il. 1957. 4.00. Wiley

Woodbury, David O. Glass giant of Palomar. il. 1953. 5.00. Dodd

TELEVISION (621.388)

American Council on Education. Teaching by closed circuit television. 1956. 1.00.
A.C.E.

Adams, John C., and others. College teaching by television. 1958. 4.00. A.C.E.

Anthony, E. Z. Profitable television troubleshooting. 1957. 7.25. McGraw

Barnhart. Radio and television announcing. 1953. 7.25. Prentice-Hall

Barnouw, Erik. Television writer. 1962. 3.95. Hill & Wang

Bellaire, Arthur. TV advertising: Handbook. il. 1959. 6.50. Harper

Bluem, A. William, and others. Television in the public interest. il. 1961.
6.95. Hastings

Bretz, Rudy. Techniques of television production. il. 1953. 10.00. McGraw

Bretz, Rudy, and Edward Stasheff. Television program: Its direction and production. il. 1962. 6.95. Hill & Wang

Buchsbaum, Walter H. Television servicing. 1958. 7.70. Prentice-Hall

Callahan, J. W. Television in school, college, and community. 1961. 6.50. Mc-
Graw

Conference on Freedom and Responsibility in Broadcasting, Northwestern
University, 1961. 5.00. Northwestern U.

Curran, Charles W. Screen writing and production techniques. 1958. 4.95.
Hastings

Elliott, William Y. Television's impact on American culture. 1956. 4.95.
Mich. State

Fischer, Bernhard, and Herbert V. Jacobs. Elements of mathematics for radio,
television, and electronics. il. 1954. 5.60. Macmillan

Fischer, Edward. Screen arts. 1960. 3.50. Sheed

Fowler, Kenneth, and Harold B. Lippert. Television fundamentals: Theory,
circuits and servicing. il. 1953. 8.00. McGraw

Grob, Bernard. Basic television. il. 1954. 9.25. McGraw

Head, Sydney. Broadcasting in America. 1956. 10.00. Houghton

Heath, Eric. T.V. writer's handbook. 1962. bds. 5.50. Western Pubs.

Henneke, Ben Graf, and Edward S. Dumit. Announcer's handbook. 1959. pap.
4.25. Holt, Rinehart & Winston

Himmelweit, Hilde T., and others. Television and the child. 1958. 6.75.
Oxford U. P.

Hyde, Stuart W. Television and radio announcing. il. 1959. 9.50. Houghton

Johnson, J. R. Television: How it works. il. 5.50. Rider

Jones, Charles Reed. Your career in motion pictures, radio and television.
3.75. Sheridan

Kiver, Milton S. Television simplified. il. 1962. 9.95. Van Nostrand

Lerch, John H. Careers in broadcasting. il. 1962. 3.95. Meredith

Lewis, Philip. Educational television guidebook. il. 1961. 6.75. McGraw

McMahan, Harry Wayne. Television production. 1957. 7.50. Hastings

Opotowsky, Stan. TV: The big picture. 1961. 4.50. Dutton

Postman, Neil. Television and the teaching of English. 1.00. Appleton

Powell, John W. Channels of learning. 1962. 4.50. Pub. Affairs

Sams, Howard W., and Co. Photofact guide to TV troubles. 1962. pap. 2.00.
Bobbs

Schramm, Wilbur L., and others. Television in the lives of our children. il.
1961. 6.00. Stanford

Schramm, Wilbur. Impact of educational educational television. 1960. 5.00.
U. of Ill.

Seehafer, Eugene F., and J. W. Laemmar. Successful television and radio
advertising. il. 1959. 9.95. McGraw

Seldes, Gilbert. Public arts. 1957. pap. 1.50. S. and S.

Siepmann, Charles A. Radio, television, and society. il. 1950. 5.00. Oxford U.P.

Stepmann, Charles A. TV and our school crisis. 1958. 3.50. Dodd

Tarbet, Donald G. Television and our schools. il. 1961. 5.00. Ronald

Tyler, Poyntz. Television and radio. 1961. 2.50. Wilson

Zettl, Herbert. Television production handbook. 1961. 6.95. Wadsworth
TEMPERANCE (178)
Holloway, Elma. Alcohol and youth. il. 1961. bds. 2.75. Vantage
McCarthy, Raymond G. Teen-agers and alcohol: A handbook for the educator. 1956. 4.00. Rutgers Center of Alcohol Studies
Monroe, Margaret E., and Jean Stewart. Alcohol education for the layman: A bibliography. 1959. 5.00. Rutgers
Ullman, Albert. To know the difference. 1960. 4.75. St. Martins
TEMPERATURE (551.5)
King, Allen L. Thermophysics. 1962. 9.50. Freeman
Winslow, C.E.A., and L. P. Herrington. Temperature and human life. 1949. 4.00. Princeton
TEMPLES (726)
Hanson, J. A. Roman theater-temples. 1958. 7.50. Princeton
TENNESSEE (976.8)
Alexander, Thomas B. Political reconstruction in Tennessee. 1950. 4.00. Vanderbilt
Davidson, Donald. Tennessee: The new river, Civil War to TVA. il. 1948. 4.50. Holt, Rinehart & Winston
Davidson, Donald. Tennessee: The old river, frontier to secession. il. 1946. 4.00. Rinehart
Hubbard, Preston J. Origins of the TVA: The Muscle Shoals controversy. 1961. 8.00. Vanderbilt
King, Judson. Conservation fight: From Theodore Roosevelt to the Tennessee Valley Authority. 1959. 6.00. Pub. Affairs
Lilienthal, David E. TVA: Democracy on the march. 1953. 5.00. Harper
Martin, Roscoe C. TVA: The first twenty years. 1956. 4.50. U. of Tenn., or U. of Ala.
Writers' Project. Tennessee. 1949. 6.50. Hastings
TENNIS (796.34)
Budge, L. Tennis made easy. 1945. 2.95. Ronald
Connolly, Maureen. Power tennis. il. 1954. 2.95. Ronald
Jaeger, Eloise, and Harry Leighton. Teaching of tennis for school and recreational programs. 1959. 3.25. Burgess
Leighton, Harry. Tennis. 1962. 1.95. Sterling
Murphy. B., and C. Tennis for beginners. 1958. 3.50. Ronald
Sports Illustrated. Sports Illustrated book of tennis. il. 1960. 2.95. Lippincott
Talbert, William F., and Bruce S. Old. Game of doubles in tennis. il. 1962. 4.95. Lippincott
Talbert, William F., and Bruce S. Old. Game of singles in tennis. il. 1962. 4.95. Lippincott
TENNYSON, ALFRED TENNYSON, BARON, 1809-1892 (928)
Buckley, Jerome H. Tennyson: The growth of a poet. 1960. 5.75. Harvard
Killham, John. Critical essays on the poetry of Tennyson. 1960. 5.50. Barnes & Noble
Killham, John. Tennyson and the Princess, reflections of an age. 1958. 5.60. Oxford U. P.
Lounsbury, Thomas R. Life and times of Tennyson. 1962. 10.00. Russell
Ryals, Clyde. Theme and symbol in Tennyson's poetry to 1850. in prep. U. of Pa.
TEXAS (976.4)
Dobie, J. Frank, and others. Texian stomping grounds. 1941. 2.50. S.M.U.
Hogan, William Ransom. Texas Republic: A social and economic history. il. 1947. 4.00. U. of Okla.
Tolbert, Frank X. Informal history of Texas. il. 1961. 3.95. Harper
Walker, Stanley. Texas. il. 1962. 8.50. Viking
Writers' Project. Texas. 1947. 6.50. Hastings
TEXTILES (677)

Atwater, Mary M. Shuttle-craft book of American hand-weaving. il. 7.95. Macmillan
Conran, Terence. Printed textile design. il. 1958. 6.50. Viking
Erickson, Janet. Block printing on textiles. il. 1961. 10.00. Watson
Hess, Katharine P. Textile fibers and their use. il. 1958. 6.95. Lippincott
Kafka, Francis J. Hand decoration of fabrics. il. 1959. 5.50. Taplinger
Moncrieff, R. W. Man made fibers. 1957. 9.75. Wiley
Potter, Maurice D., and B. P. Corbman. Fiber to fabric. 1959. 4.80. McGraw
Wingate, Isabel B. Textile fabrics and their selection. 1955. 10.60. Prentice-Hall

THACKERAY, WILLIAM MAKEPEACE, 1811-1863 (928)

Ray, G. N. Buried life: A study of the relation between Thackeray's fiction and his personal history. 1952. 2.00. Oxford U. P.
Ray, G. N. Thackeray: The age of wisdom (1847-1863) 1958. 8.00. McGraw
Ray, G. N. Thackeray: The uses of adversity. 1955. 7.00. McGraw
Tillotson, Geoffrey. Thackeray the novelist. 1954. 4.50. Cambridge U. P.

THAILAND (959.3)

American Geographical Society. Thailand. il. 1962. 10.00. Meredith
Blake, W. T. Thailand journey. il. 1960. 4.95. Taplinger
Busch, Noel F. Thailand. il. 1959. 3.50. Van Nostrand
Landon, Margaret. Anna and the King of Siam. il. 1944. 5.95. Day

THEATER (792)

Agate, James. English dramatic critics, 1660-1933. 3.95. Hill & Wang
Albright, H. D., and others. Principles of theatre art. 1955. 7.75. Houghton
Anderson, Maxwell. Off Broadway: Essays about the theater. 2.50. Sloane
Arnott, Peter. Introduction to the Greek theatre. 5.00. St. Martins
Bailey, Howard. ABC's of play producing: A handbook for the non professional. 1955. 3.95. McKay
Baker, Blanch M. Theatre and allied arts. 1953. 10.00. Wilson
Beare, William. Roman stage. 7.50. Hillary
Belkanp, S. Yancey. Guide to the performing arts. 1957. 15.00.; 1958, 1959, 1960, 9.00 ea. Scarecrow
Bentley, Eric. In search of theater. il. 1953. pap. 1.45. Vintage
Bieber, M. History of the Greek and Roman theater. 1961. 17.50. Princeton
Bowers, Faubion. Japanese theatre. il. 1952. 6.00. Nelson
Bowman, Walter P., and Robert H. Ball. Theatre language, a dictionary. 6.95. Theatre Arts
Bradbrook, Muriel C. Themes and conventions of Elizabethan tragedy. 1953. 5.00. Cambridge U. P.
Brooke, Iris. Costume in Greek drama. 6.00. Theatre Arts
Chambers, Edmund K. Mediaeval stage. il. 2 vols. 1903. 12.00. Oxford U. P.
Cheney, Sheldon. Theatre. 1959. 9.50. McKay
Cooper, Charles W. Preface to drama. 1955. 5.50. Ronald
Corry, Percy. Amateur theatrecraft. 1962. 3.95. Pitman
Crafton, A., and J. Royer. Complete acted play: From script to final curtain. il. 3.75. Appleton
Craig, Gordon. On the art of the theatre. 1925. 2.75. Theatre Arts
Dietrich, John E. Play direction. 1953. 9.65. Prentice-Hall
Dolman, John, Jr. Art of play production. 1946. 5.00. Harper
Elickinger, Ray C. Greek theater and its drama. 1946. 6.50. U. of Chicago
Friederich, Willard J., and John H. Fraser. Scenery design for the amateur stage. il. 1950. 4.50. Macmillan
Gagey, E. M. Revolution in American drama. 1947. 3.75. Columbia
Gaye, Freda. Who's who in the theatre. 1962. 20.00. Pitman (R)
Gard, Robert E., and Gertrude Burley. Community theatre. 1959. 3.75. Duell
Gassner, John. Form and idea in modern theatre. 1956. 4.90. Holt, Rinehart & Winston
Gassner, John. Theatre in our times. 1954. pap. 2.45. Crown
Gassner, John, and Philip Barber. Producing the play. 1953. 7.00. Holt, Rinehart & Winston

Gassner, John. Theatre at the crossroads: Plays and playwrights on the midcentury American stage. 1960. 5. 95. Holt, Rinehart & Winston
Gorchakov, N. A. Theater in Soviet Russia. 1957. 10. 00. Columbia
Granville-Barker, Harley. On dramatic method. 1960. 3. 00. Smith, Peter
Harrison, G. B. Elizabethan plays and players. 1956. 4. 40. U. of Mich.
Hartnoll, Phyllis. Oxford companion to the theatre. 1957. 11. 50. Oxford U. P.
Hatlen, Theodore W. Orientation to the theatre. il. 1962. pap. 2. 75. Appleton
Hewitt, Barnard W. Theatre U. S. A. , 1668-1957. 1959. 9. 95. McGraw
Hewitt, Barnard, and others. Play production: Theory and practice. il. 1959. 8. 50. Lippincott
Hotson, Leslie. Shakespeare's wooden O. il. 1960. 6. 50. Macmillan
Kerr, Walter. How not to write a play. 3. 95. Writer
Krutch, Joseph Wood. Comedy and conscience after the Restoration. 1949. 5. 00. Columbia
MacGowan, Kenneth, and W. Melnitz. Living stage: A history of the world theatre. 1955. 11. 00. Prentice-Hall
Mantle, Burns. Best plays of 1894-1961. 45 vols. 6. 00 ea. Dodd
Nathan, George Jean. Magic morror. 1960. 5. 00. Knopf
Nathan, George Jean. Theatre in the fifties. 1953. 5. 00. Knopf
Nicoll, Allardyce. British drama. 1957. 5. 50. Barnes & Noble
Nicoll, Allardyce. Development of the theatre. 10. 75. Harcourt
Nicoll, Allardyce. Theatre and dramatic theory. 1962. 3. 75. Barnes & Noble
Ommanney, Katharine A. , and P. C. Stage and the school. 1960. 5. 60. McGraw
Pickard-Cambridge, Arthur. Dramatic festivals of Athens. 1953. 8. 80. Oxford U. P.
Priestley, John B. Wonderful world of the theatre. il. 1959. 2. 95. Doubleday
Rice, Elmer. Living theater. 1959. 5. 50. Harper
Roberts, Vera M. On stage: A history of theatre. 1962. 7. 00. Harper
Samachson, Dorothy, and Joseph. Dramatic story of the theatre. il. 1955. 4. 00. Abelard
Schonberger, E. D. Fundamentals of play production. 1961. 3. 00. Denison
Selden, Samuel. Man in his theatre. 1957. 3. 00. U. of N. C.
Selden, Samuel. Stage in action. il. 3. 50. Appleton
Seldes, Gilbert. Seven lively arts. 1957. 4. 95. Sagamore
Serlio, and others. Renaissance stage. 5. 50. U. of Miami
Slonim, Marc. Russian theater, from the empire to the Soviets. il. 1961. 7. 50. World Pub.
Shaw, George Bernard. Shaw on theatre. by E. J. West. 1959. 3. 95. Hill & Wang
Shaw, Bernard. Plays and players: Essays on the theatre. 1954. 2. 25. Oxford U. P.
Shipley, Joseph T. Guide to great plays. 1956. 10. 00. Pub. Affairs
Sobel, Bernard. New theatre handbook and digest of plays. 1948. 5. 95. Crown (R)
Sobel, Bernard. Pictorial history of vaudeville. il. 1961. 6. 95. Citadel
Southern, Richard. Seven ages of the theatre. 1961. 5. 95. Hill & Wang
Tynan, Kenneth. Curtains: Selections from the drama criticism and related writings. 1961. 7. 95. Atheneum
Wright, Edward A. Primer for playgoers. 1958. 7. 00. Prentice-Hall
Wright, Edward A. Understanding today's theatre: Cinema, stage, television. il. 1959. pap. 1. 95. Prentice-Hall
Young, John Wray. Directing the play: From selection to opening night. 1958. 3. 50. Harper
Young, Stark. Immortal shadows. 3. 95. Scribner

THEATERS (792)

Burris-Meyer, Harold, and Edward C. Cole. Scenery for the theatre. il. 1938. 15. 00. Little
Cornberg, Sol, and Emanuel L. Gebauer. Stage crew handbook. il. 1957. 5. 00. Harper
Corry, Percy. Planning the stage. il. 1961. 7. 95. Pitman

Gillette, Arnold S. Stage scenery. il. 1960. 8.95. Harper
Gropius, Walter. Theatre of the Bauhaus. il. 1961. 7.50. Wesleyan U. P.
Larson, Orville K. Scene design for stage and screen. 1961. 5.00. Mich. State
Napier, Frank. Handbook of sound effects. 2.00. Wehman
Selden, Samuel, and Hunton D. Sellman. Stage scenery and lighting. il. 1959.
    7.95. Meredith
Southern, Richard. Stage setting for amateurs and professionals. 5.00. Theatre
    Arts

THEOLOGY (200)

Augustine, Saint. Basic writings. 2 vols. 1948. 7.50 ea. Random
Barth, Karl. Community, church, and state. 3.00. Smith, Peter
Cross, F. L. Oxford dictionary of the Christian church. 1957. 20.00. Oxford U. P.
    (R)
Duns, Scotus, John. Philosophical writings. by Allan Wolter. 1962. 6.50. Nelson
Edwards, Jonathan. Representative selections. by Clarence Faust, and Thomas
    Johnson. 4.25. Smith, Peter
Fosdick, Harry Emerson. Great voices of the Reformation. 2.95. Modern Lib.
Francis of Assisi, Saint. St. Francis of Assisi. il. 1960. 4.50. Harper
Freeman, D. H. Relationship between philosophy and theology. 2.75. Pres-
    byterian & Reformed
Hegel, Friedrich. On Christianity, earlier theological writings. tr. by T. M.
    Knox. 4.00. Smith, Peter
Leibrecht, Walter. Religion and culture. 1959. 7.50. Harper
Luther, Martin. Martin Luther: Selections from his writings. 1961. 6.75. Quad-
    rangle
Mather, Cotton. Selections from Cotton Mather. by Kenneth B. Murdock. 1960.
    2.45. Hafner
Parente, Pietro. Dictionary of dogmatic theology. 1951. 5.00. Bruce (R)
Pegis, A. C. Wisdom of Catholicism. 2.95. Modern Lib.
Przywara, Erich. Augustine synthesis. 1958. 4.00. Smith, Peter
Schaff, Philip, and Johann Herzog. New Schaff-Herzog encyclopedia of religious
    knowledge. 13 vols. 65.00. Baker Bk. (R)
Thomas, Aquinas, Saint. Basic writings. by Anton C. Pegis. 2 vols. 1945. 15.00.
    Random
Thomas, Aquinas, Saint. Introduction to Saint Thomas Aquinas. 1948. 1.95.
    Modern Lib.
Wesley, John. Works of John Wesley. 14 vols. 24.95. Zondervan
Woods, Ralph L. Treasury of Catholic thinking. 1962. pap. 1.95. Apollo

THERAPEUTICS (615)

Curtis, David. Learn while you sleep. 1960. 3.00. Libra
Jones, Alfred E. Scientific autosuggestion. 1957. 2.95. Assoc. Booksellers
Jung, Carl G. Modern man in search of a soul. 5.75. Harcourt

THERMODYNAMICS (536.7)

Bridgman, P. W. Nature of thermodynamics. 3.40. Smith, Peter
Callen, Herbert. Thermodynamics. il. 1960. 8.75. Wiley
Carnot, Sadi. Reflections on the motive power of fire. 3.50. Smith, Peter
Dodge, Barnett F. Chemical engineering thermodynamics. il. 1944. 11.00.
    McGraw
Faires, Virgil M. Elementary thermodynamics. il. 1948. 7.50. Macmillan
Fermi, Enrico. Thermodynamics. 1957. pap. 1.75. Dover
Hall, N. A. Thermodynamics of fluid flow. 1951. 8.65. Prentice-Hall
Hawkins, G. A. Thermodynamics. 1951. 7.00. Wiley
Weber, Harold C. , and H. P. Meissner. Thermodynamics for chemical engineers.
    1957. 8.95. Wiley
Zemansky, Mark W. Heat and thermodynamics. il. 1957. 9.50. McGraw

THOMAS, AQUINAS, SAINT, 1225?-1274 (921.9)

Ancombe, G. E. M. , and Peter T. Geach. Three philosophers. 1961. 3.50.
    Cornell

Brennan, Robert E. Thomistic psychology. 1941. 5.75. Macmillan
Chesterton, G. K. St. Thomas Aquinas. 1933. 3.00. Sheed
D'Arcy, M. C. St. Thomas Aquinas. 1954. 3.75. Newman
De La Vega, F. J. Social progress and happiness in the philosophy of St. Thomas
    Aquinas and contemporary American sociology. 1949. 1.75. Catholic U. of Am.
    Pr.
Gilby, Thomas. Political thought of Thomas Aquinas. 1958. 5.00. U. of Chicago
Gilson, Etienne. Christian philosophy of St. Thomas Aquinas. 1956. 7.50. Random
Gilson, Etienne. Elements of Christian philosophy. 6.95. Doubleday
Hutchins, Robert M. St. Thomas and the world state. 1949. 2.50. Marquette
Klocker, Harry R. Thomism and modern thought. 1962. 4.00. Appleton
Maritain, Jacques. St. Thomas and the problem of evil. 1942. 2.50. Marquette
Pieper, Josef. Guide to Thomas Aquinas. 1962. 3.95. Pantheon
THOMAS, DYLAN, 1914-1953 (928)
Bayley, John. Romantic survival: A study in poetic evolution. 1957. 3.40. Oxford
    U. P.
Brinnin, John M. Casebook of Dylan Thomas. 1960. 4.95. Crowell
Brinnin, John Malcolm. Dylan Thomas in America. 1955. 6.00. Little
Thomas, Caitlin. Leftover life to kill. 1957. 4.75. Little
Tindall, William Y. Reader's guide to Dylan Thomas. 1962. 4.95. Farrar, Straus
THOMPSON, FRANCIS, 1859-1907 (928)
Reid, J. C. Francis Thompson, man and poet. il. 1960. 4.25. Newman
Thomson, Paul. Francis Thompson. 1961. 5.00. Nelson
THOREAU, HENRY DAVID, 1817-1862 (928)
Canby, Henry S. Thoreau. 4.75. Smith, Peter
Derleth, August. Concord rebel: A life of Henry David Thoreau. il. 1962. 3.50.
    Chilton
Harding, Walter. Thoreau: A century of criticism. 1954. 3.75. S.M.U.
Harding, Walter R. Thoreau handbook. 1959. 4.50. N.Y.U.
Krutch, Joseph Wood. Henry David Thoreau. 1948. 4.75. Sloane
Metzger, Charles R. Thoreau and Whitman: A study of their esthetics. 1961.
    4.25. U. of Wash.
Stoller, Leo. After Walden: Thoreau's changing views on economic man. 1957.
    4.00. Stanford
Van Doren, Mark. Henry David Thoreau. 5.00. Russell
THOUGHT AND THINKING (153)
Chase, Stuart. Tyranny of words. 4.50. 1959. Harcourt
Dewey, John. Essays in experiemntal logic. 3.75. Smith, Peter
Dewey, John. How we think. 1933. 5.00. Heath
Dewey, John. Logic: Theory of inquiry. 1938. 6.50. Holt
Dimnet, Ernest. Art of thinking. 1928. 3.50. S. and S.
Flesch, Rudolf. Art of clear thinking. 1951. 3.50. Harper
Holloway, John. Language and intelligence. 1951. 3.50. St. Martins
Johnson, Donald M. Psychology of thought and judgement. 1955. 7.00. Harper
Larrabee, Harold A. Reliable knowledge. 1945. 6.50. Houghton
Mursell, James L. Using your mind effectively. 1951. 4.50. McGraw
Shands, Harley C. Thinking and psychotherapy. 1961. 5.75. Harvard
Snell, Bruno. Discovery of the mind: The Greek origins of European thought.
    1953. 5.50. Harvard
Thompson, Robert. Psychology of thinking. 1959. pap. 0.95. Penguin
Thouless, Robert H. How to think straight. 1939. 3.50. S. and S.
Weigel, Gustav, and Arthur Madden. Knowledge: Its value and limits. 1961. 3.95.
    Prentice-Hall
THYROID GLAND (612.44)
Fleischmann, Walter. Comparative physiology of the thyroid and parathyroid
    glands. 1951. 2.50. Thomas, C.C.
Levitt, Tobias. Thyroid, a physiological, pathological, clinical and surgical
    study. il. 1954. 20.00. Williams & Wilkins

TOPOLOGY (513. 83)

Halmos, Paul R. Measure theory. il. 1950. 7.75. Van Nostrand

Lefschetz, S. Introduction to topology. 1949. 5.00. Princeton

Newman, M. H. A. Topology of plane sets of points. 1951. 6.50. Cambridge U. P.

Patterson, Edward M. Topology. il. 1960. 1.95. Wiley

Pontryagin, L. S. Foundations of combinatorial topology. 1952. 4.00. Graylock

TORNADOES (551. 553)

Flora, Snowden D. Tornadoes of the United States. il. 1958. 3.95. U. of Okla.

TORTS (347. 5)

Bohlen, Francis H. Bohlen's Cases on torts. 1941. 6.80. Bobbs

Gregory, Charles O. , and Harry Kalven, Jr. Cases and materials on torts. 1959. 12.50. Little

TOSCANINI, ARTURO, 1867-1957 (927)

Chotzinoff, Samuel. Toscanini. il. 1956. 3.95. Knopf

Marsh, Robert Charles. Toscanini and the art of orchestral performance. 1956. 4.50. Lippincott

TOTALITARIANISM (321. 64)

Arendt, Hannah. Origins of totalitarianism. pap. 2.25. Meridian

Cantril, Hadley. Soviet leaders and the image of man. 1960. 4.00. Rutgers

Friedrich, Carl J. , and Zbigniew K. Brzezinski. Totalitarian dictatorship and autocracy. 1956. 5.50. Harvard

Fromm, Erich. Escape from freedom. 3.75. 1941. Rinehart

Hayek, Freidrich A. Road to serfdom. 1944. 5.75. U. of Chicago

Kornhauser, William. Politics of mass society. 1959. 5.00. Free Press

Lauterbach, Albert. Economic security and individual freedom: Can we have both? 2.50. Cornell

McGovern, William M. From Luther to Hitler: History of Fascist-Nazi political theory. 1941. 7.75. Houghton

Malinowski, Bronislaw. Freedom and civilization. 1960. pap. 2.25. Indiana

Schlesinger, Arthur, Jr. Vital center. 3.50. 1962. Houghton

Talmon, J. L. Origins of totalitarian democracy. 5.50. Praeger

TOTEMISM (291. 2ll)

Freud, Sigmund. Totem and taboo. 1952. 4.50. Norton

Weatherby, Hugh. Tales the totems tell. 1951. 2.95. St. Martins

TOULOUSE-LAUTREC MONFA, HENRI MARIE RAYMOND DE, 1864-1901 (927)

Julien, Edouard. Toulouse-Lautrec. il. 1959. 3.50. Crown

Lassaigne, Jacques. Toulouse-Lautrec. 1953. 5.75. World Pub.

Toulouse-Lautrec, Henri de. Toulouse-Lautrec: Portfolio with text. 1958. 1.50. World Pub.

TOXICOLOGY (615. 9)

Dreisbach, R. H. Handbook of poisoning, disgnosis and treatment. il. 1961. 3.50. Lange

Herber, Lewis. Our synthetic environment. 1962. 4.95. Knopf

TOYNBEE, ARNOLD, JOSEPH, 1889- (928)

Ashley, Montagu, M. F. Toynbee and history. 1956. 5.00. Sargent

TOYS (688. 72)

Foley, Daniel J. Toys through the ages. il. 1962. 4.95. Chilton

Hertz, Louis H. Handbook of old American toys. il. 1947. 3.95. Haber

TRACERS (BIOLOGY) (581.13356)

Kamen, Martin D. Isotopic tracers in biology: An introduction to tracer methodology 1957. 10.50. Academic Press

Sheppard, Charles W. Basic principles of the tracer methods. il. 1962. 8.00. Wiley

TRACK-ATHLETICS (796. 42)

Bresnahan, George T. , and others. Track and field athletics. il. 1960. 5.50. Mosby

Conger, R. M. Track and field. 1939. 2.95. Ronald

Cooper, John, and Jesse Mortensen. Track and field. 1959. 5.25. Prentice-Hall

Miller, Richard I. Fundamentals of track and field coaching. 1952. 5. 25. McGraw

V-Five Association of America. Track and field. il. 1950. 4. 00. U. S. Naval
Inst.

TRADE-MARKS (659.12)

Berle, Alf K. , and L. Sprague de Camp. Inventions, patents and their management.
1959. 12. 50. Van Nostrand

Jacobson, Egbert. Trademark design. 1952. 8. 75. Theobald

TRADE REGULATION (338. 9)

Anderson, Ronald A. Government and business. 1960. 7. 50. South-Western Pub.

Cotter, Cornelius P. Government and private enterprise. 1960. 7. 00. Holt,
Rinehart & Winston

Newman, P. C. Public control of business. 1955. 15. 00. Praeger

TRADE-UNIONS (331. 88)

Cole, G. D. H. Short history of the British working-class movement. 1948. 6. 75.
Macmillan

Hammond, T. T. Lenin on trade unions and revolution, 1893-1917. 1957. 3. 50.
Columbia

Harrington, Michael, and Paul Jacobs. Labor in a free society: Arden House
Symposium on Trade Unionism. 1959. 4. 00. U. of Calif.

Harrison, Martin. Trade unions and the Labour Party since 1945. 1960. 4. 95.
Wayne

Hicks, J. R. Theory of wages. 1958. 4. 00. Smith, Peter

Kernhauser, Arthur, and others. Industrial conflict. 1954. 7. 95. McGraw

Perlman, Selig. Theory of the labor movement. 1949. 3. 50. Kelley

Rose, Arthur M. Trade union wage policy. 1956. 3. 00. U. of Calif.

Tannenbaum, Frank. Philosophy of labor. 1951. 3. 00. Knopf

Unwin, George. Industrial organization in the 16th and 17th centuries. 6. 00.
Kelley

Wigham, Eric L. Trade unions. 1956. 1. 70. Oxford U. P. '

Wright, David McC. Impact of the labor union. 1956. 5. 00. Kelley

TRADE-UNIONS--U. S. (331. 88)

Adamic, Louis. Dynamite, the story of class violence in America. il. 1959.
6. 00. Smith, Peter

Barbash, Jack. Labor's grass roots. 1961. 4. 95. Harper

Barbash, Jack. Practice of unionism. 1956. 5. 75. Harper

Barbash, Jack. Unions and union leadership. 1959. 6. 00. Harper

Bradley, Philip D. Public stake in union power. 1959. 7. 00. U. of Va.

Daniels, W. M. American labor movement. 2. 00. Wilson

Foner, Philip S. History of the labor movement in the United States. vol. 1,
From Colonial times to the founding of the American Federation of Labor.
in prep; vol. 2, From the founding of the American Federation of Labor to
the emergence of American imperialism. 5. 00. Int. Pub.

Grob, Gerald N. Workers and Utopia. 1961. 6. 50. Northwestern U.

Karson, Marc. American labor unions and politics 1900-1918. 1959. 6. 50.
Southern Ill.

Leiter, Robert. Labor economics and industrial relations. 1960. pap. 1. 95.
Barnes & Noble

Lipset, Seymour M. Political man: The social bases of politics. 1959. 4. 95.
Doubleday

Perlman, Mark. Labor union theories in America: Background and development.
1958. 6. 00. Harper

Peterson, Florence. American labor unions. 1952. 4. 00. Harper

Rayback, Joseph G. History of American labor. 1959. 6. 95. Macmillan

Rees, Albert. Economics of trade unions. 1962. 3. 50. U. of Chicago

Richberg, Donald R. Labor union monopoly: A clear and present danger. 1957.
3. 50. Regnery

Shister, Joseph. Economics of the labor market. 1956. 6. 50. Lippincott

Taft, Philip. Structure and government of labor unions. il. 1954. 6. 50. Harvard

Ware, Norman. Labor movement in the United States, 1860-1895. 1959. 5.50.
Smith, Peter

TRAFFIC SAFETY (614.86)

Brody, Leon, and Herbert J. Stack. Highway safety and driver education. 1954.
9.35. Prentice-Hall
Glenn, Harold T. Youth at the wheel. 1958. 4.08. Bennett
Gordon, Albert C. Traffic accidents and how to prevent them. 3.50. Pagoda
Halsey, Maxwell N. Skillful driving. il. 1959. bds. 3.95. Doubleday
Ingraham, Joseph C. Modern traffic control. il. 1954. 4.50. Funk
Kearney, Paul W. How to drive better and avoid accidents. il. 1956. 4.95. Crowell
Lauer, A. R. Psychology of driving. il. 1961. 10.50. Thomas, C. C.
Owen, Wilfred. Metropolitan transportation problem. 1956. 4.50. Brookings

TRAGEDY (808.2)

Bowers, Fredson. Elizabethan revenge tragedy. 1958. 4.00. Smith, Peter
Bradbrook, Muriel C. Themes and conventions of Elizabethan tragedy. 1952.
5.00. Cambridge U. P.
Brooks, Cleanth. Tragic themes in Western literature. 1955. 4.00. Yale
Farnham, Willard. Medieval heritage of Elizabethan tragedy. 1957. 7.50. Barnes
& Noble
Hathorn, Richmond Y. Tragedy, myth, and mystery. 1962. 6.75. Indiana
Leech, Clifford. Shakespeare's tragedies and other studies in seventeenth
century drama. 1950. 3.80. Oxford U. P.
Lucas, F. L. Tragedy. 1953. 2.50. Macmillan
Mandel, Oscar. Definition of tragedy. 1961. 4.50. N. Y. U.
Muller, Herbert J. Spirit of tragedy. 1956. 5.75. Knopf
Myers, Henry Alonzo. Tragedy: A view of life. 1957. 3.50. Cornell
Olson, Elder. Tragedy and the theory of drama. 1961. 6.50. Wayne
Reid, Benjamin L. William Butler Yeats: The lyric of tragedy. il. 1961. 4.50.
U. of Okla.
Sewall, Richard B. Vision of tragedy. 1959. 4.00. Yale
Steiner, George. Death of tragedy. 1961. 5.00. Knopf

TRANQUILIZING DRUGS (615.788)

Himwich, Harold E. Tranquilizing drugs. 1957. 5.00. A. A. A. S.
Kline, Nathan S. Psychopharmacology frontiers. 1959. 10.00. Little

TRANSCENDENTALISM (809.91)

Frothingham, Octavius Brooks. Transcendentalism in New England. 3.75.
Smith, Peter
Goddard, Harold C. Studies in New England transcendentalism. 6.00. Hillary
Gohdes, Clarence. Periodicals of American transcendentalism. 1931. 5.00.
Duke
Gray, Henry David. Emerson. 1958. 3.50. Ungar
Miller, Perry. G. E. Transcendentalists: An anthology. 1950. 6.50. Harvard
Peel, Robert. Christian Science: Its encounter with American culture. 1958.
4.00. Holt.
Temple, William. Nature, man and God. Gifford lectures, 1932-1933 and 1933-
1934. 1953. 6.75. St. Martins

TRANSISTORS (621.38)

Bevitt, William D. Transistors handbook. il. 1956. 10.00. Prentice-Hall
Coblenz, Abraham, and H. L. Owens. Transistors. 1955. 7.50. McGraw
Cooke-Yarborough, M. A. Introduction to transistor circuits. il. 1960. 3.50.
Wiley
De Witt, D. , and A. L. Roseloff. Transistor electronics, 1957. 9.00. McGraw
Garner, Louis E. , Jr. Transistor circuit handbook. il. 4.95. Coyne
Marrows, H. E. Transistor engineering reference handbook. il. 1956. 9.95.
Rider
Pullen, Keats, Jr. Handbook of transistor circuit design. 1961. 13.00. Prentice-
Hall
Riddle, Robert L. , and Marlin P. Ristenbatt. Transistor physics and circuits.
1958. 11.00. Prentice-Hall

Shea, Richard F. Principles of transistor circuits. 1953. 11.75. Wiley

TRANSPORTATION (385-388)
Baldwin, Leland D. Keelboat age on western waters. 1960. 5.00. U. of Pittsburgh
Beckmann, M., and others. Studies in the economics of transportation. 1956. 5.00. Yale
Beebs, Lucius, and Charles Clegg. Hear the train blow: A pictorial epic of America in the railroad age. il. 12.75. Dutton
Bigham, Truman C., and Merrill J. Roberts. Transportation. il. 1952. 7.95. McGraw
Fair, Marvin L., and Ernest W. Williams, Jr. Economics of transportation. 1959. 8.00. Harper
Grossman, W. L. Fundamentals of transportation. 5.50. Simmons-Boardman
Hornung, Clarence. Wheels across America: A pictorial history of transportation il. 4.95. Barnes, A. S.
Lee, Norman E. Travel and transport through the ages. 1955. 2.95. Cambridge U. P.
Locklin, David Philip. Economics of transportation. 1960. 11.35. Irwin
Legault, Adrian R. Highway and airport engineering. 1960. 12.00. Prentice-Hall
Meyer, Balthasar H. History of transportation in the U. S. before 1860. 12.50. Smith, Peter
Savage, C. I. Economic history of transport. 2.50. Hillary
Taylor, George R. Transportation revolution: 1815-1860. il. 1951. 10.10. Holt, Rinehart & Winston
Tedlow, Joseph H. Regulation of transportation. by Lee K. Mathews. 1955. 8.00. Brown, W. C.

TREATIES (341.2)
Byrd, E. M., jr. Treaties and executive agreements in the United States. 7.50. Int. Pub. Service
Hartmann, Frederick H. Basic documents of international relations. 1951, 4.25. McGraw
Hendry, James McLeod. Treaties and federal constitutions. 1955. 4.50. Pub. Affairs
McNair, Lord. Law of treaties. 1961. 13.45. Oxford U. P.

TREES (582.16)
Anderson, Roger F. Forest and shade tree entomology. 1960. 8.50. Wiley
Ary, Sheila, and Mary Gregory. Oxford book of wild flowers. il. 1960. 8.25. Oxford U. P. (R)
Bailey, Liberty H. Cultivated conifers in North America. il. 13.50. Macmillan
Baker, F. S. Principles of silviculture. 1950. 8.00. McGraw
Blackburn, Benjamin. Trees and shrubs in eastern North America. 1952. 6.75. Oxford U. P.
Coker, William Chambers, and Henry R. Totten. Trees of the southeastern states. 1945. 4.00. U. of N. C.
Davey, Martin. Complete guide to tree care. 1961. 3.95. Holt, Rinehart & Winston
Emerson, Arthur I., and Clarence M. Weed. Our trees: How to know them. 1959. 6.50. Lippincott
Graves, Arthur Harmount. Illustrated guide to trees and shrubs. 1956. 6.50. Harper
Green, Charlotte H. Trees of the south. 1939. 5.00. U. of N. C.
Haller, John M. Tree care. il. 6.50. Macmillan
Hough, Romeyn B. Handbook of the trees of the northern states and Canada east of the Rocky Mountains. il. 1947. 10.00. Macmillan
Hough, Romeyn B. Hough's encyclopedia of American woods. 15 vols. 30.00 ea. Speller (R)
Hottes, Alfred C. Book of trees. il. 1953. 5.00. Dodd
Jane, F. W. Structure of wood. il. 9.50. Macmillan
Kieran, John. Introduction to nature. il. 1955. 6.00. Doubleday
Kieran, John. Introduction to trees. 1954. 2.95. Doubleday

Kramer, Paul J. , and Theodore T. Kozlowski. Physiology of trees. 1960. 12. 50.
    McGraw
Marx, David S. Learn the trees from leaf prints. il. 1938. 2.25. Botanic
Mathews, F. Schuyler. Field book of American trees and shrubs. il. 1915. 3. 95.
    Putnam (R)
Menninger, Edwin A. What flowering tree is that: A handbook for the tropics.
    1958. pap. 2. 00. Horticultural Bks.
Muenscher, W. C. Keys to woody plants. 1950. Cornell
Peattie, Donald Culross. Natural history of trees of eastern and central North
    America. il. 1950. 6. 00. Houghton
Petrides, George A. Field guide to the trees and shrubs. il. 1958. 4.50. Houghton
    (R)
Platt, Rutherford. 1001 questions answered about trees. il. 1959. 6. 00. Dodd
Sargent, Charles S. Manual of the trees of North America. 2 vols. il. 1962.
    4. 00 ea. Smith, Peter
Schaffner, J. H. Field manual of trees. 3. 00. Long's College Bk.
Symonds, George W. D. , and Stephen Chelminski. Tree identification book. il.
    1958. 10. 00. Barrows (R)
Thimann, K. V. Physiology of forest trees. 1958. 12. 00. Ronald
TRIALS (343. 1)
Curtis, C. P. It's your law. 1954. 3. 75. Harvard
Morris, Richard B. Fair trial. 1952. 5. 75. Knopf
Nizer, Louis. My life in court. 1961. 5. 95. Doubleday
Tracy, John E. Nine famous trials. 1960. 3. 50. Vantage
West, Rebecca. Meaning of treason. 1947. 3. 50. Viking
Williams, Brad. Due process. 1960. 4. 50. Morrow
TRIGONOMETRY (514)
Benson, Robert E. Natural trigonometric functions. 5. 00. Powner
Crowder, Norman A. , and Grace C. Martin. Trigonometry. il. 4. 95. Doubleday
Dadourian, H. M. Plane trigonometry. il. 1950. 4. 75. Addison-Wesley
Goodman, A. W. Plane trigonometry. il. 1959. 4. 50. Wiley
Hall, Dick W. , and L. O. Kattsoff. Modern trigonometry. il. 1961. 4. 95. Wiley
Heineman, E. Richard. Plane trigonometry. 1956. 4. 25. McGraw
Kells, Lyman M. , and others. Plane and spherical trigonometry. 1951. 5. 25.
    McGraw
Levi, Howard. Foundations of geometry and trigonometry. 1960. 11. 00. Prentice-
    Hall
Morgan, Frank M. Plane and spherical trigonometry with tables. 4. 25. Am. Bk.
    Co.
Mostert, Paul S. Analytic trigonometry. il. 1960. 5. 65. Prentice-Hall
Niles, Nathan O. Plane trigonometry. 1959. 3. 95. Wiley
Palmer, Irwin, and Samuel Fletcher. Trigonometry and logarithms. 1951. 3. 50.
    McGraw
Rutledge, William A. , and J. A. Pond. Modern trigonometry. 1961. 4. 95.
    Prentice-Hall
Sharp, Henry. Modern fundamentals of algebra and trigonometry. il. 9. 00.
    Prentice-Hall
Thompson, J. E. Elements of spherical trigonometry. 1942. 2. 25. Van Nostrand
Vance, Elridge P. Modern algebra and trigonometry. 1962. 7. 50. Addison-Wesley
TRISTAN (833. 912)
Bedier, Joseph. Romance of Tristan and Isuelt. tr. by Hilaire Belloc and Paul
    Rosenfled. il. 6. 00. Heritage
Robinson, Edwin Arlington. Tristram. 1928. 3. 95. Macmillan
Rougemont, Denis de. Love in the western world. 1956. 4. 50. Pantheon
TROLLOPE, ANTHONY., 1815-1882 (928)
Booth, Bradford A. Anthony Trollope. 1958. 6. 00. Indiana
Trollope, Anthony. Autobiography. 5. 00. Oxford U. P.
Walpole, Hugh. Anthony Trollope. 1. 25. St. Martins

Wildman, John Hazard. Anthony Trollope's England. 1940. 2.00. Brown U.
TROTSKY, LEON, 1879-1940 (928.917)
Deutscher, Isaac. Prophet armed: Trotsky: 1879-1921. 1954. 7.50. Oxford U. P.
Levine, Isaac D. Mind of an assassin. il. 1959. 4.50. Farrar, Straus
TROY (939.21)
Page, Denys. History and the Homeric Iliad. il. 1959. 8.00. U. of Calif.
Warner, Rex. Greeks and Trojans. il. 1953. 3.50. Mich. State
Young, Arthur M. Troy and her legend. il. 1948. 4.00. U. of Pittsburgh
TRUMAN, HARRY S., PRES. U.S., 1884- (923.173)
Daniels, Jonathan. Man of Independence. 1950. 5.00. Lippincott
Steinberg, Alfred. Man from Missouri: Life and times of Harry Truman. 1962.
    6.50. Putnam
TRUSTS (338.85)
Adams, Walter, and Horace M. Gray. Monopoly in America. 1955. 3.40. Mac-
    millan
Baldwin, William L. Antitrust and the changing corporation. il. 1961. 8.75.
    Duke
Berge, Wendell. Cartels: Challenge to a free world. 1949. 3.25. Pub. Affairs
Dewey, Donald. Monopoly in economics and law. il. 1959. 5.75. Rand McNally
Dietz, Arthur. Introduction to the anti-trust laws. 2.00. Twayne
Edwards, Corwin. Big business and the policy of competition. 3.50. Western
    Reserve
Hale, George E., and Rosemary. Market power: Size and shape under the
    Sherman act. 1958. 17.50. Little
Herling, John. Great price conspiracy: The story of the antitrust violations in
    the electrical industry. 1962. 5.50. McKay
Kaysen, Carl, and Donald F. Turner. Anti-trust policy. 1959. 7.50. Harvard
Lilienthal, David E. Big business: A new era. 1953. 3.50. Harper
Mason, Edward S, Economic concentration and the monopoly problems. il. 1957.
    6.00. Harvard
Mayall, Kenneth L. International cartels. 1951. 2.75. Tuttle
Neal, Alfred. Industrial concentration and price inflexibility. 1942. 2.75.
    Pub. Affairs
Neale, A. D. Antitrust laws of the U.S.A. 1960. 7.50. Cambridge U. P.
Stocking, George W. Workable competition and antitrust policy. 1961. 7.50.
    Vanderbilt
TUBERCULOSIS (616.995)
Dubos, Rene, and Jean. White Plague. 1952. 6.00. Little
Hetherington, H. W., and Fannie W. Eshleman. Tuberculosis. il. 1958. 6.50.
    Putnam
Pottenger, Francis Marion. Fight against tuberculosis. 1952. 4.00. Abelard
TUMBLING (796.47)
Burns, T. and T. Micoleau. Tumbling techniques illustrated. 1957. 2.95.
    Ronald
Griswold, Larry. Trampoline tumbling. il. 1962. 3.50. Barnes, A. S.
TUNISIA (961.1)
Anthony, John. Tunisia. il. 1962. 4.50. Scribner
Hammerton, Thomas. Tunisia unveiled. il. 1959. 5.00. Transatlantic
TURKEY (956.1)
Alderson, A. D. Structure of the Ottoman dynasty. 1956. 12.80. Oxford U. P.
Davis, William Stearns. Short history of the Near East: 330 A.D. to 1922. il.
    6.25. Macmillan
Gokalp, Ziya. Turkish nationalism and western civilization. 1959. 5.00. Columbia
Kilic, Altemur. Turkey and the world. 1959. 4.50. Pub. Affairs
Kinross, Lord. Turkey. il. 1960. 14.00. Viking
Lewis, Bernard. Emergence of modern Turkey. 1961. 7.70. Oxford U. P.
Lewis, Geoffrey. Turkey. 1960. 6.50. Praeger
Price, M. Phillips. History of Turkey. il. 1956. 4.75. Macmillan

Thomas, Lewis Victor, and Richard Nelson Frye. United States and Turkey and
Iran. il. 1951. 4.25. Harvard
TURTLES (598.13)
Ashley, L. M. Laboratory anatomy of the turtle. 1955. pap. 1.65. Brown, W.C.
Carr, Archie. Handbook of turtles: the turtles of the United States, Canada,
and Baja California. il. 7.50. Cornell
Pope, Clifford H. Turtles of the United States and Canada. il. 1939. 5.75. Knopf
TWELFTH CENTURY (909.1)
Haskins, Charles. Renaissance of the twelfth century. 3.75. Smith, Peter
Holmes, Urban T., Jr. Daily living in the Twelfth Century: Based on the ob-
servations of Alexander Neckam in London and Paris. il. 1952. 3.85.
U. of Wis.
TWENTIETH CENTURY (909.82)
Amory, Cleveland, and Frederic Bradlee. ,Vanity Fair; A Cavalcade of the 1920's
and 1930's. il. 1960. 10.00. Viking
Barrett, Marvin. Years between: A dramatic view of the twenties and thirites.
il. 1962. 6.95. Little
Beloff, Max. Great powers, essays in twentieth century politics. 1959. 4.50.
Macmillan
Bruun, Geoffrey, and Victor S. Mamatey. World in the twentieth century. il.
1962. 8.00. Heath
East, W. Gordon, and A. E. Moodie. Changing world. 8.50. Harcourt
Hughes, Henry Stuart. Consciousness and society. 1958. 6.00. Knopf
Hughes, H. Stuart. Consciousness and society. pap. 1.85. Vintage
Kohn, Hans. Twentieth century. 1957. 3.75. Macmillan
Linton, Ralph. Most of the world. 1949. 6.50. Columbia
Marcel, Gabriel. Man against mass society. 1962. 1.95. Regnery
Mosse, George L. Culture of western Europe. 6.50. Rand McNally
Newsweek and C. S. Hammond and Co. Five worlds of our lives. 1960. 13.95.
Hammond
TYLER, JOHN, PRES. U.S., 1790-1862 (923.173)
Morgan, Robert J. Whig embattled: The presidency under John Tyler. 1954.
3.50. U. of Nebr.
TYPEWRITING (652.3)
Grossman, Jack, and Sherwood Friedman. Handbook for typists. 1962. Pitman
Lessenberry, D. D., and others. 20th century typewriting: Complete course.
1962. 3.80. South-Western Pub.
Wanous, S. J. Personal and professional typing. 1962. 3.36. South-Western Pub.

U

UGANDA (967.61)
Apter, D. E. Political kingdom in Uganda: A study in bureaucratic nationalism.
1961. 10.00. Princeton
Ingham, K. Making of modern Uganda. 5.00. Humanities
Wild, J. V. Story of the Uganda agreement. 1.00. St. Martins
UKRAINE (947.71)
Kostiuk, Hryhory. Stalinist rule in the Ukraine. 1960. 4.95. Praeger
Manning, Clarence. Twentieth century Ukraine. 3.50. Twayne
Manning, Clarence. Ukraine under the Soviets. 3.50. Twayne
Wullivant, Robert S. Soviet politics and the Ukraine, 1917-1957. 1962. 8.50.
Columbia
ULTRASONICS (534.5)
Andrews, Alan. ABC's of ultrasonics. 1961. pap. 1.95. Bobbs
Glickstein, Cyrus. Basic ultrasonics. il. 1960. Rider
Richardson, Edward G. Ultrasonic physics. by A. E. Brown. 1962. 5.50. Am.
Elsevier
Vigoreux, Paul. Ultrasonics. 1951. 4.75. Wiley

Wood, Robert Williams. Supersonics: The science of inaudible sounds. il. 1937.
2.00. Brown, U.
UNDERDEVELOPED AREAS (338.91)
Almond, Gabriel A., and J. S. Coleman. Politics of the developing areas. 1960.
8.50. Princeton
Asher, Robert E., and others. Development of the emerging countries. 1962.
3.75. Brookings
Bauer, Peter T. Economic analysis and policy in underdeveloped countries.
1957. 3.00. Duke
Bauer, Peter, and Basil Yamey. Economics of underdeveloped countries. 1957.
pap. 1.75. U. of Chicago
Belshaw, Horace. Population growth and levels of consumption. 1956. 6.00.
Inst. of Pac. Rel.
Benham, Frederic C. Economic aid to underdeveloped countries. 1961. 2.00.
Oxford U. P.
Braibanti, Ralph J. D., and Joseph J. Spengler. Tradition, values, and
socio-economic development. 6.00. Duke
Brand, Willem. Struggle for a higher standard of living. 7.50. Free Press
Buchanan, Norman S., and Howard S. Ellis. Approaches to economic develop-
ment. 1955. 5.00. Twentieth Century
Frost, Raymond. Backward society. 1961. 5.00. St. Martins
Griffith, Alison. Role of American higher education in relation to developing
areas. 1961. 2.00. A.C.E.
Higgins, Benjamin. Economic development. 1959. 7.90. Norton
Kautsky, John H. Political change in underdeveloped countries: Nationalism
and communism. 1962. 3.95. Wiley
Krause, Walter. Economic development: The underdeveloped world and the
American interest. 1961. 8.50. Wadsworth
Kurihara, Kenneth K. Keynesian theory of economic development. 1959. 5.50.
Columbia
Lee, Douglas H. K. Climate and economic development in the tropics. 1957.
3.50. Harper
Mezerik, Avrahm G. Economic development aids for underdeveloped countries.
1961. pap. 2.50. Int. Review Service
Millikan, Max F., and Donald L. M. Blackmer. Emerging nations: Their growth
and the U.S. policy. 1961. 4.50. Little
Myrdal, Gunnar. International economy: Problems and prospects. 1956. 7.50.
Harper
Oser, Jacob. Must men starve? The Malthusian controversy. 1957. 4.50. Abelard
Pentony, DeVere E. Underdeveloped lands: A dilemma of the international
economy. 1960. pap. 1.50. Chandler Pub.
Scott, John. Democracy is not enough. 1960. 3.95. Harcourt
Shannon, Lyle W. Underdeveloped areas. 1957. 7.25. Harper
Shonfield, Andrew. Attack on world poverty. 1960. 5.00. Random
Staley, Eugene. Future of underdeveloped countires. 1961. 6.00. Harper
Tang, Peter S. H. Communist China as a developmental model for underdeveloped
countires. 1960. 1.50. Res. Inst. on Sino-Soviet Bloc
Theobald, Robert. Profit potential in the developing countires. 1962. 12.00.
Am. Management Assn.
Theobald, Robert. Rich and the poor. 1960. 4.50. Potter, C. N.
Ward, Barbara. Rich nations and the poor nations. 1962. bds. 3.75. Norton
Zook, Paul D. Foreign trade and human capital. 1962. 3.00. S.M.U.
UNDERGROUND RAILROAD (973.7)
Breyfogle, William. Make free: The story of the underground railroad. 1958.
6.00. Lippincott
UNITED NATIONS (341.13)
Alwan, Mohamed. Algeria before the United Nations. 3.50. Speller
Asher, Robert E., and others. United Nations and promotion of the general
welfare. 1957. 8.75. Brookings

Ashley, Montagu, M. F. Statement on race. 1951. 2.75. Abelard
Bailey, S. D. General Assembly of the United Nations. 6.00. Praeger
Bailey, Sydney D. Secretariat of the United Nations. 3.50. Taplinger
Bloomfield, Lincoln P. United Nations and U.S. foreign policy. 1960. 4.75. Little
Clark, Grenville, and Louis B. Sohn. World peace through world law. 1960.
    6.50. Harvard
Cohen, Benjamin V. United Nations: Constitutional developments, growth and
    pos sibilities. 1961. 2.75. Harvard
Cohen, Benjamin A. Worldmark encyclopedia of the nations. 1960. 30.00. Harper
Commission to Study the Organization of Peace. Organizing peace in the nuclear
    age. by Arthur N. Holcombe. 1959. 3.75. N. Y. U.
Cousins, Norman. In place of folly. 1961. 3.50. Harper
Coyle, David C. United Nations and how it works. 1961. 3.75. Columbia
Dallin, Alexander. Soviet Union at the United Nations. 5.75. Praeger
Eagleton, Clyde. United Nations and the United States. 1951. S.M.U.
Fenichell, Stephen. United Nations design for peace. il. 1960. Holt, Rinehart
    & Winston
Goodrich, Leland M. United Nations. il. 19591 7.50. Crowell
Goodspeed, Stephen S. Nature and function of international organization. il. 1959.
    7.50. Oxford U. P.
Green, James Frederick. United Nations and human rights. 1956. Brookings
Gross, Ernest A. United Nations: Structure for peace. 1962. 2.95. Harper
Hovet, Thomas, Jr. Bloc politics in the United Nations. 1960. 6.50. Harvard
Hulme, Kathryn. Wild place. 1953. 4.95. Little
Huxley, Julian. UNESCO: Its purpose and its philosophy. 1948. 2.00. Pub. Affairs
Lauterpacht, Elihu. United Nations emergency force. 1960. 3.50. Praeger
McClure, Wallace. World legal order. 1960. 7.50. U. of N. C.
Moore, Bernard. Second lesson: Seven years at the United Nations. 1957. 4.50.
    St. Martins
Munro, Leslie. United Nations: Hope for a divided world. 4.00. Holt, Rinehart
    & Winston
Murray, James N., Jr. United Nations trusteeship system. 1957. 4.50. U. of Ill.
National Education Association, International Relations Committee. Resources for
    teaching about the UN, with annotated bibliography. 1962. 1.50. N. E. A.
Nicholas, Herbert G. United Nations as a political institution. 1959. 3.40.
    Oxford U. P.
Riggs, Robert E. Politics in the United Nations. 1958. 4.50. U. of Ill.
Roosevelt, Eleanor, and William S. De Witt. UN: Today and tomorrow. 1953.
    4.00. Harper
Rubin, Jacob A. Pictorial history of the United Nations. il. 7.50. Yoseloff
Russell, Ruth B., and Jeannette E. Muther. History of the United Nations Charter,
    the role of the United States, 1940-1956. 1958. 10.00. Brookings
Schiffer, W. B. Legal community of mankind. 1954. 5.50. Columbia
Stone, Julius. Aggression and world order: A critique of United Nations theories
    of aggression. 1958. 5.00. U. of Calif.
United Nations. Yearbook. 1952, 1953, 12.50 ea; 1954, 1955. 10.50 ea; 1956,
    1957, 1958, 1959, 12.50 ea; 1960, 1961, 15.00 ea. Columbia
Watts, J. Orval. United Nations: Planned tyranny. 3.75. Devin
Woodbridge, G. History of UNRRA. 3 vols. 15.00. Columbia
Yearbook of the United Nations. 1959. issue. 1960. 12.50; 1960 issue. 1961. 15.00;
    1961 issue. 1962. 15.00. U. N. (R)
Zocca, Louis R., and Marie R. United Nations, action for peace. 1955. pap.
    0.50. Rutgers (R)
UNITED STATES (973)
Brockway, Wallace, and Bart Keith Winer. Homespun America. 1958. 10.00.
    S. and S.
De Voto, Bernard. Easy chair. 1955. 4.00. Houghton
Knowles, Horace A. Gentlemen, scholars and scoundrels: Selections from
    Harper's Magazine. 1850-1959. 8.50. Harper

Martin, Paul, and others. Indians before Columbus: Twenty thousand years of
North American history revealed by archeology. il. 1947. 8.50. U. of Chicago
Robbins, Roland, and Evan Jones. Hidden America. il. 1959. 5.00. Knopf

U.S. ARMY (355.310973)

Bradley, Frank X., and H. Glen Wood. Paratrooper. il. 1962. 4.50. Stackpole
Croghan, George. Army life on the western frontier. il. 1958. 4.00. U. of Okla.
Custer, Elizabeth B. Boots and saddles; or Life in Dakota with General Custer.
il. 1961. 2.00. U. of Okla.
Downey, Fairfax. Guns at Gettysburg. il. 1958. 5.00. McKay
Dupuy, R. Ernest. Compact history of the U.S. army. il. 1956. 4.95. Hawthorn
Ginzberg, Eli, and others. Ineffective soldier. 3 vols. 6.00 ea. Columbia
Higginson, Thomas W. Army life in a black regiment. 1961. 4.50. Mich. State
Jacobs, J. R. Beginning of the U.S. Army. 1947. 6.00. Princeton
Maass, A. A. Muddy waters: The Army engineers and the nation's rivers. il.
1951. 4.75. Harvard
Milhollen, Hirst D., and others. Horsemen, Blue and Gray: A pictorial history.
1960. 10.00. Oxford U. P.
Millis, Walter. Arms and men. 5.75. Putnam
Stern, Philip Van Doren. Soldier life in the Union and Confederate armies.
il. 1961. 6.95. Indiana
Walmsley, Harold. Your future in the Army. 1960. 2.95. Richards Rosen
Weigley, Russell F. Towards an American army: Military thought from Wash-
ington to Marshall. 1962. 7.50. Columbia
Wiley, Bell Irvin. Common soldier in the Civil War. il. 1958. 5.95. Grosset
Wiley, Bell Irvin. They who fought here. 10.00. Macmillan
Williams, T. Harry. Americans at war. 1960. 3.50. La. State
Nelson, Henry L. Uniforms of the United States Army. il. 1959. 14.95. Yoseloff

U.S. --BIOGRAPHY (920)

American men of science. Physical and biological sciences. vol. A-E. 1960;
vol. F-K. 1960; vol. L-R, 1961; vol. S-Z. 1961. 25.00 ea. Social and Be-
havioural sciences. 1962. 25.00 ea. Cattell (R)
Amory, Cleveland. Who killed society? il. 1960. 6.50. Harper
Brown, John Mason. Through these men. 1956. 4.50. Harper
Burger, Nash K., and John K. Bettersworth. South of Appomattox. il. 1959.
5.75. Harcourt
Burnett, Constance Buel. Five for freedom. 1953. 3.50. Abelard
Cattell, Jaques. Directory of American scholars. 1957. 20.00 net postpaid. Bowker
Cook, Fred J. What manner of men: Forgotten heroes of the American Revolution.
1959. 5.00. Morrow
Cousins, Norman. In God we trust: The religious beliefs and ideas of the
American founding fathers. 1958. 5.95. Harper
Dargan, Marion. Guide to American biography. 3.00. U. of N. Mex.
Dupuy, Richard E., and Trevor N. Brave men and great captains. 1959. 5.95.
Harper
Fishwick, Marshall, American heroes: Myth and reality. 1954. 3.75. Pub.
Affairs
Funk, and Wagnalls. Builders of America. 3 vols. 1959. 6.50 ea. Funk
Goldberg, Harvey. American radicals: Some problems and personalities. 1957.
5.00. Monthly Review
Handlin, Oscar. Library of American biography. 3.75 ea.
Hofstadter, Richard. American political tradition. 1948. 5.75. Knopf
Holbrook, Stewart H. Dreamers of the American dream. 1957. 5.75. Doubleday
Holbrook, Stewart H. Lost men of American history. il. 1946. 6.95. Macmillan
Moyer, Eva H. Sixteen exceptional Americans. il. 1959. 5.00. Vantage
Johnson, Gerald W. Lunatic fringe. 1957. 3.95. Lippincott
Koenig, Louis. Invisible presidency: The behind-the scenes story of seven
presidential confidants from Hamilton to Sherman Adams. 1960. 6.95. Holt,
Rinehart & Winston

Lillard, Richard G. American life in autobiography: A descriptive guide. 1956. pap. 3.75. Stanford

Madison, Charles A. American labor leaders. 6.50. Ungar

Madison, Charles A. Critics and crusaders: A century of American protest. 1958. 5.95. Ungar

Mason, Gabriel. Great American liberals. 1956. 3.95. Beacon

Meredith, Roy. Mr. Lincoln's contemporaries. il. 1951. 6.00. Scribner

Nye, Russel B. Baker's dozen: Thirteen unusual Americans. 1956. 5.00. Mich. State

Who was who in America. 3 vols. 20.00 ea. Marquis (R)

Who's who in America. 27.50. Marquis (R)

Who's who in commerce and industry. 24.00. Marquis (R)

Who's who in the South and the Southwest. 23.00. Marquis (R)

Who's who of American women. 25.00. Marquis (R)

U. S.--CIVILIZATION (973)

Adams, James Truslow. Provincial society, 1690-1763. il. 1938. 6.75. Macmillan

American Heritage book of great historic places. by Bruce Catton. il. 1957. 12.50. S. and S.

American Heritage. First year of American Heritage. 1958. 15.00. S. and S.

Amory, Cleveland, and Frederic Bradlee. Vanity fair: A cavalcade of the 1920s and 1930s. il. 1960. 10.00. Viking

Baldwin, Leland D. Meaning of America. 1955. 4.00. U. of Pittsburgh

Barck, Oscar Theodor, and Hugh Talmage Lefler. Colonial America. il. 7.75. Macmillan

Barrett, Donald N. Values in America. 1961. 4.50. U. of Notre Dame

Beard, Charles A. , and Mary R. America in midpassage. 1939. 10.00. Macmillan

Beard, Charles A. , and Mary R. Beards' new basic history of the United States. 1960. 4.95. Doubleday

Beard, Charles A. , and Mary R. Rise of American civilization. il. 8.50. Macmillan

Bell, Daniel. End of ideology. 1959. 7.50. Free Press

Benians, E. A. Race and nation in the United States. 1946. 1.25. Cambridge U. P.

Blankenship, Russell. American literature as an expression of the national mind. 1949. 7.50. Holt

Blegen, Theodore C. Land of their choice: The immigrants write home. 1955. 5.75. U. of Minn.

Boorstin, Daniel J. America and the image of Europe. 3.35. Smith, Peter

Boorstin, Daniel J. Image; or, What happened to the American dream. 1962. 5.00. Atheneum

Bowers, D. F. Foreign influences in American life. il. 4.00. Smith, Peter

Brogan, D. W. America in the modern world. 1960. 3.00. Rutgers

Brooks, Van Wyck. Times of Melville and Whitman. 1953. 2.95. Dutton

Bruckberger, Raymond L. Image of America. 1959. 5.00. Viking

Bryce, James. Reflections on American institutions. 2.25. Smith, Peter

Buck, Pearl S. , and Eslanda Goode Robeson. American argument. 1949. 3.00. Day

Buffum, Francis H. America at the crossroads. 1956. 1.25. Caxton

Burlingame, Roger. American conscience. 1957. 6.75. Knopf

Coelho, George V. Changing images of America: A study of Indian students' perspectives. 1958. 4.00. Free Press

Commager, Henry Steele. American mind. 1950. 6.50. Yale

Conference on Science, Philosophy, and Religion. Symposia. 6 vols. 7.50 ea. Harper

Congdon, Don. Thirties: A time to remember. 1961. 7.50. S. and S.

American Heritage. American Heritage book of the pioneer spirit. 1959. 12.95. S. and S.

Blake, Nelson M. Short history of American life. il. 1952. 6.95. McGraw

Boerstin, Daniel J. Americans: The colonial experience. 1958. 6.00. Random

Coan, Otis W. , and Richard G. Lillard. America in fiction. pap. 3.50. Stanford (R)

Cooke, Alistair. One man's America. 1952. 3. 95. Knopf

Counts, George S. Education and American civilization. 1952. 4. 00. T. C.

Curti, Merle. American paradox. 1956. 2. 75. Rutgers

Curti, Merle. Growth of American thought. 1951. 9. 00. Harper

Davidson, Marshall. Life in America. 2 vols. il. 1951. 12. 50. Houghton

Davie, Emily. Profile of America. il. 1960. 4. 95. Grosset

Dos Passos, John. Prospects of a golden age. 1959. 7. 50. Prentice-Hall

Douglas, William O. America challenged. 1960. 2. 50. Princeton

Eggleston, Edward. Transit of civilization from England to America in the 17th century. 4. 00. Smith, Peter

Faulkner, Harold U. American political and social history. il. 1957. 7. 50. Appleton

Faulkner, Harold U. Quest for social justice. 1898-1914. il. 6. 75. Macmillan

Fish, Carl R. Rise of the common man, 1830-1850. il. 1937. 6. 75. Macmillan

Gabriel, Ralph H. Course of American democratic thought. 1956. 6. 50. Ronald

Griffith, Thomas. Waist-high culture. 1959. 4. 50. Harper

Hacker, Louis M. Shaping of the American tradition. 6. 00. Columbia

Handlin, Oscar. American people in the twentieth century. 1954. 3. 75. Harvard

Horton, Rod W. , and Herbert W. Edwards. Backgrounds of American literary thought. 1952. 3. 25. Appleton

Hsu, Francis L. K. Americans and Chinese: Two ways of life. 1953. 6. 00. Abelard

Hubbell, Jay B. American life in literature. 2 vols. il. 1949. 7. 25 ea. Harper

Johnson, Gerald W. This American people. 1951. 3. 95. Harper

Jones, Howard Mumford. Guide to American literature and its backgrounds since 1890. 1959. pap. 2. 50. Harvard

Kennedy, Gail. Pragmatism and American culture. 1950. pap. 1. 50. Heath

Kluckhohn, Clyde. Mirror for man. 1949. 5. 00. McGraw

Kohn, Hans. American nationalism. 5. 00. Macmillan

Krout, John Allen, and Dixon Ryan Fox. Completion of independence, 1790-1830. il. 1944. 6. 75. Macmillan

Larrabee, Eric. American panorama. 1957. 4. 95. N. Y. U.

Labaree, Leonard W. Conservatism in early American history. pap. 1. 75. Cornell

Lerner, Max. America as a civilization. 1957. 12. 00. S. and S.

Lord, Walter. Good years. il. 1960. 5. 95. Harper

Lynes, Russell. Tastemakers. il. 1954. 6. 00. Harper

Mannes, Marya. More in anger. 3. 95. Lippincott

Maritain, Jacques. Reflections on America. 1958. 3. 50. Scribner

Meyers, Marvin. Jacksonian persuasion: Politics and belief. 5. 00. Stanford

Miers, Earl Schenck. American story. 5. 00. Channel Pr. , Manhasset, N. Y.

Miller, Perry. Errand into the wilderness. 1956. 4. 75. Harvard

Mills, C. Wright. Power elite. 1956. 6. 50. Oxford U. P.

Morley, Felix. Power in the people. 1949. 5. 00. Van Nostrand

Mowrer, Edgar A. Good time to be alive. 1959. 3. 50, Duell

Mumford, Lewis. Brown decades: A study of the arts of America 1865-1895. il. 1960. 3. 50. Smith, Peter

Mumford, Lewis. Golden day, a study in American literature and culture. 3. 50. Smith, Peter

Nettels, C. P. Roots of American civilization. il. 1938. 5. 75. Appleton

Nevins, Allan. Emergence of modern America. 1865-1878. il. 1928. 6. 75. Macmillan

Niebuhr, Reinhold. Irony of American history. 1952. 3. 50. Scribner

Parrington, Vernon Louis. Main currents in American thought. 10. 50. Harcourt

Patterson, S. Howard, and others. Problems in American democracy. il. 1961. 5. 32. Macmillan

Perry, Ralph B. Puritanism and democracy. 1944. 7. 50. Vanguard

Pochmann, Henry. German culture in America. 1956. 7. 50. U. of Wis.

Probst, G. E. Happy republic, a reader in Tocqueville's America. 4. 50. Smith, Peter

Rideout, Walter B. Radical novel in the United States, 1900-1954: Some interrelations of literature and society. 1956. 6. 50. Harvard

Rosenberg, Bernard, and David Manning White. Mass culture: The popular arts in America. 1957. 6.50. Free Press

Rossiter, Clinton. First American Revolution. 1956. pap. 1.25. Harcourt

Sanford, Charles L. Quest for paradise: Europe and the American moral imagination. 1961. 5.00. U. of Ill.

Satin, Joseph. 1950's: America's placid decade. 1960. pap. 1.75. Houghton

Schaff, Philip. America, a sketch of its political, social, and religious character. 1961. 4.25. Harvard

Schlesinger, Arthur M. Paths to the present. 5.75. Macmillan

Schneider, H. W. History of American philosophy. 1946. 6.00. Columbia

Skard, Sigmund. American myth and the European mind: American studies in Europe, 1776-1960. 1961. 4.50. U. of Pa.

Smith, Huston. Search for America. 1959. bds. 2.95. Prentice-Hall

Spiller, Robert. Changing patterns in American civilization. 1962. pap. 1.65. Barnes, A. S.

Times, London, Literary Supplement. American imagination. 4.50. Atheneum

Tolles, Frederick B. Quakers and the Atlantic culture. 1960. 3.95. Macmillan

Wecter, Dixon. Age of the Great Depression, 1929-1941. il. Macmillan

Wecter, Dixon, and others. Changing patterns in American civilization. 3.75. Smith, Peter

Wertenbaker, Thomas J. First Americans. 1607-1690. il. 6.75. Macmillan

Wish, Harvey. Society and thought in America. vol. 1, Early America. 1950. 6.75; vol. 2, Modern America. 1962. 8.75. McKay

Wright, Louis B. Atlantic Frontier: Colonial American civilization, 1607-1763. 1959. 3.75. Cornell

Wright, Louis B. Culture on the moving frontier. 1955. 3.50. Indiana

Wylie, Philip. Generation of vipers. 1955. 4.00. Holt, Rinehart & Winston

Youngdahl, Luther W. Ramparts we watch. 1961. 3.95. Denison

Commager, Henry Steele. Living ideas in America: An anthology of documents. 1951. 6.50. Harper

Golden, Harry. Enjoy! 1960. 4.00. World Pub.

Golden, Harry. For 2¢ plain. 1959. 4.00. World Pub.

Golden, Harry. Only in America. 4.00. World Pub.

Hand, Learned. Spirit of liberty: Papers and addresses of Learned Hand. 1960. 4.00. Knopf

Handlin, Oscar. American principles and issues: The national purpose. 1961. 6.00. Holt, Rinehart & Winston

Hoover, Herbert. Addresses upon the American road, 1955-1960. 1961. 7.50. Caxton.

Johnston, Edgar G. Preserving human values in an age of technology. il. 1961. 4.00. Wayne

Kallen, Horace M., and others. Cultural pluralism and the American idea. 1956. 5.00. U. of Pa.

Kwiat, Joseph J., and Mary C. Turpie. Studies in American culture. 1960. 4.75. U. of Minn.

Lerner, Max. Unfinished country. 1959. 7.50. S. and S.

Mencken, Henry L. Bathtub hoax and other blasts and bravos from the Chicago Tribune. 1958. 5.00. Knopf

Niebuhr, Reinhold. Pious and secular America. 1958. 3.00. Scribner

Pound, Ezra. Impact: Essays on ignorance and the decline of American civilization. 1960. 5.00. Regnery

U. S.--COAST GUARD (351.792)

Evans, Stephen H. United States Coast Guard, 1790-1949. il. 1949. 5.00. U. S. Naval Inst.

Willoughby, Malcolm F. United States Coast Guard in World War II. 1957. 6.00. U. S. Naval Inst.

U. S.--COMMERCE (382)

Albion, Robert J. Seaports south of Sahara. 1959. 6.00. Appleton

Barger, H. Distribution's place in the American economy since 1869. 1955. 4.50. Princeton

Barr, Robert J. American trade with Asia and the Far East. 9.00. Twayne
Davis, Marjorie V. Guide to American business directories. 1948. 3.75. Pub.
    Affairs (R)
Fayerweather, J. Facts and fallacies of international business. 1962. 3.95.
    Holt, Rinehart & Winston
Frank, Isaiah. European common market. 1961. 7.50. Praeger
Goodman, Bernard. Industrial materials in Canadian-American relations. 1961.
    7.00. Wayne
Hamilton, Alexander. Papers on public credit, commerce and finance. 1957.
    3.50. Bobbs
Humphrey, Don D. United States and the Common Market. 1962. 4.50. Praeger
National Education Association, National Council for the Social Studies Teachers
    guide to world trade. 1960. 1.00. N. E. A.
Rydell, Raymond A. Cape Horn to the Pacific: The rise and decline of an ocean
    highway. 1952. 4.00. U. of Calif.
Seelye, Alfred L. Marketing in transition. 1958. 6.00. Harper
Viner, Jacob. International economics. 1951. 6.00. Free Press
U. S. --CONGRESS (328.3)
Acheson, Dean. Citizen looks at congress. 1957. 2.95. Harper
Burnham, James. Congress and the American tradition. 1959. 6.50. Regnery
Carr, Robert K. House committee on Un-American activities, 1945-1950. 6.50.
    Cornell
Carroll, Holbert N. House of Representatives and foreign affairs. 1958. 5.00.
    U. of Pittsburgh
Chafee, Lechariah, Jr. Three human rights in the constitution. 4.00. U. of Kans.
Dahl, Robert A. Congress and foreign policy. 1950. 4.50. Harcourt
Dimock, Marshall E. Congressional investigating committees. 1929. 2.75.
    Johns Hopkins
Galloway, George B. Legislative process in Congress. 1953. 6.50. Crowell
Galloway, George B. History of the House of Representatives. il. 1962. 7.50.
    Crowell
Griffith, Ernest S. Congress: Its contemporary role. 1961. 4.50. N. Y. U.
Gross, Bertram M. Legislative struggle: A study in social combat. il. 1953.
    7.25. McGraw
Harris, Joseph P. Advice and consent of the Senate. 1953. 7.00. U. of Calif.
Haynes, George Henry. Senate of the United States. 2 vols. 1960. 15.00. Russell
Kennedy, Robert F. Enemy within. il. 1960. 4.50. Harper
Matthews, Donald R. U. S. senators and their world. 1960. 6.00. U. of N. C.
Moos, Malcolm. Politics, presidents and coattails. 1952. 4.50. Johns Hopkins
Paxton, Annabel. Women in congress. 1945. 2.00. Dietz
Robinson, James A. Congress and foreign policy-making. 1962. 5.50. Dorsey
Tucker, Ray, and Frederick R. Barkley. Sons of the wild jackass. il. 3.00.
    Farrar, Straus
White, William S. Citadel: The story of the U. S. Senate. 1957. 4.50. Harper
Wilson, Woodrow. Congressional government. 1958. 3.00. Smith, Peter
Young, R. Congressional politics in the Second World War. 1956. 4.50. Columbia
U. S. --CONSTITUTION (342.73)
Adams, John. Political writings. 1954. 3.25. Bobbs
Bartholomew, Paul C. American government under the Constitution. 1956.
    4.25. Brown, W. C.
Beard, Charles A. Economic interpretation of the Constitution of the United
    States. 1935. 4.75. Macmillan
Beard, Charles A. Supreme Court and the Constitution. 1961. 3.95. Prentice-
    Hall
Brandies, Louis Dembitz. Social and economic views of Mr. Justice Brandeis.
    by Alfred Lief. 1930. 6.00. Vanguard
Brown, R. E. Charles Beard and the Constitution. 1956. 4.00. Princeton
Carr, Robert K. Supreme Court and judicial review. 1942. pap. 2.00. Holt,
    Rinehart & Winston

Commager, Henry Steele. Majority rule and minority rights. 2.50. Smith, Peter

Corwin, Edward S. Constitution and what it means today. 1958. 6.00. Princeton

Corwin, Edward S. Liberty against government. 1948. 3.00. La. State

Corwin, Edward S., and Jack W. Peltason. Understanding the Constitution. pap. 2.50. Holt

Cotter, Cornelius P., and J. Malcolm Smith. Powers of the President during national crises. 1959. 5.00. Pub. Affairs

Crosskey, William W. Politics and the Constitution in the history of the United States. 1953. 20.00. U. of Chicago

Cushman, Robert E. Leading Constitutional decisions. 1958. 3.75. Appleton

Dietze, Gottfried. Federalist: A classic of federalism and free government. 1960. 6.50. Johns Hopkins

Douglas, William O. Almanac of liberty. 1954. 5.95. Doubleday

Douglas, William O. Living Bill of rights. 1961. 1.50. Doubleday

Drinker, Henry S. Some observations on the Four Freedoms of the First Amendment. 1957. 3.00. Boston U.

Dumbauld, Edward. Bill of Rights and what it means today. il. 1957. 3.75. U. of Okla.

Farrand, Max. Framing of the Constitution of the United States. 1913. 4.50. Yale

Garrett, Kathryn, and Lula Underwood. Story of a great document. 1961. 1.00. Steck

Gellhorn, Walter. American rights. 1960. 4.50. Macmillan

Hamilton, Alexander, and others. Federalist. 1961. 7.50. Harvard

Hockett, Homer C. Constitutional history of the United States. 2 vols. 7.75 ea. Macmillan

Holcombe, Arthur Norman. Our more perfect union: From eighteenth-century principles to twentieth-century practice. 1950. 4.50. Harvard

Holmes, Oliver Wendell. Mind and faith of Justice Holmes. 1954. 2.95. Modern Lib.

Jensen, Merrill. Articles of Confederation. 1959. 6.50. U. of Wis.

Konvitz, Milton R. Bill of Rights reader: Leading constitutional cases. 1960. 8.25. Cornell

Kurland, Philip B. Supreme Court review. 1962. 6.50. U. of Chicago

Latham, Earl. Declaration of Independence and the Constitution. 1949. pap. 1.50. Heath

McCloskey, Robert G. Essays in constitutional law. 1957. 5.75. Knopf

McDonald, Forrest. We the people: The economic origins of the Constitution. 1958. 7.80. U. of Chicago

Main, Jackson T. Antifederalists: Critics of the Constitution, 1781-1788. 1961. 7.50. U. of N. C.

Mendelson, Wallace. Constitution and the Supreme Court. 1959. 7.00. Dodd

Morley, Felix. Power in the people. 1949. 5.00. Van Nostrand

Morison, Samuel Eliot. Sources and documents illustrating the American Revolution, 1764-1788, and the formation of the federal constitution. 1929. 5.00. Oxford U. P. (R)

Pritchett, Charles H. American Constitution. 1959. 10.75. McGraw

Rossiter, Clinton. Seedtime of the republic. 1953. 7.50. Harcourt

Rutland, Robert A. Birth of the Bill of Rights: 1776-1791. 1955. 5.00. U. of N. C.

Schuyler, Robert. Constitution of the United States: An historical survey. 3.50. Smith, Peter

Schwartz, Bernard. American constitutional law. 1955. 6.00. Cambridge U. P.

Smith, James M., and Paul L. Murphy. Liberty and justice: A historical record of American constitutional development. 1958. 6.75. Knopf

Swisher, Carl B. American constitutional development. 1954. 12.50. Houghton

Swisher, Carl Brent. Growth of constitutional power in the United States. 1946. 4.00. U. of Chicago

Solberg, Winton U. Federal convention and the formation of the union of the
   American states. 1958. 5.00. Bobbs
Van Doren, Carl. Great rehearsal. 1948. 3.75. Viking
Walker, Harvey. Legislative process. 1948. 6.00. Ronald
Welch, Joseph. Constitution. il. 1956. 4.75. Houghton
U. S. --DECLARATION OF INDEPENDENCE (973.313)
Malone, Dumas. Story of the Declaration of Independence. il. 1954. 10.00.
   Oxford U. P.
U. S. --DESCRIPTION AND TRAVEL (917.3)
American Heritage. American Heritage book of great historic places. il. 1957.
   12.50. S. and S.
Crevecoeur, John. Letters from an American farmer. 1.95. Dutton
Dickens, Charles. American notes, and Pictures from Italy. il. 1957. 4.00.
   Oxford U. P.
Douglas, William O. My wilderness: East to Katahdin. il. 1961. 4.95. Doubleday
Gunther, John. Inside U. S. A. 1951. 6.50. Harper
Holiday. American panorama, east of the Mississippi. 1960. 5.00. Doubleday
Laugel, Auguste. United States during the Civil War. 1961. 6.95. Indiana
Long, Edward J. America's national monuments and historic sites. il. 5.00.
   Doubleday
Look. Look at America. il. 10.00. Houghton
Paterson, John H. North America: A regional geography. il. 1961. 6.00. Oxford
   U. P.
Pierson, George W. Tocquevile in America. 1960. 3.50. Smith, Peter
Sienkiewicz, Henry. Portrait of America. 1959. 5.00. Columbia
Steinbeck, John. Travels with Charley in search of America. 1962. 4.95. Viking
Tocqueville, Alexis de. Journey to America. by J. P. Mayer. tr. by George
   Lawrence. 1960. 6.50. Yale
Trollope, Anthony. North America. il. 1951. 6.75. Knopf
U. S. --ECONOMIC CONDITIONS (330.973)
Allen, Frederick Lewis. Big change: America transforms itself, 1900-1950.
   1952. 4.50. Harper
Barnes, Harry E. , and Oreen M. Ruedi. American way of life. 1950. 7.75.
   Prentice-Hall
Beard, Charles A. Economic interpretation of the Constitution of the United
   States. 1935. 4.75. Macmillan
Berle, Adolf A. Power without property. 1959. 3.75. Harcourt
Bining, A. C. Rise of American economic life. 1955. 6.50. Scribner
Blau, Joseph L. Social theories of Jacksonian democracy. 1954. 4.50. Bobbs
Bogue, Donald J. , and Calvin L. Beale. Economic areas of the United States. il.
   1961. 27.50. Free Press
Bowles, Chester. Coming political breakthrough. 1959. 4.00. Harper
Brainard, Harry G. Economics in action. 1959, 5.50. Oxford U. P.
Childs, Marquis W. , and Douglass Cater. Ethics in a business society. 1954.
   3.50. Harper
Cochran, Thomas C. , and William Miller. Age of enterprise: A social history of
   industrial America. 1942. 6.50. Macmillan
Cochran, T. C. American business system: A historical perspective, 1900-1955.
   1957. 4.75. Harvard
Crane, Burton. Practical economist. 1960. 3.95. S. and S.
Dewhurst, J. Frederic, and others. America's needs and resources: A new
   survey. 1955. 10.00. Twentieth Century
Fainsod, Merle, and others. Government and the American economy. 1959. 7.35.
   Norton
Faulkner, Harold. Decline of laissez faire: 1897-1917. il. 1951. 6.75. Holt, Rinehart
   & Winston
Faulkner, Harold U. Quest for social justice. 1898-1914. il. 6.75. Macmillan
Fels, Rendigs, Challenge to the American economy: An introduction to eco-
   nomics. il. 1961. 10.60. Allyn & Bacon

Fine, Sidney. Laissez faire and the general -welfare state. 1956. 7. 50. U. of Mich.
Fortune. Markets of the sixties. il. 1960. 5.00. Harper
Fortune. Readings in economics. il. 1957. pap. 2.55. Holt, Rinehart & Winston
Galbraith, John K. American capitalism. 1956. 3.50. Houghton
Galbraith, John K. Economics and the art of controversy. 1955. 2. 75. Rutgers
Galbraith, John K. Liberal hour. 1960. 3. 50. Houghton
Gustafson, A. F. , and others. Conservation in the United States. 5.00. Cornell
Hacker, Louis M. Major documents in American economic history. 2 vols. 1961.
   pap. 1. 25 ea. Van Nostrand
Hahn, Walter F. , and John C. Neff. American strategy for the nuclear age. 3. 50.
   Smith, Peter
Hession, Charles H. , and others. Dynamics of the American economy. 1956. 6.00.
   Knopf
Hicks, John D. Rehearsal for disaster: The boom and collapse of 1919-1920.
   3. 50. U. of Fla.
Hitch, Charles J. , and Roland N. McKean. Economics of defense in the nuclear
   age. 1960. 9. 50. Harvard
Kelso, Louis O. , and Mortimer J. Adler. Capitalist manifesto. 1958. 3. 75.
   Random
Kelso, Louis O. , and Mortimer J. Adler. New capitalists. il. 1961. 3. 50.
   Random
Knorr, Klaus E. , and William J. Baumol. What price economic growth? il. 1961.
   3. 95. Prentice-Hall
Kemmerer, Donald L. , and Merlin H. Hunter. Economic history of the United
   States. 1956. pap. 1. 50. Littlefield
Mitchell, Broadus. Depression decade, 1929-1941. il. 1947. 7.00. Holt, Rinehart
   & Winston
Murray, Robert K. Red scare: A study in national hysteria. il. 1955. 4. 75.
   U. of Minn.
Myers, Gustavus. History of the great American fortunes. 2. 95. Modern Lib.
Nevins, Allan. Emergence of modern America. 1865-1878. il. 1928. 6. 75. Mac-
   millan
Potter, David M. People of plenty: Economic abundance and the American charac-
   ter. 1954. 4. 25. U. of Chicago
Sears, Paul B. Deserts on the march. 1959. 2. 75. U. of Okla.
Slichter, Sumner H. Economic growth in the United States. by John T. Dunlop.
   1961. 5. 00. La. State
Slichter, Sumner H. Potentials of the American economy. by John T. Dunlop.
   1961. 7. 50. Harvard
Smith, Guy H. Conservation of natural resources. 1958. 8. 50. Wiley
Soule, George. Prosperity decade: From war to depression, 1917-1929. 1957.
   6. 50. Holt, Rinehart & Winston
Spiller, Robert E. , and Eric Larrabee. American perspectives: The national
   self-image in the twentieth century. 1961. 4. 75. Harvard
Steele, George, and Paul Kirchner. Crisis we face. il. 1960. 4. 95. McGraw
Taylor, George R. Transportation revolution: 1815-1860. il. 1951. 10.10. Holt,
   Rinehart & Winston
Wecter, Dixon. Age of the Great Depression, 1929-1941. 6. 75. Macmillan
Zeigler, Edward W. Men who make us rich. 1962. 5. 00. Macmillan
U. S. --EMIGRATION AND IMMIGRATION (325. 73)
Brown, Francis J. , and Joseph S. Roucek. One America. 1952. 10. 00. Prentice-
   Hall
Commager, Henry Steele. Immigration and American history: Essays in honor
   of Theodore C. Blegen. 1961. 4. 50. U. of Minn.
Handlin, Oscar. Immigration as a factor in American history. 1959. pap. 1. 95.
   Prentice-Hall
Jones, Maldwyn A. American immigration. il. 1960. 6. 00. U. of Chicago
U. S. --FOREIGN RELATIONS (327. 73)
Acheson, D. Power and diplomacy. 1958. 3. 00. Harvard

Adams, Ephraim. Great Britain and the American Civil War. 2 vols. bd. as l. 7.50. Russell
Aitken, Hugh G. J., and others. American economic impact on Canada. 1959. 4.50. Duke
Aitken, Thomas. Foreign policy for American business. il. 1962. bds. 4.00. Harper
Allen, Harry C. Great Britain and the United States: History of Anglo-American relations. 1783-1952. 10.00. 1955. St. Martins
Acheson, D. Power and diplomacy. 1958. 3.00. Harvard
Almond Gabriel A. American people and foreign policy. 1960. 4.00. Praeger
American Management Association. Increasing profits from foreign operations. 1957. 5.25. Am. Management Assn.
American Assembly. United States and the Far East. il. 1962. 3.95. Prentice-Hall
Bailey, Thomas A. Diplomatic history of the American people. il. 1958. 7.00. Appleton
Barnes, Harry E. Perpetual war for perpetual peace. 1953. 6.00. Caxton
Bartlett, Ruhl J. Record of American diplomacy. 1954. 7.00. Knopf
Beale, Howard K. Theodore Roosevelt and the rise of American to world power. 1956. 6.00. Johns Hopkins
Beard, Charles A. American foreign policy in the making, 1932-lo40. 1946. 6.00. Yale
Bemis, Samuel F. American foreign policy and the blessings of liberty and other essays. 1962. 10.00. Yale
Bemis, Samuel Flagg. Diplomatic history of the United States. il. 1955. 10.50. Holt, Rinehart & Winston
Bemis, Samuel Flagg. Short history of American foreign policy and diplomacy. 1959. 12.00. Holt, Rinehart & Winston
Bemis, Samuel F. Diplomacy of the American Revolution. 1957. 3.75. Smith, Peter
Bemis, Samuel Flagg. Latin American policy of the United States: An historical interpretation. il. 6.50. Harcourt
Bishop, Hillman M., and Samuel Hendel. Basic issues of American democracy. pap. 2.95. Appleton
Brookings Institution, International Studies Group Staff. Major problems of United States foreign policy. 7 vols. 1947-1954. 1947. pap. 1.50; 1948-1949, 3.00, pap. 1.50; 1949-1950, 3.00, pap. 1.50; 1950-1951. o. p; 1951-1952, 3.00, pap. 1.50; 1952-1953, 4.00, pap. 2.00; 1954- pap. 2.00. Brookings
Browder, R. Origins of Soviet-American diplomacy. 1953. 5.00. Princeton
Brown, Frencis J., and Joseph S. Roucek. One America. 1952. 10.00. Prentice-Hall
Brinton, Crane. United States and Britain. il. 1948. 4.25. Harvard
Campbell, Charles S., Jr. Anglo-American understanding, 1898-1903. 1957. 5.50. Johns Hopkins
Campbell, John C. Defense and the Middle East. 1960. 5.00. Harper
Chase, Stuart. Live and let live. 1959. 3.50. Harper
Cheever, D. S., and H. F. Haviland, Jr. American foreign policy and the separation of powers. 1952. 3.75. Harvard
Corwin, Edward S. French policy and the American alliance of 1778. 1962. 9.00. Shoe String
Cowles, Willard. Treaties and constitutional law. 1941. 4.50. Pub. Affairs
Crabb, Cecil V., Jr. American foreign policy in the nuclear age. 1960. 6.90. Harper
Curl, Peter V. Documents on American foreign relations. 1953. 5.00. Harper
Drummond, Rocoe, and Gaston Coblentz. Duel at the brink. 1960. 4.50. Doubleday
Dulles, Foster R. America's rise to world power: 1898-1954. 1955. 5.00. Harper
Dulles, John Foster, War or peace. 6.00. Macmillan

Fairbank, John King. United States and China. 1958. 5.50. Harvard
Feis, H. China tangle. 1953. 7.50. Princeton
Flynn, John T. While you slept. 1951. 3.00. Devin
Goebel, D. American foreign policy: A documentary survey, 1776-1960. 1961.
    5.50. Holt, Rinehart & Winston
Goldwin, Robert A., and others. Readings in American foreign policy. 1959. pap.
    2.75. Oxford U. P.
Graber, D. A. Crisis diplomacy. 1959. 6.75. Pub. Affairs
Griswold, A. Whitney. Far Eastern policy of the United States. 1938. 10.00. Yale
Guerrant, Edward. Roosevelt's good neighbor policy. 2.50. U. of N. Mex.
Handlin, Oscar. Uprooted. 1951. 4.75. Little
Hoover, Herbert Clark. Ordeal of Woodrow Wilson. 1958. 6.00. McGraw
Keenleyside, Hugh L., and Gerald S. Brown. Canada and the United States. 6.00.
    Knopf
Kenen, Peter B. Giant among nations: Problems in United States foreign economic
    policy. 1960. 5.00. Harcourt
Kennan, George. Realities of American foreign policy. 1954. 2.75. Princeton
Kennan, George F. American diplomacy: 1900-1950. 1952. pap. 0.60. New Am. Lib.
Kennan, G. F. Soviet-American relations, 1917-1920. 2 vols. vol. 1. Russia
    leaves the war. 1956; vol. 2, Decision to intervene. 1958. 7.50 ea. Princeton
Kennedy, John F. To turn the tide. 1962. 3.95. Harper
Kissinger, Henry A. Necessity for choice. 1961. 5.95. Harper
Kissinger, Henry A. Nuclear weapons and foreign policy. 1957. 5.00. Harper
Langer, William L., and S. Everett Gleason. Challenge to isolation: 1937-1940.
    2 vols. 16.00. Harper
Laserson, Max M. American impact on Russia, 1784-1917. pap. 1.50. Collier
Latourette, Kenneth S. American record in the Far East. 1952. 3.00. Inst. of
    Pac. Rel.
Leopold, Richard W. Growth of American foreign policy. 1962. 11.75. Knopf
Lieuwen, Edwin. Arms and politics in Latin America. 1960. 5.00. Praeger'
Lippmann, Walter. Public opinion. 5.75. Macmillan
Lippmann, Walter. Isolation and alliances: An American speaks to the British.
    1952. 2.00. Little
MacCorkle, Stuart A. American policy of recognition towards Mexico. 1933.
    1.50. Johns Hopkins
McKay, Donald Cope. United States and France. il. 1951. 4.50. Harvard
Masland, J. W., and L. I. Radway. Soldiers and scholars: Military education and
    national policy. 1957. 8.50. Princeton
May, Ernest R. Imperial democracy. 1961. 6.75. Harcourt
May, Ernest R. World War and American isolation, 1914-1917. 1959. 7.50.
    Harvard
Millis, Walter, and John C. Murray. Foreign policy and the free society. 1958.
    2.75. Oceana
Mills, Charles W. Causes of world war three. 1958. 3.50. S. and S.
Nevins, Allan. Hamilton Fish: The inner history of the Grant administration. 2
    vols. il. 12.50. Ungar
Newman, Robert P. Recognition of Communist China. 1961. 4.95. Macmillan
Niebuhr, Reinhold. Irony of American history. 1952. 3.50. Scribner
Nixon, Richard M. Challenges we face. 1960. 3.95. McGraw
Palmer, Thomas, Jr. Search for a Latin American policy. 1957. 4.50. U. of Fla.
Perkins, Dexter. America's quest for peace. 1961. 3.00. Indiana
Perkins, Dexter. American approach to foreign policy. 1962. 4.95. Harvard
Plischke, Elmer. Conduct of America diplomacy. il. 1961. 8.50. Van Nostrand
Randall, Clarence B. Communist challenge to American business. 3.50. Little
Reinhardt, George C. American strategy in the atomic age. 1955. 3.75. U. of
    Okla.
Roberts, Henry L. Russia and America: Dangers and prospects. 1956. 3.50.
    Harper
Roosevelt, James. Liberal papers. 1962. 5.00. Quadrangle
Schlamm, William S. Germany and the East-West crisis. 1959. 3.95. McKay

Schnapper, M. B. New frontiers of the Kennedy administration. 1961. 3. 75. Pub. Affairs

Stevenson, Adlai. Call to greatness. 1955. 2. 75. Harper

Stromberg, Roland N. Collective security and American foreign policy. 1962. 6. 00. Praeger

Sulzberger, C. L. What's wrong with U. S. foreign policy. 1959. 4. 50. Harcourt

Tannenbaum, Frank. American tradition in foreign policy. 1955. 3. 50. U. of Okla.

Truman, Harry S. Mr. Citizen. il. 1960. 5. 00. Random

Truman, Harry S. Truman program. 1949. 2. 95. Pub. Affairs

Tyrner-Tyrnauer, A. R. Lincoln and the emperors. il. 1962. 4. 50. Harcourt

Utley, Freda. China story. 1951. pap. 2. 00. Regnery

Warner, W. L. , and L. Srole. Social systems of American etnic groups. 1945. 6. 00. Yale

White, Theodore H. Fire in the ashes: Europe in mid-century. 1953. 5. 95. Sloane

Whitaker, Arthur Preston. United States and South America: The northern republics. il. 1948. 4. 25. Harvard

Wittke, Carl F. We who built America. pap. 3. 00. Western Reserve

Woods, Frances Jerome, Sister. Cultural values of American ethnic groups. 1956. 4. 50. Harper

U. S. --GOVERNMENT PUBLICATIONS (025.173)

Boyd, Anne M. , and Rae E. Rips. United States government publications. 1950. 6. 50. Wilson (R)

Hirshberg, Herbert S. , and Carl H. Melinat. Subject guide to U. S. government publications. 1947. 5. 00. A. L. A.

Jackson, Ellen. Manual for the administration of the federal documents collection in libraries. 1955. 3. 00. A. L. A.

Schmeckebier, Laurence F. , and Roy B. Eastin. Government publications and their use. 1961. 6. 00. Brookings

U. S. --HISTORY (973)

Adams, Henry. Great secession winter and other essays. by George Hochfield. 6. 00. Sagamore

Adams, James Truslow. Epic of America. il. 1933. 6. 50. Little

Agar, Herbert. Price of union. 1950. 8. 50. Houghton

Bailey, Thomas A. American pageant: A history of the republic. il. 1961. 8. 50. Heath

Baldwin, Leland D. Survey of American history. 8. 00. Am. Bk. Co.

Bassett, R. H. Basset, John S. Short history of the United States. 1492-1938. 7. 00. Macmillan

Beard, Charles A. , and Mary R. America in midpassage. 1939. 10. 00. Macmillan

Beard, Charles A. , and Mary R. Beards' new basic history of the United States. 1960. 4. 95. Doubleday

Beers, Henry P. Bibliographies in American history. 12. 50. Cooper (R)

Bellot, H. Hale. American history and American historians: Review of recent contributions to the interpretation of the history of the United States. 1952. 4. 00. U. of Okla.

Benet, Stephen Vincent. America. 1944. 2. 75. Holt, Rinehart & Winston

Benson, Lee. Turner and Beard: American historical writing reconsidered. 1960. 5. 00. Free Press

Botkin, Benjamin A. Civil War treasury of tales, legends, and folklore. il. 1960. 7. 95. Random

Carruth, Gorton, and staff. Encyclopedia of American facts and dates. 1962. 6. 95. Crowell (R)

Channing, Edward. History of the United States. 6 vol. 7. 00 ea. Macmillan

Coan, Otis W. , and Richard G. Lillard. America in fiction. pap. 3. 50. Stanford

Cochran, Thomas C. , and Wayne Andrews. Concise dictionary of American history. 1962. 19. 50. Scribner

Commager, Henry Steele, and Allan Nevins. Heritage of America. il. 1949. 7. 50. Heath

Craven, Avery, and W. Johnson. United States: Experiment in democracy. 1962. 7.25. Ginn
Craven, Avery, and others. Documentary history of the American people. 1951. 8.25. Ginn
Curti, Merle. Probing our past. 1959. 4.25. Smith, Peter
Davis, Burke. Our incredible Civil War. il. 1960. 4.95. Holt, Rinehart & Winston
Davis, Burke. To Appomattox: Nine April Days, 1865. il. 1959. 6.00. Holt, Rinehart & Winston
Degler, Carl N. Out of our past: The forces that shaped modern America. 1958. 6.50. Harper
Dickinson, A. T., Jr. American historical fiction. 1958. 7.50. Scarecorw (R)
Essays in American history dedicated to Frederick Jackson Turner. 3.75. Smith, Peter
Faulkner, Harold U., and Tyler Kepner. America: Its history and people. 1950. 6.48. McGraw
Freidel, Frank. American epochs series. 3 vols. 8.50 ea. Braziller
Hacker, Louis M. Shaping of the American tradition. 6.00. Columbia
Hofstadter, Richard, and others. United States: The history of a republic. 1957. 8.95. Prentice-Hall
Hurd, Charles. Treasury of great American speeches. il. 1959. 5.95. Hawthorn
Knapp, Samuel L. American cultural history, 1607-1829. il. 1960. 6.00. Scholars' Facs.
Kraus, Michael. United States to 1865. il. 1959. 7.50. U. of Mich.
Larned, Josephus N. Literature of American history. 1953. 15.00. Long's College Bk.
Leisy, Ernest E. American historical novel. 1952. 3.75. U. of Okla. (R)
Malone, Dumas, and Basil Rauch. Empire for liberty. 2 vols. il. 7.50 ea. Appleton
Martin, Michael, and Leonard Gelber. Dictionary of American history. 1959. pap. 2.50. Littlefield
Miller, William. New history of the United States. 1958. 5.00. Braziller
Morison, Samuel Eliot, and Henry Steele Commager. Growth of the American Republic. 7.50. Oxford U. P.
Morison, Samuel E. Hour of American history. 3.25. Smith, Peter
Morison, Samuel Eliot. By land and by sea. 1953. 5.75. Knopf
Morris, Richard B. Encyclopedia of American history. 1961. 8.95. Harper (R)
Nelson, Clair E. Dates you should know. 1960. 3.00. Pageant (R)
Nevins, Allan. Times of trial. il. 1958. 5.95. Knopf
Paxson, Frederic L. History of the American frontier. 1924. 6.50. Houghton
Peattie, Donald Culross. Parade with banners. 1957. 3.50. World Pub.
Perkins, Dexter, and Glydon Van Deusen. United States of America, a history. 2 vols. 7.25 ea. Macmillan
Rae, John B., and Thomas H. D. Mahoney. United States in world history. 1955. 7.95. McGraw
Schlesinger, Arthur M. New viewpoints in American history. 5.25. Macmillan
Soviet view of the American past. 1960. 3.00. Smith, Peter
Stimpson, George. Book about American history. 1950. 4.95. Harper
Thistlethwaite, Frank. Great experiment. 1955. 5.00. Cambridge U. P.
Todd, Lewis, and Merle Curti. Rise of the American nation. il. 5.96. Harcourt
Turner, Frederick Jackson. Early writings of Frederick Jackson Turner. by Everett E. Edwards. 1938. 3.50. U. of Wis.
Turner, F. J. Significance of sections in American history. 4.25. Smith, Peter
Van Loon, Hendrik Willem. Story of America. 1942. 3.95. Liveright
Van Tassell, David D. Recording America's past, 1607-1884. 1960. 6.00. U. of Chicago

U.S.--HISTORY--SOURCES (973)

Angle, Paul. By these words. 1954. 5.95. Rand McNally
Commager, Henry Steele. Documents of American history. 1949. 6.50. Appleton (R)
Commager, Henry Steele. Living ideas in America: An anthology of documents. 1951. 6.50. Harper (R)

Hacker, Louis M. Shaping of the American tradition. 6.00. Columbia

Handlin, O., and others. Harvard guide to American history. 1954. 10.00. Harvard

Hart, Albert Bushnell. American history told by contemporaries. 5 vols; vol. 1, Era of colonization, 1492-1689. 7.50; vol. 2. Building of the Republic, 1689-1783, 7.50; vol. 3, National expansion, 1783-1845. 7.50; vol. 4, Welding of the nation, 1846-1900. 7.75. vol. 5, 20th century United States, 1900-1929. 8.00; set, 35.00. Macmillan

Heffner, Richard D. Documentary history of the United States. 1956. 4.95. Indiana

Jameson, J. F. Original narratives of early American history. 19 vols. 5.75 ea.

Meyers, Marvin, and others. Sources of the American Republic. 2 vols. 1960. 3.75 ea. Scott

Morris, Richard B. Great presidential decisions. 1960. 7.50. Lippincott

University of Chicago, College, Social Sciences I staff. People shall judge; Readings in the formation of American policy. 2 vols. 5.00 ea. U. of Chicago

U.S.--HISTORY--COLONIAL PERIOD (973.2)

Adams, John Quincy, and John Adams. Selected writings. by Adrienne Kock and William Peden. 1946. 5.75. Knopf

Andrews, Charles M. Colonial period of American history. 4 vols. Settlements. vol. 1. 1936 7.00; vol. 2. 1936. 6.00; vol. 3. 1937. 7.50; vol. 4. England's commercial and colonial policy. 1938. 7.50. Yale

Andrews, C. M. Narratives of the insurrections, 1675-1690. 1915. 5.75. Barnes & Noble

Benet, Stephen Vincent. Western star. 1943. 3.50. Holt, Rinehart & Winston

Boorstin, Daniel J. Americans: The colonial experience. 1958. 6.00. Random

Channing, Edward. Century of colonial history, 1660-1760. (History of the United States. vol. 2) 7.00. Macmillan

Channing, Edward. Planting of the nation in the new world, 1000-1660. (History of the United States. vol. 1) 7.00. Macmillan

Jensen, Merrill. American colonial documents to 1776. 15.20. Oxford U. P.

Jernegan, Marcus W. American colonies, 1492-1750. 1959. 5.00. Ungar

McGuire, Edna. Brave young land. il. 1946. 4.32. Macmillan

Nettels, C. P. Roots of American civilization. (Crofts American history series) il. 1938. 5.75. Appleton

Page, Elizabeth. Tree of liberty. 1939. 6.95. Holt, Rinehart & Winston

Parkman, Francis. Half-century of conflict. pap. 1.50. Collier

Parkman, Francis. Parkman reader. il. by Samuel Eliot Morison. 1955. 6.50. Little

Savelle, Max. Foundations of American civilization: History of colonial America. il. 1942. 7.25. Holt

U.S.--HISTORY--REVOLUTION (973.3)

Abernethy, Thomas P. Western lands and the American Revolution. il. 1959. 7.50. Russell

Alden, John Richard. American Revolution: 1775-1783. 1954. 5.00. Harper

Allen, Ethan. Narrative of Colonel Ethan Allen. 3.25. Smith, Peter

Alden, John Richard. South in the Revolution, 1763-1789. 1957. 7.50. La. State

American Heritage. American Heritage book of the Revolution. 1958. 12.50. S. and S.

Andrews, Charles M. Colonial background of the American revolution. 1931. 5.00. Yale

Bakeless, John. Turncoats, traitors and heroes. il. 1959. 6.50. Lippincott

Bakeless, Katherine, and John. Spies of the revolution. 1962. 3.95. Lippincott

Britt, Albert. Hungry war. 1961. 5.00. Barre

Bruckberger, Raymond L. Image of America. 1959. 5.00. Viking

Burke, Edmund. Speech on American taxation. bd. with Speech on conciliation with America; and Letter to the sheriffs of Bristol. by F. G. Selby. 1.50. St. Martins

Clark, William Bell. Ben Franklin's Privateers: A naval epic of the American Revolution. 1956. 3.75. La. State

Commager, Henry Steele, and Richard B. Morris. Spirit of Seventy-six. il.
1958. 15. 00. Bobbs
Cook, Fred J. What manner of man: Forgotten heroes of the American Revolution.
1959. 5. 00. Morrow
Davidson, Philip G. Propaganda and the American Revolution. 1941. 5. 00. U. of
N. C.
Dickerson, O. M. Navigation acts and the American Revolution. 1951. 6. 00. U. of
Pa.
Doane, Gilbert H. Searching for your ancestors. il. 1960. 3. 95. U. of Minn.
Falkner, Leonard. Forge of liberty: The dramatic opening of the American
Revolution. il. 1959. 4. 50. Dutton
Foley, Rae. Famous American spies. 1962. 3. 00. Dodd
Gipson, Lawrence. Coming of the Revolution: 1763-1775. 1954. 5. 00. Harper
Hamilton, Alexander. Papers of Alexander Hamilton, 1768-1790. 6 vols. by
Harold C. Syrett, and Jacob E. Cooke. vol. 1, 2. 1768-1780; vols. 3, 4. 1782-
1788; vols. 5, 6. 1788-1790. 12. 50 ea; set, 60. 00. Columbia
Jameson, J. F. American Revolution considered as a social movement. 2. 50.
Smith, Peter
Jensen, Merrill. Articles of Confederation. 1959. 6. 50. U. of Wis.
Knollenberg, Bernhard. Origin of the American Revolution: 1759-1766. 1961. pap.
1. 50. Collier
Lancaster, Bruce. From Lexington to liberty. 1955. 5. 75. Doubleday
Miller, John C. Sam Adams. il. 1936. 7. 50. Stanford
Miller, John C. Triumph of freedom 1775-1783. 1948. 7. 50. Little
Mitchell, Joseph B. Decisive battles of the American Revolution. 1962. 4. 50.
Putnam
Paine, Thomas. Common sense. with the crisis. pap. 0. 95. Doubleday
Peckham, Howard H. War for independence: A military history. 1958. 4. 00. pap.
1. 75. U. of Chicago
Rossiter, Clinton. First American Revolution. 1956. pap. 1. 25. Harcourt
Schlesinger, A. M. Colonial merchants and the American Revolution, 1763-
1776. 7. 50. Ungar
Schlesinger, Arthur M. Prelude to independence. 1958. 6. 00. Knopf
Wahlke, John C. Causes of the American Revolution. 1962. pap. 1. 50. Heath
U. S. --HISTORY--1783-1809 (973. 4)
Beloff, Max. Thomas Jefferson and American democracy. 2. 50. Macmillan
Carman, Harry J. , and Arthur W. Thompson. Guide to the principal sources
for American civilization, 1800-1900, in the city of New York: Printed materials
1962. 15. 00. Columbia
Channing, Edward. Federalists and Republicans, 1789-1815. 7. 00. Macmillan
Channing, Edward. Period of transition, 1815-1848. 7. 00. Macmillan
Churchill, Winston S. Great democracies (1815-1901) 6. 00. Dodd
Cunliffe, Marcus. Nation takes shape: 1789-1837. 1959. 4. 50. U. of Chicago
Dos Passos, John. Men who made the nation. 1957. 5. 95. Doubleday
Fiske, John. Critical period of American history, 1783-1789. 6. 50. Houghton
Jensen, Merrill. New nation. 1950. 5. 75. Knopf
Krout, John, Allen, and Dixon Ryan Fox. Completion of independence, 1790-
1830. il. 1944. 6. 75. Macmillan
Malone, Dumas, and Basil Rauch. To 1865. il. 1960. 7. 50. Appleton
Miller, John C. Federalist era, 1789-1801. 1960. 5. 00. Harper
Morgan, Edmund S. Birth of the Republic: 1763-89. 1956. 3. 50. U. of Chicago
Nye, Russel B. Cultural life of the new Nation: 1776-1830. il. 1960. 5. 00. Harper
Wiltse, Charles M. New nation: 1800-1845. 4. 50. Hill & Wang
Wright, Esmond. Fabric of freedom, 1763-1800. il. 1961. 4. 50. Hill & Wang
U. S. --HISTORY--WAR OF 1812 (973. 52)
Carr, Albert Z. Coming of war. 4. 95. Doubleday
Forester, C. S. Age of fighting sail. 1956. 5. 00. Doubleday
Freidel, Frank. Splendid little war. il. 1958. 8. 50. Little

Gilpin, Alec R. War of 1812 in the old Northwest. 1958. 6.50. Mich. State
Pratt, Julius W. Expansionists of 1812. 4.25. Smith, Peter

U.S.-- ISTORY--1815-1861 (973.6)

Coit, Margaret L. Fight for union. il. 1961. 3.00. Macmillan
De Voto, Bernard. Year of decision. 1950. 7.50. Houghton
Hart, Albert Bushnell. Welding of the nation, 1846-1900. 7.50. Macmillan
Nevins, Allan. Ordeal of the Union. 2 vols. vol. 1, Fruits of manifest destiny
    1847-1852; vol. 2, House dividing, 1852-1857. il. 1947. 7.50 ea. Scribner
Stern, Philip Van Doren. Prologue to Sumter. il. 1961. 9.95. Indiana
Waggoner, Madeline S. Long haul west: The great canal era, 1817-1850. il.
    5.75. Putnam

U.S.-- HISTORY--WAR WITH MEXICO, 1845-1848

De Voto, Bernard. Year of decision. 1950. 7.50. Houghton
Fuller, John D. P. Movement for the acquisition of all Mexico, 1846-1848. 1936.
    2.50. Johns Hopkins
Grant, U.S. Personal memoirs. 2.50. Smith, Peter
Henry, Robert S. Story of the Mexican War. il. 5.00. Ungar
Singletary, Otis A. Mexican War. 1960. 3.75. U. of Chicago

U.S.--HISTORY--CIVIL WAR (973.7)

Adams, Ephraim. Great Britain and the American Civil War. 2 vols. 7.50.
    Russell
American Heritage. American Heritage picture history of the Civil War. by
    Bruce Catton. il. 1960. 19.95. Doubleday
Beatner, Mark M., III. Civil War dictionary: A concise encyclopedia. il. 1959.
    15.00. McKay
Bradford, Ned G. Battles and leaders of the Civil War. il. 8.95. Meredith
Canby, Courtlandt. Lincoln and the Civil War. 1960. 5.00. Braziller
Catton, Bruce. America goes to war. 3.00. Wesleyan U. P.
Catton, Bruce. Centennial history of the Civil War. vol. 1. Coming fury. 1961.
    7.50. Doubleday
Catton, Bruce. This hallowed ground: The story of the Union side of the Civil
    War. 1956. 4.95. Doubleday
Catton, Bruce. Army of the Potomac. 3 vols. 12.50. Doubleday
Catton, Bruce. Glory road. 1953. 4.50. Doubleday
Catton, Bruce. Grant moves south. 1960. 6.50. Little
Catton, Bruce. Mr. Lincoln's army. 1951. 4.50. Doubleday
Catton, Bruce. Stillness at Appomattox. il. 1953. 5.00. Doubleday
Channing, Edward. War for southern independence. 7.00. Macmillan
Churchill, Winston S. American Civil War. il. 1961. 3.00. Dodd
Cochran, Hamilton. Blockade runners of the Confederacy. il. 1958. 6.00. Bobbs
Cole, Arthur C. Irrepressible conflict. 1850-1865. 1934. 6.75. Macmillan
Commager, Henry Steele. Official atlas of the Civil War. 40.00. Yoseloff
Commager, Henry Steele. Photographic history of the Civil War. 5 vols. 1957.
    40.00. Yoseloff (R)
Craven, Avery O. Civil War in the making, 1815-1860. 1959. 3.00. La. State
Craven, Avery. Coming of the Civil War. 1957. 6.50. U. of Chicago
Donald, David. Lincoln reconsidered. 1956. 3.50. Knopf
Donald, David H. Divided we fought: A pictorial history of the war, 1861-1865.
    1959. 14.95. Macmillan
Dowdey, Clifford. Land they fought for: The South as the Confederacy, 1832-
    1865. 1955. 5.75. Doubleday
Dowdey, Clifford. Lee's last campaign: The story of Lee and his men against
    Grant, 1864. il. 1960. 6.00. Little
Downey, Fairfax. Clash of cavalry: The battle of Brandy Station. il. 1959. 4.95.
    McKay
Eaton, Clement. History of the Southern Confederacy. pap. 1.50. Collier
Freeman, Douglas S. Lee's lieutenants. 3 vols. il. 30.00. Scribner
Fuller, J. F. C. Grant and Lee: A study in personality and generalship. il. 1957.
    5.00. Indiana

Hesseltine, William B. Tragic conflict. 1962. 8.50. Braziller
Johnson, Ludwell H. Red River campaign: Politics and cotton in the Civil War.
    il. 1958. 5.00. Johns Hopkins
Lee, Robert E. Wartime papers. il. 1961. 15.00. Little
Liddell Hart, Basil H. Sherman. 1958. 1.95. Praeger
McElroy, John. This was Andersonville. by Roy Meredith. il. 12.50. McDowell
MacBride, Robert. Civil War ironclads. 1962. 7.50. Chilton
Marx, Karl, and Friedrich Engels. Civil War in the United States. 1961. 4.00.
    Int. Pubs.
Meredith, Roy. Mr. Lincoln's contemporaries. il. 1951. 6.00. Scribner
Miers, Earl S. Billy Yank and Johnny Reb. il. 1959. 3.50. Rand McNally
Miers, Earl S. , and Paul M. Angle. Tragic years, 1860-1865. 2 vols. 1960.
    15.001 S. and S.
Mitchell, Joseph B. Decisive battles of the Civil War. il. 1955. 4.00. Putnam
Nevins, Allan. War for the union. 2 vols. vol. 1, Improvised war. 1861-1862.
    1959; vol. 2, War becomes revolution, 1862-1863. 1960. il. 7.50 ea. Scribner
Nevins, Allan. Ordeal of the Union. 2 vols. il. 1947. 7.50 ea. Scribner
Randall, James G. , and David Donald. Civil War and Reconstruction. il. 1961.
    9.00. Heath
Randall, James G. , and David Donald. Divided Union. il. 1961. 6.50. Little
Rozwenc, Edwin C. Causes of the American Civil War. 1961. pap. 2.25.
    Heath
Sandburg, Carl. Storm over the land: A profile of the Civil War. il. 1942. 5.75.
    Harcourt
Sanger, D. B. , and T. R. Hay. James Longstreet. 1952. 6.50. La. State
Sideman, Belle B. , and Lillian Friedman. Europe looks at the Civil War. 1960.
    6.00. Orion
Stern, Philip Van Doren. End to valor. 1958. 5.75. Houghton
Strother, David H. Virginia Yankee in the Civil War: Diaries of David Hunter
    Strother. by Cecil D. Eby, Jr. il. 1961. 6.75. U. of N. C.
Swanberg, W. A. First blood: Story of Fort Sumter. il. 1957. 5.95. Scribner
Warner, Ezra. Generals in gray. 1959. 7.50. La. State
Warren, Robert Penn. Legacy of the Civil War. 1961. 2.75. Random
Welles, Gideon. Civil War and Reconstruction. 1959. 4.50. Twayne
Welles, Gideon. Lincoln's administration. 4.50. Twayne
West, Richard S. Jr. Mr. Lincoln's navy. il. 1958. 6.95. McKay
Wilson, Woodrow. Division and reunion, 1829-1889. 3.00. Smith, Peter
Young, Agatha. Women and the crisis. il. 1959. 6.00. Obolensky
U.S.--HISTORY--1865-1898 (973.8)
Buck, Paul. Road to reunion, 1865-1900. 1959. 3.25. Smith, Peter
Faulkner, Harold U. Politics, reform and expansion: 1890-1900. 1959. 5.00.
    Harper
Freidel, Frank. Splendid little war. il. 1958. 7.50. Little
U.S.--HISTORY--20TH CENTURY (973.9)
Allen, Frederick Lewis. Only yesterday. 1931. 5.00. Harper
Baldwin, Leland D. Recent American history. 7.00. Am. Bk. Co.
Hicks, John D. Republican ascendancy, 1921-1933. 1960. 5.00. Harper
Hoffman, Frederick J. Twenties: American writing in the postwar decade. 1955.
    6.00. Viking
Hoover, Herbert. Memoirs of Herbert Hoover. 3 vols. 6.00 ea. Macmillan
Lord, Walter. Good years. il. 1960. 5.95. Harper
Markmann, Charles L. , and Mark Sherwin. One week in March. il. 1961. 3.95.
    Putnam
Nixon, Richard M. Six crises. 1962. 5.95. Doubleday
Perkins, Dexter. New age of Franklin Roosevelt: 1932-45. 1957. 4.50. U. of
    Chicago
Robinson, Edgar E. Roosevelt leadership: 1933-1945. 1954. 6.00. Lippincott
Schlesinger, Arthur Jr. Age of Roosevelt. 4 vols. 6.95 ea. 1962. Houghton
Slosson, Preston W. Great crusade and after, 1914-1928. il. 1931. 6.75. Mac-
    millan

Wish, Harvey. Contemporary America. 1955. 7.50. Harper

U.S.--HISTORY, MILITARY (973)

Millis, Walter. Arms and men. 5.75. Putnam
Williams, T. Harry. Americans at war. 1960. 3.50. La. State

U.S.--INTELLECTUAL LIFE (973)

Barzun, Jacques. Teacher in America. 1945. 5.00. Little
Beer, Thomas. Mauve decade. 1961. pap. 1.10. Vintage
Blankenship, Russell. American literature as an expression of the national mind.
    1949. 7.50. Holt
Bode, Carl. Anatomy of American popular culture, 1840-1861. il. 1959. 6.00.
    U. of Calif.
Boorstin, Daniel J. Lost world of Thomas Jefferson. 4.00. Smith, Peter
Brooks, Van Wyck. America's coming of age. 1959. 3.00. Smith, Peter
Commager, Henry Steele. American mind. 1950. 6.50. Yale
Curti, Merle. Gorwth of American thought. 1951. 9.00. Harper
Curti, Merle. Probing our past. 1959. 4.25. Smith, Peter
Elliott, William Y. Television's impact on American culture. 1956. 4.95. Mich.
    State
Gabriel, Ralph H. Course of American democratic thought. 1956. 6.50. Ronald
Hart, J. D. Popular book: A history of America's literary taste. il. 1950. 6.50.
    Oxford U. P.
Horton, Rod W., and Herbert W. Edwards. Backgrounds of American literary
    thought. 1952. 3.25. Appleton
Mumford, Lewis. Golden day, a study in American literature and culture.
    3.50. Smith, Peter
Nye, Russel B. Cultural life of the new nation: 1776-1830. il. 1960. 5.00. Harper
Peyre, Henri. Observations on life, literature and learning in America. 1961.
    5.00. Southern Ill.
Rosenberg, Bernard, and David Manning White. Mass culture: The popular arts in
    America. 1957. 6.50. Free Press
Spiller, Robert E., and Eric Larrabee. American perspectives: The national
    self-image in the twentieth century. 1961. 4.75. Harvard
Wright, Louis B. Cultural life of the American colonies: 1607-1763. 1957. 5.00.
    Harper

U.S.--LAWS, STATUTES (340)

Bailey, S. K. Congress makes a law. 1950. 5.00. Columbia
Berman, Daniel M. Bill becomes a law: The Civil Rights Act of 1960. pap. 1.75.
    Macmillan
Millis, Harry A., and Emily C. Brown. From the Wagner Act to Taft-Hartley.
    1950. 9.50. U. of Chicago
Witte, Edwin E. Development of the Social security act. il. 1962. 5.75. U. of Wis.

U.S.--NAVY (359)

Chapelle, Howard I. History of American sailing navy. 18.50. Norton
Howard, Joseph L. Our modern Navy. il. 1961. 5.95. Van Nostrand
King, Ernest J., and Walter Nuir Whitehill. Fleet Admiral King. il. 1952. 12.50.
    Norton
Pratt, Fletcher. Compact history of the U. S. navy. il. 1962. 4.95. Hawthorn
Yates, Brock W. Destroyers and destroyermen. il. 1959. 3.50. Harper

U.S.--POLITICS AND GOVERNMENT (973)

Adams, Henry. Great secession winter and other essays. by George Hochfield.
    6.00. Sagamore
Angle, Paul M. Created equal? The complete Lincoln-Douglas debates of 1858. -
    1958. 7.50. U. of Chicago
Appleby, Paul H. Policy and administration. 1949. 2.50. U. of Ala.
Baird, A. Craig. American public addresses. 1956. 5.50. McGraw
Beard, Charles A. American government and politics. 1949. 7.00. Macmillan
Beard, Charles A. Republic. 1943. 3.75. Viking
Binkley, Wilfred E. American political parties. 1958. 5.75. Knopf

Binkley, Wilfred E. , and Malcolm C. Moos. Grammar of American politics: The national government. 1957. 6.00. Knopf

Birley, Robert. Speeches and documents in American history. 4 vols. 2.25 ea. Oxford U. P.

Blau, Joseph L. Social theories of Jacksonian democracy. 1954. 4.50. Bobbs

Boorstin, Daniel J. Genius of American politics. 1953. 4.00. U. of Chicago

Bowles, Chester. American politics in a revolutionary world. 1956. 2.25. Harvard

Buchanan, Lamont. Ballot for Americans: A pictorial history of American elections and electioneering, 1789-1956. il. 1956. 4.95. Dutton

Burkhart, James, and others. American government: The clash of issues. 1960. 4.25. Prentice-Hall

Calhoun, John C. Disquisition on government. 1958. 2.50. Smith, Peter

Carnegie, Andrew. Gospel of wealth and other timely essays. 1962. 4.50. Harvard

Carter, Edward W. , and Charles C. Rohlfing, American government and its work. 7.25. Macmillan

Charles, Joseph. Origins of the American party system. 3.25. Smith, Peter

Chevalier, Michael. Society, manners and politics in the United States. 3.50. Smith, Peter

Clemens, Samuel Langhorne. Mark Twain and the Government. by Svend Petersen. 1960. 3.50. Caxton

Cole, Arthur C. Whig Party in the South. 1959. 6.75. Smith, Peter

Commager, Henry Steele. Living ideas in America: An anthology on documents. 1951. 6.50. Harper

Corwin, Edward S. President: Office and powers. 1957. 6.50. N. Y. U.

Craven, Avery O. Civil War in the making, 1815-1860. 1959. 3.00. La. State

Cunningham, Noble E. , Jr. Jeffersonian Republicans: The formation of party organization, 1789-1801. 1958. 6.00. U. of N. C.

Dauer, Manning J. Adams Federalists. 1953. 6.00. Johns Hopkins

Dixon, Robert G. , Jr. , and Elmer Plischke. American government basic documents and materials. il. 1950. 4.50. Van Nostrand

Douglas, Stephen A. Letters. by Robert W. Johannsen. il. 1961. 10.00. U. of Ill.

Faulkner, Harold U. American political and social history. il. 1957. 7.50. Appleton

Ferguson, John H. , and Dean E. McHenry. American system of government. il. 1961. 7.95. McGraw

Fletcher, Cyril S. Education for public responsibility. 1961. 4.50. Norton

Fletcher, Cyril S. Education: The challenge ahead. 1962. 4.50. Norton

Franklin, Benjamin. Letters to the press, 1758-1775. 1950. 6.00. U. of N. C.

Fuchs, Lawrence. Political behavior of American Jews. 1956. 4.00. Free Press

Guitteau, William B. , and Edna M. Bohlmen. Our government today. 1938. 3.96. Houghton

Handlin, Oscar, and Mary F. Dimensions of liberty. 1961. 3.75. Harvard

Hart, James. American presidency in action, 1789. 4.00. Brown Book

Hofstadter, Richard. American political tradition. 1948. 5.75. Knopf

Hoyt, Edwin P. , Jr. Jumbos and jackasses: A popular history of the political wars. 5.95. Doubleday

Jacobson, Jacob M. Development of American political thought. 7.50. Appleton

Lincoln, Abraham, and Stephen Douglas. In the name of the people: Speeches and writings of Lincoln and Douglas in the Ohio campaign of 1859. by Harry V. Jaffa and Robert W. Johannsen. 1959. 5.00. Ohio State

Lippmann, Walter. Preface to politics. 1962. 4.40. U. of Mich.

Lipset, Seymour M. Political man: The social bases of politics. 1959. 4.95. Doubleday

MacDonald, H. Malcolm, and others. Outside readings in American government. 1957. 3.95. Crowell

McLaughlin, and Hart. Cyclopedia of American government. 3 vols. 27.00. Smith, Peter (R)

Meyers, Marvin. Jacksonian persuasion: Politics and belief. 5.00. Stanford

Miers, Earl Schenck. Great rebellion. 1958. 6.00. World Pub.

Miller, John C. Crisis in freedom: The Alien and Sedition acts. 1951. 4.75. Little
Munro, William B. Government of the United States, national, state, and local. 6.95. Macmillan
Munro, William B. National government of the United States. 6.00. Macmillan
Nash, Howard P. Third parties in American politics. il. 1958. 6.00. Pub. Affairs
Ogg, Frederic A., and P. Orman Ray. Introduction to American government: The national government. il. 7.50. Appleton
Ostrander, Gilman. Rights of man in America, 1607-1861. 1960. 6.50. U. of Missouri
Parrington, Vernon Louis. Main currents in American thought. 1 vol. 10.50. vol. 1, Colonial mind, 1620-1800; and vol. 2, Romantic revolution in America, 1800-1860. pap. 1.75 ea. Harcourt
Rossiter, Clinton. Conservatism in America. 1962. 5.00. Knopf
Schattschneider, E. E. Party government. 1942. pap. 2.50. Holt, Rinehart & Winston
Schlesinger, Arthur M. New viewpoints in American history. 5.25. Macmillan
Schlesinger, Arthur M. Paths to the present. 5.75. Macmillan
Scott, Andrew M. Political thought in America. 1959. 8.50. Holt, Rinehart & Winston
Sperber, Hans and Travis Trittschuh. American political terms: An historical dictionary. 1962. 9.00. Wayne (R)
Swisher, C. B. Theory and practice of American national government. 6.50. Houghton
Tocqueville, Alexis de. Democracy in America. 2 vols. tr. by Phillips Bradley. 1944. 7.50. Knopf
Truman, Harry S. Memoirs. 2 vols. 1958. 4.50. Doubleday
Turner, Frederick J. Rise of the new West. 1959. 6.00. Smith, Peter
White, Leonard D. Jacksonians: A study in administrative history, 1829-1861. 1954. 5.95. Macmillan
White, Leonard D. Federalists. A study in administrative history. 6.00. Macmillan
White, Leonard D. Introduction to the study of public administration. 1955. 6.75. Macmillan
Williams, Wayne C. Rail splitter for president. 3.00. Brown Book
Wilson, Francis Graham. Case for conservatism. 1951. 1.75. U. of Wash.
Wilson, Woodrow. Congressional government. 1958. 3.00. Smith, Peter
Wilson, Woodrow. Constitutional government in the United States. 1908. 3.00. Columbia
Wilson, Woodrow. Division and reunion, 1829-1889. 3.00. Smith, Peter

U.S. --POLITICS AND GOVERNMENT--CIVIL WAR (973.7)

Buck, Paul. Road to reunion, 1865-1900. 1959. 3.25. Smith, Peter
Davis, Jefferson. The rise and fall of the Confederate Government. 1958. 2 vols. boxed. 12.50. Yoseloff
Goldman, Eric F. Rendezvous with destiny. 1952. 6.95. Knopf
Hesseltine, William B. Lincoln and the war governors. 1948. 5.75. Knopf
Hicks, John D. Populist revolt. il. 1961. pap. 1.75. U. of Neb.
Hofstadter, Richard. Age of reform: From Bryan to F.D.R. 1955. 5.00. Knopf
Laugel, Auguste. United States during the Civil War. by Allan Nevins. 1961. 6.95. Indiana

U.S. --POLITICS AND GOVERNMENT--20TH CENTURY (973.9)

Agar, Herbert. Price of power: America since 1945. 1957. 4.00. U. of Chicago
American Assembly. Goals for Americans. by the President's Commission on National Goals. 1960. 3.50. Prentice-Hall
Bowles, Chester. American politics in a revolutionary world. 1956. 2.25. Harvard
Bowles, Chester. Prologue to the sixties. 1962. 4.50. Harper
Brogan, D. W. Politics in America. 1959. 6.00. Harper
Brown, John Mason. Through these men. 1956. 4.50. Harper
Daniels, Josephus. Wilson era: Years of war and after, 1917-1923. 1.30. U. of N. C.
Einaudi, Mario. Roosevelt revolution. 1959. 5.95. Harcourt

Ewing, Cortez A. M. Congressional elections, 1896-1944. 1947. 2.00. U. of Okla.
Fenton, John M. In your opinion. 1960. 3.95. Little
Forcey, Charles. Crossroads of liberalism. 1961. 7.00. Oxford U. P.
Goldwater, Barry. Conscience of a conservative. pap. 0.50. Macfadden
Harris, Seymour E. Economics of the political parties. 1962. 7.00. Macmillan
Hilliard, Charles C. Cross, the sword and the dollar. 1951. 3.00. North River
Hoover, Herbert. Addresses upon the American road, 1933-1955. 7 vols. 15.00.
    Stanford
Kennedy, John F. To turn the tide. 1962. 3.95. Harper
Lederer, William J. Nation of sheep. 1961. 3.95. Norton
Link, Arthur S. Woodrow Wilson and the progressive era: 1910-1917. 1954. 5.00.
    Harper
Martin, Joseph W. , and Robert J. Donovan. My first fifty years in politics. 1960.
    4.95. McGraw
Mencken, Henry L. On politics: A carvival of buncombe. by Malcolm Moos. 1956.
    pap. 1.45. Vintage
Regier, C. C. Era of the muckrakers. 4.25. Smith, Peter
Schlesinger, Arthur, Jr. Vital center. 3.50. 1962. Houghton
Schnapper, M. B. New frontiers of the Kennedy administration. 1961. 3.75. Pub.
    Affairs
Swados, Harvey. Years of conscience: The muckrakers, an anthology. 3.75.
    Smith, Peter
Truman, Harry S. Mr. Citizen. il. 1960. 5.00. Random
Wecter, Dixon. Age of the Great Depression, 1929-1941. Macmillan
Wilson, Woodrow. Crossroads of freedom: The 1912 campaign speeches of Woodrow
    Wilson. by J. W. Davidson. 1956. 6.00. Yale
Wolfskill, George. Revolt of the conservative: A history of the American Liberty
    League, 1934-1940. il. 1962. 5.00. Houghton
U.S. --RACE QUESTION (301.451)
Ashmore, Harry S. The other side of Jordan. il. 1960. 3.50. Norton
Baldwin, James. Nobody knows my name. 1961. 4.50. Dial
Baldwin, James. Notes of a native son. 3.25. Smith, Peter
Baruch, Dorothy W. Glass house of prejudice. 1946. 3.50. Morrow
Brown, Francis J. , and Joseph S. Roucek. One America. 1952. 10.00. Prentice-
    Hall
Frazier, Edward F. Black bourgeoisie. 1956. 4.00. Free Press
Furnas, J. C. Goodbye to Uncle Tom. il. 1956. 6.00. Sloane
Handlin, Oscar. Race and nationality in American life. 1957. 4.75. Little
La Farge, John. Catholic viewpoint on race relations. 1960. 3.50. Doubleday
Lincoln, Charles E. Black Muslims in America. 1961. 4.95. Beacon
Lomax, Louis E. Negro revolt. 1962. 3.50. Harper
Myers, Gustavus. History of bigotry in the U.S. 1943. 3.50. Random
Redding, Saunders. Lonesome road: The story of the Negro in America. 1958.
    5.75. Doubleday
Rose, Arnold, and Caroline. America divided: Minority group relations in the
    United States. 1949. 3.75. Knopf
Thompson, Edgar T. Race relations and the race problem. 1948. 6.00. Duke
U.S. --RELATIONS (327)
Boorstin, Daniel J. America and the image of Europe. 3.35. Smith, Peter
Bowles, Chester. Ideas, people and peace. 1958. 3.00. Harper
Brogan, D. W. America in the modern world. 1960. 3.00. Rutgers
Bruckberger, Raymond L. Image of America. 1959. 5.00. Viking
Buck, Pearl S. , and Carlos P. Romulo. Friend to friend. 1958. 2.95. Day
Chester, Edward W. Europe views America: A critical evaluation. 1961. 4.50.
    Pub. Affairs
Commager, Henry S. Immigration and American history: Essays in honor of
    Theodore C. Blegen. 1961. 4.50. U. of Minn.
Curti, Merle. Probing our past. 1959. 4.25. Smith, Peter
Douglas, William O. America challenged. 1960. 2.50. Princeton

Douglas, William O. Democracy's manifesto. 2. 00. Doubleday
Heilbroner, Robert L. Future as history. 1959. 4. 00. Harper
Kennedy, John F. Strategy of peace. 1960. 3. 50. Harper
Kohn, Clyde F. United States and the world today. il. 1957. 3. 50. Rand McNally
Kraus, Michael. Atlantic civilization: 18th century origins. 1961. 7. 50. Russell
Lippmann, Walter. Communist world and ours. 1959. 2. 00. Little
Schurz, William L. American foreign affairs. 1959. 4. 50. Dutton
Schwantes, Robert S. Japanese and Americans: A century of cultural relations,
    1955. 4. 00. Harper

U. S. --RELIGION (277)

Bates, Ernest S. American faith. 1957. 7. 50. Norton
Bell, Bernard Iddings. Crowd culture. Regnery
Clark, Elmer T. Small sects in America. 1949. pap. 1. 25. Abingdon
Cousins, Norman. In God we trust: The religious beliefs and ideas of the American
    founding fathers. 1958. 5. 95. Harper
Dulles, John Foster. Spiritual legacy. 1960. 3. 95. Westminster
Gaustad, Edwin S. Historical atlas of religion in America. 1962. 7. 95. Harper
Hall, Thomas Cuming. Religious background of American culture. 1959. 5. 75.
    Ungar
Hardon, John A. Protestant churches of America. 1958. 5. 00. Newman
La Farge, John, and others. Religion and our divided denominations. by Willard
    Learoyd Sperry. 1945. 1. 50. Harvard
Mead, Frank S. Handbook of denominations in the United States. 1961. 2. 95. Abingdon
    (R)
Rosten, Leo. Guide to the religions of America. 1955. 3. 95. S. and S.
Smith, J. W. , and A. L. Jamison. Religion in American life. 4 vols. 1961. 32. 50.
    Princeton

U. S. --SOCIAL CONDITIONS (300)

Adamic, Louis. Dynamite, the story of class violence in America. il. 1959. 6. 00.
    Smith, Peter
Adams, James Truslow. Provincial society, 1690-1763. 1938. 6. 75. Macmillan
Amory, Cleveland. Last resorts: A portrait of American society at play. 1952.
    5. 95. Harper
Allen, Frederick Lewis. Big change: America transforms itself, 1900-1950. 1952.
    4. 50. Harper
Barnes, Harry E. , and Oreen M. Ruedi. American way of life. 1950. 7. 75. Pren-
    tice-Hall
Barnes, Harry Elmer. Social institutions. 1942. 7. 25. Prentice-Hall
Bell, Daniel. End of ideology. 1959. 7. 50. Free Press
Bertrand, Alvin L. Rural sociology. 1958. 7. 50. McGraw
Bredemeier, Harry C. , and Jackson Toby. Social problems of America: Costs
    and casualties in an acquisitive society. il. 1960. 6. 75. Wiley
Britt, Steuart H. Selected readings in social psychology. 1950. 3. 95. Holt,
    Rinehart & Winston
Bryce, James. American commonwealth. 6. 75. Macmillan.
Calhoun, Arthur W. Social history of the American family. 3 vols. vol. 1,
    Colonial period; vol. 2, From independence through the Civil War; vol. 3,
    From 1865 to 1919. 1960. pap. 1. 95 ea. Barnes & Noble
Chevalier, Michael. Society, manners and politics in the United States. 3. 50.
    Smith, Peter
Cochran, Thomas C. , and William Miller. Age of enterprise: A social history of
    industrial America. 1942. 6. 50. Macmillan
Cuber, John F. , and others. Problems of American society: Values in conflict.
    1956. 5. 50. Holt
Curti, Merle. American issues: The social record. 1960. 7. 50. Lippincott
Dickens, Charles. American notes. 2. 00. Smith, Peter
Dulles, Foster R. America learns to play: A history of popular recreation 1607-
    1940. il. 6. 00. Smith, Peter

Earle, Alice M. Home life in colonial days. il. 1913. 5.50. Macmillan
Ebersole, Luke. American society. 1955. 6.95. McGraw
Farquhar, Margaret C. Colonial life in America. 1962. 2.50. Holt, Rinehart & Winston
Faulkner, Harold U. Quest for social justice. 1898-1914. il. 6.75. Macmillan
Fine, Sidney. Laissez faire and the general-welfare state. 1956. 7.50. U. of Mich.
Fortune. America in the sixties. il. 1960. pap. 1.85. Harper
Graham, Saxon. America culture. 1957. 6.50. Harper
Handlin, Oscar. This was America. il. 1949. 4.50. Harvard
Hoffsommer, Harold. Sociology of American life. 1958. 8.50. Prentice-Hall
Holbrook, Stewart H. Dreamers of the American dream. 1957. 5.75. Doubleday
Kahl, Joseph A. American class structure. 1957. 6.55. Holt, Rinehart & Winston
Kinross, Lord. Innocents at home. il. 1960. 3.50. Morrow
Kolb, John H., and Edmund de S. Brunner. Study of rural society. 7.50. Houghton
Lee, Elizabeth B., and Alfred M. Social problems in America: A source book. 1955. pap. 5.50. Holt, Rinehart & Winston
Lipton, Lawrence. Holy barbarians. 1959. 5.00. Messner
Lubell, Samuel. Future of American politics. 1956. pap. 0.95. Doubleday
Lynd, Robert Stoughton. Knowledge for what? 1939. 4.00. Princeton
Lynes, Russell. Surfeit of honey. 1957. 3.00. Harper
Lynes, Russell. Tastemakers. il. 1954. 6.00. Harper
McGee, Reece. Social disorganization in America. 1961. 3.25. Chandler Pub.
Martindale, Don A. American social structure. 1960. 6.00. Appleton
Miller, John C. Colonial image. 1962. 8.50. Braziller
Mills, C. Wright. Power elite. 1956. 6.50. Oxford U. P.
Morris, Clarence. Trends in modern American society. 1962. 5.00. U. of Pa.
Nevins, Allan. Emergence of modern America. 1865-1878. il. 1928. 6.75. Macmillan
Reissman, Leonard. Class in American society. 1959. 6.75. Free Press
Schlesinger, Arthur M. Rise of the city. 1878-1898. il. 6.75. Macmillan
Sinclair, Andrew. Prohibition, the era of excess. il. 1962. 7.95. Little
Sirjamaki, John. American family in the twentieth century. 1953. 4.25. Harvard
Slosson, Preston W. Great crusade and after, 1914-1928. il. 1931. 6.75. Macmillan
Smith, James Morton. Seventeenth-century America, essays on colonial history. 1959. 5.00. U. of N. C.
Soule, George. Time for living. 1955. 3.00. Viking
Trollope, Frances. Domestic manners of the Americans. 1949. pap. 1.65. Vintage
Warner, William Lloyd. American life: Dream and reality. il. 1953. 2.75. U. of Chicago
Warner, W. Lloyd, and others. Democracy in Jonesville. 1949. 4.50. Harper
Warner, William L. Social class in America. 3.75. Smith, Peter
Warner, W. Lloyd. Family of God: A symbolic study of Christian life in America. 1961. pap. 1.75. Yale
Warner, W. Lloyd. Living and the dead. 1959. 7.50. Yale
Weinberg, Arthur, and Lila. Muckrakers. 1961. 7.50. S. and S.
Weinberg, Samuel K. Social problems in our time. il. 1960. 6.95. Prentice-Hall
Wertenbaker, Thomas J. Golden age of colonial culture. 1959. pap. 1.75. Cornell
Wish, Harvey. Contemporary America. 1955. 7.50. Harper
Wright, Louis B. Cultural life of the American colonies: 1607-1763. 1957. 5.00. Harper

U. S. --SUPREME COURT (347.9)

Beard, Charles A. Supreme Court and the Constitution. 1961. 3.95. Prentice-Hall
Black, Charles L., Jr. People and the court. 1960. 5.00. Macmillan
Carr, Robert K. Supreme Court and judicial review. 1942. pap. 2.00. Holt, Rinehart & Winston
Corwin, Edward S. Court over constitution: A study of judicial review as an instrument of popular government. 3.50. Smith, Peter

Curtis, Charles P. Law as large as life. 1959. 3.50. S. and S.

Frank, John P. Marble palace: The Supreme Court in American life. il. 1958. 5.00. Knopf

Gordon, Rosalie M. Nine men against America. 3.50. Devin

Laines, Charles G. Role of the Supreme Court in American government and politics 1789-1835. 1961. 12.50. Russell

Jackson, Robert F. Supreme Court in the American system of government. 1955. 2.00. Harvard

Kurland, Philip B. Supreme Court review. 1961 and 1962. 6.00 ea. U. of Chicago

McCloskey, Robert G. American Supreme Court. 1960. 5.00. U. of Chicago

Mason, Alpheus T. Supreme Court. 1962. 4.95. U. of Mich.

Murray, William F. Rights of Americans. 1954. 2.50. Forum

Pritchett, C. Herman. Congress versus the Supreme Court, 1957-1960. 1961. 3.75. U. of Minn.

Ramaswamy, M. Creative role of the Supreme Court of the United States. 1956. 3.00. Stanford

Rodell, Fred. Nine men: A political history of the Supreme Court of the U. S. from 1790 to 1955. 1955. 5.00. Random

Warren, Charles. Supreme Court in United States history. 2 vols. 1960. 15.00. Little

U. S. --TERRITORIAL EXPANSION (973)

Anthony, P. J. America, hope of the ages. 1959. 4.75. Christopher

De Voto, Bernard. Course of empire. 1952. 6.50. Houghton

Pratt, J. W. Expansionists of 1812. 4.25. Smith, Peter

UNIVERSITIES AND COLLEGES (378)

American Council on Education. Higher education in the United States. 1961. 2.00. A. C. E.

Babbitt, Irving. Literature and the American college. 2.00. Houghton

Beck, H. P. Men who control our universities. 1947. pap. 3.50. Columbia

Bennett, M. E. Getting the most out of college. 1957. 4.75. McGraw

Berdie, Ralph F. After high school: What? 1954. 4.25. U. of Minn.

Berelson, B. Graduate education in the United States. 6.95. McGraw

Boroff, David. Campus, USA: Portraits of American colleges in action. 1961. 4.50. Harper

Bowles, Frank A. How to get into college. 2.95. 1959. Dutton

Brownstein, Samuel C. College bound: Planning for college and career. 1958. 3.95. Barrons

Brubacher, John S., and Willis Rudy. Higher education in transition: An American history, 1636-1956. 1958. 8.50. Harper

Buttrick, George A. Biblical thought and the secular university. 1960. 2.50. La. State

Carlin, Edward A., and E. B. Blackman. Curriculum building in general education. 1960. 3.25. Brown, W. C.

Conant, James B. Academical patronage and superintendence. 1938. pap. 0.25. Harvard

Deferrari, R. J. College organization and administration. 1947. 4.50. Catholic U. of Am. Pr.

Deferrari, R. J. Self-evaluation and accreditation in higher education. 1959. 3.50. Catholic U. of Am. Pr.

Deutsh, Monroe E. College from within. il. 1952. 3.00. U. of Calif.

Eddy, Edward D., Jr. Colleges for our land and time: The land-grant idea in American education. 1957. 4.50. Harper

Educational Records Bureau. College freshmen speak out. 1956. 5.00. Harper

Fine, Benjamin. How to be accepted by the college of your choice. 1960-61. 1959. 4.95. Channel Pr., Manhasset, N. Y.

Glaze, Thomas E. Business administration for colleges and universities. 1962. 6.00. La. State

Havighurst, Robert J. American higher education, in the 1960's. il. 1960. 2.50. Ohio State

Hawes, Gene R. Guide to colleges. 1962. 5. 95. Columbia (R)

Hill, A. T. Small college meets the challenge. 1959. 5. 25. McGraw

Hofstadter, Richard, and Wilson Smith. American higher education. 2 vols. 15. 00. U. of Chicago

Hollinshead, B. S. Who should go to college? 1952. 3. 00. Columbia

Hoopes, R. State universities and colleges: A guide for prospective students. 1962. 3. 50. McKay (R)

Hutchins, Robert M. Education for freedom. 1943. 2. 50. La. State

Hutchins, Robert M. Higher learning in America. 1936. 7. 50. Yale

Irwin, Mary. American universities and colleges. 1960. 13. 00. A. C. E. (R)

Keiser, Albert. College names. 3. 00. Twayne

Kidd, Charles V. American universities and federal research. 1959. 6. 00. Harvard

Leacock, Stephen. Pursuit of knowledge. 1934. 2. 00. Liveright

Lloyd-Jones, Esther, and others. Case studies in college student-staff relationships. 1956. 2. 25. T. C.

Lovejoy, Clarence. Lovejoy's college guide. 1961. 5. 95. S. and S.

McConnell, Thomas R. General pattern for American public higher education. il. 1962. 4. 95. McGraw

McHale, Kathryn. Changes and experiments in liberal arts education. NSSE, 31st yrbk. pt. 2. 1932. 2. 50. U. of Chicago

National Education Association, Association for Higher Education. Current issues in higher education. 1958, 1959, 1960. 1961. 5. 00 ea. N. E. A.

National Education Association, American Educational Research Association. Coming crisis in the selection of students for college entrance. 1960. 1. 00. N. E. A.

Ness, Frederic W. Guide to graduate study. 1960. 6. 00. A. C. E.

Perkins, John A. Plain talk from a campus. 1959. 4. 00. Univ. Pub.

Ruml, Beardsley, and D. H. Morrison. Memo to a college trustee. 1959. 2. 95. McGraw

Sanford, R. Nevitt. American college: A psychological and social interpretation of higher learning. 1962. 8. 75. Wiley

Schmidt, George P. Liberal arts college: A chapter in American cultural history. il. 1957. 6. 00. Rutgers

Selden, William K. Accreditation: A struggle over standards in higher education. 1960. 2. 50. Harper

Charpe, Russell T. , and others. Financial assistance for college students. 1946. 1. 00. A. C. E.

Smith, Richard W. , and Howard P. Snethen. Four big years. 1960. 3. 50. Bobbs

Stoke, Harold W. American college president. 1959. 3. 50. Harper

Swift, Richard N. World affairs and the college curriculum. 1959. 3. 50. A. C. E.

Tyler, Ralph W. Graduate study in education. NSSE, 50th yearbook. pt. 1. 1951. 4. 50. U. of Chicago

Veblen, Thorstein. Higher learning in America. 3. 25. Smith, Peter

Walsh, Chad. Campus gods on trial. 1962. 3. 00. Macmillan

Walter, Erich A. Religion and the state university. 1958. 6. 50. U. of Mich.

Woodburne, Lloyd S. Principles of college and university administration. 1958. 5. 00. Stanford

World of learning. annual. 23. 50. Int. Pub. Service

Wriston, H. M. Academic procession. 1959. 4. 00. Columbia

URUGUAY (989. 5)

Hudson, W. H. Purple land. il. 1927. 3. 00. Dutton

Tinker, Edward L. Life and literature of the Pampas. il. 1961. U. of Fla.

UTAH (979. 2)

Stegner, Wallace. Mormon country. 1942. 4. 00. Duell

Writers' Project. Utah. 1954. 6. 50. Hastings

UTILITARIANISM (171. 5)

Stephen, Leslie. English utilitarians, Jeremy Bentham, James Mill, John Stuart Mill. 15. 00. Smith, Peter

UTOPIAS (321. 07)
Bacon, Francis. Advancement of learning, and New Atlantis. 1938. 2. 25. Oxford
U. P.
Bacon, Francis. Essays and New Atlantis. 1942. 1. 75. Van Nostrand
Bellamy, Edward. Looking backward. 3. 00. Houghton
Bestor, Arthur E., Jr. Backwoods Utopias. 1959. 5. 00. U. of Pa.
Butler, Samuel. Erewhon. 1. 95. Dutton
Butler, Samuel. Erewhon and Erewhon revisited. 1. 95. Modern Lib.
More, Thomas. Utopia of Sir Thomas More. 1. 75. St. Martins
Morgan, Arthur E. Nowhere was somewhere. 3. 00. Community Service
Mumford, L. Story of utopias. 4. 25. Smith, Peter
Plato. Republic. 1. 95. Modern Lib.
Tuveson, Ernest Lee. Millennium and Utopia: A study in the background of the
idea of progress. 1949. 3. 50. U. of Calif.

V

VAN GOGH, VINCENT, 1853-1890 (927)
Elgar, Frank. Van Gogh, a study of his life and work. il. 1958. 5. 75. Praeger
Huyghe, Rene. Van Gogh. il. 1958. 3. 50. Crown
Knuttel, Gerard. Van Gogh. 1962. pap. 0. 75. Barnes & Noble
Van Gogh, Vincent. Dear Theo: The autobiography of Vincent Van Gogh. il. 1958.
5. 00. Doubleday
VEBLEN, THORSTEIN BUNDE, 1857-1929. (923. 3)
Dobriansky, Lev E. Veblenism: A new critique. 1957. 6. 00. Pub. Affairs
Riesman, David. Thorstein Veblen. 3. 00. Scribner
VECTOR ANALYSIS (516. 83)
Brand, L. Vectorial mechanics. 1930. 8. 95. Wiley
Constant, Frank W. Theoretical physics: Mechanics. il. 1954. 8. 75. Addison-
Wesley
Davis, Harry F. Introduction to vector analysis. il. 1961. 10. 60. Allyn & Bacon
Gibbs, J. Willard. Vector analysis. by E. B. Wilson. pap. 2. 00. Dover
Spiegel, Murray R. Outline of theory and problems of vector analysis. il. 1959.
3. 25. Schaum
VENEZUELA (987)
Lieuwen, Edwin. Venezuela. il. 1961. 4. 00. Oxford U. P.
VENICE (945. 31)
Busse, Fritz. Venice, impressions. il. 5. 95. Arts
Hutton, Edward. Venice and Venetia. 1954. 5. 00. McKay
Lane, Frederic Chapin. Venetian ships and shipbuilders of the Renaissance. il. 1934
3. 50. Johns Hopkins
Morris, James. World of Venice. il. 1960. 5. 00. Pantheon
VERDI, GIUSEPPE, 1813-1901 (927)
Hussey, Dyneley. Verdi. 1949. 3. 50. Farrar, Straus
Sheean, Vincent. Orpheus at eighty. 1958. 5. 00. Random
Walker, Frank. Man Verdi. il. 1962. 10. 75. Knopf
VERGIL (PUBLIUS VERGILIUS MARO) (928)
Bowra, Cecil Maurice. From Virgil to Milton. 4. 50. St. Martins
Knight, W. F. Jackson. Roman Vergil. 5. 00. Hillary
VERMONT (974. 3)
Fisher, Dorothy Canfield. Vermont tradition: Biography of an outlook on life.
1953. 6. 00. Little
Hill, Ralph N. Yankee kingdom: Vermont and New Hampshire. il. 1960. 5. 95.
Harper
VERTEBRATES (596)
Berrill, N. J. Origin of vertebrates. 1955. 4. 00. Oxford U. P.
Blair, W. F., and others. Vertebrates of the United States. 1957. 13. 75. McGraw
Colbert, E. H. Evolution of the vertebrates. 1955. 7. 95. Wiley
Kent, G. C. Comparative anatomy of the vertebrates. 1954. 7. 95. McGraw
Romer, Alfred S. Vertebrate paleontology. il. 1945. 8. 50. U. of Chicago

Romer, Alfred S. Vertebrate story. il. 1959. 7.00. U. of Chicago
VETERINARY MEDICINE (636.0895)
Bierer, B. W. Short history of veterinary medicine in America. 1955. 3.00.
  Mich. State
Blood. Douglas C. , and J. A. Henderson. Veterinary medicine. 1960. 15.00.
  Williams & Wilkins
Merck veterinary manual. 9.75. Merck
Seiden, Rudolph, and W. James Gough. Livestock health encyclopedia. il. 1961.
  9.50. Springer
VICTORIA, QUEEN OF GREAT BRITAIN, 1819-1901 (923.142)
Strachey, Lytton. Queen Victoria. 1949. 2.50. Harcourt
VIETNAM (959.7)
Buttinger, Joseph. Smaller dragon. 1958. 7.50. Praeger
Fall, Bernard. Two Vietnams: A political history. 6.00. Praeger
VIRGIN ISLANDS (972.972)
Eggleston, George T. Virgin Islands. il. 1959. 7.50. Van Nostrand
Harman, Jeanne P. Virgins: Magic islands. il. 1961. 4.95. Meredith
VIRGINIA (975.5)
Beverley, Robert. History and present state of Virginia. by Louis B. Wright. 1947.
  6.00. U. of N.C.
Simkins, Francis B. , and others. Virginia: History, government, geography. il.
  1957. 4.52. Scribner
Virginia: Guide to the Old Dominion. 6.50. Oxford U. P.
Wallace, Charles M. Capitol: The history of the capitol of Virginia. 1936. 1.00.
  Dietz
Wertenbaker, Thomas J. Patrician and plebeian in Virginia. 5.00. Russell
Wertenbaker, Thomas J. Planters of colonial Virginia. 5.00. Russell
Wertenbaker, Thomas J. Virginia under the Stuarts. 5.00. Russell
VIRUSES (576.6)
Burnet, Frank M. Principles of animal virology. 1960. 12.00. Academic Press
Ciba Foundation. Nature of viruses. 1957. 8.00. Little
Dalldorf, Gilbert. Introduction to virology. il. 1955. 3.50. Thomas, C.C.
Hagan, W. A., and D. W. Bruner. Infectious diseases of domestic animals. il.
  1961. 11.50. Cornell
Smith, Kenneth M. Viruses. 1962. 3.75. Cambridge U. P.
Weidel, Wolfhard. Virus. il. 1959. 4.50. U. of Mich.
Williams, Greer. Virus hunters. 1959. 6.50. Knopf
VISION (152.1)
Huxley, Aldous. Art of seeing. 1942. 3.50. Harper
Senden, Marius von. Space and sight. 10.00. Free Press
VOCABULARY (428.3)
Birkett, W. Norman. Magic of words. 1953. 1.00. Oxford U. P.
Brown, James I., and Rachel Salisbury. Building a better vocabulary. il. 1959.
  2.50. Ronald
Eaton, Helen S. English-French-German-Spanish word frequency dictionary. 1940.
  pap. 2.45. Dover
Fires, Charles C., and A. Aileen Traver. English word lists. 1950. 2.00. Wahr
Funk, Wilfred. Six weeks to words of power. 1953. 3.95. Funk
Funk, Wilfred. Way to vocabulary power and culture. 1946. 4.95. Funk
Funk, Wilfred. Word origins and their romantic stories. 1950. 4.95. Funk'
Gilmartin, John G. Building your vocabulary. 1950. 2.92. Prentice-Hall
Gilmartin, John G. Gilmartin's word study. 1955. 3.15. Prentice-Hall
Gilmartin, John G. Increase your vocabulary. 1957. 3.60. Prentice-Hall
Gilmartin, John G. Words in action. 1954. 2.88. Prentice-Hall
Hartrampf, Gustavus A. Hartrampf's vocabulary-builder. 2.49. Grosset
Lewis, Norman. Word power made easy. 1949. 3.50. Doubleday
Mathews, Mitford M. Words: How to know them. 1956. 2.00. Holt, Rinehart &
  Winston
Morsberger, Robert E. How to improve your verbal skills. 1962. 4.95. Crowell

Parkhurst, Charles Chandler, and Alice Blais. Using words effectively. Series
    A and series B. 1958. 2.50 ea. Harper
Rosenberger, Marjorie. Mark my words. 1947. 0.96. Harcourt
Weber, Christian O. Reading and vocabulary development. 1951. 3.75. Prentice-
    Hall

VOCATIONAL GUIDANCE (371.42)

Angel, Juvenal L. Looking for employment in foreign countries. 1961. 8.50.
    World Trade Academy
Angel, Juvenal L. Occupations for men and women after 45. 1962. 10.00.
    World Trade Academy
Baer, Max F., and Edward C. Roeber. Occupational information. 1958. 5.95.
    Sci. Res. Assoc.
Bailey, C. W. How to get a better job and make more money. 4.50. Carlton
Bennett, Margaret E. College and life. 1952. 4.95. McGraw
Blum, Milton L., and Benjamin Balinsky. Counseling and psychology. 1951. 6.95.
    Prentice-Hall
Borow, H., and R. Lindsey. Vocational planning for college students. 1959. 2.95.
    Prentice-Hall
Bragdon, Helen D., and others. Educational counseling of college students. 0.50.
    A.C.E.
Clifton, Mark. Opportunity unlimited. 1959. 3.95. Chilton
Cohen, Nathan M. Vocational training directory of the United States. 1958. pap.
    2.95. Potomac (R)
Darley, John G., and Theda Hagenah. Vocational interest measurement: Theory
    and practice. 1955. 5.00. U. of Minn.
Feingold, S. Norman, and Harold List. How to get that part time job. 1958. 2.50.
    Arco
Foreign Policy Association. Careers in world affairs: At home and abroad. 1961.
    pap. 1.75. Doubleday
Forrester, Gertrude. Methods of vocational guidance. 1951. 6.50. Heath
Glanvelle, Juan L. Modern vocational trends reference handbook, 1960-61. 12.50.
    World Trade Academy
Greenleaf, W. J. Occupations and careers. 1955. 6.64. McGraw
Hawkins, Layton S., and others. Development of federal legislation for vocational
    education. 1962. 7.50. Am. Tech. Soc.
Hodnett, Edward. So you want to go into industry. 1960. 3.50. Harper
Hoppock, Robert. Occupational information. 1957. 7.50. McGraw (R)
Jones, Walter B. Problems in teaching industrial arts and vocational education.
    1958. 3.00. Bruce
Kaplan, Oscar J. Encyclopedia of vocational guidance. 2 vols. 1948. 7.50. Assoc.
    Booksellers (R)
Kitson, Harry Dexter. I find my vocation. 1954. 3.96. McGraw
Larison, Ruth H. How to get and hold the job you want. 1950. 4.50. McKay
Layton, Wilbur L. Strong vocational interest blank. 1960. pap. 3.50. U. of Minn.
Lofquist, L. H., and G. N. England. Problems in vocational counselling. 1960.
    3.50. Brown, W. C.
Lovejoy, Clarence. Lovejoy's vocational school guide. 1955. 5.95. S. and S. (R)
Magoun, Frederick Alexander. Successfully finding yourself and your job. 1959.
    3.75. Harper
Martinson, William D. Educational and vocational planning. 1959. 1.25. Scott
Mays, A. Principles and practices of vocational education. 1948. 5.75. McGraw
Morgan, Arthur E. Business of my own. 1946. 3.00. Community Service
Morris, Mark. Career opportunities: Guide to 100 leading occupations. 1946. 3.75.
    Pub. Affairs
Myers, George E. Principles and techniques of vocational guidance. 1941. 6.25.
    McGraw
New York Life Insurance Company. Guide to career information. 1957. 4.00. Harper
Prosser, Charles A., and Calvin S. Sifferd. Selecting an occupation. 1959. 3.00.
    Taplinger

Prosser, Charles A., and Thomas H. Quigley. Vocational education in a democracy. 1949. 7.25. Am. Tech. Soc.
Roberts, Roy W. Vocational and practical arts education. 1957. 6.50. Harper
Sargent, Porter. Junior colleges, specialized schools and colleges. 1959. 5.00. Sargent (R)
Science Research Associates. Handbook of job facts. 1959. 3.95. Sci. Res. Assoc.
Shartle, Carroll L. Occupational information: Its development and application. 10.00. Prentice-Hall
Struck, F. T. Creative teaching. 1938. 7.95. Wiley
Thomas, L. G. Occupational structure and education. 1956. 9.00. Prentice-Hall
Zapoleon, Marguerite. College girl looks ahead. 1956. 4.50. Harper

VOICE (808.5)
Anderson, Virgil A. Training the speaking voice. 1961. 5.00. Oxford U. P.
Bender, James F. How to talk well. 1949. 5.50. McGraw
Brodnitz, Friedrich S. Keep your voice healthy. il. 1953. 3.95. Harper
Defosses, Beatrice. Your voice and your speech. 1959. 4.95. Hill & Wang
Fairbanks, Grant. Voice and articulation drillbook. 1960. 3.50. Harper
Gray, Giles W., and Claude Merton Wise. Bases of speech. 1959. 7.00. Harper
Iellier, Marjorie. How to develop a better speaking voice. 1.00. Borden
McClosky, David Blair. Your voice at its best. 1959. 3.50. Little
Van Dusen, Clarence Raymond. Training the voice for speech. 1953. 5.50. McGraw
Van Riper, Charles. Speech correction: Principles and methods. 1954. 7.95. Prentice-Hall

VOLCANOES (551.2)
Poole, Lynn, and Gray. Volcanoes in action: Science and legend. 1962. 3.00. McGraw

VOLTAIRE, FRANCOIS MARIE AROUET DE, 1694-1778 (928)
Brumfitt, J. H. Voltaire, historian. 1958. 4.00. Oxford U. P.
Goldsmith, Oliver. Voltaire, bd. with Hugo, Victor. Voltaire. 0.95. Yoseloff
Lauer, Rosemary. Mind of Voltaire. 1961. 3.50. Newman

VOTING (324)
Berelson, Bernard R., and others. Voting: A study of opinion formation in a presidential campaign. il. 1954. 7.50. U. of Chicago
Black, Duncan. Theory of committees and elections. 1958. 5.50. Cambridge U.P.
Burdick, Eugene, and Arthur Brodbeck. American voting behavior. 7.50. Free Press
Lazarsfeld, P. F., and others. People's choice. 1948. 3.75. Columbia
Lipset, Seymour M. Political man: The social bases of politics. 1959. 4.95. Doubleday

VOYAGES AND TRAVELS (910)
Clemens, Samuel Langhorne. Innocents abroad. il. 1869. 4.50. Harper
Clemens, Samuel Langhorne. Travels of Mark Twain. by Charles Neider. il. 1961. 7.50. Coward
Cocteau, Jean. My journey round the world. il. 5.00. Transatlantic
Cook, James. Voyages of discovery. 1906. 1.95. Dutton
Dana, Richard H. Two years before the mast. il. 3.75. Dodd
Freuchen, Peter. Peter Freuchen's book of the seven seas. 1957. 8.95. Messner
Innes, Hammond. Harvest of journeys. il. 1960. 5.00. Knopf
London, Jack. Cruise of the Snark. il. 1928. 4.50. Macmillan
Polo, Marco. Travels. 1931. 1.95. Modern Lib.
Slocum, Joshua. Sailing alone around the world. 1.95. Grosset
Spectorsky, Auguste C. Book of the sea. il. 1958. 4.95. Grosset
Thomas, Lowell. Seven wonders of the world. il. 1959. 3.50. Doubleday

W

WAGES (331.2)
Bergson, A. Structure of Soviet wages. 1944. 4.00. Harvard

Bry, Gerhard. Wages in Germany, 1871-1945. 1960. 10.00. Princeton
Garvy, G. Appraisal of the 1950 census income data. 1958. 10.00. Princeton
Gilboy, E. W. Wages in eighteenth century England. 1934. 5.00. Harvard
Harrington, Carl C. Job evaluation and wage incentives. 1949. 5.00. Chilton
Reynolds, L. G., and C. H. Taft. Evolution of wage structure. 1956. 5.00. Yale
Taylor, George W., and Frank C. Pierson. New concepts in wage determination.
   1957. 6.95. McGraw
WAGNER, RICHARD, 1813-1883 (927)
Barzun, Jacques. Darwin, Marx, Wagner: Critique of a heritage. 3.00. Smith,
   Peter
Gilman, Lawrence. Wagner's operas. 1937. 3.00. Rinehart
Heline, Corinne. Esoteric music: The Wagerian music dramas. 3.50. New Age
Jacobs, Robert L. Wagner. il. 1949. 3.50. Farrar, Straus
Newman, Ernest. Life of Richard Wagner. 4 vols. il. 1933-1946. 7.50 ea. set,
   25.00. Knopf
Stein, Jack M. Richard Wagner and the synthesis of the arts. 1960. 5.00. Wayne
WALES (942.9)
Defoe, Daniel. Tour through the whole island of Great Britain. 2 vols. 1928. 1.95
   ea. Dutton
Rees, W. Historical atlas of Wales. 4.50. Hillary
WALPOLE, HORACE, 4TH EARL OF OXFORD, 1717-1797 (928)
Lewis, Wilmarth. Collector's progress. 1951. 5.75. Knopf
Lewis, Wilmarth S. Horace Walpole. il. 1961. 6.50. Pantheon
WAR (355)
Curtiss, Harriette A., and Frank H. Philosophy of war. 2.00. DeVorss
Gaulle, Charles de. Edge of the sword. 1960. 3.50. Criterion
Knieriem, Auguste von. Nuremberg trials. 1959. 12.50. Regnery
Knorr, K. War potential of nations. 1956. 5.00. Princeton
Wright, Quincy. Study of war. 2 vols. il. 1942. 20.00. U. of Chicago
WASHINGTON, GEORGE, PRES. U.S., 1732-1799 (923.173)
Cunliffe, Marcus. George Washington, man and monument. il. 1958. 4.00. Little
Freeman, Douglas S. George Washington. 7 vols. set, 70.00. Scribner (R)
Stephenson, N. W., and W. H. Dunn. George Washington. 2 vols. il. 15.00.
   Oxford U. P.
Weems, M. L. Life of George Washington. Harvard
Wright, Esmond. Washington and the American Revolution. 2.50. Macmillan
WASHINGTON (STATE) (979.7)
Avery, Mary W. History and government of the State of Washington. il. 1961.
   6.00. U. of Wash.
Federal Writers' Program. Washington: A guide to the Evergreen State. il. 5.00.
   Binfords (R)
WASHINGTON, D.C. (975.3)
Feeley, Stephen V. Story of the capitol. 0.95. Stewart
Frome, Michael. Washington: A modern guide to the nation's capital. il. 2.50.
   Doubleday
Green, C. M. Washington: Village and capital, 1800-1878. 1962. 8.50. Princeton
Jensen, Amy L. White House and its thirty-two families. 1958. 12.50. McGraw
Kimmel, Stanley. Mr. Lincoln's Washington. il. 1957. 7.50. Coward
Roberts, Chalmers. Washington past and present. il. 1950. 6.00. Pub. Affairs
WATER (333.9)
King, Thomson. Water. 1953. 4.95. Macmillan
Klein, Louis. River pollution: Guide to chemical analysis. 1959. 6.00. Academic
   Press
Murphy, Earl F. Water purity: A study in legal control of natural resources. 1961.
   4.75. U. of Wis.
Philps, Earle B. Stream sanitation. 1944. 7.50. Wiley
Prescott, S. C., and others. Water bacteriology. 1946. 5.75. Wiley
Russell, M. B. Water in relation to soil and crops. 1960. 4.00. Academic Press

WATER-COLOR PAINTING (751. 42)

Cooper, Mario. Flower painting in watercolor. 1962. 10.00. Reinhold

Dehn, Adolf. Water color, gouache, and casein painting. il. 1955. 5.95. Viking

Fabry, Alois. Water-color painting is fun. il. 1960. 3.75. Viking

Flint, Francis M. Russell. Water color out of doors. il. 1959. 5.00. Viking

Guptill, Arthur L. Watercolor painting step-by-step. 5.75. Watson

Hill, Adrian Keith Graham. On the mastery of water color painting. 1939. 6.95.
   Pitman

Kautzky, Theodore. Painting trees and landscapes in watercolor. 1952. 9.95.
   Reinhold

Schimmel, William B. Water color. il. 6.00. Macmillan

Smith, Marcella. Flower painting in water color. 1956. 3.50. Pitman

WAVE MECHANICS (530)

Brillouin, Leon. Wave propagation and group velocity. 1960. 6.00. Academic Press

Collin, Robert E. Field theory of guided waves. 16.50. McGraw

Feather, Norman. Introduction to the physics of vibrations and waves. il. 6.00.
   Aldine

Heitler, W. Elementary wave mechanics: With application to quantum chemistry.
   1956. 3.40. Oxford U. P.

Lamont, H. R. L. Wave guides. 1950. 2.25. Wiley

Lindsay, Robert B. Mechanical radiation. 1960. 10.50. McGraw

Linnett, J. W. Wave mechanics and valency. 1960. 4.00. Wiley

WEALTH (339)

Creamer, Daniel. Bibliography on income and wealth. vol. 1, 1937-1947. 1952.
   10.00. Quadrangle

Heilbroner, Robert. Quest for wealth. 1956. 5.00. S. and S.

WEATHER (551. 59)

Atkin, J. Myron, and R. Will Burnett. Air, winds, and weather. 1958. 1.00.
   Rinehart

Byers, Horace R. General meteorology. il. 1959. 10.00. McGraw

Fisher, Robert Moore. How about the weather? il. 1958. 3.95. Harper

Humphreys, W. J. Ways of the weather. 1942. 4.50. Ronald

Kimble, George H. T. Our American weather. il. 1961. pap. 1.95. Indiana

Sager, Raymond M., and others. Weathercaster. 1961. 3.00. Dial

Trewartha, Glenn T. Introduction to climate. il. 1954. 8.25. McGraw

Wells, Robert. Weather forecasting as a hobby. 1.00. Hammond

WEEDS (632. 58)

Meunscher, W. C. Weeds. il. 1955. 10.00. Macmillan

Robbins, Wilfred W., and others. Weed control. il. 1952. 9.00. McGraw

WELDING (671. 52)

Bruckner, Walter H. Metallurgy of welding. 1954. 7.50. Pitman

Morris, Joe L. Welding principles for engineers. 10.65. Prentice-Hall

Oates, J. A. Welding engineer's handbook. il. 5.50. Transatlantic

Rigsby, Herbert P. Welding fundamentals. 1949. 4.25. Pitman

Rossi, Boniface E. Welding and its application. 1941. 6.00. McGraw

WELLINGTON, ARTHUR WELLESLEY, 1ST DUKE OF, 1769-1852 (923. 5)

Gleig, G. R. Life of the Duke of Wellington. 1.95. Dutton

WESLEY, JOHN, 1703-1791 (922)

Brailsford, Mabel R. Tale of two brothers: John and Charles Wesley. 1954. 4.50.
   Oxford U. P.

Sherwin, Oscar. John Wesley, friend of the people. 5.00. Twayne

Williams, Colin W. John Wesley's theology today. 1960. 4.50. Abingdon

THE WEST (978)

Billington, Ray A. Far western frontier: 1830-1860. 1956. 5.00. Harper

Billington, Ray Allen. Westward expansion: History of the American frontier.
   8.00. Macmillan

Clemens, Samuel Langhorne. Roughing it. il. 1875. 3.95. Harper

De Voto, Bernard. Journals of Lewis and Clark. 1953. 6.50. Houghton

De Voto, Bernard. Across the wide Missouri. il. 1947. 10. 95. Houghton
De Voto, Bernard. Year of decision. 1950. 7. 50. Houghton
Fremont, J. C. Narratives of exploration and adventure. 1956. 8. 50. McKay
Gregg, Jacob Ray. History of the Oregon Trail, Santa Fe Trail and other trails.
 il. 1955. 5. 00. Binfords
Irving, Washington. Adventures of Captain Bonneville, U. S. A. il. 1961. 7. 95.
 U. of Okla.
Jackson, Donald. Letters of the Lewis and Clark expedition. 1783-1854. il. 1962.
 10. 00. U. of Ill.
Koran, James D., and Paul Sann. Pictorial history of the wild West. il. 1954.
 5. 95. Crown
Lewis, Oscar. War in the Far West, 1861-1865. 3. 95. Doubleday
Paxson, Frederic L. History of the American frontier. 1924. 6. 50. Houghton
Pioneer atlas of the American West. 5. 95. Rand McNally
Remington, Frederic. Frederic Remington's own west, by Harold McCracken. il.
 1960. 7. 50. Dial
Ruxton, George F. Life, in the Far West. by LeRoy R. Hafen. il. 1959. 5. 00. U.
 of Okla.
Stegner, Wallace. Beyond the hundredth meridian. 6. 00. 1962. Houghton
Turner, Frederick J. Frontier and section: Selected essays. 1961. 3. 95. Prentice-
 Hall
Turner, Frederick Jackson. Frontier in American history. 1959. 5. 45. Holt,
 Rinehart & Winston
Turner, Frederick J. Rise of the new West. 1959. 6. 00. Smith, Peter
Wellman, Paul I. Indian wars of the West. il. 1954. 5. 95. Doubleday
Wolfe, Thomas. Western journal. il. 1951. 1. 98. U. of Pittsburgh
WEST INDIES (972. 9)
Arciniegas, German. Caribbean: Sea of the New World. il. 1946. 6. 75. Knopf
Parry, J. H., and P. M. Sherlock. Short history of the West Indies. 1956. 5. 00.
 St. Martins
WEST VIRGINIA (975. 4)
Lambert, Oscar D. West Virginia and its government. 1951. 6. 00. Heath
Summers, F. P., and C. H. Ambler. West Virginia: The Mountain State. 1957.
 8. 65. Prentice-Hall
WHALING (639. 28)
Church, Albert C. Whale ships and whaling. il. 1960. 8. 50. Norton
Robertson, R. B. Of whales and men. il. 1954. 5. 00. Knopf
Stackpole, Edouard A. Sea-hunters. il. 1953. 7. 50. Lippincott
WHARTON, EDITH NEWBOLD (JONES) 1862-1937 (928)
Nevius, Blake. Edith Wharton: A study of her fiction. 1953. 5. 00. U. of Calif.
WHEAT (633. 11)
Vavilov, N. I. Origin, variation, immunity and breeding of cultivated plants.
 1951. 7. 50. Ronald
WHITEHEAD, ALFRED NORTH, 1861-1947 (925)
Black, Max. Nature of mathematics. 1950. 5. 00. Humanities
WHITMAN, MARCUS, 1802-1847 (923. 9)
Jones, Nard. Great command. 1959. 5. 00. Little
WHITMAN, WALT, 1819-1892 (928)
Allen, Gay Wilson. Solitary singer: A critical biography of Walt Whitman. il.
Allen, Gay Wilson. Walt Whitman. 3. 35. Smith, Peter
Allen, Gay W. Walt Whitman as man, poet, and legend. 1961. 6. 50. Southern
Asselineau, Roger. Evolution of Walt Whitman: The creation of a personality. 1960.
 7. 50. Harvard
Dutton, Geoffrey. Whitman. 3. 00. Smith, Peter
Miller, James E. Walt Whitman. 3. 50. Twayne
Musgrove, Sydney. T. S. Eliot and Walt Whitman. 1952. 2. 00. Cambridge U. P.
WHITTIER, JOHN GREENLEAF, 1807-1892 (928)
Leary, Lewis. John Greenleaf Whittier. 3. 50. Twayne

WILD FLOWERS (582.13)
Gabrielson, Ira N. Wildlife conservation. il. 1959. 5.95. Macmillan
Hylander, Clarence J. Macmillan wild flower book. il. 1954. 9.95. Macmillan
Lemmon, Robert S., and Charles C. Johnson. Wildflowers of North America. il.
   1961. 9.95. Doubleday
Morton, Julia F. Wild plants for survival in south Florida. il. 1962. pap. 2.95.
   Hurricane
Roosevelt, Theodore. Theodore Roosevelt's America. by Farida A. Wiley. il.
   1962. pap. 1.45. Doubleday
Wherry, Edgar T. Wild flower guide. il. 1948. 3.95. Doubleday
Wing, L. W. Practice of wildlife conservation. 1951. 6.50. Wiley
WILDE, OSCAR, 1854-1900 (928)
Finzi, John Charles, comp. Oscar Wilde and his literary circle. il. 1957. 5.00.
   U. of Calif.
Harris, Frank. Oscar Wilde. 1959. 7.00. Mich. State
Winwar, Frances. Oscar Wilde and the yellow nineties. 1958. 5.50. Harper
WILLIAM IV, KING OF GT. BRIT,, 1765-1837 (923.142)
Fulford, Roger. Hanover to Windsor. il. 1960. 5.00. Macmillan
WILLIAMS, ROGER, 1604?-1683 (922.1)
Miller, Perry. Roger Williams: His contribution to American tradition. 1962.
   pap. 1.25. Atheneum
Winslow, Ola Elizabeth. Master Roger Williams. il. 7.50. Macmillan
WILLIAMS, TENNESSEE, 1914- (928)
Falk, Signi. Tennessee Williams. 3.50. Twayne
Nelson, Benjamin. Tennessee Williams: the man and his work. 1961. 5.00.
   Obolensky
Tischler, Nancy M. Tennessee Williams: Rebellious Puritan. 1961. 5.00. Citadel
WILLS (347.65)
Grange, William J., and others. Wills, executors, and trustees. 1950. 8.50.
   Ronald
WILSON, WOODROW, PRES. U.S., 1856-1924 (923.173)
Buehrig, Edward H. Wilson's foreign policy in perspective. 1957. 4.50. Indiana
Craig, Hardin. Woodrow Wilson at Princeton. il. 1960. 3.75. U. of Okla.
Dudden, Arthur P. Woodrow Wilson and the world of today. 1957. 2.75. U. of Pa.
George, Alexander L., and Juliette L. Woodrow Wilson and Colonel House: A
   personality study. 1956. 6.00. Day
Link, Arthur S. Wilson the diplomatist: A look at his major foreign policies. 1957.
   4.00. Johns Hopkins
Link, A. S. Wilson: The struggle for neutrality, 1914-1915. 1960. 10.00. Princeton
WISCONSIN (977.5)
Maxwell, Robert S. La Follette and the rise of the Progressives in Wisconsin. il.
   1956. 4.50. Wis. State Hist. Soc.
Writers' Project. Wisconsin. 1954. 6.50. Hastings
WIT AND HUMOR (808.7)
Burnett, Whit. This is my best humor. 1955. 5.00. Dial
Century of humourous verse. pap. 1.35. Dutton
Esar, Evan. Dictionary of humorous quotations. 4.95. Horizon (R)
Freud, Sigmund. Jokes and their relation to the unconscious. by James Strachey.
   1960. 4.50. Norton
Prochnow, Herbert V., and Herbert V., Jr. Dictionary of wit, wisdom, and
   satire. 1962. 4.95. Harper (R)
Whiting, Percy H. How to speak and write with humor. 1959. 4.95. McGraw
WITCHCRAFT (133.4)
Gardner, G. B. Meaning of witchcraft. 6.00. Wehman
Kittredge, George L. Witchcraft in Old and New England. 1958. 8.00. Russell
Kluckhohn, Clyde. Navaho witchcraft. 1962. 4.95. Beacon
Robbins, Rossell H. Encyclopedia of witchcraft and demonology. 7.50. Crown (R)
Starkey, Marion L. Devil in Massachusetts, a modern inquiry into the Salem witch
   trials. 3.50. Smith, Peter

Summers, Montague. History of witchcraft and demonology. 1956. 6.00. U. Books
WOMAN (396)
Anderson, Mary, and Mary Winslow. Woman at work: The autobiography of Mary
  Anderson. il. 1951. 3.50. Univ. of Minn.
Beard, Mary R. Woman as force in history. pap. 1.50. Collier
Dexter, Elisabeth A. Career women of America, 1776-1840. 1950. 4.00. Jones,
  Marshall
Fairchild, Johnson E. Women, society and sex. 1952. 4.00. Sheridan
Flexner, Eleanor. Century of struggle: The woman's rights movement in the
  United States. il. 1959. 6.00. Harvard
Jephcott, P., and others. Married women working. 7.00. Humanities
Maule, Frances. Executive careers for women. 1961. 3.95. Harper
Mill, John Stuart. Subjection of women. 1.95. Dutton
Monro, Kate M., and Isabel S. Clubwoman's manual. 4.50. Macmillan
Muller, Leo, and Ouida. New horizons for college women. 1960. 3.25. Pub. Affairs
Smuts, Robert W. Women and work in America. 1959. 4.50. Columbia
Woolf, Virginia. Room of one's own. 1929. 3.75. Harcourt
Zapoleon, Marguerite W. Occupational planning for women. 1960. 5.00. Harper
WOOD (674.1)
Biggs, John R. Woodcuts. il. 1959. 5.95. Sterling
Gibbia, S. W. Wood finishing and refinishing. 1954. 6.95. Van Nostrand
Hiratsuka, Un-ichi. Selected woodcuts. il. 1958. 7.50. Tuttle
Hunt, George M., and George A. Garratt. Wood preservation. il. 1953. 9.50.
  McGraw
Rood, John. Sculpture in wood. il. 1950. 5.75. U. of Minn.
WOOL (677.3)
Alexander, P., and R. F. Hudson. Wool: Its chemistry and physics. 8.50. Textile
  Bk.
Onions, W. J. Wool. 1962. 9.50. Wiley
WOOLF, VIRGINIA (STEPHEN) 1882-1941 (928)
Bennett, J. Virginia Woolf. 1945. 2.50. Cambridge U. P.
Brewster, Dorothy. Virginia Woolf's London. 1960. 3.00. N. Y. U.
WORDSWORTH, WILLIAM, 1770-1850 (928.142)
Beatty, Arthur. William Wordsworth: His doctrine and art in their historical
  relations. 1960. 5.00. U. of Wis.
Coe, Charles N. Wordsworth and the literature of travel. 3.00. Twayne
Havens, Raymond D. Mind of a poet. 2 vols. 1952. 4.00 ea. set, 7.50. Johns
  Hopkins
WORK (331)
Berkowitz, Monroe. Workmen's compensation. 1959. 6.00. Rutgers
De Grazia, Sebastian. Of time, work, and leisure. 1962. 6.00. Twentieth Century
Dittmar, William R. State workmen's compensation laws. 1959. 2.00. Oceana
Herzberg, Frederick, and others. Motivation to work. 1959. 4.50. Wiley
Leontiev, A. Work under capitalism and socialism. 0.75. Int. Pubs.
Levenstein, Aaron. Why people work. 1962. 3.95. Crowell-Collier
Lintern, D. G., and R. J. S. Curtis. Work measurement and incentives. 1958.
  5.00. Pitman
Rotroff, Virgil H. Work measurement. il. 1959. 4.85. Reinhold
WORLD HISTORY (909)
Cheney, L. J. History of the western world. 1959. 4.95. Pitman
Cordier, Ralph and Edward Robert. History of early peoples. 3.40. Rand McNally
Easton, Stewart C. Heritage of the past: From the earliest times to 1715. 1957.
  8.50. Holt, Rinehart & Winston
Kahler, Erich. Man the measure. 1956. 6.50. Braziller
Langer, William L. Encyclopedia of world history. 1952. 9.00. Houghton (R)
Mazour, Anatole G., and John M. Peoples. Men and nations: A world history.
  1961. 6.00. Harcourt
Shotwell, James T. Long way to freedom. 1960. 8.50. Bobbs

Smith, Goldwin. Heritage of man. il. 1960. 12.50. Scribner
Wells, H. G. Outline of history. 2 vols. 1956. 4.95. Doubleday
WORLD POLITICS (327)
Acheson, D. Power and diplomacy. 1958. 3.00. Harvard
Agar, Herbert. Price of power: America since 1945. 1957. 4.00. U. of Chicago
Berle, A. A., Jr. Tides of crisis: A primer of foreign relations. 1957. 3.75.
  Reynal
Borkenau, F. World Communism. 1962. 4.40. U. of Mich.
Bowles, Chester. Ideas, people and peace. 1958. 3.00. Harper
Burnham, James. Managerial revoltuion. 1960. pap. 1.95. Indiana
Calvocoressi, Peter, and Coral Bell. Survey of international affairs, 1953.
  1956. 7.70. Oxford U. P.
Carr, Edward H. International relations between the two world wars 1919-1939.
  2.25. St. Martins
Chamberlin, William H. America: Partner in world rule. 3.00. Vanguard
Chamberlin, William H. Evolution of a conservative. 1959. 5.50. Regnery
Churchill, Winston S. Sinews of peace. 1949. 3.50. Houghton
Crozier, Brian. Rebels. 1960. 3.95. Beacon
Dirksen, Herbert von. Moscow, Tokyo, London: Twenty years of German foreign
  policy. il. 1952. 4.00. U. of Okla.
Eden, Anthony. Days for decision. 1950. 3.00. Houghton
Eisenhower, Dwight D. Peace with justice. 1961. 4.00. Columbia
Engel, Julien. Security of the free world. 1960. 2.50. Wilson
Everett, Samuel, and Christian O. Arndt. Teaching world affairs in American
  schools. 1956. 4.00. Harper
Finletter, Thomas K. Foreign policy: The next phase. 1960. 4.00. Harper
Fischer, Louis. Russia, America, and the world. 1961. 5.00. Harper
Fischer, Louis. This is our world. il. 1956. 6.00. Harper
Fromm, Erich. May man prevail. 1961. 4.50. Doubleday
Gaitskell, H. Challenge of coexistence. 1957. 2.50. Harvard
Gathorne-Hardy, G. M. Short history of international affairs, 1920-1939. 1950. 4.80.
  Oxford U. P.
Hasluck, E. L. Foreign affairs. 1919-1937. 1938. 3.00. Cambridge U. P.
Hsieh, Alice L. Communist China's strategy in the nuclear era. 1962. 4.50. Pren-
  tice-Hall
Hughes, Emmet J. America the vincible. 1959. 3.95. Doubleday
Huntington, Samuel P. Changing patterns of military politics. 1962. 7.50. Free
  Press
Hyamson, A. M. Dictionary of international affairs. 1947. 3.75. Pub. Affairs (R)
Jacobson, Harold K. America's foreign policy. 1960. 6.50. Random
Kennan, George F. Russia, the atom and the west. 1958. 3.00. Harper
Kenworthy, Leonard. Free and inexpensive material on world affairs. 1954.
  1.25. Pub. Affairs
Kertesz, Stephen D., and M. A. Fitzsimons. American diplomacy in a new era.
  1961. 10.00. U. of Notre Dame
Langer, William L., and Hamilton F. Armstrong. Foreign affairs bibliography.
  1919-1932. 1961. 15.00. Russell (R)
Lasswell, Harold, and others. Study of power. 1950. 7.50. Free Press
Lerner, Max. Age of overkill. 1962. 6.50. S. and S.
Leddell, Hart, B. Deterrent or defense. 1960. 4.95. Praeger
Lindsay, Michael. Is peaceful co-existence possible? 1960. 5.00. Mich. State
Lippmann, Walter. Coming tests with Russia. 1961. 2.50. Little
Mallory, Walter H. Political handbook of the world. 1960 and 1961, 4.50. ea; 1962,
  4.95. Harper (R)
Mauldin, Bill. What's got your back up 1961. 3.95. Harper
Mezerik, Avrahm G. Atom tests and radiation hazards; test ban efforts, UN, cold
  war conferences, chronology. 1962. pap. 2.50. Int. Review Service
Montgomery, Bernard Law. Approach to sanity. 1959. 2.75. World Pub.
Moon, Parker T. Imperialism and world politics. 6.50. Macmillan

Morgenstern, Oskar. Question of national defense. 1959. 3.95. Random

O'Conor, John F. Cold war and liberation. il. 7.50. Vantage

Power, Paul F. Gandhi on world affairs. 1960. 3.25. Pub. Affairs

Russell, Bertrand. Common sense and nuclear warfare. 1959. 2.50. S. and S.

Stebbins, Richard P. United States in world affairs, 3 vols. vol. 1, United States in world affairs, 1959; vol. 2, United States in world affairs, 1960. pap. 1.45 ea. vol. 3, United States in world affairs, 1961. pap. 1.65. Vintage

Stevenson, Adlai E. Putting first things first, a Democratic view. 1960. 3.00. Random

Swift, Richard N. World affairs and the college curriculum. 1959. 3.50. A.C.E.

Thomas, Norman. Prerequisites for peace. 1959. 3.50. Norton

Toynbee, Philip. Fearful choice: A debate on nuclear policy. 1959. 2.50. Wayne

Van Valkenburg, Samuel, and Carl L. Stotz. Elements of political geography. 1954. 10.65. Prentice-Hall

Wadsworth, James. Price of peace. 3.95. Praeger

Wilson, Thomas W., Jr. Cold war and common sense. il. 1962. 4.95. N.Y. Graphic

WORLD WAR, 1939-1945 (940.53)

Benson, Oliver. Through the diplomatic looking-glass: Immediate origins of the war in Europe. il. 1939. 2.00. U. of Okla.

Churchill, Winston L.S. Gathering storm. 1948. Their finest hour. 1949. Grand alliance. 1950. Hinge of fate. 1950. Closing the ring. 1951. Triumph and tragedy. 1953. 6.50 ea. Houghton

Churchill, Winston L.S. Memoirs of the Second World War. by Denis Kelly. il. 1959. 8.75. Houghton

Chruchill, Winston L.S. Second World War. il. 1959. 25.00. Houghton

Churchill, Winston S., and the Editors of Life. Second World War. il. 1960. 7.99. Golden Press

Eisenhower, Dwight D. Crusade in Europe. il. 1948. 4.50. Doubleday

Flower, Desmond, and James Reeves. Taste of courage: The war. 1939-1945. 1960. 10.00. Harper

Harding, Lord. Mediterranean strategy, 1939-45. 1960. 0.75. Cambridge U.P.

Howarth, David A. D-Day. il. 1959. 4.95. McGraw

Langsam, Walter Consuelo. World since 1919. il. 1954. 6.75. Macmillan

Liddell Hart, B.H. German generals talk. il. 1948. 4.50. Morrow

Love, Edmund G. War is a private affair. 1959. 3.75. Harcourt

Montgomery, Bernard L. Memoirs. 1958. 6.00. World Pub.

Morgenstern, George. Pearl Harbor, the story of the secret war. 3.50. Devin

Meyer, Robert Jr. Stars and stripes story of World War II. il. 1960. 5.95. McKay

Morison, Samuel Eliot. Invasion of France and Germany, 1944-1945. 1957. 7.50. Little

Morison, Samuel Eliot. Sicily-Salerno-Anzio, January 1943-June 1944. 1954. 7.50. Little

Morison, Samuel Eliot. Strategy and compromise. 1958. 3.00. Little

Pyle, Ernie. Brave men. 1944. 1.98. Grosset

Rommel, Edwin. Rommel papers. by B.H. Liddell Hart. 7.50. Harcourt

Rooney, Andrew A. Fortunes of war: Four great battles of World War II. il. 1962. 6.95. Little

Ryan, Cornelius. Longest day: June 6, 1944. 1959. 4.95. S. and S.

Smith, W.B. Eisenhower's six great decisions: Europe 1944-45. 1956. 3.95. McKay

Snyder, Louis L. War: A concise history. 1939-1945. il. 1960. 7.95. Messner

Speidel, Hans. Invasion - 1944. il. 1950. 4.00. Regnery

Steinbeck, John. Once there was a war. 1958. 3.95. Viking

Taylor, Alan J.P. Origins of the Second World War. il. 1962. 4.50. Atheneum

Theobald, R.A. Final secret of Pearl Harbor. 1954. 3.50. Devin

U.S. Dept. of the Army. Command decisions. 1959. 5.95. Harcourt

Waller, George M. Pearl Harbor: Roosevelt and the coming of the war. 1953. pap. 1.50. Heath

Wilmot, Chester. Struggle for Europe: History, World War II. 1952. il. 6.95.
Harper
WORTH (121.8)
Hall, Everett W. Our knowledge of fact and value. 1961. 5.00. U. of N. C.
Hall, Everett W. What is value? 1952. 6.00. Humanities
Hourani, George F. Ethical value. 1956. 4.50. U. of Mich.
Kohler, Wolfgang. Place of value in a world of facts. 4.50. Liveright
Lepley, R. Language of value. 1957. 6.50. Columbia
Maslow, Abraham H. New knowledge in human values. 1959. 4.95. Harper
Mead, George Herbert. Philosophy of the act. 1959. 8.50. U. of Chicago
Parker, Dewitt H. Human values. 1944. 3.00. Wahr
Parker, DeWitt H. Philosophy of value. 1957. 5.00. U. of Mich.
WRIGHT, FRANK LLOYD, 1869-1959. (927)
Farr, Finis. Frank Lloyd Wright. il. 1961. 5.95. Scribner
Manson, Grant F. Frank Lloyd Wright: The first golden age. 1958. vol. 1, 5.00.
Reinhold
Wright, Frank Lloyd. Autobiography. 1943. 15.00. Duell
WRITING (652)
Diringer, David. Writing: Its origins and early history. il. 1962. 6.95. Praeger
Etiemble, Rene. Orion book of the written word. il. 1961. 6.95. Orion
Fairbank, Alfred, and Berthold Wolpe. Renaissance handwriting. il. 1960. 12.50.
World Pub.
Irwin, Keith Gordon. Romance of writing: From Egyptian hieroglyphics to modern
letters, numbers, and signs. il. 1956. 3.75. Viking
Marinaccio, Anthony. Exploring the graphic arts. il. 1959. 6.25. Van Nostrand
Tschichold, J. Illustrated history of writing and lettering. 1952. 4.00. Columbia
Tsien, T. H. Written on bamboo and silk. il. 1962. 7.50. U. of Chicago
WYOMING (978.7)
Trachsel, Herman H., and Ralph M. Wade. Government and administration of
Wyoming. 1953. 6.75. Crowell
Wyoming: Guide to its history, highways, and people. 6.50. Oxford U. P.

X

X-RAYS (537.535)
Bleich, Alan R. Story of X-rays from Rontgen to isotopes. 1960. pap. 1.35. Dover
Compton, Arthur H., and Samuel K. Allison. X-rays in theory and experiment.
1935. 17.50. Van Nostrand
Klug, H. P., and L. E. Alexander. X-ray diffraction procedures. 1954. 17.50.
Wiley

Y

YACHT RACING (797.14)
Cole, Guy. Ocean crusing. 1959. pap. 1.25. De Graff
Curry, Manfred. Yacht racing. il. 1948. 10.00. Scribner
Fox, Uffa. Sail and power. 1936. 10.00. De Graff
Hiscock, Eric. Wandering under sail. 1948. 3.00. De Graff
YEATS, WILLIAM BUTLER, 1865-1939 (928)
Ellmann, Richard. Identity of Yeats. 1954. 6.00. Oxford U. P.
Gordon, D. J. W. B. Yeats: Images of a poet. 1961. 3.75. Barnes & Noble
Stock, A. G. W. B. Yeats: His poetry and thought. 1961. 5.50. Cambridge U. P.
Yeats, William Butler. Autobiography. 1953. 6.00. Macmillan
YOGA (181.45)
Bahm, Archie J. Yoga. 1961. 3.50. Ungar
Francis, P. G. Yoga: Life science. 2.00. Wehman
YOUTH (136.7)
Clark, Dick. Your happiest years. 1959. 2.95. Random
Felsen, Henry Gregor. Letters to a teen-age son. 1962. 3.00. Dodd

Geisel, John B. Personal problems. 1949. 3. 96. Houghton
Hollingshead, A. B. Elmtown's youth. 1949. 5. 50. Wiley
Powers and Partington. John Robert Powers way to teenage beauty, charm and
    popularity. 1962. 3. 95. Prentice-Hall
Warters, Jane. Achieving maturity. 1949. 5. 95. McGraw
White House Conference on Children and Youth, 1960. Values and ideals of
    American youth. by E. Ginzberg. 1961. 6. 00. Columbia
YUGOSLAVIA (949. 7)
Brown, Alec. Yugoslav life and landscape. il. 4. 00. Ungar
Farrell, R. Barry. Yugoslavia and the Soviet Union, 1948-1956. 1956. 5. 00. Shoe
    String
Kerner, Robert J. Yugoslavia. il. 1949. 6. 50. U. of Calif.
West, Rebecca. Black lamb and grey falcon. il. 1941. 6. 95. Viking

Z

ZEN (SECT) (294. 329)
Ames, Van Meter. Zen and American thought. 4. 50. U. of Hawaii
Chang, Chen-Chi. Practice of Zen. 1959. 4. 00. Harper
Ogata, Sohaku. Zen for the West. il. 1959. 3. 75. Dial
Suzuki, D. T. Introduction to Zen Buddhism. 3. 00. Wehman
Suzuki, Daisetz T. Zen and Japanese Buddhism. il. 1958. 3. 25. Tuttle
ZOLA, EMILE, 1840-1902 (928)
Grant, Richard B. Zola's Son excellence Eugene Rougon, an historical and critical
    study. 1960. 4. 00. Duke
Wilson, Angus. Emile Zola. 3. 50. Smith, Peter
ZOOLOGY (591)
Aristotle. Generation of animals. 1943. 3. 50. Harvard
Black, J. D. Biological conservation. 1954. 6. 50. McGraw
 Brown, Mary J. Scientific vocabulary for beginning zoology students and non-
    scientific students. 1957. 3. 00. Pageant
Cain, A. J. Animal species and their evolution. 1954. 2. 50. Hillary
Carrighar, Sally. One day on Beetle Rock. il. 1944. 4. 50. Knopf
Carter, G. S. Animal evolution. il. 4. 50. Macmillan
Eddy, Samuel, and Alexander C. Hodson. Taxonomic keys to the common animals
    of the North Central states. 1961. 3. 25. Burgess
Elton, Charles. Animal ecology. il. 3. 75. Macmillan
Hanson, Earl D. Animal diversity. 1961. 3. 75. Prentice-Hall
Harmer, S. F., and A. E. Shipley. Cambridge natural history. 10 vols. il. set.
    140. 00. Hafner
Hegner, Robert W., and Karl A. Stiles. College zoology. il. 1957. 7. 75. Macmillan
Hegner, Robert W. Parade of the animal kingdom. il. 1935. 6. 95. Macmillan
Life. Wonders of life on earth. 1961. 5. 00. Golden Press
Manter, Harold W., and Dwight D. Miller. Introduction to zoology. il. 1959. 8. 00.
    Harper
Mayr, E., and others. Methods and the principles of systematic zoology. 1953.
    8. 50. McGraw
Morgan, A. H. Kinships of animals and men. 1955. 7. 95. McGraw
Rothschild, Nathaniel M. V. Classification of living animals. 1961. 4. 75. Wiley
Schenk, Edward T., and John H. McMasters. Procedure in taxonomy. 1956. 4. 00.
    Stanford
Smith, Roger C. Guide to the literature of the zoological sciences. 1962. 4. 00.
    Burgess
Terres, John K. Discovery: Great moments of the lives of outstanding naturalists.
    il. 1961. 6. 50. Lippincott
Vessel, M. F., and E. J. Harrington. Common native animals. 1961. 4. 95.
    Chandler Pub.
Winchester, A. M., and Harvey B. Lovell. Zoology. il. 1961. 8. 00. Van Nostrand

1,000 VITAL LITERARY WORKS (NOVELS, DRAMAS, POETRY, ESSAYS)

A

Addison, Joseph. Sir Roger de Coverley Papers. 2.28. Houghton
Aeschylus. Tragedies. 2 vols. 3.50 ea. Harvard
Agee, James. Death in the family. 1957. 4.50. Obolensky
Aiken, Conrad. Collected poems. 1953. 11.00. Oxford U. P.
Aiken, Conrad. Collected short stories of Conrad Aiken. 1960. 6.00. World Pub.
Aldington, Richard. Viking book of poetry of the English-speaking world. 2 vols. 1958. 12.50. Viking
Aleichem, Sholom. Selected stories. 1.95. Modern Lib.
Algren, Nelson. A walk on the wild side. 0.50. pap. Fawcett
Anderson, Maxwell. Eleven verse plays. 1929-1939. il. 10.00. Harcourt
Anderson, Sherwood. Portable Sherwood Anderson. ed. by Horace Gregory. 1949. 2.95. Viking
Anderson, Sherwood. Winesburg, Ohio. 1960. 3.50. Viking
Anouilh, Jean. Lark. tr. by Christopher Fry. 1956. 3.50. Oxford U. P.
Anouilh, Jean. Ring round the moon. 1950. tr. by Christopher Fry. 3.00. Oxford U. P.
Apuleius, Lucius. Golden asse. tr. by Adlington. 3.95. Liveright
Aristophanes. Eleven comedies. 4.50. Liveright
Aristotle. Works: The Oxford translation. 12 vols. Oxford U. P.
Armour, Margaret. The Nibelungenlied. 6.00. Heritage
Arnold, Matthew. Essays, letters, and reviews. il. 1960. 9.00. Harvard
Arnold, Matthew. Poems. 1.95. Dutton
Arnold, Matthew. Poetical works. ed. by C. B. Tinker and H. F. Lowry. 1950. 4.50. Oxford U. P.
Arnold, Matthew. Portable Matthew Arnold. ed. by Lionel Trilling. 1949. 2.95. Viking
Asch, Sholem. Apostle. 6.00. Putnam
Asch, Sholem. Mary. 5.00. Putnam
Asch, Sholem. Nazarene. 6.00. Putnam
Asch, Sholem. Prophet. 1955. 5.00. Putnam
Atherton, Gertrude. Conqueror. 1943. 4.95. Lippincott
Auden, W. H. Collected poetry. 4.75. Random
Auden, W. H. Portable Greek reader. 1948. 2.95. Viking
Austen, Jane. Complete novels. 2.95. Modern Lib.

B

Balzac, Honore de. Bachelor's house. 3.50. Juniper
Balzac, Honore de. Cousin Bette. 1.95. Modern Lib.
Balzac, Honore de. Droll stories. ed. by Ernest Boyd. 3.95. Liveright
Balzac, Honore de. Eugenie Grandet. 1.95. Dutton
Balzac, Honore de. Old Goriot. 1.95. Dutton
Balzac, Honore de. Short novels. 1948. 6.00. Dial
Barrie, James M. Representative plays. 1954. 3.48. Scribner
Baudelaire, Charles. One hundred poems from Les fleurs du mal. 1947. il. 5.00. U. of Calif.
Beaumarchais, Pierre A. Marriage of Figaro, and The barber of Seville. 1962. 2.95. Barron's
Beaumont, Francis, and John Fletcher. Plays. vols. 1-5, 1905-1912. 6.50 ea. Cambridge U. P.
Beaumont, Francis. Coxcomb. 6.50. Cambridge U. P.
Beaumont, Francis. Woman hater. 6.50. Cambridge U. P.

Beckett, Samuel. Krapp's last tape, and other dramatic pieces. 1960. pap. 1.95. Grove
Beckett, Samuel. Watt. 1959. pap. 2.45. Grove
Beckett, Samuel. Three novels: Malone, Malone dies, and the Unamable. 6.50. Grove.
Beckett, Samuel. Waiting for Godot. 1956. pap. 1.25. Grove
Beddoes, Thomas Lovell. Plays and poems. 1950. 2.50. Harvard
Bellamy, Edward. Looking backward. 1959. 1.40. Harper
Belloc, Hilaire. Selected essays. 1955. 3.25. British Bk.
Bellow, Saul. Adventures of Augie March. 1953. 5.00. Viking
Bellow, Saul. Henderson, the rain king. 1959. 4.50. Viking
Bemelmans, Ludwig. Holiday in France. 1957. 5.00. Houghton
Benavente, Jacinto. Los malhechores del bien. ed. by Irving A. Leonard, and Robert K. Spaulding. 1961. 2.85. Macmillan
Benchley, Robert. Benchley beside himself. il. 1943. 3.95. Harper
Benet, Stephen Vincent. Devil and Daniel Webster. il. 1937. 2.50. Rinehart
Benet, Stephen Vincent. John Brown's Body. 1928. il. 5.00. Rinehart
Benet, Stephen Vincent. Selected works. 1942. 6.00. Rinehart
Benet, Stephen Vincent. Western star. 1943. 3.50. Holt, Rinehart & Winston
Bennett, Arnold. Old wives' tale. 1.95. Modern Lib.
Bernanos, Georges. The diary of a country priest. 1.75. Doubleday
Blackmore, Richard D. Lorna Doone. 1946. 2.64. Globe
Blake, William. Portable Blake. il. ed. by Alfred Kazin. 1946. 2.95. Viking
Boccaccio, Giovanni. Decameron. 3.95. Liveright
Bowen, Elizabeth. Death of the heart. 1939. 4.95. Knopf
Boyle, Kay. Collected poems. 1962. 4.00. Knopf
Bradford, Roark. Ol' man Adam an' his chillun. il. 1928. 3.50. Harper
Brecht, Bertolt. Seven plays. ed. by Eric Bentley. 1961. 8.50. Grove
Bridges, Robert. Poetry and Prose. 1955. 1.55. Oxford U. P.
Bridges, Robert. Testament of beauty. 1930. 6.00. Oxford U. P.
Bromfield, Louis. Bromfield galaxy: The green bay tree, Early autumn, A good woman. 1957. 5.00. Harper
Bronte, Charlotte. Jane Eyre. il. 3.75. Dodd
Bronte, Emily. Wuthering Heights. 3.25. Collins
Brooke, Rupert. Poems. 1.50. Nelson
Browning, Elizabeth Barrett. Complete poetical works. 6.00. Houghton
Browning, Elizabeth Barrett. Sonnets from the Portuguese. il. 1950. 5.00. Crowell
Browning, Robert. Complete poetical works. ed. by Horace E. Scudder. 7.50. Houghton
Buchan, John. Greenmantle. 1.50. Nelson
Buck, Pearl S. Good earth. 1949. 5.50. Day
Buck, Pearl S. Come, my beloved. 1953. 4.00. Day
Buck, Pearl S. Imperial woman. 1956. 5.50. Day
Buck, Pearl S. Letter from Peking. 1957. 3.75. Day
Buck, Pearl S. Pavilion of women. 1946. 4.95. Day
Burns, Robert. Complete poetical works. 6.00. Houghton
Burton, Richard, tr. Arabian nights. 1.95. Modern Lib.
Burton, Robert. Anatomy of melancholy. 1955. 3.95. Tudor
Butler, Samuel. Way of all flesh. il. 1957. 3.75. Dodd
Byron, George Gordon. Complete poetical works. ed. by. Paul E. More. 7.50. Houghton
Byron, George Gordon. Don Juan. 1.95. Modern Lib.

C

Cabell, James B. Between friends. 1962. 7.50. Harcourt
Cabell, James B. Jurgen. pap. 1.45. Crown
Caldwell, Erskine. Complete stories of Erskine Caldwell. 1953. 5.95. Little
Caldwell, Erskine. God's little acre. 1.95. Modern Lib.

Caldwell, Erskine. Tobacco Road. 1.95. Modern Lib.
Caldwell, Erskine. Trouble in July. 1940. 3.50. Little
Caldwell, Taylor. Dear and glorious physician. 1959. 3.95. Doubleday
Caldwell, Taylor. Prologue to love. 1961. 5.95. Doubleday
Camus, Albert. Caligula and three other plays. 1958. 5.00. Knopf
Camus, Albert. Fall. 1957. 3.00. Knopf
Camus, Albert. Myth of Sisyphus and other essays. 1955. 4.00. Knopf
Camus, Albert. Plague. 1948. 3.95. Knopf
Camus, Albert. Rebel. 1954. 4.00. Knopf
Camus, Albert. Stranger. 1946. 3.00. Knopf
Canby, Henry S. Classic Americans. 6.00. Russell
Capote, Truman. Breakfast at Tiffany's. 1958. 3.50. Random
Capote, Truman. Other voices, other rooms. pap. 0.95. Vintage
Carroll, Lewis. Alice in Wonderland. il. 1956. 1.49. Doubleday
Cary, Joyce. Herself surprised. 1948. 1.40. Harper
Cary, Joyce. Horse's mouth. 1950. 1.40. Harper
Cather, Willa. Death comes for the Archbishop. 1927. 3.95. Knopf
Cather, Willa. Lost lady. 1923. 3.50. Knopf
Cather, Willa. My Antonia. 5.00. 1961. Houghton
Cather, Willa. My mortal enemy. 1926. 3.50. Knopf
Cather, Willa. O Pioneers! 4.00. Knopf
Catullus. Works. ed. by Elmer T. Merrill. 1893. 3.25. Harvard
Catullus. Carmina. ed. by R.A.B. Mynors. 1958. 1.75. Oxford U. P.
Catullus. Collected poems. tr. by Jack Lindsay. 2.50. Transatlantic
Cerf, Bennett A. Try and stop me. 1944. 3.00. S. and S.
Cervantes, Miguel de. Don Quixote. il. 2.95. Modern Lib.
Cervantes, Miguel de. Six exemplary novels. 1961. pap. 1.50. Barron's
Chapman, Maristan. Doubloons. 2.95. Barnes, A.S.
Chaucer, Geoffrey. Complete works. ed. by W.W. Skeat. 1933. 4.50. Oxford U. P.
Chaucer, Geoffrey. Canterbury tales. il. 1961. 5.00. Golden Press
Chekhov, Anton. Portable Chekhov. 1947. 2.95. Viking
Chekhov, Anton. Plays and stories. 1.95. Dutton
Chesterton, G. K. Collected poems. 1911. 5.00. Dodd
Chesterton, G. K. Man who was Thursday. 3.50. Dodd
Chesterton, G. K. Selected essays. 1951. 3.25. British Bk.
Child, Francis. English and Scottish ballads. 40.00. 3 vols. Cooper
Ciardi, John. As if: Poems new and selected. 1955. 3.50. Rutgers
Cicero. Brutus: Orator. 3.50. Harvard
Cicero. Pro Milone. 1902. 1.70. Oxford U. P.
Cicero. Tusculan disputations. 3.50. Harvard
Cicero. Verrine orations. 2 vols. 3.50 ea. Harvard
Clark, Walter Van Tiburg. Ox-Bow incident. pap. 1.25. Vintage
Clemens, Samuel Langhorne. Adventures of Tom Sawyer. il. 1958. 3.75. Dodd
Clemens, Samuel Langhorne. Connecticut Yankee in King Arthur's court. il.
    1889. 3.95. Harper
Clemens, Samuel Langhorne. Huckleberry Finn. il. 1955. 2.75. Dutton
Clemens, Samuel Langhorne. Life on the Mississippi. il. 4.50. Harper
Clemens, Samuel Langhorne. Mysterious stranger and other stories. 1916. 4.50.
    Harper
Clemens, Samuel Langhorne. Pudd'nhead Wilson. 1962. 3.50. Harvard
Cobb, Irvin S. Speaking of operations. il. 1.50. Doubleday
Coffin, Robert P. Tristram. Collected poems. 6.75. Macmillan
Coleridge, Samuel Taylor. Complete poetical works. 2 vols. 11.20. Oxford U. P.
Collette. Break of day. 1961. 3.75. Farrar, Straus
Collette. Claudine married. 1960. 3.50. Farrar, Straus
Collette. Gigi. bd. with Chance acquaintances, and Julie de Carneilhan. il. 1952.
    3.50. Farrar, Straus
Collins, Wilkie. Moonstone. 1955. 3.75. Dodd
Collins, Wilkie. Woman in white. 1.95. Dutton

Conan Doyle, Arthur. Complete Sherlock Holmes. 2 vol. ed. 1953. 7.50; 1 vol. ed. 1952. 4.95. Doubleday
Confucius. Analects. 1938. 3.50. Macmillan
Congreve, William. Complete plays. pap. 1.75. Hill & Wang
Connelly, Marc. Green pastures. 1935. 3.00. Rinehart
Conrad, Joseph. Heart of darkness: With backgrounds and criticisms. ed. by Leonard Dean. il. 1960. pap. 2.50. Prentice-Hall
Conrad, Joseph. Lord Jim. il. 1961. 3.75. Dodd
Conrad, Joseph. Nigger of the Narcissus. 1952. 1.40. Harper
Conrad, Joseph. Nostromo. 1951. 1.95. Modern Lib.
Conrad, Joseph. Secret agent. 1.50. Nelson
Conrad, Joseph. Shadow-line. bd. with Typhoon, and Secret sharer. 1959. pap. 0.95. Doubleday
Conrad, Joseph. Tales of the east and west. 1958. 3.95. Doubleday
Conrad, Joseph. Victory. 1932. 1.95. Modern Lib.
Cooper, James Fenimore. Deerslayer. pap. 0.95. Collier
Cooper, James Fenimore. Last of the Mohicans. il. 1951. 3.75. Dodd
Cooper, James Fenimore. Pathfinder. il. 1954. 3.75. Dodd
Cooper, James Fenimore. Pioneers. il. 1958. 3.75. Dodd
Cooper, James Fenimore. Prairie. pap. 1.45. Doubleday
Cooper, James Fenimore. Satanstoe. 1962. pap. 1.95. U. of Nebr.
Cooper, James Fenimore. Spy. il. 1949. 3.75. Dodd
Corneille, Pierre. Chief plays of Corneille. 1957. 5.00. Princeton
Corneille, Pierre. Le Cid. 1.25. Cambridge U. P.
Costain, Thomas B. Magnificent century. 1951. 4.50. Doubleday
Coward, Noel. Noel Coward song book. il. 1953. 7.50. S. and S.
Coward, Noel. Pomp and circumstance. 4.50. Doubleday
Cowley, Malcolm. Exile's return. 1959. 3.25. Smith, Peter
Cowper, William. Letters. 1.95. Dutton
Cozzens, James G. By love possessed. 1957. 5.00. Harcourt
Cozzens, James Gould. Guard of honor. 1948. 5.95. Harcourt
Cozzens, James Gould. Just and the unjust. 1950. 2.50. Harcourt
Crabbe, G. New Poems. ed. by A. Pollard. 1960. 6.00. Lounz
Crane, Hart. Collected poems, including The bridge. 3.95. Liveright
Crane, Stephen. Red badge of courage and other stories. 2.75. Oxford U. P.
Costain, Thomas B. Below the salt. 1957. Doubleday
Costain, Thomas B. Black rose. 1945. 3.95. Doubleday
Costain, Thomas B. Chord of steel. 1960. 3.95. Doubleday
Costain, Thomas B. Conquerors. 1949. 4.50. Doubleday
Costain, Thomas B. Darkness and the dawn. 1959. 3.95. Doubleday
Costain, Thomas B. High towers. 1949. 3.00. Doubleday
Costain, Thomas B. Moneyman. 1951. 4.50. Doubleday
Costain, Thomas B. Ride with me. 1944. 3.75. Doubleday
Costain, Thomas B. Silver chalice. 1954. 3.95. Doubleday
Cronin, A. J. Citadel. 1937. 4.95. Little
Cronin, A. J. Green years. 1944. 4.95. Little
Cronin, A. J. Hatter's castle. 1931. 5.75. Little
Cronin, A. J. Judas tree. 1961. 4.95. Little
Cronin, A. J. Keys of the kingdom. 1941. 4.95. Little
Cronin, A. J. Spanish gardener. 1950. 4.95. Little
Cronin, A. J. Stars look down. 1935. 5.75. Little
Cronin, A. J. Three loves. 1957. 4.95. Little
Crouse, Russel, and Howard Lindsay. Life with Father. il. 1953. 5.00. Knopf
Cummings, E. E. Collected poems. 5.50. Harcourt
Cummings, E. E. Enormous room. 1934. 1.95. Modern Lib.
Cummings, E. E. Poems: 1923-1954. 1954. 6.75. Harcourt

Daudet, Alphonse. Tartarin of Tarascon, and Tartarin on the Alps. 1.95. Dutton
Davenport, Marcia. Constant image. 1960. 3.95. Scribner
Davenport, Marcia. Of Lena Geyer. 1936. 4.50. Scribner
Davies, W. H. Farewell to poesy and other pieces. 1.00. Humphries
Davis, H. L. Honey in the horn. 1957. 4.95. Morrow
Day, Clarence. Best of Clarence Day. il. 1948. 5.75. Knopf
Day, Clarence. Life with father. 1935. 3.50. Knopf
Day, Lewis, Cecil. Poet's task. 1951. 0.35. Oxford U. P.
Day, Lewis, Cecil. Short is the time: Poems 1936-1943. 1943. 2.25. Oxford U. P.
Defoe, Daniel. Captain Singleton. 1.95. Dutton
Defoe, Daniel. Journal of the plague year. 1.95. Dutton
Defoe, Daniel. Moll Flanders. 1.95. Dutton
Dekker, Thomas. Shoemaker's holiday. 1.10. St. Martins
Delacroix, Eugene. Journal of Eugene Delacroix. il. 1951. 3.75. N. Y. Graphic
De La Mare, Walter. Come hither. il. 1957. 7.50. Knopf
De La Mare, Walter. Rhymes and verses. il. 1947. 5.00. Holt, Rinehart & Winston
De La Roche, Mazo. Jaina. 1927. 4.50. Little
Demosthenes. Private orations. 3 vols. 3.50 ea. Harvard
De Quincey, Thomas. Confessions of an English opium eater. 1.95. 1961. Dutton
Derleth, August. Bright journey. 3.50. Arkham
Dickens, Charles. Novels of Charles Dickens. 16 vols. lea. 52.00. Collins
Dickinson, Emily. Bolts of melody: New poems of Emily Dickinson. il. 1945. 5.50.
  Harper
Dickinson, Emily. Complete poems of Emily Dickinson. ed. by Thomas H. Johnson.
  1960. 10.00. Little
Dickinson, Emily. Poems: First and second series. il. pap. 1.95. World Pub.
Dinesen, Isak. Seven Gothic tales. 1.95. Modern Lib.
Disraeli, Benjamin. Coningsby. 1.95. Dutton
Disraeli, Benjamin. Lothair. 1.50. Nelson
Dobson, Austin. Selected poems. 2.25. Oxford U. P.
Donald, David. Lincoln's Herndon: A biography. il. 1948. 5.75. Knopf
Donne, John. Complete poetry and selected prose. 1.95. Modern Lib.
Donne, John. Essays in divinity. ed. by E. M. Simpson. 1952. 3.40. Oxford U. P.
Donne, John. Poems. 1.95. Dutton
Donne, John. Poetry and prose. 1946. 1.55. Oxford U. P.
Donne, John. Selected poems. ed. by J. Hayward. pap. 0.85. Penguin
Donne, John. Some poems and a devotion. 1.00. New Directions
Dos Passos, John. Big money. 3.50. Houghton
Dos Passos, John. 42nd parallel. 3.50. Houghton
Dos Passos, John. Manhattan transfer. 1943. 4.95. Houghton
Dos Passos, John. Midcnetury. 1961. 5.95. Houghton
Dos Passos, John. Three soldiers. 1947. 3.00. Houghton
Dos Passos, John. U.S.A. 2.95. Modern Lib.
Dostoyevsky, Feodor. Brothers Karamazov. 1956. 2.49. Grosset
Dostoyevsky, Fyodor. Crime and punishment. 1.95. Dutton
Dostoevsky, Fyodor. Letters from the underworld. 1.95. Dutton
Dostoevsky, Fyodor. House of the dead. 3.75. Macmillan
Dostoyevsky, Fyodor. Idiot. 2.95. Modern Lib.
Dostoyevsky, Fyodor M. Possessed. il. 6.00. Dial
Dostoyevsky, Fyodor. White nights. tr. by Constance Garnett. 3.75. Macmillan
Douglas, Lloyd C. Big fisherman. 1948. 4.50. Houghton
Douglas, Lloyd C. Doctor Hudson's secret journal. 2.75. Houghton
Douglas, Lloyd C. Green light. 1935. 3.00. Houghton
Douglas, Lloyd C. Living faith. 1955. 3.75. Houghton
Douglas, Lloyd C. Magnificent obsession. 3.00. Houghton
Douglas, Lloyd C. Robe. 1947. 6.00. Houghton
Douglas, Norman. South wind. 1.95. Modern Lib.
Dreiser, Theodore. American tragedy. il. 4.95. World Pub.
Dreiser, Theodore. Best short stories. 1956. 3.75. World Pub.

Dreiser, Theodore. Financier. 3.75. World Pub.
Dreiser, Theodore. Genius. 3.95. World Pub.
Dreiser, Theodore. Jennie Gerhardt. 3.75. World Pub.
Dreiser, Theodore. Sister Carrie. 3.95. World Pub.
Dreiser, Theodore. Titan. 3.75. World Pub.
Drinkwater, John. Abraham Lincoln. 2.04. Houghton
Drury, Allen. Advise and consent. 1959. 5.75. Doubleday
Dryden, John. All for love. ed. by Ben Griffity. il. 1961. 1.95. Barron's
Dryden, John. Essays of John Dryden. 2 vols. 1961. 15.00. Russell
Dryden, John. Poems and fables. ed. by James Kinsley. 1962. 5.00. Oxford U. P.
Dryden, John. Poetry, prose and plays. 1952. 4.75. Harvard
Dumas, Alexander. Count of Monte Cristo. 4.95. Grosset
Dumas, Alexandre. Dame de Monsoreau. 2 vols. il. 3.50 ea. Farrar, Straus
Dumas, Alexandre. Journal of Madame Giovanni. tr. by Marguerite E. Wilbur.
    3.95. Liveright
Dumas, Alexandre. Marguerite de Valois. il. 3.50. Farrar, Straus
Dumas, Alexandre. Three musketeers. il. 6.00. Dial
Dumas, Alexandre. Twenty years after. il. 6.00. Dial
Dumas, Alexandre. Vicomte de Bragelonne. 5 vols. il. 3.50 ea. Farrar, Straus
Dumas, Alexandre. Camille. 1.95. Modern Lib.
Du Maurier, Daphne. King's general. 3.95. Doubleday
Du Maurier, Daphne. Rebeca. 1948. 3.95. Doubleday
Du Maurier, Daphne. Scapegoat. 1957. 3.95. Doubleday
Du Maurier, George. Trilby. 1.95. Dutton
Dunbar, Paul Laurence. Complete poems. il. 1940. 4.00. Dodd
Durrell, Lawrence. Balthazar. 1958. 3.95. Dutton
Durrell, Lawrence. Bitter Lemons. 3.75. 1959. Dutton
Durrell, Lawrence. Black Book. 1960. 4.95. Dutton
Durrell, Lawrence G. Clea. 1960. 3.95. Dutton
Durrell, Lawrence. Esprit de corps. il. 1957. 2.75. Dutton
Durrell, Lawrence. Justine. 1957. 3.95. Dutton
Durrell, Lawrence. Mountolive. 1959. 3.95. Dutton

E

Eberhart, Richard. Collected poems. 1930-1960. 1960. 6.00. Oxford U. P.
Eddy, Mary Baker. Christ and Christmas, an il. poem. 3.00. Christian Science
Edgeworth Maria. Castle Rackrent, and Absentee. 1.95. Dutton
Edman, Irwin. Philosopher's holiday.
Eggleston, Edward. Hoosier schoolmaster. 3.00. Smith, Peter
Ehrenburg, Ilya. Change of season. 1962. 4.50. Knopf
Eliot, George. Adam Bede. 3.75. Dodd
Eliot, George. Daniel Deonda. 4.25. Smith, Peter
Eliot, George. Middlemarch. 1962. 3.50. Harcourt
Eliot, George. Mill on the Floss. il. 1960. 3.75. Dodd
Eliot, George. Romola. 2.75. Oxford U. P.
Eliot, George. Silas Marner. il. 3.75. Dodd
Eliot, T. S. Cocktail party. 3.75. Harcourt
Eliot, T. S. Collected poems. 3.95. Harcourt
Eliot, T. S. Complete poems and plays. 1909-1950. 1952. 6.00. Harcourt
Eliot, T. S. Four quartets. 3.00. Harcourt
Eliot, T. S. Idea of a Christian society. 2.75. Harcourt
Eliot, T. S. Murder in the cathedral. 2.50. Harcourt
Eliot, T. S. Sacred wood. 1950. 2.50. Barnes & Noble
Emerson, Ralph Waldo. Essays. 1951. 3.25. Crowell
Erasmus, Desiderius. In praise of folly. 1.95. Modern Lib.
Ervine, St. John. Bernard Shaw: His life, work and friends. il. 1956. 7.50.
    Morrow
Euripides. Alcestis. 1954. 2.40. Oxford U. P.

Euripides. Electra. 1939. 2.40. Oxford U. P.
Euripides. Helen. 1951. 1.50. Mich. State
Euripides. Medea. 1952. 3.00. Oxford U. P.
Euripides. Plays. 2 vols. 1.95 ea. Dutton
Evelyn, John. Diary. 2 vols. 1.95 ea. Dutton

F

Falkner, John Meade. Moonfleet. il. 1951. 4.75. Little
Farquhar, George. Four plays. 3.00. Hill & Wang
Farrell, James T. Short stories. pap. 2.95. Grosset
Farrell, James T. Studs Lonigan. 1935. 6.00. Vanguard
Fast, Howard. Citizen Tom Paine. il. pap. 1.95. World Pub.
Faulkner, William. Absalom, Absalom. 1.95. Modern Lib.
Faulkner, William. Collected stories. 6.50. Random
Faulkner, William. Go down Moses and other stories. 3.50. Random
Faulkner, William. Intruder in the dust. 3.95. Random
Faulkner, William. Knight's gambit. 3.50. Random
Faulkner, William. Light in August. 1.95. Modern Lib.
Faulkner, William. Portable Faulkner. 1946. 2.95.
Faulkner, William. Requiem for a nun. 3.00. Random
Faulkner, William. Reivers. 1962. 4.95. Random House
Faulkner, William. Sanctuary. 1962. 4.95. Random
Faulkner, William. Sartoris. 4.75. Random
Faulkner, William. Soldiers' pay. 3.95. Liveright
Faulkner, William. Sound and the fury, and As I Lay dying. 1.95. Modern Lib.
Faulkner, William. Wild palms. 3.95. Random
Ferber, Edna. American beauty. 1951. 3.95. Doubleday
Ferber, Edna. Cimarron. 1951. 3.95. Doubleday
Ferber, Edna. Great son. 3.95. Doubleday
Ferber, Edna. Ice palace. 1958. 4.50. Doubleday
Ferber, Edna. Saratoga Trunk. 1951. 3.95. Doubleday
Ferber, Edna. Show boat. 1.95. Grosset
Ferber, Edna. So big. 3.95. Doubleday
Field, Rachel. All this, and heaven too. 1943. 5.95. Macmillan
Fielding, Henry. Amelia. 2 vols. 1.95 ea. Dutton
Fielding, Henry. Joseph Andrews. 1.95. Dutton
Fielding, Henry. Tom Jones. 2 vols. 1.95 ea. Dutton
Fitzgerald, F. Scott. Last tycoon. 3.50. Scribner
Fitzgerald, F. Scott. Stories. 1951. 5.50. Scribner
Fitzgerald, F. Scott. Tender is the night. by Arthur Mizener. 4.50. Scribner
Fitzgerald, F. Scott. This side of paradise. 1920. 3.95. Scribner
Flaubert, Gustave. Madame Bovary. 1.95. Dutton
Flaubert, Gustave. Salammbo. 1.95. Dutton
Flaubert, Gustave. Sentimental education. 1.95.
Flavin, Martin. Journey in the dark. pap. 0.50. Avon
Ford, Ford Madox. Parade's end. 1961. 7.50. Knopf
Ford, John. Plays. 1957. pap. 1.65. Hill & Wang
Ford, Paul L. Janice Meredith. 3.95. Dodd
Forester, Cecil S. African Queen. 1.95. Modern Lib.
Forester, C. S. Captain from Connecticut. 1941. 4.95. Little
Forester, Cecil S. Captain Horatio Hornblower. il. 1939. 5.00. Little
Forester, C. S. Good shepherd. 1955. 3.95. Little
Forester, Cecil S. Lieutenant Hornblower. 1952. 4.95. Little
Forester, Cecil S. Lord Hornblower. 1.95. Grosset
Forster, E. M. Longest journey. 1922. 4.00. Knopf
Forster, E. M. Room with a view. 1923. 4.00. Knopf
Forster, E. M. Two cheers for democracy. 1962. pap. 1.95. Harcourt
Fowler, Gene. Skyline. 1961. 5.00. Viking

France, Anatole. Penguin Island. 1. 95. Modern Lib.
France, Anatole. Revolt of the angels. 1.45. Crown
Freneau, Philip. Poetry of Freneau. 2.45. Hafner
Frost, Robert. Complete poems of Robert Frost. 1949. 6.00. Holt
Fry, Christopher. Boy with a cart. 1952. 3.00. Oxford U. P.
Fry, Christopher. Dark is light enough. 1954. 3.50. Oxford U. P.
Fry, Christopher. Lady's not for burning. 1950. 3.50. Oxford U. P.
Fry, Christopher. Phoenix too frequent. il. 1959. 3.50. Oxford U. P.
Fry, Christopher. Sleep of prisoners: A play. 1951. 3.50. Oxford U. P.
Fry, Christopher. Venus observed. 1950. 3.50. Oxford U. P.

G

Gallico, Paul. Snow goose. 1941. 1.50. Knopf
Gallico, Paul. Snowflake. il. 1953. 2.00. Doubleday
Galsworthy, John. Forsyte saga. 1922. 7.50. Scribner
Galsworthy, John. Representative plays. 1923. 3.40. Scribner
Garcia, Lorca, Federico. Five plays. comedies and tragicomedies. 4.75. New
    Directions
Garland, Hamlin. Main-Travelled roads, 615. 3.00. Harper
Garland, Hamlin. Son of the middle border. il. 4.95. Macmillan
Garnett, David. Flowers of the forest. 1956. 4.50. Harcourt
Gide, Andre. Corydon. 1950. 3.75. Farrar, Straus
Gide, Andre. Counterfeiters. 1.95. Modern Lib.
Gide, Andre. Fruits of the earth. 1949. 3.50. Knopf
Gide, Andre. Immoralist. 1948. 3.50. Knopf
Gide, Andre. Isabelle. 1947. 1.95. Appleton
Gide, Andre. Starit is the gate. 1943. 3.50. Knopf
Giraudoux, Jean. Four plays. pap. 1.75. Hill & Wang
Glasgow, Ellen. Barren ground. 3.50. Smith, Peter
Glasgow, Ellen. Vein of iron. 2.50. Harcourt
Goethe, Johann W. Wilhelm Mister's apprenticeship, 1136. 1.50. Collier
Goethe, Johann Wolfgang von. Faust: A tragedy in two parts. by Bayard Taylor.
    2.75. Oxford U. P.
Gogol, Nikolai. Dead souls. 1.95. Modern Lib.
Golding, William. Free fall. 3.95. Harcourt
Golding, William. Lord of the flies. 5.00. Coward
Goldsmith, Oliver. Poems and plays. 1.95. Dutton
Goldsmith, Oliver. Selected works. 1951. 4.75. Harvard
Goldsmith, Oliver. She stoops to conquer. ed. by Vincent F. Hopper and Gerald
    B. Lahey. 1958. 1.95. Barron's
Goldsmith, Oliver. Vicar of Wakefield and other writings. 1.95. Modern Lib.
Goncharov, Ivan A. Oblomov. 1.95. Dutton
Goodrich, Marcus. Delilah. 1953. 4.00. Rinehart
Gorky, Maxim. Selected short stories. 1959. 3.75. Ungar
Goudge, Elizabeth. Castle on the hill. 1942. 3.95. Coward
Graves, Robert. Hercules, my shipmate. 1945. 4.50. Farrar, Straus
Graves, Robert. I, Claudius. 1.95. Modern Lib.
Gray, Thomas. Poems. 1898. 1.25. Cambridge U. P.
Green, Paul. Common glory. 1948. 1.00. U. of N. C.
Green, Paul. Lost colony. 1954. 2.50. U. of N. C.
Greene, Graham. Brighton Rock. 3.50. 1956. Viking
Greene, Graham. Burnt-out case. 1961. 3.95. Viking
Greene, Graham. Heart of the matter. 1948. 3.50. Viking
Greene, Graham. Potting shed. 3.00. Viking
Greene, Graham. Power and the glory. 1946. 3.75. Viking
Greene, Graham. Quiet American. 1956. 3.95. Viking
Greene, Graham. Twenty-one stories. 1962. 3.95. Viking
Greenslet, Ferris. Under the bridge. 3.00. Houghton

Guareschi, Giovanni. Little world of Don Camillo. il. 1951. 3.00. Farrar, Straus
Guest, Edgar A. Collected verse. 6.00. Reilly & Lee
Gulbranssen, Trygve. Beyond sing the woods. 1954. 5.00. Putnam
Guthrie, Alfred B., Jr. Big sky. 4.50. Houghton

H

Haggard, H. Rider. King Solomon's mines. il. 2.75. British Bk.
Halsey, Margaret. With malice toward some. il. 1959. pap. 1.45. S. and S.
Hamalian, Leo, and Edmond L. Volpe. Ten modern short novels. 1958. 4.95.
    Putnam
Hardy, Thomas. Collected poems. 1926. 10.00. Macmillan
Hardy, Thomas. Far from the madding crowd. 1895. 5.00. Harper
Hardy, Thomas. Jude the obscure. 1.95. Modern Lib.
Hardy, Thomas. Mayor of Casterbridge. 1.95. Modern Lib.
Hardy, Thomas. Return of the native. 3.75. Dodd
Hardy, Thomas. Selected poems. 2.25. St. Martins
Hardy, Thomas. Tess of the d'Urbervilles. il. 1953. 4.25. St. Martins
Hardy, Thomas. Trumpet-major. 1887. 3.50. St. Martins
Hardy, Thomas. Two on a tower. 3.50. St. Martins
Hardy, Thomas. Under the greenwood tree. 3.50. St. Martins
Hardy, Thomas. Wessex tales. 3.50. St. Martins
Hardy, Thomas. Woodlanders. 3.50. St. Martins
Harte, Bret. Luck of Roaring Camp and other stories. il. 1961. 3.75. Dodd
Hawthorne, Nathaniel. Blithedale romance. 1958. pap. 1.25. Norton
Hawthorne, Nathaniel. House of the seven gables. 1.95. Dutton
Hawthorne, Nathaniel. Marble faun. pap. 0.95. Doubleday
Hawthorne, Nathaniel. Portable Hawthorne. 1948. 2.95. Viking
Hawthorne, Nathaniel. Scarlet letter. il. 3.75. Dodd
Hawthorne, Nathaniel. Twice-told tales. 1.95. Dutton
Hazlitt, William. Selected essays. 1917. 2.00. Cambridge U. P.
Hazlitt, William. Table talk. 1.95. Dutton
Heggen, Thomas. Mister Roberts. 3.50. Houghton
Heine, Heinrich. Poems. il. by Fritz Kredel. 5.00. Heritage
Hellman, Lillian. Six plays. 1.95. Modern Lib.
Hemingway, Ernest. Death in the afternoon. il. 10.00. Scribner
Hemingway, Ernest. Farewell to arms. 1953. 4.50. Scribner
Hemingway, Ernest. For whom the bell tolls. 1940. 4.95. Scribner
Hemingway, Ernest. Green hills of Africa. il. 1935. 4.50. Scribner
Hemingway, Ernest. Hemingway reader. 5.95. Scribner
Hemingway, Ernest. Old man and the sea. 3.50. Scribner
Hemingway, Ernest. Short stories. 1954. 6.00. Scribner
Hemingway, Ernest. Sun also rises. 3.95. Scribner
Hemingway, Ernest. To have and have not. 1954. 3.95. Scribner
Harris, Joel C. Tales of Uncle Remus, 1049. 7.50. Houghton
Hazlitt, William. Spirit of the age; or, Contemporary portraits. 1904. 2.25. Oxford
    U. P.
Henry, O. Best stories of O. Henry. 1954. 2.50. Doubleday
Henry, O. Complete works. 1953. 5.95. Doubleday
Herrick, Robert. Poems. 2.75. Oxford U. P.
Hersey, John. Bell for Adano. 1944. 3.95. Knopf
Hersey, John. Child buyer. 1960. 4.00. Knopf
Hersey, John. Wall. 1950. 5.95. Knopf
Hersey, John. War lover. 1959. 5.00. Knopf
Hesse, Hermann, Siddhartha. 1951. 2.00. New Directions
Hesse, H. Steppenwolf. 3.00. Ungar
Hillyer, Robert. Collected poems. 1961. 4.75. Knopf
Hilton, James. Good-bye, Mr. Chips. il. 1953. 2.95. Little
Hilton, James. Lost horizon. il. 1933. 3.50. Morrow

Hilton, James. Random Harvest. 1943. 4.50. Little
Holmes, Oliver Wendell. Autocrat of the breakfast table. 2.50. Houghton
Homer. Complete works. 2.95. Modern Lib.
Hope, Anthony. Prisoner of Zenda. 3.25. Dutton
Hopkins, Gerard Manley. Poems. 1948. 5.00. Oxford U. P.
Horace. Collected works. 1.95. Dutton
Housman, A. E. Manuscript poems. 4.50. U. of Minn.
Housman, A. E. Shropshire lad. 1946. 1.50. Colby
Howells, William Dean. Hazard of new fortunes. 1952. 2.95. Dutton
Howells, W. D. Rise of Silas Lapham. 2.75. Oxford U. P.
Howells, William Dean. Their wedding journey. il. 3.00. Houghton
Howells, William Dean. Traveller from Altruria. 3.35. Smith, Peter
Hudson, W. H. Birds of La Plata. il. 12.00. Dutton
Hudson, W. H. Green mansions. il. 3.75. Dodd
Hughes, Thomas. Tom Brown's school days. il. by S. Van Abbe. 2.75. Dutton
Hugo, Victor. Hunchback of Notre Dame. il. 3.75. Dodd
Hugo, Victor. Les miserables. il. 1925. 4.50. Dodd
Hugo, Victor. Toilers of the sea. 1.95. Dutton
Hulme, Kathryn. Nun's story. 1956. 4.95. Little
Huxley, Aldous. Antic hay. 1923. 3.50. Harper
Huxley, Aldous. Ape and essence. 1948. 3.50. Harper
Huxley, Aldous. Brave new world. 1932. 3.50. Harper
Huxley, Aldous. Brave new world revisited. 1958. 3.50. Harper
Huxley, Aldous. Collected essays of Aldous Huxley. 1959. 5.50. Harper
Huxley, Aldous. Crome yellow. 1922. 4.50. Harper
Huxley, Aldous. Devils of Loudun. 1952. 5.00. Harper
Huxley, Aldous. Ends and means. 1937. 5.50. Harper
Huxley, Aldous. Point counter-point. 1928. 4.00. Harper
Huxley, Aldous. Time must have a stop. 1944. 4.50. Harper

I

Ibsen, Hendrik. Doll's house, and Wild duck, and Lady from the sea. 1.95. Dutton
Ibsen, Henrik. Eleven plays. 2.95. Modern Lib.
Ibsen, Hendrik. Peer Gynt. 1.95. Dutton
Inge, William. Four plays. 1958. 5.00. Random
Ingoldsby, Thomas. Ingoldsby legends. 1.95. Dutton
Ionesco, Eugene. Plays (Rhinoceros and other plays) 3.75. Smith, Peter
Irving, Washington. Rip Van Winkle, and Legend of Sleepy Hollow. 1.50. McKay
Irving, Washington. Sketch book. il. 1954. 3.75. Dodd
Irving, Washington. Washington Irving, representative selections. 1934. 2.00. Am.
   Bk. Co.
Isherwood, Christopher. Berlin stories. 1954. 3.50. New Directions
Isherwood, Christopher. Prater violet. pap. 0.95. Modern Lib.

J

Jackson, Charles. Lost weekend. 1944. 3.95. Farrar, Straus
Jackson, Helen Hunt. Ramona. 1952. 2.64. Globe
James, Henry. Ambassadors. 1.95. Dutton
James, Henry. American. 1907. 6.00. Scribner
James, Henry. Bostonians. 1.95. Modern Lib.
James, Henry. Complete plays. il. 1949. 10.00. Lippincott
James, Henry. Confidence. 4.50. Vanguard
James, Henry. Daisy Miller. 1946. 5.00. Holt, Rinehart & Winston
James, Henry. Golden bowl. 1959. pap. 2.95. Grove
James, Henry. Portrait of a lady. 2 vols. 6.00 ea. Scribner
James, Henry. Princess Casamassima. 2 vols. 6.00 ea. Scribner
James, Henry. Roderick Hudson. 3.75. Smith, Peter

James, Henry. Selected letters. 1955. 4.75. Farrar, Straus
James, Henry. Small boy and others. 3.75. Smith, Peter
James, Henry. Tragic muse. 1960. 4.25. Smith, Peter
James, Henry. Turn of the screw, and the Aspern papers. 1.95. Dutton
James, Henry. Washington Square. 1.95. Modern Lib.
James, Henry. Wings of the dove. 1.95. Modern Lib.
James, Marquis. Andrew Jackson: Portrait of a president. 1.95. Grosset
Jeans, J. H. Universe around us. 5.00. 1960. Cambridge U. P.
Jeffers, Robinson. Selected poetry. 1938. 5.95. Random
Jensen, Johannes V. Long journey. 1945. 6.95. Knopf
Jewett, Sarah Orne. Best stories of Sarah Orne Jewett. 1960. 5.00. Houghton
Jewett, Sarah Orne. Country of the pointed firs. 3.00. Houghton
Johnson, Josephine. Now in November. 1934. 3.50. S. and S.
Johnson, Osa. I married adventure. il. 1940. 5.00. Lippincott
Jones, James. From here to eternity. 1951. 5.95. Scribner
Jones, James. Some came running. 1958. 5.95. Scribner
Jonson, Ben. Works. 11 vols. 1925-1952. 8.80 ea. Oxford U. P.
Jonson, Ben. Complete plays. 2 vols. 1.95 ea. Dutton
Josephus, Flavius. Complete works. 1960. 6.95. Kregel
Joyce, James. Collected poems. il. 1957. pap. 0.95. Viking
Joyce, James. Dubliners. 1.95. Modern Lib.
Joyce, James. Portrait of the artist as a young man. 3.50. 1956. Viking
Joyce, James. Ulysses. 6.00. Random
Joyce, James A. Capital punishment. 1962. pap. 1.95. Grove
Juvenal. Satires. 2.75. Cambridge U. P.

K

Kafka, Franz. Amerika. 1947. 4.50. Schocken
Kafka, Franz. Briefe an Milena. 1952. 4.50. Schocken
Kafka, Franz. Briefe, 1902-1924. ed. by Max Brod. 1958. 6.00. Schocken
Kafka, Franz. Penal colony. 1948. 4.50. Schocken
Kafka, Franz. Tagebuecher. 5.50. Schocken
Kafka, Franz. Trial. 1937. 4.50. Knopf
Kantor, MacKinlay. Andersonville. 1955. 5.00. World Pub.
Kantor, MacKinlay. Spirit Lake. 1961. 6.95. World Pub.
Kantor, MacKinlay. Voice of Bugle Ann. 1935. 3.00. Coward
Kaye-Smith, Sheila. Superstition corner. 1955. 3.75. Regnery
Kazin, Alfred. On native grounds. 6.75. Harcourt
Keats, John. Poems. ed. by Edmund Blunden. 3.25. Collins
Keats, John. Selected letters. ed. by Lionel Trilling. 1951. 4.75. Farrar, Straus
Kelley, Amy. Eleanor of Aquitaine and the four kings. il. 1950. 5.50. Harvard
Kennedy, John P. Swallow barn. 2.75. Hafner
Kerouac, Jack. On the road. 1957. Viking
Kimbrough, Emily. And a right good crew. il. 1958. 4.50. Harper
Kimbrough, Emily and Cornelia Otis Skinner. Our hearts were young and gay. il. 3.50. Dodd
Kingsley, Charles. Westward ho! 3.75. Dodd
Kipling, Rudyard. Choice of Kipling's verse. pap. 1.25. Doubleday
Kipling, Rudyard. Kim. il. 1962. 3.75. Dodd
Koestler, Arthur. Arrival and departure. pap. 0.35. Berkley
Koestler, Arthur. Darkness at noon. 1.95. Modern Lib.
Koestler, Arthur. Reflections on hanging. 4.95. Macmillan
Koestler, Arthur. Thieves in the night. pap. 0.50. Berkley
Krutch, Joseph Wood. Desert year. 3.75. Sloane

L

La Farge, Oliver. Laughing Boy. 4.00. Houghton
Lagerkvist, Par. Barabbas. pap. 1.25. Vintage

Lamb, Charles. Complete works and letters. 2.95. Modern Lib.
Lamb, Charles. Essays of Elia. 1.95. Dutton
Lamb, Charles. Letters. 2 vols. 1930. 1.95 ea. Dutton
Landor, Walter S. Imaginary conversations. 1.95 Dutton
Langland, William. Piers Plowman. 1931. 1.95. Dutton
Lanier, Sidney. Poems and poem outlines. 6.00. Johns Hopkins
Lardner, Ring. Best short stories of Ring Lardner. 1958. 4.50. Scribner
Lawrence, D. H. Portable D. H. Lawrence. 1947. 2.95. Viking
Lawrence, D. H. Rainbow. 1.95. Modern Lib.
Lawrence, D. H. Plummed Serpent. 5.00. Knopf
Lawrence, D. H. Sons and lovers. 1.95. Modern Lib.
Lawrence, D. H. Women in love. 1.95. Modern Lib.
Lawrence, T. E. Seven pillars of wisdom: A triumph. il. 1947. 6.00. Doubleday
Lea, Tom. Brave bulls. il. 1949. 4.95. Little
Lederer, William J., and Eugene Burdick. Ugly American. 1958. 3.95. Norton
Lee, Harper. To kill a mockingbird. 1960. 3.95. Lippincott
Lewis, C. S. Out of the silent planet. 1943. 4.50. Macmillan
Lewis, C. S. Pilgrim's regress. 1959. 3.00. Eerdmans
Lewis, C. S. Screwtape letters. 1943. 3.50. Macmillan
Lewis, Lloyd. Captain Sam Grant. 1950. 6.50. Little
Lewis, Matthew G. The monk. 2.45. Grove
Lewis, Sinclair. Arrowsmith. 1949. 2.50. Harcourt
Lewis, Sinclair. Babbitt. 1949. 2.50. Harcourt
Lewis, Sinclair. Cass Timberlane. 1.95. Modern Lib.
Lewis, Sinclair. Dodsworth. 1.95. Modern Lib.
Lewis, Sinclair. Main Street. 1950. 2.50. Harcourt
Lewisohn, Ludwig. Don Juan. 3.00. Liveright
Lindsay, Vachel. Collected poems. il. 1925. 7.95. Macmillan
Llewellyn, Richard. How green was my valley. 4.50. Macmillan
Locke, John. Essay concerning human understanding. 2 vols. il. 1959. pap. 2.25.
    Dover
Lockridge, Ross, Jr. Raintree County. 10.00. Houghton
London, Jack. Call of the wild. il. 6.00. Dial
London, Jack. Martin Eden. 1956. pap. 1.25. Holt, Rinehart & Winston
London, Jack. Sea-wolf. 4.50. Macmillan
London, Jack. South Sea tales. 1961. 3.75. Macmillan
London, Jack. White Fang. 4.50. Macmillan
Longfellow, Henry Wadsworth. Evangeline. 4.50. McKay
Longfellow, Henry W. Poems. 1.95. Modern Lib.
Longus. Daphnis and Chloe. bd. with Parthenius. Love romances. 3.50. Harvard
Loti, Pierre. Iceland fisherman. 1.95. Dutton
Louys, Pierre. Aphrodite. 1.95. Modern Lib.
Lovelace, Richard. Poems. 5.60. Oxford U. P.
Lowell, Amy. Poetry and poets. 2.25. Houghton
Lowell, James Russell. Complete poetical works. 5.50. Houghton
Lowry, Malcolm. Selected poems. 1962. pap. 1.50. City Lights
Lucian. Dialogues. 7 vols. 3.50 ea. Harvard
Lyle, John H. Dry and lowless years. 1960. 4.95. Prentice-Hall
Lynd, Robert. Essays on life and literature. 1.95. Dutton

M

Macaulay, T. B. Essays. 2 vols. 1.95 ea. Dutton
McCullers, Carson. Ballad of the sad cafe. Omnibus containing 3 novels; Member
    of the wedding; Reflections in a golden eye; Heart is a lonely hunter. 6.50. Houghton
McCullers, Carson. Heart is a lonely hunter. 4.00. Houghton
McCullers, Carson. Member of the wedding. 3.00. New Directions
McKenney, Ruth. My sister Eileen. 3.50. Harcourt
MacLeish, Archibald. Collected poems, 1917-1952. 1952. 5.00. Houghton

MacLeish, Archibald. J. B. 1958. 3.50. Houghton
MacNeice, Louis. Eighty-five poems. 1959. 3.50. Oxford U. P.
Mailer, Norman. Norman. Naked and the dead. 1948. 5.00. Rinehart
Mallory, Sir Thomas. Le morte d'Arthur. 2 vols. 1.95. Dutton
Malraux, Andre. L'Espoir. pap. 1.15. Macmillan
Malraux, Andre. Man's fate. 1936. 1.95. Modern Lib.
Mann, Thomas. Buddenbrooks. 1938. 5.00. Knopf
Mann, Thomas. Confessions of Felix Drull, confidence man. 1955. 4.95. Knopf
Mann, Thomas. Doctor Fautus. 1948. 4.95. Knopf
Mann, Thomas. Essays of three decades. 1947. 5.00. Knopf
Mann, Thomas. Joseph and his brothers. tetralogylin 1 vol. 1948. 7.50. Knopf
Mann, Thomas. Magic mountain. 1927. 6.00. Knopf
Mann, Thomas. Stories of three decades. 2.95. Modern Lib.
Mansfield, Katherine. Short stories of Katherine Mansfield. 1937. 6.75. Knopf
Manzoni, Alessandro. Bethrothed. 1.95. Dutton
Marlowe, Christopher. Plays and poems. 2.95. Dutton
Marquand, John P. H. M. Pulham, esquire. 1941. 5.00. Little
Marquand, John P. Late George Apley. 1937. 5.00. Little
Marquand, John P. Point of no return. 1949. 5.75. Little
Marquis, Don. Best of Don Marquis. 1959. 3.95. Doubleday
Masefield, John. Poems. 1953. 10.50. Macmillan
Masters, Edgar Lee. Spoon River anthology with additional poems. 3.95. Macmillan
Maturin, Charles Robert. Melmoth, the wonderer. 1961. pap. 2.40. U. of Nebr.
Maugham, W. Somerset. Complete short stories. 2 vols. vol. 1, East and West;
    vol. 2, The world over. 1952. 12.50. Doubleday
Maugham, W. Somerset. Magician. 1957. 3.75. Doubleday
Maugham, W. Somerset. Moon and sixpence. 1.95. Modern Lib.
Maugham, W. Somerset. Of human bondage. 1.95. Modern Lib.
Maugham, W. Somerset. Points of View; Five essays. 1959. 4.50. Doubleday
Maugham, W. Somerset. Razor's edge. 1959. 3.50. Doubleday
Maugham, W. Somerset. Summing up. 1943. 3.95. Doubleday
Maupassant, Guy de. Best short stories. 1.95. Modern Lib.
Maupassant, Guy de. Mademoiselle Fifi and other stories. il. 2.00. Starvon
Maupassant, Guy de. Odd number. 1889. 2.50. Harper
Maupassant, Guy de. Quinze contes. ed. by F. C. Green. 1943. 1.50. Cambridge
    U. P.
Mauriac, Francois. Son of Man. 1960. 3.00. World Pub.
Mauriac, Francois. Therese. 3.50. Farrar, Straus
Mauriac, Francois. Vipers' tangle. 3.00. Sheed
Maxwell, William. Folded leaf. 1959. pap. 1.25. Vintage
Means, Florence Crannell. Moved-outers. ill. 3.00. Houghton
Means, Florence Crannell. Shuttered windows. ill. 3.00. Houghton
Melville, Herman. Billy Budd. 1946. 5.00. Holt, Rinehart & Winston
Melville, Herman. Moby Dick. 1950. 2.64. Globe
Melville, Herman. Omoo. il. 1924. 4.50. Dodd
Melville, Herman. Portable Melville. 1952. 2.95. Viking
Melville, Herman. Typee. 1959. 1.40. Harper
Mencken, H. L. Prejudices. 1.45. Vintage
Meredith, George. Egoist. 2.75. Oxford U. P.
Meredith, George. Ordeal of Richard Feverel. 1956. 1.95. Dutton
Merejcovski, Dmitri. Romance of Leonardo Da Vinci. il. 1953. 3.95. Heritage
Merton, Thomas. Seven story mountain. 3.95. Harcourt
Merton, Thomas. Sign of Jonas. 3.50. Harcourt
Meyer, Conrad Ferdinand. Poetry of Conrad Ferdinand Meyer. 1954. 4.50. U. of
    Wis.
Meynell, Alice. Essays. 1947. 2.75. Newman
Michener, James A. Hawaii. 6.95. Random
Michener, James A. Sayonara. 1954. 3.50. Random
Michener, James A. Tales of the South Pacific. 1947. 4.50. Macmillan

Millay, Edna St. Vincent. Collected lyrics. 1943. 7.50. Harper
Millay, Edna St. Vincent. Collected sonnets. 1941. 6.00. Harper
Miller, Arthur. Collected plays. 1957. 6.00. Viking
Miller, Arthur. Death of a salesman. 3.00. 1949. Viking
Miller, Caroline. Lamb in his bosom. pap. 0.50. Avon
Millis, Walter. Arms and men. 5.75. Putnam
Milton, John. Areopagitica and other prose works. 1.95. Dutton
Milton, John. Complete poetry and selected prose. 1.95. Modern Lib.
Milton, John. Paradise lost. 2.50. Odyssey
Milton, John. Prose selections. ed. by Merritt Y. Hughes. 2.50. Odyssey
Mitchell, Margaret. Gone with the wind. il. 1939. 4.95. Macmillan
Moliere, Jean Baptiste. Misanthrope. 1959. bds. 2.95. Barron's
Moliere, Jean Baptiste. Six prose comedies of Moliere. tr. by George Graveley.
   1956. 5.00. Oxford U. P.
Moliere, Jean Baptiste. Tartuffe. tr. by Renee Waldinger. 1959. bds. 2.95. Barron's
Montaigne, M. E. de. Essays. 1946. 3.50. Oxford U. P.
Montherlant, Henri de. Selected essays. tr. 1961. 5.00. Macmillan
Moore, George. Esther Waters. 1956. 1.95. Dutton
Moore, George. Heloise and Abelard. 3.95. Liveright
Moore, Marianne. Collected poems. 3.95. Macmillan
Moravia, Alberto. Bitter honeymoon. 1956. 3.50. Farrar, Straus
Moravia, Alberto. Roman tales. 1957. 3.75. Farrar, Straus
Moravia, Alberto. Two women. 1958. 4.95. Farrar, Straus
Morgan, Charles. Fountain. 1932. 4.95. Knopf
Morley, Christopher. Haunted bookshop. il. 1955. 3.95. Lippincott
Morley, Christopher. Parnassus on wheels. il. 1955. 3.95. Lippincott
Muir, John. Stickeen. 1909. 1.96. Houghton

N

Nash, Ogden. Selected verse. 1.95. Modern Lib.
Nashe, Thomas. Unfortunate traveller; or, Jack Wilton. 1960. 2.50. Putnam
Nathan, George Jean. Magic mirror. 1960. 5.00. Knopf
Nathan, Robert. Portrait of Jennie. 1940. 3.50. Knopf
Newman, John H. Apologia pro vita sua. 1.95. Dutton
Nordhoff, Charles, and James Norman Hall. Mutiny on the Bounty. 1932. 4.95. Little
Norris, Frank. Oxtopus. 1947. 3.95. Doubleday

O

O'Casey, Sean. Juno and the Paycock. 1.75. Martins
O'Casey, Sean. Selected plays. 1955. 6.50. Braziller
O'Connor, Flannery. Good man is hard to find. 1955. 3.75. Harcourt
O'Connor Flannery. Violent bear it away. 1960. 3.75. Farrar, Straus
Odets, Clifford. Six plays. 1.95. Modern Lib.
O'Flaherty, Liam. Two lovely beasts. il. 3.00. Devin
O'Hara, John. From the terrace. 1958. 6.95. Random
O'Hara, John. Selected short stories. 1.95. Modern Lib.
Omar Khayyam. Rubaiyat. tr. by Edward Fitzgerald. il. 1950. 2.00. Crowell
O'Neill, Eugene. Long voyage home: Seven plays of the sea. 1.95. Modern Lib.
O'Neill, Eugene. Nine plays. 2.95. Modern Lib.
O'Neill, Eugene. The touch of the poet. 3.75. Yale
Ortega y Gasset, Jose. Revolt of the masses. 1932. 3.95. Norton
Orwell, George. Animal farm. il. 1954. 2.95. Harcourt
Orwell, George. Burmese days. 3.50. Harcourt
Orwell, George. Clergyman's daughter. 1960. 4.75. Harcourt
Orwell, George. Coming up for air. 3.95. Harcourt
Orwell, George. Homage to Catalonia. 3.50. Harcourt
Orwell, George. Nineteen eighty-four. 4.75. Harcourt

Orwell, George. Shooting an elephant. 3.00. Harcourt
Oursler, Fulton. Greatest story ever told. il. 1949. 3.50. Doubleday
Ovid. Selected works. 1.95. Dutton
Ovid. Tristia. 1.25. Cambridge U. P.

P

Paine, Tom. The selected works. 2.95. Modern Lib.
Palgrave, Francis T. Golden treasury. 1.95. Modern Lib.
Parker, Dorothy. Collected poetry. 1.95. Modern Lib.
Parker, Dorothy. Collected stories. 1942. 1.95. Modern Lib.
Parrish, Anne. Clouded star. 1948. 3.95. Harper
Partridge, Bellamy. Going, going, gone. il. 1958. 3.95. Dutton
Pascal, Blaise. Pensees. 1.45. Doubleday
Pascal Balise. Thoughts. 3.00. Smith, Peter
Pasternak, Boris. Doctor Zhivago. 2.95. Modern Lib.
Patchen, Kenneth. Selected poems. 1958. 2.00. New Directions
Paton, Alan. Cry, the beloved country. 1948. 3.95. Scribner
Paton, Alan. Too late the Phalarope. 1953. 3.95. Scribner
Perelman, S. J. Best of S. J. Perelman. 1.95. Modern Lib.
Perse, St. John. Anabasis, 32. 4.00. Harcourt
Pindar. Odes. ed. and tr. by Richard Lattimore. 1947. 4.25. U. of Chicago
Pirandello, Luigi. Right you are. 1954. 4.00. Columbia
Plautus. Menaechmi. ed. by P. T. Jones. 1918. 1.70. Oxford U. P.
Pliny, the Younger. Letters. 2 vols. 3.50 ea. Harvard
Poe, Edgar Allan. Complete tales and poems. 2.95. Modern Lib.
Poe, Edgar Allan. Tales. 3.75. Dodd
Pope, Alexander. Poems. 1.50. Nelson
Porter, Katherine Anne. Flowering judas, and other stories. 1.95. Modern Lib.
Porter, Katherine Anne. Leaning tower and other stories. 4.00. Harcourt
Porter, Katherine Anne. Pale horse, pale rider. 1.95. Modern Lib.
Porter, Katherine Anne. Ship of fools. 6.50. Brown
Pound, Ezra. Poems. 3.50. New Directions
Proust, Marcel. Remembrance of things past. 2 vols. 8.00. Random
Puahkin, A. S. The poems, plays, and plays. 2.95. Modern Lib.
Pushkin, Alexander. Captain's daughter and other tales. 1961. 1.95. Dutton

R

Rabelais, Francois. Complete works. 2.95. Modern Lib.
Racine, Jean Baptiste. Audromache. tr. by Herma Briffault. 2.95. Barron's
Racine, Jean, and Pierre Corneille. Six plays. 1.95. Modern Lib.
Random, John Crowe. Selected poems. 1945. 3.50. Knopf
Rawlings, Marjorie K. Cross Creek. 1942. 4.50. Scribner
Rawlings, Marjorie K. Yearling. 1961. 4.50. Scribner
Reade, Charles. Cloister and the hearth. 3.75. Dodd
Remarque, Erich Maria. All quiet on the Western Front. 1929. 4.50. Little
Richardson, Samuel. Clarissa. 1950. 1.95. Modern Lib.
Richardson, Samuel. Pamela. 1958. pap. 1.45. Norton
Richter, Conrad. Trees, with Fields, and Town. 3 vols. 10.50. Knopf
Richter, Conrad. Waters of Kronos. 1960. 3.50. Knopf
Riley, James Whitcomb. Complete poetical works. 3.95. Grosset
Rilke, Rainer Maria. Letters to a young poet. 1945. 3.95. Norton
Roberts, Elizabeth M. The time of man. 1.65. Viking
Roberts, Kenneth. Arundel. 4.00. Doubleday
Roberts, Kenneth. Northwest Passage. 1959. 4.95. Doubleday
Roberts, Kenneth. Rabble in arms. 1947. 4.50. Doubleday
Robinson, Edwin Arlington. Collected poems. 12.00. Macmillan
Rossetti, Dante G. Poems and translations. 1.95. Dutton

Rostrand, Edmond. Cyrano de Bergerac. il. 1921. 3.50. Oxford U. P.
Rousseau, Jean-Jacques. Confessions. 1945. 1.95. Modern Lib.
Rousseau, Jean-Jacques. Emile. ed. by William H. Boyd. 1962. 2.95. T.C.
Runyon, Damon. Treasury of Damon Runyon. 1.95. Modern Lib.

S

Sabatini, Rafael. Captain Blood. 4.50. Houghton
Sabatini, Rafael. Scaramouche. 1.95. Grosset
Sagan, Francoise. Bonjour tristesse. 1955. 2.95. Dutton
Saki. Short stories. 1.95. Modern Lib.
Salinger, J. D. Catcher in the rye. 1951. 4.50. Little
Salinger, J. D. Franny and Zooey. 1961. 4.00. Little
Salinger, J. D. Nine stories. 1959. 1.95. Modern Lib.
Sand, Georges. Consuelo. 1961. pap. 0.75. Fawcett
Sandburg, Carl. Complete poems. 8.00. Harcourt
Sandoz, Mari. Crazy horse, the strange man of the Oglalas. pap. 1.60. U. of Nebr.
Sandoz, Mari. Old Jules. 1955. 4.95. Hastings
Saroyan, William. Human comedy. il. 4.75. 1944. Harcourt
Saroyan, William. My name is Aram. il. 1940. 2.50. Harcourt
Sartre, Jean-Paul. Age of reason. 1947. 4.50. Knopf
Sartre, Jean-Paul. Reprieve. 1947. 4.50. Knopf
Sartre, Jean-Paul. Troubled sleep. 1951. 4.50. Knopf
Schulberg, Budd. What makes Sammy run? 1.95. Modern Lib.
Scott, Walter. Complete poetical works. 7.50. Houghton
Scott, Sir Walter. Guy Mannering. 1.95. Dutton
Scott, Walter. Heart of Midlothian. 1.95. Dutton
Scott, Walter. Ivanhoe. il. 3.75. Dutton
Scott, Walter. Kenilworth. il. 1956. 3.75. Dodd
Scott, Walter. Old Mortality. 1.95. Dutton
Scott, Walter. Poetical works. 1904. 4.50. Oxford U. P.
Scott, Walter. Quentin Durward. il. 3.75. Dodd
Scott, Walter. Redgauntlet. 1.50. Nelton
Scott, Walter. Talisman. 1.95. Dutton
Scott, Walter. Waverley. il. 6.00. Heritage
Scott, Walter. Woodstock. 1.50. Nelson
Service, Robert. Collected poems. 1944. 4.95. Dodd
Shapiro, Karl. Poems, 1940-1953. 1953. 3.00. Random
Shaw, George Bernard. Complete plays with prefaces. 6 vols. 1962. 7.50 ea.
Shaw, Irwin. Mixed company: Collected stories. 3.95. Random
Shaw, Irwin. Selected stories. 1.95. Modern Lib.
Shaw, Irwin. Two weeks in another town. 1960. 4.95. Random
Shaw, Irwin. Young lions. 1.95. Modern Lib.
Shelley, Percy Bysshe. Complete poetical works. ed. by G. E. Woodberry. 6.75. Houghton
Sheridan, R. B. Plays. 1.95. Dutton
Sholokhov, Mikhail. Silent Don. 10.00. Knopf
Shulman, Max. Rally round the flag, boys. 1957. 3.50. Doubleday
Shute, Nevil. Legacy. 1950. 3.75. Morrow
Shute, Nevil. On the beach. 1957. 3.95. Morrow
Shute, Nevil. Trustee from the toolroom. 1959. 3.95. Morrow
Sienkiewicz, Henryk. Quo Vadis. 1955. 3.75. Dodd
Silone, Ignazio. Bread and wine. 1962. 5.95. Atheneum
Silone, Ignazio. Fontamara. 4.00. Atheneum
Silone, Ignazio. Secret of Juca. 1958. 3.50. Harper
Simms, William Gilmore. The Yemassee. pap. 2.75. Hafner
Sinclair, Upton. Jungle. 1951. 1.40. Harper
Sitwell, Sacheverell. Arabesque and honeycomb. il. 1958. 6.00. Random
Sitwell, Sacheverell. Bridge of the Brocada Sash. il. 1960. 8.50. World Pub.

Skinner, Cornelia Otis. Ape in me. il. 1959. 3.00. Houghton
Skinner, Cornelia Otis. That's me all over. il. 3.75. Dodd
Smith, Betty. Tree grows in Brooklyn. il. 1947. 5.00. Harper
Smith, Lillian. Strange fruit. 3.00. Harcourt
Smith, Logan Pearsall. All trivia. new and rev. ed. 2.75. Harcourt
Smollett, Tobias. Expedition of Humphry Clinker. 2.25. Oxford U. P.
Smollett, Tobias. Humphry Clinker. 1.95. Modern Lib.
Smollett, Tobias. Roderick Random. 1.95. Dutton
Sophocles. Antigone. ed. by M. A. Bayfield. 1.75. St. Martins
Sophocles. Tragedies. 2 vols. vol. 1. Oedipus the king, Oedipus at Colonus, Antigone
    vol. 2. Ajax, Electra, Trachiniae, Philoctetes. 3.50 ea. Harvard
Spender, Stephen. Collected poems. 1955. 4.00. Random
Spenser, Edmund. Complete poetical works. 1908. 7.00. Houghton
Spenser, Edmund. Faerie queens. 2 vols. 1.95 ea. Dutton
Spinoza, Benedict de. Works of Spinoza. 2 vols. tr. by Elwes. 7.00. Smith, Peter
Stein, Gertrude. Selected writings. ed. by Carl Van Vechten. 1.95. Modern Lib.
Steinbeck, John. East of Eden. 2.98. Grosset
Steinbeck, John. Grapes of wrath. 1939. 6.00. Viking
Steinbeck, John. In dubious battle. 1.95. Modern Lib.
Steinbeck, John. Of mice and men. 1.95. Modern Lib.
Steinbeck, John. Pearl. il. 1947. 2.75. Viking
Steinbeck, John. Portable Steinbeck. 1946. 2.95. Viking
Steinbeck, John. Red pony. il. 1959. 2.75. Viking
Steinbeck, John. Tortilla flat. 1.95. Modern Lib.
Steinbeck, John. Winter of our discontent. 1961. 4.50. Viking
Stendhal, M. de. Charterhouse of Parma. 3.95. Tudor
Stendhal, M. de. On love. 3.95. Liveright
Stendhal, M. de. Red and the black. 3.95. Liveright
Stephens, James. Crock of gold. il. 4.50. Macmillan
Sterne, Laurence. Sentimental journey, and Journal, and Letters of Eliza. 1.95.
    Dutton
Sterne, Laurence. Tristram Shandy. 1.95. Dutton
Stevens, Wallace. Collected poems of Wallace Stevens. 1954. 7.50. Knopf
Stevenson, Robert Louis. Essays. 1959. pap. 1.25. Regnery
Stevenson, Robert Louis. Inland voyage, and Travels with a donkey. 1.95. Dutton
Stevenson, Robert Louis. Kidnapped. il. 3.75. Dodd
Stevenson, Robert Louis. Master of Ballantrae, and Weir of Hermiston. 1.95. Dutton
Stevenson, Robert Louis. Treasure island. il. 1956. 3.75. Dodd
Stewart, George R. Storm. 1.95. Modern Lib.
Stockton, Frank R. Casting away of Mrs. Lecks and Mrs. Aleshine. il. 3.95.
    Meredith
Stoker, Bram. Dracula. 1959. 2.95. Doubleday
Stone, Irving. Agony and the ecstasy. 1961. 5.95. Doubleday
Stone, Irving. Clarence Darrow for the defense. 1949. 5.00. Doubleday
Stone, Irving. Love is eternal; Mary Todd and Abraham Lincoln. 1954. 3.95.
    Doubleday
Stone, Irving. Lust for life. 1.95. Modern Lib.
Stone, Irving. President's lady. 1959. 3.95. Doubleday
Stowe, H. B. Uncle Tom's cabin. 1.95. Dutton
Strindberg, August. Plays. 3 vols. 3.75 ea. Humphries
Stuart, Jesse. Hie to the hunters. 1950. 4.50. McGraw
Stuart, Jesse. Man with a bull-tongue plow. 1959. pap. 1.65. Dutton
Styron, William. Lie down in darkness. 1.45. Viking
Swift, Jonathan. Gulliver's travels. il. 3.75. Dodd
Swift, Jonathan. Portable Swift. 2.95. Viking
Sue, Eugene. The wandering jew. 2.95. Modern Lib.
Swinburne, A. C. Selected poems. ed. by Laurence Binyon. 2.25. Oxford U. P.
Synge, John M. Complete works. 6.00. Random
Synge, J. M. Riders to the sea. 0.75. Humphries

Tacitus. Dialogue, Agricola, and Germania. 1.60. Oxford U. P.
Tarkington, Booth. Alice Adams. 1.95. Grosset
Tarkington, Booth. Penrod. 1.50. Grosset
Tate, Allen. Collected essays. 1959. 6.00. Swallow, A.
Tate, Allen. Poems. pap. 1.85. Swallow, A.
Teasdale, Sara. Collected poems. 1937. 5.50. Macmillan
Tennyson, Alfred. Complete poetical works. ed. by W. J. Rolfe. 7.00. Houghton
Tennyson, Alfred. Poems and plays. 2.95. Modern Lib.
Thackeray, William Makepeace. Henry Esmond. 1959. 1.65. Norton
Thackeray, W. M. Pendennis. 2 vols. 1.95 ea. Dutton
Thackeray, William M. Vanity Fair. 3.75. Dodd
Thomas, Dylan. Adventures in the skin trade and other stories. 1955. 3.50. New
    Directions
Thomas, Dylan. Collected poems of Dylan Thomas. 3.75. New Directions
Thomas, Aquinas, Saint. Basic writings. 2 vols. 1945. 15.00. Random
Thompson, Francis. Poems. 4.00. Appleton
Thoreau, Henry David. Cape Cod. il. 1951. 5.50. Norton
Thoreau, Henry David. Excursions. 3.75. Smith, Peter
Thoreau, Henry D. Heart of Thoreau's journals. 3.50. Smith, Peter
Thoreau, Henry David. Maine woods. il. 1950. 5.50. Norton
Thoreau, Henry David. Portable Thoreau. 1947. pap. 1.65. Viking
Thoreau, H. D. Walden. 1.95. Dutton
Thucydides. Complete writings. 1934. 1.95. Modern Lib.
Thurber, James. Thurber cranival. il. 4.95. Harper
Thurber, James. White deer. il. 1945. 3.50. Harcourt
Tibullus, and Catullus. Works. 3.50. Harvard
Tolstoy, Leo. Anna Karenina. 3.00. Oxford U. P.
Tolstoy, Leo. Kreutzer sonata, The devil, and other tales. 2.75. Oxford U. P.
Tolstoy, Leo. Resurrection. 1952. 2.75. Oxford U. P.
Tolstoy, Leo. War and peace. 1956. 3.50. Grosset
Trollope, Anthony. Barchester Towers. 1.85. Collins
Trollope, Anthony. Doctor Thorne. 2.75. Oxford U. P.
Trollope, Anthony. Framley Parsonage. 1962. 3.50. Harcourt
Trollope, Anthony. Last chronicle Barset. 1962. 3.50. Harcourt
Trollope, Anthony. Rachel Ray. 1952. 4.95. Knopf
Trollope, Anthony. Small house at Allington. 1962. 3.50. Harcourt
Trollope, Anthony. Warden. il. 1952. 5.00. Oxford U. P.
Turgenev, Ivan. Fathers and sons. il. 5.00. Dial
Twain, Mark. Innocents abroad. 4.50. Harper

U

Ulman, James Ramsey. White tower. 1959. 5.95. Lippincott
Undset, Sigrid. Kristin Lavransdatter. 1935. 6.50. Knopf
Updike, John. Same door. 1959. 3.75. Knopf

V

Van Doren, Mark. Collected stories. 1962. 5.95. Hill & Wang
Van Dyke, Henry. Mansion. il. 1911. 1.75. Harper
Van Dyke, Henry. Story of the other wise man. 1.50. Grosset
Verne, Jules. Around the world in eighty days. 1956. 1.50. Grosset
Verne, Jules. From the earth to the moon and a trip around it. 2.50. Lippincott
Verne, Jules. Journey to the center of the earth. 3.00. Assoc. Booksellers
Verne, Jules. Mysterious island. 1956. 1.95. Grosset
Verne, Jules. Twenty thousand leagues under the sea. il. 3.75. Dodd
Villon, Francois. Complete poems. 3.95. Liveright

Voltaire, Francois. Marie Arouet de. Candide. 4.95. Peter Pauper
Voltaire, Francois. Portable Voltaire. ed. by Ben Ray Redman. 1949. 2.95. Viking

W

Wallace, Lew. Ben-Hur. il. 6.00. Heritage
Waln, Nora. House of exile. il. 1933. 5.00. Little
Walpole, Hugh. Cathedral. 2.00. St. Martins
Walpole, Hugh. Fortitude. 1.95. Modern Lib.
Walpole, Hugh. Jeremy and Hamlet. 2.00. St. Martins
Waltari, Mika. Egyptian. 5.00. Putnam
Walton, Izaak. Compleat angler. 1.95. Dutton
Warren, Robert Penn. All the king's men. 5.75. Harcourt
Warren, Robert Penn. Band of angels. 1955. 3.95. Random
Warren, Robert Penn. Cave. 1959. 4.95. Random
Warren, Robert Penn. World enough and time. 3.50. Random
Waugh, Evelyn. Brideshead revisited. 1956. pap. 0.75. Dell
Waugh, Evelyn. Helena. 1950. 4.50. Little
Waugh, Evelyn. Loved one. 1943. 3.50. Little
Webster, John. Duchess of Malfi. il. 1959. 1.95. Barron's
Webster, John. White devil. 1960. 4.25. Harvard
Wells, H. G. Tono Bungay. 1.95. Modern Lib.
Wells, H. G. War of the worlds and Time machine. 1956. 2.64. Globe
Welty, Eudora. Delta wedding. 3.75. Harcourt
Welty, Eudora. Ponder heart. 1954. 3.00. Harcourt
Welty, Eudora. Wide net and other stories. 3.00. Harcourt
West, Rebecca. Black lamb and grey falcon. il. 1941. 6.95. Viking
Weston, Christine. Indigo. 3.75. Smith, Peter
Wharton, Edith. Age of innocence. 1920. 4.95. Meredith
Wharton, Edith. Best short stories of Edith Wharton. 1958. 4.50. Scribner
Wharton, Edith. Ethan Frome. 1938. 3.00. Scribner
Wharton, Edith. House of mirth. 1905. 3.50. Smith, Peter
Walpole, Horace. The castle of Otranto in three eighteenth century romances. pap.
    0.65. Collier
West, Nathanael. Day of the locust. 6.50. Viking
Wilde, Oscar. Dorian Gray and De Profundis. 1.95. Modern Lib.
White, T. H. The once and future king. 5.95. Putnam
White, Stewart Edward. Gold. 1954. 3.95. Doubleday
Whitman, Walt. Leaves of grass. 1954. 3.95. Doubleday
Whittier, John Greenleaf. Poems. 6.00. Houghton
Wilde, Oscar. Complete plays. 1959. 1.65. Norton
Wilde, Oscar. Essays and poems. 1959. 1.65. Norton
Wilder, Thornton. Bridge of San Luis Rey. 1.50. Grosset
Wilder, Thornton. Heaven's my destination. 1957. 4.50. Harper
Wilder, Thornton. Ides of March. 1948. 4.95. Harper
Wilder, Thornton. Three plays. Our town, Skin of our teeth, Matchmaker. 1957.
    5.50. Harper
Williams, Ben Ames. House divided. 8.50. Houghton
Williams, Tennessee. Baby Doll. 3.00. New Directions
Williams, Tennessee. Camino real. 3.00. New Directions
Williams, Tennessee. Cat on a hot tin roof. 1955. 3.25. New Directions
Williams, Tennessee. Glass menagerie. pap. 2.25. New Directions
Williams, Tennessee. Hard candy: Book of stories. 1959. 4.50. New Directions
Williams, Tennessee. In the winter of cities. 1955. 3.50. New Directions
Williams, Tennessee. Roman spring of Mrs. Stone. 1950. 2.75. New Directions
Williams, Tennessee. Rose tattoo. 3.25. New Directions
Williams, Tennessee. Streetcar named Desire. 1947. 3.75. New Directions
Williams, Tennessee. Suddenly last summer. 1958. 2.75. New Directions
Williams, Tennessee. Summer and smoke. 2.75. New Directions

Williams, Tennessee. Sweet bird of youth. 1959. 3.25. New Directions
Williams, Tennessee. The milk train doesn't stop here any more. 4.50. New
  Directions
Williams, Tennessee. 27 wagons full of cotton. 1953. 3.50. New Directions
Williams, William Carlos. Collected earlier poems. 5.00. New Directions
Williams, William Carlos. Farmers' daughters and other stories. 1961. 4.50.
Williams, William Carlos. Paterson. 1948. 2.50. New Directions
Williams, William Carlos. Picture's from Brueghel. pap. 2.25. New Directions
Wilson, Edmund. Axel's castle. 1931. 4.50. Scribner
Wister, Owen. Virginian. 2.49. Grosset
Wolfe, Thomas. Hills beyond. 1941. 5.00. Harper
Wolfe, Thomas. Look homeward, angel. il. 1929. 5.95. Scribner
Wolfe, Thomas. Web and the rock. 1960. 2.98. Grosset
Wolfe, Thomas. You can't go home again. 1940. 6.95. Harper
Woolf, Virginia. Haunted house and other short stories. 1944. 3.50. Harcourt
Woolf, Virginia. Orlando, a biography. 1950. pap. 0.50. New Am. Lib.
Woolf, Virginia. Mrs. Dalloway. 1949. 2.50. Harcourt
Woolf, Virginia. To the lighthouse. 1949. 2.50. Harcourt
Wordsworth, William. Poetical works. 5 vols. ed. by Ernest de Selincourt and
  Helen Darbishire. vol. 1, 1940. 5.60; vol. 2, 1952. 6.10; vol. 3, 1954. 6.10;
  vol. 4, 1947. 7.20; vol. 5, 1949. 7.20. Oxford U. P.
Wouk, Herman. Marjorie Morningstar. 1955. 4.95. Doubleday
Wouk, Herman. Caine mutiny. 1955. 3.95. Doubleday'
Wright, Richard. Native son. 1.40. Harper
Wylie, Philip. Disappearance. 1951. 4.00. Rinehart
Wylie, Philip. Essay on morals. 1947. 5.50. Rinehart
Wylie, Philip. Generation of vipers. 1955. 4.00. Holt, Rinehart & Winston
Wylie, Philip. Opus 21. 1949. 3.50. Rinehart
Wylie, Philip. Disappearance
Wylie, Elinor. Collected poems. 1932. 5.75. Knopf

X

Xenophon. Anabasis. 3.50. McKay
Xenophon. Hellenica, Anabasis, Symposium and Apology. 3 vols. 3.50 ea.
  Harvard

Y

Yarmolinsky, Avrahm. Treasury of great Russian short stories. 1944. 9.75.
  Macmillan
Yeats, William Butler. Collected plays. 6.00. Macmillan
Yeats, William Butler. Selected poems. 1962. pap. 1.95. Macmillan
Yerby, Frank. Woman called Fancy. 1951. 4.95. Dial
Young, Stark. So red the rose. 1935. 3.95. Scribner

Z

Zamiatin, Eugene. We, the basis for Orwell's 1984. 1.45. Dutton
Zola, Emile. Germinal. 1937. 4.00. Knopf
Zola, Emile. Nana. 1.95. Modern Lib.

SECTION III

VITAL REFERENCE WORKS FOR JUNIOR COLLEGE LIBRARIES

BOOK SELECTION TOOLS

AMERICAN BOOK PUBLISHING RECORD. 12 issues a year. 1960. $10.00.
Bowker
BOOK BUYER'S HANDBOOK. American Booksellers Assn. 1959-60.
BOOK REVIEW DIGEST. Wilson, 1905- (monthly except February and July) $12.00
BOOKLIST AND SUBSCRIPTION BOOKS BULLETIN. American Library Association
1956- $6.00
BOOKS IN PRINT. An Index to the Publisher's Trade List Annual. Bowker, 1962.
$18.00 (annual)
THE CUMULATIVE BOOK INDEX. Wilson, Service Basis. 1898
GRAHAM, B. READER'S ADVISER AND BOOKMAN'S MANUAL. 9th edition, revised
& enlarged by Hester R. Hoffman, Bowker, 1960, $15.00.
LITERARY MARKET PLACE. 1962-63, $7.45. Bowker
PUBLISHERS' TRADE LIST ANNUAL. Bowker, 1962, 2 vols. $8.50
PUBLISHERS WEEKLY. Bowker. $11.00 a year.
SHORES, LOUIS. Basic Reference Sources: An Introduction to Materials and
Methods, American Library Association. 1954, $6.25. A.L.A.
SUBJECT GUIDE TO BOOKS IN PRINT. Bowker, 1962, $17.50
TRINKNER, C.L. Basic Books for Junior College Libraries: 20,000 Vital Titles.
Colonial Press, 1963. $20.00
WINCHELL CONSTANCE M. Guide to Reference Books. 7th ed. 1951, $10.00.
A.L.A.

INDEXES

AYER'S DIRECTORY OF NEWSPAPERS AND PERIODICALS. Ed. William McCalliste
1880- (annual) $30.00. Ayer
THE BIBLIOGRAPHIC INDEX: A Cumulative Bibliography of Bibliographies. 1937-
(Service Basis) Wilson
BIOGRAPHICAL INDEX. (Service Basis) Wilson
CLAPP, JANE, Art in Life. $12.50. 1959. Scarecrow
ESSAY AND GENERAL LITERATURE INDEX. 1930- (Service Basis) Wilson
INTERNATIONAL INDEX TO PERIODICALS. 1928- (Service Basis) Wilson
LOVELL, E.C. AND HALL, R.M. Index to Handicrafts, Model-Making and
Workshop Projects. $8.00. Faxon
MONRO, I.S. AND COOK, D.E. Costume Index. $6.00. Wilson
NEW YORK TIMES INDEX. 1913- (bi-weekly), Annual. 60.00 yr. New York Times
Company
PUBLIC AFFAIRS INFORMATION SERVICE. 1915. $50.00. Wilson
READERS' GUIDE TO PERIODICAL LITERATURE. 1900. Service Basis. Wilson
ULRICH'S PERIODICAL DIRECTORY. 10th edition, 1963. $22.50. Bowker
VANCE, L.E. Illustration Index. 1956. $5.00 (w. supplement) Scarecrow
VERTICAL FILE INDEX OF PAMPHLETS. 1932- (monthly except August) $8.00
yr. Wilson

ENCYCLOPEDIAS

General Adult Encyclopedias

COLLIER'S ENCYCLOPEDIA. Ed. Louis Shores, 20 vols. , 1960. $299.50. Collier
& Macmillan
ENCYCLOPEDIA AMERICANA. The international reference work. Ed. Lavinia P.
Dudley. 30 vols. 1962. $329.50. The Americana Corp.
ENCYCLOPEDIA BRITANNICA. A new survey of universal knowledge, Ed. John
V. Dodge. 24 vols. , 1962. $398.00. Encyclopedia Britannica Inc.

One-Volume Encyclopedias

COLUMBIA ENCYCLOPEDIA. 2nd edition, 1959. $35.00. Columbia University
   Press
THE LINCOLN LIBRARY OF ESSENTIAL INFORMATION. Ed. Clyde W. Park.
   1961. $34.50. The Frontier Press Company.

Encyclopedia Supplements

AMERICANA ANNUAL; An encyclopedia of the events. 1923- (annual) $12.00. Watts
BRITANNICA BOOK OF THE YEAR; A record of the March Events, 1938- (annual)
   $5.30. Encyclopedia Britannica
COLLIER'S ENCYCLOPEDIA YEAR BOOK. 1938- (annual) $10.00. Collier &
   Macmillan
THE NEW INTERNATIONAL YEAR BOOK. Ed. Susan V. Brady, 1963. $10.00.
   Funk & Wagnalls

DICTIONARIES

THE AMERICAN COLLEGE DICTIONARY. by Clarency L. Barnhart. 1959. $5.00.
   Random House
BERRY, L. V. The American Thesaurus of Slang. 1953. $15.00. Crowell
CRAIGIE, SIR W. A. & HULBERT, J. R., eds. A Dictionary of American English
   on Historical Principles. 100.00. Univ. of Chicago
EVANS, BERGEN. Dictionary of Contemporary American Usage. 1957. $5.95.
   Random House
FOWLER, H. W. A Dictionary of Modern English Usage. 1937. $4.50. Oxford
   Univ. Press
FUNK AND WAGNALLS NEW "STANDARD" DICTIONARY OF THE ENGLISH
   LANGUAGE. (unabridged) $40.00. Funk and Wagnalls
JANE'S ALL THE WORLD'S AIRCRAFT. 1961-62. $35.00. McGraw
LEWIS, NORMAN. New Roget's Thesaurus of the English Language in Dictionary
   Form. 1961. $3.50. Doubleday
MURRAY, SIR J. A. H., Ed. The Oxford English Dictionary. 13 vols. $300.00.
   Oxford Univ. Press
THE NEW CENTURY DICTIONARY. By H. G. Emery and K. G. Brewster. 2 vols
   $30.00. Appleton
COLLEGE STANDARD DICTIONARY. 1956. $5.50. Funk & Wagnalls
PARTRIDGE, ERIC. A Dictionary of Slang and Unconventional English. 5th ed.
   1961. $16.00. Macmillan
ROGET, PETER MARK. Thesaurus of English Words and Phrases. 1946. $4.25.
   Crowell
WEBSTER'S DICTIONARY OF SYNONYMS. 1951. $6.00. Merriam
WEBSTER'S NEW COLLEGIATE DICTIONARY. 6th ed. 1956. $5.00. Merriam
WEBSTER'S NEW INTERNATIONAL DICTIONARY. William A. Neilson, G. 2 v.
   $47.50. Merriam
WEBSTER'S NEW TWENTIETH CENTURY DICTIONARY OF THE ENGLISH
   LANGUAGE. 1958, (unabridged) $39.50. World Publishing Co.
WOOD, CLEMENT. Complete Rhyming Dictionary. Garden City. 1943. $3.50.
   Doubleday

French

CASSELL'S NEW FRENCH-ENGLISH DICTIONARY. 1951. $7.50. Funk and Wagnalls

German

CASSELL'S GERMAN DICTIONARY. 1958. $7.50. Funk and Wagnalls

Italian

CASSELL'S ITALIAN DICTIONARY. By Piero Rebora. 1959. $7.50. Funk and
Wagnalls

Russian

SMIRNITSKY, A. I. Russian-English Dictionary. 1959. $7.95. Dutton

Spanish

CUYAS, ARTURO. Appleton's Revised Guyas Dictionary. 1960. $7.50. Appleton

ALMANACS AND FACT FINDERS AND YEARBOOKS

DICTIONARY OF DATES. ed. by C. Arnold-Baker, A. Dent. 1954. $4.25. Dutton
DOUGLAS, GEORGE W. The American Book of Days. 1948. $6.00. Wilson
ENCYCLOPEDIA OF AMERICAN FACTS AND DATES, ed. by Gorton Carruth.
1962. $6.95. Crowell
HAZELTINE, MARY E. Anniversaries and Holidays. 1944. $6.00
INFORMATION PLEASE ALMANAC. Dan Golenpaul. 1959. $2.50. Macmillan
KANE, J. N. Famous First Facts. 1950. $7.00. Wilson
THE NEW CENTURY CLASSICAL HANDBOOK. Edited by Catherine B. Avery.
$15.00. Appleton
WEIDEMAN, HUGH, ed. The Rapid Fact Finder. 1958. $4.95. Crowell
WHITAKER, JOSEPH. Whitaker's Almanac Annual. 1869. $6.00. British Book
WORLD ALMANAC. An Almanac and Book of Facts. (Annual) 1868-date. Ed.
Harry Hansen. World-Telegram & Sun. $2.00

Yearbooks

YEARBOOK OF AMERICAN CHURCHES... information on all faiths in the U.S.A.
N. Y. National Council of the Churches of Christ. 1916-date. $4.00
THE ANNUAL REGISTER OF WORLD EVENTS: A Review of the Year 1962. $25.00
St . Martins
BOOK OF THE STATES... v. 1, 1935-date. Chicago Council of State Governments.
(1935) $10.00
DEMOGRAPHIC YEAR BOOK. 1948-date. $8.00. U.N.
FACTS ON FILE. 1940. Ed. Fred McGhee. $30.00
INTERNATIONAL YEARBOOK AND STATESMAN'S WHO'S WHO. Annual $25.00.
Int. Publishing Service
OFFICIAL HOTEL RED BOOK AND DIRECTORY, 1886-date. New York American
Hotel Assn. $6.00
STATESMAN'S YEAR-BOOK. 1864. (annual) $9.50. St. Martins
STATISTICAL YEAR BOOK. 1948-date. 1962. $10.00. U.N.
U.S. DEPARTMENT OF AGRICULTURE. Yearbook of Agriculture. 1894-date
Govt. Printing Office
THE YEARBOOK OF THE UNITED NATIONS. 1962. $15.00. U.N.

PHILOSOPHY, PSYCHOLOGY, AND RELIGION

BALDWIN, JAMES. Dictionary of Philosophy and Psychology. 1940. $15.00.
Smith, Peter
HARRIMAN, PHILIP. New Dictionary of Psychology. 1947. $5.00
HINSIE, LELAND. Psychiatric Dictionary with Encyclopedia Treatment of Modern
Terms. 1953. $17.50. Oxford Univ. Press
MAGILL, FRANK NORTHEN. Masterpieces of World Philosophy. $8.95. 1961.
Harper
RUNES, DAGOBERT. Dictionary of Philosophy. New York Philosophical Library.
1942. $6.00

WARREN, HOWARD. Dictionary of Psychology. 1934. $4.00. Houghton

RELIGION

Encyclopedias

FERM, V. T. A. The Encyclopedia of Religion. 1959. pap. 2.95. Littlefield
HASTINGS, JAMES. Encyclopedia of Religion and Ethics. 1927. $65.00.
  Scribner
JULIAN, JOHN. Dictionary of Hymnology Setting Forth the Origin and History of
  Christian Hymns of all Ages and Nations. 1957. $12.50. Scribner
MILLER, MADELEINE. Encyclopedia of Bible Life. 1955. $6.95. Harper
MILLER, MADELEINE. Harper's Bible Dictionary. 1952. $8.95. Harper

Bible Sources

BLACK, MATTHEW & OTHERS, ed. Peake's Commentary on the Bible. $15.00.
  Nelson
BUTTRICK, GEORGE ARTHUR & OTHERS, eds. The Interpreter's Dictionary of
  the Bible. 4 vols. $45.00. Abington,
DUMMELOW, J.R., Commentary on the Holy Bible. 1947. $5.95. Macmillan
ELLICOTT, CHARLES JOHN. Commentary on the Whole Bible. 1954. 4 vols.
  $24.95. Zondervan
HARMON, NOLAN B., The Interpreter's Bible. 1951-1957. 12 vols. set, $89.50.
  Abingdon
HOLY BIBLE, DOUAY VERSION. Catholic Publishing Company. 1948. $4.20.
HOLY BIBLE, KING JAMES VERSION. Prices Vary
HOLY BIBLE, REVISED STANDARD VERSION. 1952. $6.00. Nelson
KRAELING, EMIL GOTTLIEB HEINRICH. Historical Atlas of the Holy Land.
  $2.95. Rand McNally
MEAD, FRANK SPENCER. Handbook of Denominations in the United States.
  $2.95. Abingdon
THE NEW ENGLISH BIBLE. New Testament. Oxford Press. $4.95
STRONG, JAMES. Exhaustive Concordance of the Bible. $14.75. Abingdon
THE APROCRYPHA: An American Translation. By E.J. Goodspeed. Univ. of
  Chicago Press. 1938. $5.00
BROWNE, LEWIS. The World's Great Scriptures. 1956. $7.50. Macmillan
BURROWS, MILLAR. The Dead Sea Scrolls. 1955. $6.50. Viking
CHAMPION, SELWYN. The Eleven Religions and Their Proverbial Lore, a
  Comparative Study. 1945. $4.00. Dutton
BROWNE, LEWIS. The World's Great Scriptures. $7.50. Macmillan
EDITORS OF LIFE. The World's Great Religions. Simon & Schuster. 1957. $13.50.
STEVENSON, BURTON. Home Book of Bible Quotations. 1949. $7.95. Harper
WRIGHT, G.E. Westminister Historical Atlas to the Bible. 1956. $7.50. Westminister

SOCIAL SCIENCES

BALLENTINE, JAMES ARTHUR. Law Dictionary With Pronunciations. 1948.
  $15.00. Lawyers Co-Operative Pub. Co.,
BOOK OF THE STATES. 1935. Council of State Governments, (Biennial) $10.00
COMMODITY YEAR BOOK. 1939. New York, Commodity Research Bureau. $14.50
CONSUMERS'S RESEARCH BULLETIN. (Report) Sept. 1931. Washington, N.J.,
  Consumers' Research, 1931- Monthly. Annual, $3.00 per yr.
DICTIONARY OF SOCIOLOGY, ed. by Henry Pratt Fairchild. Littlefield. $1.95.
ECONOMIC ALMANAC FOR 1940-date. National Industrial Conference. (Annual)
  $5.00
ENCYCLOPAEDIA OF THE SOCIAL SCIENCES. E.R. Seligman and Alvin Johnson.
  Macmillan, Reissue 1948. 8 vols. $110.00
JANE'S FIGHTING SHIPS. v. 1-, 1898 Lond., S. Low. il. Annual. $35.00. McGraw
SMITH, EDWARD CONRAD, AND ZURCHER, ARNOLD JOHN eds. New Dictionary
  of American Politics. 1955. $4.95. Barnes & Noble

THOMAS' REGISTER OF AMERICAN MANUFACTURERS. Thomas Pub. Co. 3v. and index, $12.50
YOUNG, EARL FISKE. Dictionary of Social Welfare. Social Sciences. 1948

Costumes

EVANS, MARY. Costume Throughout the Ages. Rev. ed. 1950. $6.00. Lippincott
GORSLINE, DOUGLAS. What People Wore. $10.00. Viking
HANSEN, H.H. Costumes and Styles. The Evolution of Fashion from Early Egypt to the Present. 1956. $7.50. Dutton
MONRO, ISABEL S. Costume Index Supplement. 1957. $6.00. Wilson

Business

THE SECRETARY'S HANDBOOK. 8th ed. rev. Faintor, Sarah A. 5.95. Macmillan

Education

ALEXANDER, CARTER, AND BURKE, ARVID J. How to Locate Educational Information and data.. Columbia Univ. 1958. $6.25.
AMERICAN ASSOCIATION OF JUNIOR COLLEGES. Junior College Directory. 1927- Washington Assoc., Annual. $1.00
AMERICAN JUNIOR COLLEGES. by Edmund J. Gleazer, Jr. Latest Edition. $9.00. A.C.E.
AMERICAN UNIVERSITIES AND COLLEGES. ED. by Mary Irvin. (8th edition) 1960. $13.00
BAIRDS MANUAL OF AMERICAN COLLEGE FRATERNITIES. 1963. $8.00. George Banta Co.
BROWNSTEIN, SAMUEL C. You Can Win A Scholarship. Barron's Education Service. 1958. $4.95.
CHAMBERS, MERRITT MADISON, ed. Universities of the World Outside U.S.A. Wash. American Council on Education. 1950. $12.00

Education

DANIEL, ROBERT S. AND LOUTIT, C.M. Professional Problems in Psychology. 1953. $5.95. Prentice-Hall
ENCYCLOPEDIA OF EDUCATIONAL RESEARCH. Ed. Chester W. Harris. 1960. $25.00. Macmillan
THE FIFTH MENTAL MEASUREMENTS YEARBOOK. Oscar K. Buros. 1959. $22.50. The Gryphon Press
GOOD, CARTER V. Dictionary of Education. 1959. $10.75. McGraw_Hill
HARRIS, CHESTER, ed. Encyclopedia of Educational Research. $25.00. Macmillan
JUNIOR COLLEGES, SPECIALIZED SCHOOLS AND COLLEGES. 1954. $5.00. Sargent
LOVEJOY, C.E. AND THEODORE S. JONES. LoveJoy-Jones College Scholarships Guide. 1957. $2.25. S&S
UNESCO. World Survey of Education. 3 vols. 34.00. Int. Doc. Service-Columbia
U.S. OFFICE OF EDUCATION. Educational Directory. 1912 (annual) $0.70. G.P.O.

Etiquette

POST, EMILY. Etiquette: The Blue Book of Social Usage. 1955. $5.00. Funk & Wagnalls
VANDERBILT, AMY. Amy Vanderbilt's Complete New Book of Etiquette. 1962. $5.50. Doubleday
VOGUE BOOK OF ETIQUETTE. A Complete Guide to Traditional Forms and Modern Usage. 1948. $6.50. S&S

Guidance

DICTIONARY OF OCCUPATIONAL TITLES. 1939-44. 4 vols. U.S. Employment
    Service. Wash. , Govt. Printing Office.
FORRESTER, GERTRUDE. Occupational Literature, An Annotated Bibliography.
    1958. $6.50. Wilson
OCCUPATIONAL INDEX. 1936- (quarterly) $7.50 yr. New York University
U.S. LABOR STATISTICS BUREAU. Occupational Outlook Handbook. 1957. $4.00.
    G.P.O.

SCIENCE AND TECHNOLOGY

Biological Sciences

BAILEY, L.H. Manual of Cultivated Plants. 1949. $19.50. Macmillan
COLLINGWOOD, G.H. Knowing your Trees. American Forestry Association.
    $6.00
DITMARS, R.L. Reptiles of the World. 1936. $6.95. Macmillan
GRAY, ASA. Manual of Botany. American Book Company. 1950. $15.00
HYLANDER, C.J. Macmillan Wild Flower Book. 1954. $9.95. Macmillan
LUTZ, F.E. Field Book of Insects. 1935. $3.95. Putnam
MATHEWS, F.S. Field Book of American Trees and Shrubs. 1915. $3.95. Putnam
MATHEWS, F.S. Field Book of American Wild Flowers. $5.00. Putnam
NATIONAL GEOGRAPHIC SOCIETY. Book of Fishes. N.G. Society. 1952. $6.50.
PETERSON, R.T. Field Guide to the Birds. 1947. $4.95. Houghton

Chemistry

ANDERSON, H.V. Chemical Calculations. 1955. $4.95. McGraw
BENNETT, HARRY, Ed. Concise Chemical and Technical Dictionary. Tudor,
    Chemical Publishing Co. 1962. $15.00

Medical Science

DORLAND, W.A.N. Illustrated Medical Dictionary. (latest ed) $12.50. Saunders
FISHBEIN, MORRIS. Popular Medical Encyclopedia. 1956. $4.95. Doubleday
PHARMACOPEIA OF THE U.S.A. 14th rev. 1950. $10.00. Mack
MERCK INDEX OF CHEMICALS AND DRUGS. An Encyclopedia for the Chemist,
    Pharmacist, Physician, and Allied Professions. Merck & Co. (latest ed). $12.00

Encyclopedia

Encyclopedia of Chemical Technology. 15 volumes. ed. by Raymond E. Kirk.
    400.00. Wiley

Physical Sciences

AMERICAN INSTITUTE OF PHYSICS HANDBOOK. ed. by Dwight E. Gray. 1957.
    $18.50
COMRIE, L.J. ed. Barlow's Tables of Squares, Cubes, Square Roots, Cube Roots
    and Reciprocals of all Instegers. Up to 12,500. 4th ed. Tudor. $4.95
GLASSTONE, SAMUEL. Source Book of Atomic Energy. 2nd ed. 1958. $4.40.
    Van Nostrand
HACH'S CHEMICAL DICTIONARY. 3rd ed. 1956. $12.50. Blakiston
HENDERSON, I.F. AND W.D. Dictionary of Scientific Terms. 7th ed. by J.H.
    Kenneth. 1961. $12.50. Nostrand
INTERNATIONAL DICTIONARY OF PHYSICS AND ELECTRONICS. 1961. $27.85.
    Van Nostrand

JAMES, GLEN AND ROBERT C. eds. Mathematics Dictionary. 1959. $15.00. Van Nostrand

SPACE ENCYCLOPEDIA. rev. ed. Jones, Harold Spencer. $8.95. Dutton

VAN NOSTRAND'S SCIENTIFIC ENCYCLOPEDIA. 3rd ed. 1958. $29.75. Van Nostrand

FINE ARTS

Art and Architecture

GARDNER, Helen. Art Through the Ages. 1959. $9.50. Harcourt

FLETCHER, Banister Flight. A History of Architecture. 1961. $16.75. 17th ed. Scribner

HUYGHE, Rene. Larousse Encyclopedia of Prehistoric and Ancient Art. 1962. $17.95. Prometheus

MAILLARD, Robert. Dictionary of Modern Sculpture. 1962. $7.95. Tudor

MONRO, Isabel Stevenson. Index to Reproductions of American Paintings. 1948. $8.50. Wilson

PIERSON, William H. Jr., & DAVIDSON, Martha. The Arts of the United States. 1960. $9.95. McGraw-Hill

REINACH, Salomon. Apollo; An Illustrated Manual of the History of Art Throughout the Ages. 1935. $3.00. Scribner

WHITTICK, Arnold. Symbols, Signs, and Their Meaning. 1960. $10.00. London

Music and Opera

APEL, Willi. Harvard Dictionary of Music. 1944. $9.50. Harvard

BAKER, Theodore. Baker's Biographical Dictionary of Musicians. 5th edition. 1958. $18.00. Schirmer

BROCKWAY, Wallace. The World of Opera. 1962. $10.00. Pantheon

EWEN, David. The Book of European Light Opera. 1962. $7.50. Holt

EWEN, David. Composers of Yesterday. 1937. $5.00. Wilson

EWEN, David. Living Musicians. 1940. $5.00. Wilson

EWEN, David. Popular American Composers. 1962. $7.00. Wilson

GRAVE, Sir George. Dictionary of Music, and Musicians. 5th edition, 10 vols. 1954. $142.00. St. Martins Press

HARTNOLL, Phyllis. The Oxford Companion to the Theater. 2nd ed. 1957. 11.50. Oxford U.P.

KOBBE, Gustav. Complete Opera Book. 1954. $10.00. Putnam

LANG, Paul Henry, & BETTMANN, Otto. A Pictorial History of Music. 1961. $10.00. Norton

McSPADDEN, J. Walker. Operas and Musical Comedies. 3rd edition. 1955. $4.50. Crowell

MARTIN, George Whitney. The Opera Companion. 1961. $12.50. Dodd, Mead

THOMPSON, Oscar. International Cyclopedia of Music and Musicians. 8th edition. 1956. $25.00. Dodd

DRAMA

LOVELL, John. Digests of Great American Plays. 1961. $5.95. Crowell

LITERATURE

BAUGH, Albert C. ed. A Literary History of England. Century-Crofts. $14.95. Appleton

BENET, William Rose. The Reader's Encyclopedia. 1955. $7.95. Crowell

BERNHARDT, William F., ed. Granger's Index to Poetry. 1962. $65.00. Columbia

CAMBRIDGE BIBLIOGRAPHY OF ENGLISH LITERATURE. ed. by F.W. Aateson 1957. $45.00. Cambridge U.P.

CAMBRIDGE HISTORY OF ENGLISH LITERATURE. ed. by A.W. Ward and A.R. Waller. 1932. $65.00. Cambridge U.P.

COLUMBIA DICTIONARY OF MODERN EUROPEAN LITERATURE. Horatio Smith, ed. 1947. $10.00. Columbia Univ. Press

COOK, Doroth Y, and MUNRO, I.S. Short Story Index. N.Y. Wilson. 1953. $14.00

HAYDN, Hiram & Fuller, Edmund, Thesaurus of Book Digests. 1949. pap. $1.95. Crown

HOFFMAN, Hester R. Reader's Adviser and Bookman's Manual. 9th ed. 1960. $15.00

HOME BOOK OF MODERN VERSE. An Extension of the Home Book of Verse. 1950. $10.00. Holt

LITERARY HISTORY OF THE UNITED STATES. Ed. by Robert E. Spiller and others. 1948. 1 vol. ed. $8.75. Bibliography and Supplement, 1962, $12.50. Macmillan

LOGASA, Hannah, and VER NOOY, Winfred. Index to One-Act Plays. 1924-50. 4 v. $7.50 ea. Faxon

MAGILL, F.N. Masterpieces of World Literature in Digest form. 3 series. $8.50 ea. Harper

OTTEMILLER, John H. Index to Plays in Collections. 3rd ed. 1957. $9.50. Scarecrow Press

OXFORD DICTIONARY OF QUOTATIONS. 2nd ed. Oxford Univ. Press. 1953. $10.50.

SHIPLEY, Joseph Twadell. Dictionary of World Literature. Criticism Forms-Technique. Philosophical Library. 1953. $7.50. Littlefield

STEVENSON, Burton Egbert. Home Book of Quotations, Classical and Modern 9th ed. 1959. $25.00. Dodd

STEVENSON, Burton Egbert. Home Book of Verse. 9th ed. 1953. 2 v. $25.00. Holt

THRALL, W.F. & ADDISON, Hibbard. A Handbook to Literature. rev. ed. 1960. 3.75. Odyssey

WEST, Dorothy H. and PEAKE, D.M. Play Index. 1949-1952. 1953. $5.00. Wilson

Literature (Dictionaries)

CASSELL'S ENCYCLOPEDIA OF WORLD LITERATURE. Ed. by Sigfried H. Steinbert. 1954. 2 v. $25.00. Funk

BURKE, WILLIAM JERMIAH, AND HOWE, W.D. eds. American Authors and Books Crown. 1943. $8.50

HART, JAMES DAVID. Oxford Companion to American Literature. 3rd ed. 1956. $10.00. Oxford U.P.

OXFORD CLASSICAL DICTIONARY. Ed. by M. Cary and Others. $13.50. Oxford U.P.

OXFORD COMPANION TO CLASSICAL LITERATURE. 2nd ed. by Paul Harvey. $4.50. Oxford U.P.

OXFORD COMPANION TO ENGLISH LITERATURE. 3rd ed. Paul Harvey, editor. 1946. Oxford U.P. $10.00

Literature Quotations

HOYT, JEHIEL KEELER. New Cyclopedia of Practical Quotations. Rev. ed. 1922. $7.50. Funk

BARTLETT, JOHN. Familiar Quotations. 1955. $10.00. Little

SMITH, WILLIAM GEORGE. Oxford Dictionary of English Proverbs. 2nd ed. by Sir Paul Harvey. Oxford Univ. Press. 1948. $7.20.

STEVENSON, BURTON EGBERT. Home Book of Proverbs, Maxims, and Familiar Phrases. 1948. $35.00. Macmillan

BREWER'S DICTIONARY OF PHRASE AND FABLE. Brewer, E.C. 1953. $5.95. Harper

ADAMS, J. T. Album of American History. 1944-49. 5 v. $46.50. Scribner
ADAMS, JAMES TRUSLOW. Atlas of American History. 1943. $15.00. Scribner
ADAMS, J. T. ed. Dictionary of American History. 2nd ed. 1942. 6 v. $60.00.
  Scribner
ANNUAL REGISTER OF WORLD EVENTS. 1961. $25.00. St. Martins Press
BOYD, ANDREW. Atlas of World Affairs, rev. ed. 1959. $3.50. Praeger
COMMAGER, H. S. Ed. Documents of American History. 6th ed. 1958. $6.50.
  Appleton-Crofts
FACTS ON FILE. Yearbooks. 1943. $30.00 ea.
GUIDE TO HISTORICAL LITERATURE. ed. by George F. Howe and Others. $16.50
  Macmillan
HANDLIN, OSCAR. Harvard Guide to American History. 1954. $10.00. Belknap
  Harvard
LANGER, WILLIAM L. An Encyclopaedia of World History, Ancient, Medieval,
  and Modern, Chronologically Arranged. Rev. Ed. Houghton. 1952. $9.00
MORRIS, R. B. ed. Encyclopaedia of World History, Rev. Ed. 1961. $8.95. Harper
PUTNAM, GEORGE PALMER AND PUTNAM, GEORGE HAVEN. Dictionary of
  Events; A Handbook of Universal History. 1936. $10.00. Grosset and Dunlap
SHEPHERD, WILLIAM ROBERT. Historical Atlas. 8th ed. N. Y. Barnes & Noble
  1956. $15.00

Bibliographies and Dictionaries

MARTIN, MICHAEL, RHETA AND LOVETT, G. H. An Encyclopedia of Latin-
  American History. 1956. $5.00. N. Y. Abelard-Schuman
MOTT, FRANK LUTHER. History of American Magazines. 1930-57. 4 vols. v. 1,
  $10.00. v. 2, $8.50. v. 3, $9.00. v. 4, $12.50. Cambridge, Harvard U. P.

BIOGRAPHICAL SOURCES

AMERICAN AUTHORS, 1600-1900. 1938. $6.00. Wilson
AMERICAN MEN OF SCIENCE. Ed. Jaques Cattell. 10th ed. $25.00. Cattell
BIOGRAPHY INDEX. A Cumulative Index to Biographical Material in Books and
  Magazines. 4 vols. 1946-48. Vol 5. 1958-61. Sold on Service Basis. Wilson
BRITISH AUTHORS BEFORE 1800. 1952. $6.00. Wilson
BRITISH AUTHORS OF THE NINETEENTH CENTURY. 1955. $5.00. Wilson
CHAMBERS BIOGRAPHICAL DICTIONARY. The Great of All Nations and All
  Times. Rev. by J.O. Horne. $15.00. St. Martins
CONTEMPORARY AUTHORS. 1962. $25.00. Gale Press
CURRENT BIOGRAPHY. Who's News and Why. 1940-date. N. Y. Wilson. 1940-date
  Service basis
CURRENT BIOGRAPHY. Yearbooks, 1946-1961. $7.00 ea. Wilson
DEFORD, MIRIAM A. Who Was When? A Dictionary of Contemporaries. 1950.
  $6.00. Wilson
DICTIONARY OF AMERICAN BIOGRAPHY. Ed. by Allen Johnson and Dumas Malone.
  1928-44. 21 vols. and Index, $184.00. Scribner
DIRECTORY OF AMERICAN SCHOLARS. Ed. Jaques Cattell. 3rd ed. $20.00.
  Bowker
DICTIONARY OF NATIONAL BIOGRAPHY. Ed. Sir Leslie Stephen and Sir Sidney
  Lee. Inc. 1882-1949. 22 vols. (Including 1st Supplement) $208.00. Supplements
  2,3,4.5, $960 ea. Supplement 6.16.80, Concise Dictionary 2 pts, pt. 1, to
  1900, $9.60 ea., pt. 2, 1901-1950, $6.75. Oxford Univ. Press
THE INTERNATIONAL WHO'S WHO. Rev. Annually. $22.00. Int. Pub. Service
KUNTZ, STANLEY J., AND HAYCRAFT, HOWARD. Twentieth Century Authors;
  a biographical Dictionary of Modern Literature. 1942. $8.50. Wilson

MAGILL, FRANK N. Ed. Cyclopedia of World Authors. 1958. $8.95. Harper
NEW CENTURY CYCLOPEDIA OF NAMES. N.Y. Appleton, 1954. 3 vols. $39.50.
TWENTIETH CENTURY AUTHORS. First Supplement. ed. Stanley J. Kunitz.
  1955. $8.00. Wilson
WEBSTER'S BIOGRAPHICAL DICTIONARY. 1943. $8.50. Merriam
WHO WAS WHO, 1941-50. (English) Macmillan. $15.00.
WHO WAS WHO IN AMERICA. A companion Biographical Reference Work to
  Who's Who in America. v. 1, 1897-1942. v. 2, 1943-53. 1942-50. $10.00.
  1951-60 $20.00 ea. Marquis
WHO'S WHO IN AMERICA. Vol 30, 1958-59. A.N. Marquis Co. 1959. $25.00
WHO'S WHO IN COMMERCE AND INDUSTRY. 12th International ed. 1961-62
  $24.00. Marquis
THE WORLD OF LEARNING. Europa Publications. $23.50.
WHO's WHO IN AMERICAN EDUCATION. By Robert C. Cook, and Mary A. Smith
  v. 1, 1928- Biennial. $10.00

ATLASES AND GAZETTEERS

ADAMS, JAMES TRUSLOW. Ed. R.V. Coleman. Atlas of American History
  1943, $15.00. Scribner
EKWALL, EILERT. Concise Oxford Dictionary of English Place names. $8.80.
  Oxford Univ. Press
ENCYCLOPAEDIA BRITANNICA WORLD ATLAS. 1962. $29.50. Encyclopedia
  Britannica
FOX, EDWARD W. ed. Atlas of European History. 1957. $7.00. Oxford U.P.
GOODE, JOHN PAUL. World Atlas; Physical, Political and Economic. 9th ed.
  by Edward B. Espenshade, Jr. 1953. $7.25. Chic. Rand
HAMMOND'S NEW INTERNATIONAL WORLD ATLAS. 1947. $2.95. Hammond
JORDAN, E.L. Nature Atlas of America. il. 1952. $9.95. Hammond
LORD, CLIFFORD L AND ELIZABETH LORD. Historical Atlas of the U.S. 1953.
  $5.50. Holt
PAULLIN, CHARLES O. Atlas of the Historical Geography of the United States.
  Ed. by John K. Wright. 1932. Carnegie Pub. #901. $15.00
RAND McNALLY & CO. Commercial Atlas and Marketing Guide. 89th ed. Chic.
  Rand, 1958. $45.00. Annually
RAND McNALLY & CO. Cosmopolitan World Atlas. 1962. $14.95. Rand McNally
SHEPHERD, WILLIAM R. Historical Atlas. 8th rev. ed. 1956. $15.00. Barnes
  & Noble
STEWART, GEORGE R. Names on the Land. rev. ed. 1958. $6.00. Houghton
TIMES ATLAS OF THE WORLD. 5 vols. ed. by John Bartholomew. 1960. $25.00. ea.
  Houghton
WEBSTER'S GEOGRAPHICAL DICTIONARY. 1955. $8.50. rev. ed. Merriam Co.,
  G. and C.
WRIGHT, J. KIRTLAND, AND PLATT, ELIZABETH. Aids to Geographical Research;
  Bibliographies, Periodicals, Atlases, Gazetteers and other Reference Books.
  2nd ed. 1947. $5.00. Columbia Univ. Press

Gazetteers

COLUMBIA LIPPINCOTT GAZETTEER OF THE WORLD. ed. by Leon E. Seltzer
  $65.00, including supple. Columbia U.P.

GOVERNMENT DOCUMENTS

BARNES, William. The Foreign Service of the United States, Origin, Development,
  and Functions. 1961. Wash., D.C. Dept. of State. $3.50
HISTORICAL STATISTICS OF THE UNITED STATES. 1789-1945. Washington
  Govt. Printing Office. 1949.

MONTHLY CATALOG OF UNITED STATES. Government Publications. $3.00.
MORRISON, D. G. , Criteria for the Establishment of 2-year Colleges. U. S.
Office of Education Bulletin. 1961.
U. S. AIR FORCE RESERVE OFFICERS' TRAINING CORPS. $3.00. Maxwell Air
Force Base, 1958.
U. S. BUREAU OF THE BUDGET. The Federal Budget in Brief. Annual
U. S. BUREAU OF THE CENSUS. Census of Business; Latest ed. G. P. O.
U. S. BUREAU OF THE CENSUS. Historical Statistics of the United States. 1960.
$6.00
U. S. BUREAU OF THE CENSUS. Statistical Abstract of the United States. 1878-
date. Washington Govt. Printing Office. $3.75.
U. S. BUREAU OF THE CENSUS. Census Catalog and Subject Guide. Washington
Govt. Pringint Office. 1945- Quarterly. $2.50 per yr.
U. S. BUREAU OF FOREIGN AND DOMESTIC COMMERCE. Foreign Commerce
yearbook. 1933, 1935-39- 1948-51. Washington Govt. Printing Office
U. S. COMMISSION ON CIVIL RIGHTS. Report 1959- (1959 report summary of
Commission 1957-59 $2.00. 1960 Reports. 5 vols. Voting, Education, Employ-
ment, Housing and Justice. $5.25.
U. S. COMMISSION ON ORGANIZATION OF THE EXECUTIVE BRANCH OF THE
GOVERNMENT. 1949. McGraw-Hill
U. S. CONGRESS. Biographical Directory of the American Congress, 1774-1927.
Washington Govt. Printing Office, 1928. $4.50
U. S. CONGRESS. Committee on Un-American Activities. Facts on Communism
1960- V. 1, The Communist Ideology. $.45, Vol. 2, The Soviet Union. $1.25.
U. S. CONGRESS. Senate. Committee on Labor and Public Welfare. Migratory
Labor. 1961-62.
U. S. CONGRESS. Official Congressional Directory... 1809-date. Washington Govt.
Printing Office.
U. S. CONSTITUTION. The Constitution of the United States of America, Analysis
and Interpretation. $6.25. 1953.
U. S. CONSTITUTION. The United States Constitution; text with analytical index...
$.30. 1961
U. S. DEPARTMENT OF AGRICULTURE. Yearbook of Agriculture. Various prices.
Annual. (GPO)
U. S. LAWS, STATUTES, ETC. Index to the Federal Statutes (1789-1873) (1874-
1931) Washington Govt. Printing Office, 1911-33, 2 vols. $3.50
U. S. LIBRARY OF CONGRESS. Descriptive Cataloging Division. Rules for
Descriptive Cataloging. $1.75. 1949. Supplement, $0.20, 1949-51.
U. S. LIBRARY OF CONGRESS. Division of Documents. 1910-date. Washington
Govt. Printing Office
U. S. LIBRARY OF CONGRESS. General Reference and Bibliography Division.
A Guide to the Study of the United States of America, 1960. $7.00. G. P. O.
U. S. LIBRARY OF CONGRESS. Subject Cataloging Division Music Subject Headings
used, 1952. $1.50
UNITED STATES GOVERNMENT ORGANIZATION MANUAL. Annual, $1.50. G. P. O.
U. S. OFFICE OF EDUCATION. Accreditation in Higher Education. $1.00. 1959.
U. S. OFFICE OF EDUCATION. Accredited Higher Institutions. Approximately
Every 4 years. Latest 11th ed. , 1960
U. S. OFFICE OF EDUCATION. Education Directory. Annual, 4 parts. $.70.
G. P. O.
U. S. OFFICE OF EDUCATION. Library Statistics of College and Universities.
Annual, $0.50. G. P. O.
U. S. POST OFFICE DEPARTMENT. United States Official Postal Guide 1874-
Washington Govt. Printing Office. Postal Manual. 1954- G. P. O.
U. S. PRESIDENT. Economic Report... $1.25. Annual G. P. O.
U. S. SUPERINTENDENT OF DOCUMENTS. Selected United States Government
Publications... 1928-date. Govt. Printing Office
U. S. SUPERINTENDENT OF DOCUMENTS. United States Government Printing
Publications. Monthly Catalog. 1895-Washington Govt. Printing Office

ONE HUNDRED AND FIFTY RECOMMENDED PERIODICALS
FOR THE JUNIOR COLLEGE LIBRARY

Abstracts of the English Studies. (National Council of Teachers of English) 1958. (10 times a year) $4.00. 508 S. Sixth St., Champaign, Illinois.

ALA Bulletin. Monthly (bi-monthly July-August) 50 E. Huron St., Chicago 11, Illinois, Membership.

American Academy of Political and Social Science. Annals. 1890— Bi-monthly. 3937 Chestnut St., Philadelphia 4, Pa. $7.00.

American Artist. 1937— Monthly (except July and August). Watson-Guptill Publications, Inc., 24 West 40th St., New York 18, N. Y. $7.00.

American Builder. 1905— Monthly, 30 Church St., New York 7, N. Y. $3.50.

American Economic Review. 1911— (5 times a year). Northwestern University, Evanston, Illinois, $6.00.

American Dietetic Association. 1925— Monthly, 620 N. Michigan Ave., Chicago 11, Ill. $8.00.

American Fabrics. 1946— Quarterly, 24 E. 38th Street, New York 16, N. Y. $12.00.

American Heritage. 1949— Bi-monthly, 551 Fifth Ave., New York 17, N. Y. $15.00.

American Historical Review. 1895— Quarterly. 60 Fifth Ave., New York 11, N. Y. $10.00.

American Home. 1928— Monthly. 300 Park Ave., New York 22, N. Y. $3.00.

American Journal of Nursing. 1900— Monthly. 10 Columbus Circle, New York 19, N. Y. $5.00.

American Journal of Psychology. 1887— Quarterly. Banta Publishing Co., Menasha, Wisconsin. $7.00.

American Journal of Sociology. 1895— Bi-monthly. 5750 Ellis Ave., Chicago 37, Illinois. $6.00.

American Literature. 1929— Quarterly. Duke University Press, Durham, N. C. $5.00.

American Political Science Review. 1906— Quarterly. 1726 Massachusetts Ave., N. W., Washington 6, D. C. $10.00.

American Speech. 1925— Quarterly. 2960 Broadway, New York 27, New York. $6.00.

Antioch Review. 1914— Quarterly. Yellow Springs, Ohio. $3.00.

Architectural Forum. 1892— Monthly. 9 Rockefeller Plaza, New York 20, N. Y. $6.50.

Architectural Record. 1891— Monthly. 119 W. 40th St., N.Y. 18, N.Y. $5.50.

Art News. 1902— Monthly. 32 East Fifty-seventh Street, New York 22, N. Y. $11.50.

Athletic Journal. 1921— Monthly (Sept.-June) 1719 Howard St., Evanston, Illinois, $2.00.

Atlantic Monthly. 1857— Monthly. 8 Arlington St., Boston 16, Mass. $7.50.

Audubon Magazine. 1899— Bi-monthly. 1130 Fifth Ave., New York 28, N. Y. $5.00.

Aviation Week. 1916— Weekly. 330 West 42nd St., New York 36, N. Y. $7.00.

Better Homes and Gardens. 1922— Monthly. 1716 Locust St., Meredith Building, Des Moines 3, Iowa. $3.00.

Booklist and Subscription Books Bulletin. 1905— Semi-monthly (monthly, August). 50 East Huron St., Chicago 11, Illinois. $6.00.

Bulletin of the Atomic Scientists. 1945— Monthly (except July and August). 5750 Ellis Ave., Chicago 37, Illinois. $6.00.

Business Education World. 1920— Monthly, (except July and August). 330 West 42nd St., New York 36, New York. $4.00.

Business Week. 1929— Weekly. 330 West 42nd Street, New York 36, N. Y. $6.00.

Catholic World. 1865— Monthly. 180 Barick St., N. Y. 14, N. Y. $6.00.

Changing Times. 1947— Monthly. 1729 H. St., N.W., Washington 6, D. C. $6.00.

Chemical and Engineering News. Weekly. 1155 Sixteenth St., N. W., Washington 6, D. C. $7.00.

Christian Century. 1884— Weekly. 407 South Deaborn St., Chicago 5, Illinois. $7.50.

College and Research Libraries. 1939— Bi-monthly. 1201-05 Bluff Street, Fulton, Missouri. $5.00.

College English. 1939— Monthly (except June-September). National Council of Teachers of English, 704 South Sixth St., Champaign, Illinois. $4.00.

Commonweal. 1924— Weekly. 386 Fourth Ave., New York 16, N. Y. $8.00.

Congressional Digest. 1921— Monthly (except July-August). 1631 K Street, N. W., Washington 6, D. C. $10.00.

Congressional Record. 1937— (Daily while Congress is in session). U. S. Government Printing Office, Washington 25, D. C. $1.50 per month.

Consumer Bulletin and Annal. 1931— Consumers' Research Inc., Washington, N. J. Monthly, $5.00.

Consumer Reports. 1936— Monthly. Consumers Union of U. S., Inc., 256 Washington Street, Mount Vernon, N. Y. $6.00.

Craft Horizons. 1941— Bi-monthly. 29 West 53rd Street, New York 19, N. Y. $6.00.

Current Biography. 1940— Monthly. (Sept.-July) 950 Univ. Ave., New York 52, N. Y. $6.00.

Current History. 1941— Monthly. 1822 Ludlow Street, Philadelphia 3, Pa. $7.50.

Dance Magazine. 1926— Monthly. 231 W. 58th Street, New York 19, N. Y. $6.00.

Department of State Bulletin. 1939— Weekly. U. S. Government Printing Office, Washington 25, D. C. $8.50.

Design. 1899— Bi-monthly (except July and August). 337 South High Street, Columbus, Ohio, $4.50.

Economic Geography. Quarterly. Clarke University. Worcester 10, Mass. $7.00.

Educational Theatre Journal. 1949— Quarterly. 10 Watson Place, Columbia, Missouri. $5.00.

English Journal. 1912— Monthly. (except Sept.-May) 508 South St., St. Champaign, Ill. $5.00.

Electronics World. 1919— Monthly. 434 South Wabash Ave., Chicago 5, Illinois. $5.00.

Federal Reserve Bulletin. 1915— Monthly. Board of Governors of the Federal Reserve System, Washington 25, D. C. $6.00.

Field and Stream. 1896— Monthly. 383 Madison Ave., New York, N. Y. $3.50.

Foreign Affairs. 1922— Quarterly. 58 East 68th Street, New York 21, N.Y. $6.00.

Flying. 1927— Monthly. 1 Park Ave., New York 16, N. Y. $5.00.

Fortune. 1930— Monthly. 540 North Michigan Avenue, Chicago 11, Illinois, $10.00.

Forum. (University News Service and Office of Development) 1956— Quarterly. University of Houston, Houston, Texas, $3.00.

French Review. 1927— (6 times a year) Mount Royal and Guilford Avenues, Baltimore 2, Maryland. $5.00.

German Quarterly. 1928— Quarterly. South Memorial Drive, Appleton. $5.50.

Germanic Review. 1926— Quarterly. 2960 Broadway, New York 27, N.Y. $6.00.

Good Housekeeping. 1885— Monthly. 57th Street at 8th Ave., New York 19, N. Y. $3.50.

Harper's Magazine. 1850— Monthly. 49 East 33rd Street, New York 16, N. Y. $6.00.

Harvard Business Review. Bi-monthly. 1922— Soldiers Field, Boston 63, Mass. $10.00.

Higher Education. 1945— Monthly (except June-August). U. S. Government Printing Office, Washington 25, D. C. $.75.

Hispania. 1948— Quarterly. Depauw University, Greecastle, Ind. $5.00.

Holiday. 1946— Monthly. Independence Square, Philadelphia 5, Pa. $5.95.

Horizon. 1958— Bi-monthly. 551 Fifth Avenue, New York 17, N. Y. $18.00.

House Beautiful. 1896— Monthly. 250 West 55th St., New York 19, N. Y. $6.00.

Industrial Arts and Vocational Education. 1914— Monthly (except July and August) 400 North Broadway, Milwaukee 1, Wisconsin. $3.75.

Journal of Applied Psychology. 1917— Bi-monthly. 1333 Sixteenth St., N.W., Washington 6, D. C. $10.00.

Journal of Chemical Education. 1924— Monthly. 20th & Northampton Sts., Easton, Pa. $4.00.

Journal of Educational Research. 1920— (9 times a year) Dembar Publications, Inc., Box 737, Madison 3, Wisconsin. $7.50.

Journal of Geography. 1902—Monthly (except June-August) 3333 Elston Ave., Chicago 18, Illinois. $5.00.

Journal of Health - Physical Education - Recreation. 1896— Monthly (except bi-monthly May-June; not pub. July-August) 1201 Sixteenth St., N.W. Washington 6, D. C. $10.00.

Journal of Higher Education. 1930— Monthly. (except July-September) Ohio State University Press, Columbus 10, Ohio. $6.00.

Journal of Home Economics. 1909— Monthly (except July and August) 1600 Twentieth St., N.W., Washington 8, D.C. $6.00.

Journal of Modern History. 1929— Quarterly. Univ. of Chicago, 5750 Ellis Ave., Chicago 37, Illinois. $7.50.

Junior College Journal. 1930— Monthly. (except June-August) 1785 Massachusetts Ave., N. W., Washington 6, D. C. $4.00.

The Kenyon Review. 1939—Quarterly. Kenyon College, Gambier, Ohio. $4.00.

Library Journal. 1876— Semi-Monthly (monthly in July and August) 62 West 45th St., New York 36, N. Y. $10.00.

Library Resources and Technical Services. 1957— Quarterly. 50 E. Huron Street, Chicago 11, Illinois, $5.00.

Library Trends. 1952— Quarterly. University of Illinois Library School, Urbana, Illinois, $5.00.

Life. 1936— Weekly. 540 North Michigan Ave., Chicago, Illinois. $5.95.

Look. 1937— Bi-weekly. Look Building, Des Moines 4, Iowa. $4.00.

Mademoiselle. 1935— Monthly. 304 East 45th St., New York 17, N. Y. $5.00.

Marriage and Family Living. 1938— Quarterly. George Banta and Co., Menasha, Wisconsin, $7.50.

Mathematics Teacher. 1908— Monthly (except June-September) National Council of Teachers of Mathematics, 1201 Sixteenth St., N. W., Washington 6, D. C. $6.00.

Mental Hygiene. 1917— Quarterly. 10 Columbus Circle, New York 19, N. Y. $6.00.

Modern Language Association of America. 1884— (5 times a year) 6 Washington Square, North, New York 3, N. Y. $10.00.

The Modern Language Journal. 1956— Monthly (except June-September) 450 Ahnaip St., Menasha, Wisconsin, $4.00.

Monthly Labor Review. 1915— Monthly. U. S. Government Printing Office, Washington 25, D. C. $6.25.

Musical America. 1998— Monthly. (except semi-monthly Nov., Dec., & Jan.) 34 North Crystal St., E. Stroudsburg, Penn. $5.00.

Musical Quarterly. Quarterly. 3 East 43rd St., New York 17, N.Y., $5.00.

Nation. 1865— Weekly. (except for omission of four summer issues) 333 Sixth Ave., New York 14. $8.00.

National Education Association Journal. 1913—Monthly (except June-August) 1201 16th St., N. W., Washington 6, D. C. Membership.

NEA Research Division Reports and Monographs. 1923— (4 times a year) 1201 Sixteenth St., N.W., Washington 6, D. C. $2.00.

National Geographic Magazine. 1889— Monthly. 16th and M Street, Washington 6, D.C. $8.00.

Nation's Business. 1912— Monthly. 1615 H. St., N. W., Washington 6, D. C. $18.00.

Natural History. 1900— Monthly. (bi-monthly, June-September) Central Park West at 79th St., New York 24, N. Y. $5.00.

New Republic. Weekly. (except for omissions of four summer issues) 1244 19th St., N.W., Washington 6, D. C. $8.00.

New York Times Book Review. 1896— Weekly. Times Square, New York 36, N. Y. $6.50.

New York Times Magazine. 1896— Weekly. Times Square, New York 36, N.Y.
New Yorker. 1925— 25 West 43rd St., New York 36, N. Y. $7.00.
Newsweek. 1933— Weekly. 350 Dennison Ave., Dayton 1, Ohio. $6.00.
Nursing Outlook. 1953— Monthly. 10 Columbus Circle, New York 19, N. Y. $5.00.
Opera News. 1936— Weekly. 654 Madison Ave., New York 21, N. Y. $6.00.
Overview. 1960— Monthly. 470 Park Ave., S., New York 16, N. Y. $5.00.
P.M.L.A. 1884— (5 times a year.) 6 Washington Square, New York 3, N. Y. $10.00.
Parents' Magazine and Family Home Guide. 1926—Monthly. Bergenfield, New Jersey, $4.00.
Personnel and Guidance Journal. 1921— Monthly (except June-August) 1605 New Hampshire Ave., N.W., Washington 9, D. C. $9.00.
Poetry. 1912— Monthly. 1018 North State St., Chicago 10, Illinois. $5.00.
Political Science Quarterly. 1886— (4 times a year) Columbia University, New York 27, N. Y. $6.00.
Popular Photography. 1937— Monthly. 434 South Wabash Ave., Chicago 5, Illinois, $5.00.
Popular Science Monthly. 1872— Monthly. 355 Lexington Ave., New York 17, N. Y. $3.40.
Popular Mechanics Magazine. 1902— Monthly. 200 E. Ontario St., Chicago 11, Illinois, $3.50.
Practical Home Economics. 1956— (9 times a year) 33 W. 42nd Street, New York 22, N. Y. $3.50.
Publishers' Weekly. 1872— Weekly. 3rd and Hunting Park Ave., Philadelphia 40, Pa.
Quarterly Journal of Speech. 1915— (4 times a year) Indiana Univ. Bloomington, Ind. $5.50.
Reader's Digest. 1922— Monthly. Pleasantville, N. Y. $4.00.
Reader's Digest (French edition) Selection du Reader's Digest. 1947— Monthly. 1015 Cote du Beaver Hall, Montreal, Quebec. $4.00.
Reader's Digest (German edition) Das Beste aus Reader's Digest. 1948— Monthly. Stuttgart W, Paulinenatrasse 44, Germany.
Reader's Digest (Spanish edition) Seleciones del Reader's Digest. 1940— Monthly. Call 23 # 105, Vedado, Havana, Cuba. $3.85.
Recreation. 1907— Monthly. (except July and August) 8 West Eight St., New York 11, N. Y. $5.00.
The Reporter. 1949— Fortnightly. 136 East 57th St., New York 22, N. Y. $6.00.
Review of Educational Research. 1931— (5 times a yr.) 1201 6th St., N.W. Washington, D. C.
Sales Management. 1918— (6 times a year) 630 Third Ave., New York 17, N. Y. $7.00.
Saturday Evening Post. 1728— Weekly. Independence Square, Philadelphia 5, Pa. $5.95.
Saturday Review. 1924— Weekly. 25 West 4th St., New York 36, N. Y. $7.00.
School and Society. 1915— Bi-weekly. (except July and August) 1834 Broadway, New York 23, N. Y. $7.50.
School Arts. 1901— Monthly. (except July and August) Printers Building, Worcester 8, Massachusetts. $6.00.
School Life. 1918— Monthly. (except June-August) U. S. Government Office, Washington 25, D. C. $1.75.
Science. 1883— Weekly. 1515 Massachusetts Ave., N. W., Washington 5, D. C. $8.50.
Science Digest. 1937— Monthly. 200 East Ontario St., Chicago 11, Illinois. $3.50.
Science News Letter. 1921— Weekly. 1719 N. St., N. W., Washington 6, D.C. $5.50.
Sewanee Review. 1892— Quarterly. Univ. of the South, Sewanee, Tennessee, $4.00.
Scientific American. 1845— Monthly. 415 Madison Ave., New York 17, N. Y. $6.00.

Sky and Telescope. 1941— Monthly. Harvard College Observatory, Cambridge 38, Mass. $5.00.
Sports Illustrated. 1954— Weekly. 540 North Michigan Ave., Chicago 11, Illinois. $6.75.
Survey of Current Business. 1921— Monthly. U. S. Government Printing Office. Washington 25, D. C. $4.00.
Theatre Arts. 1916— Monthly. 1421 East Main St., Saint Charles, Illinois, $7.50.
Time. 1923— Weekly. 520 North Michigan Ave., Chicago 11, Illinois. $7.00.
The Times Literary Supplement. Weekly. (Times, London) 25 E. 54th St., N. Y. 22, N. Y. $7.50.
Todays Health. 1923— Monthly. 535 North Dearborn St., Chicago 10, Illinois. $4.00.
Travel. 1901— Monthly. 50 West 57th St., New York 19, N. Y. $5.00.
United Nations Review. 1954— Monthly. Columbia University Press, 2960 Broadway, New York 27, N. Y. $6.00.
United States News and World Report. 1933— Weekly. 2300 N. St., N. W., Washington 7, D. C. $7.00.
Vital Speeches of the Day. 1934— Semi-monthly. 33 West 42nd St., New York 36, N. Y. $7.00.
Wilson Library Bulletin. 1914— Monthly (except July-August) 950-972 University Ave., New York 52, N. Y. $4.00.
The Writer. 1887— Monthly. 8 Arlington St., Boston 16, Mass. $4.00.
Yale Review. 1911— Quarterly. Yale University Press, 28 Hillhouse Ave., New Haven. $4.00.

CONTRIBUTORS

The following contributors were responsible for coordinating the book selection work of over 2600 subject specialists and librarians.

EUGENIA ADAMSON, Librarian, Virginia Intermont College, Bristol, Virginia
SISTER MARY ANN, Librarian, Sisters of St. Francis, Duns Scotus Library, Sylvania, Ohio
ELLA B. ANDERSON, Librarian, Bethany Lutheran College Library, Mankato, Minnesota
ERNEST R. ANDERSON, Highline College, Seattle 88, Washington
DONALD J. ANDREKOVICK, Librarian, Pennsylvania State University, Dubois, Pennsylvania
THERON H. ATKINSON, Librarian, Ricks College, Rexburg, Idaho
FRANCES ATWOOD, Librarian, Lasell Junior College, Auburndale 66, Massachusetts
MARGARET S. ATWOOD, Librarian, York Junior College, York, Pennsylvania
HARRY BACH, Librarian, Riverside City College, Riverside, California
MARGARET BATTLE, Librarian, Suwannee River Junior College, Madison, Florida
DOROTHY GRACE BECK, Librarian, Fort Smith Junior College, Fort Smith, Arkansas
BARBARA BELL, Librarian, Grand View College, Des Moines 16, Iowa
LEROY BERG (Subject Specialist), College Of The Sequoias, Visalia, California
FRANCES BERKIHISER, Librarian, Evangel College, Springfield 2, Missouri
MARIE BEZOLD, Librarian, Independent School District No. 697, Eveleth, Minnesota
ORA BIZZELL, Librarian, Hiwassee College, Madisonville, Tennessee
MATTIE BLACKWELL, Librarian, Connors State Agricultural College, Warner, Oklahoma
WARD BLANCHARD, Librarian, Southwestern College, Chula Vista, California
IMOGENE I. BOOK, Librarian, Mt. Vernon Community College, Mt. Vernon, Illinois
MARCIA BRADSHAW, Librarian, Mitchell College, Statesville, North Carolina
MARGARET BRIDGES, Librarian, Mars Hill College Library, Mars Hill, North Carolina
HARLAN C. BROWN, Librarian, St. Mary's Junior College, Raleigh, North Carolina
HELEN ABLE BROWN, Librarian, St. Mary's Junior College, Raleigh, North Carolina
M. M. BROWN, Librarian, Roosevelt Junior College, West Palm Beach, Florida
KATHERINE M. BRUBECK, Librarian, Baltimore Junior College, Baltimore 15, Maryland
OSBORNE Y. BRULAND, Librarian, Waldorf College, Forest City, Iowa
VIRGINIA BUCHANAN, Librarian, Montreat-Anderson College, Montreat, North Carolina
ANNALEE M. BUNDY, Librarian, The College of Guam, Agana, Guam
RUTH CAGLEY, Librarian, Canton Community College Library, Canton, Illinois
LOUISE CAHN, Librarian, Fresno City College Library, Fresno 4, California
MARGARET CAMPAGNA, Librarian, Burdett College, Boston 16, Massachusetts
CATHERINE CARDEW, Librarian, Briarcliff College, Briarcliff Manor, New York
LORRAINE CARTER, Librarian, Olympic College, Bremerton, Washington
ANNABETH CASH, Librarian, Sullins College, Bristol, Virginia
MOTHER M. JANE CHANTAL R.S.H.M., Librarian, Marymount Junior College, Arlington 7, Virginia
CLARA CLEAVELAND, Librarian, Penn Hall Junior College, Chambersburg, Pennsylvania
LORRAINE A. CLINE, Librarian, Fergus Falls Junior College, Fergus Falls, Minnesota
GERALDINE COLLINS, Librarian, Paul Smith's College, Paul Smiths, New York
SISTER MARY CONSUELO, C.R.S.M., Librarian, Gwynedd-Mercy Junior College, Gwynedd Valley, Pennsylvania
L. GRIFFIN COPELAND, Librarian, Florida Christian College, Temple Terrace, Florida
CARMELA A. COREY, Librarian, Los Angeles Metropolitan College of Business, Los Angeles 15, California
CARLISLE CROSS, Subject Specialist, Pensacola Junior College, Pensacola, Florida
MILDRED S. COUNCILL, Librarian, Mount Olive Junior College, Mount Olive, North Carolina
ALICE COX, Librarian, Clarke Memorial College, Newton, Mississippi
DOROTHY R. CRAWFORD, Librarian, Mecklenburg College Library, Charlotte, North Carolina
SARA CRITTENDEN, Head Librarian, St. Petersburg Junior College, St. Petersburg 10, Florida
LELAND COREY, Librarian, Hannibal-Language College Extension Center, St. Louis 10, Maryland
H. E. DAVIS, Librarian, Wright Junior College, Chicago 34, Illinois
DOUGLAS DAY, Subject Specialist, University of Virginia, Charlottesville, Virginia
L. R. DE GARMO, Librarian, Compton College, Compton, California
NOYES DEVOR, Librarian, Central College Library, McPherson, Kansas

ARMAND J. DE ROSSET, Librarian, Frederick Community College, Frederick, Maryland
PAUL T. DIETZ, Librarian, Concordia College, Milwaukee 8, Wisconsin
EVA J. DIXON, Librarian, Chipola College, Marianna, Florida
ALMA DOBBERFUHL, Librarian, Concordia College and High School, Portland, Oregon
JOHN B. DOOLEY, Head Librarian, Chabot College, San Leandro, California
MABEL N. DORSETT, Librarian, Holmes Junior College, Goodman, Mississippi
NORMAN DUPREY, Librarian, Becker Junior College, Worcester 9, Massachusetts
MARY JOINES DURHAM, Librarian, Norman College, Norman Park, Georgia
HELEN M. EALS, Librarian, Lower Columbia Junior College, Longview, Washington
HELEN K. EARNSHAW, Librarian, Los Angeles Trade Technical College, Los Angeles 15, California
J. S. EBLE, (Mrs.), Librarian, Highland Park Junior College, Highland Park 3, Michigan
RUTH G. EDDY, Librarian, Fisher Junior College, Boston 16, Massachusetts
SHIRLEY EDSALL, Librarian, Corning Community College Library, Corning, New York
PEARL ELLIS, Librarian, Southwestern Bible Institute, Waxahachie, Texas
GEORGE ELSER, Librarian, Chaffey College, Alta Loma, California
LOIS ENGLER, Librarian, Bismarck Junior College, Bismarck, North Dakota
MARIE L. ERWIN, Librarian, Sacramento City College, Sacramento 22, California
HARRY E. FOSTER, Librarian, Anne Arundel Community College, Severna Park, Maryland
GEORGE A. FOX, Librarian, Joliet Township High School and Junior College, Joliet, Illinois
ELIZABETH G. FREEMAN, Librarian, Wilmington College Library, Wilmington, North Carolina
FLY, (MRS.) Librarian, Cumberland University, Cumberland, Tennessee
ANGELA GARRETT, Librarian, Northwest Community College, Powell, Wyoming
MARGARET GIBBS, Librarian, Decatur Baptist College, Decatur, Texas
CAROLYN H. GODDARD, Librarian, Franklin Institute of Boston, Boston 16, Massachusetts
DON GRAY, Librarian, University Of Minnesota, Morris, Minnesota
MACY B. GRAY, Librarian, Georgia Southwestern College, Americus, Georgia
GLADYS Y. GREENE, Librarian, Volusia County Community College, Daytona Beach, Florida
ETHLYN GREENWOOD, Librarian, Bay Path Junior College, Longmeadow, Massachusetts
SARA M. GREGORY, Librarian, Emory At Oxford, Oxford, Georgia
ALICE B. GRIFFITH, Librarian, Mohawk Valley Technical Institute At Utica, Utica, New York
JAMES GUEST, Subject Specialist, Pensacola Junior College, Pensacola, Florida
SISTER JUSTINA GROTHE S.M.I.C., Librarian, Tombrock Junior College, Paterson, New Jersey
MARY GUM, Librarian, Belleville Junior College, Belleville, Illinois
THELMA GUNNING, Librarian, Eastern Oklahoma Agricultural and Mechanical College, Wilburton, Oklahoma
JULE F. HARTWICK (MR.), Librarian, Alpena Community College, Alpena, Michigan
GRACE HATHCOCK, Librarian, Alamogordo Community College, Alamogordo, New Mexico
IRENE D. HEAPS, Librarian, Hershey Junior College, Hershey, Pennsylvania
EDITH HEGWER, Librarian, Casper College, Casper, Wyoming
SISTER MARY HELEN, RSM, Librarian, Mercy Junior College, St. Louis 31, Missouri
WILLIAM HESSEL, Librarian, Community College Library, Venton Harbor, Michigan
DOROTHY HICKS, Librarian, The Southern Union College, Wadley, Alabama
ELOISE HILBERT, Librarian, Auburn Community College, Auburn, New York
GRACE HILDERBRAND, Librarian, The Packer Collegiate Institute, Brooklyn, New York
GAY HILDRETH, Librarian, Pensacola Junior College, Pensacola, Florida
JOHN J. HODNETT, Rev. C.M., Librarian, Saint Joseph's College, Princeton, New Jersey
JOHN HOFEN, Subject Specialist, Pensacola Junior College, Pensacola, Florida
LAUREL HOLCOMB, Librarian, Olympic College, Bremerton, Washington
ELIZABETH J. HOLDER, Librarian, Brevard College, Brevard, North Carolina
BETTY HOLIFIELD, Librarian, Utica Junior College, Utica, Mississippi
LOUISE HOLZAPFEL, Librarian, Allegany Community College, Cumberland, Maryland
B. C. HOMEYER, Librarian, The Zachary Taylor Library, Brownsville, Texas
MONROE HOPKINS, Librarian, Hannibal-LaGrange College, Hannibal, Missouri
LOIS HOWARD, Librarian, Gibbs Junior College, St. Petersburg 12, Florida
ORA HUGHES, Librarian, Washington Junior College, Pensacola, Florida
RALPH HUNT, Subject Specialist, Pensacola Junior College, Pensacola, Florida
GEORGE HYNES, Librarian, North Dakota School Of Forestry, Bottineau, North Dakota
MERLE INGLI, Rochester Junior College, Rochester, Minnesota
LOUISE JACKSON, Librarian, Gordon Military College, Barnesville, Georgia

BROOKS A. JENKINS, Librarian, Clark College, Vancouver, Washington
MINNIE JOHNSON, Librarian, Chicago Teachers College Library, Chicago 12, Illinois
NELLIE E. JOHNSON, Librarian, Brewton-Parker College Library, Mount Vernon, Georgia
W. T. JOHNSTON, Librarian, Abraham Baldwin Agricultural College, Tifton, Georgia
MARY C. JONES, Librarian, Henry Duckworth Library, Young Harris, Georgia
SISTER M. BERNARD JOSEPH, Librarian, Mount Saint Mary College, Newburgh, New York
HAZEL KEENER, Librarian, Christian College, Columbia, Missouri
LIBBIE KESSLER, Librarian, Delta College Library, University Center, Michigan
JOHN J. KIRVAN, Resident Librarian, St. Peter's College Library, Baltimore 29, Maryland
ROBERT KLASSEN, Librarian, Pacific Collége, Fresno 2, California
ADELE KNEPLEY, Librarian, Valley Forge Military Academy, Wayne, Pennsylvania
G. A. KORNTHEUER, Librarian, St. John's College, Winfield, Kansas
A. W. LANGERAK, Dean, Webster City Junior College, Webster City, Iowa
CHARLES L. LAUBENTHAL, Head, Technical Processes, Pensacola Junior College, Pensacola, Florida
JULIAN LEGERE, (FATHER) Librarian, Father Judge Mission Seminary Library, Monroe, Virginia
CHRIS LEGGE, Librarian, Bradford Junior College, Bradford, Massachusetts
FERN LEOPOLD, Librarian, Skagit Valley College, Mount Vernon, Washington
HELEN M. LEWIS, Librarian, Clinch Valley College, Wise, Virginia
ODEAL LOCKE, Librarian, Cameron State Agricultural College, Lawton, Oklahoma
ARTHUR LONG, Librarian, Fort Lewis A & M College, Durango Colorado
FLORA H. MACKENZIE, Librarian, Mary Holmes Junior College, West Point, Mississippi
GENE MAGNER, Librarian, State University Of New York, Morrisville, New York
SISTER THIRISE MARIE, S.N.D. Librarian, Villa Julie College, Stevenson, Maryland
SISTER MARIETTA, P.B.V.M. Librarian, Presentation Junior College, Aberdeen, South Dakota
JESSIE MATHEWS, Librarian, Rutgers University Law Library, Camden 2, New Jersey
MARJORIE MAULDING, Librarian, Kellogg Community College Library, Battle Creek, Michigan
MURIEL B. McCALL, Librarian, Armstrong College Of Savannah, Savannah, Georgia
IONE WILLIAMS McCLAIN, Librarian, Sheridan College Library, Sheridan, Wyoming
JAMES F. MCCOY, Librarian, Trenton Junior College, Trenton 8, New Jersey
MAURINE MCINNIS, Librarian, Mississippi Delta Junior College, Moorhead, Mississippi
FRANCES L. MEALS, Librarian, Colby Junior College, New London, New Hampshire
ROGER M. MILLER, Librarian, Centralia Junior College, Centralia, Washington
PEARL JEFFORDS MINOR, Librarian, Mason City Junior College Library, Mason City, Iowa
RUTH K. MITCHELL, Librarian, Milwaukee School Of Engineering, Milwaukee 1, Wisconsin
NORMA J. MONGEON, Librarian, Worcester Junior College, Worcester 8, Massachusetts
HELEN-JEAN MOORE, Librarian, Point Park Junior College, Pittsburgh 22, Pennsylvania
WOODY S. MOORE (MRS.), Librarian, The Marion Institute, Marion, Alabama
SISTER M. THOMAS MORE, Librarian, Sisters of St. Francis Dun Scotus Library, Sylvania, Ohio
SISTER MYRA, Librarian, Immaculata Junior College, Washington, D. C.
THEODORA B. NEWLANDS, (MRS.), Librarian, Hartford College, Hartford 5, Connecticut
INDIA A. NEWTON, (MISS), Librarian, Shasta College, Redding, California
WILLIAM J. NICHOLS, Librarian, Dutchess Community College, Poughkeepsie, N.Y.
LEON NOVAR, Librarian, Wilson Junior College, Chicago, Illinois
HUMPHREY A. OLSEN, Librarian, Vincennes University, Vincennes, Indiana
ROBERT S. PALM, (Mrs.), Librarian, Leicester Junior College, Leicester, Massachusetts
J. CARLYLE PARKER, Librarian, The Church College of Hawaii, Laie, Hawaii
MARY G. PARKER, Librarian, State University of New York, Canton, New York
NORMA LEE PECK, Librarian, Multnomah College, Portland 5, Oregon
DON S. PELKEY, Librarian, The Lansing Libraries, Lansing 33, Michigan
MYRNA PERRY, Librarian, Freed-Hardeman College, Henderson, Tennessee
DOROTHY POTEAT, Librarian, Emmanuel College Library, Franklin Springs, Georgia
DAVID S. PRATT, Librarian, Brevard Junior College, Cocoa, Florida
SYBIL PRICE, Librarian, Spartanburg Junior College Library, Spartanburg, S. C.
MARJORIE N. QUIGLEY, Librarian, The Pennsylvania State University, Altoona, Pennsylvania
CATHERINE RICKMAN, (MRS.), Librarian, Stratford Junior College, Danville, Virginia

GRACE J. RIDER, Librarian, Canal Zone Junior College Library, Balboa, Canal Zone
RUTH RIGGS, Librarian, Cazenovia College, Cazenovia, New York
BERNARD C. RINK, Librarian, Northwestern Michigan College, Traverse City, Michigan
EMMY LOU RITZ, Librarian, Porterville College Library, Porterville, California
KENNETH ROACH, Librarian, Howard County Junior College, Big Springs, Texas
ADA V. ROBINSON, Librarian, Puerto Rico Junior College, Rio Piedras, Puerto Rico
NORMA M. ROBINSON, Librarian, St. Johns River Junior College, Palatka, Florida
SISTER M. ROSARIA, Librarian, Sisters of St. Francis Dons Scotus Library, Slyvania, Ohio
JONNIE ROWAN, Librarian, Amarillo College, Amarillo, Texas
RAY ROWLAND, Librarian, Augusta College, Augusta, Georgia
LOU SANDS, Librarian, North Florida College, Madison, Florida
ESTHER B. SCHROEDER, Librarian, Brainerd Junior College, Brainerd, Minnesota
TONY SCHULZETENBERGE, Librarian, Ely Junior College, Ely, Minnesota
W. W. SCOTT, Librarian, Sinclair College, Dayton 2, Ohio
KATHLEEN YORK SERGOTT, Librarian, Massachusetts Bay Community College, Boston, Massachusetts
ELLANOR S. SEWELL, Librarian, Monticello College Library, Alton, Illinois
H. W. SHELTON, (MRS.), Librarian, University of Baltimore, Baltimore 1, Maryland
JAYNIE M. SHELTON, Librarian, Voorhees Junior College, Denmark, South Carolina
WILLIAM A. SHIMER, Librarian, Maunaolu College, Maui, Hawaii
ROSE SHULA, Librarian, Olympic College, Bremerton, Washington
LUCILLE SHULL, Librarian, Northeastern Junior College, Sterling, Colorado
WILLIAM R. SIEBEN, Librarian, St. Mary's Of The Late Seminary, Chicago, Illinois
FREDONIA SIKES, Librarian, Kilgore College, Kilgore, Texas
FRIEDA SILER, Librarian, Bluefield College, Bluefield, Virginia
ROBERT W. SILLEN, Librarian, Quincy Junior College, Quincy 69, Massachusetts
ETHEL SLONAKER, Librarian, Shenandoah College, Winchester, Virginia
ALMA VAN SLYKE, Librarian, Suomi College, Hancock, Michigan
ETHEL K. SMITH, Librarian, Wingate College, Wingate, North Carolina
ROGER MAE SMITH, (MISS), Librarian, South Plains College, Levelland, Texas
JEAN B. SPAULDING, Librarian, Marjorie Webster Junior College, Washington 12, D. C.
WILLIAM J. STIGALL, JR. (MRS.), Librarian, Lincoln College, Lincoln, Illinois
JOEL A. STOWERS, Librarian, Berry College, Mount Berry, Georgia
EVELYNE STRICKLAND, Librarian Alvin Junior College, Alvin, Texas
VIOLA THEORELL, Librarian, Black Hawk College, Moline, Illinois
ELIZABETH THOMAS, Librarian, Mount Vernon Junior College, Washington 7, D. C.
BARTH K. THOMPSEN, Librarian, Ketchikan Community College, Ketchikan, Alaska
MIRIAM THOMPSON, Librarian, Suffolk County Community College, Selden, New York
SANDRA J. TOLLMAN, Northwest Community College, Powell, Wyoming
JAMES R. TOLMAN, Librarian, Weber College, Ogden, Utah
ELMA TROMBLE, Librarian, Garden City Junior College, Garden City, Kansas
BARBARA TWISS, The Baptist Institute, Bryn Mawr, Pennsylvania
J. P. VAGT, Librarian, Odessa College, Odessa, Texas
FATHER GORDON VAN HORF, O.S.C., Librarian, Crosier Seminary, Onamia, Minnesota
MARY C. VAN NORT, Librarian, Keystone Junior College, La Plume, Pennsylvania
FRITZ VEIT, Librarian, Chicago City Junior College, Chicago 21, Illinois
MATTIE MAE VIVERETTE, Librarian, Jones County Junior College, Ellisville, Mississippi
HARRY R. VOIGT, Librarian, St. Paul's Junior College, Concordia, Missouri
RICHARD WADDLE, Librarian, Yakima Valley College, Yakima, Washington
JAMES O. WALLACE, Librarian, San Antonio College, San Antonio 12, Texas
GARNAR V. WALSH, Dean, Miner Institute, Chazy, New York
BEVERLEY WALTERS, (MRS.), Librarian, Olympic College, Bremerton, Washington
DOROTHY M. WARD, Librarian, Ranger College, Ranger, Texas
EDITH F. WATERMAN, Librarian, The Montgomery Junior College, Takoma Park 12, Maryland
MARY C. WEEKS, Librarian, Ellsworth College, Iowa Falls, Iowa
IMOGENE WHITE, (MRS.), Librarian, Oklahoma Military Academy, Claremore, Oklahoma
WILLIAM W. WICKER, Librarian, Frederick College, Portsmouth, Virginia
ROY H. WIEGERT, Librarian, Keokuk Community College, Keokuk, Iowa
RUTH WIEST, Librarian, Southwestern Junior College, Keene, Texas
RACHEL WILKES, Librarian, Centralia Township High School And Junior College, Centralia, Illinois
PARKER WILLIAMS, (MISS), San Jacinto College, Pasadena, Texas
FLORENCE C. WILMER, Librarian, Catonsville Community College, Catonsville 28, Maryland
EULA WINDHAM, Librarian, Middle Georgia College, Cochran, Georgia
LORING YOUNCE, REV., Librarian, Concordia College, Edmonton, Alberta, Canada
LOIS ZARAGOZA, Librarian, Washington Junior College, Pensacola, Florida
MARGUETITE ZIMMERMANN, Librarian, Springfield Junior College, Springfield, Ill.

REPRESENTING VITAL TITLES FOR JUNIOR COLLEGES

ABELARD-SCHUMAN, 6 W. 57 St., New York 19.

ABINGDON PR., 201 8th. Ave., S., Nashville 3, Tenn.

ABRAMS, HARRY N., 6 W. 57 St., New York 19.

ACADEMIC PRESS, 111 5rh Ave., New York 3.

ACADEMY GUILD PRESS, 1317 Van Ness Ave., Fresno 15, Calif.

ACADEMY OF POLITICAL SCIENCE, Columbia University, 116 St. and Broadway, New York 27

ACE BOOKS, 1120 Avenue of the Americas, New York 36.

ADDISON-WESLEY PUBLISHING CO., Reading, Mass.

AERO PUBLISHERS, 2162 Sunset Blvd., Los Angeles 26.

AFFILIATED PUBLISHERS, 630 Fifth Ave., New York 20.

AHRENS PUBLISHING CO., INC., 230 Park Ave., New York 17.

ALDINE PUB. CO., 64 East Van Buren St., Chicago 5.

ALL SAINTS PRESS, INC., 630 Fifth Ave., New York 20.

ALLEN, H., P.O. Box 1810 University Ctr. Sta., Cleveland 6, Ohio.

ALLENSON, ALEC R., INC., 635 E. Ogden Ave., Naperville, Ill.

ALL-PETS BOOKS, Box 151, Fond du Lac, Wis.

ALLYN & BACON, 150 Tremont St., Boston, 11.

AMERICAN ASSOCIATION FOR THE ADVANCEMENT OF SCIENCE, 1515 Massachusetts Ave., N.W., Washington 5, D. C.

AMERICAN BAR FOUNDATION, 1155 E. 60 St., Chicago 37.

AMERICAN BOOK CO., 55 Fifth Ave., New York 3.

AMERICAN COUNCIL ON EDUCATION, 1785 Massachusetts Ave., N.W., Washington 6, D. C.

AMERICAN ELSEVIER PUBLISHING CO., 52 Vanderbilt Ave., New York 17.

AMERICAN HERITAGE PUB. CO., 551 Fifth Ave., New York 17.

AMERICAN LIBRARY ASSOCIATION, 50 E. Huron St., Chicago 11.

AMERICAN MANAGEMENT ASSOCIATION, 1515 Broadway, New York 36.

AMERICAN PHILOSOPHICAL SOCIETY, 104 S. 5 St., Philadelphia 6.

AMERICAN PHOTOGRAPHIC BOOK PUBLISHING CO., 33 W. 60 St., New York 23.

AMERICAN SOCIETY FOR TESTING & MATERIALS, 1916 Race St., Philadelphia 3, Pa.

AMERICAN TECHNICAL SOCIETY, 848 East 58th St., Chicago 37.

AMERICANA CORPORATION, 575 Lexington Ave., New York 22.

ANDERSON, W. H., CO. 646 Main St., Cincinnati 2, Ohio

ANGEL ISLAND PUBLICATIONS, Box 755, Sausalito, Calif.

ANNUAL REVIEWS, 231 Grant Ave., Palo Alto, Calif.

APPOLLO EDITIONS, INC. 425 Park Ave., S., New York 16.

APPLETON-CENTURY-CROFTS, 35 W. 32 St. New York 1.

ARCADIA HOUSE, 419 Park Ave., S., New York 16.

ARCO PUBLISHING CO., 480 Lexington Ave., New York 17.

ARKHAM HOUSE, Sauk City, Wis.

ARTS, INC., 667 Madison Ave., New York 21.

ASIA PUBLISHING HOUSE, 119 W. 57 St., New York 19, N. Y.

ASSOCIATED BOOKSELLERS, 1582 E. State St. Westport, Conn

ATHENEUM PUBLISHERS, 162 E. 38 St., New York 16

ATLANTIC MONTHLY PRESS 8 Arlington St. Boston 16, Mass.

AUGSBURG PUBLISHING HOUSE, 426 S. 5th Street, Minneapolis 15, Minn.

AUGUSTANA BOOK CONCERN, 639 38th St., Rock Island, Ill.

AUGUSTIN, J. J., Locust Valley, N. Y.

AVON BOOKS, DIVISION OF THE HEARST CORP., 572 Madison Ave., New York 22.

BAHA'I PUBLISHING TRUST, 110 Linden Ave., Wilmette, Ill.

BAKER, VOORHIS, 30 Smith Ave. Mt. Kisco, N. Y.

BAKER BOOK HOUSE, 1019 Wealthy St., S. E., Grand Rapids 6 Mich.

BALLANTINE BOOKS, 101 Fifth Ave., New York 3.

BANTAM BOOKS, 271 Madison Ave., New York 16.

BARNES, A. S. & CO., 11 E. 36 St. New York 16.

BARNES & NOBLE, 105 Fifth Ave. New York 3.

BARRE PUB. CO., South Street, Barre, Mass.

BARRON'S EDUCATIONAL SERIES, 343 Great Neck Rd., Great Neck, N. Y.

BARTHOLOMEW HOUSE, 205 E. 42 St., New York 17.

BASIC BOOKS PUBLISHING CO., 404 Park Ave. South, New York 16.

BEACON PRESS, 25 Beacon St., Boston 8.

BELLMAN PUB. CO., P.O. Box 172, Cambridge 38, Mass.

BELMONT BOOKS, 66 Leonard St., New York 13, N. Y.

BENDER, MATTHEW, AND CO., 253 Orange, Albany, N. Y.

BENEFIC PRESS, 1900 N. Narragansett, Chicago 39, Ill.

BENJAMIN, W. A., 2465 Broadway, New York

BENNETT, CHAS. A., CO., 237 N. Monroe St., Peoria 3, Ill.

BENTLEY, ROBERT, 993 Massachusetts Ave., Cambridge 38, Mass.

BENZIGER BROTHERS, 7 E. 51 St. New York 22.

BERKLEY PUBLISHING CORPORATION, 15 E. 26 St., New York 10.

BETHANY PRESS, 2640 Pine Blvd., St. Louis 3, Mo.

BIBLIO AND TANNEN, 63 4th Ave., New York

BINFORDS & MORT, 5205 S.E. 11 Ave., Portland 2, Oreg.

BLAISDELL PUB. CO. 501 Madison Ave., New York 22, N. Y.

BLOCH PUBLISHING COMPANY, 31 W. 31 St., New York 1.

BOARDMAN, CLARK CO., 22 Park Pl., New York

BOBBS-MERRILL COMPANY, 4300 W. 62 St., Indianapolis 6, Ind.

BOLLINGEN FOUNDATION, 140 E. 62 St., New York 21

BOUREGY THOMAS & CO., 22 E. 60 St. New York 22.

BOWKER, R. R., CO., 62 W. 45 St. New York 36.

BRANFORD, C. T., CO., 75 Union St., Newton Center 59, Mass.

BRAZILLER, GEORGE, 215 Park Ave., S., New York 3.

BRETHREN PRESS, 1451 Dundee Ave., Elgin, Ill.

BRITISH BOOK CENTRE, 122 E. 55 St., New York 22.

BROADMAN PRESS, 127 Ninth Ave., N., Nashville 3, Tenn.

BROOKINGS INSTITUTION, 1775 Massachusetts Ave., N.W., Washington 6, D.C.

BROWN, W. C. CO., 135 S. Locust St., Dubuque, Iowa

BRUCE PUBLISHING CO., 400 N. Broadway, Milwaukee 1, Wis.

BRUCE PUBLISHING CO., 2642 University Ave., St. Paul 14, Minn.

BUREAU OF NATIONAL AFFAIRS, 1231 24 Street, N.W., Washington 7, D.C.

BURGESS PUBLISHING CO., 426 S. 6 Street, Minneapolis 15, Minn.

CALLAGHAN, Mundelein, Ill.

CAMBRIDGE BOOK CO., 45 Kraft Ave., Bronxville, N. Y.

CAMBRIDGE UNIVERSITY PRESS, 32 E. 57th Street, New York 22, N. Y.

CATHOLIC UNIVERSITY OF AMERICA PRESS, 620 Michigan Ave., N.E. Washington 17, D.C.

CATTELL, JAQUES PRESS, Annex 15, Arizona State University, Tempe, Ariz.

CAXTON PRINTERS, Caldwell, Idaho

CENTURY HOUSE, Watkins Glen, N. Y.

CHANDLER PUBLISHING CO., 604 Mission Street, San Francisco 5, Calif.

CHANNEL PRESS, 400 Community Drive, Manhasset, L. I., N. Y.

CHANTICLEER PRESS, 457 Madison Ave., New York 22, N. Y.

CHELSEA PUBLISHING CO., 50 E. Fordham Rd., New York 58, N. Y.

CHEMICAL PUBLISHING CO., 212 Fifth Ave., New York 10, N. Y.

CHILDRENS PRESS, Jackson Blvd., & Racine Ave., Chicago 7.

CHILMARK PRESS, 457 Madison Ave., New York 22, N. Y.

CHILTON CO., 56 & Chestnut Sts., Philadelphia 39, Pa.

CHRISTIAN EDUCATION PRESS, 1505 Race St., Philadelphia.

CITADEL PRESS, 222 Park Ave., S., New York 3, N. Y.

CITY LIGHTS POCKET BOOKSHOP, 261 Columbus Ave., San Francisco 11, Calif.

CLARKE & WAY, 55 W. 13 St., New York 10, N. Y.

COLLEGE AND UNIVERSITY PRESS, 263 Chapel St., New Haven 13, Conn.

COLLEGE ENTRANCE PUBLICATIONS, 104 5th Ave., New York 11.

COLLINS, WILLIAM AND SONS, 425 Park Ave., S., New York 16, N. Y.

COLONIAL PRESS, Northport, Ala.

COLONIAL PUBLISHING, 175 Purchase St., Boston 10, Mass.

COLONIAL WILLIAMSBURG, 383 Madison Ave., New York 17, N. Y.

COLUMBIA UNIVERSITY PRESS, 2960 Broadway, New York 27, N. Y.

COMMERCE CLEARING HOUSE, 4025 W. Peterson Ave., Chicago 46.

COMPTON, F. E., 1000 N. Dearborn St., Chicago 10.

CONCORDIA PUBLISHING HOUSE, 3558 S. Jefferson Ave., St. Louis 18, Mo.

CONSULTANTS BUREAU ENTERPRISES, INCORPORATED, 227 W. 17 Street, New York 11.

COOPER SQUARE PUBLISHERS, 59 Fourth Ave., New York.

CORNELL MARITIME PRESS, Box 109, Cambridge, Md.

CORNELL UNIVERSITY PRESS, Ithaca, N. Y.

CORNERSTONE LIBRARY, 630 Fifth Ave., New York 20.

CORTINA, R. D., COMPANY, 136 W. 52 Street, New York

COWARD-McCANN, INC., 210 Madison Ave., New York 16.

CRITERION BOOKS, 6 W. 57 Street, New York 19.

CROFT EDUCATION SERVICES, 100 Garfield Ave., New London, Conn.

CROWELL, THOMAS Y., 201 Park Ave., S., New York 3.

CROWELL-COLLIER PRESS, 640 Fifth Ave., New York.

CROWN PUBLISHERS, 419 Park Ave., S., New York 16.

DARTNELL CORP., 4660 Ravenswook Avenue, Chicago, Illinois.

DAUGHTERS OF ST. PAUL, 50 St. Paul's Ave., Jamaica Plain, Boston 30, Mass.

DAVIS, F. A., COMPANY, 1914 Cherry St., Philadelphia 3, Pa.

DAVIS PUBLICATIONS, 19-61 Printers Bldg., Worcester 8, Mass.

DAWSON'S BOOK SHOP, 550 S. Figueroa St., Los Angeles 17, Calif.

DELL PUBLISHING CO., 750 Third Ave., New York 16.

DENISON, T. S., & CO., 321 Fifth Ave., S., Minneapolis 15, Minn.

DESCLEE COMPANY, 280 Broadway, New York 7.

DEVIN'-ADAIR CO., 25 E., 26 St., New York 10.

DIAL PRESS, 461 Park Ave., S., New York 16.

DODD, MEAD & CO., 432 Park Ave., S., New York 16.

DODGE, F. W., CORP., 119 W. 40 St., New York 18.

DONOHUE, M. A., 711 Dearborn St., Chicago 5.

DOUBLEDAY & CO., Garden City, N. Y.

DOVER PUBLICATIONS, 180 Varick St., New York 14.

DRAMATISTS PLAY SERVICE, INC., 14 E. 38 St., New York 16.

DUELL, SLOAN & PEARCE, 1716 Locust St., Des Moines 3, Iowa

DUFOUR EDITIONS, Chester Springs, Pa.

DUKE UNIVERSITY PRESS, 6697 College Station, Durham, N. C.

DUQUESNE UNIVERSITY, 801 Bluff St., Pittsburg, Pa.

DUTTON, E. P., & COMPANY, 201 Park Ave., New York 3.

EDUCATIONAL PUBLISHING CORP., 23 Leroy Ave., Darien, Conn.

EMERSON BOOKS, 251 W. 19 St., New York 11.

ENCYCLOPAEDIA BRITANNICA, 425 N. Michigan Ave., Chicago 11, Ill.

EPSTEIN & CARROLL, 457 Madison Ave., New York 22.

EQUITY PUBLISHING CORPORATION, Oxford, N.H.

ERICKSSON, PAUL S., 119 W. 57 St., New York 19.

FAIRCHILD PUBLICATIONS, INC., 7 E. 12 St., New York 3.

FARRAR, STRAUS & CO., 19 Union Sq. W., New York 3.

FAWCETT PUBLICATIONS, Fawcett Pl., Greenwich, Conn.

F. W. FAXON CO., 91 Francis St., Boston, Mass.

FEARON PUBLISHERS, 828 Valencia St., San Francisco 10, Calif.

FELL, FREDERICK, INC., 386 Park Ave., S., New York 16.

FERGUSON, L. G., PUBLISHING CO., 6 N. Michigan Ave., Chicago 2.

FIDELER CO., 31 Ottawa Ave., N. W., Grand Rapids 2, Mich.

FIDES PUBLISHERS, Box 507, Notre Dame, Ind.

FLEET PUBLISHING CO., 230 Park Ave., New York 17.

FOLLETT PUBLISHING CO., 1000-1018 W. Washington, Chicago 7.

FORDHAM UNIVERSITY PRESS, 441 E., Fordham Rd., New York 58.

FORIEGN POLICY ASSOCIATION, 345 E. 46 St., New York 17.

FOUNDATION PRESS, 268 Flatbush Ave., Ext., Brooklyn 1, N. Y.

FRANCISCAN HERALD PRESS, 1434 W. 51 St., Chicago 9, Ill.

FRANKLIN, BURT, 514 W. 113 St. , New York 25.

FREE PRESS OF GLENCOE, INC. , 60 Fifth Ave. , New York

FREEMAN, W. H. , AND CO. , 660 Market St. , San Francisco 4, Calif.

FRENCH, SAMUEL, INC. , 25 W. 45 St. , New York 36.

FRIENDSHIP PRESS, 475 Riverside Dr. , New York 27.

FUNK & WAGNALLS CO. , 360 Lexington Ave. , New York 17.

GEIS, BERNARD, ASSOCIATES, 130 E. 56 St. , New York 22.

GEORGETOWN UNIVERSITY PRESS, Washington 7, D. C.

GERNSBACK LIBRARY, 154 W. 14 St. , New York 11.

GINN & CO. , Back Bay P.O. 191, Boston 17, Mass.

GLOBE BOOK CO. , 175 Fifth Ave. , New York 10.

GONOME PRESS, P.O. Box 161, Hicksville, N. Y.
GOLD MEDAL BOOKS, Fawcett Pl. , Greenwich, Conn

GOODHEART-WILLCOX CO. , 18250 Harwood Ave. , Homewood, Ill

GORDON & BREACH, 150 Fifth Ave. , New York 11.

GOSPEL TRUMPET PRESS, 1200 E. Fifth St. , Anderson, Ind.

GREENE, STEPHEN, PRESS, 120 Main St. , Brattleboro, Vt.

GROLIER, INC. , 575 Lexington Ave. , New York 22.

GROSSET & CUNLAP, INC. , 1107 Broadway, New York 10.

GROVE PRESS, 64 University Pl. , New York 3.

GRUNE & STRATTON, INC. , 381 Park Ave. , S. , New York 16.

GULF PUBLISHING CO. , Box 2608, Houston, Tex.

HAFNER PUBLISHING CO. , 31 E. 10 St. , New York 3.

HARCOURT, BRACE & WORLD, 750 Third Ave. , New York 17.

HARIAN PUBLICATIONS, 1000 Prince St. , Greenlawn, N. Y.

HARLOW PUBLISHING CORPORATION, 532 N. W. Second St. , Oklahoma City, Okla.

HARPER & ROW, 49 E. 33 St. , New York 16.

HART PUBLISHING CO. , 74 Fifth Ave. , New York 13.

HARVARD UNIVERSITY, Graduate School of Business Administration, Soldiers Field, Boston 63, Mass.

HARVARD UNIVERSITY PRESS, Kittredge Hall, 79 Graden St. , Cambridge 38, Mass.

HARVEY HOUSE, 5 S. Buckhout St., Irvington-on-Hudson, N. Y.

HASTINGS HOUSE, 151 E. 50 St., New York 22.

HAWTHORN BOOKS, INC., 70 Fifth Ave., New York 11.

HEARTHSIDE PRESS, 118 E. 28 St., New York 16.

HEATH D. C., & CO., 285 Columbus Ave., Boston 16.

HEBREW UNION COLLEGE PRESS, Clifton Ave., Cincinnati, Ohio

HERALD PRESS, 610 Walnut Ave., Scottdale, Pa.

HERALD PUBLISHING HOUSE, P.O. Box 477, 103 S. Osage St., Independence, Mo.

HERDER & HERDER, 232 Madison Avenue, New York 16.

HERDER, B., BOOK CO., 17 S. Broadway, St. Louis 2, Mo.

HERMAN PUBLISHING SERVICE, Stamford House, Stamford, Conn.

HERZL, THEODOR, PRESS, 515 Park Ave., New York

HILL & WANG, 141 Fifth Ave., New York 11.

HOLIDAY HOUSE, 8 W. 13 St., New York 11.

HOLMAN, A. J., CO. 1222-26 Arch St., Philadelphia 7, Pa.

HOLT, RINEHART & WINSTON, 383 Madison Ave., New York 17.

HORIZON PRESS, INC., 156 Fifth Avenue, New York 10.

HORN BOOK, INC., 585 Boylston St., Boston 16, Mass.

HOUGHTON MIFFLIN CO., 2 Park St., Boston 7, Mass.

HOWELL BOOK HOUSE, 575 Lexington Ave., New York 22, N. Y.

HOWELL-NORTH PRESS, 1050 Parker St., Berkeley 10, Calif.

HUMANITIES PRESS, 303 Fourth Ave., New York 10.

HUMPHRIES, BRUCE, INC., 48 Melrose St., Boston 16.

INDIANA UNIVERSITY PRESS, Bloomington, Ind.

INDUSTRIAL PRESS, 93 Worth St., New York 13.

INSTITUTE OF EARLY AMERICAN HISTORY AND CULTURE, Williamsburg, Va.

INSTITUTE OF LANGUAGE STUDY, 24 Clinton Ave., Montclair, N. J.

INTERNATIONAL UNIVERSITIES PRESS, 227 W. 13 St., New York 11.

INTERSCIENCE. 440 Park Ave. S., New York 16, N. Y.

INTERSTATE, THE, 19 N. Jackson St., Danville, Ill.

IOWA STATE UNIVERSITY PRESS, Ames, Iowa.

IRWIN, R. D., INC., 1818 Ridge Rd., Homewood, Ill.

JEWISH PUBLICATION SOCIETY OF AMERICA. 222 N. 15 St., Philadelphia 2, Pa.

JOHN DAY CO., 62 W. 45 St., New York 36, N. Y.

JOHN KNOX PRESS, 8 N. Sixth St., Box 1176, Richmond 9, Virginia

JOHNS HOPKINS PRESS, Baltimore 18, Maryland

JUDD, ORANGE, PUBLISHING CO., 15 East 26th Street, New York 10.

JUDY PUBLISHING CO., Box 5270, Main P. O. Chicago 80.

JULIAN PRESS, 80 E. 11 St., New York 3.

KENEDY, P. J. & SONS, 2 Barclay St., New York 7.

KNOPF, ALFRED A., INC., 501 Madison Ave., New York 22.

KREGEL'S PUBLICATIONS, 525 Eastern Ave., S.E., Grand Rapids 6, Mich.

LAIDLAW BROTHERS, THATCHER & MADISON AVENUES, River Forest, Ill.

LANE BOOK COMPANY, Menlo Park, Calif.

LANGE MEDICAL PUBLICATIONS, P.O. Box 1215, Los Altos, Calif.

LANTERN PRESS, 257 Park Ave., S., New York 10.

LAS AMERICAS PUBLISHING CO., 152 E. 23 St., New York 10.

LATIN AMERICA INSTITUTE PRESS, 200 Park Ave., New York 3.

LEA & FEBIGER, 600 S. Washington Sq., Philadelphia 6, Pa.

LERNER PUBLICATIONS CO., 133 1st Avenue North, Minneapolis 1, Minn.

LIPPINCOTT, J. B., CO., 227 S. 6 St., E. Washington Sq., Philadelphia 5.

LITTLE, BROWN & CO., 34 Beacon St., Boston 6.

LITTLEFIELD, ADAMS & CO., 128 Oliver St., Paterson 1, N. J.

LIVERIGHT PUBLISHING CO., 386 Park Avenue, S., New York 16.

LOIZEAUX BORS., 19 W. 21 St., New York 10.

LONGMANS, 119 W. 40 St., New York 18, N. Y.

LOOKING GLASS LIBRARY, 457 Madison Ave., New York 22, N. Y.

LOUISIANA STATE UNIVERSITY PRESS., Baton Rouge 3, La.

LOYOLA UNIVERSITY PRESS, 3441 N. Ashland Ave., Chicago 13.

LUCE, ROBERT B., 1816 Jefferson Pl., N. W., Washington D. C. (See also McKay)

LYONS & CARNAHAN, 407 E. 25 St. , Chicago 16, Ill.

MD PUBLICATIONS, 30 E. 60 St. , New York 22.

McCORMICH-MATHERS PUBLISHING CO. , 1440 E. English St. , (Box 2212),
Wichita 1, Kansas

MACFADDEN BOOKS, INC. , (MACFADDEN-BARTELL CORP.), 205 East 42nd
St. , New York 17.

MCGRAW-HILL BOOK CO. , INC. , 330 W. 42 St. , New York 36.

MCKAY, DAVID CO. , INC. , 119 W. 40 St. , New York 18.

MCKNIGHT & MCKNIGHT PUBLISHING CO. , U.S. Route 66 at Tonawanda Ave. ,
Bloomington, Ill.

MACMILLAN CO. , THE, 60 Fifth Avenue, New York 11.

MCNALLY & LOFTIN, 510 W. Fourth St. , Charlotte 2, N.C.

MACRAE-SMITH CO. , 225 S. 15 St. , Philadelphia 2.

MACY, GEORGE, CO. , INC. , 595 Madison Ave. , New York 22. (See Dial Press.)

MARQUIS, A. N. & CO. , MARQUIS---WHO'S WHO, INC. , 210 E. Ohio St. ,
Chicago 11.

MAXTON PUBLISHERS, 15 E. 26 St. , New York 10. (See also Follett)

MEDICAL BOOKS FOR CHILDREN. 133 First Ave. N. Minneapolis 1, Minn.

MEREDITH PUBLISHING CO. , 1716 Locust St. , Des Moines 3, Iowa

MERIDIAN BKS. 2231 W. 110 St. , Cleveland 2, Ohio

MERRIAM, G. & C. , CO. , 47 Federal St. , Springfield 2, Mass.

MERRILL, CHARLES E. , CO. , 1300 Alum Creek Dr. , Columbus 16, Ohio

MESSNER, JULIAN, INC. , 8 W. 40 St. , New York 18.

MICHIGAN STATE UNIV. , BUREAU OF BUS. & ECON. RESEARCH, GRADUATE
SCHOOL OF BUSINESS ADM. , East Lansing, Mich.

MODERN LIBRARY, 457 Madison Ave. , New York 22, N. Y.

MONARCH BOOKS, INC. , 386 Park Avenue, S. , New York 16.

MONTHLY REVIEW PRESS, 333 6th Avenue, New York 14.

MOODY PRESS, 820 N. LaSalle St. , Chicago 10.

MOREHOUSE-BARLOW CO. , 14 E. 41 St. , New York 17.

MORGAN & MORGAN, 101 Park Ave. , New York 17.

MORROW, WILLIAM, & CO. , 425 Park Avenue S. , New York 16.

MOSBY, C. V. , CO. , 3207 Washington Blvd. , St. Louis 3.

MUHLENBERG PRESS, 2900 Queen Lane, Philadelphia 29.

MUNICIPAL MANUAL PUBLISHERS, Freeport, Me.

MUSEUM OF MODERN ART, 11 W. 53 St., New York 19.

MUSEUM OF PRIMITIVE ART, N. Y., 239 Park Ave. S., New York 3, N. Y.

N-P PUBLICATIONS, 850 Hansen Way, Palo Alto, Calif.

NATIONAL ACADEMY OF SCIENCES---NATIONAL RESEARCH COUNCIL, 2101 Constitution Ave., N.W., Washington 25, D.C.

NATIONAL BUREAU OF ECONOMIC RESEARCH, 261 Madison Ave., New York 16.

NATIONAL EDUCATION ASSOCIATION, 1201 16 St. N.W., Washington 6, D.C.

NATIONAL FOREMEN'S INSTITUTE. Englewood Cliffs, N. J.

NATIONAL GEOGRAPHIC SOCIETY, 16 & M Sts., N.W., Washington 6, D.C.

NATIONAL INDUSTRIAL CONFERENCE BOARD, 460 Park Ave., New York 22.

NATIONAL PLANNING ASSOCIATION, 1606 New Hampshire Ave., N.W., Washington 9, D.C.

NATIONAL PRESS. 850 Hansen Way, Palo Alto, Calif.

NAYLOR CO., 918 N. St. Mary's St., San Antonio 6, Tex.

NELSON, THOMAS, AND SONS, 18 East 41st St., New York 17.

NEW AMERICAN LIBRARY OF WORLD LITERATURE, INC., 501 Madison Ave., New York 22.

NEW DIRECTIONS, 333 Sixth Avenue, New York 14.

NEW YORK GRAPHIC SOCIETY, 95 E. Putnam Ave., Greenwich, Conn.

NEW YORK UNIVERSITY PRESS, Washington Sq., New York 3.

NEWMAN PRESS, 69 W. Main St., Westminster, Md.

NOBLE & NOBLE, INC., 67 Irving Pl., New York 3.

NOONDAY PRESS. 19 Union Square W., New York 3, N. Y.

NORTON, W. W. & CO., 55 Fifth Ave., New York 3.

NOURSE PUBLISHING CO., P.O. Box 398, San Carlos, Calif.

OBOLENSKY, IVAN, 341 E. 62nd St., New York 21.

OCEANA PUBLICATIONS, 40 Cedar St., Dobb's Ferry, N. Y.

ODYSSEY PRESS, 55 Fifth Ave., New York 3.

OHIO STATE UNIVERSITY PRESS, 164 W. 19 Ave., Columbus, 10, Ohio.

OPEN COURT PUBLISHING CO. , LaSalle, Ill.

ORION PRESS, 116 E. 19 St. , New York 3.

OTTENHEIMER PUBLISHERS, 4805 Nelson Ave. , Baltimore 15.

OXFORD BOOK CO. , 71 Fifth Avenue, New York 3.

OXFORD UNIVERSITY PRESS, 417 Fifth Ave. , New York 16.

PACIFIC BOOKS, P.O. Box 558, Palo Alto, Calif.

PACIFIC COAST PUBLISHERS, Campbell Ave. at Scott Dr. , Menlo Park, Calif.

PACIFIC PRESS PUBLISHING ASSOCIATION, 1350 Villa St. , Mountain View, Calif.

PANTHEON BOOKS, INC. , 22 E. 51 St. New York 22.

PAPERBACK LIBRARY, 260 Park Ave. , S. , New York 10.

PARENTS' MAGAZINE ENTERPRISES, 52 Vanderbilt Ave. , New York 17.

PARNASUS PRESS, 33 Parnassus Rd. , Berkeley 8, Calif.

PAULIST PRESS, 401 W. 59 St. , New York 19.

PEGGY CLOTH-BOOKS. 200 Fifth Ave. , New York 10, N. Y.

PENDLE HILL PAMPHLETS, 338 Plush Mill Rd. , Wallingford, Pa.

PENGUIN BOOKS, 3300 Clipper Mill Rd. Baltimore 11.

PENNSYLVANIA STATE UNIVERSITY PRESS, 310 Old Main, University Park, Pa.

PERGAMON PRESS, 122 E. 55 St. , New York 22.

PERKINS ORIENTAL BOOKS, 255 Seventh Ave. , New York 1.

PETER PAUPER PRESS, 629 MacQuestern Parkway, Mount Vernon, N. Y.

PHILOSOPHICAL LIBRARY, INC. , 15 E. 40 St. , New York 16.

PILGRIM PRESS. 1505 Race St. , Philadelphia 2, Pa.

PLATT AND MUNK CO. , 200 Fifth Ave. , New York 10,

PLAYS, INC. , 8 Arlington St. , Boston 16.

POCKET BOOKS, 630 Fifth Ave. , New York 20.

POPULAR LIBRARY, 355 Lexington Ave. , New York 17.

POPULAR MECHANICS PRESS, 200 E. Ontario St. , Chicago 11, Ill.

POTTER, CLARKSON N. , INC. , 23 E. 67 St. New York 21.

PRAEGER FREDERICK A. , INC. , 61 University Pl. , New York 3.

PRENTICE-HALL, INC. , Englewood Cliffs, N. J.

PRINCETON UNIVERSITY, INDUSTRIAL RELATIONS SECTION, Princeton, N.J.

PRIORY PRESS, Asbury Rd. , Dubuque, Iowa.

PUBLIC ADMINISTRATION SERVICE, 1313 E. 60 St. , Chicago 37.

PUBLIC AFFAIRS PRESS, 419 New Jersey Ave. , S.E. , Washington 3, D.C.

PUTNAM'S, G.P. , SONS,210 Madison Ave. , New York 16.

PYRAMID BOOKS, 444 Madison Ave. , New York 22.

QUADRANGLE BOOKS, 119 W. Lake St. , Chicago 1.

RAND MCNALLY CO. , P.O. Box 7600, Chicago 80.

RANDOM HOUSE, INC. , 457 Madison Ave. , New York 22.

READER'S DIGEST ASSOCIATION, Pleasantville, N. Y.

REGNERY, HENRY, CO. , 14 E. Jackson Blvd. , Chicago 4.

REINHOLD,PUBLISHING CORP. , 430.Park Ave. , New York 22.

REVELL, FLEMING H. , CO. , Booker St. , Westwood, N. J.

REVIEW AND HERALD PUBLISHING ASSOCIATION, 6856 Eastern Ave. , N.W. ,
Washington D.C.

REYNAL & CO. , 221 E. 49 St. , New York 17, N.Y.

RICHARDS CO. , 595 Madison Ave. , New York 22.

RIDER, JOHN F. , PUBLISHERS, INC. , 116 W. 14 St. , New York 11.

RITCHIE, WARD, PRESS, ANDERSON, RITCHIE & SIMON, 1932 Hyperion Ave. ,
Los Angeles 27.

RODALE BOOKS, 6th and Minor Sts. Emmaus, Pa.

ROTHMAN, F.B. AND CO. , 57 Leuning St. , S. Hackensack, N.J.

ROW, PETERSON, 49 E. 33 St. , New York 16, N. Y.

ROWMAN & LITTLEFIELD, 84 Fifth Ave. , New York 11.

ROY PUBLISHERS, 30 E. 74 St. , New York 21.

RUSSELL AND RUSSELL, 80 E. 11 St. , New York 3.

RUTGERS UNIVERSITY PRESS, 30 College Ave. , New Brunswick, N.J.

ST. ANTHONY GUILD PRESS, 508 Marshall St. , Paterson 3, N.J.

ST. MARTIN'S PRESS, INC. , 175 Fifth Ave. , New York 10.

SAMS, HOWARD W. , & CO. , 2201 W. 46 St. , Indianapolis 5.

SAN LUCAS PRESS. 239 Park Ave. , S. , New York 3, N.Y.

SARGENT, PORTER, 11 Beacons St. , Boston, Mass.

SAUNDERS, W.B. , CO. , 218 W. Washington Sq. , Philadelphia 5.

SCARECROW PRESS, 257 Park Ave. , S. , New York 10.

SCHOCKEN BOOKS, 67 Park Ave. , New York 16.

SCHOLARS' FACSIMILES AND REPRINTS, 1605 N.W. , 14 Ave. , Gainesville, Fla.

SCHOLASTIC BOOK SERVICES, 33 W. 42 St. , New York 36.

SCIENCE EDITIONS, 440 Park Ave. , S. , New York 16, N. Y.

SCIENCE RESEARCH ASSOCIATES, 259 E. Erie St. , Chicago 10.

SCOTT, FORESMAN AND CO. , 433 E. Eriek St. , Chicago 11.

SCOTT, WILLIAM R. , 8 W. 13 St. , New York 11.

SCRIBNER'S CHARLES, SONS, 597 Fifth Ave. , New York 17.

SEABURY PRESS, 1 Fawcett Pl. , Greenwich, Conn.

SEAHORSE PRESS, 620 Esplanade, Pelham 65, N. Y.

SHEED AND WARD, 64 University Pl. , New York 3.

SHENGOLD PUBLICATIONS, 45 W. 45 St. , New York 36.

SHERIDAN HOUSE, 257 Park Ave. , S. , New York 10.

SHOE STRING PRESS, 965 Dixwell Ave. , Hamden 14, Conn.

SHOREWOOD PUBLISHING CO. , 304 E. 45 St. , New York 17.

SIERRA CLUB, 1050 Mills Tower, San Francisco 4, Calif.

SILVER BURDETT CO. , Park Ave. , & Columbia Rd. Morristown, N. J.

SIMMONS-BOARDMAN PUBLISHING CO. , 30 Church St. , New York 7.

SIMON & SCHUSTER, INC. , 639 Fifth Ave. , New York 20.

SINGER, L. W. , CO. , 249-259 W. Erie Blvd. Syracuse 2, N. Y.

SMITH, PETER, 20 Railroad Ave. , Gloucester, Mass.

SOCCER ASSOCIATES. Box 634, New Rochelle, N. Y.

SOUTHERN ILLINOIS UNIVERSITY PRESS, Carbondale, Ill.

SOUTHERN METHODIST UNIVERSITY PRESS, Dallas 22.

SOUTH-WESTERN PUBLISHING CO. , 5101 Madison Ave. , Cincinnati 27.

SPELLER, ROBERT, AND SONS, 33 W. 42 St. , New York 36.

STACKPOLE CO. , 100 Telegraph Pr. Bldg. , Cameron & Kelker Sts. , Harrisburg, Pa.

STANDARD PUBLISHING FOUNDATION, 8100 Hamilton Ave. , Cincinnati 31.

STANDARD REFERENCE WORKS PUBLISHING CO. , 53 E. 77 St. , New York 21.

STANFORD UNIVERSITY PRESS, Stanford, Calif.

STATE HISTORICAL SOCIETY OF WISCONSIN, 816 State St. , Madison 6.

STECK CO. , Box 16, Austin 61, Tex.

STEINER, RUDOLF, PUBLICATIONS, 65 S. Greenbush Rd. , West Nyack, N.Y.

STERLING PUBLISHING CO. , 419 Park Ave. , S. , New York 16.

STUART, LYLE, 239 Park Ave. , South, New York 3.

SUMMY-BIRCHARD PUBLISHING CO. , 1834 Ridge Ave. , Evanston, Ill.

SWALLOW, ALAN, 2679 S. York St. , Denver 10.

SYRACUSE UNIVERSITY PRESS, 920 Irving Place (Box 87) University Station, Syracuse 10, N.Y.

TAPLINGER PUBLISHING COMPANY, 119 W. 57 Street, New York 19.

TEACHER'S COLLEGE, BUREAU OF PUBLICATIONS, 525 W. 120. Street, N. Y.

TEACHER'S PRACTICAL PRESS, 47 Frank St. , Valley Stream L.I. , N.Y.

TEMPLEGATE, 719 Adams St. , Springfield, Ill.

TENNESSEE BOOK CO. , 126 Third Avenue, N. , Nashville 3.

THEATRE ARTS BOOKS, 333 Sixth Ave. , New York 14.

THOMAS, CHARLES C. , Publisher, 301 E. Lawrence Ave. , Springfield, Ill.

THOR PUBLISHING CO. , P.O. Box 27608', Hollywood 27, Calif.

TIME INC. , Time & Life Bldg. , Rockefeller Center, New York 20.

TRANSATLANTIC ARTS, Hollywood-by-the-Sea, Fla.

TUDOR PUBLISHING CO. , 221 Park Ave. , S. , New York 3.

TUTTLE, CHARLES E. , CO. , 28 S. Main St. , Rutland, Vt.

TWAYNE PUBLISHERS, INC. , 31 Union Sq. , W. , New York 3.

TWENTIETH CENTURY FUND, 41 E. 70 St. , New York 21.

UNGAR, FREDERICK, Publishing Co., 1313 E. 23 St. , New York 10.

UNION OF AMERICAN HEBREW CONGREGATIONS, 838 Fifth Ave. , New York 21.

UNITED EDUCATORS, INC. , Tangley Oaks Educational Ctr. , Lake Bluff, Ill.

UNITED STATES NAVAL INSTITUTE, Annapolis, Md.

UNIVERSE BOOKS, INC. , 381 Park Avenue, S. , New York 16.

UNIVERSITY BOOKS, INC., 1601 Jericho Turnpike, New Hyde Park, L.I., N.Y.

UNIVERSITY OF ALABAMA PRESS, University, Ala.

UNIVERSITY OF CALIFORNIA, Bureau of Public Administration, Berkeley 4, Calif.

UNIVERSITY OF CHICAGO PRESS, 5750 Ellis Ave., Chicago 37.

UNIVERSITY OF COLORADO PRESS, Boulder, Colo.

UNIVERSITY OF FLORIDA PRESS, 15 N.W. 15th St., Gainesville, Fla.

UNIVERSITY OF HAWAII PRESS, Honolulu 14, Hawaii.

UNIVERSITY OF ILLINOIS PRESS, Urbana, Ill.

UNIVERSITY OF KANSAS PRESS, 114 Flint Hall, Lawrence, Kansas

UNIVERSITY OF KENTUCKY PRESS, McVey Hall, University of Kentucky, Lexington 29, Ky.

UNIVERSITY OF MICHIGAN, W.L. Clements Library, Ann Arbor, Mich.

UNIVERSITY OF MINNESOTA PRESS, 2037 University Ave., S.E., Minneapolis 14.

UNIVERSITY OF MISSOURI, Engineering Experimental Station, Columbia, Mo.

UNIVERSITY OF NEBRASKA PRESS, Lincoln 8, Nebr.

UNIVERSITY OF NEW MEXICO PRESS, Albuquerque, N. Mex.

UNIVERSITY OF NORTH CAROLINA PRESS, Chapel Hill, N.C.

UNIVERSITY OF NOTRE DAME, Mediaeval Institute, Notre Dame, Inc.

UNIVERSITY OF OKLAHOMA PRESS, Faculty Exchange, Norman, Okla.

UNIVERSITY OF PENNSYLVANIA PRESS, 3436 Walnut St., Philadelphia 4.

UNIVERSITY OF PITTSBURGH PRESS, 3309 Cathedral of Learning, Pittsburgh 13, Pa.

UNIVERSITY OF SOUTH CAROLINA PRESS, Columbia 1, S.C.

UNIVERSITY OF TENNESSEE PRESS, Publication Bldg., Knoxville 16, Tenn.

UNIVERSITY OF TEXAS, College of Business Administration Foundation, Austin, Tex.

UNIVERSITY OF VIRGINIA PRESS, Box 3786, University Sta., Charlottesville, Va.

UNIVERSITY OF WASHINGTON PRESS, 1405 E. 41st St., Seattle 5, Wash.

UNIVERSITY OF WISCONSIN PRESS, 430 Sterling Ct., Madison 6, Wis.

UNIVERSITY PUBLISHERS, INC., 239 Park Avenue, S., New York 3.

VANDERBILT UNIVERSITY PRESS, Nashville 5.

VANGUARD PRESS, INC., 424 Madison Ave., New York 17.

VAN NOSTRAND, D., CO., INC., 120 Alexander St., Princeton, N.J.

VEDANTA PRESS, 1946 Vedanta Pl., Hollywood 28, Calif.

WAGNER, HARR, PUBLISHING CO., 609 Mission St., San Francisco 5.

WALCK, HENRY Z., INC., 101 Fifth Avenue, New York 3.

WALKER & CO., 10 West 56th St., New York 19.

WARNE, FREDERICK, & CO., INC., 210 Fifth Ave., New York 10.

WASHINGTON SQUARE PRESS, INC., 630 Fifth Ave., New York 20.

WATSON-GUPTILL PUBLICATIONS, INC., 111 Fourth Ave., New York 3.

WATTS, FRANKLIN, INC., 575 Lexington Ave., New York 22.

WAYNE STATE UNIVERSITY PRESS, 5980 Cass Ave., Detroit 2.

WEBSTER PUBLISHING CO., 1154 Reco Ave., St. Louis 26.

WESLEYAN UNIVERSITY PRESS, 356 Washington St., Middletown, Conn.

WEST PUBLISHING CO., 50 W. Kellogg Blvd., St. Paul 2, Minn.

WESTENLORE PRESS, 5040 Eagle Rock Blvd., Los Angeles 41.

WESTERN PUBLISHING CO., 1220 Mound Ave., Racine, Wis.

WESTMINSTER PRESS, Witherspoon Bldg., Philadelphia 7.

WHEELRIGHT, BOND, CO., Porter's Landing, Freeport, Maine

WHITMAN, ALBERT, AND CO., 560 W. Lake St., Chicago 6.

WHITMAN PUBLISHING CO., 1220 Mound Ave., Racine, Wis.

WILDE, W.A., CO., 10 Huron Dr., Natick, Mass.

WILEY, JOHN, & SONS, INC., 440 Park Ave. S., New York 16.

WILLIAMS & WILKINS CO., 428 E. Preston St., Baltimore 2.

WILSON, H.W., CO., 950 University Ave., New York 22.

WISE WILLIAM H. & CO., 370 Seventh Ave., New York 1.

WITTENBORN, INC., 1018 Madison Ave., New York 21.

WORLD PUBLISHING CO., 2231 W. 110 St., Cleveland 2.

WRITER, THE, INC., 8 Arlington St., Boston 16.

YALE UNIVERSITY LIBRARY, New Haven, Conn.

YEAR BOOK MEDICAL PUBLISHERS, 35 E. Wacker Dr., Chicago 1.

YOSELOFF, THOMAS, INC., 11 E. 35 St. New York 36, N.Y.

ZONDERVAN PUBLISHING HOUSE, 1415 Lake Dr., S.E., Grand Rapids 6, Mich.

541.37	Electrolytes	551.5	Meteorology
541.38	Isotopes	551.5	Meteorology as a Profession
541.39	Chemical Reactions	551.5	Temperature
541.39	Chemical Reaction--Conditions & Laws	551.55	Storms
541.39	Chemical Reaction, Rate of	551.552	Hurricanes
541.362	Combustion	551.553	Tornadoes
541.372	Ionization	551.559	Dust Storms
541.372	Ions	551.559	Hail
541.383	Quantum Chemistry	551.56	Lightning
541.392	Chemical Equilibruim	551.572	Clouds
541.396	Coordination Compounds	551.59	Weather
543	Chemistry, Analytic	551.7	Earth--Age
543.01	Chemical Tests and Reagents	551.7	Geology, Stratigraphic
543.1	Food--Analysis	551.9	Geochemistry
544	Chemistry, Analytic--Qualitative	551.96	Coral Reefs and Islands
544	Microchemistry	553.2	Coal
544.1	Radicals (Chemistry)	553.28	Oil Fields
544.5	Diffusion	553.6	Sulphur
544.92	Chromatographic Analysis	553.8	Precious Stones
545	Chemistry, Analytic--Quantitative	560	Paleontology
545.812	Colorimetry	561	Paleobotany
546	Chemistry, Inorganic	563	Protozoa
546.391	Beryllium	565.3	Crustacea
546.532	Chromium	569	Mammals, Fossil
546.683	Silicon	571	Excavations (Archaeology)
546.71	Nitrogen	571	Kensington Rune Stone
546.731	Fluorine	571	Man, Prehistoric
546.75	Gases, Rare	571	Man, Prehistoric--America
547	Chemistry, Organic	571	Man, Prehistoric--Europe
547	Hydrocarbons	571	Man, Primitive
547.473	Auxin	571	Mycenae
547.596	Nucleic Acids	571	Stone Age
547.611	Benzene	571.3	Bronze Age
547.637	Amino Acids	571.3	Copper Age
547.73	Cholesterol	571.7	Cave-Drawings
547.75	Proteins	571.73	Sculpture, Greek
547.78	Carbohydrates	571.9	Mounds
547.843	Plastics	572	Anthropology
548	Crystallography	572	Ethnology
548.9	Luminescence	572	Society, Primitive
549	Diamonds	572.081	Boas, Franz, 1858-1942
549.1	Mineralogy	573	Man
550	Earth	573	Man--Constitution
550	Geological Research	573.2	Man--Origin
550	Geology	573.4	Man--Influence of Environment
550	Geology--Antarctic Regions	573.6	Body Size
550	Geology--North America	574	Bioenergetics
550	Geology, Structural	574	Biology
551	Geophysics	574	Biology--Dictionaries
551.4	Caves	574	Biology--History
552	Petrology	574	Biology--Philosophy
552	Rocks	574	Biology--Tables, Etc.
551.2	Volcanoes	574	Biology--Terminology
551.22	Earthquakes	574.1	Biological Physics
551.312	Glaciers	574.192	Biological Chemistry
551.4	Caves--U.S.	574.192	Histochemistry
551.4	Physical Geography	574.193	Enzymes
551.41	Continents	574.194	Hormones
551.41	Drift	574.3	Embryology
551.43	Mountains	574.5	Adaptation (Biology)
551.45	Deserts	574.5	Ecology
551.46	Ocean	574.82	Histology
551.46	Oceanography	574.87	Cells
551.46	Tides	574.87	Cytogenetics
551.471	Gulf Stream	574.87	Cytology
551.48	Limnology	574.9	Natural History
551.49	Hydrology	574.92	Seashore Biology
551.5	Atmosphere	574.92074	Aquariums
551.5	Climatology	574.929	Fresh-Water Biology
551.5	Low Temperature Research	574.973	Natural History--U.S.
551.5	Low Temperatures.	575	Evolution
		575	Origin of Species

780.974	Carnegie Hall, New York	792.84	Ballet
781	Music--Theory	793	Ballroom Dancing
781	Musical Notation	793	Paper Work
781.15	Music--Psychology	793	Skits, Stunts, Etc.
781.3	Harmony	793.3	Dancing
781.4	Counterpoint	793.3	Delsarte System
781.4	Fugue	793.31	Folk Dancing
781.5	Musical Form	793.74	Games of Strategy (Mathematics)
781.55	Dance Music	793.74	Mathematical Recreations
781.61	Composition (Music)	793.8	Conjuring
781.63	Conducting	794.1	Chess
781.63	Instrumentation & Orchestration	794.2	Board Games
781.71	Music, Primitive	794.2	Checkers
781.91	Musical Instruments	794.6	Bowling
782	Librettists	795	Card Tricks
782.1	Opera	795	Gambling
782.95	Ballets--Stories, Plots, Etc.	795.01	Chance
783	Church Music	795.415	Contract Bridge
783.28	Christmas Music	796	Athletics
783.5	Chants	796	Athletics--Apparatus & Equipment
783.6	Carols	796	Athletics--History
783.9	Hymns	796	Sports
784	Choirs (Music)	796.007	Basketball Coaching
784	Songs	796.077	Coaching (Athletics)
784.1	Choral Music	796.2	Automobile Racing
784.1	Madrigal	796.3	Baseball--Biography
784.3	English Ballads and Songs	796.3	Baseball--History
784.3	English Ballads and Songs--	796.31	Hand Ball
	History and Criticism	796.323	Basketball
784.4	American Ballads and Songs	796.332	Football
784.4	Cowboys--Songs and Music	796.34	Lacrosse
784.4	Folk Songs	796.34	Tennis
784.4	Folk-Songs, American	796.352	Golf
784.4	Folk-Songs, English	796.357	Baseball
784.6	Conducting (Choral)	796.3578	Softball
784.71	National Songs	795.4	Cards
784.9	Singing	796.4	College Sports
784.94	Ear Training	796.4	Gymnastics
785	Instrumental Music	796.42	Track Athletics
785.1	Orchestra	796.47	Tumbling
785.11	Symphonies	796.48	Olympic Games
785.12	Bands (Music)	796.5	Outdoor Life
785.1207	Drum Majors	796.52	Mountaineering
785.42	Jazz Music	796.54	Camp Counselors
785.7	Chamber Music	796.54	Camping
789.5	Bells	796.54	Camps
790	Chatauquas	796.6	Cycling
790	Games	796.8	Jiu-Jitsu
790	Geishas	796.8	Karate
790	Play	796.83	Boxing
790	Recreation	796.93	Skis and Skiing
790.196	Handicapped	796.962	Hockey
790.2	Hobbies	797	Aquatic Sports
790.345	Badminton (Game)	797.1	Boats and Boating
791	Bible Plays	797.122	Canoes and Canoeing
791	Lyceums	797.124	Sailing
791.3	Circus--History	797.14	Yacht Racing
791.43	Moving-Pictures	797.2	Swimming
791.53	Puppets and Puppet Plays	797.23	Diving
791.82	Bull-Fights	798.46	Harness Racing
792	Ballet Dancing	799	Game and Game-Birds--North
792	Ballet--History		America
792	London--Theaters	799.1	Fishing
792	Stage Lighting	799.16	Salt-Water Fishing
792	Theater	799.2	Game and Game-Birds
792	Theaters	799.2	Hunting
792.022	Amateur Theatricals	799.277	Bison, American
792.027	Make-Up, Theatrical	799.277	Deer Hunting
792.028	Acting	799.32	Archery
792.0952	Japanese Drama--History and	800	Literature
	Criticism	800	Literature, Comparative--
792.8	Choreography		American & English

809	Literature--History & Criticism
809	Literature, Medieval
809	Literature, Medieval--History & Criticism
809	Literature, Modern--History & Criticism
809.1	Poetry--History & Criticism
809.2	Drama--History & Criticism
809.2	Drama--History & Criticism
809.2	Drama--History and Criticism-- 20th Century
809.3	Fiction--History & Criticism
809.7	Humorists
809.9	Romanticism
809.91	Symbolism, Literature
809.91	Transcendentalism
809.93	Law in Literature
810	American Literature--Addresses, Essays, Lectures
810	American Literature (Selections: Extracts, Etc.)
810	Canadian Literature--History & Criticism
810.03	American Literature--Dictionaries, Indexes, Etc.
810.08	American Literature (Collections)
810.08	American Prose Literature (Collections)
810.09	American Literature--History & Criticism
811	Crane, Hart, 1899-1932
811	Cummings, Edward Estlin, 1894-1962
811	Dunbar, Paul Lawrence, 1872-1906
811.016	American Poetry--Bibliography
811.04	Ballads, American
811.08	American Poetry (Collections)
811.08	American Poetry (Collections) 19th Century
811.08	American Poetry (Collections) 20th Century
811.104	Ballads, Irish
811.4	Howe, Julia (Ward) 1819-1910
811.5	Eliot, Thomas Stearns, 1888-
811.5	Jeffers, Robinson, 1887-
811.52	Frost, Robert, 1874-
811.9	American Poetry--History & Criticism
812	Gideon, Judge of Israel--Drama
812	Lincoln, Abraham, Pres. U.S.-- Drama
812.08	American Drama (Collections)
812.09	American Drama--History & Criticism
813	Austen, Jane, 1775-1817
813	Bowen, Elizabeth (Mrs. Alan Charles Cameron)1899
813	Hawthorne, Nathaniel, 1804-1864
813.08	American Fiction (Collections)
813.09	American Fiction--History & Criticism
813.09	Historical Fiction
813.24	Cooper, James Fenimore, 1789-1851
813.3	Melville, Herman, 1819-1891
813.4	Clemens, Samuel Langhorne, 1835-1910
813.4	Crane, Stephen, 1871-1900
813.4	Howells, William Dean, 1837-1920
813.5	Dos Passos, John Roderigo, 1896-
813.5	Dreiser, Theodore, 1871-1945
813.5	Fitzgerald, Francis Scott Key, 1896-1940
813.5	Gozzens, James Gould, 1903-
813.5	Hemingway, Ernest, 1898-1961
813.52	Cather, Willa Sibert
813.52	Faulkner, William 1897-1962
814.08	American Essays
814.36	Emerson Ralph Waldo, 1803-1882
817	American Wit and Humor
815	American Orations
817	Gilbreth, Frank Bunker, 1868-1924
819.1	Canadian Poetry (Collections)
819.1	Canadian Poetry--History & Criticism
820	English Literature (Collections)
820	English Literature (Collections)
820	English Literature (Collections) 18th Century
820	English Literature (Collections) 19th Century
820	English Literature (Collections) 20th Century
820	English Literature (Collections) Middle English, 1100-1500
820	English Prose Literature (Collections) Early Modern (To 1700)
820	English Prose Literature (Collections) 18th Century
820	English Prose Literature (Collections) 19th Century
820	English Prose Literature (Collections) 20th Century
820	English Prose Literature --History & Criticism
820	English Wit And Humor
820.016	English Literature--Bibliography
820.3	English Literature--Dictionaries, Indexes, Etc.
820.4	English Literature--Addresses, Essays, Lectures
820.7	English Literature--Outlines, Syllabi, Etc.
820.7	English Literature--Study & Teaching
820.8	English Prose Literature (Collections)
820.82	English Literature (Selections: Extracts, Etc.)
820.81	Cary, Joyce, 1888-1957
820.9	English Literature--History & Criticism
820.9	English Literature--History & Criticism--18th Century
820.9	English Literature--History & Criticism--19th Century
820.903	English Literature--History & Criticism Early Modern (To 1700)
820.903	English Literature--History & Criticism--Middle English (1100-1500)
820.904	English Literature--Irish Authors
821	Byron, George Gordon Noel Byron, 6th Baron, 1788-1824
821	Coleridge, Samuel Taylor, 1722-1834
821	Cowper, William, 1731-1800
821	Crashaw, Richard, 1613-1649
821	Donne, John, 1573-1631
821	Dryden, John, 1631-1700
821	English Poetry (Selections, Extracts, Etc.)
821.04	Ballads, English
821.04	Ballads, English--Discography
821.08	English Poetry (Collections)
821.09	English Poetry--History & Criticism
821.1	English Poetry (Collections) Middle English (1100-1500)

850	Italian Literature		890	English Literature--Translations From Oriental Literature
851.15	Dante Alighieri, 1265-1321		891.1	Indic Literature
852	Italian Drama		891.1	Mahabharata, Bhagavadgita
860	Brazilian Literature--Translations into English		891.62	Irish Literature
860	Cervates Saavedra, Miguel de, 1547-1616		891.62	Irish Poetry (Collections)
			891.63	Short Stories, Irish
860	Mexican Fiction--History & Criticism		891.7	Russian Drama
860	Mexican Literature--Translations into English		891.7	Russian Fiction
			891.7	Russian Literature
860	Mexican Poetry--Translations into English		891.73	Short Stories, Russian
			891.85	Polish Literature
860	Spanish Literature		892.19	Assyro-Babylonian Literature
862	Spanish Drama		892.4	Jewish Literature
863.08	Short Stories, Spanish'		893	Book of the Dead
869	English Literature--Translations From Portuguese		893	Dostoevskii, Fedor Mikhailovich, 1821-1881
870	English Literature--Translations From Latin		895	Chang, Heng, 78-139
870	Latin-American Literature (Collections)		895	Chinese Poetry--History & Criticism
			895	Li Po, 705-762
870	Latin-American Literature--History and Criticism		895.1	Chinese Poetry--Translations into English
870	Latin Drama--History & Criticism		895.6	Haiku
870	Latin Drama--Translations into English		895.6	Japanese Literature--History & Criticism
870	Latin Drama, Medieval & Modern		895.61082	Japanese Poetry--Translations into English
870	Latin Fiction--History & Criticism		895.62	No (Japanese Drama)
870	Latin Literature (Selections, Extracts, Etc.)		897.4	Aztec Literature
			899.6	Australian Literature--History & Criticism
870	Latin Literature, History & Criticism		901	Civilization, Occidental
870	Latin Literature--Translations into English		901	Civilization, Occidental--History Sources
870	Latin Literature, Medieval & Modern--History & Criticism		901	Civilization, Oriental
			901	Civilization--Philosophy
871	Horace (Quintus Horatius Flaccus)		901	Civilization, Roman
871	Latin Poetry (Collections)		901	Europe--Civilization
871	Latin Poetry--History & Criticism		901	History
871	Latin Poetry, Medieval & Modern History & Criticism		901	History--Philosophy
			901.6	History--Sources
871	Latin Poetry, Medieval & Modern Translations into English		901.9	Civilization
			901.9	Civilization--History
871	Latin Poetry--Translations into English		901.9	Civilization--History--Outlines, Syllabi, Etc.
880	Classical Literature--History & Criticism		901.9	Civilization--History--Sources
			901.94	Civilization, Modern
880	Classical Literature--Translations into English		901.94	Civilization, Modern--Addresses, Essays, Lectures
880	Dithyramb		903	History--Dictionaries
880	Greek Drama--Translations into English		904	Battles
			905.8	History--Yearbooks
880	Greek Literature (Collections)		907.2	Historiography
880	Greek Literature--History & Criticism		907.2	History--Methodology
			909	Courts and Courtiers
880	Greek Literature--Translations into English		909	East and West
			909	History, Modern
881	Greek Poetry (Collections)		909	World History
881	Greek Poetry--History & Criticism		909.1	Twelfth Century
881	Greek Poetry--Translations into English		909.5	Sixteenth Century
			909.6	Seventeenth Century
882	Orpheus		909.7	Eighteenth Century
882.2	Sophocles, 496?-406 B.C.		909.81	Nineteenth Century
882.9	Greek Drama--History & Criticism		909.82	Twentieth Century
			910	Discoveries (Geography)
883	Homer		910	Geography
883	Ovid		910	Macao-Descriptions
883.1	Civilization, Homeric		910	Voyages and Travels
885	Greek Orations		910.07	Geography--Study & Teaching
890	Chinese Literature--Translations into English		910.3	Geography--Dictionaries
			910.3	Names, Geographical
890	Oriental Literature		910.45	Seafaring Life

923.1 Stalin, Joseph (Iosif Stalin) 1879-1953

923.1 Tiberius, Emperor of Rome, 42 B.C.-37 A.D.

923.142 Catharine Howar, Consort of Henry VIII, King of England

923.142 Catharine of Aragon, Consort of Henry VIII, 1485-1536

923.142 Charles II, King of England 1630-1685

923.142 Edward I, King of England, 1239-1307

923.142 Edward VI, King of England

923.142 Edward VII, King of Gt. Brit, 1814-1910

923.142 Edward VIII, King of Gt. Brit, 1894-

923.142 Edward, Prince of Wales, called the Black Prince, 1330-1376

923.142 Eleanor, of Aquitaine, Consort of Henry II, 1122-1204

923.142 Elizabeth, Queen of England, 1533-1603

923.142 Elizabeth II, Queen of Gt. Brit., 1926-

923.142 George III, King of Gt. Brit., 1737-1820

923.142 George IV, King of Gt. Brit., 1762-1830

923.142 George V, King of Gt. Brit., 1865-1936

923.142 George VI, King of Gt. Brit., 1895-1952

923.142 Henry II, King of England, 1133-1189

923.142 Henry III, King of England, 1207-1272

923.142 Henry VIII, King of England, 1491-1547

923.142 John, King of England, 1167-1216

923.142 Margaret, Princess of Gt. Brit., 1930-

923.142 Mary I, Queen of England, 1516-1558

923.142 Mary Stuart, Queen of the Scots, 1542-1587

923.142 Richard II, King of England, 1367-1400

923.142 Richard III, King of England, 1452-1485

923.142 Victoria, Queen of Gt. Brit., 1819-1901

923.142 William IV, King of Gt. Brit., 1765-1837

923.143 Hitler, Adolf, 1889-1945

923.144 Marie Antoinette, Consort of Louis XVI, King of France, 1755-1793

923.145 Caesar, C. Julius

923.145 Claudius, Emperor of Rome, B.C. 10-A.D. 54.

923.145 Mussolini, Benito, 1883-1945

923.1455 Medici, Lorenze De, 1449-1492

923.147 Peter I, The Great, Emperor of Russia, 1672-1725

923.151 Chiang Kai-Shek, 1886-

923.151 Mao Tse-Tung, 1893-

923.153 Ibn Saud, King of Saudi Arabia, 1880-1953

923.173 Adams, John, Pres. U.S., 1735-1826

923.173 Adams, John Quincy, Pres. U.S., 1767-1848

923.173 Arthur, Chester Alan, Pres. U.S., 1830-1886

923.173 Buchanan, Hames, Pres. U.S., 1791-1868

923.173 Cleveland, Grover, Pres. U.S., 1837-1908

923.173 Coolidge, Calvin, Pres. U.S., 1872-1933

923.173 Eisenhower, Dwight David, Pres. U.S., 1890-

923.173 Fillmore, Millard, Pres. U.S., 1800-1874

923.173 Grant, Ulysses Simpson, Pres. U.S., 1822-1885

923.173 Harrison, Benjamin, Pres. U.S., 1833.1901

923.173 Jackson, Andrew, Pres. U.S.

923.173 Jefferson, Thomas, Pres. U.S., 1743-1826

923.173 Lincoln, Abraham, Pres. U.S., --Assasination

923.173 Lincoln, Abraham, Pres. U.S., 1809-1865

923.173 Madison, James, Pres. U.S., 1751-1836

923.173 McKinley, William, Pres. U.S., 1843-1901

923.173 Monroe, James, Pres. U.S., 1758-1831

923.173 Polk, James, Knox, Pres. U.S., 1795-1849

923.173 Roosevelt, Franklin Delano, Pres. U.S., 1882-1945

923.173 Truman, Harry S., Pres. U.S., 1884-

923.173 Tyler, John, Pres. U.S., 1790-1862

923.173 Washington, George, Pres. U.S., 1732-1799

923.173 Wilson, Woodrow, Pres. U.S., 1856-1924

923.198 Bolivar, Simon, 1783-1830

923.2 Bacon, Francis, Viscount St. Albans, 1561-1626

923.2 Bancroft, Frederic

923.2 Barkley, Alben William

923.2 Baruch, Bernard Mannes, 1870

923.2 Becker, Carl Lotus, 1873-1945

923.2 Benson, Ezra Taft

923.2 Borah, William Edgar, 1865-1940

923.2 Bradford, William, 1588-1657

923.2 Cicero, Marcus Tullius, 106-43 B.C.

923.2 Cromwell, Oliver, 1599-1658

923.2 Cromwell, Thomas, Earl of Essex, 1485-1540

923.2 Davis, Jefferson, 1808-1889

923.2 Debs, Eugene Victor, 1855-1926

923.2 Dulles, John Foster, 1888-1959

921 Gallatin, Albert, 1761-1849

923.2 Garibaldi, Giuseppe, 1807-1882

923.2 Gibbon, Edward, 1737-1794

923.2 Gramont, Antoine, Duc De, 1604-1678

923.2 Griffith, Arthur, 1872-1922

923.2 Hammarskjold, Dag Hjalmar Agne Carl, 1905-1961

923.2 Kellogg, Frank Billings, 1856-1937

923.2 King, William Lyon MacKenzie, 1874-1950

923.2 Knox, John, 1505-1572

923.2 Lafayette, Marie Joseph Paul Yves Roch Gilbert Du Motier, Marquis De, 1757-1834

923.2 La Follette, Robert M., 1855-1925

923.2 Laguardia, Fiorello Henry, 1882-1947

928	Stein, Gertrude, 1874-1946
928	Steinbeck, John Ernst, 1902-
928	Stendhal, (Marie Henri Beyle) 1783-1842
928	Stevens, Wallace
928	Stevenson, Robert Louis, 1850-1894
928	Stowe, Harriet Elizabeth (Beecher) 1811-1896
928	Strachey, Giles Lytton, 1880-1932
928	Stuart, Jesse, 1907-
928	Swift, Jonathan, 1667-1745
928	Synge, John Millington, 1871-1909
928	Tarkington, Booth
928	Tennyson, Alfred Tennyson, Baron, 1809-1892
928	Thackeray, William M., 1811-1863
928	Thomas, Dylan, 1914-1953
928	Thompson, Francis, 1859-1907
928	Thoreau, Henry David, 1817-1862
928	Tocqueville, Alexis Charles Henri Maurice Clerel De, 1805-1859
928.917	Tolstoi, Lev Nikolaevich, Graf, 1828-1910
928	Toynbee, Arnold, Joseph, 1889-
928	Trollope, Anthony, 1815-1882
928	Vergil (Publius Vergilius Maro)
928	Voltaire, Francois Marie Arouet De, 1694-1778
928	Walpole, Horace, 4th Earl of Oxford, 1717-1797
928	Wharton, Edith Newbold (jones) 1862-1937
928	Whittier, John Greenleaf, 1807-1892
928	Whitman, Walt, 1819-1892
928	Wilde, Oscar, 1854-1900
928	Williams, Tennessee, 1914-
928	Woolf, Virginia (Stephen) 1882-1941
928	Yeats, William Butler, 1865-1939
928	Zola, Emile, 1840-1902
928.1	Bierce, Ambrose, 1842-1914
928.1	Dickinson, Emily Norcross, 1830-1886
928.1	Mansfield, Katherine, 1888-1923
928.11	Pound, Ezra Loomis, 1885-
928.13	Poe, Edgar Allan, 1809-1849
928.142	Clough, Arthur Hugh, 1819-1861
928.142	Wordsworth, William, 1770-1850
928.144	Colet, Louise (Revoil) 1810-1876
928.144	Saint Exupery, Antoine De, 1900-1944
928.2	Boswell, James, 1740-1795
928.2	Bronte Family
928.2	Bronte, Patrick Branwell, 1817-1848
928.2	Maugham, William Somerset, 1874-
928.21	Pope, Alexander, 1688-1744
928.23	Shaw, George Bernard, 1856-1950
928.3	Mann, Thomas, 1875-1955
928.3	Novelists
928.344	Colette, Sidonie Gabrielle, 1873-1954
928.4	Manet, Edouard, 1832-1883
928.42	Gide, Andre Paul Guillaume, 1869-1951
928.42	Goldsmith, Oliver, 1728.1774
928.424	Moliere, Jean Baptiste Poquelin, 1622-1673
928.44	Belloc, Hilaire, 1870-1953
928.443	Montaigne, Mochel Eyquem De, 1533-1592
928.7	Marquand, John Phillips
928.73	Bemelman, Ludwig

928.73	Benchley, Robert Charles, 1889-1945
928.73	Benet, Stephen Vincent, 1898-1943
928.841	Cocteau, Jean, 1889-
928.917	Pushkin, Alesksandr Sergeevich, 1799-1837
928.917	Trotsky, Leon, 1879-1940
928.942	Collier, Jeremy, 1650-1726
928.973	Douglas, Frederick, 1817?-1895
928.973	O'Neill, Eugene Gladstone, 1888-1953
928.973	Porter, William Sydney, 1862-1910
929	Bridger, James, 1804-1881
929	Browne, Sir Thomas, 1605-1682
929	Burr, Aaron, 1756-1836
929.1	Genealogy
929.4	Names
929.4	Names, Personal
929.5	Epitaphs
929.6	Heraldry
929.8	Emblems, National
929.8	Gilds
929.9	Flags
930	Carthage
930	Cities and Towns, Ancient
930	Cities and Towns, Medieval
930	Civilization, Ancient
930	Darius I, 521 B.C.-486 B.C.
930	Hannibal, 247-183 B.C.
930	History, Ancient
932	Egypt--History, 1882-1952
932	Egypt--History, 1952
932	Egypt--History--Ancient, to 640
935	Assyria
935	Babylon
935	Babylonia
935	Babylonia--Antiquities
935	Mesopotamia--Antiquities
936.32	Civilization, Anglo-Saxon
936.36	Goths
936.4	Celts
936.7	Slavs
937	Pompeii
937	Rome--History
937	Rome (City)--Social Life & Customs
937.04	Punic Wars
938	Athens--Description--Views
938	Athens--Politics & Government
938	Civilization, Greco-Roman
938	Civilization, Greek
938	Greece--Antiquities
938	Greece--History
938	Greece--History--Sources
938	Greece--Politics & Government
938	Greece--Social Life & Customs
938.5	Athens--Antiquities
938.9	Greece--History--Historiography
939	Hittites
939.18	Crete--Antiquities
939.18	Knossos (Grete)
939.21	Troy
939.32	Galatia--Politics & Government
939.47	Civilization, Arabic
940	Atlantic Ocean
940	Conscientious Objectors
940	Europe, Eastern
940	Europe--Politics
940.1	Civilization, Medieval
940.1	Europe--History--476-1492
940.1	Manors
940.1	Middle Ages
940.1	Middle Ages--History
940.1	Middle Ages--History--Sources